Biology

Concepts and Applications 9e

About the Cover Photo

Despite their awkward waddle on land, emperor penguins soar through the sea. Once they dive into the water, these animals are both graceful and unbelievably fast. Scientists have now discovered the secret to a swimming penguin's speed: A layer of air that stays between the water and their dense coat of feathers acts as a lubricant.

When an emperor penguin swims, it is slowed by the friction between its body and the water, keeping its maximum speed somewhere between four and nine feet per second. But in short bursts the penguin can double or even triple its speed by releasing air from its feathers in the form of tiny bubbles. The bubbles reduce the density and viscosity of the water around the penguin's body, cutting drag and enabling the bird to reach speeds that would otherwise be impossible—and that help the penguins avoid fast-moving predators such as leopard seals.

The key to this talent is in the penguin's feathers. Like other birds, emperors have the capacity to fluff their feathers and insulate their bodies with a layer of air. Unlike most birds, which have rows of feathers with bare skin between them, emperor penguins have a dense, uniform coat of feathers. And because the bases of their feathers include tiny filaments—just 20 microns in diameter, less than half the width of a thin human hair—air is trapped in a fine, downy mesh and released as microbubbles so tiny that they form a lubricating coat on the feather surface.

Though feathers are not an option for ships, technology may finally be catching up with biology. In 2010 a Dutch company started selling systems that lubricate the hulls of container ships with bubbles. Last year Mitsubishi announced that it had designed an air-lubrication system for supertankers. But so far no one has designed anything that can gun past a leopard seal and launch over a wall of sea ice. That's still proprietary technology.

Join photographer Paul Nicklen as he captures unique video of emperor penguins soaring through the sea and launching their bodies out of the water onto the ice at *http://ngm .nationalgeographic.com/2012/11/emperor -penguins/behind-the-scenes-video.*

Biology

Concepts and Applications 9e

Cecie Starr
Christine A. Evers
Lisa Starr

Australia • Brazil • Japan • Korea • Mexico • Singapore • Spain • United Kingdom • United States

Biology: Concepts and Applications,
Ninth Edition
Cecie Starr, Christine A. Evers, Lisa Starr

Senior Product Manager: Peggy Williams

Content Developer: Jake Warde

Product Assistant: Victor Luu

Media Developer: Lauren Oliveira

Executive Brand Manager: Nicole Hamm

Senior Marketing Development Manager:
Tom Ziolkowski

Content Project Manager: Hal Humphrey

Senior Art Director: Pamela Galbreath

Manufacturing Planner: Karen Hunt

Senior Rights Acquisitions Specialist:
Dean Dauphinais

Production Service:
Grace Davidson & Associates, Inc.

Photo Researcher: Christina Ciaramella,
PreMedia Global

Text Researcher: Melissa Tomaselli and
Sunetra Mukudan, PreMedia Global

Copy Editor: Anita Wagner

Illustrators: Lisa Starr, ScEYEnce Studios,
Precision Graphics

Text and Cover Designer: Irene Morris

Cover and Title Page Image: Emperor penguins;
PAUL NICKLEN/National Geographic Creative

Compositor: Lachina

For product information and technology assistance, contact us at
Cengage Learning Customer & Sales Support, 1-800-354-9706

For permission to use material from this text or product,
submit all requests online at **www.cengage.com/permissions.**
Further permissions questions can be e-mailed to
permissionrequest@cengage.com.

Library of Congress Control Number: 2013946059

Paper Edition

ISBN-13: 978-1-285-42781-2

ISBN-10: 1-285-42781-5

High School Edition

ISBN-13: 978-1-285-42785-0

ISBN-10: 1-285-42785-8

Cengage Learning
200 First Stamford Place, 4th Floor
Stamford, CT 06902
USA

Cengage Learning is a leading provider of customized learning solutions with office locations around the globe, including Singapore, the United Kingdom, Australia, Mexico, Brazil, and Japan. Locate your local office at **www.cengage .com/global.**

Cengage Learning products are represented in Canada by Nelson Education, Ltd.

To learn more about Cengage Learning Solutions, visit **www.cengage.com.**

Purchase any of our products at your local college store or at our preferred online store **www.cengagebrain.com.**

Printed in the United States of America
1 2 3 4 5 6 7 17 16 15 14 13

Contents in Brief

Detailed Contents

Preface

We wrote this book to provide an accessible and appealing introduction to the study of life. Most students who use it will not become biologists, but all can benefit from an enhanced understanding of biological processes. For example, knowing how cells and bodies work helps a person make informed decisions about nutrition, life-style, and medical care. Recognizing the breadth of biodiversity, the mechanisms by which it arises, and the ways in which species interact brings to light the threats posed by human-induced extinctions. Realizing how living and nonliving components of ecosystems interact makes it clear why human activities such as adding greenhouse gases to the atmosphere puts us and other species at risk.

Our quest to educate and edify is shared by the National Geographic Society, with whom we have partnered for this edition. You will see the fruits of this partnership throughout the text—in spectacular new photographs, informative illustrations, and text features that highlight the wide variety of work supported by the society.

FEATURES OF THIS EDITION

SETTING THE STAGE

Each chapter opens with a dramatic two-page photo spread. A brief Links to Earlier Concepts paragraph reminds students of relevant information that has been covered in previous chapters, and concise Key Concept statements summarize the current chapter's content. An eye-catching image that appears in icon form next to each key concept also occurs within a relevant section, as part of a visual message that threads through the chapter.

CONCEPT SPREADS

The content of every chapter is organized as a series of Concepts, each explored in a section that is two pages or less. A section's Concept is reflected in its title, which is posed as a question that the student should be able to answer after reading the text. Bulleted sentences in the Take Home Message summarize and reinforce the Concept and supporting information provided in the section.

PEOPLE MATTER

Our new People Matter feature illustrates the relevance of ongoing research, and also highlights the diversity of the modern scientific community. Individuals whose work is spotlighted in this feature include well-established scientists, young scientists who are just beginning their careers, and a few nonscientists; most are National Geographic Explorers or Grantees.

ON-PAGE GLOSSARY

A new On-Page Glossary comprises boldface key terms introduced in each section. This section-by-section glossary offers definitions in alternate wording, and can also be used as a quick study aid. All glossary terms also appear in boldface in the Chapter Summary.

EMPHASIS ON RELEVANCE

Each chapter ends with an Application section that explains a current topic in light of the chapter content. For example, in Chapter 29, students use what they just learned about neural control to understand how sports-induced concussions permanently injure the brain—which is under intense study by scientific and athletic communities at this writing. Each Application also relates to a core interest of the National Geographic Society: Education, Conservation, Exploration, Get Involved, or Sustainability.

SELF-ASSESSMENT TOOLS

Many figure captions now include a Figure-It-Out Question and answer that allow students to quickly check their understanding of the illustration. At the end of each chapter, Self-Quiz and Critical Thinking Questions provide additional self-assessment material. A new chapter-end Data Analysis Activity sharpens analytical skills by asking the student to interpret data presented in graphic or tabular form. The data is related to the chapter material, and is from a published scientific study in most cases. For example, the Activity in Chapter 13 (Observing Patterns in Inherited Traits) asks the student to interpret data from an experiment revealing the suppressive effect of cystic fibrosis mutations on cellular uptake of *Salmonella* bacteria. This Activity continues the explanation of cystic fibrosis inheritance patterns begun in the chapter's Application section.

CHAPTER-SPECIFIC CHANGES This new edition contains 275 new photographs and almost 200 new or updated illustrations. In addition, the text of every chapter has been updated and revised for clarity. A page-by-page guide to new content and figures is available upon request, but we summarize the highlights here.

Chapter 1, Invitation to Biology
Renewed and updated emphasis on the relevance of new species discovery and the process of science; new features spotlight Smithsonian curator Kris Helgen and marine biologist Tierney Thys.

Chapter 2, Life's Chemical Basis
New graphics illustrate elements and radioactive decay; new feature spotlights volcanologist Ken Sims sampling radioisotopes in lava.

Chapter 3, Molecules of Life
New illustrations of carbon rings and tertiary structure; new feature spotlights discovery of carbohydrates in gas surrounding a sunlike star.

Chapter 4, Cell Structure
New photos illustrate surface-to-volume ratio, prokaryotes, biofilms, food vacuoles, chloroplasts, amyloplasts, basal bodies, and *E. coli* on food. New art illustrates plant cell walls, plasmodesmata, and cell junctions. Comparison of microscopy techniques updated using *Paramecium*. New features highlight electrical engineer Aydogan Ozcan's cell phone microscope, and astrobiologist Kevin Hand's work with NASA.

Chapter 5, Ground Rules of Metabolism
New photos illustrate potential energy, activation energy, energy transfer in redox reactions, turgor, phagocytosis, and alcohol abuse. Temperature-dependent enzyme activity now illustrated with polymerases. New feature highlights pressure-tolerant enzymes of deep sea amphipods. Expanded material on cofactors consolidated with ATP into new section. New activity requires interpretation of pH activity graphs of four enzymes from an extremophile archaean.

Chapter 6, Where It Starts—Photosynthesis
New photos illustrate phycobilins, and adaptations of C4 plants. New feature highlights conservation work of forester Willie Smits.

Chapter 7, How Cells Release Chemical Energy
New photos illustrate alcoholic and lactate fermentation, mitochondria, and mitochondrial disease. Revised art shows aerobic respiration's third stage. New feature highlights Benjamin Rapoport's glucose-driven, implantable fuel cell.

Chapter 8, DNA Structure and Function
Chromosome and DNA artwork has been revised for consistency throughout unit; DNA replication art updated. New photos illustrate DNA, x-ray diffraction, and mutation. New section consolidates material on DNA damage and mutations. New Figure spotlights marine biologist Mariana Fuentes, who studies how global warming is impacting sex ratios in sea turtle populations. Sex determination figure removed (text content remains).

Chapter 9, From DNA to Protein
New feature highlights Jack Horner's discovery of *T. rex* collagen in an ancient fossil. Expanded material on the effects of mutation includes new micrograph of a sickled blood cell. Ricin essay expanded to include other RIPs along with new photos and illustrations. New activity requires interpretation of data on the effects of an engineered RIP on cancer cells.

Chapter 10, Control of Gene Expression
New photos illustrate a polytene chromosome, *antennapedia* gene and mutation, X chromosome inactivation, *Arabidopisis* mutations, and breast cancer survivors; new feature details evolution of lactose tolerance. New section covers epigenetics; new activity requires analysis of retrospective data on an epigenetic effect.

Chapter 11, How Cells Reproduce
New photos illustrate mitosis, the mitotic spindle; new section details telomeres. New feature highlights behavioral ecologist Iain Couzin's hypothesis about collective behavior in metatstatic cells.

Chapter 12, Meiosis and Sexual Reproduction
New features highlight evolutionary biologist Maurine Neiman's work on the selective advantage of asexuality in the New Zealand mud snail, and asexuality in bdelloid rotifers. New photos illustrate crossovers and DNA repair during mitosis and meiosis.

Chapter 13, Observing Patterns in Inherited Traits
New figure illustrates how genotype gives rise to phenotype; new photos illustrate epistasis and continuous variation. Coverage of environmental effects on gene expression expanded and updated with new epigenetics research and new feature highlighting psychologist Gay Bradshaw's work on PTSD in elephants.

Chapter 14, Human Inheritance
New feature spotlights geneticist Nancy Wexler's work on Huntington's disease; new photo illustrates albinism.

Chapter 15, Biotechnology
Coverage of personal genetic testing updated with new medical applications, including photo of Angelina Jolie. New photos show recent examples of genetically modified animals. New "who's the daddy" critical thinking question offers students an opportunity to analyze a paternity test based on SNPs.

Chapter 16, Evidence of Evolution
Photos of analogous plants replaced with classic examples; new photo in morphological convergence section illustrates the difference. Photos of 19th century naturalists added to emphasize the process of science that led to natural selection theory. Expanded coverage of fossils includes how banded iron formations provide evidence of evolution of photosynthesis, and new feature spotlighting paleontologist Paul Sereno. New series of paleogeographic maps from Ron Blakey.

Chapter 17, Processes of Evolution
Added simple graphic to illustrate founder effect, and replaced hypothetical example in text with reduced diversity of ABO alleles in Native Americans. Consolidated and expanded material on antibiotic resistance into new Application section that covers overuse of antibiotics in livestock. New feature highlights evolutionary biologist Julia Day's work on speciation in African cichlids. New photos illustrate behavioral isolation in peacock spiders; new graphics illustrate stasis in coelacanths, and parsimony analysis. Added example of using cladistics to study viral evolution.

Chapter 18, Life's Origin and Early Evolution
Added information about earliest evidence of liquid water on Earth, a new contender for oldest fossil cells, and Robert Ballard's discovery of deep sea hydrothermal vents.

Chapter 19, Viruses, Bacteria, and Archaea
New feature about virologist Nathan Wolfe, increased coverage of viral recombination and of the roles of bacteria in human health and as decomposers.

Chapter 20, The Protists
New graphic illustrating primary and secondary endosymbiosis; added information about diatoms as a source of petroleum; new feature about Ken Banks, who created a text messaging system now used to track malaria outbreaks; coverage of choanoflagellates (the modern protists most closely related to animals) moved to this chapter.

Chapter 21, Plant Evolution
Updated life cycle graphics; improved photos of liverworts and horworts; new feature about Jeff Benca's studies of lycophytes, new coverage of seed banks as stores of plant diversity.

Chapter 22, Fungi
New graphics illustrating fungal phylogeny and a generalized fungal life cycle; new feature about DeeAnn Reeder, who studies white nose syndrome in bats; new coverage of fungi that infect insects and use of fungi in biotechnology and research; new coverage of the chytrid implicated in many amphibian declines.

Chapter 23, Animals I: Major Invertebrate Groups
New graphic comparing body plans in acolomate, pseudocoelomate, and coelomate worms; new feature about David Gruber's studies of biofluorescence in cnidarians; added information about penis fencing in marine flatworms and regeneration in planarians, similarity between larvae of annelids and mollusks as evidence of shared ancestry.

Chapter 24, Animals II: The Chordates
Updated evolutionary tree diagrams for chordates showing monophyly of jawless fishes; dropped discussion of "craniates"; updated and revised discussion of primate subgroups and human evolution with new photos and graphics; new feature about paleontologists Meave and Louise Leakey; new discussion of health problems related to our bipedalism.

Chapter 25, Plant Tissues
Reorganized to consolidate growth patterns into a single section. Many new photos added to illustrate internal structure of stems, leaves, roots. Two new features highlight the work of plant biologist Mark Olson and plant ecologist Jon Keeley.

Chapter 26, Plant Nutrition and Transport
New feature highlights the work of agroecologist Jerry Glover. Many new photos and updated art pieces. Illustration of Casparian strip integrated with new micrograph.

Chapter 27, Plant Reproduction and Development
Updated material on bee pollination behavior and colony collapse. Expanded coverage of asexual reproduction includes seedless crops, and historical information on John Chapman and *Phylloxera*. Plant development heavily revised to reflect paradigm shifts driven by recent breakthroughs in research. Expanded material on hormones organized by section. New features highlight the work of ethnobotanist Grace Gobbo and entomologist Dino Martins. New photos illustrate UV-reflecting patterns in flowers, mammal and bird pollination, embryonic development, internal anatomy of eudicot seeds, ABA mutation, chloroplast tropism, abscission, hypersensitive response, honeybee pollination. New art shows apical dominance, ethylene production during fruit formation, stomata function, gibberellin function in seed germination, circadian cycles of gene expression.

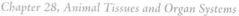

Chapter 28, *Animal Tissues and Organ Systems*
New feature about Brenda Larison's investigation into the adaptive value of zebra stripes, new information about walrus blubber (a specialized adipose tissue); improved coverage of organ systems; added information about tissue regeneration in nonhuman animals to discussion of stem cells.

Chapter 29, *Neural Control*
Added a subsection about methods of studying the human brain. New feature highlights the work of Diana Reiss, who studies dolphin cognition. New coverage of concussions and traumatic brain injury.

Chapter 30, *Sensory Perception*
New graphic of neurons involved in olfaction; new information about loss of sweet receptors in cats and some other carnivores and about newly discovered taste receptor for fatty acids; new feature about Fernando Montealegre-Z's studies of insect hearing; new section about cochlear implants.

Chapter 31, *Endocrine Control*
New coverage of the roles of thyroid hormone in amphibian metamorphosis and of melatonin in seasonal coat color changes in arctic hares; updated coverage of phthalates as endocrine disrupters.

Chapter 32, *Structural Support and Movement*
New opening section about mechanisms of animal locomotion; new feature about Kakani Katija Young's investigation into how marine animals mix the seas; new information about muscles of an elephant's trunk and the composition of muscle fibers in loris limbs.

Chapter 33, *Circulation*
New graphic showing the structure of and relationship among blood vessels; improved description of and depiction of capillary exchange; added information about circulation in giraffes and about cardiocerebral resuscitation.

Chapter 34, *Immunity*
Added material on neutrophil nets, chronic inflammation, cytokine storm, public confidence as a factor in the success of vaccination programs. Updated material on HIV/AIDS treatment strategies. New photos illustrate T cell/APC interaction, skin as a surface barrier, neutrophil nets, IgM polymers, leukocytes populating a lymph node, cytotoxic T cells killing a cancer cell, contact allergy. New feature highlights biochemist Mark Merchant's work discovering and characterizing crocodilian antimicrobial peptides.

Chapter 35, *Respiration*
Added a photo of horseshoe crab hemolymph and information about modification of nostril position in vertebrates; updated information about first aid for choking. New feature about Cynthia Beall's study of humans who live at high altitude.

Chapter 36, *Digestion and Human Nutrition*
New graphic illustrates organs that contribute material to the small intestine; new table summarizes chemical digestion. New feature highlights the work of epidemiologist Christopher Golden, who studies the nutritional importance of bushmeat. New application about health effects of obesity.

Chapter 37, *Maintaining the Internal Environment*
New feature highlights biological anthropologist Cheryl Knott's use of urinalysis in studies of orangutans. New information about climate-related genetic adaptations in humans.

Chapter 38, *Reproduction and Development*
Major reorganization—the overview of development now precedes the discussion of humans. New feature highlights the work of zoologist Stewart Nicol, who studies sexual anatomy and behavior of echidnas. Improved depiction of the ovarian cycle.

Chapter 39, *Animal Behavior*
Added information about epigenetic effects on behavior. New feature highlights biologist Isabelle Charrier's work studying vocal recognition in animals. Improved discussion of parental care variation among animal groups.

Chapter 40, *Population Ecology*
New feature highlights the work of biologist Karen DeMatteo, who studies predator populations. Revised coverage of life history strategies.

Chapter 41, *Community Ecology*
New feature highlights population geneticist Nayuta Yamashita's study of resource partitioning in lemurs.

Chapter 42, *Ecosystems*
New feature highlights conservationist Jonathan Waterman's journey along the water-deprived Colorado River. Updated information about current level of atmospheric carbon dioxide; expanded discussion of the nitrogen cycle.

Chapter 43, *The Biosphere*
Improved general description of biomes. Added information about desert crust. New feature highlights biogeochemist Katey Walter Anthony's studies of arctic methane.

Chapter 44, *Human Effects on the Biosphere*
New feature about Paula Kahumbu's conservation efforts in Africa; sustainable uses of resources. Updated information about acid rain, ozone depletion.

STUDENT AND INSTRUCTOR RESOURCES

INSTRUCTOR COMPANION SITE Everything you need for your course in one place! This collection of book-specific lecture and class tools is available online via *www.cengage.com/login*. Access and download PowerPoint presentations, images, instructor's manuals, videos, and more.

CENGAGE LEARNING TESTING POWERED BY COGNERO A flexible online system that allows you to:
• author, edit, and manage test bank content from multiple Cengage Learning solutions
• create multiple test versions in an instant
• deliver tests from your LMS, your classroom or wherever you want

STUDENT INTERACTIVE WORKBOOK Labeling exercises, self-quizzes, review questions, and critical thinking exercises help students with retention and better test results.

THE BROOKS/COLE BIOLOGY VIDEO LIBRARY 2009 FEATURING BBC MOTION GALLERY Looking for an engaging way to launch your lectures? The Brooks/Cole series features short high-interest segments: Pesticides: Will More Restrictions Help or Hinder?; A Reduction in Biodiversity; Are Biofuels as Green as They Claim?; Bone Marrow as a New Source for the Creation of Sperm; Repairing Damaged Hearts with Patients' Own Stem Cells; Genetically Modified Virus Used to Fight Cancer; Seed Banks Helping to Save Our Fragile Ecosystem; The Vanishing Honeybee's Impact on Our Food Supply.

MINDTAP A personalized, fully online digital learning platform of authoritative content, assignments, and services that engages your students with interactivity while also offering you choice in the configuration of coursework and enhancement of the curriculum via web-apps known as MindApps. MindApps range from ReadSpeaker (which reads the text out loud to students), to Kaltura (allowing you to insert inline video and audio into your curriculum). MindTap is well beyond an eBook, a homework solution or digital supplement, a resource center website, a course delivery platform, or a Learning Management System. It is the first in a new category—the Personal Learning Experience.

APLIA FOR BIOLOGY The Aplia system helps students learn key concepts via Aplia's focused assignments and active learning opportunities that include randomized, automatically graded questions, exceptional text/art integration, and immediate feedback. Aplia has a full course management system that can be used independently or in conjunction with other course management systems such as MindTap, D2L, or Blackboard. Visit *www.aplia.com/biology*.

Acknowledgments

We are incredibly grateful for the ongoing input of the instructors, listed on the following page, who helped us polish our text and shape our thinking. Key Concepts, Data Analysis Activities, On-Page Glossaries, custom videos—such features are direct responses to their comments and suggestions.

This edition benefits from a collaborative association with the National Geographic Society in Washington D.C. The Society has graciously allowed us to enhance our presentation with its extensive resources, including beautiful maps and images, Society explorer and grantee materials, and online videos.

Thanks to Yolanda Cossio and Peggy Williams at Cengage Learning for continuing to encourage us to improve and innovate, and for suggesting that we collaborate with National Geographic. Jake Warde ensured that this collaboration ran smoothly and Grace Davidson did the same for the project as a whole. Leila Hishmeh, Anna Kistin, Jen Shook, and Wesley Della Volla helped us acquire National Geographic maps and photos; Melissa Tomaselli and Sunetra Mukundan obtained text permissions.

This edition's sleek new look is a product of talented designer Irene Morris. Thanks also to Christina Ciaramella for photoresearch and photo permissions. Copyeditor Anita Wagner and proofreader Diane Miller helped us keep our text clear, concise, and correct; tireless editorial assistant Victor Luu organized meetings, reviews, and paperwork. Lauren Oliveira created a world-class technology package for both students and instructors.

—Lisa Starr, Chris Evers, and Cecie Starr 2013

Influential Class Testers and Reviewers

Brenda Alston-Mills
North Carolina State University

Kevin Anderson
Arkansas State University - Beebe

Norris Armstrong
University of Georgia

Tasneem Ashraf
Coshise College

Dave Bachoon
Georgia College & State University

Neil R. Baker
The Ohio State University

Andrew Baldwin
Mesa Community College

David Bass
University of Central Oklahoma

Lisa Lynn Boggs
Southwestern Oklahoma State University

Gail Breen
University of Texas at Dallas

Marguerite "Peggy" Brickman
University of Georgia

David Brooks
East Central College

David William Bryan
Cincinnati State College

Lisa Bryant
Arkansas State University - Beebe

Katherine Buhrer
Tidewater Community College

Uriel Buitrago-Suarez
Harper College

Sharon King Bullock
Virginia Commonwealth University

John Capehart
University of Houston - Downtown

Daniel Ceccoli
American InterContinental University

Tom Clark
Indiana University South Bend

Heather Collins
Greenville Technical College

Deborah Dardis
Southeastern Louisiana University

Cynthia Lynn Dassler
The Ohio State University

Carole Davis
Kellogg Community College

Lewis E. Deaton
University of Louisiana - Lafayette

Jean Swaim DeSaix
University of North Carolina - Chapel Hill

(Joan) Lee Edwards
Greenville Technical College

Hamid M. Elhag
Clayton State University

Patrick Enderle
East Carolina University

Daniel J. Fairbanks
Brigham Young University

Amy Fenster
Virginia Western Community College

Kathy E. Ferrell
Greenville Technical College

Rosa Gambier
Suffok Community College - Ammerman

Tim D. Gaskin
Cuyahoga Community College - Metropolitan

Stephen J. Gould
Johns Hopkins University

Laine Gurley
Harper College

Marcella Hackney
Baton Rouge Community College

Gale R. Haigh
McNeese State University

John Hamilton
Gainesville State

Richard Hanke
Rose State Community College

Chris Haynes
Shelton St. Community College

Kendra M. Hill
South Dakota State University

Juliana Guillory Hinton
McNeese State University

W. Wyatt Hoback
University of Nebraska, Kearney

Kelly Hogan
University of North Carolina

Norma Hollebeke
Sinclair Community College

Robert Hunter
Trident Technical College

John Ireland
Jackson Community College

Thomas M. Justice
McLennan College

Timothy Owen Koneval
Laredo Community College

Sherry Krayesky
University of Louisiana - Lafayette

Dubear Kroening
University of Wisconsin - Fox Valley

Jerome Krueger
South Dakota State University

Jim Krupa
University of Kentucky

Mary Lynn LaMantia
Golden West College

Dale Lambert
Tarrant County College

Kevin T. Lampe
Bucks County Community College

Susanne W. Lindgren
Sacramento State University

Madeline Love
New River Community College

Dr. Kevin C. McGarry
Kaiser College - Melbourne

Ashley McGee
Alamo College

Jeanne Mitchell
Truman State University

Alice J. Monroe
St. Petersburg College - Clearwater

Brenda Moore
Truman State University

Erin L. G. Morrey
Georgia Perimeter College

Rajkumar "Raj" Nathaniel
Nicholls State University

Francine Natalie Norflus
Clayton State University

Harold Olivey
Indiana University Northwest

Alexander E. Olvido
Virginia State University

John C. Osterman
University of Nebraska, Lincoln

Bob Patterson
North Carolina State University

Shelley Penrod
North Harris College

Carla Perry
Community College of Philadelphia

Mary A. (Molly) Perry
Kaiser College - Corporate

John S. Peters
College of Charleston

Carlie Phipps
SUNY IT

Michael Plotkin
Mt. San Jacinto College

Ron Porter
Penn State University

Karen Raines
Colorado State University

Larry A. Reichard
Metropolitan Community College - Maplewood

Jill D. Reid
Virginia Commonwealth University

Robert Reinswold
University of Northern Colorado

Ashley E. Rhodes
Kansas State University

David Rintoul
Kansas State University

Darryl Ritter
Northwest Florida State College

Amy Wolf Rollins
Clayton State University

Sydha Salihu
West Virginia University

Jon W. Sandridge
University of Nebraska

Robin Searles-Adenegan
Morgan State University

Erica Sharar
IVC; National University

Julie Shepker
Kaiser College - Melbourne

Rainy Shorey
Illinois Central College

Eric Sikorski
University of South Florida

Phoebe Smith
Suffolk County Community College

Robert (Bob) Speed
Wallace Junior College

Tony Stancampiano
Oklahoma City Community College

Jon R. Stoltzfus
Michigan State University

Peter Svensson
West Valley College

Jeffrey L. Travis
University at Albany

Nels H. Troelstrup, Jr.
South Dakota State University

Allen Adair Tubbs
Troy University

Will Unsell
University of Central Oklahoma

Rani Vajravelu
University of Central Florida

Jack Waber
West Chester University of Pennsylvania

Kathy Webb
Bucks County Community College

Amy Stinnett White
Virginia Western Community College

Virginia White
Riverside Community College

Robert S. Whyte
California University of Pennsylvania

Kathleen Lucy Wilsenn
University of Northern Colorado

Penni Jo Wilson
Cleveland State Community College

Robert Wise
University of Wisconsin Oshkosh

Michael L. Womack
Macon State College

Maury Wrightson
Germanna Community College

Mark L. Wygoda
McNeese State University

Lan Xu
South Dakota State University

Poksyn ("Grace") Yoon
Johnson and Wales University

Muriel Zimmermann
Chaffey College

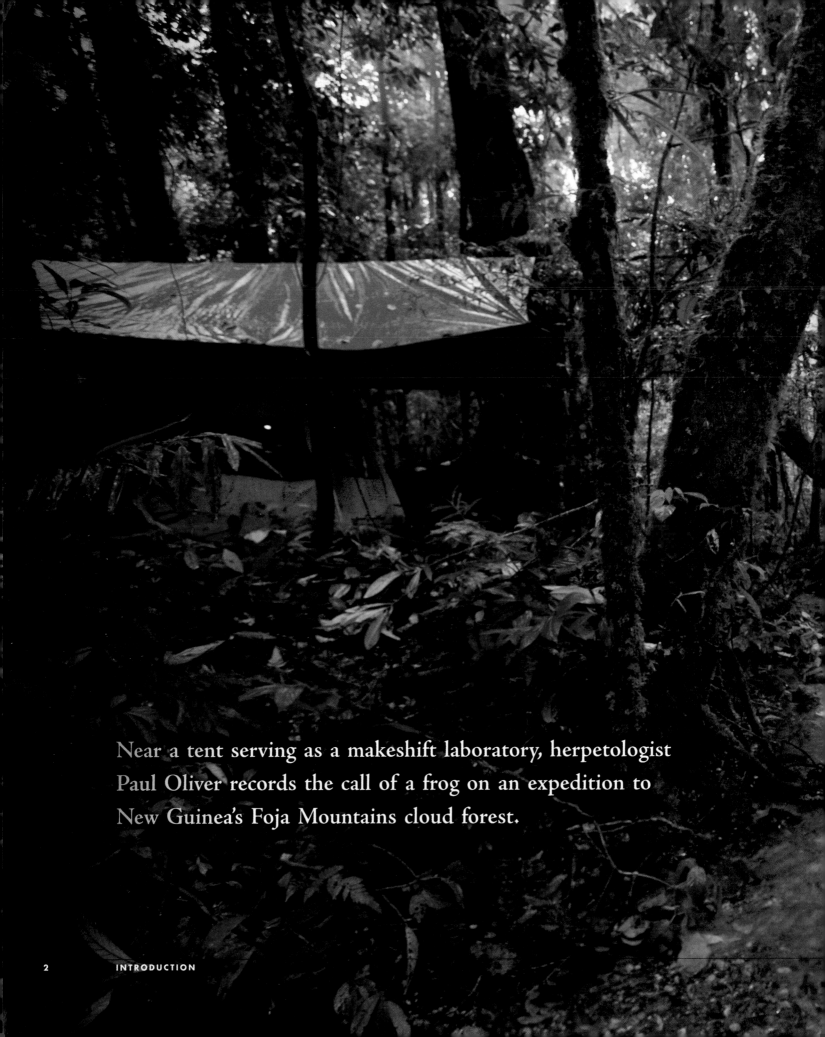

Near a tent serving as a makeshift laboratory, herpetologist Paul Oliver records the call of a frog on an expedition to New Guinea's Foja Mountains cloud forest.

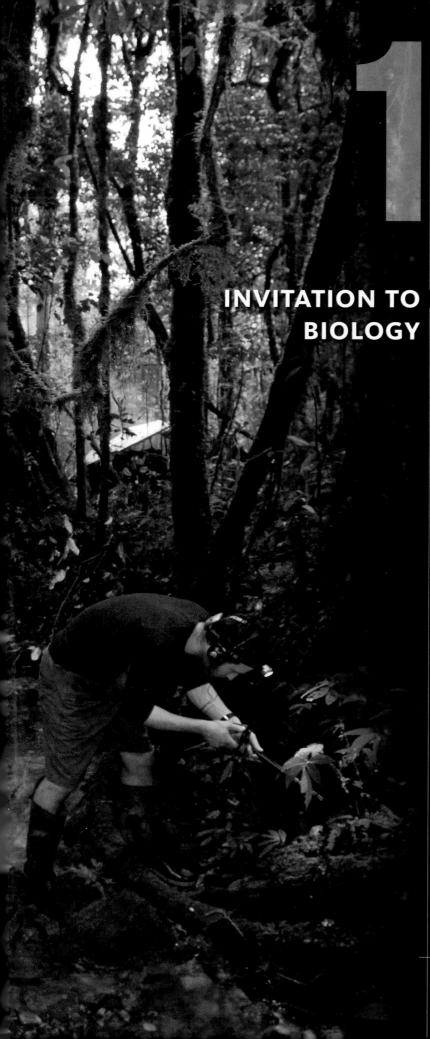

1

INVITATION TO BIOLOGY

Links to Earlier Concepts

Whether or not you have studied biology, you already have an intuitive understanding of life on Earth because you are part of it. Every one of your experiences with the natural world—from the warmth of the sun on your skin to the love of your pet—contributes to that understanding.

KEY CONCEPTS

THE SCIENCE OF NATURE
We can understand life by studying it at many levels, starting with atoms that are components of all matter, and extending to interactions of organisms with their environment.

LIFE'S UNITY
All living things require ongoing inputs of energy and raw materials; all sense and respond to change; and all have DNA that guides their functioning.

LIFE'S DIVERSITY
Observable characteristics vary tremendously among organisms. Various classification systems help us keep track of the differences.

THE NATURE OF SCIENCE
Carefully designing experiments helps researchers unravel cause-and-effect relationships in complex natural systems.

LIMITATIONS OF SCIENCE
Science addresses only testable ideas about observable events and processes. It does not address anything untestable, such as beliefs and opinions.

LIFE IS MORE THAN THE SUM OF ITS PARTS

Biology is the study of life, past and present. What, exactly, is the property we call "life"? We may never actually come up with a good definition, because living things are too diverse, and they consist of the same basic components as nonliving things. When we try to define life, we end up only identifying properties that differentiate living from nonliving things.

Complex properties, including life, often emerge from the interactions of much simpler parts. To understand why, take a look at this drawing:

The property of "roundness" emerges when the parts are organized one way, but not other ways. Characteristics of a system that do not appear in any of the system's components are called **emergent properties**. The idea that structures with emergent properties can be assembled from the same basic building blocks is a recurring theme in our world, and also in biology.

LIFE'S ORGANIZATION

Through the work of biologists, we are beginning to understand an overall pattern in the way life is organized. We can look at life in successive levels of organization, with new emergent properties appearing at each level (FIGURE 1.1).

Life's organization starts with interactions between atoms. **Atoms** are fundamental building blocks of all substances ❶. Atoms join as **molecules** ❷. There are no atoms unique to living things, but there are unique molecules. In today's world, only living things make the "molecules of life," which are lipids, proteins, DNA, RNA, and complex carbohydrates. The emergent property of "life" appears at the next level, when many molecules of life become organized as a cell ❸. A **cell** is the smallest unit of life. Cells survive and reproduce themselves using energy, raw materials, and information in their DNA.

Some cells live and reproduce independently. Others do so as part of a multicelled organism. An **organism**

❶ atom
Atoms are fundamental units of all substances, living or not. This image shows a model of a single atom.

❷ molecule
Atoms join other atoms in molecules. This is a model of a water molecule. The molecules special to life are much larger and more complex than water.

❸ cell
The cell is the smallest unit of life. Some, like this plant cell, live and reproduce as part of a multicelled organism; others do so on their own.

❹ tissue
Organized array of cells that interact in a collective task. This is epidermal tissue on the outer surface of a flower petal.

❺ organ
Structural unit of interacting tissues. Flowers are the reproductive organs of many plants.

FIGURE 1.1 {Animated} An overall pattern in the way life is organized. New emergent properties appear at each successive level.

is an individual that consists of one or more cells. A poppy plant is an example of a multicelled organism ❼.

In most multicelled organisms, cells are organized as tissues ❹. A **tissue** consists of specific types of cells organized in a particular pattern. The arrangement

CREDITS: (in text) © Cengage Learning 2015; (1) 1, 2: © Cengage Learning; 3, 4: © Umberto Salvagnin, www.flickr.com/photos/kaibara.; 5: California Poppy, © 2009, Christine M. Welter.

6 organ system
A set of interacting organs. The shoot system of this poppy plant includes its aboveground parts: leaves, flowers, and stems.

7 multicelled organism
Individual that consists of more than one cell. Cells of this California poppy plant are part of its two organ systems: aboveground shoots and belowground roots.

8 population
Group of single-celled or multicelled individuals of a species in a given area. This population of California poppy plants is in California's Antelope Valley Poppy Reserve.

9 community
All populations of all species in a specified area. These plants are part of a community called the Antelope Valley Poppy Reserve.

10 ecosystem
A community interacting with its physical environment through the transfer of energy and materials. Sunlight and water sustain the community in the Antelope Valley.

11 biosphere
The sum of all ecosystems: every region of Earth's waters, crust, and atmosphere in which organisms live. No ecosystem in the biosphere is truly isolated from any other.

flower is an organ of reproduction in plants; a heart, an organ that pumps blood in animals. An **organ system** is a set of organs and tissues that interact to keep the individual's body working properly ❻. Examples of organ systems include the aboveground parts of a plant (the shoot system), and the heart and blood vessels of an animal (the circulatory system).

A **population** is a group of individuals of the same type, or species, living in a given area ❽. An example would be all of the California poppies that are living in California's Antelope Valley Poppy Reserve. At the next level, a **community** consists of all populations of all species in a given area. The Antelope Valley Reserve community includes California poppies and all other organisms—plants, animals, microorganisms, and so on—living in the reserve ❾. Communities may be large or small, depending on the area defined.

The next level of organization is the **ecosystem**, which is a community interacting with its environment ❿. The most inclusive level, the **biosphere**, encompasses all regions of Earth's crust, waters, and atmosphere in which organisms live ⓫.

atom Fundamental building block of all matter.
biology The scientific study of life.
biosphere All regions of Earth where organisms live.
cell Smallest unit of life.
community All populations of all species in a given area.
ecosystem A community interacting with its environment.
emergent property A characteristic of a system that does not appear in any of the system's component parts.
molecule An association of two or more atoms.
organ In multicelled organisms, a grouping of tissues engaged in a collective task.
organism Individual that consists of one or more cells.
organ system In multicelled organisms, set of organs engaged in a collective task that keeps the body functioning properly.
population Group of interbreeding individuals of the same species that live in a given area.
tissue In multicelled organisms, specialized cells organized in a pattern that allows them to perform a collective function.

TAKE-HOME MESSAGE 1.1

Biologists study life by thinking about it at different levels of organization, with new emergent properties appearing at each successive level.

All things, living or not, consist of the same building blocks: atoms. Atoms join as molecules.

The unique properties of life emerge as certain kinds of molecules become organized into cells.

Higher levels of life's organization include multicelled organisms, populations, communities, ecosystems, and the biosphere.

allows the cells to collectively perform a special function such as protection from injury (dermal tissue), movement (muscle tissue), and so on.

An **organ** is an organized array of tissues that collectively carry out a particular task or set of tasks ❺. For example, a

CREDITS: (1) 6: Lady Bird Johnson Wildflower Center; 7: Michael Szoenyi/Science Source; 8: Photographers Choice RF/ SuperStock; 9: © Sergei Krupnov, www.flickr.com/photos/7969319@N03; 10: © Mark Koberg Photography; 11: NASA.

① producer acquiring energy and nutrients from the environment

② consumer acquiring energy and nutrients by eating a producer

ENERGY IN SUNLIGHT

③ Producers harvest energy from the environment. Some of that energy flows from producers to consumers.

PRODUCERS
plants and other self-feeding organisms

④ Nutrients that get incorporated into the cells of producers and consumers are eventually released back into the environment (by decomposition, for example). Producers then take up some of the released nutrients.

CONSUMERS
animals, most fungi, many protists, bacteria

⑤ All of the energy that enters the world of life eventually flows out of it, mainly as heat released back to the environment.

FIGURE 1.2 {Animated} The one-way flow of energy and cycling of materials through the world of life.

Even though we cannot precisely define "life," we can intuitively understand what it means because all living things share a set of key features. All require ongoing inputs of energy and raw materials; all sense and respond to change; and all pass DNA to offspring (**TABLE 1.1**).

TABLE 1.1

Three Key Features of Living Things

Requirement for energy and nutrients	Ongoing inputs of energy and nutrients sustain life.
Homeostasis	Each living thing has the capacity to sense and respond to change.
Use of DNA as hereditary material	DNA is passed to offspring during reproduction.

ORGANISMS REQUIRE ENERGY AND NUTRIENTS

Not all living things eat, but all require energy and nutrients on an ongoing basis. Both are essential to maintain the functioning of individual organisms and the organization of life. A **nutrient** is a substance that an organism needs for growth and survival but cannot make for itself.

Organisms spend a lot of time acquiring energy and nutrients (**FIGURE 1.2**). However, the source of energy and the type of nutrients required differ among organisms. These differences allow us to classify all living things into two categories: producers and consumers. **Producers** make their own food using energy and simple raw materials they get from nonbiological sources ①. Plants are producers that use the energy of sunlight to make sugars from water and carbon dioxide (a gas in air), a process called **photosynthesis**. By contrast, **consumers** cannot make their own food. They get energy and nutrients by feeding on other organisms ②. Animals are consumers. So are decomposers, which feed on the wastes or remains of other organisms. The leftovers from consumers' meals end up in the environment, where they serve as nutrients for producers. Said another way, nutrients cycle between producers and consumers.

Unlike nutrients, energy is not cycled. It flows through the world of life in one direction: from the environment ③, through organisms ④, and back to the environment ⑤. This flow maintains the organization of every living cell and body, and it also influences how individuals interact with one another and their environment. The energy flow is one-way, because with each transfer, some energy escapes as heat, and cells cannot use heat as an energy source. Thus, energy that enters the world of life eventually leaves it (we return to this topic in Chapter 5).

ORGANISMS SENSE AND RESPOND TO CHANGE

An organism cannot survive for very long in a changing environment unless it adapts to the changes. Thus, every living thing has the ability to sense and respond to change both inside and outside of itself (**FIGURE 1.3**). For example, after you eat, the sugars from your meal enter your bloodstream. The added sugars set in motion a series of events that causes cells throughout the body to take up sugar faster, so the sugar level in your blood quickly falls. This response keeps your blood sugar level within a certain range, which in turn helps keep your cells alive and your body functioning.

The fluid portion of your blood is a component of your internal environment, which is all of the body fluids outside of cells. Unless that internal environment is kept within certain ranges of temperature and other conditions, your body cells will die. By sensing and adjusting to change, you and all other organisms keep conditions in the internal environment within a range that favors survival. **Homeostasis** is the name for this process, and it is one of the defining features of life.

ORGANISMS USE DNA

With little variation, the same types of molecules perform the same basic functions in every organism. For example, information in an organism's **DNA** (deoxyribonucleic acid) guides ongoing functions that sustain the individual through its lifetime. Such functions include **development**: the process by which the first cell of a new individual gives rise to a multicelled adult; **growth**: increases in cell number, size, and volume; and **reproduction**: processes by which individuals produce offspring.

FIGURE 1.3 Living things sense and respond to their environment. This baby orangutan is laughing in response to being tickled. Apes and humans make different sounds when being tickled, but the airflow patterns are so similar that we can say apes really do laugh.

Individuals of every natural population are alike in certain aspects of their body form and behavior because their DNA is very similar: Orangutans look like orangutans and not like caterpillars because they inherited orangutan DNA, which differs from caterpillar DNA in the information it carries. **Inheritance** refers to the transmission of DNA to offspring. All organisms inherit their DNA from one or two parents.

DNA is the basis of similarities in form and function among organisms. However, the details of DNA molecules differ, and herein lies the source of life's diversity. Small variations in the details of DNA's structure give rise to differences among individuals, and also among types of organisms. As you will see in later chapters, these differences are the raw material of evolutionary processes.

---

consumer Organism that gets energy and nutrients by feeding on tissues, wastes, or remains of other organisms.
development Multistep process by which the first cell of a new multicelled organism gives rise to an adult.
DNA Deoxyribonucleic acid; carries hereditary information that guides development and other activities.
growth In multicelled species, an increase in the number, size, and volume of cells.
homeostasis Process in which an organism keeps its internal conditions within tolerable ranges by sensing and responding to change.
inheritance Transmission of DNA to offspring.
nutrient Substance that an organism needs for growth and survival but cannot make for itself.
photosynthesis Process by which producers use light energy to make sugars from carbon dioxide and water.
producer Organism that makes its own food using energy and nonbiological raw materials from the environment.
reproduction Processes by which parents produce offspring.

TAKE-HOME MESSAGE 1.2

Continual inputs of energy and the cycling of materials maintain life's complex organization.

Organisms sense and respond to change inside and outside themselves. They make adjustments that keep conditions in their internal environment within a range that favors cell survival, a process called homeostasis.

All organisms use information in the DNA they inherited from their parent or parents to develop, grow, and reproduce. DNA is the basis of similarities and differences in form and function among organisms.

CREDIT: (3) © Dr. Marina Davila Ross, University of Portsmouth.

A **Prokaryotes** are single-celled, and have no nucleus. As a group, they are the most diverse organisms.

B **Eukaryotes** consist of cells that have a nucleus. Eukaryotic cells are typically larger and more complex than prokaryotes.

bacteria are the most numerous organisms on Earth. Top, this bacterium has a row of iron crystals that functions like a tiny compass; bottom, a resident of human intestines.

archaea resemble bacteria, but they are more closely related to eukaryotes. Top: two types from a hydrothermal vent on the seafloor. Bottom, a type that grows in sulfur hot springs.

protists are a group of extremely diverse eukaryotes that range from microscopic single cells (top) to giant multicelled seaweeds (bottom).

fungi are eukaryotic consumers that secrete substances to break down food outside their body. Most are multicelled (top), but some are single-celled (bottom).

FIGURE 1.4 A few representatives of life's diversity: **A** some prokaryotes; **B** some eukaryotes.

Living things differ tremendously in their observable characteristics. Various classification schemes help us organize what we understand about the scope of this variation, which we call Earth's **biodiversity**.

For example, organisms can be grouped on the basis of whether they have a **nucleus**, which is a sac with two membranes that encloses and protects a cell's DNA. **Bacteria** (singular, bacterium) and **archaea** (singular, archaeon) are organisms whose DNA is *not* contained within a nucleus. All bacteria and archaea are single-celled, which means each organism consists of one cell (**FIGURE 1.4A**). Collectively, these organisms are the most diverse representatives of life. Different kinds are producers or consumers in nearly all regions of Earth. Some inhabit such extreme environments as frozen desert rocks, boiling sulfurous lakes, and nuclear reactor waste. The first cells on Earth may have faced similarly hostile environments.

Traditionally, organisms without a nucleus have been called **prokaryotes**, but this designation is now used only informally. This is because, despite the similar appearance of bacteria and archaea, the two types of cells are less related to one another than we once thought. Archaea

turned out to be more closely related to **eukaryotes**, which are organisms whose DNA is contained within a nucleus. Some eukaryotes live as individual cells; others are multicelled (**FIGURE 1.4B**). Eukaryotic cells are typically larger and more complex than bacteria or archaea.

Structurally, **protists** are the simplest eukaryotes, but as a group they vary dramatically, from single-celled consumers to giant, multicelled producers.

animal Multicelled consumer that develops through a series of stages and moves about during part or all of its life.
archaea Group of single-celled organisms that lack a nucleus but are more closely related to eukaryotes than to bacteria.
bacteria The most diverse and well-known group of single-celled organisms that lack a nucleus.
biodiversity Scope of variation among living organisms.
eukaryote Organism whose cells characteristically have a nucleus.
fungus Single-celled or multicelled eukaryotic consumer that breaks down material outside itself, then absorbs nutrients released from the breakdown.
nucleus Sac that encloses a cell's DNA; has two membranes.
plant A multicelled, typically photosynthetic producer.
prokaryote Single-celled organism without a nucleus.
protist Member of a diverse group of simple eukaryotes.

CREDITS: (4A) top left, Dr. Richard Frankel; top right, © Dr. Harald Huber, Dr. Michael Hohn, Prof. Dr. K.O. Stetter, University of Regensburg, Germany; bottom left, © Biophoto Associates/Science Source; bottom right, Dr. Terry Beveridge, Visuals Unlimited Inc.; (4B) Protists: top, Courtesy of Allen W. H. Bé and David A. Caron; bottom, © worldswildlifewonders/ Shutterstock.com; Fungi: top, © JupiterImages; bottom, Visuals Unlimited/Masterfile.

plants are multicelled eukaryotes. Most are photosynthetic, and have roots, stems, and leaves.

animals are multicelled eukaryotes that ingest tissues or juices of other organisms. All actively move about during at least part of their life.

Fungi (singular, fungus) are eukaryotic consumers that secrete substances to break down food externally, then absorb nutrients released by this process. Many fungi are decomposers. Most fungi, including those that form mushrooms, are multicellular. Fungi that live as single cells are called yeasts.

Plants are multicelled eukaryotes; the majority are photosynthetic producers that live on land. Besides feeding themselves, plants also serve as food for most other land-based organisms.

Animals are multicelled consumers that consume tissues or juices of other organisms. Unlike fungi, animals break down food inside their body. They also develop through a series of stages that lead to the adult form. All kinds actively move about during at least part of their lives.

TAKE-HOME MESSAGE 1.3

Organisms differ in their details; they show tremendous variation in observable characteristics, or traits.

We can divide Earth's biodiversity into broad groups based on traits such as having a nucleus or being multicellular.

PEOPLE MATTER

National Geographic Explorer
KRISTOFER HELGEN

Kristofer Helgen discovers new animals. Deep in a New Guinea rain forest. High on an Andean mountainside. Resting in a museum's specimen drawer. "Conventional wisdom would have it that we know all the mammals of the world," he notes. "In fact, we know so little. Unique species, profoundly different from anything ever discovered, are out there waiting to be found." His own efforts prove this. Helgen himself has discovered approximately 100 new species of mammals previously unknown to science. "Since I was three years old, I've been transfixed by animals," he recalls. "Even then, my excitement revolved around figuring out how many different kinds there were."

Helgen's search plunges him into the wild on almost every continent. Yet about three times as many new finds are made within the walls of museums. "An expert can go into any large natural history museum and identify kinds of animals no one knew existed," he explains. When only a few specimens of a species exist, and reside in museums scattered across the globe, sheer logistics often prevent researchers from connecting the dots and pinpointing a new find. "Collections build up over centuries," he says, "It's virtually impossible to fully interpret that wealth of material. Every day brings surprises." As Curator of Mammals for the Smithsonian Institution's National Museum of Natural History, he oversees not only the collection's use as an invaluable research resource, but also its continued expansion through exploration.

Each time we discover a new **species**, or unique kind of organism, we name it. **Taxonomy**, a system of naming and classifying species, began thousands of years ago, but naming species in a consistent way did not become a priority until the eighteenth century. At the time, European explorers who were just discovering the scope of life's diversity started having more and more trouble communicating with one another because species often had multiple names. For example, the dog rose (a plant native to Europe, Africa, and Asia) was alternately known as briar rose, witch's briar, herb patience, sweet briar, wild briar, dog briar, dog berry, briar hip, eglantine gall, hep tree, hip fruit, hip rose, hip tree, hop fruit, and hogseed—and those are only the English names! Species often had multiple scientific names too, in Latin that was descriptive but often cumbersome. The scientific name of the dog rose was *Rosa sylvestris inodora seu canina* (odorless woodland dog rose), and also *Rosa sylvestris alba cum rubore, folio glabro* (pinkish white woodland rose with smooth leaves).

An eighteenth-century naturalist, Carolus Linnaeus, standardized a naming system that we still use. By the Linnaean system, every species is given a unique two-part scientific name. The first part is the name of the **genus** (plural, genera), a group of species that share a unique set of features. The second part is the **specific epithet**. Together, the genus name and the specific epithet designate one species. Thus, the dog rose now has one official name, *Rosa canina*, that is recognized worldwide.

Genus and species names are always italicized. For example, *Panthera* is a genus of big cats. Lions belong to the species *Panthera leo*. Tigers belong to a different species in the same genus (*Panthera tigris*), and so do leopards (*P. pardus*). Note how the genus name may be abbreviated after it has been spelled out once.

A ROSE BY ANY OTHER NAME . . .

The individuals of a species share a unique set of inherited characteristics, or **traits**. For example, giraffes normally have very long necks, brown spots on white coats, and so on. These are morphological traits (*morpho–* means form). Individuals of a species also share biochemical traits (they make and use the same molecules) and behavioral traits (they respond the same way to certain stimuli, as when hungry giraffes feed on tree leaves).

We can rank species into ever more inclusive categories based on shared sets of traits. Each rank, or **taxon** (plural, taxa), is a group of organisms that share a unique set of traits. Each category above species—genus, family, order, class, phylum (plural, phyla), kingdom, and domain— consists of a group of the next lower taxon (**FIGURE 1.5**). Using this system, we can sort all life into a few categories (**FIGURE 1.6** and **TABLE 1.2**).

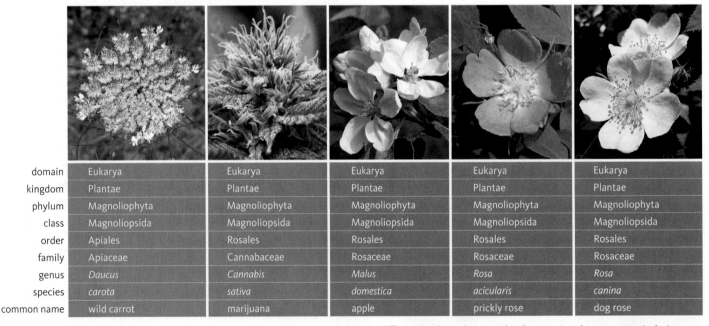

domain	Eukarya	Eukarya	Eukarya	Eukarya	Eukarya
kingdom	Plantae	Plantae	Plantae	Plantae	Plantae
phylum	Magnoliophyta	Magnoliophyta	Magnoliophyta	Magnoliophyta	Magnoliophyta
class	Magnoliopsida	Magnoliopsida	Magnoliopsida	Magnoliopsida	Magnoliopsida
order	Apiales	Rosales	Rosales	Rosales	Rosales
family	Apiaceae	Cannabaceae	Rosaceae	Rosaceae	Rosaceae
genus	*Daucus*	*Cannabis*	*Malus*	*Rosa*	*Rosa*
species	*carota*	*sativa*	*domestica*	*acicularis*	*canina*
common name	wild carrot	marijuana	apple	prickly rose	dog rose

FIGURE 1.5 Linnaean classification of five species that are related at different levels. Each species has been assigned to ever more inclusive groups, or taxa: in this case, from genus to domain.

 FIGURE IT OUT: Which of the plants shown here are in the same order?

Answer: Marijuana, apple, prickly rose, and dog rose

CREDITS: (5) from left, © xania.g, www.flickr.com/photos/52287712@N00; © kymkemp.com; Nigel Cattlin/Visuals Unlimited, Inc.; Courtesy of Melissa S. Green, www.flickr.com/photos/henkimaa; © Grodana Sarkotic.

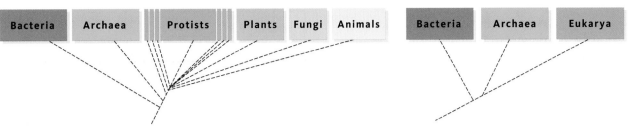

A **Six-kingdom classification system.** The protist kingdom includes the most ancient multicelled and all single-celled eukaryotes.

B **Three-domain classification system.** The Eukarya domain includes protists, plants, fungi, and animals.

FIGURE 1.6 {Animated} Two ways to see the big picture of life. The lines in such diagrams indicate evolutionary connections.

It is easy to tell that orangutans and caterpillars are different species because they appear very different. Distinguishing species that are more closely related may be much more challenging (**FIGURE 1.7**). In addition, traits shared by members of a species often vary a bit among individuals, such as eye color does among people. How do we decide if similar-looking organisms belong to different species or not? The short answer to that question is that we rely on whatever information we have. Early naturalists studied anatomy and distribution—essentially the only methods available at the time—so species were named and classified according to what they looked like and where they lived. Today's biologists are able to compare traits that the early naturalists did not even know about, including biochemical ones.

FIGURE 1.7 **Four butterflies, two species: Which are which?**

The top row shows two forms of the species *Heliconius melpomene*; the bottom row, two forms of *H. erato*.

H. melpomene and *H. erato* never cross-breed. Their alternate but similar patterns of coloration evolved as a shared warning signal to predatory birds that these butterflies taste terrible.

genus A group of species that share a unique set of traits.
species Unique type of organism.
specific epithet Second part of a species name.
taxon Group of organisms that share a unique set of traits.
taxonomy The science of naming and classifying species.
trait An observable characteristic of an organism or species.

The discovery of new information sometimes changes the way we distinguish a particular species or how we group it with others. For example, Linnaeus grouped plants by the number and arrangement of reproductive parts, a scheme that resulted in odd pairings such as castor-oil plants with pine trees. Having more information today, we place these plants in separate phyla.

Evolutionary biologist Ernst Mayr defined a species as one or more groups of individuals that potentially can interbreed, produce fertile offspring, and do not interbreed with other groups. This "biological species concept" is useful in many cases, but it is not universally applicable. For example, we may never know whether separate populations could interbreed even if they did get together. As another example, populations often continue to interbreed even as they diverge, so the exact moment at which two populations become two species is often impossible to pinpoint. We return to speciation and how it occurs in Chapter 17, but for now it is important to remember that a "species" is a convenient but artificial construct of the human mind.

TABLE 1.2

All of Life in Three Domains

Bacteria	Single cells, no nucleus. Most ancient lineage.
Archaea	Single cells, no nucleus. Evolutionarily closer to eukaryotes than bacteria.
Eukarya	Eukaryotic cells (with a nucleus). Single-celled and multicelled species of protists, plants, fungi, and animals.

TAKE-HOME MESSAGE 1.4

Each type of organism, or species, is given a unique, two-part scientific name.

Classification systems group species on the basis of shared, inherited traits.

CREDITS: (6) © Cengage Learning 2015; (7) © 2006 Axel Meyer, "Repeating Patterns of Mimicry." *PLoS Biology* Vol. 4, No. 10, e341 doi:10.1371/journal.pbio.0040341. Used with Permission; (Table 1.2) © Cengage Learning.

Most of us assume that we do our own thinking, but do we, really? You might be surprised to find out how often we let others think for us. Consider how a school's job (which is to impart as much information to students as quickly as possible) meshes perfectly with a student's job (which is to acquire as much knowledge as quickly as possible). In this rapid-fire exchange of information, it is sometimes easy to forget about the quality of what is being exchanged. Anytime you accept information without questioning it, you let someone else think for you.

THINKING ABOUT THINKING

Critical thinking is the deliberate process of judging the quality of information before accepting it. "Critical" comes from the Greek *kriticos* (discerning judgment). When you use critical thinking, you move beyond the content of new information to consider supporting evidence, bias, and alternative interpretations. How does the busy student manage this? Critical thinking does not necessarily require extra time, just a bit of extra awareness. There are many ways to do it. For example, you might ask yourself some of the following questions while you are learning something new:

> *What message am I being asked to accept?*
> *Is the message based on facts or opinion?*
> *Is there a different way to interpret the facts?*
> *What biases might the presenter have?*
> *How do my own biases affect what I'm learning?*

Such questions are a way of being conscious about learning. They can help you decide whether to allow new information to guide your beliefs and actions.

THE SCIENTIFIC METHOD

Critical thinking is a big part of **science**, the systematic study of the observable world and how it works (**FIGURE 1.8**). A scientific line of inquiry usually begins with curiosity about something observable, such as, say, a decrease in the number of birds in a particular area. Typically, a scientist will read about what others have discovered before making a **hypothesis**, a testable explanation for a natural phenomenon. An example of a hypothesis would be, "The number of birds is decreasing because the number of cats is increasing." Making a hypothesis this way is an example of **inductive reasoning**, which means arriving at a conclusion based on one's observations. Inductive reasoning is the way we come up with new ideas about groups of objects or events.

A **prediction**, or statement of some condition that should exist if the hypothesis is correct, comes next. Making predictions is called the if–then process, in which the "if"

TABLE 1.3

The Scientific Method

1. **Observe** some aspect of nature.

2. **Think of an explanation** for your observation (in other words, form a hypothesis).

3. **Test the hypothesis.**
   a. Make a prediction based on the hypothesis.
   b. Test the prediction using experiments or surveys.
   c. Analyze the results of the tests (data).

4. **Decide** whether the results of the tests support your hypothesis or not (form a conclusion).

5. **Report** your experiment, data, and conclusion to the scientific community.

---

part is the hypothesis, and the "then" part is the prediction. Using a hypothesis to make a prediction is a form of **deductive reasoning**, the logical process of using a general premise to draw a conclusion about a specific case.

Next, a scientist will devise ways to test a prediction. Tests may be performed on a **model**, or analogous system, if working with an object or event directly is not possible. For example, animal diseases are often used as models of similar human diseases. Careful observations are one way to test predictions that flow from a hypothesis. So are **experiments**: tests designed to support or falsify a prediction. A typical experiment explores a cause-and-effect relationship.

Researchers often investigate causal relationships by changing and observing **variables**, characteristics or events that can differ among individuals or over time.

---

control group Group of individuals identical to an experimental group except for the independent variable under investigation.
critical thinking Judging information before accepting it.
data Experimental results.
deductive reasoning Using a general idea to make a conclusion about a specific case.
dependent variable In an experiment, a variable that is presumably affected by an independent variable being tested.
experiment A test designed to support or falsify a prediction.
experimental group In an experiment, a group of individuals who have a certain characteristic or receive a certain treatment.
hypothesis Testable explanation of a natural phenomenon.
independent variable Variable that is controlled by an experimenter in order to explore its relationship to a dependent variable.
inductive reasoning Drawing a conclusion based on observation.
model Analogous system used for testing hypotheses.
prediction Statement, based on a hypothesis, about a condition that should exist if the hypothesis is correct.
science Systematic study of the observable world.
scientific method Making, testing, and evaluating hypotheses.
variable In an experiment, a characteristic or event that differs among individuals or over time.

"When it comes to fishes, the mola really pushes the boundary of fish form," says National Geographic Explorer Tierney Thys. "It seems a somewhat counterintuitive design for plying the waters of the open seas—a rather goofy design—and yet the more I learn about it, the more respect and admiration I have for it."

FIGURE 1.8 Tierney Thys travels the world's oceans to study the giant sunfish (mola). This mola is carrying a satellite tracking device.

An **independent variable** is defined or controlled by the person doing the experiment. A **dependent variable** is an observed result that is supposed to be influenced by the independent variable. For example, an independent variable in an investigation of our observed decrease in the number of birds may be the removal of cats in the area. The dependent variable in this experiment would be the number of birds.

Biological systems are complex, with many interacting variables. It can be difficult to study one variable separately from the rest. Thus, biology researchers often test two groups of individuals simultaneously. An **experimental group** is a set of individuals that have a certain characteristic or receive a certain treatment. This group is tested side by side with a **control group**, which is identical to the experimental group except for one independent variable: the characteristic or the treatment being tested. Any differences in experimental results between the two groups is likely to be an effect of changing the variable.

Test results—**data**—that are consistent with the prediction are evidence in support of the hypothesis.

Data inconsistent with the prediction are evidence that the hypothesis is flawed and should be revised.

A necessary part of science is reporting one's results and conclusions in a standard way, such as in a peer-reviewed journal article. The communication gives other scientists an opportunity to evaluate the information for themselves, both by checking the conclusions drawn and by repeating the experiments.

Forming a hypothesis based on observation, and then systematically testing and evaluating the hypothesis, are collectively called the **scientific method** (TABLE 1.3).

TAKE-HOME MESSAGE 1.5

Judging the quality of information before accepting it is called critical thinking.

The scientific method consists of making, testing, and evaluating hypotheses. It is a way of critical thinking.

Experiments measure how changing an independent variable affects a dependent variable.

There are many different ways to do research, particularly in biology. Some biologists make surveys; they observe without making hypotheses. Some make hypotheses and leave experimentation to others. Despite a broad range of approaches, however, researchers typically try to design experiments in a consistent way. They change one independent variable at a time, and carefully measure the effects of the change on a dependent variable.

To give you a sense of how biology experiments work, we summarize two published studies here.

POTATO CHIPS AND STOMACHACHES

In 1996 the U.S. Food and Drug Administration (the FDA) approved Olestra® (a fat replacement manufactured from sugar and vegetable oil) for use as a food additive. Potato chips were the first Olestra-containing food product on the market in the United States. Controversy soon raged. Many people complained of intestinal problems after eating the chips and thought that the Olestra was at fault.

Two years later, researchers at Johns Hopkins University School of Medicine designed an experiment to test the hypothesis that this food additive causes cramps. The researchers predicted *if* Olestra causes cramps, *then* people who eat Olestra will be more likely to get cramps than people who do not. To test their prediction, they used a Chicago theater as a "laboratory," and asked 1,100 people between the ages of thirteen and thirty-eight to eat potato chips while watching a movie. Each person got an unmarked bag that contained 13 ounces of chips. In this experiment, individuals who ate Olestra-containing potato chips constituted the experimental group, and individuals who ate regular chips were the control group. The independent variable was the presence or absence of Olestra in the chips.

A few days after the experiment was finished, the researchers contacted everyone and collected reports of any post-movie cramps (the dependent variable). Of the 563 people in the experimental (Olestra-eating) group, 89 (15.8 percent) complained about cramps. However, so did 93 of the 529 people (17.6 percent) making up the control group—who had eaten the regular chips. In this experiment, people were about as likely to get cramps whether or not they ate chips made with Olestra. These results did not support the prediction, so the researchers concluded that eating Olestra does not cause cramps (**FIGURE 1.9**).

BUTTERFLIES AND BIRDS

A 2005 experiment investigated whether certain peacock butterfly behaviors defend these insects from predatory birds. The researchers performing this experiment began with two observations. First, when a peacock butterfly rests, it folds its wings, so only the dark underside shows (**FIGURE 1.10A**). Second, when a butterfly sees a predator approaching, it repeatedly flicks its wings open, while also moving them in a way that produces a hissing sound and a series of clicks (**FIGURE 1.10B**).

The researchers were curious about why the peacock butterfly flicks its wings. After they reviewed earlier studies, they came up with two hypotheses that might explain the wing-flicking behavior:

1. Although wing-flicking probably attracts predatory birds, it also exposes brilliant spots that resemble owl eyes. Anything that looks like owl eyes is known to startle small, butterfly-eating birds, so exposing the wing spots might scare off predators.
2. The hissing and clicking sounds produced when the peacock butterfly moves its wings may be an additional defense that deters predatory birds.

A Hypothesis
Olestra® causes intestinal cramps.

B Prediction
People who eat potato chips made with Olestra will be more likely to get intestinal cramps than those who eat potato chips made without Olestra.

C Experiment	Control Group Eats regular potato chips	Experimental Group Eats Olestra potato chips
D Results	93 of 529 people get cramps later (17.6%)	89 of 563 people get cramps later (15.8%)

E Conclusion
Percentages are about equal. People who eat potato chips made with Olestra are just as likely to get intestinal cramps as those who eat potato chips made without Olestra. These results do not support the hypothesis.

FIGURE 1.9 The steps in a scientific experiment to determine if Olestra causes cramps. A report of this study was published in the *Journal of the American Medical Association* in January 1998.

FIGURE IT OUT: What was the dependent variable in this experiment?

Answer: Whether or not a person got cramps

CREDITS: (9) photo, © Superstock; artwork, © Cengage Learning 2015.

A With wings folded, a resting peacock butterfly resembles a dead leaf.

B When a bird approaches, a butterfly repeatedly flicks its wings open. This behavior exposes brilliant spots and also produces hissing and clicking sounds.

C Researchers tested whether peacock butterfly wing flicking and hissing reduce predation by blue tits.

FIGURE 1.10 Testing peacock butterfly defenses. Researchers painted out the spots of some butterflies, cut the sound-making part of the wings on others, and did both to a third group; then exposed each butterfly to a hungry blue tit. Results, listed below in Table 1.4, support the hypotheses that peacock butterfly spots and sounds can deter predatory birds.

 FIGURE IT OUT: What was the dependent variable in this series of experiments?

Answer: Being eaten

TABLE 1.4

Results of Peacock Butterfly Experiment*

Wing Spots	Wing Sound	Total Number of Butterflies	Number Eaten	Number Survived
Spots	Sound	9	0	9 (100%)
No spots	Sound	10	5	5 (50%)
Spots	No sound	8	0	8 (100%)
No spots	No sound	10	8	2 (20%)

* Proceedings of the Royal Society of London, Series B (2005) 272: 1203–1207.

The researchers then used their hypotheses to make the following predictions:

1. If peacock butterflies startle predatory birds by exposing their brilliant wing spots, then individuals with wing spots will be less likely to get eaten by predatory birds than those without wing spots.
2. If peacock butterfly sounds deter predatory birds, then sound-producing individuals will be less likely to get eaten by predatory birds than silent individuals.

The next step was the experiment. The researchers used a marker to paint the wing spots of some butterflies black, and scissors to cut off the sound-making part of the wings of others. A third group had both treatments: Their wings were painted and cut. The researchers then put each butterfly into a large cage with a hungry blue tit (**FIGURE 1.10C**) and watched the pair for thirty minutes.

TABLE 1.4 lists the results of the experiment. All of the butterflies with unmodified wing spots survived, regardless of whether they made sounds. By contrast, only half of the butterflies that had spots painted out but could make sounds survived. Most of the silenced butterflies with painted-out spots were eaten quickly. The test results confirmed both predictions, so they support the hypotheses. Predatory birds are indeed deterred by peacock butterfly sounds, and even more so by wing spots.

TAKE-HOME MESSAGE 1.6

Natural processes are often influenced by many interacting variables.

Researchers unravel cause-and-effect relationships in complex natural processes by performing experiments in which they change one variable at a time.

SAMPLING ERROR

When researchers cannot directly observe all individuals of a population, all instances of an event, or some other aspect of nature, they may test or survey a subset. Results from the subset are then used to make generalizations about the whole. For example, a survey team may catalog the number of beetles in a given area of a very large forest. If that given area is one-thousandth of the forest, then an estimate of the number of beetles in the entire forest would be one thousand times their result. However, this type of generalization is risky because the subset may not be representative of the whole. In our beetle survey, for example, if the only nest of beetles in the entire forest happened to be located in the area that was surveyed, then the generalized result would be in error. **Sampling error**

is a difference between results obtained from a subset, and results from the whole (**FIGURE 1.11A**).

Sampling error may be unavoidable, but knowing how it can occur helps researchers design their experiments to minimize it. For example, sampling error can be a substantial problem with a small subset, so experimenters try to start with a relatively large sample, and they repeat their experiments (**FIGURE 1.11B**). To understand why these practices reduce the risk of sampling error, think about flipping a coin. There are two possible outcomes of each flip: The coin lands heads up, or it lands tails up. Thus, the chance that the coin will land heads up is one in two (1/2), which is a proportion of 50 percent. However, when you flip a coin repeatedly, it often lands heads up, or tails up, several times in a row. With just 3 flips, the proportion of times that heads actually land up may not even be close to 50 percent. With 1,000 flips, however, the overall proportion of times the coin lands heads up is much more likely to approach 50 percent.

In cases such as flipping a coin, it is possible to calculate **probability**, which is the measure, expressed as a percentage, of the chance that a particular outcome will occur. That chance depends on the total number of possible outcomes. For instance, if 10 million people enter a drawing, each has the same probability of winning: 1 in 10 million, or (an extremely improbable) 0.00001 percent.

Analysis of experimental data often includes probability calculations. If a result is very unlikely to have occurred by chance alone, it is said to be **statistically significant**. In this context, the word "significant" does not refer to the result's importance. It means that the result has been subjected to a rigorous statistical analysis that shows it has a very low probability (usually 5 percent or less) of being skewed by sampling error.

Variation in data is often shown as error bars on a graph (**FIGURE 1.12**). Depending on the graph, error bars may indicate variation around an average for one sample set, or the difference between two sample sets.

BIAS IN INTERPRETING RESULTS

Particularly when studying humans, changing a single variable apart from all others is not often possible. For example, remember that the people who participated in the Olestra experiment were chosen randomly. That means the study was not controlled for gender, age, weight, medications taken, and so on. Such variables may have influenced the results.

Human beings are by nature subjective, and scientists are no exception. Experimenters risk interpreting their results in terms of what they want to find out. That is why they often

A Natalie chooses a random jelly bean from a jar. She is blindfolded, so she does not know that the jar contains 120 green and 280 black jelly beans.

The jar is hidden from Natalie's view before she removes her blindfold. She sees one green jelly bean in her hand and assumes that the jar must hold only green jelly beans. This assumption is incorrect: 30 percent of the jelly beans in the jar are green, and 70 percent are black. The small sample size has resulted in sampling error.

B Still blindfolded, Natalie randomly picks out 50 jelly beans from the jar. She ends up choosing 10 green and 40 black ones.

The larger sample leads Natalie to assume that one-fifth of the jar's jelly beans are green (20 percent) and four-fifths are black (80 percent). The larger sample more closely approximates the jar's actual green-to-black ratio of 30 percent to 70 percent.

The more times Natalie repeats the sampling, the greater the chance she has of guessing the actual ratio.

FIGURE 1.11 {Animated} Demonstration of sampling error, and the effect of sample size on it.

CREDIT: (11) © Gary Head.

design experiments to yield quantitative results, which are counts or some other data that can be measured or gathered objectively. Such results minimize the potential for bias, and also give other scientists an opportunity to repeat the experiments and check the conclusions drawn from them.

This last point gets us back to the role of critical thinking in science. Scientists expect one another to recognize and put aside bias in order to test their hypotheses in ways that may prove them wrong. If a scientist does not, then others will, because exposing errors is just as useful as applauding insights. The scientific community consists of critically thinking people trying to poke holes in one another's ideas. Their collective efforts make science a self-correcting endeavor.

THE LIMITS OF SCIENCE

Science helps us be objective about our observations in part because of its limitations. For example, science does not address many questions, such as "Why do I exist?" Answers to such questions can only come from within as an integration of all the personal experiences and mental connections that shape our consciousness. This is not to say subjective answers have no value, because no human society can function for long unless its individuals share standards for making judgments, even if they are subjective. Moral, aesthetic, and philosophical standards vary from one society to the next, but all help people decide what is important and good. All give meaning to our lives.

Neither does science address the supernatural, or anything that is "beyond nature." Science neither assumes nor denies that supernatural phenomena occur, but scientists may cause controversy when they discover a natural explanation for something that was thought to have none. Such controversy often arises when a society's moral standards are interwoven with its understanding of nature. For example, Nicolaus Copernicus proposed in 1540 that Earth orbits the sun. Today that idea is generally accepted, but the prevailing belief system had Earth as the immovable center of the universe. In 1610, astronomer Galileo Galilei published evidence for the Copernican model of the solar system, an act that resulted in his imprisonment. He was publicly forced to recant his work, spent the rest of his life under house arrest, and was never allowed to publish again.

probability The chance that a particular outcome of an event will occur; depends on the total number of outcomes possible.
sampling error Difference between results derived from testing an entire group of events or individuals, and results derived from testing a subset of the group.
statistically significant Refers to a result that is statistically unlikely to have occurred by chance.

FIGURE 1.12 Example of error bars in a graph. This graph was adapted from the peacock butterfly research described in Section 1.6.

The researchers recorded the number of times each butterfly flicked its wings in response to an attack by a bird.

The dots represent average frequency of wing flicking for each sample set of butterflies. The error bars that extend above and below the dots indicate the range of values—the sampling error.

FIGURE IT OUT: What was the fastest rate at which a butterfly with no spots or sound flicked its wings?

Answer: 22 times per minute

As Galileo's story illustrates, exploring a traditional view of the natural world from a scientific perspective can be misinterpreted as a violation of morality. As a group, scientists are no less moral than anyone else, but they follow a particular set of rules that do not necessarily apply to others: Their work concerns only the natural world, and their ideas must be testable by other scientists.

Science helps us communicate our experiences without bias. As such, it may be as close as we can get to a universal language. We are fairly sure, for example, that the laws of gravity apply everywhere in the universe. Intelligent beings on a distant planet would likely understand the concept of gravity. We might well use gravity or another scientific concept to communicate with them, or anyone, anywhere. The point of science, however, is not to communicate with aliens. It is to find common ground here on Earth.

TAKE-HOME MESSAGE 1.7

Checks and balances inherent in the scientific process help researchers to be objective about their observations.

Researchers minimize sampling error by using large sample sizes and by repeating their experiments.

Probability calculations can show whether a result is likely to have occurred by chance alone.

Science is a self-correcting process because it is carried out by an aggregate community of people systematically checking one another's ideas.

TABLE 1.5

Examples of Scientific Theories

Atomic theory	All substances consist of atoms.
Big bang	The universe originated with an explosion and continues to expand.
Cell theory	All organisms consist of one or more cells, the cell is the basic unit of life, and all cells arise from existing cells.
Evolution	Change occurs in the inherited traits of a population over generations.
Global warming	Human activities are causing Earth's average temperature to increase.
Plate tectonics	Earth's crust is cracked into pieces that move in relation to one another.

Suppose a hypothesis stands even after years of tests. It is consistent with all data ever gathered, and it has helped us make successful predictions about other phenomena. When a hypothesis meets these criteria, it is considered to be a **scientific theory** (**TABLE 1.5**). To give an example, all observations to date have been consistent with the hypothesis that matter consists of atoms. Scientists no longer spend time testing this hypothesis for the compelling reason that, since we started looking 200 years ago, no one has discovered matter that consists of anything else. Thus, scientists use the hypothesis, now called atomic theory, to make other hypotheses about matter.

Scientific theories are our best objective descriptions of the natural world, but they can never be proven absolutely because to do so would necessitate testing under every possible circumstance. For example, in order to prove atomic theory, the composition of all matter in the universe would have to be checked—an impossible task even if someone wanted to try.

Like all hypotheses, a scientific theory can be disproven by one observation or result that is inconsistent with it. For example, if someone discovers a form of matter that does not consist of atoms, atomic theory would be revised until no one could prove it to be incorrect. This potentially falsifiable nature of scientific theories is part of science's built-in system of checks and balances. The theory of evolution, which states that change occurs in a line of descent over time, still holds after a century of observations

and testing. As with all other scientific theories, no one can be absolutely sure that it will hold under all possible conditions, but it has a very high probability of not being wrong. Few other theories have withstood as much scrutiny.

You may hear people apply the word "theory" to a speculative idea, as in the phrase "It's just a theory." This everyday usage of the word differs from the way it is used in science. Speculation is an opinion, belief, or personal conviction that is not necessarily supported by evidence. A scientific theory differs because it is supported by a large body of evidence, and it is consistent with all known facts.

A scientific theory also differs from a **law of nature**, which describes a phenomenon that has been observed to occur in every circumstance without fail, but for which we do not have a complete scientific explanation. The laws of thermodynamics, which describe energy, are examples. As you will see in Chapter 5, we understand *how* energy behaves, but not exactly *why* it behaves the way it does.

---

law of nature Generalization that describes a consistent natural phenomenon for which there is incomplete scientific explanation.
scientific theory Hypothesis that has not been disproven after many years of rigorous testing.

TAKE-HOME MESSAGE 1.8

A scientific theory is a time-tested hypothesis that is consistent with all known facts. It is our most objective way of describing the natural world.

1.9 Application: THE SECRET LIFE OF EARTH

Researcher Paul Oliver discovered this tiny tree frog perched on a sack of rice during a particularly rainy campsite lunch in New Guinea's Foja Mountains. The explorers dubbed the new species "Pinocchio frog" after the Disney character because the male frog's long nose inflates and points upward during times of excitement.

Exploration

IN THIS ERA OF DETAILED CELL PHONE GPS, could there possibly be any places left on Earth that humans have not yet explored? Actually, there are plenty. For example, a 2-million-acre cloud forest in New Guinea was only recently penetrated by explorers. How did the explorers know they had landed in uncharted territory? For one thing, the forest was filled with plants and animals unknown even to native peoples that have long inhabited other parts of the region. Team member Bruce Beehler remarked, "I was shouting. This trip was a once-in-a-lifetime series of shouting experiences." The team members discovered many new species, including a rhododendron plant with flowers the size of plates and a frog the size of a pea. They also came across hundreds of species that are on the brink of extinction in other parts of the world, and some that supposedly had been extinct for decades.

Each new species is a reminder that we do not yet know all of the organisms that share our planet. We don't even know how many to look for. Why does that matter? Understanding the scope of life on Earth gives us perspective on where we fit into it. For example, the current rate of extinctions is about 1,000 times faster than ever recorded, and we now know that human activities are responsible for the acceleration. At this rate, we will never know about most of the species that are alive today. Is that important? Biologists think so. Whether or not we are aware of it, humans are intimately connected with the world around us. Our activities are profoundly changing the entire fabric of life on Earth. The changes are, in turn, affecting us in ways we are only beginning to understand.

Ironically, the more we learn about the natural world, the more we realize we have yet to learn. But don't take our word for it. Find out what biologists know, and what they do not, and you will have a solid foundation upon which to base your own opinions about the human connection—your connection—with all life on Earth.

Summary

SECTION 1.1   **Biology** is the scientific study of life. Biologists think about life at different levels of organization, with **emergent properties** appearing at successive levels. All matter consists of **atoms**, which combine as **molecules**. **Organisms** are individuals that consist of one or more **cells**, the level at which life emerges. Cells of larger multicelled organisms are organized as **tissues, organs**, and **organ systems**. A **population** is a group of interbreeding individuals of a species in a given area; a **community** is all populations of all species in a given area. An **ecosystem** is a community interacting with its environment. The **biosphere** includes all regions of Earth that hold life.

SECTION 1.2   All organisms require energy and **nutrients** to sustain themselves. **Producers** harvest energy from the environment to make their own food by processes such as **photosynthesis**; **consumers** eat other organisms, their wastes, or remains. Organisms keep the conditions in their internal environment within ranges that their cells tolerate—a process called **homeostasis. DNA** contains information that guides an organism's **growth**, **development**, and **reproduction**. The passage of DNA from parents to offspring is called **inheritance**.

SECTION 1.3   The many types of organisms that currently exist on Earth differ greatly in details of body form and function. **Biodiversity** is the sum of differences among living things. **Bacteria** and **archaea** are both **prokaryotes**, single-celled organisms whose DNA is not contained within a **nucleus**. The DNA of single-celled or multicelled **eukaryotes** (**protists, plants, fungi**, and **animals**) is contained within a nucleus.

SECTION 1.4   Each **species** has a two-part name. The first part is the **genus** name. When combined with the **specific epithet**, it designates the particular species. With **taxonomy**, species are ranked into ever more inclusive **taxa** on the basis of shared **traits**.

SECTION 1.5   **Critical thinking**, the self-directed act of judging the quality of information as one learns, is an important part of **science**. Generally, a researcher observes something in nature, uses **inductive reasoning** to form a **hypothesis** (testable explanation) for it, then uses **deductive reasoning** to make a testable **prediction** about what might occur if the hypothesis is correct. **Experiments** with **variables** may be performed on an **experimental group** as compared with a **control group**, and sometimes on **models**. A researcher changes an **independent variable**, then observes the effects of the change on a **dependent variable**. Conclusions are drawn from the resulting **data**. The **scientific method** consists of making, testing, and evaluating hypotheses, and sharing results.

SECTION 1.6   Biological systems are usually influenced by many interacting variables. Research approaches differ, but experiments are typically designed in a consistent way, in order to study a single cause-and-effect relationship in a complex natural system.

SECTION 1.7   Small sample size increases the potential for **sampling error** in experimental results. In such cases, a subset may be tested that is not representative of the whole. Researchers design experiments carefully to minimize sampling error and bias, and they use **probability** rules to check the **statistical significance** of their results. Science is ideally a self-correcting process because scientists check and test one another's ideas. Science helps us be objective about our observations because it is only concerned with testable ideas about observable aspects of nature. Opinion and belief have value in human culture, but they are not addressed by science.

SECTION 1.8   A **scientific theory** is a long-standing hypothesis that is useful for making predictions about other phenomena. It is our best way of describing reality. A **law of nature** describes something that occurs without fail, but has an incomplete scientific explanation.

SECTION 1.9   We know about only a fraction of the organisms that live on Earth, in part because we have explored only a fraction of its inhabited regions.

Self-Quiz   Answers in Appendix VII

1. _____ are fundamental building blocks of all matter.
   a. Atoms   c. Cells
   b. Molecules   d. Organisms

2. The smallest unit of life is the _____ .
   a. atom   c. cell
   b. molecule   d. organism

3. Organisms require _____ and _____ to maintain themselves, grow, and reproduce.

4. By sensing and responding to change, organisms keep conditions in the internal environment within ranges that cells can tolerate. This process is called _____ .

5. DNA _____ .
   a. guides form   c. is transmitted from
      and function   parents to offspring
   b. is the basis of traits   d. all of the above

6. A process by which an organism produces offspring is called _____ .

7. _____ is the transmission of DNA to offspring.
   a. Reproduction   c. Homeostasis
   b. Development   d. Inheritance

8. A butterfly is a(n) _____ (choose all that apply).
   a. organism   e. consumer
   b. domain   f. producer
   c. species   g. prokaryote
   d. eukaryote   h. trait

CREDIT: Scientific Paper; Adrian Vallin, Sven Jakobsson, Johan Lind and Christer Wiklund, *Proc. R. Soc. B* (2005 272, 1203, 1207). Used with permission of The Royal Society and the author.

Data Analysis Activities

Peacock Butterfly Predator Defenses The photographs below represent experimental and control groups used in the peacock butterfly experiment discussed in Section 1.6. See if you can identify the experimental groups, and match them up with the relevant control group(s). *Hint*: Identify which variable is being tested in each group (each variable has a control).

A Wing spots painted out   **B** Wing spots visible; wings silenced   **C** Wing spots painted out; wings silenced   **D** Wings painted but spots visible   **E** Wings cut but not silenced   **F** Wings painted, spots visible; wings cut, not silenced

9. _____ move around for at least part of their life.

10. A bacterium is _____ (choose all that apply).
    a. an organism
    b. single-celled
    c. an animal
    d. a eukaryote

11. Bacteria, Archaea, and Eukarya are three _____ .

12. A control group is _____ .
    a. a set of individuals that have a certain characteristic or receive a certain treatment
    b. the standard against which an experimental group is compared
    c. the experiment that gives conclusive results

13. Fifteen randomly selected students are found to be taller than 6 feet. The researchers concluded that the average height of a student is greater than 6 feet. This is an example of _____ .
    a. experimental error
    b. sampling error
    c. a subjective opinion
    d. experimental bias

14. Science only addresses that which is _____ .
    a. alive
    b. observable
    c. variable
    d. indisputable

15. Match the terms with the most suitable description.
    ___ life
    ___ probability
    ___ species
    ___ hypothesis
    ___ prediction
    ___ producer
    a. if–then statement
    b. unique type of organism
    c. emerges with cells
    d. testable explanation
    e. measure of chance
    f. makes its own food

Critical Thinking

1. A person is declared dead upon the irreversible ceasing of spontaneous body functions: brain activity, blood circulation, and respiration. Only about 1% of a body's cells have to die in order for all of these things to happen. How can a person be dead when 99% of his or her cells are alive?

2. Explain the difference between a one-celled organism and a single cell of a multicelled organism.

3. Why would you think twice about ordering from a restaurant menu that lists the specific epithet but not the genus name of its offerings? *Hint*: Look up *Homarus americanus*, *Ursus americanus*, *Ceanothus americanus*, *Bufo americanus*, *Lepus americanus*, and *Nicrophorus americanus*.

4. Once there was a highly intelligent turkey that had nothing to do but reflect on the world's regularities. Morning always started out with the sky turning light, followed by the master's footsteps, which were always followed by the appearance of food. Other things varied, but food always followed footsteps. The sequence of events was so predictable that it eventually became the basis of the turkey's theory about the goodness of the world. One morning, after more than 100 confirmations of this theory, the turkey listened for the master's footsteps, heard them, and had its head chopped off.

Any scientific theory is modified or discarded upon discovery of contradictory evidence. The absence of absolute certainty has led some people to conclude that "theories are irrelevant because they can change." If that is so, should we stop doing scientific research? Why or why not?

5. In 2005, researcher Woo-suk Hwang reported that he had made immortal stem cells from human patients. His research was hailed as a breakthrough for people affected by degenerative diseases, because stem cells may be used to repair a person's own damaged tissues. Hwang published his results in a peer-reviewed journal. In 2006, the journal retracted his paper after other scientists discovered that Hwang's group had faked their data.

Does the incident show that results of scientific studies cannot be trusted? Or does it confirm the usefulness of a scientific approach, because other scientists discovered and exposed the fraud?

CENGAGE brain.com To access course materials, please visit www.cengagebrain.com.

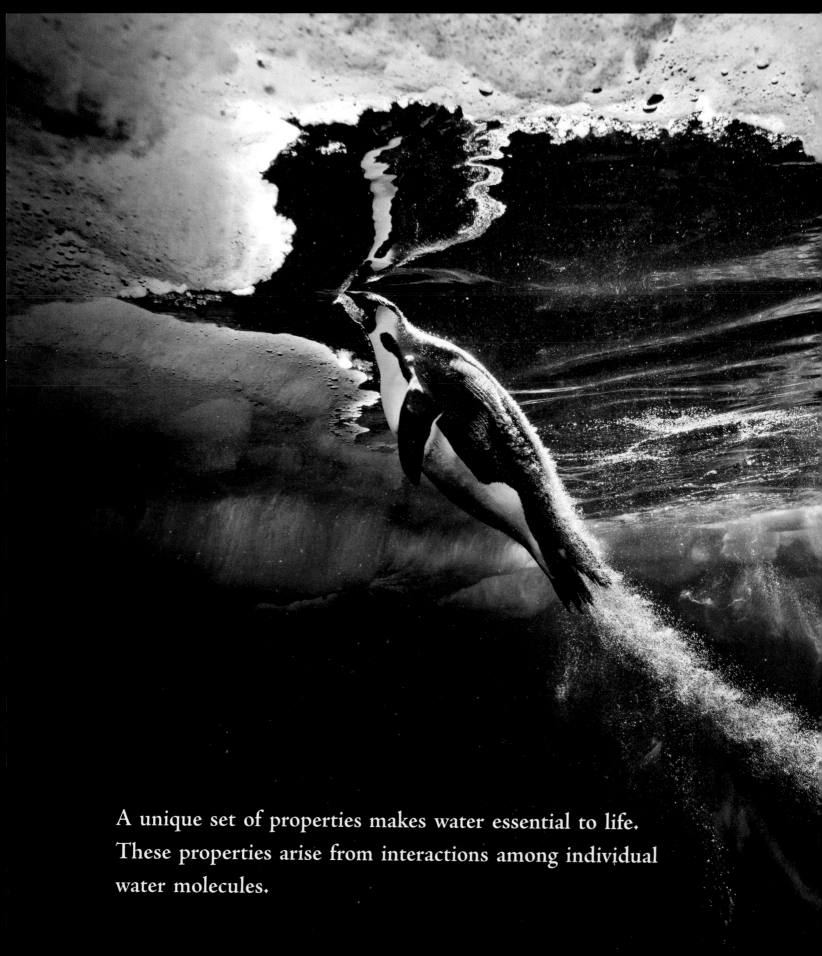

A unique set of properties makes water essential to life. These properties arise from interactions among individual water molecules.

2

LIFE'S CHEMICAL BASIS

Links to Earlier Concepts

In this chapter, you will explore the first level of life's organization—atoms—as you encounter the first example of how the same building blocks, arranged different ways, form different products (Section 1.1). You will also see one aspect of homeostasis, the process by which organisms keep themselves in a state that favors cell survival (1.2).

KEY CONCEPTS

ATOMS AND ELEMENTS
Atoms, the building blocks of all matter, differ in their numbers of protons, neutrons, and electrons. Atoms of an element have the same number of protons.

WHY ELECTRONS MATTER
Whether an atom interacts with other atoms depends on the number of electrons it has. An atom with an unequal number of electrons and protons is an ion.

ATOMS BOND
Atoms of many elements interact by acquiring, sharing, and giving up electrons. Interacting atoms may form ionic, covalent, or hydrogen bonds.

WATER
Hydrogen bonding among individual molecules gives water properties that make life possible: temperature stabilization, cohesion, and the ability to dissolve many other substances.

HYDROGEN POWER
Most of the chemistry of life occurs in a narrow range of pH, so most fluids inside organisms are buffered to stay within that range.

Photograph by Paul Nicklen, National Geographic Creative.

Even though atoms are about 20 million times smaller than a grain of sand, they consist of even smaller subatomic particles. Positively charged **protons** (p+) and uncharged **neutrons** occur in an atom's core, or **nucleus**. Negatively charged **electrons** (e−) move around the nucleus (**FIGURE 2.1A**). **Charge** is an electrical property: Opposite charges attract, and like charges repel.

A typical atom has about the same number of electrons and protons. The negative charge of an electron is the same magnitude as the positive charge of a proton, so the two charges cancel one another. Thus, an atom with the same number of electrons and protons carries no charge.

All atoms have protons. The number of protons in the nucleus is called the **atomic number**, and it determines the type of atom, or element. **Elements** are pure substances, each consisting only of atoms with the same number of protons in their nucleus (**FIGURE 2.1B**). For example, the atomic number of carbon is 6, so all atoms with six protons in their nucleus are carbon atoms, no matter how many electrons or neutrons they have. Carbon, the substance, consists only of carbon atoms, and all of those atoms have six protons.

Knowing the numbers of electrons, protons, and neutrons in atoms helps us predict how elements will behave. In 1869, chemist Dmitry Mendeleyev arranged the elements known at the time by their chemical properties. The arrangement, which he called the **periodic table** (**FIGURE 2.1C**), turned out to be by atomic number, even though subatomic particles would not be discovered until the early 1900s.

In the periodic table, each element is represented by a symbol that is typically an abbreviation of the element's Latin or Greek name. For instance, Pb (lead) is short for *plumbum*; the word "plumbing" is related—ancient Romans made their water pipes with lead. Carbon's symbol, C, is from *carbo*, the Latin word for coal (which is mostly carbon).

ISOTOPES AND RADIOISOTOPES

All atoms of an element have the same number of protons, but they can differ in the number of other subatomic particles. Those that differ in the number of neutrons are called **isotopes**. We define isotopes by their **mass number**, which is the total number of protons and neutrons in their nucleus. Mass number is written as a superscript to the left of an element's symbol. For example, hydrogen, the simplest atom, has one proton and no neutrons, so it is designated ^1H. The most common isotope of carbon has six protons and six neutrons, so it is ^{12}C, or carbon 12. The other naturally occurring isotopes of carbon are ^{13}C (six protons, seven neutrons), and ^{14}C (six protons, eight neutrons).

Carbon 14 is a **radioisotope**, or radioactive isotope. Atoms of a radioisotope have an unstable nucleus that breaks up

---

FIGURE 2.1 {Animated} Atoms and elements.

A Atoms consist of electrons moving around a nucleus of protons and neutrons. Models such as this one do not show what atoms look like. Electrons move in defined, three-dimensional spaces about 10,000 times bigger than the nucleus.

⊕ proton
◉ neutron
⊖ electron

B Example of an element.

atomic number
element symbol
mass number
elemental substance
element name
carbon

C The periodic table of the elements.

---

atomic number Number of protons in the atomic nucleus; determines the element.
charge Electrical property. Opposite charges attract, and like charges repel.
electron Negatively charged subatomic particle.
element A pure substance that consists only of atoms with the same number of protons.
isotopes Forms of an element that differ in the number of neutrons their atoms carry.
mass number Of an isotope, the total number of protons and neutrons in the atomic nucleus.
neutron Uncharged subatomic particle in the atomic nucleus.
nucleus Core of an atom; occupied by protons and neutrons.
periodic table Tabular arrangement of all known elements by their atomic number.
proton Positively charged subatomic particle that occurs in the nucleus of all atoms.
radioactive decay Process by which atoms of a radioisotope emit energy and/or subatomic particles when their nucleus spontaneously breaks up.
radioisotope Isotope with an unstable nucleus.
tracer A molecule with a detectable component.

CREDITS: (1A, B right, C) © Cengage Learning 2015; (1B) left, Theodore Gray/ Visuals Unlimited, Inc.

spontaneously. As a nucleus breaks up, it emits radiation—subatomic particles, energy, or both—a process called **radioactive decay**. The atomic nucleus cannot be altered by ordinary means, so radioactive decay is unaffected by external factors such as temperature, pressure, or whether the atoms are part of molecules.

Each radioisotope decays at a predictable rate into predictable products. For example, when carbon 14 decays, one of its neutrons splits into a proton and an electron. The nucleus emits the electron as radiation. Thus, a carbon atom with eight neutrons and six protons (^{14}C) becomes a nitrogen atom, with seven neutrons and seven protons (^{14}N):

nucleus of ^{14}C, with   nucleus of ^{14}N, with
6 protons, 8 neutrons   7 protons, 7 neutrons

This process is so predictable that we can say with certainty that about half of the atoms in any sample of ^{14}C will be ^{14}N atoms after 5,730 years. The predictable rate of radioactive decay makes it possible for scientists to estimate the age of a rock or fossil by measuring its isotope content (we return to this topic in Section 16.4).

TRACERS

All isotopes of an element generally have the same chemical properties regardless of the number of neutrons in their atoms. This consistent chemical behavior means that organisms use atoms of one isotope the same way that they use atoms of another. Thus, radioisotopes can be used as tracers to study biological processes. A **tracer** is any substance with a detectable component. For example, a molecule in which an atom (such as ^{12}C) has been replaced with a radioisotope (such as ^{14}C) can be used as a radioactive tracer. When delivered into a biological system such as a cell, body, or ecosystem, this tracer may be followed as it moves through the system with instruments that detect radiation.

TAKE-HOME MESSAGE 2.1

All matter consists of atoms, tiny particles that in turn consist of electrons moving around a nucleus of protons and neutrons.

An element is a pure substance that consists only of atoms with the same number of protons. Isotopes are forms of an element that have different numbers of neutrons.

Unstable nuclei of radioisotopes break down spontaneously (decay) at a predictable rate to form predictable products.

National Geographic Explorer
KENNETH SIMS

A volcano is a force of nature most of us prefer to observe from a very long and safe distance. Not volcanologist Ken Sims. The National Geographic explorer could never be satisfied with anything less than standing on the edge of an erupting volcano. In fact, even standing on the edge of an erupting volcano wasn't enough for Sims. As part of his research, he rappelled down into the mouth of Nyiragongo, a volcano in the Democratic Republic of the Congo, to gather fresh lava from a molten lake boiling at 1800°F.

Sims says, "While many think of me as a volcanologist, I am actually an isotope geochemist and, as such, I have pondered and written professional papers on a wide range of problems, including chemical oceanography; the Earth's paleo-climate; oceanic and continental crustal growth; continental crustal weathering; ground water transport; and, of course, the genesis and evolution of volcanic systems. The measurement of radioactive isotopes in natural systems allows me to quantify fundamental processes that would otherwise be limited to qualitative observation. This may make me sound like a nerd but to be able to quantify the Earth's processes is truly inspiring."

ELECTRONS MATTER

Electrons are really, really small. How small are they? If they were as big as apples, you would be about 3.5 times taller than our solar system is wide. Simple physics explains the motion of, say, an apple falling from a tree, but electrons are so tiny that such everyday physics cannot explain their behavior. For example, electrons carry energy, but only in incremental amounts. An electron gains energy only by absorbing the exact amount needed to boost it to the next energy level. Likewise, it loses energy only by emitting the exact difference between two energy levels. This concept will be important to remember when you learn how cells harvest and release energy.

A lot of electrons may be zipping around in the same atom. Despite moving really fast (around 3 million meters per second), they never collide. Why not? For one reason, electrons in an atom occupy different orbitals, which are defined volumes of space around the atomic nucleus.

To understand how orbitals work, imagine that an atom is a multilevel apartment building, with the nucleus in the basement. Each "floor" of the building corresponds to a certain energy level, and each has a certain number of "rooms" (orbitals) available for rent. Two electrons can occupy each room. Pairs of electrons populate rooms from the ground floor up; in other words, they fill orbitals from lower to higher energy levels. The farther an electron is from the nucleus in the basement, the greater its energy. An electron can move to a room on a higher floor if an energy input gives it a boost, but it immediately emits the extra energy and moves back down.

A **shell model** helps us visualize how electrons populate atoms (**FIGURE 2.2**). In this model, nested "shells" correspond to successively higher energy levels. Thus, each shell includes all of the rooms (orbitals) on one floor (energy level) of our atomic apartment building.

We draw a shell model of an atom by filling it with electrons (represented as balls or dots), from the innermost shell out, until there are as many electrons as the atom has protons. There is only one room on the first floor, one orbital at the lowest energy level. It fills up first. In hydrogen, the simplest atom, a single electron occupies that room (**FIGURE 2.2A**). Helium, with two protons, has two electrons that fill the room—and the first shell. In larger atoms, more electrons rent the second-floor rooms (**FIGURE 2.2B**). When the second floor fills, more electrons rent third-floor rooms (**FIGURE 2.2C**), and so on.

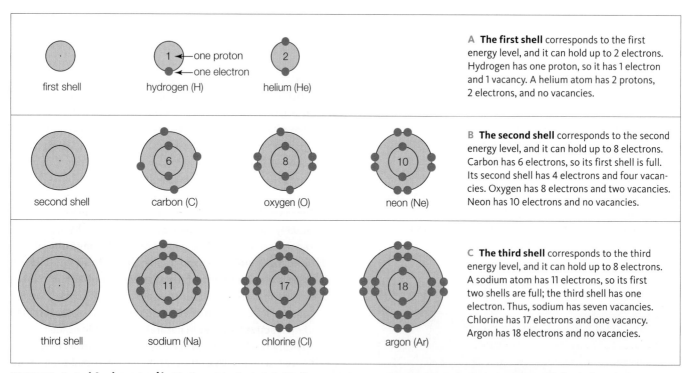

A **The first shell** corresponds to the first energy level, and it can hold up to 2 electrons. Hydrogen has one proton, so it has 1 electron and 1 vacancy. A helium atom has 2 protons, 2 electrons, and no vacancies.

B **The second shell** corresponds to the second energy level, and it can hold up to 8 electrons. Carbon has 6 electrons, so its first shell is full. Its second shell has 4 electrons and four vacancies. Oxygen has 8 electrons and two vacancies. Neon has 10 electrons and no vacancies.

C **The third shell** corresponds to the third energy level, and it can hold up to 8 electrons. A sodium atom has 11 electrons, so its first two shells are full; the third shell has one electron. Thus, sodium has seven vacancies. Chlorine has 17 electrons and one vacancy. Argon has 18 electrons and no vacancies.

FIGURE 2.2 {Animated} Shell models. Each circle (shell) represents one energy level. To make these models, we fill the shells with electrons from the innermost shell out, until there are as many electrons as the atom has protons. The number of protons in each model is indicated.

FIGURE IT OUT: Which of these models have unpaired electrons in their outer shell?   Answer: Hydrogen, carbon, oxygen, sodium, and chlorine

vacancy

no vacancy

ABOUT VACANCIES

When an atom's outermost shell is filled with electrons, we say that it has no vacancies. Any atom is in its most stable state when it has no vacancies. Helium, neon, and argon are examples of elements with no vacancies. Atoms of these elements are chemically stable, which means they have no tendency to interact with other atoms. Thus, these elements occur most frequently in nature as solitary atoms.

By contrast, when an atom's outermost shell has room for another electron, it has a vacancy. Atoms with vacancies tend to get rid of them by interacting with other atoms; in other words, they are chemically active. For example, the sodium atom (Na) depicted in **FIGURE 2.2C** has one electron in its outer (third) shell, which can hold eight. With seven vacancies, we can predict that this atom is chemically active.

In fact, this particular sodium atom is not just active, it is extremely so. Why? The shell model shows that a sodium atom has an unpaired electron, but in the real world, electrons really like to be in pairs when they occupy orbitals. Solitary atoms that have unpaired electrons are called **free radicals**. With some exceptions, free radicals are very unstable, easily forcing electrons upon other atoms or ripping electrons away from them. This property makes free radicals dangerous to life (we return to this topic in Section 5.5).

A free radical sodium atom can easily evict its one unpaired electron, so that its second shell—which is full of electrons—becomes its outermost, and no vacancies remain. This is the atom's most stable state. The vast majority of sodium atoms on Earth are like this one, with 11 protons and 10 electrons.

Atoms with an unequal number of protons and electrons are called **ions**. Ions carry a net (or overall) charge. Sodium ions (Na^+) offer an example of how atoms gain a positive charge by losing an electron (**FIGURE 2.3A**). Other atoms gain a negative charge by accepting an electron. For example, an uncharged chlorine atom has 17 protons and 17 electrons. The outermost shell of this atom can hold eight electrons,

---

free radical Atom with an unpaired electron.
ion Charged atom.
shell model Model of electron distribution in an atom.

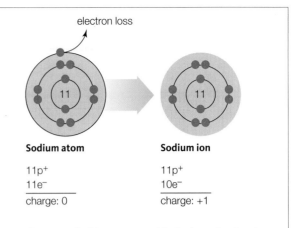

electron loss

Sodium atom

11p+
11e−
charge: 0

Sodium ion

11p+
10e−
charge: +1

A A sodium atom (Na) becomes a positively charged sodium ion (Na+) when it loses the single electron in its third shell. The atom's full second shell is now its outermost, so it has no vacancies.

electron gain

Chlorine atom

17p+
17e−
charge: 0

Chloride ion

17p+
18e−
charge: −1

B A chlorine atom (Cl) becomes a negatively charged chloride ion (Cl−) when it gains an electron and fills the vacancy in its third, outermost shell.

FIGURE 2.3 **Ion formation.**

but it has only seven. With one vacancy and one unpaired electron, we can predict—correctly—that this atom is chemically very active. An uncharged chlorine atom easily fills its third shell by accepting an electron. When that happens, the atom becomes a chloride ion (Cl−) with 17 protons, 18 electrons, and a net negative charge (**FIGURE 2.3B**).

TAKE-HOME MESSAGE 2.2

An atom's electrons are the basis of its chemical behavior.

Shells represent all electron orbitals at one energy level in an atom. When the outermost shell is not full of electrons, the atom has a vacancy.

Atoms with vacancies tend to interact with other atoms.

An atom can get rid of vacancies by participating in a chemical bond with another atom. A **chemical bond** is an attractive force that arises between two atoms when their electrons interact. Chemical bonds link atoms into molecules. In other words, each molecule consists of atoms held together in a particular number and arrangement by chemical bonds. For example, a water molecule consists of three atoms: two hydrogen atoms bonded to the same oxygen atom (**FIGURE 2.4**). A water molecule is also a **compound**, which means it has atoms of two or more elements. Other molecules, including molecular oxygen (a gas in air), have atoms of one element only.

The term "bond" applies to a continuous range of atomic interactions. However, we can categorize most bonds into distinct types based on their properties. Which type forms depends on the atoms taking part in the molecule.

IONIC BONDS

Two ions may stay together by the mutual attraction of their opposite charges, an association called an **ionic bond**. Ionic bonds can be quite strong. Ionically bonded sodium and chloride ions make up sodium chloride (NaCl), which we know as common table salt. A crystal of this substance consists of a cubic lattice of sodium and chloride ions interacting in ionic bonds (**FIGURE 2.5A**).

Ions retain their respective charges when participating in an ionic bond (**FIGURE 2.5B**). Thus, one "end" of an ionic bond has a positive charge, and the other "end" has a negative charge. Any such separation of charge into distinct positive and negative regions is called **polarity** (**FIGURE 2.5C**). A sodium chloride molecule is polar because the chloride ion keeps a very strong hold on its extra electron. In other words, it is strongly electronegative. **Electronegativity** is a measure of an atom's ability to pull electrons away from another atom. Electronegativity is not the same thing as charge. Rather, an atom's electronegativity depends on its size, how many vacancies it has, and what other atoms it is interacting with.

An ionic bond is very polar because the atoms that are participating in it have a very large difference in electronegativity. When atoms with a lower difference in electronegativity interact, they tend to form chemical bonds that are less polar than ionic bonds.

COVALENT BONDS

Covalent bonds form between atoms with a small difference in electronegativity or none at all. In a **covalent bond**, two atoms share a pair of electrons, so each atom's vacancy is partially filled (**FIGURE 2.6**). Sharing electrons links the two atoms, just as sharing a pair of earphones links two friends (*above*). Covalent bonds can be stronger than ionic bonds, but they are not always so.

TABLE 2.1 shows different ways of representing covalent bonds. In structural formulas, a line between two

---

FIGURE 2.4 The water molecule. Each water molecule has two hydrogen atoms bonded to the same oxygen atom.

one oxygen atom
two hydrogen atoms

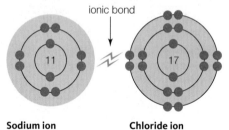

Na⁺ Cl⁻

A Each crystal of table salt consists of many sodium and chloride ions locked together in a cubic lattice by ionic bonds.

ionic bond

B The strong mutual attraction of opposite charges holds a sodium ion and a chloride ion together in an ionic bond.

Sodium ion

$11p^+$
$10e^-$
charge: +1

Chloride ion

$17p^+$
$18e^-$
charge: −1

C Ions taking part in an ionic bond retain their charge, so the molecule itself is polar. One side is positively charged (represented by a blue overlay); the other side is negatively charged (red overlay).

positive charge ←→ negative charge

FIGURE 2.5 Ionic bonds in table salt, or NaCl.

TABLE 2.1

Ways of Representing Molecules

Common name:	Water	Familiar term.
Chemical name:	Dihydrogen monoxide	Describes elemental composition.
Chemical formula:	H_2O	Indicates unvarying proportions of elements. Subscripts show number of atoms of an element per molecule. The absence of a subscript means one atom.
Structural formula:	H—O—H	Represents each covalent bond as a single line between atoms.
Structural model:		Shows relative sizes and positions of atoms in three dimensions.
Shell model:		Shows how pairs of electrons are shared in covalent bonds.

MOLECULAR HYDROGEN (H—H)

Two hydrogen atoms, each with one proton, share two electrons in a nonpolar covalent bond.

MOLECULAR OXYGEN (O=O)

Two oxygen atoms, each with eight protons, share four electrons in a double covalent bond.

WATER (H—O—H)

Two hydrogen atoms share electrons with an oxygen atom in two covalent bonds. The bonds are polar because the oxygen exerts a greater pull on the shared electrons than the hydrogens do.

FIGURE 2.6 {Animated} Covalent bonds, in which atoms fill vacancies by sharing electrons. Two electrons are shared in each covalent bond. When sharing is equal, the bond is nonpolar. When one atom exerts a greater pull on the electrons, the bond is polar.

atoms represents a single covalent bond, in which two atoms share one pair of electrons. For example, molecular hydrogen (H_2) has one covalent bond between hydrogen atoms (H—H). Two, three, or even four covalent bonds may form between atoms when they share multiple pairs of electrons. For example, two atoms sharing two pairs of electrons are connected by two covalent bonds, which are represented by a double line between the atoms. A double bond links the two oxygen atoms in molecular oxygen (O=O). Three lines indicate a triple bond, in which two atoms share three pairs of electrons. A triple covalent bond links the two nitrogen atoms in molecular nitrogen (N≡N). Comparing bonds between the same two atoms: A triple bond is stronger than a double bond, which is stronger than a single bond.

Double and triple bonds are not distinguished from single bonds in structural models, which show positions and relative sizes of the atoms in three dimensions. The bonds

are shown as one stick connecting two balls, which represent atoms. Elements are usually coded by color:

carbon   hydrogen   oxygen   nitrogen   phosphorus

Atoms share electrons unequally in a polar covalent bond. A bond between an oxygen atom and a hydrogen atom in a water molecule is an example. One atom (the oxygen, in this case) is a bit more electronegative. It pulls the electrons a little more toward its side of the bond, so that atom bears a slight negative charge. The atom at the other end of the bond (the hydrogen) bears a slight positive charge. Covalent bonds in compounds are usually polar. By contrast, atoms participating in a nonpolar covalent bond share electrons equally. There is no difference in charge between the two ends of such bonds. The bonds in molecular hydrogen (H_2), oxygen (O_2), and nitrogen (N_2) are nonpolar.

chemical bond An attractive force that arises between two atoms when their electrons interact.
compound Molecule that has atoms of more than one element.
covalent bond Chemical bond in which two atoms share a pair of electrons.
electronegativity Measure of the ability of an atom to pull electrons away from other atoms.
ionic bond Type of chemical bond in which a strong mutual attraction links ions of opposite charge.
polarity Separation of charge into positive and negative regions.

TAKE-HOME MESSAGE 2.3

A chemical bond forms between atoms when their electrons interact. A chemical bond may be ionic or covalent depending on the atoms taking part in it.

An ionic bond is a strong mutual attraction between two ions of opposite charge. Ionic bonds are very polar.

Atoms share a pair of electrons in a covalent bond. When the atoms share electrons unequally, the bond is polar.

2.4 WHAT ARE LIFE-SUSTAINING PROPERTIES OF WATER?

HYDROGEN BONDING IN WATER

Water has unique properties that arise from the two polar covalent bonds in each water molecule. Overall, the molecule has no charge, but the oxygen atom carries a slight negative charge; the hydrogen atoms, a slight positive charge. Thus, the molecule itself is polar (FIGURE 2.7A).

The polarity of individual water molecules attracts them to one another. The slight positive charge of a hydrogen atom in one water molecule is drawn to the slight negative charge of an oxygen atom in another. This type of interaction is called a hydrogen bond. A **hydrogen bond** is an attraction between a covalently bonded hydrogen atom and another atom taking part in a separate polar covalent bond (FIGURE 2.7B). Like ionic bonds, hydrogen bonds form by the mutual attraction of opposite charges. However, unlike ionic bonds, hydrogen bonds do not make molecules out of atoms, so they are not chemical bonds.

Hydrogen bonds are on the weaker end of the spectrum of atomic interactions, and they form and break much more easily than covalent or ionic bonds. Even so, many of them form, and collectively they are quite strong. As you will see, hydrogen bonds stabilize the characteristic structures of biological molecules such as DNA and proteins. They also form in tremendous numbers among water molecules (FIGURE 2.7C). Extensive hydrogen bonding among water molecules gives liquid water several special properties that make life possible.

WATER'S SPECIAL PROPERTIES

Water Is an Excellent Solvent The polarity of the water molecule and its ability to form hydrogen bonds make water an excellent **solvent**, which means that many other substances easily dissolve in it. Substances that dissolve easily in water are **hydrophilic** (water-loving). Ionic solids such as sodium chloride (NaCl) dissolve in water because the slight positive charge on each hydrogen atom in a water molecule attracts negatively charged ions (Cl$^-$), and the slight negative charge on the oxygen atom attracts positively charged ions (Na$^+$). Hydrogen bonds among many water molecules are collectively stronger than an ionic bond between two ions, so the solid dissolves as water molecules tug the ions apart and surround each one (*right*).

Sodium chloride is called a **salt** because it releases ions other than H$^+$ and OH$^-$ when it dissolves in water (more about these ions in the next section). When a substance such as NaCl dissolves, its component ions disperse uniformly among the molecules of liquid, and it becomes a **solute**. A uniform mixture such as salt dissolved in water is called a **solution**. Chemical bonds do not form between molecules of solute and solvent, so the proportions of the two substances in a solution can vary.

Nonionic solids such as sugars dissolve easily in water because their molecules can form hydrogen bonds with water molecules. Hydrogen bonding with water does not break the covalent bonds of such molecules; rather, it dissolves the substance by pulling individual molecules away from one another and keeping them apart.

Water does not interact with **hydrophobic** (water-dreading) substances such as oils. Oils consist of nonpolar molecules, and hydrogen bonds do not form between nonpolar molecules and water. When you mix oil and water, the water breaks into small droplets, but quickly begins to cluster into larger drops as new hydrogen bonds form among its molecules. The bonding excludes molecules of oil and

slight negative charge

slight positive charge

A Polarity of the water molecule. Each of the hydrogen atoms in a water molecule bears a slight positive charge (represented by a blue overlay). The oxygen atom carries a slight negative charge (red overlay).

a hydrogen bond

B A hydrogen bond is an attraction between a hydrogen atom and another atom taking part in a separate polar covalent bond.

C The many hydrogen bonds that form among water molecules impart special properties to liquid water.

FIGURE 2.7 {Animated} Hydrogen bonds in water.

CREDITS: (7A) © Cengage Learning 2015; (7B,C, inset) © Cengage Learning.

pushes them together into drops that rise to the surface of the water. The same interactions occur at the thin, oily membrane that separates the watery fluid inside cells from the watery fluid outside of them. As you will see in Chapter 3, such interactions give rise to the structure of cell membranes.

Water Has Cohesion Molecules of some substances

resist separating from one another, and the resistance gives rise to a property called **cohesion**. Water has cohesion because hydrogen bonds collectively exert a continuous pull on its individual molecules. You can see cohesion in water as surface tension, which means that the surface of liquid water behaves a bit like a sheet of elastic (*left*).

Cohesion plays a role in many processes that sustain multicelled bodies. As one example, water molecules constantly escape from the surface of liquid water as vapor, a process called **evaporation**. Evaporation is resisted by hydrogen bonding among water molecules. In other words, overcoming water's cohesion takes energy. Thus, evaporation sucks energy (in the form of heat) from liquid water, and this lowers the water's surface temperature. Evaporative water loss helps you and some other mammals cool off when you sweat in hot, dry weather. Sweat, which is about 99 percent water, cools the skin as it evaporates.

Cohesion works inside organisms, too. Consider how plants absorb water from soil as they grow. Water molecules evaporate from leaves, and replacements are pulled upward from roots. Cohesion makes it possible for columns of liquid water to rise from roots to leaves inside narrow pipelines of vascular tissue. In some trees, these pipelines extend hundreds of feet above the soil (Section 26.4 returns to this topic).

---

cohesion Property of a substance that arises from the tendency of its molecules to resist separating from one another.
evaporation Transition of a liquid to a vapor.
hydrogen bond Attraction between a covalently bonded hydrogen atom and another atom taking part in a separate covalent bond.
hydrophilic Describes a substance that dissolves easily in water.
hydrophobic Describes a substance that resists dissolving in water.
salt Compound that releases ions other than H^+ and OH^- when it dissolves in water.
solute A dissolved substance.
solution Uniform mixure of solute completely dissolved in solvent.
solvent Liquid that can dissolve other substances.
temperature Measure of molecular motion.

FIGURE 2.8 **{Animated}** Hydrogen bonds lock water molecules in a rigid lattice in ice. The molecules in this lattice pack less densely than in liquid water, which is why ice floats on water. A covering of ice can insulate water underneath it, thus keeping aquatic organisms from freezing during harsh winters.

Water Stabilizes Temperature All atoms jiggle nonstop, so the molecules they make up jiggle too. We measure the energy of this motion as degrees of **temperature**. Adding energy (in the form of heat, for example) makes the jiggling faster, so the temperature rises.

Hydrogen bonding keeps water molecules from jiggling as much as they would otherwise, so it takes more heat to raise the temperature of water compared with other liquids. Temperature stability is an important part of homeostasis, because most of the molecules of life function properly only within a certain range of temperature.

Below 0°C (32°F), water molecules do not jiggle enough to break hydrogen bonds, and they become locked in the rigid, lattice-like bonding pattern of ice (**FIGURE 2.8**). Individual water molecules pack less densely in ice than they do in water, which is why ice floats on water. Sheets of ice that form on the surface of ponds, lakes, and streams can insulate the water under them from subfreezing air temperatures. Such "ice blankets" protect aquatic organisms during cold winters.

CREDITS: (in text) © Herbert Schnekenburger; (8) top, Vicki Rosenberg, www.flickr.com/photots/roseofredrock; bottom, © Cengage Learning.

2.5 WHY ARE HYDROGEN IONS IMPORTANT IN BIOLOGICAL SYSTEMS?

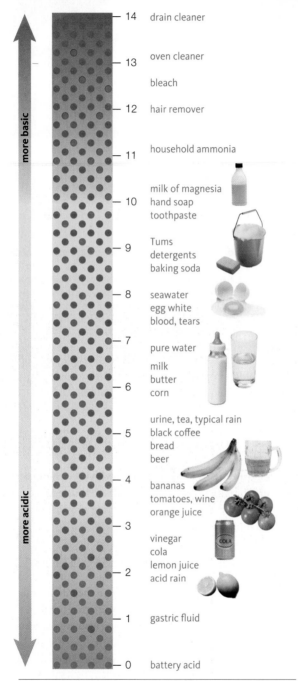

FIGURE 2.9 A pH scale. Here, red dots signify hydrogen ions (H+) and blue dots signify hydroxyl ions (OH−). Also shown are the approximate pH values for some common solutions.

This pH scale ranges from 0 (most acidic) to 14 (most basic). A change of one unit on the scale corresponds to a tenfold change in the amount of H+ ions.

 FIGURE IT OUT: What is the approximate pH of cola?

Answer: 2.5

When water is liquid, some of its molecules spontaneously separate into hydrogen ions (H+) and hydroxide ions (OH−). These ions can combine again to form water:

$$H_2O \longrightarrow H^+ + OH^- \longrightarrow H_2O$$

water   hydrogen   hydroxide   water
              ions   ions

Concentration refers to the amount of a particular solute dissolved in a given volume of fluid. Hydrogen ion (H+) concentration is a special case. We measure the amount of hydrogen ions in a solution using a value called **pH**. When the number of H+ ions equals the number of OH− ions in the liquid, the pH is 7, or neutral. The higher the number of hydrogen ions, the lower the pH. A one-unit decrease in pH corresponds to a tenfold increase in the number of H+ ions, and a one-unit increase corresponds to a tenfold decrease in the number of H+ ions (**FIGURE 2.9**).

One way to get a sense of the pH scale is to taste dissolved baking soda (pH 9), pure water (pH 7), and lemon juice (pH 2). Nearly all of life's chemistry occurs near pH 7. Most of your body's internal environment (tissue fluids and blood) stays between pH 7.3 and 7.5.

Substances called **bases** accept hydrogen ions, so they can raise the pH of fluids and make them basic, or alkaline (above pH 7). **Acids** give up hydrogen ions when they dissolve in water, so they lower the pH of fluids and make them acidic (below pH 7).

Strong acids ionize completely in water to give up all of their H+ ions; weak acids give up only some of them. Hydrochloric acid (HCl) is an example of a strong acid: its H+ and Cl− ions stay separated in water. Inside your stomach, the H+ from HCl makes gastric fluid acidic (pH 1–2). Carbonic acid is an example of a weak acid. It forms when carbon dioxide gas (CO2) dissolves in the watery, fluid portion of human blood:

$$CO_2 + H_2O \longrightarrow H_2CO_3$$

carbon dioxide   carbonic acid

A carbonic acid molecule can break apart into a hydrogen ion and a bicarbonate ion, which in turn can recombine to form carbonic acid again:

$$H_2CO_3 \longrightarrow H^+ + HCO_3^- \longrightarrow H_2CO_3$$

carbonic acid   bicarbonate   carbonic acid

Together, carbonic acid and bicarbonate constitute a **buffer**, a set of chemicals that can keep the pH of a solution stable by alternately donating and accepting ions that contribute to pH. For example, when a base is added to an unbuffered fluid, the number of OH− ions increases, so the pH rises. However, if the fluid is buffered, the addition of base causes the buffer to release H+ ions. These combine with OH− ions to form water, which has no effect on pH. Excess hydrogen ions combine with the buffer, so they do not contribute to pH. Thus, the pH of a buffered fluid stays the same when base or acid is added.

CREDITS: (9) art: © Cengage Learning 2015; photos: © JupiterImages Corporation; (in text) © Cengage Learning 2015.

Under normal circumstances, the fluids inside cells (as well as those inside bodies) stay within a consistent range of pH because they are buffered. For example, excess OH^- in blood combines with the H^+ from carbonic acid to form water, which does not contribute to pH. Excess H^+ in blood combines with bicarbonate, so it does not affect pH. This exchange of ions keeps the blood pH stable, but only up to a certain point. A buffer can neutralize only so many ions; even slightly more than that limit and the pH of the fluid will change dramatically.

Most biological molecules can function properly only within a narrow range of pH. Even a slight deviation from that range can halt cellular processes, so buffer failure can be catastrophic in a biological system. For instance, when breathing is impaired suddenly, carbon dioxide gas accumulates in tissues, so too much carbonic acid forms in blood. The resulting decline in blood pH may cause the person to enter a coma (a dangerous level of unconsciousness). By contrast, hyperventilation (sustained rapid breathing) causes the body to lose too much CO_2. The loss results in a rise in blood pH. If blood pH rises too much, prolonged muscle spasm (tetany) or coma may occur.

Burning fossil fuels such as coal releases sulfur and nitrogen compounds that affect the pH of rain and other forms of precipitation. Rainwater is not buffered, so the addition of acids or bases has a dramatic effect. In places with a lot of fossil fuel emissions, the rain and fog can be more acidic than vinegar. The corrosive effect of this acid

 rain is visible in urban areas (*left*). Acid rain also drastically changes the pH of water in soil, lakes, and streams. Such changes can overwhelm the buffering capacity of fluids inside organisms, with lethal effects. We return to acid rain in Section 44.4.

acid Substance that releases hydrogen ions in water.
base Substance that accepts hydrogen ions in water.
buffer Set of chemicals that can keep the pH of a solution stable by alternately donating and accepting ions that contribute to pH.
concentration Amount of solute per unit volume of solution.
pH Measure of the number of hydrogen ions in a fluid.

TAKE-HOME MESSAGE 2.5

The number of hydrogen ions in a fluid determines its pH. Most biological systems function properly only within a narrow range of pH.

Acids release hydrogen ions in water; bases accept them. Salts release ions other than H^+ and OH^-.

Buffers help keep pH stable. Inside organisms, they are part of homeostasis.

Application: Sustainability

FIGURE 2.10 Mercury that falls on Earth's oceans accumulates in the bodies of tuna and other large predatory fish.

MERCURY IS A TOXIC ELEMENT. Most of it is safely locked away in rocks, but volcanic activity and other geologic processes release it into the atmosphere. So do human activities, especially burning coal. Airborne mercury can drift long distances before settling to Earth's surface, where microbes combine it with carbon to form a substance called methylmercury.

Unlike mercury alone, methylmercury easily crosses skin and mucous membranes. In water, it ends up in the tissues of aquatic organisms. All fish and shellfish contain it. Humans contain it too, mainly as a result of eating seafood. When mercury enters the body, it damages the nervous system, brain, kidneys, and other organs. An average-sized adult who ingests as little as 200 micrograms of methylmercury may experience blurred vision, tremors, itching or burning sensations, and loss of coordination. Exposure to larger amounts can result in thought and memory impairment, coma, and death. Methylmercury in a pregnant woman's blood passes to her unborn child, along with a legacy of permanent developmental problems.

It takes months or even years for mercury to be cleared from the body, so the toxin can build up to high levels if even small amounts are ingested on a regular basis. That is why large predatory fish have a lot of mercury in their tissues (FIGURE 2.10). It is also why the U.S. Environmental Protection Agency recommends that adult humans ingest less than 0.1 microgram of mercury per kilogram of body weight per day. For an average-sized person, that limit works out to be about 7 micrograms per day, which is not a big amount if you eat seafood. A typical 6-ounce can of albacore tuna contains about 60 micrograms of mercury, and the occasional can has many times that amount. It does not matter if the fish is canned, grilled, or raw, because methylmercury is unaffected by cooking. Eat a medium-sized tuna steak, and you could be getting more than 700 micrograms of mercury along with it.

Summary

SECTION 2.1 Atoms consist of **electrons**, which carry a negative **charge**, moving about a **nucleus** of positively charged **protons** and uncharged **neutrons** (**TABLE 2.2**). The **periodic table** lists **elements** in order of **atomic number**. **Isotopes** of an element differ in the number of neutrons. The total number of protons and neutrons is the **mass number**. **Tracers** can be made with **radioisotopes**, which, by a process called **radioactive decay**, emit particles and energy when their nucleus spontaneously breaks up.

SECTION 2.2 Which atomic orbital an electron occupies depends on its energy. A **shell model** represents successive energy levels as concentric circles. Atoms tend to get rid of vacancies. Many do so by gaining or losing electrons, thereby becoming **ions**. Unpaired electrons make **free radicals** chemically active.

SECTION 2.3 A **chemical bond** is an attractive force that unites two atoms as a molecule. A **compound** consists of two or more elements. Atoms form different types of bonds depending on their **electronegativity**. The mutual attraction of opposite charges can hold atoms together in an **ionic bond**, which is completely polar (**polarity** is separation of charge). Atoms share a pair of electrons in a **covalent bond**, which is nonpolar if the sharing is equal, and polar if it is not.

SECTION 2.4 Two polar covalent bonds give each water molecule an overall polarity. **Hydrogen bonds** that form among water molecules in tremendous numbers are the basis of water's unique properties. Water has **cohesion** and a capacity to act as a **solvent** for **salts** and other polar **solutes**; and it resists **temperature** changes. **Hydrophilic** substances dissolve easily in water to form **solutions**; **hydrophobic** substances do not. **Evaporation** is the transition of liquid to vapor.

SECTION 2.5 A solute's **concentration** refers to the amount of solute in a given volume of fluid; **pH** reflects the number of hydrogen ions (H^+). **Acids** release hydrogen ions in water; **bases** accept them. A **buffer** can keep a solution within a consistent range of pH. Most cell and body fluids are buffered because most molecules of life work only within a narrow range of pH.

SECTION 2.6 Interactions between atoms make the molecules that sustain life, and also some that destroy it. Mercury in air pollution ends up in the bodies of fish, and in turn, in the bodies of humans.

TABLE 2.2

Players in the Chemisty of Life

Atoms	Particles that are basic building blocks of all matter.
Proton (p^+)	Positively charged particle of an atom's nucleus.
Electron (e^-)	Negatively charged particle that can occupy a defined volume of space (orbital) around an atom's nucleus.
Neutron	Uncharged particle of an atom's nucleus.
Element	Pure substance that consists entirely of atoms with the same, characteristic number of protons.
Isotopes	Atoms of an element that differ in the number of neutrons.
Radioisotope	Unstable isotope that emits particles and energy when its nucleus breaks up.
Tracer	Molecule that has a detectable component such as a radioisotope. Used to track the movement or destination of the molecule in a biological system.
Ion	Atom that carries a charge after it has gained or lost one or more electrons. A single proton without an electron is a hydrogen ion (H^+).
Molecule	Two or more atoms joined in a chemical bond.
Compound	Molecule of two or more different elements in unvarying proportions (for example, water: H_2O).
Solute	Substance dissolved in a solvent.
Hydrophilic	Refers to a substance that dissolves easily in water. Such substances consist of polar molecules.
Hydrophobic	Refers to a substance that resists dissolving in water. Such substances consist of nonpolar molecules.
Acid	Compound that releases H^+ when dissolved in water.
Base	Compound that accepts H^+ when dissolved in water.
Salt	Ionic compound that releases ions other than H^+ or OH^- when dissolved in water.
Solvent	Substance that can dissolve other substances.

Self-Quiz Answers in Appendix VII

1. What atom has only one proton?
   - a. hydrogen
   - b. an isotope
   - c. a free radical
   - d. a radioisotope

2. A molecule into which a radioisotope has been incorporated can be used as a(n) _____ .
   - a. compound
   - b. tracer
   - c. salt
   - d. acid

3. Which of the following statements is incorrect?
   - a. Isotopes have the same atomic number and different mass numbers.
   - b. Atoms have about the same number of electrons as protons.
   - c. All ions are atoms.
   - d. Free radicals are dangerous because they emit energy.

4. In the periodic table, symbols for the elements are arranged according to _____ .
   - a. size
   - b. charge
   - c. mass number
   - d. atomic number

5. An ion is an atom that has _____ .
   - a. the same number of electrons and protons
   - b. a different number of electrons and protons
   - c. electrons, protons, and neutrons

Data Analysis Activities

Radioisotopes in PET Scans Positron-emission tomography (PET) helps us "see" a functional process inside the body. By this procedure, a radioactive sugar or other tracer is injected into a patient, who is then moved into a scanner. Inside the patient's body, cells with differing rates of activity take up the tracer at different rates. The scanner detects radioactive decay wherever the tracer is, then translates that data into an image.

1. What conclusion does **FIGURE 2.11** and its caption suggest about the behavior of a smoker compared with that of a nonsmoker?

2. What is an alternate interpretation of the differences between the results of these two PET scans?

3. This experiment compares two human individuals, who undoubtedly differ in factors other than smoking. What would be an appropriate control for this study?

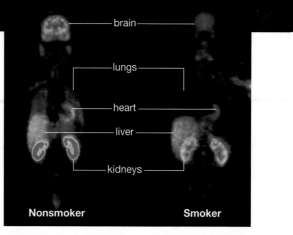

FIGURE 2.11 Two PET scans showing the activity of a molecule called MAO-B in the body of a nonsmoker (*left*) and a smoker (*right*). The activity is color-coded from red (highest activity) to purple (lowest). Low MAO-B activity is associated with violence, impulsiveness, and other behavioral problems.

---

6. The measure of an atom's ability to pull electrons away from another atom is called _____ .
   a. electronegativity   b. charge   c. polarity

7. The mutual attraction of opposite charges holds atoms together as molecules in a(n) _____ bond.
   a. ionic   c. polar covalent
   b. hydrogen   d. nonpolar covalent

8. Atoms share electrons unequally in a(n) _____ bond.
   a. ionic   c. polar covalent
   b. hydrogen   d. nonpolar covalent

9. A(n) _____ substance repels water.
   a. acidic   c. hydrophobic
   b. basic   d. polar

10. A salt does not release _____ in water.
    a. ions   b. energy   c. H^+

11. Hydrogen ions (H^+) are _____ .
    a. indicated by a pH scale   c. in blood
    b. protons   d. all of the above

12. When dissolved in water, a(n) _____ donates H^+; a(n) _____ accepts H^+.
    a. acid; base   c. buffer; solute
    b. base; acid   d. base; buffer

13. A(n) _____ can help keep the pH of a solution stable.
    a. covalent bond   c. buffer
    b. hydrogen bond   d. pH

14. A _____ is dissolved in a solvent.
    a. molecule   b. solute   c. salt

15. Match the terms with their most suitable description.
    ___ hydrophilic   a. protons > electrons
    ___ atomic number   b. number of protons in nucleus
    ___ hydrogen bonds   c. polar; dissolves easily in water
    ___ positive charge   d. collectively strong
    ___ temperature   e. protons < electrons
    ___ negative charge   f. measure of molecular motion

Critical Thinking

1. Alchemists were medieval scholars and philosophers who were the forerunners of modern-day chemists. Many spent their lives trying to transform lead (atomic number 82) into gold (atomic number 79). Explain why they never did succeed in that endeavor.

2. Draw a shell model of a lithium atom (Li), which has 3 protons, then predict whether the majority of lithium atoms on Earth are uncharged, positively charged, or negatively charged.

3. Polonium is a rare element with 33 radioisotopes. The most common one, ^{210}Po, has 82 protons and 128 neutrons. When ^{210}Po decays, it emits an alpha particle, which is a helium nucleus (2 protons and 2 neutrons). ^{210}Po decay is tricky to detect because alpha particles do not carry very much energy compared to other forms of radiation. They can be stopped by, for example, a sheet of paper or a few inches of air. This property is one reason why authorities failed to discover toxic amounts of ^{210}Po in the body of former KGB agent Alexander Litvinenko until after he died suddenly and mysteriously in 2006. What element does an atom of ^{210}Po change into after it emits an alpha particle?

4. Some undiluted acids are not as corrosive as when they are diluted with water. That is why lab workers are told to wipe off splashes with a towel before washing. Explain.

CENGAGE **brain**.com To access course materials, please visit www.cengagebrain.com.

Rice has been cultivated for thousands of years. Carbohydrate-packed seeds make this grain the most important food source for humans worldwide.

3

Links to Earlier Concepts

Having learned about atomic interactions (Section 2.3), you are now in a position to understand the structure of the molecules of life. Keep the big picture in mind by reviewing Section 1.1. You will be building on your knowledge of covalent bonding (2.3), acids and bases (2.5), and the effects of hydrogen bonds (2.4).

MOLECULES OF LIFE ⟩ KEY CONCEPTS

STRUCTURE DICTATES FUNCTION

Complex carbohydrates and lipids, proteins, and nucleic acids are assembled from simpler molecules. Functional groups add chemical character to a backbone of carbon atoms.

CARBOHYDRATES

Cells use carbohydrates as structural materials, for fuel, and to store and transport energy. They can build different complex carbohydrates from the same simple sugars.

LIPIDS

Lipids are the main structural component of all cell membranes. Cells use them to make other compounds, to store energy, and as waterproofing or lubricating substances.

PROTEINS

Proteins are the most diverse molecules of life. They include enzymes and structural materials. A protein's function arises from and depends on its structure.

NUCLEIC ACIDS

Nucleotides are building blocks of nucleic acids; some have additional roles in metabolism. DNA stores a cell's heritable information. RNA helps put that information to use.

THE STUFF OF LIFE: CARBON

The same elements that make up a living body also occur in nonliving things, but their proportions differ. For example, compared to sand or seawater, a human body contains a much larger proportion of carbon atoms. Why? Unlike sand or seawater, a body consists of a very high proportion of the molecules of life—complex carbohydrates and lipids, proteins, and nucleic acids—which in turn consist of a high proportion of carbon atoms. Molecules that have primarily hydrogen and carbon atoms are said to be **organic**. The term is a holdover from a time when these molecules were thought to be made only by living things, as opposed to the "inorganic" molecules that formed by nonliving processes.

Carbon's importance to life arises from its versatile bonding behavior. Carbon has four vacancies (Section 2.2), so it can form four covalent bonds with other atoms, including other carbon atoms. Many organic molecules have a backbone—a chain of carbon atoms—to which other atoms attach. The ends of a backbone may join to form a carbon ring structure (**FIGURE 3.1**). Carbon's ability to form chains and rings, and also to bond with many other elements, means that atoms of this element can be assembled into a wide variety of organic compounds.

We represent organic molecules in several ways. The structure of many organic molecules is quite complex (**FIGURE 3.2A**). For clarity, we may omit some of the bonds in a structural formula. Hydrogen atoms bonded to a carbon backbone may also be omitted. Carbon rings are often represented as polygons (**FIGURE 3.2B**). If no atom is shown at a corner or at the end of a bond, a carbon is implied there. Ball-and-stick models are useful for representing smaller organic compounds (**FIGURE 3.2C**). Space-filling models show a molecule's overall shape (**FIGURE 3.2D**). Proteins and nucleic acids are often represented as ribbon structures, which, as you will see in Section 3.4, show how the backbone folds and twists.

FROM STRUCTURE TO FUNCTION

An organic molecule that consists only of hydrogen and carbon atoms is called a **hydrocarbon**. Hydrocarbons are generally nonpolar. Methane, the simplest kind, is one carbon atom bonded to four hydrogen atoms. Other organic

---

FIGURE 3.1 Carbon rings.

A Carbon's versatile bonding behavior allows it to form a variety of structures, including rings.

B Carbon rings form the framework of many sugars, starches, and fats (such as those found in doughnuts).

A A structural formula for an organic molecule—even a simple one—can be very complicated. The overall structure is obscured by detail.

B Structural formulas of organic molecules are typically simplified by using polygons as symbols for rings, omitting some bonds and element labels.

C A ball-and-stick model is often used to show the arrangement of atoms and bonds in three dimensions.

D A space-filling model can be used to show a molecule's overall shape. Individual atoms are visible in this model. Space-filling models of larger molecules often show only the surface contours.

FIGURE 3.2 Modeling an organic molecule. All of these models represent the same molecule: glucose.

---

condensation Chemical reaction in which an enzyme builds a large molecule from smaller subunits; water also forms.

enzyme Organic molecule that speeds up a reaction without being changed by it.

functional group An atom (other than hydrogen) or a small molecular group bonded to a carbon of an organic compound; imparts a specific chemical property.

hydrocarbon Compound or region of one that consists only of carbon and hydrogen atoms.

hydrolysis Water-requiring chemical reaction in which an enzyme breaks a molecule into smaller subunits.

metabolism All of the enzyme-mediated chemical reactions by which cells acquire and use energy as they build and break down organic molecules.

monomers Molecules that are subunits of polymers.

organic Describes a molecule that consists mainly of carbon and hydrogen atoms.

polymer Molecule that consists of multiple monomers.

reaction Process of molecular change.

A Condensation. Cells build a large molecule from smaller ones by this reaction. An enzyme removes a hydroxyl group from one molecule and a hydrogen atom from another. A covalent bond forms between the two molecules; water also forms.

B Hydrolysis. Cells split a large molecule into smaller ones by this water-requiring reaction. An enzyme attaches a hydroxyl group and a hydrogen atom (both from water) at the cleavage site.

FIGURE 3.3 {Animated} Two common metabolic processes by which cells build and break down organic molecules.

TABLE 3.1

Some Functional Groups in Biological Molecules

Group	Structure	Character	Formula	Found in:
acetyl		polar, acidic	$-COCH_3$	some proteins, coenzymes
aldehyde		polar, reactive	$-CHO$	simple sugars
amide		weakly basic, stable, rigid	$-C(O)N-$	proteins nucleotide bases
amine		very basic	$-NH_2$	nucleotide bases amino acids
carboxyl		very acidic	$-COOH$	fatty acids amino acids
hydroxyl	$-O-H$	polar	$-OH$	alcohols sugars
ketone		polar, acidic	$-CO-$	simple sugars nucleotide bases
methyl	$-CH_3$	nonpolar	$-CH_3$	fatty acids some amino acids
sulfhydryl	$-S-H$	forms rigid disulfide bonds	$-SH$	cysteine many cofactors
phosphate		polar, reactive	$-PO_4$	nucleotides DNA, RNA phospholipids proteins

molecules, including the molecules of life, have at least one functional group. A **functional group** is an atom (other than hydrogen) or small molecular group covalently bonded to a carbon atom of an organic compound. These groups impart chemical properties such as acidity or polarity (**TABLE 3.1**). The chemical behavior of the molecules of life arises mainly from the number, kind, and arrangement of their functional groups.

All biological systems are based on the same organic molecules, a similarity that is one of many legacies of life's common origin. However, the details of those molecules differ among organisms. Just as atoms bonded in different numbers and arrangements form different molecules, simple organic building blocks bonded in different numbers and arrangements form different versions of the molecules of life. These small organic molecules—simple sugars, fatty acids, amino acids, and nucleotides—are called **monomers** when they are used as subunits of larger molecules. Molecules that consist of multiple monomers are called **polymers**.

Cells build polymers from monomers, and break down polymers to release monomers. These and any other processes of molecular change are called chemical **reactions**. Cells constantly run reactions as they acquire and use energy to stay alive, grow, and reproduce—activities that are collectively called **metabolism**. Metabolism requires **enzymes**, which are organic molecules (usually proteins) that speed up reactions without being changed by them.

In many metabolic reactions, large organic molecules are assembled from smaller ones. With **condensation**, an enzyme covalently bonds two molecules together. Water (H—O—H) usually forms as a product of condensation when a hydroxyl group (—OH) from one of the molecules combines with a hydrogen atom (—H) from the other molecule (**FIGURE 3.3A**). With **hydrolysis**, the reverse of condensation, an enzyme breaks apart a large organic molecule into smaller ones. During hydrolysis, a bond between two atoms breaks when a hydroxyl group gets attached to one of the atoms, and a hydrogen atom gets attached to the other (**FIGURE 3.3B**). The hydroxyl group and hydrogen atom come from a water molecule, so this reaction requires water.

We will revisit enzymes and metabolic reactions in Chapter 5. The remainder of this chapter introduces the different types of biological molecules and the monomers from which they are built.

TAKE-HOME MESSAGE 3.1

The molecules of life are organic, which means they consist mainly of carbon and hydrogen atoms. Functional groups bonded to their carbon backbone impart chemical characteristics to these molecules.

Cells assemble large polymers from smaller monomer molecules. They also break apart polymers into monomers.

CREDITS: (3) From Starr/Taggart/Evers/Starr, Biology, 12E. © 2009 Cengage Learning; (Table 3.1) © Cengage Learning.

3.2 WHAT IS A CARBOHYDRATE?

glycolaldehyde

Molecules of glycolaldehyde, a simple sugar, were recently discovered floating in gas surrounding a young, sunlike star. The finding is important because glycolaldehyde can react with other molecules found in space gas to form ribose, the five-carbon monosaccharide component of RNA. "What is really exciting about our findings is that the sugar molecules are falling in towards one of the stars of the system," says team member Cécile Favre. "The sugar molecules are not only in the right place to find their way onto a planet, but they are also going in the right direction." The discovery does not prove that life has developed elsewhere in the universe—but it implies that there is no reason it could not. It shows that the carbon-rich molecules that are the building blocks of life can be present even before planets have begun forming.

FIGURE 3.4 Astronomers made a sweet discovery in 2012.

Carbohydrates are organic compounds that consist of carbon, hydrogen, and oxygen in a 1:2:1 ratio. Cells use different kinds as structural materials, for fuel, and for storing and transporting energy. The three main types of carbohydrates in living systems are monosaccharides, oligosaccharides, and polysaccharides.

SIMPLE SUGARS

"Saccharide" is from *sacchar*, a Greek word that means sugar. Monosaccharides (one sugar) are the simplest type of carbohydrate. These molecules have extremely important biological roles. Common monosaccharides have a backbone of five or six carbon atoms (carbon atoms of sugars are numbered in a standard way: 1′, 2′, 3′, and so on, as illustrated in the model of glucose on the *right*).

glucose

Glucose has six carbon atoms. Five-carbon monosaccharides are components of the nucleotide monomers of DNA and RNA (**FIGURE 3.4**). Two or more hydroxyl (—OH) groups impart solubility to a sugar molecule, which means that monosaccharides move easily through the water-based internal environments of all organisms.

Cells use monosaccharides for cellular fuel, because breaking the bonds of sugars releases energy that can be harnessed to power other cellular processes (we return to this important metabolic process in Chapter 7). Monosaccharides are also used as precursors, or parent molecules, that are remodeled into other molecules; and as structural materials to build larger molecules.

POLYMERS OF SIMPLE SUGARS

Oligosaccharides are short chains of covalently bonded monosaccharides (*oligo–* means a few). Disaccharides consist of two monosaccharide monomers. The lactose in milk, with one glucose and one galactose, is a disaccharide. Sucrose, the most plentiful sugar in nature, has a glucose and a fructose unit (sucrose extracted from sugarcane or sugar beets is our table sugar). Oligosaccharides attached to lipids or proteins have important functions in immunity.

Foods that we call "complex" carbohydrates consist mainly of polysaccharides: chains of hundreds or thousands of monosaccharide monomers. The chains may be straight or branched, and can consist of one or many types of monosaccharides. The most common polysaccharides are cellulose, starch, and glycogen. All consist only of glucose monomers, but as substances their properties are very different. Why? The answer begins with differences in patterns of covalent bonding that link their monomers.

Cellulose, the major structural material of plants, is the most abundant biological molecule on Earth. Its long, straight chains are locked into tight, sturdy bundles by hydrogen bonds (**FIGURE 3.5A**). The bundles form tough fibers that act like reinforcing rods inside stems and other plant parts, helping these structures resist wind and other forms of mechanical stress. Cellulose does not dissolve in water, and it is not easily broken down. Some bacteria and fungi make enzymes that can break it apart into its component sugars, but humans and other mammals do not. Dietary fiber, or "roughage," usually refers to the cellulose in our vegetable foods. Bacteria that live in the guts of termites and grazers such as cattle and sheep help these animals digest the cellulose in plants.

In starch, a different covalent bonding pattern between glucose monomers makes a chain that coils up into a spiral (**FIGURE 3.5B**). Like

CREDITS: (4) photo, NASA/JPL-Caltech/UCLA; inset, © Cengage Learning 2015; (in text) © Cengage Learning.

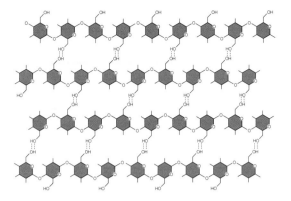

A **Cellulose**
Cellulose is the main structural component of plants.
Above, in cellulose, chains of glucose monomers stretch side by side and hydrogen-bond at many —OH groups. The hydrogen bonds stabilize the chains in tight bundles that form long fibers. Very few types of organisms can digest this tough, insoluble material.

B **Starch**
Starch is the main energy reserve in plants, which store it in their roots, stems, leaves, seeds, and fruits. Below, in starch, a series of glucose monomers form a chain that coils up.

C **Glycogen**
Glycogen functions as an energy reservoir in animals, including people. It is especially abundant in the liver and muscles. Above, glycogen consists of highly branched chains of glucose monomers.

FIGURE 3.5 **{Animated}** Three of the most common complex carbohydrates and their locations in a few organisms. Each polysaccharide consists only of glucose subunits, but different bonding patterns result in substances with very different properties.

cellulose, starch does not dissolve easily in water, but it is more easily broken down than cellulose. These properties make starch ideal for storing sugars in the watery, enzyme-filled interior of plant cells. Most plant leaves make glucose during the day, and their cells store it by building starch. At night, hydrolysis enzymes break the bonds between starch's glucose monomers. The released glucose can be broken down immediately for energy, or converted to sucrose that is transported to other parts of the plant. Humans also have hydrolysis enzymes that break down starch, so this carbohydrate is an important component of our food.

Animals store their sugars in the form of glycogen. The covalent bonding pattern between glucose monomers in glycogen forms highly branched chains (**FIGURE 3.5C**). Muscle and liver cells contain most of the body's stored

glycogen. When the sugar level in blood falls, liver cells break down stored glycogen, and the released glucose subunits enter the blood.

In chitin, a polysaccharide similar to cellulose, long, unbranching chains of nitrogen-containing monomers are linked by hydrogen bonds. As a structural material, chitin is durable, translucent, and flexible. It strengthens hard parts of many animals, including the outer cuticle of lobsters (*left*), and it reinforces the cell wall of many fungi.

carbohydrate Molecule that consists primarily of carbon, hydrogen, and oxygen atoms in a 1:2:1 ratio.
cellulose Tough, insoluble carbohydrate that is the major structural material in plants.

TAKE-HOME MESSAGE 3.2

Cells use simple carbohydrates (sugars) for energy and to build other molecules.

Glucose monomers, bonded in different ways, form complex carbohydrates, including cellulose, starch, and glycogen.

CREDITS: (5A–C), © Cengage Learning 2015; middle, © JupiterImages Corporation; (bottom right inset) David Liittschwager/National Geographic Creative.

Lipids are fatty, oily, or waxy organic compounds. Many lipids incorporate **fatty acids**, which are small organic molecules that consist of a long hydrocarbon "tail" with a carboxyl group "head" (FIGURE 3.6). The tail is hydrophobic; the carboxyl group makes the head hydrophilic (and acidic). You are already familiar with the properties of fatty acids because these molecules are the main component of soap. The hydrophobic tails of fatty acids in soap attract oily dirt, and the hydrophilic heads dissolve the dirt in water.

Saturated fatty acids have only single bonds linking the carbons in their tails. In other words, their carbon chains are fully saturated with hydrogen atoms (FIGURE 3.6A). Saturated fatty acid tails are flexible and they wiggle freely. Double bonds between carbons of unsaturated fatty acid tails limit their flexibility (FIGURE 3.6B,C).

FATS

The carboxyl group head of a fatty acid can easily form a covalent bond with another molecule. When it bonds to a glycerol, a type of alcohol, it loses its hydrophilic character and becomes part of a fat. **Fats** are lipids with one, two,

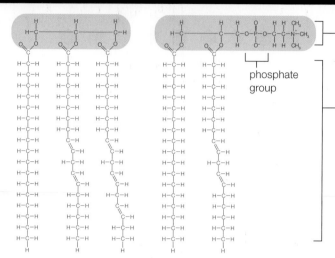

A The three fatty acid tails of a triglyceride are attached to a glycerol head.

B The two fatty acid tails of this phospholipid are attached to a phosphate-containing head.

phosphate group

FIGURE 3.7 {Animated} Lipids with fatty acid tails.

or three fatty acids bonded to the same glycerol. A fat with three fatty acid tails is called a **triglyceride** (FIGURE 3.7A). Triglycerides are entirely hydrophobic, so they do not dissolve in water. Most "neutral" fats, such as butter and vegetable oils, are examples. Triglycerides are the most abundant and richest energy source in vertebrate bodies. Gram for gram, fats store more energy than carbohydrates.

Butter, cream, and other high-fat animal products have a high proportion of **saturated fats**, which means they consist mainly of triglycerides with three saturated fatty acid tails. Saturated fats tend to be solid at room temperature because their floppy saturated tails can pack tightly. Most vegetable oils are **unsaturated fats**, which means they consist mainly of triglycerides with one or more unsaturated fatty acid tails. Each double bond in a fatty acid tail makes a rigid kink. Kinky tails do not pack tightly, so unsaturated fats are typically liquid at room temperature.

FIGURE 3.6 {Animated} Fatty acids. **A** The tail of stearic acid is fully saturated with hydrogen atoms. **B** Linoleic acid, with two double bonds, is unsaturated. The first double bond occurs at the sixth carbon from the end, so linoleic acid is called an omega-6 fatty acid. Omega-6 and **C** omega-3 fatty acids are "essential fatty acids." Your body does not make them, so they must come from food.

hydrophilic "head" (acidic carboxyl group)

hydrophobic "tail"

A stearic acid (saturated)

B linoleic acid (omega-6)

C linolenic acid (omega-3)

fat Lipid that consists of a glycerol molecule with one, two, or three fatty acid tails.
fatty acid Organic compound that consists of a chain of carbon atoms with an acidic carboxyl group at one end.
lipid Fatty, oily, or waxy organic compound.
lipid bilayer Double layer of lipids arranged tail-to-tail; structural foundation of cell membranes.
phospholipid A lipid with a phosphate group in its hydrophilic head, and two nonpolar tails typically derived from fatty acids.
saturated fat Triglyceride that has three saturated fatty acid tails.
steroid Type of lipid with four carbon rings and no tails.
triglyceride A fat with three fatty acid tails.
unsaturated fat Triglyceride that has one or more unsaturated fatty acid tails.
wax Water-repellent mixture of lipids with long fatty acid tails bonded to long-chain alcohols or carbon rings.

CREDITS: (6) From Starr/Evers/Starr, Biology Today and Tomorrow with Physiology, 4E. © Cengage Learning; (7) © Cengage Learning.

hydrophilic head

one layer of lipids

two hydrophobic tails

one layer of lipids

A Phospholipid molecule

B A lipid bilayer

FIGURE 3.8 {Animated} Phospholipids as components of cell membranes. A double layer of phospholipids—the lipid bilayer—is the structural foundation of all cell membranes. You will read more about the structure of cell membranes in Chapter 4.

an estrogen

testosterone

HO

O

OH

O

female

male

FIGURE 3.9
Steroids. Estrogen and testosterone are steroid hormones that govern reproduction and secondary sexual traits. The two hormones are the source of gender-specific traits in many species, including wood ducks.

PHOSPHOLIPIDS

A **phospholipid** consists of a phosphate-containing head with two long hydrocarbon tails that are typically derived from fatty acids (**FIGURE 3.7B**). The tails are hydrophobic, but the highly polar phosphate group makes the head hydrophilic. These opposing properties give rise to the basic structure of cell membranes, which consist mainly of phospholipids. In a cell membrane, phospholipids are arranged in two layers—a **lipid bilayer** (**FIGURE 3.8**). The heads of one layer are dissolved in the cell's watery interior, and the heads of the other layer are dissolved in the cell's fluid surroundings. All of the hydrophobic tails are sandwiched between the hydrophilic heads.

WAXES

A **wax** is a complex, varying mixture of lipids with long fatty acid tails bonded to alcohols or carbon rings. The molecules pack tightly, so waxes are firm and water-repellent. Plants secrete waxes onto their exposed surfaces to restrict water loss and keep out parasites and other pests. Other types of waxes protect, lubricate, and soften skin and hair. Waxes, together with fats and fatty acids, make feathers waterproof. Bees store honey and raise new generations of bees inside a honeycomb of secreted beeswax.

STEROIDS

Steroids are lipids with no fatty acid tails; they have a rigid backbone that consists of twenty carbon atoms arranged in a characteristic pattern of four rings (**FIGURE 3.9**). Functional groups attached to the rings define the type of steroid. These molecules serve varied and important physiological functions in plants, fungi, and animals. Cells remodel cholesterol, the most common steroid in animal tissue, to produce many other molecules, including bile salts (which help digest fats), vitamin D (required to keep teeth and bones strong), and steroid hormones.

TAKE-HOME MESSAGE 3.3

Lipids are fatty, waxy, or oily organic compounds.

Fats have one, two, or three fatty acid tails; triglyceride fats are an important energy reservoir in vertebrate animals.

Phospholipids arranged in a lipid bilayer are the main component of cell membranes.

Waxes have complex, varying structures. They are components of water-repelling and lubricating secretions.

Steroids serve varied and important physiological roles in plants, fungi, and animals.

CREDITS: (8A) From Starr/Evers/Starr, Biology Today and Tomorrow with Physiology, 4E. © 2013 Cengage Learning; (8B) From Starr/Taggart, Biology: The Unity & Diversity of Life, w/CD & InfoTrac, 10E © 2004 Cengage Learning; (9) art, © Cengage Learning 2015; photo, Tim Davis/Science Source.

FIGURE 3.11 {Animated} Peptide bond formation.
A condensation reaction joins the carboxyl group of one amino acid and the amine group of another to form a peptide bond. In this example, a peptide bond forms between methionine and valine.

❶ A protein's primary structure consists of a linear sequence of amino acids (a polypeptide chain). Each type of protein has a unique primary structure.

FIGURE 3.12 {Animated} Protein structure.

AMINO ACID SUBUNITS

With a few exceptions, cells can make all of the thousands of different proteins they need from only twenty kinds of monomers called amino acids. An **amino acid** is a small organic compound with an amine group (—NH₂), a carboxyl group (—COOH, the acid), and a side chain called an "R group" that defines the kind of amino acid. In most amino acids, all three groups are attached to the same carbon atom (FIGURE 3.10).

FIGURE 3.10 **Generalized structure of an amino acid.**
See Appendix V for the complete structures of the twenty most common amino acids found in eukaryotic proteins.

The covalent bond that links amino acids in a protein is called a **peptide bond**. During protein synthesis, a peptide bond forms between the carboxyl group of the first amino acid and the amine group of the second (FIGURE 3.11). Another peptide bond links a third amino acid to the second, and so on (you will learn more about the details of protein synthesis in Chapter 9). A short chain of amino acids is called a **peptide**; as the chain lengthens, it becomes a **polypeptide**. **Proteins** consist of polypeptides that are hundreds or even thousands of amino acids long.

STRUCTURE DICTATES FUNCTION

Of all biological molecules, proteins are the most diverse. Structural proteins support cell parts and, as part of tissues, multicelled bodies. Feathers, hooves, and hair, as well as tendons and other body parts, consist mainly of structural proteins. A tremendous number of different proteins, including some structural types, participate in all processes that sustain life. Most enzymes that help cells carry out metabolic reactions are proteins. Proteins also function in movement, defense, and cellular communication.

One of the fundamental ideas in biology is that structure dictates function. This idea is particularly appropriate for proteins, because a protein's biological activity arises from and depends on its structure (FIGURE 3.12).

The linear series of amino acids in a polypeptide chain is called primary structure ❶, which defines the type of protein. The protein's three-dimensional shape begins to arise during synthesis, when hydrogen bonds that form among amino acids cause the lengthening polypeptide chain to twist and fold. Parts of the polypeptide form loops, helixes (coils), or flat sheets, and these patterns constitute secondary structure ❷. The primary structure of each type of protein is unique, but most proteins have similar patterns of secondary structure.

Much as an overly twisted rubber band coils back upon itself, hydrogen bonding between nonadjacent regions of a protein makes its loops, helices, and sheets fold up into even more compact domains (FIGURE 3.13A). These domains are called tertiary structure ❸. Tertiary structure makes a protein a working molecule. For example, the helices and loops in a globin chain fold up together to form a pocket that can hold a heme, which is a small compound essential to the finished protein's function. Sheets, loops, and helices of other proteins roll up into complex structures that resemble barrels, propellers, sandwiches, and so on. Large proteins typically have several domains, each contributing a particular structural or functional property to the molecule. For example, some barrel domains rotate like motors in

CREDITS: (10, 11) © Cengage Learning 2015; (12) 2–4: 1BBB, A third quaternary structure of human hemoglobin A at 1.7-A resolution. Silva, M.M., Rogers, P.H., Arnone, A., Journal: (1992) J.Biol.Chem. 267: 17248–17256; 1, 5 left: © Cengage Learning; 5 right: © JupiterImages Corporation.

oline — **glutamic ac...**

2 Secondary structure arises as a polypeptide chain twists into a helix (coil), loop, or sheet held in place by hydrogen bonds.

3 Tertiary structure occurs when loops, helices, and sheets fold up into a domain. In this example, the helices of a globin chain form a pocket.

4 Many proteins have two or more polypeptide chains (quaternary structure). Hemoglobin, shown here, consists of four globin chains (green and blue). Each globin pocket now holds a heme group (red).

5 Some types of proteins aggregate into much larger structures. As an example, organized arrays of keratin, a fibrous protein, compose filaments that make up your hair.

---

small molecular machines (**FIGURE 3.13B**). Other barrels function as tunnels for small molecules, allowing them to pass, for example, through a cell membrane.

Many proteins also have quaternary structure, which means they consist of two or more polypeptide chains that are closely associated or covalently bonded together **4**. Most enzymes are like this, with multiple polypeptide chains that collectively form a roughly spherical shape.

Fibrous proteins aggregate by many thousands into much larger structures, with their polypeptide chains organized into strands or sheets. The keratin in your hair is an example **5**. Some fibrous proteins contribute to the structure and organization of cells and tissues. Others help cells, cell parts, and multicelled bodies move.

Enzymes often attach sugars or lipids to proteins. A glycoprotein forms when oligosaccharides are attached to a polypeptide. The molecules that allow a tissue or a body to recognize its own cells are glycoproteins, as are other molecules that help cells interact in immunity.

Some lipoproteins form when enzymes covalently bond lipids to a protein. Other lipoproteins are aggregate structures that consist of variable amounts and types of proteins and lipids (**FIGURE 3.14**).

A In this protein, loops (green), coils (red), and a sheet (yellow) fold up together into a chemically active pocket. The pocket gives this protein the ability to transfer electrons from one molecule to another. Many other proteins have the same pocket structure.

B This barrel domain is part of a rotary mechanism in a larger protein. The protein functions as a molecular motor that pumps hydrogen ions through cell membranes.

FIGURE 3.13 Examples of protein domains.

FIGURE 3.14 A lipoprotein particle. The one depicted here (HDL, often called "good" cholesterol) consists of thousands of lipids lassoed into a clump by two protein chains.

lipids —

protein —

amino acid Small organic compound that is a subunit of proteins. Consists of a carboxyl group, an amine group, and a characteristic side group (R), all typically bonded to the same carbon atom.
peptide bond A bond between the amine group of one amino acid and the carboxyl group of another. Joins amino acids in proteins.
peptide Short chain of amino acids linked by peptide bonds.
polypeptide Long chain of amino acids linked by peptide bonds.
protein Organic molecule that consists of one or more polypeptides.

TAKE-HOME MESSAGE 3.4

Proteins are chains of amino acids. The order of amino acids in a polypeptide chain dictates the type of protein.

Polypeptide chains twist and fold into coils, sheets, and loops, which fold and pack further into functional domains.

A protein's function arises from its three-dimensional shape.

CREDITS: (13A, 14) Castrignanò T, De Meo PD, Cozzetto D, Talamo IG, Tramontano A. (2006). The PMDB Protein Model Database. Nucleic Acids Research, 34: D306-D309. (13B) pdb ID2W5J, Vollmar, M., Shlieper, D., Winn M., Buechner, C., Groth, G. "Structure of the C14 rotor ring of the proton translocating chloroplast ATP synthase." (2009) J. Biol. Chem. 284:18228.

3.5 WHY IS PROTEIN STRUCTURE IMPORTANT?

FIGURE 3.15 Variant Creutzfeldt–Jakob disease (vCJD). Characteristic holes and prion protein fibers radiating from several deposits are visible in this slice of brain tissue from a person with vCJD.

Protein shape depends on hydrogen bonding, which can be disrupted by heat, some salts, shifts in pH, or detergents. Such disruption causes proteins to **denature**, which means they lose their three-dimensional shape. Once a protein's shape unravels, so does its function.

Consider three fatal diseases: scrapie in sheep, mad cow disease (BSE, bovine spongiform encephalopathy), and variant Creutzfeldt–Jakob disease (vCJD) in humans. All begin with a glycoprotein called PrPC that occurs normally in cell membranes of the mammalian body. Sometimes, a PrPC protein spontaneously misfolds. A single misfolded protein molecule should not pose much of a threat, but when this particular protein misfolds it becomes a **prion**, or infectious protein. The altered shape of a misfolded PrPC protein causes normally folded PrPC proteins to misfold too. Because each protein that misfolds becomes infectious, the number of prions increases exponentially.

The shape of misfolded PrPC proteins allows them to align tightly into long fibers. In the brain, these fibers accumulate in water-repellent patches that disrupt brain cell function, resulting in relentlessly worsening symptoms of confusion, memory loss, and lack of coordination. Holes form in the brain as its cells die (**FIGURE 3.15**).

In the mid-1980s, an epidemic of mad cow disease in Britain was followed by an outbreak of vCJD in humans. The cattle became infected by the prion after eating feed prepared from the remains of scrapie-infected sheep, and people became infected by eating beef from infected cattle. The use of animal parts in livestock feed is now banned in many countries, and the number of cases of BSE and vCJD has since declined.

denature To unravel the shape of a protein or other large biological molecule.
prion Infectious protein.

TAKE-HOME MESSAGE 3.5

Protein shape can unravel if hydrogen bonds are disrupted.

A protein's function depends on its structure, so conditions that alter a protein's structure also alter its function.

3.6 WHAT ARE NUCLEIC ACIDS?

A **nucleotide** is a small organic molecule that consists of a sugar with a five-carbon ring bonded to a nitrogen-containing base and one, two, or three phosphate groups (**FIGURE 3.16A**). When the third phosphate group of a nucleotide is transferred to another molecule, energy is transferred along with it. The nucleotide **ATP** (adenosine triphosphate) serves an especially important role as an energy carrier in cells.

Nucleic acids are polymers, chains of nucleotides in which the sugar of one nucleotide is bonded to the phosphate group of the next (**FIGURE 3.16B**). An example is ribonucleic acid, or **RNA**, named after the ribose sugar of its component nucleotides. An RNA molecule is a chain of four kinds of nucleotide monomers, one of which is ATP. RNA molecules carry out protein synthesis. Deoxyribonucleic acid, or **DNA**, is a nucleic acid named after the deoxyribose sugar of its component nucleotides. A DNA molecule consists of two chains of nucleotides twisted into a double helix. Hydrogen bonds between the nucleotides hold the chains together. Each cell's DNA holds all information necessary to build a new cell and, in the case of multicelled organisms, a new individual.

FIGURE 3.16 Nucleic acids.

A ATP (a nucleotide)

phosphate groups
ribose sugar
base (adenine)

B RNA (a nucleic acid)

ATP Adenosine triphosphate. Nucleotide that serves an important role as an energy carrier in cells.
DNA Deoxyribonucleic acid. Consists of two chains of nucleotides twisted into a double helix.
nucleic acid Polymer of nucleotides; DNA or RNA.
nucleotide Monomer of nucleic acids; has a five-carbon sugar, a nitrogen-containing base, and one, two, or three phosphate groups.
RNA Ribonucleic acid. Single-stranded chain of nucleotides.

TAKE-HOME MESSAGE 3.6

Nucleotides are monomers of nucleic acids. ATP has an important metabolic role as an energy carrier.

RNA carries out protein synthesis. DNA holds information necessary to build cells and multicelled individuals.

CREDITS: (15) Sherif Zaki, MD PhD, Wun-Ju Shieh, MD PhD; MPH/ CDC; (16A) From Starr/Evers/Starr, Biology Today and Tomorrow with Physiology, 4E. © 2013 Cengage Learning; (16B) © Cengage Learning 2015.

oleic acid has a *cis* bond:

elaidic acid has a *trans* bond:

FIGURE 3.17 *Trans* fats, an unhealthy food. Double bonds in the tail of most naturally occurring fatty acids are *cis*, which means that the two hydrogen atoms flanking the bond are on the same side of the carbon backbone. Hydrogenation creates abundant *trans* bonds, with hydrogen atoms on opposite sides of the tail.

FATS ARE NOT INERT MOLECULES THAT SIMPLY ACCUMULATE IN STRATEGIC AREAS OF OUR BODIES. They are major constituents of cell membranes, and as such they have powerful effects on cell function. As you learned in Section 3.3, the long carbon backbone of fatty acid tails can vary a bit in structure. *Trans* fats have unsaturated fatty acid tails with a particular arrangement of hydrogen atoms around the double bonds (**FIGURE 3.17**). Small amounts of *trans* fats occur naturally, but the main source of these fats in the American diet is an artificial food product called partially hydrogenated vegetable oil. Hydrogenation is a manufacturing process that adds hydrogen atoms to oils in order to change them into solid fats. In 1908, Procter & Gamble Co. developed partially hydrogenated soybean oil as a substitute for the more expensive solid animal fats they had been using to make candles. However, the demand for candles began to wane as more households in the United States became wired for electricity, and P&G looked for

another way to sell its proprietary fat. Partially hydrogenated vegetable oil looks like lard, so the company began aggressively marketing it as a revolutionary new food: a solid cooking fat with a long shelf life, mild flavor, and lower cost than lard or butter. By the mid-1950s, hydrogenated vegetable oil had become a major part of the American diet, and it is still found in many manufactured and fast foods. For decades, it was considered healthier than animal fats, but we now know otherwise. *Trans* fats raise the level of cholesterol in our blood more than any other fat, and they directly alter the function of our arteries and veins. The effects of such changes are quite serious. Eating as little as 2 grams a day (about 0.4 teaspoon) of hydrogenated vegetable oil measurably increases a person's risk of atherosclerosis (hardening of the arteries), heart attack, and diabetes. A small serving of french fries made with hydrogenated vegetable oil contains about 5 grams of *trans* fat.

CREDIT: (17) photo, Kentoh, 2009/Used under license from Shutterstock.com; art, © Cengage Learning 2015.

Summary

SECTION 3.1 Complex carbohydrates and lipids, proteins, and nucleic acids are **organic**, which means they consist mainly of carbon and hydrogen atoms. **Hydrocarbons** have only carbon and hydrogen atoms.

Carbon chains or rings form the backbone of the molecules of life. **Functional groups** attached to the backbone influence the chemical character of these compounds, and thus their function.

Metabolism includes chemical **reactions** and all other processes by which cells acquire and use energy as they make and break the bonds of organic compounds. In reactions such as **condensation**, **enzymes** build **polymers** from **monomers** of simple sugars, fatty acids, amino acids, and nucleotides. Reactions such as **hydrolysis** release the monomers by breaking apart the polymers.

SECTION 3.2 Enzymes build complex **carbohydrates** such as **cellulose**, glycogen, and starch from simple carbohydrate (sugar) subunits. Cells use carbohydrates for energy, and as structural materials.

SECTION 3.3 **Lipids** are fatty, oily, or waxy compounds. All are nonpolar. **Fats** have **fatty acid** tails; **triglycerides** have three. **Saturated fats** are mainly triglycerides with three saturated fatty acid tails (only single bonds link their carbons). **Unsaturated fats** are mainly triglycerides with one or more unsaturated fatty acids.

A **lipid bilayer** (that consists primarily of **phospholipids**) is the basic structure of all cell membranes. **Waxes** are part of water-repellent and lubricating secretions. **Steroids** occur in cell membranes, and some are remodeled into other molecules such as hormones.

SECTION 3.4 Structurally and functionally, **proteins** are the most diverse molecules of life. The shape of a protein is the source of its function. Protein structure begins as a series of **amino acids** (primary structure) linked by **peptide bonds** into a **peptide**, then a **polypeptide**. Polypeptides twist into helices, sheets, and coils (secondary structure) that can pack further into functional domains (tertiary structure). Many proteins, including most enzymes, consist of two or more polypeptides (quaternary structure). Fibrous proteins aggregate into much larger structures.

SECTION 3.5 A protein's structure dictates its function, so changes in a protein's structure may also alter its function. A protein's shape may be disrupted by shifts in pH or temperature, or exposure to detergent or some salts. If that happens, the protein unravels, or **denatures**, and so loses its function. **Prion** diseases are a fatal consequence of misfolded proteins.

SECTION 3.6 **Nucleotides** are small organic molecules that consist of a five-carbon sugar, a nitrogen-containing base, and one, two, or three phosphate groups. Nucleotides are monomers of **DNA** and **RNA**, which are **nucleic acids**. Some, especially **ATP**, have additional functions such as carrying energy. DNA encodes information necessary to build cells and multicelled individuals. RNA molecules carry out protein synthesis.

SECTION 3.7 All organisms consist of the same kinds of molecules. Seemingly small differences in the way those molecules are put together can have big effects inside a living organism.

Self-Quiz Answers in Appendix VII

1. Organic molecules consist mainly of _____ atoms.
   a. carbon
   b. carbon and oxygen
   c. carbon and hydrogen
   d. carbon and nitrogen

2. Each carbon atom can bond with as many as _____ other atom(s).

3. _____ groups are the "acid" part of amino acids and fatty acids.
   a. Hydroxyl (—OH)
   b. Carboxyl (—COOH)
   c. Methyl (—CH$_3$)
   d. Phosphate (—PO$_4$)

4. _____ is a simple sugar (a monosaccharide).
   a. Glucose
   b. Sucrose
   c. Ribose
   d. Starch
   e. both a and c
   f. a, b, and c

5. Unlike saturated fats, the fatty acid tails of unsaturated fats incorporate one or more _____ .
   a. phosphate groups
   b. glycerols
   c. double bonds
   d. single bonds

6. Is this statement true or false? Unlike saturated fats, all unsaturated fats are beneficial to health because their fatty acid tails kink and do not pack together.

7. Steroids are among the lipids with no _____ .
   a. double bonds
   b. fatty acid tails
   c. hydrogens
   d. carbons

8. Name three kinds of carbohydrates that can be built using only glucose monomers.

9. Which of the following is a class of molecules that encompasses all of the other molecules listed?
   a. triglycerides
   b. fatty acids
   c. waxes
   d. steroids
   e. lipids
   f. phospholipids

10. _____ are to proteins as _____ are to nucleic acids.
    a. Sugars; lipids
    b. Sugars; proteins
    c. Amino acids; hydrogen bonds
    d. Amino acids; nucleotides

11. A denatured protein has lost its _____ .
    a. hydrogen bonds
    b. shape
    c. function
    d. all of the above

12. _____ consist(s) of nucleotides.
    a. Sugars   b. DNA   c. RNA   d. b and c

Data Analysis Activities

Effects of Dietary Fats on Lipoprotein Levels Cholesterol that is made by the liver or that enters the body from food cannot dissolve in blood, so it is carried through the bloodstream by lipoproteins. Low-density lipoprotein (LDL) carries cholesterol to body tissues such as artery walls, where it can form deposits associated with cardiovascular disease. Thus, LDL is often called "bad" cholesterol. High-density lipoprotein (HDL) carries cholesterol away from tissues to the liver for disposal, so HDL is often called "good" cholesterol.

	Main Dietary Fats			
	cis fatty acids	*trans* fatty acids	saturated fats	optimal level
LDL	103	117	121	<100
HDL	55	48	55	>40
ratio	1.87	2.44	2.2	<2

In 1990, Ronald Mensink and Martijn Katan published a study that tested the effects of different dietary fats on blood lipoprotein levels. Their results are shown in **FIGURE 3.18**.

1. In which group was the level of LDL ("bad" cholesterol) highest?
2. In which group was the level of HDL ("good" cholesterol) lowest?
3. An elevated risk of heart disease has been correlated with increasing LDL-to-HDL ratios. Which group had the highest LDL-to-HDL ratio?
4. Rank the three diets from best to worst according to their potential effect on heart disease.

FIGURE 3.18 Effect of diet on lipoprotein levels. Researchers placed 59 men and women on a diet in which 10 percent of their daily energy intake consisted of *cis* fatty acids, *trans* fatty acids, or saturated fats.

Blood LDL and HDL levels were measured after three weeks on the diet; averaged results are shown in mg/dL (milligrams per deciliter of blood). All subjects were tested on each of the diets. The ratio of LDL to HDL is also shown.

13. In the following list, identify the carbohydrate, the fatty acid, the amino acid, and the polypeptide:
    a. NH_2—CH_2—$COOH$ c. (methionine)$_{20}$
    b. $C_6H_{12}O_6$ d. $CH_3(CH_2)_{16}COOH$

14. Match the molecules with the best description.
    ___ wax   a. sugar storage in plants
    ___ starch   b. richest energy source
    ___ triglyceride c. water-repellent secretions

15. Match each polymer with the appropriate monomer(s).
    ___ protein   a. phosphate, fatty acids
    ___ phospholipid   b. amino acids, sugars
    ___ glycoprotein   c. glycerol, fatty acids
    ___ fat   d. nucleotides
    ___ nucleic acid   e. glucose only
    ___ wax   f. sugar, phosphate, base
    ___ nucleotide   g. amino acids
    ___ lipoprotein   h. glucose, fructose
    ___ sucrose   i. lipids, amino acids
    ___ glycogen   j. fatty acids, carbon rings

Critical Thinking

1. Lipoproteins are relatively large, spherical clumps of protein and lipid molecules (see **FIGURE 3.14**) that circulate in the blood of mammals. They are like suitcases that move cholesterol, fatty acid remnants, triglycerides, and phospholipids from one place to another in the body. Given what you know about the insolubility of lipids in water, which of the four kinds of lipids would you predict to be on the outside of a lipoprotein clump, bathed in the water-based fluid portion of blood?

2. In 1976, a team of chemists in the United Kingdom was developing new insecticides by modifying sugars with chlorine (Cl_2), phosgene (Cl_2CO), and other toxic gases. One young member of the team misunderstood his verbal instructions to "test" a new molecule. He thought he had been told to "taste" it. Luckily for him, the molecule was not toxic, but it was very sweet. It became the food additive sucralose.

Sucralose has three chlorine atoms substituted for three hydroxyl groups of sucrose (table sugar). It binds so strongly to the sweet-taste receptors on the tongue that the human brain perceives it as 600 times sweeter than sucrose. Sucralose was originally marketed as an artificial sweetener called Splenda®, but it is now available under several other brand names.

Researchers investigated whether the body recognizes sucralose as a carbohydrate by feeding sucralose labeled with ^{14}C to volunteers. Analysis of the radioactive molecules in the volunteers' urine and feces showed that 92.8 percent of the sucralose passed through the body without being altered. Many people are worried that the chlorine atoms impart toxicity to sucralose. How would you respond to that concern?

sucrose

sucralose

CENGAGE brain .com To access course materials, please visit www.cengagebrain.com.

Each cell making up this seedling contains a nucleus (orange spots), which is the defining characteristic of eukaryotes. Rigid walls surround but do not isolate plant cells from one another.

CELL STRUCTURE

Links to Earlier Concepts

Reflect on the overview of life's levels of organization in Section 1.1. In this chapter, you will see how the properties of lipids (3.3) give rise to cell membranes; consider the location of DNA (3.6) and the sites where carbohydrates are built and broken apart (3.1, 3.2); and expand your understanding of the vital roles of proteins in cell function (3.4, 3.5). You will also revisit the philosophy of science (1.5, 1.8) and tracers (2.1).

KEY CONCEPTS

COMPONENTS OF ALL CELLS
Every cell has a plasma membrane separating its interior from the exterior environment. Its interior contains cytoplasm, DNA, and other structures.

THE MICROSCOPIC WORLD
Most cells are too small to see with the naked eye. We use different types of microscopes to reveal different details of their structure.

CELL MEMBRANES
All cell membranes consist of a lipid bilayer with various proteins embedded in it and attached to its surfaces. A membrane controls the kinds and amounts of substances that cross it.

PROKARYOTIC CELLS
Archaea and bacteria have no nucleus. In general, they are smaller and structurally more simple than eukaryotic cells, but they are by far the most numerous and diverse organisms.

EUKARYOTIC CELLS
Protists, plants, fungi, and animals are eukaryotes. Cells of these organisms differ in internal parts and surface specializations, but all start out life with a nucleus.

CELL THEORY

No one knew cells existed until after the first microscopes were invented. By the mid-1600s, Antoni van Leeuwenhoek had constructed a crude instrument, and was writing about the tiny moving organisms he spied in rainwater, insects, fabric, sperm, feces, and other samples. In scrapings of tartar from his teeth, Leeuwenhoek saw "many very small animalcules, the motions of which were very pleasing to behold." He (incorrectly) assumed that movement defined life, and (correctly) concluded that the moving "beasties" he saw were alive. Leeuwenhoek might have been less pleased to behold his animalcules if he had grasped the implications of what he saw: Our world, and our bodies, teem with microbial life.

Today we know that a cell carries out metabolism and homeostasis, and reproduces either on its own or as part of a larger organism. By this definition, each cell is alive even if it is part of a multicelled body, and all living organisms consist of one or more cells. We also know that cells reproduce by dividing, so it follows that all existing cells must have arisen by division of other cells (later chapters discuss the processes by which cells divide). As a cell divides, it passes its hereditary material—its DNA—to offspring. Taken together, these generalizations constitute the **cell theory**, which is one of the foundations of modern biology (**TABLE 4.1**).

COMPONENTS OF ALL CELLS

Cells vary in shape and function, but all have at least three components in common: a plasma membrane, cytoplasm, and DNA (**FIGURE 4.1**). A cell's **plasma membrane** is its outermost, separating the cell's contents from the external environment. Like all other cell membranes, a plasma membrane is selectively permeable, which means that only certain materials can cross it. Thus, a plasma membrane controls exchanges between the cell and its environment.

The plasma membrane encloses a jellylike mixture of water, sugars, ions, and proteins called **cytoplasm**. A major part of a cell's metabolism occurs in the cytoplasm, and the cell's internal components, including organelles, are suspended in it. **Organelles** are structures that carry out special functions inside a cell. Membrane-enclosed organelles allow a cell to compartmentalize activities.

All cells start out life with DNA, though a few types lose it as they mature. In nearly all bacteria and archaea, the DNA is suspended directly in cytoplasm. By contrast, all eukaryotic cells start out life with a **nucleus** (plural, nuclei), an organelle with a double membrane that contains the cell's DNA. All protists, fungi, plants, and animals are eukaryotes. Some of these organisms are independent, free-living cells; others consist of many cells working together as a body.

TABLE 4.1

Cell Theory

1. Every living organism consists of one or more cells.

2. The cell is the structural and functional unit of all organisms. A cell is the smallest unit of life, individually alive even as part of a multicelled organism.

3. All living cells arise by division of preexisting cells.

4. Cells contain hereditary material, which they pass to their offspring when they divide.

A bacterial cell — DNA, cytoplasm, plasma membrane

A plant cell — cytoplasm, DNA in nucleus, plasma membrane

An animal cell — cytoplasm, DNA in nucleus, plasma membrane

FIGURE 4.1 {Animated} All cells start out life with a plasma membrane, cytoplasm, and DNA. Archaea are similar to bacteria in overall structure; both are typically much smaller than eukaryotic cells. If the cells depicted here had been drawn to the same scale, the bacterium would be about this big:

Sticky secretions hold these pill-shaped cells together end to end, forming a long strand of algae. The arrangement allows each algal cell to exchange substances directly with the surrounding water. Secretions also anchor the strand to a solid surface (such as the plant on the left).

20 μm

FIGURE 4.3 An example of a colonial algae.

Diameter (cm)	2	3	6
Surface area (cm²)	12.6	28.2	113
Volume (cm³)	4.2	14.1	113
Surface-to-volume ratio	3:1	2:1	1:1

FIGURE 4.2 Examples of surface-to-volume ratio. This physical relationship between increases in volume and surface area limits the size and influences the shape of cells.

CONSTRAINTS ON CELL SIZE

Almost all cells are too small to see with the naked eye. Why? The answer begins with the processes that keep a cell alive. A living cell must exchange substances with its environment at a rate that keeps pace with its metabolism. These exchanges occur across the plasma membrane, which can handle only so many exchanges at a time. The rate of exchange across a plasma membrane depends on its surface area: the bigger it is, the more substances can cross it during a given interval. Thus, cell size is limited by a physical relationship called the **surface-to-volume ratio**. By this ratio, an object's volume increases with the cube of its diameter, but its surface area increases only with the square.

Apply the surface-to-volume ratio to a round cell. As **FIGURE 4.2** shows, when a cell expands in diameter, its volume increases faster than its surface area does. Imagine that a round cell expands until it is four times its original diameter. The volume of the cell has increased 64 times (4^3), but its surface area has increased only 16 times (4^2). Each unit of plasma membrane must now handle exchanges with four times as much cytoplasm ($64 \div 16 = 4$). If the cell gets too big, the inward flow of nutrients and the outward flow of wastes across that membrane will not be fast enough to keep the cell alive.

Surface-to-volume limits also affect the form of colonial types and multicelled ones too. For example, small cells attach end to end to form strandlike algae, so each can interact directly with the environment (**FIGURE 4.3**). Muscle cells in your thighs are as long as the muscle in which they occur, but each is thin, so it exchanges substances efficiently with fluids in the surrounding tissue.

cell theory Theory that all organisms consist of one or more cells, which are the basic unit of life; all cells come from division of preexisting cells; and all cells pass hereditary material to offspring.
cytoplasm Semifluid substance enclosed by a cell's plasma membrane.
nucleus Of a eukaryotic cell, organelle with a double membrane that holds the cell's DNA.
organelle Structure that carries out a specialized metabolic function inside a cell.
plasma membrane A cell's outermost membrane.
surface-to-volume ratio A relationship in which the volume of an object increases with the cube of the diameter, and the surface area increases with the square.

TAKE-HOME MESSAGE 4.1

Observations of cells led to the cell theory: All organisms consist of one or more cells; the cell is the smallest unit of life; each new cell arises from another cell; and a cell passes hereditary material to its offspring.

All cells start life with a plasma membrane, cytoplasm, and a region of DNA, which, in eukaryotic cells only, is enclosed by a nucleus.

The surface-to-volume ratio limits cell size and influences cell shape.

CREDITS: (2) © Cengage Learning; (3) © Frank Fox Shaw & Todd, Inc.

Most cells are 10–20 micrometers in diameter, about fifty times smaller than the unaided human eye can perceive (FIGURE 4.4). One micrometer (µm) is one-thousandth of a millimeter, which is one-thousandth of a meter (TABLE 4.2). We use microscopes to observe cells and other objects in the micrometer range of size.

Light microscopes use visible light to illuminate samples. As you will learn in Chapter 6, all light travels in waves, a property that makes it bend when it passes through a curved glass lens. Curved lenses inside a light microscope focus light that passes through a specimen, or bounces off of one, into a magnified image (FIGURE 4.5A). Photographs of images enlarged with a microscope are called micrographs. Microscopes that use polarized light can yield images in which the edges of some structures appear in three-dimensional relief (FIGURE 4.5B).

Most cells are nearly transparent, so their internal details may not be visible unless they are first stained (exposed to dyes that only some cell parts soak up). Parts that absorb the most dye appear darkest. Staining results in an increase in contrast (the difference between light and dark parts) that allows us to see a greater range of detail.

Researchers often use light-emitting tracers (Section 2.1) to pinpoint the location of a molecule of interest within a cell. When illuminated with laser light, the tracer fluoresces (emits light), and an image of the emitted light can be captured with a fluorescence microscope (FIGURE 4.5C).

Other microscopes can reveal even finer details. For example, electron microscopes use magnetic fields to focus a beam of electrons onto a sample; these instruments resolve details thousands of times smaller than light microscopes do. Transmission electron microscopes direct electrons through a thin specimen, and the specimen's internal details appear as shadows in the resulting image—a transmission electron micrograph, or TEM (FIGURE 4.5D). Scanning electron microscopes direct a beam of electrons across the surface of a specimen that has been coated with a thin layer of metal. The irradiated metal emits electrons and x-rays, which can be converted into an image (a scanning electron micrograph, or SEM) of the surface (FIGURE 4.5E). SEMs and TEMs are always black and white; colored versions have been digitally altered to highlight specific details.

TABLE 4.2

Equivalent Units of Length

| Unit | Equivalent | |
	Meter	Inch
centimeter (cm)	1/100	0.4
millimeter (mm)	1/1000	0.04
micrometer (µm)	1/1,000,000	0.00004
nanometer (nm)	1/1,000,000,000	0.00000004
meter (m)	100 cm 1,000 mm 1,000,000 µm 1,000,000,000 nm	

TAKE-HOME MESSAGE 4.2

Most cells are visible only with the help of microscopes.

We use different microscopes and techniques to reveal different aspects of cell structure.

FIGURE 4.4 **Relative sizes.** Most cells are between 1 and 100 micrometers in diameter. See also Units of Measure, Table 4.2 and Appendix VI.

FIGURE IT OUT: Which one is smallest: a protein, a virus, or a bacterium?

Answer: A protein

electron microscopes | light microscopes

small molecules | molecules of life | viruses | mitochondria, chloroplasts | most bacteria | most eukaryotic cells

lipids carbohydrates proteins DNA

0.1 nm | 1 nm | 10 nm | 100 nm | 1 µm | 10 µm

A The green blobs visible in this light micrograph of a living cell are ingested algal cells (also visible in **B** and **D**). Fine, hairlike structures on the cell's surface (also visible in **E**) are waving cilia that propel this motile organism through its fluid surroundings.

100 µm

B A light micrograph taken with polarized light shows edges in relief. This technique reveals some internal structures not visible in **A**.

C In this fluorescence micrograph, yellow pinpoints the location of a particular type of protein in the membrane of organelles called contractile vacuoles. These organelles are also visible in **B**.

D A colorized transmission electron micrograph (TEM) reveals several types of internal structures in a plane (slice) through the sample. Ingested algal cells are clearly visible.

E A colorized scanning electron micrograph (SEM) shows details of the cell's surface. The cell ingests its food via the indentation (also visible in **A**).

FIGURE 4.5 Different microscopy techniques reveal different characteristics of the same organism, a protist (*Paramecium*).

 FIGURE IT OUT: About how big are these cells?

Answer: About 250 µm long

National Geographic Explorer
DR. AYDOGAN OZCAN

Aydogan Ozcan is developing a revolutionary global health solution using one of the most common forms of technology available—the smart phone. Using readily available parts that cost less than $50, Ozcan builds adapters that transform a smart phone into a mobile medical lab with the capability to test and diagnose diseases like HIV, malaria, and tuberculosis in remote communities.

Conventional microscopes, the mainstay of diagnosis for centuries, are impractical on a global level. "They are too heavy and powerful to be cost-effectively miniaturized. They also can't quickly capture and screen the large number of cells needed for statistically viable diagnoses," he says. What's more, because technicians in remote areas may be poorly trained, they often interpret images inaccurately. "In some parts of Africa, 70 percent of malaria diagnoses are incorrect false-positives." Ozcan's invention solves these problems by arming cell phones with sophisticated algorithms that do the interpreting. To tackle the most expensive part of microscopes—lenses—his team simply eliminated them. Ozcan's modified phone uses a special light source and the phone's camera to capture an image of a blood sample, essentially turning the phone into a lens-free microscope able to resolve structures smaller than one micron.

human eye (no microscope)

frog eggs

small animals

largest organisms

| 100 µm | 1 mm | 1 cm | 10 cm | 1 m | 10 m | 100 m |

CREDITS: (4) Louse, Edward S. Ross; Frog egg, From Starr/Taggart/Evers/Starr, Biology, 13E. © 2013 Cengage Learning; Ant, Frog, © A Cotton Photo/Shutterstock; Rat, © Pakhnyushcha/Shutterstock; Goose, © Vasyl Helevachuk/Shutterstock; Boy, © Piotr Marcinski/Shutterstock; Giraffe, © Valerie Kalyuznnyy/Photos.com; Whale, © Dorling Kindersley/the Agency Collection/Getty Images; Tree, © Cengage Learning. (5A) © Nancy Nehring/iStockphoto.com; (5B) Michael Abbey/Science Source; (5C) © Dennis Kunkel Microscopy, Inc./PhototakeUSA.com; (5D) © Microworks/PhototakeUSA.com; (5E) Dr. Stanley Flegler/Visuals Unlimited/Corbis; (6) Dr. Aydogan Ozcan.

A plasma membrane physically separates a cell's external environment from its internal one, but that is not its only function. For example, you learned in Section 4.1 that a cell's plasma membrane allows some substances, but not others, to cross it. Membranes around organelles do this too. We return to membrane functions in Chapter 5; here, we explore the structure that gives rise to these functions.

THE FLUID MOSAIC MODEL

The foundation of almost all cell membranes is a lipid bilayer that consists mainly of phospholipids. Remember from Section 3.3 that a phospholipid has a phosphate-containing head and two fatty acid tails. The polar head is hydrophilic, which means that it interacts with water molecules. The nonpolar tails are hydrophobic, so they do not interact with water molecules. As a result of these opposing properties, phospholipids swirled into water will spontaneously organize themselves into lipid bilayer sheets or bubbles (*left*), with hydrophobic tails together, hydrophilic heads facing the watery surroundings (**FIGURE 4.6A**).

Other molecules, including cholesterol, proteins, glycoproteins, and glycolipids, are embedded in or attached to the lipid bilayer of a cell membrane. Many of these molecules move around the membrane more or less freely. We describe a eukaryotic or bacterial cell membrane as a **fluid mosaic** because it behaves like a two-dimensional liquid of mixed composition. The "mosaic" part of the name comes from the many different types of molecules in the membrane. A cell membrane is fluid because its phospholipids are not chemically bonded to one another; they stay organized in a bilayer as a result of collective hydrophobic and hydrophilic attractions. These interactions are, on an individual basis, relatively weak. Thus, individual phospholipids in the bilayer drift sideways and spin around their long axis, and their tails wiggle.

A cell membrane's properties vary depending on the types and proportions of molecules composing it. For example, membrane fluidity decreases with increasing cholesterol content. A membrane's fluidity also depends on the length and saturation of its phospholipids' fatty acid tails (Section 3.3). Archaea do not even use fatty acids to build their phospholipids. Instead, they use molecules with reactive side chains, so the tails of archaeal phospholipids form covalent bonds with one another. As a result of this rigid crosslinking, archaeal phospholipids do not drift, spin, or wiggle in a bilayer. Thus, membranes of archaea are stiffer than those of bacteria or eukaryotes, a characteristic that may help these cells survive in extreme habitats.

A In a watery fluid, phospholipids spontaneously line up into two layers: the hydrophobic tails cluster together, and the hydrophilic heads face outward, toward the fluid. This lipid bilayer forms the framework of all cell membranes. Many types of proteins intermingle among the lipids; a few that are typical of plasma membranes are shown *opposite*.

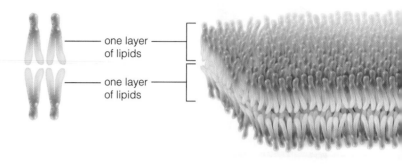

one layer of lipids

one layer of lipids

FIGURE 4.6 {Animated} Cell membrane structure.
A Organization of phospholipids in cell membranes.
B–E Examples of common membrane proteins.

TABLE 4.3

Common Membrane Proteins

Category	Function	Examples
Passive transport protein	Allows ions or small molecules to cross a membrane to the side where they are less concentrated.	Porin; glucose transporter
Active transport protein	Pumps ions or molecules through membranes to the side where they are more concentrated. Requires energy input, as from ATP.	Calcium pump; serotonin transporter
Receptor	Initiates change in a cell activity by responding to an outside signal (e.g., by binding a signaling molecule or absorbing light energy).	Insulin receptor; B cell receptor
Adhesion protein	Helps cells stick to one another, to cell junctions, and to extracellular matrix.	Integrins; cadherins
Recognition protein	Identifies a cell as self (belonging to one's own body or tissue) or nonself (foreign to the body).	MHC molecule
Enzyme	Speeds a specific reaction. Membranes provide a relatively stable reaction site for enzymes that work in series with other molecules.	Cytochrome c oxidase

CREDIT: (in text) © Cengage Learning 2015; (6A left) From Starr/Taggart, Biology: The Unity and Diversity of Life w/ CD & InfoTrac, 10E. © 2004 Cengage Learning; (6A right) From Starr/Evers/Starr, Biology Today and Tomorrow with Physiology, 3E. © 2010 Cengage Learning; (Table 4.3) © Cengage Learning.

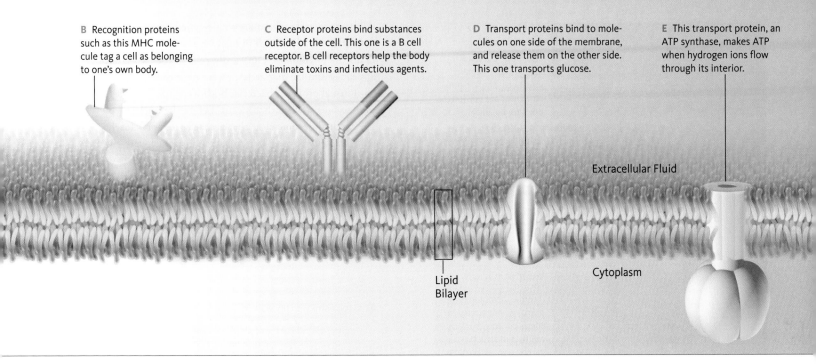

B Recognition proteins such as this MHC molecule tag a cell as belonging to one's own body.

C Receptor proteins bind substances outside of the cell. This one is a B cell receptor. B cell receptors help the body eliminate toxins and infectious agents.

D Transport proteins bind to molecules on one side of the membrane, and release them on the other side. This one transports glucose.

E This transport protein, an ATP synthase, makes ATP when hydrogen ions flow through its interior.

Extracellular Fluid

Cytoplasm

Lipid Bilayer

PROTEINS ADD FUNCTION

Many types of proteins are associated with a cell membrane (**TABLE 4.3**). Some are temporarily or permanently attached to one of the lipid bilayer's surfaces. Others have a hydrophobic domain that anchors the protein in the bilayer. Filaments inside the cell fasten some membrane proteins in place, including those that cluster as rigid pores.

Each type of protein in a membrane imparts a specific function to it. Thus, different cell membranes can have different functions depending on which proteins are associated with them. A plasma membrane has certain proteins that no internal cell membrane has. For example, cells in some animal tissues are fastened together by **adhesion proteins** in their plasma membranes, an arrangement that strengthens these tissues. **Recognition proteins** in the plasma membrane function as unique identity tags for an individual or a species (**FIGURE 4.6B**). As you will see in Chapter 34, being able to recognize "self"

imparts the potential ability to distinguish nonself (foreign) cells or particles.

Plasma membranes and some internal membranes incorporate **receptor proteins**, which trigger a change in the cell's activities upon binding a particular substance (**FIGURE 4.6C**). Different receptors bind to hormones or other signaling molecules, toxins, or molecules on another cell. The response triggered may involve metabolism, movement, division, or even cell death.

All cell membranes have some types of proteins, including enzymes. **Transport proteins** move specific substances across a membrane, typically by forming a channel through it (**FIGURE 4.6D,E**). These proteins are important because lipid bilayers are impermeable to most substances, including ions and polar molecules. Some transport proteins are open channels through which a substance moves on its own across a membrane. Others use energy to actively pump a substance across.

adhesion protein Protein that helps cells stick together in animal tissues.
fluid mosaic Model of a cell membrane as a two-dimensional fluid of mixed composition.
receptor protein Membrane protein that triggers a change in cell activity after binding to a particular substance.
recognition protein Plasma membrane protein that identifies a cell as belonging to self (one's own body or species).
transport protein Protein that passively or actively assists specific ions or molecules across a membrane.

CREDITS: (6B–E) © Cengage Learning 2015.

A *Escherichia coli*, a common bacterial inhabitant of human intestines. Short, hairlike structures are pili; longer ones are flagella.

0.5 µm

B *Dermocarpa*, a type of cyanobacteria. Like other members of this ancient lineage, *Dermocarpa* has internal membranes (in green) where photosynthesis occurs. The dark, multisided structures are carboxysomes, proteinenclosed organelles that assist photosynthesis.

1 µm

C *Helicobacter pylori*, a bacterium that can cause stomach ulcers when it infects the lining of the stomach. In unfavorable conditions, this species takes on a ball-shaped form (shown) that may offer the cells protection from environmental challenges such as antibiotic treatment.

0.5 µm

D *Thermococcus gammatolerans*, an archaeon discovered at a deep-sea hydrothermal vent, where it lives under extreme conditions of salt, temperature, and pressure. It is by far the most radiation-resistant organism ever discovered, capable of withstanding thousands of times more radiation than humans can.

0.5 µm

FIGURE 4.7 Some representatives of bacteria (A–C) and an archaeon (D).

All bacteria and archaea are single-celled organisms (**FIGURE 4.7**), though in many types the cells form filaments or colonies. Outwardly, cells of the two groups appear so similar that archaea were once thought to be an unusual group of bacteria. Both were classified as prokaryotes, a word that means "before the nucleus." By 1977, it had become clear that archaea are more closely related to eukaryotes than to bacteria, so they were given their own separate domain. The term "prokaryote" is now an informal designation.

FIGURE 4.8 {Animated} Generalized body plan of a prokaryote (a bacterium or archaeon).

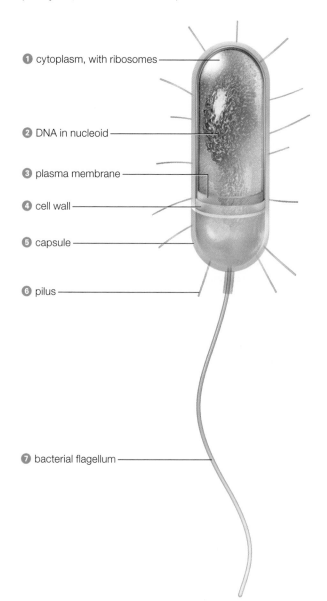

❶ cytoplasm, with ribosomes

❷ DNA in nucleoid

❸ plasma membrane

❹ cell wall

❺ capsule

❻ pilus

❼ bacterial flagellum

CREDITS: (7A) © Biophoto Associates/Science Photo Library; (7B) © Dr. Dennis Kunkel/Visuals Unlimited; (7C) Biomedical Imaging Unit, Southhampton General Hospital/Science Photo Library; (7D) Archivo Angels Tapias y Fabrice Confalonieri; (8) From Starr/Taggart/Evers/Starr, Biology, 13E. © 2013 Cengage Learning.

Bacteria and archaea are the smallest and most metabolically diverse forms of life that we know about. They inhabit nearly all of Earth's environments, including some extremely hostile places. The two kinds of cells differ in structure and metabolism. Chapter 19 revisits them in more detail; here we present an overview of structures shared by both groups (**FIGURE 4.8**).

Compared with eukaryotic cells, prokaryotes have little in the way of internal framework, but they do have protein filaments under the plasma membrane that reinforce the cell's shape and act as scaffolding for internal structures. The cytoplasm of these cells ❶ contains many **ribosomes** (organelles upon which polypeptides are assembled), and in some species, additional organelles. Cytoplasm also contains **plasmids**, small circles of DNA that carry a few genes (units of inheritance) that can provide advantages, such as resistance to antibiotics. The cell's remaining genes typically occur on one large circular molecule of DNA located in an irregularly shaped region of cytoplasm called the **nucleoid** ❷. In a few species, the nucleoid is enclosed by a membrane. Other internal membranes carry out special metabolic processes such as photosynthesis in some prokaryotes (**FIGURE 4.7B**).

Like all cells, bacteria and archaea have a plasma membrane ❸. In nearly all prokaryotes, a rigid **cell wall** ❹ surrounding the plasma membrane protects the cell and supports its shape. Most archaeal cell walls consist of proteins; most bacterial cell walls consist of a polymer of peptides and polysaccharides. Both types are permeable to water, so dissolved substances easily cross.

Polysaccharides form a slime layer or capsule ❺ around the wall of many types of bacteria. These sticky structures help the cells adhere to many types of surfaces, and they also offer protection against some predators and toxins.

Protein filaments called **pili** (singular, pilus) ❻ project from the surface of some prokaryotes. Pili help these cells move across or cling to surfaces. Many prokaryotes also have one or more **flagella** (singular, flagellum) ❼, which are long, slender cellular structures used for motion. A bacterial flagellum rotates like a propeller that drives the cell through fluid habitats.

BIOFILMS

Bacterial cells often live so close together that an entire community shares a layer of secreted polysaccharides and proteins. A communal living arrangement in which single-celled organisms live in a shared mass of slime is called a **biofilm**. A biofilm is often attached to a solid surface, and may include bacteria, algae, fungi, protists, and/or archaea. Participating in a biofilm allows the cells to linger in a

FIGURE 4.9 Oral bacteria in dental plaque, a biofilm. This micrograph shows two species of bacteria (tan, green) and a yeast (red) sticking to one another and to teeth via a gluelike mass of shared, secreted polysaccharides (pink). Other secretions of these organisms cause cavities and periodontal disease.

favorable spot rather than be swept away by fluid currents, and to reap the benefits of living communally. For example, rigid or netlike secretions of some species serve as permanent scaffolding for others; species that break down toxic chemicals allow more sensitive ones to thrive in habitats that they could not withstand on their own; and waste products of some serve as raw materials for others. Later chapters discuss medical implications of biofilms, including the dental plaque that forms on teeth (**FIGURE 4.9**).

biofilm Community of microorganisms living within a shared mass of secreted slime.
cell wall Rigid but permeable structure that surrounds the plasma membrane of some cells.
flagellum Long, slender cellular structure used for motility.
nucleoid Of a bacterium or archaeon, region of cytoplasm where the DNA is concentrated.
pilus A protein filament that projects from the surface of some prokaryotic cells.
plasmid Small circle of DNA in some bacteria and archaea.
ribosome Organelle of protein synthesis.

TAKE-HOME MESSAGE 4.4

Bacteria and archaea do not have a nucleus. Most kinds have a cell wall around their plasma membrane. The permeable wall reinforces and imparts shape to the cell body.

The structure of bacteria and archaea is relatively simple, but as a group these organisms are the most diverse forms of life.

In addition to the nucleus, a typical eukaryotic cell has many other organelles, including endoplasmic reticulum, Golgi bodies, ribosomes, and at least one mitochondrion (**TABLE 4.4** and **FIGURE 4.10**). Organelles with membranes can regulate the types and amounts of substances that enter and exit. Such control maintains a special internal environment that allows the organelle to carry out its particular function—for example, isolating toxic or sensitive substances from the rest of the cell, moving substances through cytoplasm, maintaining fluid balance, or providing a favorable environment for a special process.

In this section, we detail the nucleus, which is the defining characteristic of eukaryotes. The remaining sections of the chapter introduce the functions of other organelles typical of eukaryotic cells.

THE NUCLEUS

A cell nucleus (**FIGURE 4.11**) serves multiple functions. First, it keeps the cell's genetic material—its one and only copy of DNA—safe from metabolic processes that might damage it. Isolated in its own compartment, the DNA stays separated from the bustling activity of the cytoplasm. The nucleus also allows some molecules, but not others, to access the DNA. The nuclear membrane, which is called

TABLE 4.4

Some Organelles in Eukaryotic Cells

Organelles with membranes

Nucleus	Protecting and controlling access to DNA
Endoplasmic reticulum (ER)	Making, modifying new polypeptides and lipids; other tasks
Golgi body	Modifying and sorting new polypeptides and lipids
Vesicle	Transporting, storing, or breaking down substances
Mitochondrion	Making ATP by glucose breakdown
Chloroplast	Making sugars in plants, some protists
Lysosome	Intracellular digestion
Peroxisome	Breaking down fatty acids, amino acids, toxins
Vacuole	Storage, breaking down food or waste

Organelles without membranes

Ribosome	Assembling polypeptides
Centriole	Anchor for cytoskeleton

Other components

Cytoskeleton	Contributes to cell shape, internal organization, movement

FIGURE 4.10 Some components of eukaryotic cells.

endoplasmic reticulum   nucleus   mitochondrion   cell wall   Golgi body   vacuole

An animal cell (a white blood cell of a guinea pig)

A plant cell (from a root of thale cress)

CREDITS: (10) left, Don W. Fawcett/Science Source; right, Biophoto Associates/Science Source; (Table 4.4) © Cengage Learning.

nuclear pore

the **nuclear envelope**, carries out this function. A nuclear envelope consists of two lipid bilayers folded together as a single membrane. Membrane proteins aggregate into thousands of tiny pores (*left*) that span the nuclear envelope. The pores are anchored by the nuclear lamina, a dense mesh of fibrous proteins that supports the inner surface of the membrane. Some bacteria have membranes around their DNA, but we do not consider the bacteria to have nuclei because there are no pores in these membranes.

As you will see in Chapter 5, large molecules, including RNA and proteins, cannot cross a lipid bilayer on their own. Nuclear pores function as gateways for these molecules to enter and exit a nucleus. Protein synthesis offers an example of why this movement is important. Protein synthesis occurs in cytoplasm, and it requires the participation of many molecules of RNA. RNA is produced in the nucleus. Thus, RNA molecules must move from nucleus to cytoplasm, and they do so through nuclear pores. Proteins that carry out RNA synthesis must move in the opposite direction, because this process occurs in the nucleus. A cell can regulate the amounts and types of proteins it makes at a given time by selectively restricting the passage of certain molecules through nuclear pores. (Later chapters return to details of protein synthesis and controls over it.)

The nuclear envelope encloses **nucleoplasm**, a viscous fluid similar to cytoplasm, in which the cell's DNA is suspended. The nucleus contains at least one **nucleolus** (plural, nucleoli), a dense, irregularly shaped region of proteins and nucleic acid where subunits of ribosomes are produced.

nuclear envelope A double membrane that constitutes the outer boundary of the nucleus. Pores in the membrane control which substances can cross.
nucleolus In a cell nucleus, a dense, irregularly shaped region where ribosomal subunits are assembled.
nucleoplasm Viscous fluid enclosed by the nuclear envelope.

TAKE-HOME MESSAGE 4.5

All eukaryotic cells start life with a nucleus and other membrane-enclosed organelles.

A nucleus protects and controls access to a eukaryotic cell's DNA.

The nuclear envelope is a double lipid bilayer. Proteins embedded in the bilayer form pores that control the passage of molecules between the nucleus and cytoplasm.

A Nucleus of a liver cell (in pink).

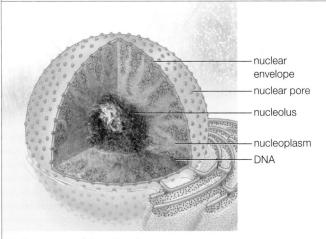

nuclear envelope
nuclear pore
nucleolus
nucleoplasm
DNA

B Components of the cell nucleus.

nuclear pore

nuclear envelope

cytoplasm

C The nuclear envelope consists of two lipid bilayers folded together as a single membrane and studded with thousands of nuclear pores. Each nuclear pore is an organized cluster of membrane proteins that selectively allows certain substances to cross it on their way into and out of the nucleus.

FIGURE 4.11 {Animated} The cell nucleus.

CREDITS: (11A) Dr. David Furness, Keele University/Science Source; (11B,C) © Cengage Learning; (inset) © Martin W. Goldberg, Durham University, UK.

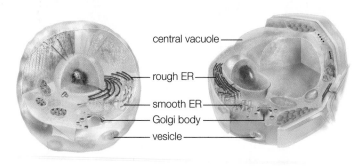

central vacuole
rough ER
smooth ER
Golgi body
vesicle

The **endomembrane system** is a series of interacting organelles between the nucleus and the plasma membrane (*above*). Its main function is to make lipids, enzymes, and proteins for insertion into the cell's membranes or secretion to the external environment. The endomembrane system also destroys toxins, recycles wastes, and has other special functions. Components of the system vary among different types of cells, but here we present an overview of the most common ones (**FIGURE 4.12**).

A VARIETY OF VESICLES

Small, membrane-enclosed sacs called **vesicles** form by budding from other organelles or when a patch of plasma membrane sinks into the cytoplasm ❶. Vesicles have a variety of functions. Many transport substances from one organelle to another, or to and from the plasma membrane. Some are a bit like trash cans that collect and dispose of waste, debris, or toxins. Enzymes in **peroxisomes** break down fatty acids, amino acids, and poisons such as alcohol. They also break down hydrogen peroxide, a toxic

by-product of fatty acid metabolism. **Lysosomes** take part in intracellular digestion. They contain powerful enzymes that can break down cellular debris and wastes (carbohydrates, proteins, nucleic acids, and lipids). Vesicles in cells such as amoebas or white blood cells deliver ingested bacteria, cell parts, and other debris to lysosomes for breakdown.

Vacuoles form by the fusion of multiple vesicles. They have different functions in different kinds of cells. Many isolate or break down waste, debris, toxins, or food (**FIGURE 4.13**). Amino acids, sugars, ions, wastes, and toxins accumulate in the water-filled interior of a plant cell's large **central vacuole**. Fluid pressure in a central vacuole keeps plant cells plump, so stems, leaves, and other plant parts stay firm.

---

central vacuole   Fluid-filled vesicle in many plant cells.
endomembrane system   Series of interacting organelles (endoplasmic reticulum, Golgi bodies, vesicles) between nucleus and plasma membrane; produces lipids, proteins.
endoplasmic reticulum (ER)   Organelle that is a continuous system of sacs and tubes extending from the nuclear envelope. Smooth ER makes lipids and breaks down carbohydrates and fatty acids; ribosomes on the surface of rough ER synthesize proteins.
Golgi body   Organelle that modifies proteins and lipids, then packages the finished products into vesicles.
lysosome   Enzyme-filled vesicle that breaks down cellular wastes and debris.
peroxisome   Enzyme-filled vesicle that breaks down amino acids, fatty acids, and toxic substances.
vacuole   A fluid-filled organelle that isolates or disposes of waste, debris, or toxic materials.
vesicle   Small, membrane-enclosed organelle; different kinds store, transport, or break down their contents.

FIGURE 4.12 Some interactions among components of the endomembrane system.

nuclear envelope   vesicle   rough ER   new protein

❶ Vesicles
Vesicles are membrane-enclosed sacs that often form by budding from other components of the endomembrane system. Many transport substances among organelles of the ER, and to and from the plasma membrane. Other vesicles store or break down substances.

❷ Rough ER
Ribosomes attached to the rough ER use RNA in the cytoplasm to make polypeptides. The newly synthesized polypeptide chains enter rough ER, where they take on tertiary structure and assemble with other polypeptide chains.

CREDITS: (in text) © Cengage Learning; (12-1) © Kenneth Bart; (12-2, 12-3) Don W. Fawcett/Visuals Unlimited; (12-4) Micrograph, Gary Grimes; (12) art, © Cengage Learning 2015.

ENDOPLASMIC RETICULUM

The membrane of the **endoplasmic reticulum** (**ER**) is an extension of the nuclear envelope. Its interconnected tubes and flattened sacs form a single compartment that houses many enzymes. Two kinds of ER, rough and smooth, are named for their appearance. Thousands of ribosomes that attach to the outer surface of rough ER give this organelle its "rough" appearance. These ribosomes make polypeptides that thread into the interior of the ER as they are assembled ❷. Inside the ER, the polypeptide chains fold and take on their tertiary structure, and many assemble with other polypeptide chains (Section 3.4). Cells that make, store, and secrete proteins have a lot of rough ER. For example, ER-rich cells in the pancreas make digestive enzymes that they secrete into the small intestine.

Some proteins made in rough ER become part of its membrane. Others migrate through the ER compartment to smooth ER. Smooth ER has no ribosomes, so it does not make its own proteins ❸. Some proteins that arrive in smooth ER are immediately packaged into vesicles for delivery elsewhere. Others are enzymes that stay and become part of the smooth ER. Some of these enzymes break down carbohydrates, fatty acids, and some drugs and poisons. Others make lipids for the cell's membranes.

GOLGI BODIES

A **Golgi body** has a folded membrane that often looks like a stack of pancakes ❹. Enzymes inside of it put finishing touches on proteins and lipids that have been delivered from ER. These enzymes attach phosphate groups or

The protist *Nassula* (round cell) uses a distinctive oral basket to feed on strands of algae. Ingested cells are packaged in food vacuoles that change color (green to purple to brown to gold) as the chlorophyll molecules inside them break down.

FIGURE 4.13 An example of vacuole function.

carbohydrates, and cleave certain proteins. The finished products (such as membrane proteins, proteins for secretion, and enzymes) are sorted and packaged in new vesicles. Some of the vesicles deliver their cargo to the plasma membrane; others become lysosomes.

> **TAKE-HOME MESSAGE 4.6**
>
> Rough ER produces enzymes, membrane proteins, and secreted proteins. Smooth ER produces lipids and breaks down carbohydrates, fatty acids, and toxins.
>
> Golgi bodies modify proteins and lipids.

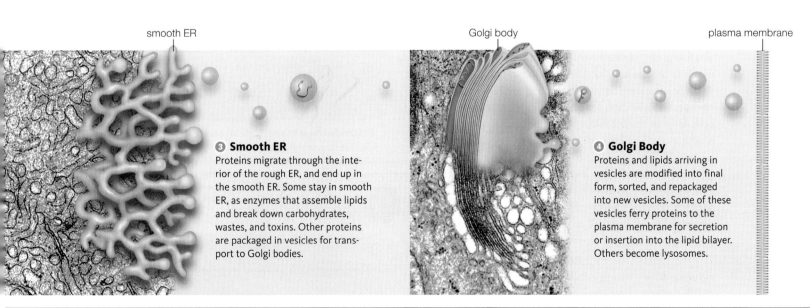

smooth ER

❸ Smooth ER
Proteins migrate through the interior of the rough ER, and end up in the smooth ER. Some stay in smooth ER, as enzymes that assemble lipids and break down carbohydrates, wastes, and toxins. Other proteins are packaged in vesicles for transport to Golgi bodies.

Golgi body   plasma membrane

❹ Golgi Body
Proteins and lipids arriving in vesicles are modified into final form, sorted, and repackaged into new vesicles. Some of these vesicles ferry proteins to the plasma membrane for secretion or insertion into the lipid bilayer. Others become lysosomes.

mitochondrion

As you will see in Chapter 5, biologists think of the nucleotide ATP as a type of cellular currency because it carries energy between reactions. Cells require a lot of ATP. The most efficient way they can produce it is by aerobic respiration, a series of oxygen-requiring reactions that harvests the energy in sugars by breaking their bonds. In eukaryotes, aerobic respiration occurs inside organelles called **mitochondria** (singular, mitochondrion). With each breath, you are taking in oxygen mainly for the mitochondria in your trillions of aerobically respiring cells.

The structure of a mitochondrion is specialized for carrying out reactions of aerobic respiration. Each mitochondrion has two membranes, one highly folded inside the other (**FIGURE 4.14**). This arrangement creates two compartments: an outer one (between the two membranes), and an inner one (inside the inner membrane). Hydrogen ions accumulate in the outer compartment. The buildup pushes the ions across the inner membrane, into the inner compartment, and this flow drives ATP formation. Chapter 7 returns to the details of aerobic respiration.

Nearly all eukaryotic cells (including plant cells) have mitochondria, but the number varies by the type of cell and by the organism. For example, single-celled organisms such as yeast often have only one mitochondrion, but human skeletal muscle cells have a thousand or more. In general, cells that have the highest demand for energy tend to have the most mitochondria.

Typical mitochondria are between 1 and 4 micrometers in length. These organelles can change shape, split in two, branch, or fuse together. They resemble bacteria in size, form, and biochemistry. They have their own DNA, which is circular and otherwise similar to bacterial DNA. They divide independently of the cell, and have their own ribosomes. Such clues led to a theory that mitochondria evolved from aerobic bacteria that took up permanent residence inside a host cell (we return to this topic in Section 18.5).

Some eukaryotes that live in oxygen-free environments have modified mitochondria that produce hydrogen in addition to ATP. Like mitochondria, these organelles have two membranes, but they have lost the ability to divide independently because they lack their own DNA.

mitochondrion Double-membraned organelle that produces ATP by aerobic respiration in eukaryotes.

A **Each mitochondrion has two membranes, one highly folded inside the other.**

outer membrane
inner membrane
outer compartment
inner compartment

0.5 μm

B Mitochondrion in a cell from bat pancreas.

FIGURE 4.14 {Animated} The mitochondrion, a eukaryotic organelle that specializes in producing ATP.

FIGURE IT OUT: What organelle is visible in the upper right-hand corner of the TEM?　Answer: Rough ER

TAKE-HOME MESSAGE 4.7

Mitochondria are eukaryotic organelles specialized to produce ATP by aerobic respiration.

CREDITS: (in text) © Cengage Learning; (14A) © Cengage Learning 2015; (14B) Keith R Porter.

chloroplast

Plastids are double-membraned organelles that function in photosynthesis, storage, or pigmentation in plant and algal cells. Photosynthetic cells of plants and many protists contain **chloroplasts**, which are plastids specialized for photosynthesis (**FIGURE 4.15**). Most chloroplasts are oval or disk-shaped. Each has two outer membranes enclosing a semifluid interior, the stroma, that contains enzymes and the chloroplast's own DNA. In the stroma, a third, highly folded membrane forms a single, continuous compartment. Photosynthesis occurs at this inner membrane.

The innermost membrane of a chloroplast incorporates many pigments, including a green one called chlorophyll (the abundance of chlorophyll in plant cell chloroplasts is the reason most plants are green). During photosynthesis, these pigments capture energy from sunlight, and pass it to other molecules that require energy to make ATP. The resulting ATP is used inside the stroma to build sugars from carbon dioxide and water. (Chapter 6 returns to details of these processes.) In many ways, chloroplasts resemble the photosynthetic bacteria that they evolved from.

Chromoplasts are plastids that make and store pigments other than chlorophylls. They often contain red or orange carotenoids that color flowers, leaves, roots, and fruits (**FIGURE 4.16**). Chromoplasts are related to chloroplasts, and the two types of plastids are interconvertible. For example, as fruits such as tomatoes ripen, green chloroplasts in their cells are converted to red chromoplasts, so the color of the fruit changes.

Amyloplasts are unpigmented plastids that make and store starch grains. They are notably abundant in cells of stems, tubers (underground stems), fruits, and seeds. Like chromoplasts, amyloplasts are related to chloroplasts, and one type can change into the other. Starch-packed amyloplasts are dense and heavy compared to cytoplasm; in some plant cells, they function as gravity-sensing organelles (we return to this topic in Chapter 27).

chloroplast Organelle of photosynthesis in the cells of plants and photosynthetic protists.
plastid One of several types of double-membraned organelles in plants and algal cells; for example, a chloroplast or amyloplast.

TAKE-HOME MESSAGE 4.8

Plastids occur in plants and some protists; they function in photosynthesis, storage, and pigmentation.

Chloroplasts are plastids that carry out photosynthesis.

A Chloroplast-packed cells make up a leaf of a flowering plant.

two outer membranes
stroma
inner membrane

B Each chloroplast has two outer membranes. Photosynthesis occurs at a much-folded inner membrane. The electron micrograph shows a chloroplast from a leaf of corn.

FIGURE 4.15 {**Animated**} The chloroplast.

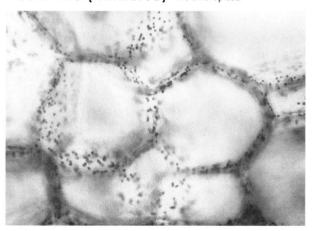

FIGURE 4.16 **Chromoplasts**. The color of a red bell pepper arises from chromoplasts in its cells.

CREDITS: (in text) © Cengage Learning; (15A) Heiti Paves/Science Photo Library; (15B) top, Dr. George Chapman/Visuals Unlimited, Inc.; bottom, © Cengage Learning 2015; (16) © David T. Webb.

Between the nucleus and plasma membrane of all eukaryotic cells is a system of interconnected protein filaments collectively called the **cytoskeleton**. Elements of the cytoskeleton reinforce, organize, and move cell structures, and often the whole cell. Some are permanent; others form only at certain times.

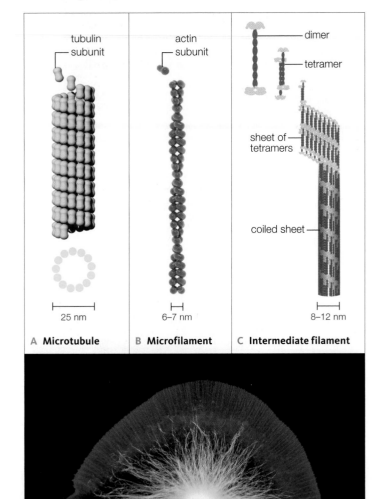

A **Microtubule**   B **Microfilament**   C **Intermediate filament**

tubulin
— subunit

actin
— subunit

— dimer

— tetramer

sheet of tetramers

coiled sheet —

25 nm   6–7 nm   8–12 nm

D A fluorescence micrograph shows microtubules (yellow) and microfilaments (blue) in the growing end of a nerve cell. These cytoskeletal elements support and guide the cell's lengthening in a particular direction.

FIGURE 4.17 {Animated} Cytoskeletal elements.

Microtubules are long, hollow cylinders that consist of subunits of the protein tubulin (**FIGURE 4.17A**). They form a dynamic scaffolding for many cellular processes, rapidly assembling when they are needed, disassembling when they are not. For example, before a eukaryotic cell divides, microtubules assemble, separate the cell's duplicated DNA molecules, then disassemble. As another example, microtubules that form in the growing end of a young nerve cell support its lengthening in a particular direction (**FIGURE 4.17D**).

Microfilaments are fibers that consist primarily of subunits of the globular protein actin (**FIGURE 4.17B**). These fine fibers strengthen or change the shape of eukaryotic cells, and have a critical function in cell migration, movement, and contraction. Crosslinked, bundled, or gel-like arrays of them make up the **cell cortex**, a reinforcing mesh under the plasma membrane. Microfilaments also connect plasma membrane proteins to other proteins inside the cell.

Intermediate filaments are the most stable elements of the cytoskeleton, forming a framework that lends structure and resilience to cells and tissues in multicelled organisms. Several types of intermediate filaments are assembled from different proteins (**FIGURE 4.17C**). For example, intermediate filaments that make up your hair consist of keratin, a fibrous protein (Section 3.4). Intermediate filaments that form the nuclear lamina consist of lamins, another type of fibrous protein.

Motor proteins that associate with cytoskeletal elements move cell parts when energized by a phosphate-group transfer from ATP (Section 3.6). A cell is like a bustling train station, with molecules and structures being moved continuously throughout its interior. Motor proteins are like freight trains, dragging cellular cargo along tracks of microtubules and microfilaments (**FIGURE 4.18**). The motor protein myosin interacts with microfilaments to bring about muscle cell contraction. Another motor protein, dynein, interacts with microtubules to bring about movement of flagella and cilia in eukaryotes. Eukaryotic flagella whip back and forth to propel cells such as sperm (*right*) through fluid. **Cilia** (singular, cilium) are short, hairlike structures that project from the surface of some cells. The coordinated

— flagellum

sperm

CREDITS: (17A–C) From Starr/Taggart/Evers/Starr, Biology, 12E. © 2009 Cengage Learning; (in text) © Cengage Learning; (17D) © Dylan T. Burnette and Paul Forscher.

waving of many cilia propels some cells through fluid, and stirs fluid around other cells that are stationary. The waving movement of eukaryotic flagella and cilia, which differs from the propeller-like rotation of prokaryotic flagella, arises from their internal architecture. Microtubules extend lengthwise through them, in what is called a 9+2 array (**FIGURE 4.19**). The array consists of nine pairs of microtubules ringing another pair in the center. The microtubules grow from a barrel-shaped organelle called the **centriole**, which remains below the finished array as a **basal body**.

Amoebas (*left*) and other types of eukaryotic cells form **pseudopods**, or "false feet." As these temporary, irregular lobes bulge outward, they move the cell and engulf a target such as prey. Elongating microfilaments force the lobe to advance in a steady direction. Motor proteins that are attached to the microfilaments drag the plasma membrane along with them.

basal body Organelle that develops from a centriole.
cell cortex Mesh of cytoskeletal elements under a plasma membrane.
centriole Barrel-shaped organelle from which microtubules grow.
cilium Short, movable structure that projects from the plasma membrane of some eukaryotic cells.
cytoskeleton Network of interconnected protein filaments that support, organize, and move eukaryotic cells and their parts.
intermediate filament Stable cytoskeletal element that structurally supports cell membranes and tissues.
microfilament Cytoskeletal element that is a fiber of actin subunits. Reinforces cell membranes; functions in muscle contractions.
microtubule Cytoskeletal element involved in movement; hollow filament of tubulin subunits.
motor protein Type of energy-using protein that interacts with cytoskeletal elements to move the cell's parts or the whole cell.
pseudopod A temporary protrusion that helps some eukaryotic cells move and engulf prey.

TAKE-HOME MESSAGE 4.9

A cytoskeleton of protein filaments is the basis of eukaryotic cell shape, internal structure, and movement.

Microtubules organize eukaryotic cells and help move their parts. Networks of microfilaments reinforce cell shape and function in movement. Intermediate filaments strengthen and maintain the shape of cell membranes and tissues, and form external structures such as hair.

When energized by ATP, motor proteins move along tracks of microtubules and microfilaments. As part of cilia, flagella, and pseudopods, they can move the whole cell.

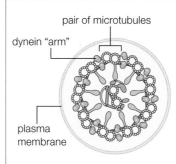

A A 9+2 array, which consists of a ring of nine pairs of microtubules plus one pair at their core, runs lengthwise through a eukaryotic flagellum or cilium. Stabilizing spokes and linking elements connect the microtubules and keep them aligned in this pattern. Projecting from each pair of microtubules in the outer ring are "arms" of the motor protein dynein.

pair of microtubules
dynein "arm"
plasma membrane

B Microtubules of a developing 9+2 array grow from a centriole, which remains below the finished array as a basal body. The micrograph *below* shows basal bodies underlying cilia of the protist pictured in **FIGURE 4.5**.

basal body

C Phosphate-group transfers from ATP cause the dynein arms in a 9+2 array to repeatedly bind the adjacent pair of microtubules, bend, and then disengage. The dynein arms "walk" along the microtubules, so adjacent microtubule pairs slide past one another. The short, sliding strokes of the dynein arms occur in a coordinated sequence around the ring, down the length of the microtubules. The movement causes the entire structure to bend.

FIGURE 4.19 {Animated} How eukaryotic flagella and cilia move.

CREDITS: (18, 19A–C) From Starr/Taggart/Evers/Starr, Biology, 13E. © 2013 Cengage Learning; (in text) Astrid & Hanns-Frieder Michler/Science Source; (19B left) Dennis Kunkel Microscopy, Inc./Visuals Unlimited, Inc.

plasma membrane   primary wall

cytoplasm

middle lamella

A Plant cell secretions form a primary wall. The middle lamella cements adjoining cells together.

B Plant cells also secrete materials in layers on the inner surface of their primary wall. These layers form a sturdy secondary wall. In some tissues, the wall remains after the cells die, becoming part of pipelines that carry water through the plant.

secondary wall

primary wall

C Plasmodesmata are channels that connect cytoplasm and ER of adjacent plant cells.

ER
cytoplasm
plasma membrane
cell wall

FIGURE 4.20 {Animated} Plant cell walls.

CELL MATRIXES

Many cells secrete an **extracellular matrix (ECM)**, a complex mixture of molecules that often includes polysaccharides and fibrous proteins. The composition and function of ECM vary by the type of cell that secretes it.

A cell wall is an example of ECM. Among eukaryotes, fungi and some protists have walls, as do plant cells (as shown in this chapter's opening photo). The composition of the wall differs among these groups. Like a prokaryotic cell wall, a eukaryotic cell wall is porous: Water and solutes easily cross it on the way to and from the plasma membrane.

In plants, the cell wall forms as a young cell secretes pectin and other polysaccharides onto the outer surface of its plasma membrane. The sticky coating is shared between adjacent cells, and it cements them together. Each cell then forms a **primary wall** by secreting strands of cellulose into the coating. Some of the pectin coating remains as the middle lamella, a sticky layer in between the primary walls of abutting plant cells (**FIGURE 4.20A**).

Being thin and pliable, a primary wall allows a growing plant cell to enlarge and change shape. In some plants, mature cells secrete material onto the primary wall's inner surface. These deposits form a firm **secondary wall** (**FIGURE 4.20B**). One of the materials deposited is **lignin**, an organic compound that makes up as much as 25 percent of the secondary wall of cells in older stems and roots. Lignified plant parts are stronger, more waterproof, and less susceptible to plant-attacking organisms than younger tissues.

Animal cells have no walls, but some types secrete an extracellular matrix called basement membrane. Despite the name, basement membrane is not a cell membrane because it does not consist of a lipid bilayer. Rather, it is a sheet of fibrous material that structurally supports and organizes

FIGURE 4.21   A plant ECM. Section through a plant leaf showing cuticle, a protective covering secreted by living cells.

cuticle   outer cell of leaf   photosynthetic cell inside leaf

CREDITS: (20A,B) © Cengage Learning 2015; (20C) top, From Starr/Taggart/Evers/Starr, Biology, 13E. © Cengage Learning; bottom, © Cengage Learning; (21) George S. Ellmore.

tissues, and it has roles in cell signaling. Bone is an ECM composed mostly of the fibrous protein collagen, and hardened by deposits of calcium and phosphorus.

A **cuticle** is a type of ECM secreted by cells at a body surface. In plants, a cuticle of waxes and proteins helps stems and leaves fend off insects and retain water (**FIGURE 4.21**). Crabs, spiders, and other arthropods have a cuticle that consists mainly of chitin (Section 3.2).

CELL JUNCTIONS

In multicelled species, cells can interact with one another and their surroundings by way of cell junctions. **Cell junctions** are structures that connect a cell directly to other cells and to its environment. Cells send and receive substances and signals through some junctions. Other junctions help cells recognize and stick to each other and to ECM.

Three types of cell junctions are common in animal tissues (**FIGURE 4.22A**). In tissues that line body surfaces and internal cavities, rows of adhesion proteins form **tight junctions** between the plasma membranes of adjacent cells. These junctions prevent body fluids from seeping between the cells (**FIGURE 4.22B**). For example, the lining of the stomach is leak-proof because tight junctions seal its cells together. These junctions keep gastric fluid, which contains acid and destructive enzymes, safely inside the stomach. If a bacterial infection damages the stomach lining, gastric fluid leaks into and damages the underlying layers. A painful peptic ulcer is the result.

Adhering junctions, which fasten cells to one another and to basement membrane, also consist of adhesion proteins. These junctions make a tissue quite strong because they connect to cytoskeletal elements inside the cells. Contractile tissues (such as heart muscle) have a lot of adhering

A Three types of cell junctions in animal tissues.

free surface of epithelial tissue

tight junctions

gap junction

adhering junction

basement membrane

B In this fluorescence micrograph, a profusion of tight junctions (green) seals abutting surfaces of kidney cell membranes and forms a leak-proof tissue. The DNA in each cell nucleus appears red.

FIGURE 4.22 {Animated} Cell junctions.

junctions, as do tissues subject to abrasion or stretching (such as skin).

Gap junctions are closable channels that connect the cytoplasm of adjoining animal cells. When open, they permit water, ions, and small molecules to pass directly from the cytoplasm of one cell to another. These channels allow entire regions of cells to respond to a single stimulus. Heart muscle and other tissues in which the cells perform a coordinated action have many gap junctions.

In plants, open channels called **plasmodesmata** (singular, plasmodesma) extend across plant cell walls to connect the cytoplasm of adjacent cells. Like gap junctions, plasmodesmata also allow substances to flow quickly from cell to cell.

adhering junction Cell junction composed of adhesion proteins that connect to cytoskeletal elements. Fastens cells to each other and basement membrane.
cell junction Structure that connects a cell to another cell or to extracellular matrix.
cuticle Secreted covering at a body surface.
extracellular matrix (ECM) Complex mixture of cell secretions; its composition and function vary by cell type.
gap junction Cell junction that forms a closable channel across the plasma membranes of adjoining animal cells.
lignin Material that strengthens cell walls of vascular plants.
plasmodesmata Cell junctions that form an open channel between the cytoplasm of adjacent plant cells.
primary wall The first cell wall of young plant cells.
secondary wall Lignin-reinforced wall that forms inside the primary wall of a plant cell.
tight junctions Arrays of adhesion proteins that join epithelial cells and collectively prevent fluids from leaking between them.

CREDITS: (22A) From Starr/Taggart/Evers/Starr, Biology, 13E. © 2013 Cengage Learning; (22B) © ADVANCELL/ Advanced In Vitro Cell Technologies.

TAKE-HOME MESSAGE 4.10

Many cells secrete an extracellular matrix (ECM). ECM varies in composition and function depending on the cell type.

Plant cells, fungi, and some protists have a porous wall around their plasma membrane. Animal cells do not have walls.

Cell junctions structurally and functionally connect cells in tissues. In animal tissues, cell junctions also connect cells with basement membrane.

You learned in Section 1.1 that the cell is the smallest unit with the properties of life. In this chapter, you learned that a living cell has at minimum a plasma membrane, cytoplasm, and a region of DNA; most cells have many other components in addition to these things. So what is it, exactly, that makes it alive? A cell does not spring to life from cellular components mixed in the right amounts and proportions. According to evolutionary biologist Gerald Joyce, the simplest definition of life might well be "that which is squishy." He says, "Life, after all, is protoplasmic and cellular. It is made up of cells and organic stuff and is undeniably squishy."

However, defining life more unambiguously than "squishy" is challenging, if not impossible. We can more easily describe what sets the living apart from the nonliving, but even that can be tricky. For example, living things have a high proportion of the organic molecules of life, but so do the remains of dead organisms in seams of coal. Living things use energy to reproduce themselves, but computer viruses, which are arguably not alive, can do that too.

So how do biologists, who study life as a profession, define it? The short answer is that their best definition is a long list of properties that collectively describe living things. You already know about two of these properties:

1. They make and use the organic molecules of life.
2. They consist of one or more cells.

The remainder of this book details the others:

3. They engage in self-sustaining biological processes such as metabolism and homeostasis.
4. They change over their lifetime, for example by growing, maturing, and aging.
5. They use DNA as their hereditary material when they reproduce.
6. They have the collective capacity to change over successive generations, for example by adapting to environmental pressures.

Collectively, these properties characterize living things as different from nonliving things.

TAKE-HOME MESSAGE 4.11

We describe the characteristic of "life" in terms of a set of properties. The set is unique to living things.

In living things, the molecules of life are organized as one or more cells that engage in self-sustaining biological processes.

Organisms make and use the organic molecules of life.

Living things change over lifetimes, and over generations.

National Geographic Explorer
DR. KEVIN PETER HAND

Today's weather forecast for Europa, Jupiter's fourth-largest moon, is –280°F. A layer of ice several miles thick coats its fractured surface, with 1,000-foot ice cliffs piercing a pitch-black sky. It is devoid of atmosphere, bombarded by fierce radiation—and National Geographic Explorer Kevin Hand can hardly wait to get there.

Hand works at the Jet Propulsion Laboratory (JPL), where he is helping NASA plan a mission to Jupiter's moons—an orbiting probe that will give Earthlings a closer look at Europa. Beneath Europa's icy shell lies a vast global liquid water ocean that Hand thinks could be a great place for life. "I want to know if DNA is the only game in town. Are there different biochemical pathways that could lead to other kinds of life? That's at the heart of why I want to go to Europa—to find something living in that ocean we can poke at and use to understand and define life in a much more comprehensive way."

For the first time, we have the technological capability of taking our search for life to distant worlds. "Nevertheless, our understanding of life as a phenomenon remains largely qualitative and poorly constrained," Hand says. In other words, without an exact definition of "life," how do we determine whether it exists on Europa? "Biology preferentially uses specific organic subunits to build larger compounds while abiotic organic chemistry proceeds randomly," says Hand. "The structures of life arise from a relatively small set of universal building blocks; thus, when we search for life we look for patterns indicative of life's structural biases."

Exploration

FIGURE 4.23 *Escherichia coli* cells sticking to the surface of a lettuce leaf. Some strains of this bacteria can cause a serious intestinal illness when they contaminate human food.

CELL FOR CELL, BACTERIA THAT LIVE IN AND ON A HUMAN BODY OUTNUMBER THE PERSON'S OWN CELLS BY ABOUT TEN TO ONE. One of the most common intestinal bacteria of warm-blooded animals (including humans) is *Escherichia coli*. Most of the hundreds of types, or strains, of *E. coli* are harmless, but a few strains make a toxic protein that can severely damage the lining of the intestine. After ingesting as few as ten cells of a toxic strain, a person may become ill with severe cramps and bloody diarrhea that lasts up to ten days. In some people, complications of infection result in kidney failure, blindness, paralysis, and death. Each year, about 265,000 people in the United States become infected with toxin-producing *E. coli*.

Strains of *E. coli* that are toxic to people live in the intestines of other animals—mainly cattle, deer, goats, and sheep—apparently without sickening them. Humans are exposed to the bacteria when they come into contact with feces of animals that harbor it, for example, by eating contaminated ground beef. During slaughter, meat can come into contact with feces. Bacteria in the feces stick to the meat, then get thoroughly mixed into it during the grinding process. Unless contaminated meat is cooked to at least 71°C

(160°F), live bacteria will enter the digestive tract of whoever eats it.

People also become infected with toxic *E. coli* by eating fresh fruits and vegetables that have come into contact with animal feces. Washing produce with water does not remove all of the bacteria because they are sticky (FIGURE 4.23). In June 2011, more than 4,000 people in Germany and France were sickened after eating sprouts, and 49 of them died. The outbreak was traced to a single shipment of contaminated sprout seeds from Egypt.

The impact of such outbreaks, which occur with unfortunate regularity, extends beyond casualties. The contaminated sprouts cost growers in the European Union at least $600 million in lost sales. In 2011 alone, the United States Department of Agriculture (USDA) recalled 36.7 million pounds of ground meat products contaminated with toxic bacteria, at a cost in the billions of dollars. Such costs are eventually passed to taxpayers and consumers.

Food growers and processors are implementing new procedures intended to reduce the number and scope of these outbreaks. Meat and produce are being tested for some bacteria before sale, and improved documentation should allow a source of contamination to be pinpointed more quickly.

Summary

SECTION 4.1   **Cell theory** is the foundation of modern biology. By this theory, all organisms consist of one or more cells; the cell is the smallest unit of life; each new cell arises from another, preexisting cell; and a cell passes hereditary material to its offspring.

All cells start out life with **cytoplasm**, DNA, and a **plasma membrane** that controls the types and kinds of substances that cross it. Most cells have many additional components (**TABLE 4.5** and **FIGURE 4.24**). In eukaryotes, a cell's DNA is contained within a **nucleus**, which is a membrane-enclosed **organelle**.

A cell's surface area increases with the square of its diameter, while its volume increases with the cube. This **surface-to-volume ratio** limits cell size and influences cell (and body) shape.

SECTION 4.2   Most cells are far too small to see with the naked eye, so we use microscopes to observe them. Different types of microscopes and techniques reveal different internal and external details of cells.

SECTION 4.3   A cell membrane is a mosaic of proteins and lipids (mainly phospholipids) organized as a lipid bilayer. The membranes of bacteria and eukaryotic cells can be described as a **fluid mosaic**; those of archaea are not fluid. Proteins contribute to membrane function. All cell membranes have enzymes, and all have **transport proteins** that help substances move across the membrane. Plasma membranes also incorporate **receptor proteins** that bind specific substances, **adhesion proteins** that lock cells together in tissues, and **recognition proteins** that identify a cell as belonging to a tissue or body.

SECTION 4.4   Bacteria and archaea, informally grouped as prokaryotes, are the most diverse forms of life that we know about. These single-celled organisms have no nucleus, but they do have **nucleoids** and **ribosomes**. Many also have a protective, rigid **cell wall** and a sticky capsule, and some have motile structures (**flagella**) and other projections (**pili**). There are often **plasmids** in addition to the single circular molecule of DNA. Bacteria and other microbial organisms may live together in a shared mass of slime as **biofilms**.

SECTION 4.5   All eukaryotic cells start out life with a nucleus and other membrane-enclosed organelles. Membranes allow organelles to compartmentalize tasks and substances that may be sensitive or dangerous to the rest of the cell. A nucleus protects and controls access to a eukaryotic cell's DNA. A double membrane studded with pores constitutes the **nuclear envelope**. The pores serve as gateways for molecules passing into and out of the nucleus.

TABLE 4.5

Summary of Typical Components of Cells

Cell Component	Main Function(s)	Bacteria, Archaea	Eukaryotes			
			Protists	Fungi	Plants	Animals
Cell wall	Protection, structural support	✔	✔	✔	✔	None
Plasma membrane	Control of substances moving into and out of cell	✔	✔	✔	✔	✔
Nucleus	Protecting and controlling access to DNA	None	✔	✔	✔	✔
DNA	Encoding of hereditary information	✔	✔	✔	✔	✔
RNA	Protein synthesis	✔	✔	✔	✔	✔
Ribosome	Protein synthesis	✔	✔	✔	✔	✔
Endoplasmic reticulum (ER)	Protein, lipid synthesis; carbohydrate and fatty acid breakdown	None	✔	✔	✔	✔
Golgi body	Final modification of proteins; lipid assembly	None	✔	✔	✔	✔
Lysosome	Intracellular digestion	None	✔	✔	✔	✔
Peroxisome	Breakdown of fatty acids, amino acids, and toxins	None	✔	✔	✔	✔
Mitochondrion	Production of ATP by aerobic respiration	None	✔	✔	✔	✔
Photosynthetic pigments	Capturing light for photosynthesis	✔	✔	None	✔	None
Chloroplast	Photosynthesis; starch storage	None	✔	None	✔	None
Vacuole	Isolation and breakdown of food, wastes, toxins	None	✔	✔	✔	None
Vesicle	Storage, transport, or breakdown of contents	✔	✔	✔	✔	✔
Flagellum	Locomotion through fluid surroundings	✔	✔	✔	✔	✔
Cilium	Movement through (and of) fluid	✔	✔	None	✔	✔
Cytoskeleton	Physical reinforcement; internal organization; movement of the cell and its parts	✔	✔	✔	✔	✔

CREDIT: (Table 4.5) © Cengage Learning.

A Typical plant cell components.

Cell Wall
Protects, structurally supports cell

Chloroplast
Specializes in photosynthesis

Central Vacuole
Increases cell surface area; stores metabolic wastes

nuclear envelope
nucleolus
DNA in nucleoplasm

Nucleus
Keeps DNA separated from cytoplasm; makes ribosome subunits; controls access to DNA

Cytoskeleton
Structural support, development, cell division, organelle movement

microtubules
microfilaments

Ribosomes
(attached to rough ER and free in cytoplasm) Sites of protein synthesis

Rough ER
Modifies proteins made by ribosomes attached to it

Mitochondrion
Energy powerhouse; produces many ATP by aerobic respiration

Smooth ER
Makes lipids, breaks down carbohydrates and fats, inactivates toxins

Plasmodesma
Communication junction between adjoining cells

Golgi Body
Finishes, sorts, ships lipids, enzymes, and proteins

Plasma Membrane
Selectively controls the kinds and amounts of substances moving into and out of cell; helps maintain cytoplasmic volume, composition

Lysosome-Like Vesicle
Digests, recycles materials

B Typical animal cell components.

nuclear envelope
nucleolus
DNA in nucleoplasm

Nucleus
Keeps DNA separated from cytoplasm; makes ribosome subunits; controls access to DNA

Cytoskeleton
Structurally supports, imparts shape to cell; moves cell and its components

microtubules
microfilaments
intermediate filaments

Ribosomes
(attached to rough ER and free in cytoplasm) Sites of protein synthesis

Rough ER
Modifies proteins made by ribosomes attached to it

Mitochondrion
Energy powerhouse; produces many ATP by aerobic respiration

Smooth ER
Makes lipids, breaks down carbohydrates and fats, inactivates toxins

Centrioles
Special centers that produce and organize microtubules

Golgi Body
Finishes, sorts, ships lipids, enzymes, and proteins

Plasma Membrane
Selectively controls the kinds and amounts of substances moving into and out of cell; helps maintain cytoplasmic volume, composition

Lysosome
Digests, recycles materials

FIGURE 4.24 {**Animated**} Organelles and structures typical of **A** plant cells and **B** animal cells.

CREDIT: (24) © Cengage Learning 2014.

Inside the nuclear envelope, the cell's DNA is suspended in viscous **nucleoplasm**. Also inside the nucleus, ribosome subunits are assembled in dense, irregularly shaped areas called **nucleoli**.

SECTION 4.6 The **endomembrane system** is a series of organelles (endoplasmic reticulum, Golgi bodies, vesicles) that interact mainly to make lipids, enzymes, and proteins for insertion into membranes or secretion. **Endoplasmic reticulum (ER)** is a continuous system of sacs and tubes extending from the nuclear envelope. Ribosome-studded rough ER makes proteins; smooth ER makes lipids and breaks down carbohydrates and fatty acids. **Golgi bodies** modify proteins and lipids before sorting them into vesicles. Different types of **vesicles** store, break down, or transport substances through the cell. Enzymes in **peroxisomes** break down substances such as amino acids, fatty acids, and toxins. **Lysosomes** contain enzymes that break down cellular wastes and debris. Fluid-filled **vacuoles** store or break down waste, food, and toxins. Fluid pressure inside a **central vacuole** keeps plant cells plump, thus keeping plant parts firm.

SECTION 4.7 Double-membraned **mitochondria** specialize in making ATP by breaking down organic compounds in the oxygen-requiring metabolic pathway of aerobic respiration.

SECTION 4.8 Different types of **plastids** are specialized for photosynthesis or storage in plants and algal cells. In eukaryotes, photosynthesis takes place inside **chloroplasts**. Pigment-filled chromoplasts and starch-filled amyloplasts are used for storage; many of these plastids serve additional roles.

SECTION 4.9 Elements of a **cytoskeleton** reinforce, organize, and move cell structures, and often the whole cell. Cytoskeletal elements include **microtubules**, **microfilaments**, and **intermediate filaments**.

Interactions between ATP-driven **motor proteins** and hollow, dynamically assembled microtubules bring about the movement of cell parts. A microfilament mesh called the **cell cortex** reinforces plasma membranes. Elongating microfilaments bring about movement of **pseudopods**. Intermediate filaments lend structural support to cells and tissues, and they help support the nuclear membrane. **Centrioles** give rise to a special 9+2 array of microtubules inside **cilia** and eukaryotic flagella, then remain beneath these motile structures as **basal bodies**.

SECTION 4.10 Many cells secrete a complex mixture of fibrous proteins and polysaccharides onto their surfaces. The secretions form an **extracellular matrix (ECM)** that has different functions depending on the cell type. In animals, a secreted basement membrane supports and organizes cells in tissues. Among the eukaryotes, plant cells, fungi, and many protists secrete a cell wall around their plasma membrane. Older plant cells secrete a rigid, **lignin-**containing **secondary wall** inside their pliable **primary wall**. Many eukaryotic cell types also secrete a protective **cuticle**.

Plasmodesmata are open **cell junctions** that connect the cytoplasm of adjacent plant cells. In animals, **gap junctions** are closable channels between adjacent cells. **Adhering junctions** that connect to cytoskeletal elements fasten cells to one another and to basement membrane. **Tight junctions** form a waterproof seal between cells.

SECTION 4.11 We describe the quality of "life" as a set of properties that are collectively unique to living things. Living things consist of cells that engage in self-sustaining biological processes, pass their hereditary material (DNA) to offspring by mechanisms of reproduction, and have the capacity to change over successive generations.

SECTION 4.12 Bacteria are found in all parts of the biosphere, including the human body. Huge numbers inhabit our intestines, but most of these are beneficial. A few can cause disease. Contamination of food with disease-causing bacteria can result in food poisoning that is sometimes fatal.

Self-Quiz Answers in Appendix VII

1. Despite the diversity of cell type and function, all cells have these three things in common:
   a. cytoplasm, DNA, and organelles with membranes.
   b. a plasma membrane, DNA, and a nuclear envelope.
   c. cytoplasm, DNA, and a plasma membrane.
   d. a cell wall, cytoplasm, and DNA.

2. Every cell is descended from another cell. This idea is part of _____ .
   a. evolution   c. the cell theory
   b. the theory of heredity d. cell biology

3. Unlike eukaryotic cells, prokaryotic cells _____ .
   a. have no plasma membrane   c. have no nucleus
   b. have RNA but not DNA   d. a and c

4. The surface-to-volume ratio _____ .
   a. does not apply to prokaryotic cells
   b. constrains cell size
   c. is part of the cell theory
   d. b and c

5. Cell membranes consist mainly of _____ and _____ .
   a. lipids; carbohydrates   c. lipids; carbohydrates
   b. phospholipids; protein   d. phospholipids; ECM

6. In a lipid bilayer, the _____ of all the lipid molecules are sandwiched between all of the _____ .
   a. hydrophilic tails; hydrophobic heads
   b. hydrophilic heads; hydrophilic tails
   c. hydrophobic tails; hydrophilic heads
   d. hydrophobic heads; hydrophilic tails

Data Analysis Activities

Abnormal Motor Proteins Cause Kartagener Syndrome An abnormal form of a motor protein called dynein causes Kartagener syndrome, a genetic disorder characterized by chronic sinus and lung infections. Biofilms form in the thick mucus that collects in the airways, and the resulting bacterial activities and inflammation damage tissues.

Affected men can produce sperm but are infertile (**FIGURE 4.25**). They can become fathers after a doctor injects their sperm cells directly into eggs. Review **FIGURE 4.20**, then explain how abnormal dynein could cause these observed effects.

A   B

FIGURE 4.25 Cross-section of the flagellum of a sperm cell from **A** a man affected by Kartagener syndrome and **B** an unaffected man.

7. Most of a membrane's diverse functions are carried out by _____ .
   a. proteins
   b. phospholipids
   c. nucleic acids
   d. hormones

8. What controls the passage of molecules into and out of the nucleus?
   a. endoplasmic reticulum, an extension of the nucleus
   b. nuclear pores, which consist of membrane proteins
   c. nucleoli, in which ribosome subunits are made

9. The main function of the endomembrane system is _____ .
   a. building and modifying proteins and lipids
   b. isolating DNA from toxic substances
   c. secreting extracellular matrix onto the cell surface
   d. producing ATP by aerobic respiration

10. Which of the following statements is correct?
    a. Ribosomes are only found in bacteria and archaea.
    b. Some animal cells are prokaryotic.
    c. Only eukaryotic cells have mitochondria.
    d. The plasma membrane is the outermost boundary of all cells.

11. Enzymes contained in _____ break down worn-out organelles, bacteria, and other particles.
    a. lysosomes
    b. mitochondria
    c. endoplasmic reticulum
    d. peroxisomes

12. Put the following structures in order according to the pathway of a secreted protein:
    a. plasma membrane
    b. Golgi bodies
    c. endoplasmic reticulum
    d. post-Golgi vesicles

13. No animal cell has a _____ .
    a. plasma membrane
    b. flagellum
    c. lysosome
    d. cell wall

14. _____ connect the cytoplasm of plant cells.
    a. Plasmodesmata
    b. Adhering junctions
    c. Tight junctions
    d. Adhesion proteins

15. Match each cell component with its function.
    ___ mitochondrion
    ___ chloroplast
    ___ ribosome
    ___ nucleus
    ___ cell junction
    ___ flagellum
    ___ cell membrane

    a. connects cells
    b. movement
    c. ATP production
    d. protects DNA
    e. protein synthesis
    f. maintains internal environment
    g. photosynthesis

Critical Thinking

1. In a classic episode of *Star Trek*, a gigantic amoeba engulfs an entire starship. Spock blows the cell to bits before it can reproduce. Think of at least one inaccuracy that a biologist would identify in this scenario.

2. In plants, the cell wall forms as a young plant cell secretes polysaccharides onto the outer surface of its plasma membrane. Being thin and pliable, this primary wall allows the cell to enlarge and change shape. At maturity, cells in some plant tissues deposit material onto the primary wall's inner surface. Why doesn't this secondary wall form on the outer surface of the primary wall?

3. Which structures can you identify in the organism *below*? Is it prokaryotic or eukaryotic? How can you tell?

CREDITS: (25) From "Tissue & Cell", Vol. 27, pp.421–427, Courtesy of Bjorn Afzelius, Stockholm University; (in text) P.L. Walne and J. H. Arnott, *Planta*, 77:325–354, 1967.

A single-celled protist with the common name Sea Sparkle glows blue when agitated—for example, by breaking waves. The light is energy released from chemical reactions that run inside these cells. Light emitted by a living organism is called bioluminescence.

5 GROUND RULES OF METABOLISM

Links to Earlier Concepts

In this chapter, you will gain insight into the one-way flow of energy through the world of life (Sections 1.1, 1.2) as you learn more about specific types of energy (2.4) and the laws of nature (1.8) that describe it. The chapter also revisits the structure and function of atoms (2.2), molecules (2.3, 3.1–3.6), and cells (4.3, 4.6, 4.7, 4.9).

KEY CONCEPTS

ENERGY FLOW
Each time energy is transferred, some of it disperses. An organism can sustain its life only as long as it continues to harvest energy from the environment.

HOW ENZYMES WORK
Enzymes increase the rate of chemical reactions. They are assisted by cofactors, and affected by temperature, salinity, pH, and other environmental factors.

THE NATURE OF METABOLISM
Sequences of enzyme-mediated reactions build, remodel, and break down organic molecules. Controls that govern steps in these pathways quickly shift cell activities.

MOVEMENT OF FLUIDS
Gradients drive the directional movements of solutes. Water moves across cell membranes to regions where solute concentration is higher.

MEMBRANE TRANSPORT
Transport proteins control solute concentrations in cells and organelles by helping substances move across membranes. Substances also move across cell membranes inside vesicles.

FIGURE 5.1 **Entropy**. Entropy tends to increase, which means that energy tends to spread out spontaneously.

FIGURE 5.2 It takes more than 10,000 pounds of soybeans and corn to raise a 1,000-pound steer. Where do the other 9,000 pounds go? About half of the steer's food is indigestible and passes right through it. The animal's body breaks down molecules in the remaining half to access energy stored in chemical bonds. Only about 15% of that energy goes toward building body mass. The rest is lost during energy conversions, as metabolic heat.

A Energy In
Sunlight reaches environments on Earth. Producers in those environments capture some of its energy and convert it to other forms that can drive cellular work.

PRODUCERS

B Some of the energy captured by producers ends up in the tissues of consumers.

CONSUMERS

C Energy Out
With each energy transfer, some energy escapes into the environment, mainly as heat. Living things do not use heat to drive cellular work, so energy flows through the world of life in one direction overall.

FIGURE 5.3 {Animated} Energy flows from the environment into living organisms, and then back to the environment. The flow drives a cycling of materials among producers and consumers.

ENERGY DISPERSES

Energy is formally defined as the capacity to do work, but this definition is not very satisfying. Even brilliant physicists who study energy cannot say exactly what it is. However, we do have an intuitive understanding of energy just by thinking about familiar forms of it, such as light, heat, electricity, and motion. We also understand intuitively that one form of energy can be converted to another. Think about how a lightbulb changes electricity into light, or how an automobile changes gasoline into the energy of motion, which is also called **kinetic energy**.

The formal study of heat and other forms of energy is thermodynamics (*therm* is a Greek word for heat; *dynam* means energy). By making careful measurements, thermodynamics researchers discovered that the total amount of energy before and after every conversion is always the same. In other words, energy cannot be created or destroyed—a phenomenon that is the **first law of thermodynamics**. Remember, a law of nature describes something that occurs without fail, but our explanation of why it occurs is incomplete (Section 1.8).

Energy also tends to spread out, or disperse, until no part of a system holds more than another part. In a kitchen, for example, heat always flows from a hot pan to cool air until the temperature of both is the same. We never see cool air raising the temperature of a hot pan. **Entropy** is a measure of how much the energy of a particular system has become dispersed. We can use the hot pan in a cool kitchen as an example of a system. As heat flows from the pan into the air, the entropy of the system increases (**FIGURE 5.1**). Entropy continues to increase until the heat is evenly distributed throughout the kitchen, and there is no longer a net (or overall) flow of heat from one area to another. Our system has now reached its maximum entropy with respect to heat. The tendency of entropy to increase is the **second law of thermodynamics**. This is the formal way of saying that energy tends to spread out spontaneously.

Biologists use the concept of entropy as it applies to chemical bonding, because energy flow in living things occurs mainly by the making and breaking of chemical bonds. How is entropy related to chemical bonding? Think about it just in terms of motion. Two unbound atoms can vibrate, spin, and rotate in every direction, so they are at high entropy with respect to motion. A covalent bond between the atoms restricts their movement, so they are able to move in fewer ways than they did before bonding. Thus, the entropy of two atoms decreases when a bond forms between them. Such entropy changes are part of the reason why some reactions occur spontaneously and others require an energy input, as you will see in the next section.

ENERGY'S ONE-WAY FLOW

Work occurs as a result of energy transfers. Consider how it takes work to push a box across a floor. In this case, a body (you) transfers energy to another body (the box) to make it move. Similarly, a plant cell works to make sugars. Inside the cell, one set of molecules harvests energy from light, then transfers it to another set of molecules. The second set of molecules uses the energy to build the sugars from carbon dioxide and water. This particular energy transfer involves the conversion of light energy to chemical energy. Most other types of cellular work occur by the transfer of chemical energy from one molecule to another.

As you learn about such processes, remember that every time energy is transferred, a bit of it disperses. Energy lost from a transfer is usually in the form of heat. As a simple example, a typical incandescent lightbulb converts only about 5 percent of the energy of electricity into light. The remaining 95 percent of the energy ends up as heat that disperses from the bulb.

Dispersed heat is not very useful for doing work, and it is not easily converted to a more useful form of energy (such as electricity). Because some of the energy in every transfer disperses as heat, and heat is not useful for doing work, we can say that the total amount of energy available for doing work in the universe is always decreasing.

Is life an exception to this inevitable flow? An organized body is hardly dispersed. Energy becomes concentrated in each new organism as the molecules of life organize into cells. Even so, living things constantly use energy—to grow, to move, to acquire nutrients, to reproduce, and so on—and some energy is lost in every one of these processes (**FIGURE 5.2**). Unless those losses are replenished with energy from another source, the complex organization of life will end.

The energy that fuels most life on Earth comes from the sun. That energy flows through producers such as plants, then consumers such as animals (**FIGURE 5.3**). During this journey, the energy is transferred many times. With each transfer, some energy escapes as heat until, eventually, all of it is permanently dispersed. However, the second law of thermodynamics does not say how quickly the dispersal has to happen. Energy's spontaneous dispersal is resisted by chemical bonds. The energy in chemical bonds is a type of **potential energy**, which is energy stored in the position or

energy The capacity to do work.
entropy Measure of how much the energy of a system is dispersed.
first law of thermodynamics Energy cannot be created or destroyed.
kinetic energy The energy of motion.
potential energy Stored energy.
second law of thermodynamics Energy disperses spontaneously.

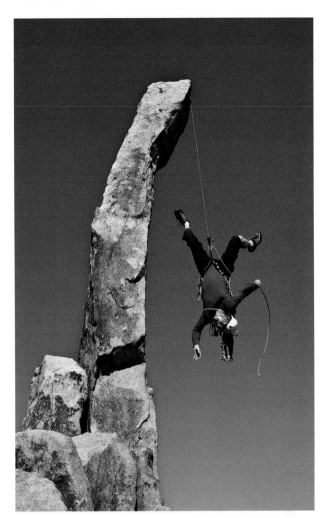

FIGURE 5.4 Illustration of potential energy. By opposing the downward pull of gravity, the rope attached to the rock prevents the man from falling. Similarly, a chemical bond keeps two atoms from moving apart.

arrangement of objects in a system (**FIGURE 5.4**). Think of all the bonds in the countless molecules that make up your skin, heart, liver, fluids, and other body parts. Those bonds hold the molecules, and you, together—at least for the time being.

TAKE-HOME MESSAGE 5.1

Energy, which is the capacity to do work, cannot be created or destroyed.

Energy disperses spontaneously.

Energy can be transferred between systems or converted from one form to another, but some is lost (as heat, typically) during every such exchange.

Sustaining life's organization requires ongoing energy inputs to counter energy loss. Organisms stay alive by replenishing themselves with energy they harvest from someplace else.

Remember from Section 3.1 that chemical reactions change molecules into other molecules. During a reaction, one or more **reactants** (molecules that enter a reaction and become changed by it) become one or more **products** (molecules that are produced by the reaction). Intermediate molecules may form between reactants and products.

We show a chemical reaction as an equation in which an arrow points from reactants to products:

$$2H_2 + O_2 \longrightarrow 2H_2O$$
(hydrogen)   (oxygen)   (water)

A number before a chemical formula in such equations indicates the number of molecules; a subscript indicates the number of atoms of that element per molecule. Note that atoms shuffle around in a reaction, but they never disappear: The same number of atoms that enter a reaction remain at the reaction's end (**FIGURE 5.5**).

CHEMICAL BOND ENERGY

Every chemical bond holds a certain amount of energy. That is the amount of energy required to break the bond, and it is also the amount of energy released when the bond forms. The particular amount of energy held by a

Reactants   **Products**

$$2H_2 + O_2 \longrightarrow 2H_2O$$
(hydrogen) (oxygen)   (water)

4 hydrogen + 2 oxygen   4 hydrogen atoms
atoms   atoms   + 2 oxygen atoms

FIGURE 5.5 Chemical bookkeeping. In equations that represent chemical reactions, reactants are written to the left of an arrow that points to the products. A number before a formula indicates the number of molecules. Atoms may shuffle around in a reaction, but the same number of atoms that enter the reaction remain at the reaction's end.

bond depends on which elements are taking part in it. For example, two covalent bonds—one between an oxygen and a hydrogen atom in a water molecule, the other between two oxygen atoms in molecular oxygen (O_2)—both hold energy, but different amounts of it.

Bond energy and entropy both contribute to a molecule's free energy, which is the amount of energy that is available ("free") to do work. In most reactions, the free energy of reactants differs from the free energy of products. If the reactants have less free energy than the products, the reaction will not proceed without a net energy input. Such reactions are **endergonic**, which means "energy in" (**FIGURE 5.6A**). If the reactants have more free energy than the products, the reaction will end with a net release of energy. Such reactions are **exergonic**, which means "energy out" (**FIGURE 5.6B**).

WHY EARTH DOES NOT GO UP IN FLAMES

The molecules of life release energy when they combine with oxygen. For example, think of how a spark ignites wood. Wood is mostly cellulose, which consists of long chains of repeating glucose monomers (Section 3.2). A spark starts a reaction that converts cellulose (in wood) and oxygen (in air) to water and carbon dioxide. The reaction is highly exergonic, which means it releases a lot of energy—enough to initiate the same reaction with other cellulose and oxygen molecules. That is why wood keeps burning after it has been lit.

Earth is rich in oxygen—and in potential exergonic reactions. Why doesn't it burst into flames? Luckily, chemical bonds do not break without at least a small input of energy, even in an energy-releasing reaction. We call this input activation energy. **Activation energy**, the minimum amount of energy required to get a chemical reaction started, is a bit like a hill that reactants must climb before they can coast down the other side to become products (**FIGURE 5.7**).

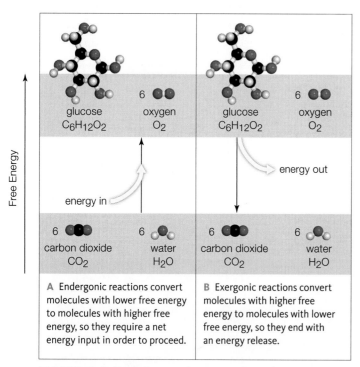

A Endergonic reactions convert molecules with lower free energy to molecules with higher free energy, so they require a net energy input in order to proceed.

B Exergonic reactions convert molecules with higher free energy to molecules with lower free energy, so they end with an energy release.

FIGURE 5.6 Energy inputs and outputs in chemical reactions.

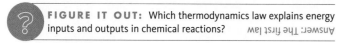

FIGURE IT OUT: Which thermodynamics law explains energy inputs and outputs in chemical reactions?

Answer: The first law

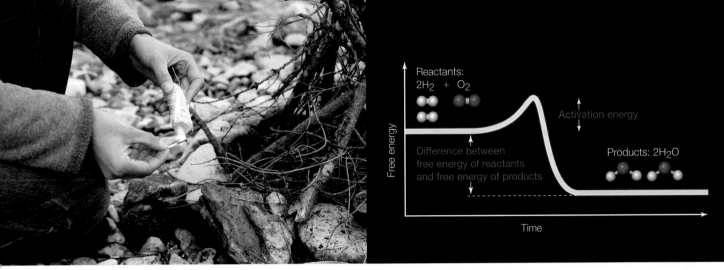

FIGURE 5.7 {Animated} Activation energy. Most reactions will not begin without an input of activation energy, which is shown in the graph as a bump in a free energy hill. Reactants in this example have more energy than the products. Activation energy keeps this and other reactions, including exergonic ones such as burning wood cellulose, from starting spontaneously.

Both endergonic and exergonic reactions have activation energy, but the amount varies with the reaction. Consider guncotton (nitrocellulose), a highly explosive derivative of cellulose. Christian Schönbein accidentally discovered a way to manufacture it when he used his wife's cotton apron to wipe up a nitric acid spill on his kitchen table, then hung it up to dry next to the oven. The apron exploded. Being a chemist in the 1800s, Schönbein immediately thought of marketing guncotton as a firearm explosive, but it proved to be too unstable to manufacture. So little activation energy is needed to make guncotton react with oxygen that it tends to explode unexpectedly. Several manufacturing plants burned to the ground before guncotton was abandoned for use as a firearm explosive. The substitute? Gunpowder, which has a higher activation energy for a reaction with oxygen.

ENERGY IN, ENERGY OUT

Cells store energy by running endergonic reactions that build organic compounds (FIGURE 5.8A). For example, light energy drives the overall reactions of photosynthesis, which produce sugars such as glucose from carbon dioxide and water. Unlike light, glucose can be stored in a cell. Cells harvest energy by running exergonic reactions that break the bonds of organic compounds (FIGURE 5.8B). Most cells do this when they carry out the overall reactions of aerobic respiration, which releases the energy of glucose by

breaking the bonds between its carbon atoms. You will see in the next few sections how cells use energy released from some reactions to drive others.

FIGURE 5.8 {Animated} Cells store and retrieve energy in the chemical bonds of organic molecules.

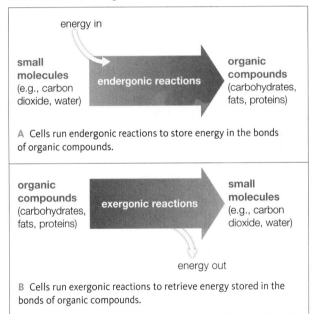

A Cells run endergonic reactions to store energy in the bonds of organic compounds.

B Cells run exergonic reactions to retrieve energy stored in the bonds of organic compounds.

---

activation energy Minimum amount of energy required to start a reaction.
endergonic Describes a reaction that requires a net input of free energy to proceed.
exergonic Describes a reaction that ends with a net release of free energy.
product A molecule that is produced by a reaction.
reactant A molecule that enters a reaction and is changed by participating in it.

TAKE-HOME MESSAGE 5.2

Endergonic reactions will not run without a net input of energy. Exergonic reactions end with a net release of energy.

Both endergonic and exergonic reactions require an input of activation energy to begin.

Cells store energy in chemical bonds by running endergonic reactions that build organic compounds. To release this stored energy, they run exergonic reactions that break the bonds.

THE NEED FOR SPEED

Metabolism requires enzymes. Why? Consider that sugar can break down to carbon dioxide and water on its own, but it might take decades. That same conversion takes just seconds inside your cells. Enzymes make the difference.

FIGURE 5.9 How an active site works.

A An active site binds substrates that are complementary in shape, size, polarity, and charge.

B The binding squeezes substrates together, influences their charge, or causes some change that lowers activation energy, so the reaction proceeds.

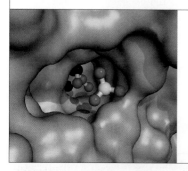

C The product leaves the active site after the reaction is finished. The enzyme is unchanged, so it can work again.

D For simplicity, enzymes are often depicted as blobs or geometric shapes. This model shows the actual contours of an active site in an enzyme (hexokinase) that adds a phosphate group to a six-carbon sugar. Both substrates are shown.

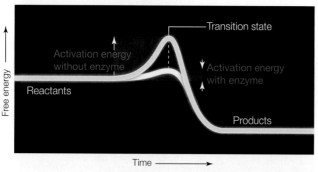

FIGURE 5.10 {Animated} The transition state. An enzyme enhances the rate of a reaction by lowering activation energy.

FIGURE IT OUT: Is the reaction shown in this graph endergonic or exergonic?

Answer: Exergonic

In a process called **catalysis**, an enzyme makes a reaction run much faster than it would on its own. The enzyme is unchanged by participating in the reaction, so it can work again and again.

Some enzymes are RNAs, but most are proteins. Each kind of enzyme recognizes specific reactants, or **substrates**, and alters them in a specific way. For instance, the enzyme hexokinase adds a phosphate group to the hydroxyl group on the sixth carbon of glucose. Such specificity occurs because an enzyme's polypeptide chains fold up into one or more **active sites**, which are pockets where substrates bind and where reactions proceed (**FIGURE 5.9**). An active site is complementary in shape, size, polarity, and charge to the enzyme's substrate. This fit is the reason why each enzyme acts in a specific way on a specific substrate.

When we talk about activation energy, we are really talking about the energy required to bring reactant bonds to their breaking point. At that point, which is called the transition state, the reaction can run without any additional energy input. Enzymes help bring on the transition state by lowering activation energy (**FIGURE 5.10**). They do so by the following four mechanisms.

Forcing Substrates Together Binding at an active site brings substrates together. The closer the substrates are to one another, the more likely they are to react.

Orienting Substrates Substrate molecules in a solution collide from random directions. By contrast, binding at an active site positions substrates optimally for reaction.

Inducing Fit By the **induced-fit model**, an enzyme's active site is not quite complementary to its substrate. Interacting with a substrate molecule causes the enzyme to change shape so that the fit between them improves. The improved fit may result in a stronger bond between enzyme and substrate, or it may better bring on the transition state.

Shutting Out Water Metabolism occurs in water-based fluids, but water molecules can interfere with certain reactions. The active sites of some enzymes repel water, and keep it away from the reactions.

active site Pocket in an enzyme where substrates bind and a reaction occurs.
catalysis The acceleration of a reaction rate by a molecule that is unchanged by participating in the reaction.
induced-fit model Substrate binding to an active site improves the fit between the two.
substrate Of an enzyme, a reactant that is specifically acted upon by the enzyme.

CREDITS: (9A–C, 10) © Cengage Learning; (9D) PDB ID: 1GZX; Paoli, M., Liddington, R., Tame, J., Wilinson, A., Dodson, G.; Crystal Structure of T state hemoglobin with oxygen bound at all four haems. J. Mol.Bio., v256, pp. 775–792, 1996.

The Mariana Trench's Challenger Deep, at almost 11,000 meters (36,000 feet) below sea level, is Earth's deepest spot. Here, despite crushing pressure, shrimp-like *Hirondellea gigas* swarm the ocean floor. *H. gigas* grow up to 2 inches (5 centimeters) long, more than twice the size of their common beachside relative, the sandhopper. Very little organic carbon makes its way down into the Challenger Deep, so how do *H. gigas* get enough food to grow so big? Researchers discovered that these crustaceans eat "wood fall"—tree and plant debris swept into the ocean that occasionally sinks. If a ship happened to sink into the Mariana Trench, "*H. gigas* would gladly eat it," said researcher Hideki Kobayashi. "In fact, a few of them bit into the wooden parts of our camera system." Special enzymes allow *H. gigas* to digest the cellulose in wood. Not surprisingly, these wood-busting enzymes work best under high-pressure conditions.

FIGURE 5.11 An organism (and its enzymes) adapted to life in a particular environment.

ENZYME ACTIVITY

Environmental factors such as pH, temperature, and salt influence an enzyme's shape, which in turn influences its function (Sections 3.4 and 3.5). Each enzyme functions best in a particular range of conditions that reflect the environment in which it evolved (**FIGURE 5.11**).

Consider pepsin, a digestive enzyme that works best at low pH (**FIGURE 5.12A**). Pepsin begins the process of protein digestion in the very acidic environment of the stomach (pH 2). During digestion, the stomach's contents pass into the small intestine, where the pH rises to about 9. Pepsin denatures (unfolds) above pH 5.5, so this enzyme becomes inactivated in the small intestine. Here, protein digestion continues with the assistance of trypsin, an enzyme that functions well at the higher pH.

Adding heat boosts free energy, which is why molecular motion increases with temperature. The greater the free energy of reactants, the closer they are to activation energy. Thus, the rate of an enzymatic reaction typically increases with temperature—but only up to a point. An enzyme denatures above a characteristic temperature. Then, the reaction rate falls sharply as the shape of the enzyme changes and it stops working (**FIGURE 5.12B**). Body temperatures above 42°C (107.6°F) adversely affect the function of many of your enzymes, which is why severe fevers are dangerous.

The activity of many enzymes is also influenced by the amount of salt in the surrounding fluid. Too little salt, and polar parts of the enzyme attract one another so strongly that the enzyme's shape changes. Too much salt interferes with the hydrogen bonds that hold the enzyme in its characteristic shape, and the enzyme denatures.

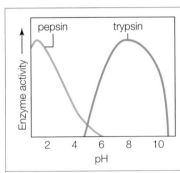

A The pH-dependent activity of two digestive enzymes, pepsin and trypsin. Pepsin acts in the stomach, where the normal pH is 2. Trypsin acts in the small intestine, where the normal pH is 9.

B Comparison of temperature-dependent activity of a DNA synthesis enzyme from two species of bacteria: *E. coli*, which inhabits the gut (normally 37°C); and *Thermus aquaticus*, which lives in hot springs around 70°C.

FIGURE 5.12 Each enzyme functions best within a characteristic range of conditions—generally, the same conditions that occur in the environment in which the enzyme evolved.

TAKE-HOME MESSAGE 5.3

Enzymes greatly enhance the rate of specific reactions.

Binding at an enzyme's active site causes a substrate to reach its transition state. In this state, the substrate's bonds are at the breaking point, and the reaction can run spontaneously.

Each enzyme works best at certain environmental conditions that include temperature, pH, and salt concentration.

Metabolism, remember, refers to the activities by which cells acquire and use energy as they build, break down, or remodel organic molecules. These activities often occur stepwise, in a series of enzymatic reactions called a **metabolic pathway**. Some metabolic pathways are linear, meaning that the reactions run straight from reactant to product (**FIGURE 5.13A**), and others are cyclic. In a cyclic pathway, the last step regenerates a reactant for the first step (**FIGURE 5.13B**). Both linear and cyclic pathways are common in cells; both can involve thousands of molecules and be quite complex. Later chapters detail the steps in some important pathways.

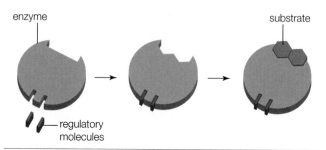

A   A linear pathway runs straight from reactant to product.

B   The last step of a cyclic pathway regenerates a reactant for the first step.

FIGURE 5.13 Metabolic pathways.

CONTROLS OVER METABOLISM

Cells conserve energy and resources by making only what they need at any given moment—no more, no less. Several mechanisms help a cell maintain, raise, or lower its production of thousands of different substances. Consider that reactions do not only run from reactants to products. Many also run in reverse at the same time, with some of the products being converted back to reactants. The rates of the forward and reverse reactions often depend on the concentrations of reactants and products: A high concentration of reactants pushes the reaction in the forward direction, and a high concentration of products pushes it in the reverse direction.

Other mechanisms more actively regulate enzymatic reactions. Certain substances—regulatory molecules or ions—can influence enzyme activity. In some cases, a regulatory substance activates or inhibits an enzyme by binding directly to the active site. In other cases, the regulatory substance binds outside of the active site, a mechanism called **allosteric regulation** (*allo*– means other; steric means structure). Binding of an allosteric regulator alters the shape of the enzyme in a way that enhances or inhibits its function (**FIGURE 5.14**).

Regulation of a single enzyme can affect an entire metabolic pathway. For example, the end product of a series of enzymatic reactions often inhibits the activity of one of the enzymes in the series (**FIGURE 5.15**). This regulatory mechanism is an example of **feedback inhibition**, in which a change that results from an activity decreases or stops the activity.

FIGURE 5.14 {Animated} Allosteric regulation, in which regulatory molecules bind to a region of an enzyme that is not the active site. The binding changes the shape of the enzyme, and thus alters its activity.

FIGURE IT OUT: Does the binding of regulatory molecules help or hinder this enzyme's function?

Answer: It helps

FIGURE 5.15 {Animated} Feedback inhibition. In this example, three different enzymes act in sequence to convert a substrate to a product. The product inhibits the activity of the first enzyme.

FIGURE IT OUT: Is this metabolic pathway cyclic or linear?

Answer: Linear

allosteric regulation Control of enzyme activity by a regulatory molecule or ion that binds to a region outside the enzyme's active site.
electron transfer chain Array of enzymes and other molecules that accept and give up electrons in sequence, thus releasing the energy of the electrons in steps.
feedback inhibition Regulatory mechanism in which a change that results from some activity decreases or stops the activity.
metabolic pathway Series of enzyme-mediated reactions by which cells build, remodel, or break down an organic molecule.
redox reaction Oxidation–reduction reaction, in which one molecule accepts electrons (it becomes reduced) from another molecule (which becomes oxidized). Also called electron transfer.

CREDITS: (13A, 14, 15) © Cengage Learning; (13B) From Starr/Evers/Starr, Biology Today and Tomorrow with Physiology, 4E. © 2013 Cengage Learning.

glucose
+
oxygen

carbon
dioxide
+
water

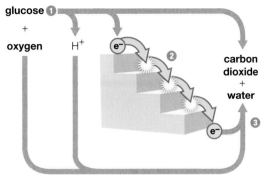

glucose ❶
+
oxygen   H⁺   e⁻

❷

carbon
dioxide
+
water

❸

e⁻

B In cells, the same overall reaction occurs in a stepwise fashion that involves an electron transfer chain, represented here by a staircase. Energy is released in amounts that cells are able to use.

❶ An input of activation energy splits glucose into carbon dioxide, electrons, and hydrogen ions (H⁺).

❷ Electrons lose energy as they move through an electron transfer chain. Energy released by electrons is harnessed for cellular work.

❸ Electrons, hydrogen ions, and oxygen combine to form water.

A Left, glucose in a metal spoon reacts (burns) with oxygen inside a glass jar. Energy in the form of light and heat is released all at once as CO_2 and water form.

FIGURE 5.16 {Animated} Comparing uncontrolled and controlled energy release.

ELECTRON TRANSFERS

The bonds of organic molecules hold a lot of energy that can be released in a reaction with oxygen. Burning is one type of reaction with oxygen, and it releases the energy of organic molecules all at once—explosively (**FIGURE 5.16A**). Cells use oxygen to break the bonds of organic molecules, but they have no way to harvest the explosive burst of energy that occurs during burning. Instead, they break the molecules apart in pathways that release the energy in small, manageable steps. Most of these steps are oxidation–reduction reactions, or redox reactions for short. In a typical **redox reaction**, one molecule accepts electrons (it becomes reduced) from another molecule (which becomes oxidized). To remember what reduced means, think of how the negative charge of an electron "reduces" the charge of a recipient molecule.

An oxidation always occurs together with a reduction (**FIGURE 5.17**). In the next two chapters, you will learn about the importance of this concept in electron transfer chains. An **electron transfer chain** is a series of membrane-bound enzymes and other molecules that give up and accept electrons in turn. Electrons are at a higher energy level (Section 2.2) when they enter a chain than when they leave. Energy given off by an electron as it drops to a lower energy level is harvested by molecules of the electron transfer chain (**FIGURE 5.16B**).

Many electrons are delivered to electron transfer chains in photosynthesis and aerobic respiration. Energy released at certain steps in those chains helps drive the synthesis of ATP. These pathways will occupy our attention in chapters to come.

FIGURE 5.17 Visible evidence of oxidation–reduction: a glowing protist, *Noctiluca scintillans* (*below*). The pathway that produces the glow involves an enzyme, luciferase, and its substrate, luciferin. It occurs when the cells are mechanically stimulated, as by waves (shown in the chapter opening photo) or an attack by a protist-eating predator.

$$\text{luciferin—H}_2 \ + \ O_2 \ \xrightarrow{\text{luciferase}} \ \text{luciferin} = O \ + \ H_2O \ + \ \textbf{light}$$

Luciferin is oxidized during the reactions, which are summarized above. At the same time, an oxygen atom is reduced when it combines it with electrons and hydrogen, so water forms.

TAKE-HOME MESSAGE 5.4

A metabolic pathway is a series of enzyme-mediated reactions that builds, breaks down, or remodels an organic molecule.

Cells conserve energy and resources by producing only what they require at a given time. This metabolic control arises from regulatory molecules and other mechanisms that influence metabolic pathways and individual reactions.

Many metabolic pathways involve electron transfers. Electron transfer chains are important sites of energy exchange.

CREDITS: (16) left, Martyn F. Chillmaid/Science Source; right, © Cengage Learning; (17) top, © Cengage Learning 2015; bottom, © Wim van Egmond/Visuals Unlimited/Corbis.

Most enzymes cannot function properly without assistance from metal ions or small organic molecules. Such enzyme helpers are called **cofactors**. Many dietary vitamins and minerals are essential because they are cofactors or are precursors for them.

Some metal ions that act as cofactors stabilize the structure of an enzyme, in which case the enzyme denatures if the ions are removed. In other cases, metal cofactors play a functional role in a reaction by interacting with electrons in nearby atoms. Atoms of metal elements readily lose or gain electrons, so a metal cofactor can help bring on the transition state by donating electrons, accepting them, or simply tugging on them.

FIGURE 5.18 Example of a coenzyme. Coenzyme Q_{10} (above) is an essential part of the ATP-making machinery in your mitochondria. It carries electrons between enzymes of electron transfer chains during aerobic respiration. Your body makes it, but some foods—particularly red meats, soy oil, and peanuts—are rich dietary sources.

Organic cofactors are called **coenzymes** (**TABLE 5.1** and **FIGURE 5.18**). Coenzymes carry chemical groups, atoms, or electrons from one reaction to another, and often into or out of organelles. Unlike enzymes, many coenzymes are modified by taking part in a reaction. They are regenerated in separate reactions.

Consider NAD^+ (nicotinamide adenine dinucleotide), a coenzyme derived from niacin (vitamin B_3). NAD^+ can accept electrons and hydrogen atoms, thereby becoming reduced to NADH. When electrons and hydrogen atoms are removed from NADH (an oxidation reaction), NAD^+ forms again:

$$NAD^+ + electrons + H^+ \longrightarrow \boxed{\textbf{NADH}} \longrightarrow NAD^+ + electrons + H^+$$

In some reactions, cofactors participate as separate molecules. In others, they stay tightly bound to the enzyme. Catalase, an enzyme of peroxisomes, has four tightly bound cofactors called hemes. A heme is a small organic compound with an iron atom at its center (**FIGURE 5.19**). Catalase's substrate is hydrogen peroxide (H_2O_2), a highly reactive molecule that forms during some normal metabolic reactions. Hydrogen peroxide is dangerous because it can easily oxidize and destroy the organic molecules of life, or form free radicals that do. Catalase neutralizes this threat. When the enzyme binds to hydrogen peroxide, it holds the molecule close to a heme. Interacting with the iron atom in the heme causes peroxide molecules to break down to water.

Substances such as catalase that interfere with the oxidation of other molecules are called **antioxidants**. Antioxidants are essential to health because they reduce the amount of damage that cells sustain as a result of oxidation by free radicals or other molecules. Oxidative damage is associated with many diseases, including cancer, diabetes, atherosclerosis, stroke, and neurodegenerative problems such as Alzheimer's disease.

TABLE 5.1

Some Common Coenzymes

Coenzyme	Example of Function
ATP	Transfers energy with a phosphate group
NAD, NAD^+	Carries electrons during glycolysis
NADP, NADPH	Carries electrons, hydrogen atoms during photosynthesis
FAD, FADH, $FADH_2$	Carries electrons during aerobic respiration
CoA	Carries acetyl group ($COCH_3$) during glycolysis
Coenzyme Q_{10}	Carries electrons in electron transfer chains of aerobic respiration
Heme	Accepts and donates electrons
Ascorbic acid	Carries electrons during peroxide breakdown (in lysosomes)
Biotin (vitamin B_7)	Carries CO_2 during fatty acid synthesis

iron atom

FIGURE 5.19 **Heme.** This organic molecule is part of the active site in many enzymes (such as catalase). In other contexts, it carries oxygen (e.g., in hemoglobin), or electrons (e.g., in molecules of electron transfer chains).

FIGURE IT OUT: Is heme a cofactor or a coenzyme?

Answer: It is both.

CREDITS: (18 left) © Cengage Learning 2015; (in text) From Starr/Evers/Starr, Biology Today and Tomorrow with Physiology, 4E. © 2013 Cengage Learning; (19, Table 5.1) © Cengage Learning; (18 right) © Valentyn Volkov/Shutterstock.com.

ATP—A SPECIAL COENZYME

In cells, the nucleotide ATP (adenosine triphosphate, Section 3.6) functions as a cofactor in many reactions. Bonds between phosphate groups hold a lot of energy compared to other bonds. ATP has two of of these bonds holding its three phosphate groups together (**FIGURE 5.20A**). When a phosphate group is transferred to or from a nucleotide, energy is transferred along with it. Thus, the nucleotide can receive energy from an exergonic reaction, and it can contribute energy to an endergonic one. ATP is such an important currency in a cell's energy economy that we use a cartoon coin to symbolize it.

A reaction in which a phosphate group is transferred from one molecule to another is called a **phosphorylation**. ADP (adenosine diphosphate) forms when an enzyme transfers a phosphate group from ATP to another molecule (**FIGURE 5.20B**). Cells constantly run this reaction in order to drive a variety of endergonic reactions. Thus, they must constantly replenish their stockpile of ATP—by running exergonic reactions that phosphorylate ADP. The cycle of using and replenishing ATP is called the **ATP/ADP cycle** (**FIGURE 5.20C**).

The ATP/ADP cycle couples endergonic reactions with exergonic ones (**FIGURE 5.21**). As you will see in Chapter 7, cells harvest energy from organic compounds by running metabolic pathways that break them down. Energy that cells harvest in these pathways is not released to the environment, but rather stored in the high-energy phosphate bonds of ATP molecules and in electrons carried by reduced coenzymes. Both the ATP and the reduced cofactors that form in these pathways can be used to drive many of the different kinds of endergonic reactions that a cell runs.

antioxidant Substance that prevents oxidation of other molecules.
ATP/ADP cycle Process by which cells regenerate ATP. ADP forms when a phosphate group is removed from ATP, then ATP forms again as ADP gains a phosphate group.
coenzyme An organic cofactor.
cofactor A metal ion or organic compound that associates with an enzyme and is necessary for its function.
phosphorylation A phosphate-group transfer.

TAKE-HOME MESSAGE 5.5

Cofactors associate with enzymes and assist their function.

Many coenzymes carry chemical groups, atoms, or electrons from one reaction to another.

When a phosphate group is transferred from ATP to another molecule, energy is transferred along with it. This energy drives cellular work.

A ATP. Bonds between its phosphate groups hold a lot of energy.

B After ATP loses one phosphate group, the nucleotide is ADP (adenosine diphosphate); after losing two, it is AMP (adenosine monophosphate).

C The ATP/ADP cycle. ADP forms in a reaction that removes a phosphate group from ATP (P_i is an abbreviation for phosphate group). Energy released in this reaction drives other reactions that are the stuff of cellular work. ATP forms again in reactions that phosphorylate ADP.

FIGURE 5.20 ATP, an important energy currency in metabolism.

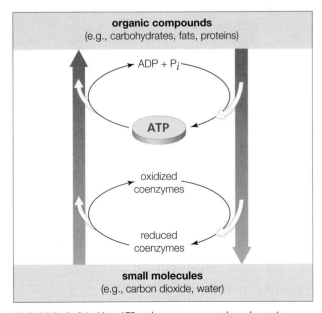

FIGURE 5.21 How ATP and coenzymes couple endergonic reactions with exergonic reactions. Yellow arrows indicate energy flow. Compare **FIGURES 5.8** and **5.20C**.

Metabolic pathways require the participation of molecules that must move across membranes and through cells. **Diffusion** (*left*) is the spontaneous spreading of molecules or ions, and it is an essential way in which substances move into, through, and out of cells. An atom or molecule is always jiggling, and this internal movement causes it to randomly bounce off of nearby objects, including other atoms or molecules. Rebounds from such collisions propel solutes through a liquid or gas, with the result being a gradual and complete mixing. How fast this occurs depends on five factors:

Size It takes more energy to move a large object than it does to move a small one. Thus, smaller molecules diffuse more quickly than larger ones.

Temperature Atoms and molecules jiggle faster at higher temperature, so they collide more often. Thus, the higher the temperature, the faster the rate of diffusion.

Concentration A difference in solute concentration (Section 2.4) between adjacent regions of solution is called a concentration gradient. Solutes tend to diffuse "down" their concentration gradient, from a region of higher concentration to one of lower concentration. Why? Consider that moving objects (such as molecules) collide more often as they get more crowded. Thus, during a given interval, more molecules get bumped out of a region of higher concentration than get bumped into it.

Charge Each ion or charged molecule in a fluid contributes to the fluid's overall electric charge. A difference in charge between two regions of the fluid can affect the rate and direction of diffusion between them. For example, positively charged substances (such as sodium ions) will tend to diffuse toward a region with an overall negative charge.

Pressure Diffusion may be affected by a difference in pressure between two adjoining regions. Pressure squeezes objects—including atoms and molecules—closer together. Atoms and molecules that are more crowded collide and rebound more frequently. Thus, diffusion occurs faster at higher pressures.

SEMIPERMEABLE MEMBRANES

Remember from Section 4.3 that lipid bilayers are selectively permeable: Water can cross them, but ions and most polar molecules cannot (**FIGURE 5.22**). When two

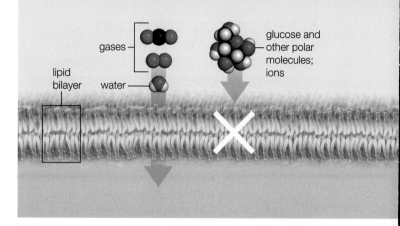

FIGURE 5.22 {Animated} Selective permeability of lipid bilayers. Hydrophobic molecules, gases, and water molecules can cross a lipid bilayer on their own. Ions in particular and most polar molecules such as glucose cannot.

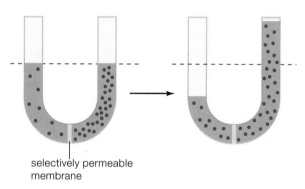

selectively permeable membrane

FIGURE 5.23 Osmosis. Water moves across a selectively permeable membrane that separates two fluids of differing solute concentration. The fluid volume changes in the two compartments as water diffuses across the membrane from the hypotonic solution to the hypertonic one.

fluids with different solute concentrations are separated by a selectively permeable membrane, water will diffuse across the membrane. The direction of water movement depends on the relative solute concentration of the two fluids. Tonicity refers to the solute concentration of one fluid relative to another that is separated by a selectively permeable membrane. Fluids that are **isotonic** have the same overall solute concentration. If the overall solute concentrations of the two fluids differ, the fluid with the lower concentration of solutes is said to be **hypotonic** (*hypo–*, under). The other one, with the higher solute concentration, is **hypertonic** (*hyper–*, over).

When a selectively permeable membrane separates two fluids that are not isotonic, water will move across the membrane from the hypotonic fluid into the hypertonic one (**FIGURE 5.23**). The diffusion will continue until the two fluids are isotonic, or until pressure against the

CREDITS: (in text) Andrew Lambert Photography/Science Source; (22, 23) From Starr/Taggart/Evers/Starr, Biology, 13E. © 2013 Cengage Learning.

hypertonic fluid counters it. The movement of water across membranes is so important in biology that it is given a special name: **osmosis**.

If a cell's cytoplasm is hypertonic with respect to the fluid outside of its plasma membrane, water diffuses into it. If the cytoplasm is hypotonic with respect to the fluid on the outside, water diffuses out. In either case, the solute concentration of the cytoplasm may change. If it changes enough, the cell's enzymes will stop working, with potentially lethal results. Many cells have built-in mechanisms that compensate for differences in solute concentration between cytoplasm and extracellular (external) fluid. In cells with no such mechanism, the volume—and solute concentration—of cytoplasm will change as water diffuses into or out of the cell (**FIGURE 5.24**).

TURGOR

The rigid cell walls of plants and many protists, fungi, and bacteria can resist an increase in the volume of cytoplasm even in hypotonic environments. In the case of plant cells, cytoplasm usually contains more solutes than soil water does. Thus, water usually diffuses from soil into a plant—but only up to a point. Stiff walls keep plant cells from expanding very much, so an inflow of water causes pressure to build up inside them. Pressure that a fluid exerts against a structure that contains it is called **turgor**. When enough pressure builds up inside a plant cell, water stops diffusing into its cytoplasm. The amount of turgor that is enough to stop osmosis is called **osmotic pressure**.

Osmotic pressure keeps walled cells plump, just as high air pressure inside a tire keeps it inflated. A young land plant can resist gravity to stay erect because its cells are plump with cytoplasm (**FIGURE 5.25A**). When soil dries out, it loses water but not solutes, so the concentration of solutes increases in soil water. If soil water becomes hypertonic with respect to cytoplasm, water will start diffusing out of the plant's cells, so their cytoplasm shrinks (**FIGURE 5.25B**). As turgor inside the cells decreases, the plant wilts.

---

diffusion Spontaneous spreading of molecules or ions.
hypertonic Describes a fluid that has a high solute concentration relative to another fluid separated by a semipermeable membrane.
hypotonic Describes a fluid that has a low solute concentration relative to another fluid separated by a semipermeable membrane.
isotonic Describes two fluids with identical solute concentrations and separated by a semipermeable membrane.
osmosis Diffusion of water across a selectively permeable membrane; occurs in response to a difference in solute concentration between the fluids on either side of the membrane.
osmotic pressure Amount of turgor that prevents osmosis into cytoplasm or other hypertonic fluid.
turgor Pressure that a fluid exerts against a structure that contains it.

A Red blood cells in an isotonic solution (such as the fluid portion of blood) have a normal, indented disk shape.

B Water diffuses out of red blood cells immersed in a hypertonic solution, so they shrivel up.

C Water diffuses into red blood cells immersed in a hypotonic solution, so they swell up. Some of these have burst.

2 μm

FIGURE 5.24 {Animated} Effects of tonicity in human red blood cells. These cells have no mechanism to compensate for differences in solute concentration between cytoplasm and extracellular fluid.

A Osmotic pressure keeps plant parts erect. These cells in an iris petal are plump with cytoplasm.

B Cells from a wilted iris petal. The cytoplasm shrank, and the plasma membrane moved away from the wall.

FIGURE 5.25 Turgor, as illustrated in cells of iris petals.

TAKE-HOME MESSAGE 5.6

Molecules or ions tend to diffuse into an adjoining region of fluid in which they are not as concentrated. The steepness of a concentration gradient as well as temperature, molecular size, charge, and pressure affect the rate of diffusion.

When two fluids of different solute concentration are separated by a selectively permeable membrane, water diffuses from the hypotonic to the hypertonic fluid. This movement, osmosis, is opposed by turgor.

A A glucose molecule (here, in extracellular fluid) binds to a glucose transporter (gray) in the plasma membrane.

B Binding causes the transport protein to change shape.

C The transport protein releases the glucose on the other side of the membrane (here, in cytoplasm) and resumes its original shape.

FIGURE 5.26 {Animated} Facilitated diffusion.

FIGURE IT OUT: In this example, which fluid is hypotonic: the extracellular fluid or cytoplasm?

Answer: Cytoplasm

TRANSPORT PROTEIN SPECIFICITY

Substances that cannot diffuse directly through lipid bilayers—ions in particular—cross cell membranes only with the help of transport proteins (Section 4.3). Each transport protein allows a specific substance to cross: Calcium pumps pump only calcium ions; glucose transporters transport only glucose; and so on. This specificity is an important part of homeostasis. For example, the composition of cytoplasm depends on the movement of particular solutes across the plasma membrane, which in turn depends on the transporters embedded in it. Glucose is an important source of energy for most cells, so they normally take up as much as they can from extracellular fluid. They do so with the help of glucose transporters in the plasma membrane. As soon as a molecule of glucose enters cytoplasm, an enzyme (hexokinase) phosphorylates it. Phosphorylation traps the molecule inside the cell because the transporters are specific for glucose, not phosphorylated glucose. Thus, phosphorylation prevents the molecule from moving back through the transporter and leaving the cell.

FACILITATED DIFFUSION

Osmosis is an example of **passive transport**, which is a membrane-crossing mechanism that requires no energy input. Diffusion of solutes through transport proteins is another example. In this case, the movement of the solute (and the direction of its movement) is driven entirely by the solute's concentration gradient. Some transport proteins form permanently open channels through a membrane. Others are gated, which means they open and close in response to a stimulus such as a shift in electric charge or binding to a particular signaling molecule.

With a passive transport mechanism called **facilitated diffusion**, a solute binds to a transport protein, which then changes shape so the solute is released to the other side of the membrane. A glucose transporter is an example of a transport protein that works in facilitated diffusion (**FIGURE 5.26**). This protein changes shape when it binds to a molecule of glucose. The shape change moves the solute to the opposite side of the membrane, where it detaches from the transport protein. Then, the transporter reverts to its original shape.

ACTIVE TRANSPORT

Maintaining a particular solute's concentration at a certain level often means transporting the solute against its gradient, to the side of the membrane where it is more concentrated. Pumping a solute against its gradient takes energy. In **active transport**, a transport protein uses energy to pump a solute against its gradient across a cell membrane.

CREDIT: (26) From Starr/Taggart/Evers/Starr, Biology, 13E. © 2013 Cengage Learning.

After a solute binds to an active transport protein, an energy input (for example, in the form of a phosphate-group transfer from ATP) changes the shape of the protein. The change causes the transporter to release the solute to the other side of the membrane.

A calcium pump moves calcium ions across cell membranes by active transport (**FIGURE 5.27**). Calcium ions act as potent messengers inside cells, and they affect the activity of many enzymes, so their concentration in cytoplasm is very tightly regulated. Calcium pumps in the plasma membrane of all eukaryotic cells can keep the concentration of calcium ions in cytoplasm thousands of times lower than it is in extracellular fluid.

Another example of active transport involves sodium–potassium pumps (**FIGURE 5.28**). Nearly all of the cells in your body have these transport proteins. Sodium ions in cytoplasm diffuse into the pump's open channel and bind to its interior. A phosphate-group transfer from ATP causes the pump to change shape so that its channel opens to extracellular fluid, where it releases the sodium ions. Then, potassium ions from extracellular fluid diffuse into the channel and bind to its interior. The transporter releases the phosphate group and reverts to its original shape. The channel opens to the cytoplasm, where it releases the potassium ions.

Bear in mind that the membranes of all cells, not just those of animals, have active transport proteins. In plants, for example, active transport proteins in the plasma membranes of leaf cells pump sucrose into tubes that thread throughout the plant body.

---

active transport Energy-requiring mechanism in which a transport protein pumps a solute across a cell membrane against its concentration gradient.
facilitated diffusion Passive transport mechanism in which a solute follows its concentration gradient across a membrane by moving through a transport protein.
passive transport Membrane-crossing mechanism that requires no energy input.

TAKE-HOME MESSAGE 5.7

Transport proteins move specific ions or molecules across a cell membrane. The amounts and types of these substances that cross a membrane depend on the transport proteins embedded in it.

In a type of passive transport called facilitated diffusion, a solute binds to a transport protein that releases it on the opposite side of the membrane. The movement is driven by the solute's concentration gradient.

In active transport, a transport protein pumps a solute across a membrane against its concentration gradient. The movement is driven by an energy input, as from ATP.

A Two calcium ions (blue) bind to the transport protein (gray).

B A phosphate group from ATP causes the protein to change shape so that the calcium ions are ejected to the opposite side of the membrane.

C After it loses the calcium ions, the transport protein resumes its original shape.

FIGURE 5.27 {Animated} Active transport of calcium ions.

FIGURE 5.28 The sodium–potassium pump. This transport protein (gray) actively transports sodium ions (Na^+) from cytoplasm to extracellular fluid, and potassium ions (K^+) in the other direction. The transfer of a phosphate group (P) from ATP provides energy required for transporting the ions against their concentration gradient.

CREDITS: (27) From Starr/Taggart/Evers/Starr, Biology 13E. © 2013 Cengage Learning; (28) © Cengage Learning.

5.8 HOW DO LARGE PARTICLES AND BULK SUBSTANCES MOVE ACROSS CELL MEMBRANES?

A **Exocytosis**. A vesicle in cytoplasm fuses with the plasma membrane. Lipids and proteins of the vesicle's membrane become part of the plasma membrane as its contents are expelled to the environment.

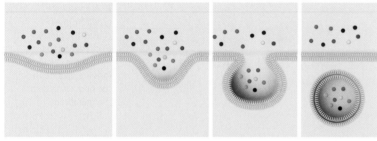

B **Bulk-phase endocytosis**. A pit in the plasma membrane traps molecules, fluid, and particles near the cell's surface in a vesicle as it deepens and sinks into the cytoplasm.

C **Receptor-mediated endocytosis**. Receptors on the cell surface bind a target molecule and trigger a pit to form in the plasma membrane. The target molecules are trapped in a vesicle as the pit deepens and sinks into the cell's cytoplasm. This mode is more selective about what is taken into the cell than bulk-phase endocytosis.

lipoprotein particle

vesicle

D Receptor-mediated endocytosis of lipoprotein particles.

FIGURE 5.29 {Animated} Exocytosis and endocytosis.

VESICLE MOVEMENT

Think back on the structure of a lipid bilayer (Section 4.3). When a bilayer is disrupted, it seals itself. Why? The disruption exposes the fatty acid tails of the phospholipids to their watery surroundings. Remember, in water, phospholipids spontaneously rearrange themselves so that their nonpolar tails stay together. A vesicle forms when a patch of membrane bulges into the cytoplasm because the hydrophobic tails of the lipids in the bilayer are repelled by the watery fluid on both sides. The fluid "pushes" the phospholipid tails together, which helps round off the bud as a vesicle, and also seals the rupture in the membrane.

Vesicles are constantly carrying materials to and from a cell's plasma membrane. This movement typically requires ATP because it involves motor proteins that drag the vesicles along cytoskeletal elements. We describe the movement based on where and how the vesicle originates, and where it goes.

By **exocytosis**, a vesicle in the cytoplasm moves to the cell's surface and fuses with the plasma membrane. As the exocytic vesicle loses its identity, its contents are released to the surroundings (**FIGURE 5.29A**).

There are several pathways of **endocytosis**, but all take up substances in bulk near the cell's surface (as opposed to one molecule or ion at a time via transport proteins). In bulk-phase endocytosis, a small patch of plasma membrane balloons inward, and then it pinches off after sinking farther into the cytoplasm. The membrane patch becomes the outer boundary of a vesicle (**FIGURE 5.29B**).

With receptor-mediated endocytosis, molecules of a hormone, vitamin, mineral, or another substance bind to receptors on the plasma membrane. The binding triggers a shallow pit to form in the membrane patch under the receptors. The pit sinks into the cytoplasm and traps the target substance in a vesicle as it closes back on itself (**FIGURE 5.29C,D**). LDL and other lipoproteins (Section 3.4) enter cells this way.

Phagocytosis (which literally means "cell eating") is a type of receptor-mediated endocytosis in which motile cells engulf microorganisms, cellular debris, or other large particles (**FIGURE 5.30**). Many single-celled protists such as amoebas feed by phagocytosis. Some of your white blood cells use phagocytosis to engulf viruses and bacteria, cancerous body cells, and other threats.

Phagocytosis begins when receptor proteins bind to a particular target. The binding causes microfilaments to assemble in a mesh under the plasma membrane. The microfilaments contract, forcing a lobe of membrane-enclosed cytoplasm to bulge outward as a pseudopod (Section 4.9). Pseudopods that merge around a target

CREDITS: (29 A–C) © Cengage Learning 2015; (29D) © R.G.W. Anderson, M.S. Brown and J.L. Goldstein. *Cell* 10:351 (1977).

FIGURE 5.30 {Animated} Phagocytosis. A phagocytic white blood cell's pseudopods surround bacteria. A vesicle will form around the bacteria as the pseudopod membranes fuse around them. The vesicle will sink into the cytoplasm, where it will fuse with a lysosome that digests its contents.

trap it inside a vesicle that sinks into the cytoplasm. Material taken in by phagocytosis is typically digested by lysosomes, and the resulting molecular bits may be recycled by the cell, or expelled by exocytosis.

MEMBRANE TRAFFICKING

The composition of a plasma membrane begins in the ER. There, membrane proteins and lipids are made and modified, and both become part of vesicles that transport them to Golgi bodies for final modification. New plasma membrane forms when the finished proteins and lipids are repackaged as vesicles that travel to the plasma membrane and fuse with it.

As long as a cell is alive, exocytosis and endocytosis continually replace and withdraw patches of its plasma membrane. If the cell is not enlarging, the total area of the plasma membrane remains more or less constant. Membrane lost as a result of endocytosis is replaced by membrane arriving as exocytic vesicles.

---

endocytosis Process by which a cell takes in a small amount of extracellular fluid (and its contents) by the ballooning inward of the plasma membrane.
exocytosis Process by which a cell expels a vesicle's contents to extracellular fluid.
phagocytosis "Cell eating"; an endocytic pathway by which a cell engulfs particles such as microbes or cellular debris.

TAKE-HOME MESSAGE 5.8

Exocytosis and endocytosis move materials in bulk across plasma membranes.

In exocytosis, a cytoplasmic vesicle fuses with the plasma membrane and releases its contents to the outside of the cell.

In endocytosis, a patch of plasma membrane sinks inward and forms a vesicle in the cytoplasm.

Some cells can engulf large particles by phagocytosis.

5.9 Application: A TOAST TO ALCOHOL DEHYDROGENASE

FIGURE 5.31 A tailgate party at a Notre Dame–Alabama football game. During 2012 alone, Indiana State police arrested 138 Notre Dame students for underage drinking at tailgate parties.

MOST COLLEGE STUDENTS ARE UNDER THE LEGAL DRINKING AGE, but alcohol abuse continues to be the most serious drug problem on college campuses throughout the United States (**FIGURE 5.31**). Every year, drinking kills more than 1,700 students and injures about 500,000 more; it is also a factor in 600,000 assaults and 100,000 rapes on college campuses.

Tens of thousands of undergraduate students have been polled about their drinking habits in recent surveys. More than half of them reported that they regularly drink five or more alcoholic beverages within a two-hour period.

Each alcoholic drink—a bottle of beer, glass of wine, shot of vodka, and so on—contains the same amount of alcohol or, more precisely, ethanol. Ethanol molecules move quickly from the stomach and small intestine into the bloodstream. Almost all of the ethanol ends up in the liver, a large organ in the abdomen. Liver cells have impressive numbers of enzymes. One of them, ADH (alcohol

dehydrogenase), helps break down ethanol and other toxic compounds.

ADH converts ethanol to acetaldehyde, an organic molecule even more toxic than ethanol and the most likely source of various hangover symptoms. A different enzyme, ALDH, very quickly converts acetaldehyde to nontoxic acetate. Both ADH and ALDH use the coenzyme NAD^+ to accept electrons and hydrogen atoms. Thus, the overall pathway of ethanol metabolism in humans is:

$$\text{ethanol} \xrightarrow[\substack{NAD^+ \quad NADH}]{ADH} \text{acetaldehyde} \xrightarrow[\substack{NAD^+ \quad NADH}]{ALDH} \text{acetate}$$

In the average healthy adult, this metabolic pathway can detoxify between 7 and 14 grams of ethanol per hour. The typical alcoholic beverage contains between 10 and 20 grams of ethanol.

If you put more ethanol into your body than your enzymes can deal with, then you will damage it. Ethanol and acetaldehyde kill liver cells, so the more

Normal, healthy human liver

Cirrhotic human liver

a person drinks, the fewer liver cells are left for detoxification . Ethanol also interferes with normal metabolic processes. For example, in the presence of ethanol, oxygen that would ordinarily take part in breaking down fatty acids is diverted to breaking down the ethanol. This is why fats accumulate as large globules in the tissues of heavy drinkers.

Long-term heavy drinking causes alcoholic hepatitis, a disease characterized by inflammation and destruction of liver tissue; and cirrhosis, a condition in which the liver becomes so scarred, hardened, and filled with fat that it loses its function. (The term cirrhosis is from the Greek *kirros*, meaning orange-colored, after the abnormal skin color of people with the disease.) The liver is the largest gland in the human body, and it has many important functions. A cirrhotic liver stops making the protein albumin, so the solute balance of body fluids is disrupted, and the legs and abdomen swell with watery fluid. It can no longer remove drugs and other toxins from the blood, so they accumulate in the brain—which impairs mental functioning and alters personality. Restricted blood flow through the liver causes veins to enlarge and rupture, so internal bleeding is a risk. The damage

to the body results in a heightened susceptibility to diabetes and liver cancer. Once cirrhosis has been diagnosed, a person has about a 50 percent chance of dying within 10 years (FIGURE 5.32).

FIGURE 5.32 Gary Reinbach, who died at the age of 22 from alcoholic liver disease shortly after this photograph was taken, in 2009. The odd color of his skin is a symptom of cirrhosis.

Transplantation is a last-resort treatment for a failed liver, but there are not nearly enough liver donors for everyone who needs a transplant. Reinbach was refused a transplant that would have saved his life because he had not abstained from drinking for the prior 6 months.

Summary

SECTION 5.1 **Kinetic energy** and **potential energy** are different forms of **energy**, the capacity to do work. Energy, which cannot be created or destroyed (**first law of thermodynamics**), tends to disperse spontaneously (**second law of thermodynamics**). **Entropy** is a measure of how much the energy of a system is dispersed. A bit disperses at each energy transfer, usually in the form of heat.

SECTION 5.2 Cells store and retrieve energy by making and breaking chemical bonds in reactions that convert **reactants** to **products**. **Endergonic** reactions require a net input of energy to proceed. **Exergonic** reactions end with a net release of energy. **Activation energy** is the minimum energy required to start a reaction.

SECTION 5.3 Enzymes greatly enhance the rate of reactions without being changed by them, a process called **catalysis**. They lower a reaction's activation energy, for example by boosting local concentrations of **substrates** or improving the fit between a substrate and the enzyme's **active site** (**induced-fit model**). Each enzyme works best within a characteristic range of conditions that reflect its evolutionary context.

SECTION 5.4 Cells build, convert, and dispose of substances in enzyme-mediated reaction sequences called **metabolic pathways**. Regulating these pathways allows a cell to conserve energy and resources. With **allosteric regulation**, a regulatory molecule or ion alters the activity of an enzyme by binding to it in a region other than the active site. Some products of metabolic pathways inhibit their own production, a regulatory mechanism called **feedback inhibition**. **Redox** (oxidation–reduction) **reactions** in **electron transfer chains** allow cells to harvest energy in small, manageable steps.

SECTION 5.5 Most enzymes require **cofactors**, which are metal ions or organic **coenzymes**. Some enzymes that act as **antioxidants** have cofactors that help them prevent dangerous oxidation reactions.

When a phosphate group is transferred from ATP to another molecule, energy is transferred along with it. Phosphate-group transfers (**phosphorylations**) to and from ATP couple exergonic with endergonic reactions. Cells regenerate ATP in the **ATP/ADP cycle**.

SECTION 5.6 The steepness of a concentration gradient, temperature, solute size, charge, and pressure influence the rate of **diffusion**. **Osmosis** is the diffusion of water across a selectively permeable membrane, from a **hypotonic** fluid toward a **hypertonic** fluid. There is no net movement of water between **isotonic** solutions. **Osmotic pressure** is the amount of **turgor** (fluid pressure against a cell membrane or wall) sufficient to halt osmosis.

SECTION 5.7 The types of transport proteins in a membrane determine which substances cross it. Ions and most polar molecules cross membranes with the help of a transport protein. With **facilitated diffusion**, a solute follows its concentration gradient across a membrane through a transport protein. Facilitated diffusion is a type of **passive transport** (no energy input is required). With **active transport**, a transport protein uses energy to pump a solute across a membrane against its concentration gradient. A phosphate-group transfer from ATP often supplies the necessary energy for active transport.

SECTION 5.8 Substances can be moved across plasma membranes in bulk by two ATP-requiring processes. With **exocytosis**, a cytoplasmic vesicle fuses with the plasma membrane, and its contents are released to the outside of the cell. With **endocytosis**, a patch of plasma membrane balloons into the cell, and forms a vesicle that sinks into the cytoplasm. Some cells engulf large particles such as prey or cell debris by the endocytic pathway of **phagocytosis**.

SECTION 5.9 Currently the most serious drug problem on college campuses is binge drinking, which is often a symptom of alcoholism. Drinking more alcohol than the body's enzymes can detoxify can be lethal in both the short term and the long term.

Self-Quiz   Answers in Appendix VII

1. _____ is life's primary source of energy.
   a. Food   b. Water   c. Sunlight   d. ATP

2. Which of the following statements is not correct?
   a. Energy cannot be created or destroyed.
   b. Energy cannot change from one form to another.
   c. Energy tends to disperse spontaneously.

3. Entropy _____ .
   a. disperses   c. always increases, overall
   b. is a measure of disorder   d. b and c

4. If we liken a chemical reaction to an energy hill, then a(n) _____ reaction is an uphill run.
   a. endergonic   c. catalytic
   b. exergonic   d. both a and c

5. If we liken a chemical reaction to an energy hill, then activation energy is like _____ .
   a. a burst of speed
   b. coasting downhill
   c. a bump at the top of the hill

6. _____ are always changed by participating in a reaction. (Choose all that are correct.)
   a. Enzymes   b. Cofactors   c. Reactants   d. Coenzymes

7. Name one environmental factor that typically influences enzyme function.

8. A metabolic pathway may _____ .
   a. build or break down molecules   c. generate heat
   b. include an electron transfer chain d. all of the above

Data Analysis Activities

Deep inside one of the most toxic sites in the United States: Iron Mountain Mine, in California. The water in this stream, which is about 1 meter (3 feet) wide in this view, is hot (around 40°C, or 104°F), heavily laden with arsenic and other toxic metals, and has a pH of zero. The slime streamers growing in it are a biofilm dominated by a species of archaea, *Ferroplasma acidarmanus*.

FIGURE 5.33 pH anomaly of *Ferroplasma* enzymes. Above are pH activity profiles of four enzymes isolated from *Ferroplasma*. Researchers had expected these enzymes to function best at the cells' cytoplasmic pH (5.0).

One Tough Bug *Ferroplasma acidarmanus* is a species of archaea discovered in an abandoned California copper mine. These cells use an energy-harvesting pathway that combines oxygen with iron–sulfur compounds in minerals such as pyrite. The reaction dissolves the minerals, so groundwater that seeps into the mine ends up with high concentrations of metal ions such as copper, zinc, cadmium, and arsenic. The reaction also produces sulfuric acid, which lowers the pH of the water around the cells to zero. *F. acidarmanus* cells maintain their internal pH at a cozy 5.0 despite living in an environment similar to hot battery acid. Thus, researchers investigating *Ferroplasma* were surprised to discover that most of the cells' enzymes function best at very low pH (**FIGURE 5.33**).

1. What does the dashed line in the graph signify?
2. Of the four enzymes, how many function optimally at a pH lower than 5?
3. What is the optimal pH for the carboxylesterase?

9. All antioxidants _____ .
   a. prevent other molecules from being oxidized
   b. are necessary in the human diet
   c. balance charge
   d. deoxidize free radicals

10. Solutes tend to diffuse from a region where they are _____ (more/less) concentrated to an adjacent region where they are _____ (more/less) concentrated.

11. _____ cannot easily diffuse across a lipid bilayer.
    a. Water   c. Ions
    b. Gases   d. all of the above

12. A transport protein requires ATP to pump sodium ions across a membrane. This is a case of _____ .
    a. passive transport   c. facilitated diffusion
    b. active transport   d. a and c

13. Immerse a human blood cell in a hypotonic solution, and water _____ .
    a. diffuses into the cell   c. shows no net movement
    b. diffuses out of the cell d. moves in by endocytosis

14. Vesicles form during _____ .
    a. endocytosis   c. phagocytosis
    b. exocytosis   d. a and c

15. Match each term with its most suitable description.
    ___ reactant   a. assists enzymes
    ___ phagocytosis   b. forms at reaction's end
    ___ first law of   c. enters a reaction
        thermodynamics   d. requires energy input
    ___ product   e. one cell engulfs another
    ___ cofactor   f. energy cannot be created
    ___ concentration gradient   or destroyed
    ___ passive transport   g. basis of diffusion
    ___ active transport   h. no energy input required

Critical Thinking

1. Often, beginning physics students are taught the basic concepts of thermodynamics with two phrases: First, you can never win. Second, you can never break even. Explain.

2. How do you think a cell regulates the amount of glucose it brings into its cytoplasm from the extracellular environment?

3. The enzyme trypsin is sold as a dietary enzyme supplement. Explain what happens to trypsin that is taken with food.

4. Catalase combines two hydrogen peroxide molecules ($H_2O_2 + H_2O_2$) to make two molecules of water. A gas also forms. What is the gas?

CREDITS: (33) left, Katrina J. Edwards; right, From Golyshina et al., *Environmental Microbiology*, 8(3): 416–425. © 2006 John Wiley and Sons. Used with permission of the publisher.

Raindrops can separate light from the sun into its different component wavelengths, which we see as different colors in a rainbow.

98   UNIT 1
PRINCIPLES OF
CELLULAR LIFE

6

WHERE IT STARTS—PHOTOSYNTHESIS

Links to Earlier Concepts

This chapter explores the main metabolic pathways (Section 5.4) by which organisms harvest energy from the sun (5.1). We revisit experimental design (1.6), electrons and energy levels (2.2), bonds (2.3), carbohydrates (3.2), membrane proteins (4.3), plastids (4.8), antioxidants (5.5), and concentration gradients (5.6).

KEY CONCEPTS

THE RAINBOW CATCHERS

The main flow of energy through the biosphere starts when photosynthetic pigments absorb light. In plants and other eukaryotes, these pigments occur in chloroplasts.

WHAT IS PHOTOSYNTHESIS?

Photosynthesis is a metabolic pathway that occurs in two stages. Light energy harvested in the first stage is used to make molecules that power sugar formation in the second.

MAKING ATP AND NADPH

In the first stage of photosynthesis, light drives ATP synthesis in one of two pathways. A cyclic pathway makes ATP alone. A noncyclic pathway makes ATP and NADPH, and it releases oxygen.

MAKING SUGARS

Sugars are assembled from carbon dioxide (CO_2) during the second stage of photosynthesis. In plants, the reactions run on ATP and NADPH—molecules that formed in the first stage.

ALTERNATE PATHWAYS

Metabolic pathways are shaped by evolution. Variations in photosynthetic pathways are evolutionary adaptations that allow plants to thrive in a variety of environments.

Photograph by Robbie George, National Geographic Creative.

Energy flow through nearly all ecosystems on Earth begins when plants and other photosynthesizers intercept sunlight. These organisms are called producers because they produce the food that sustains ecosystems. Producers are **autotrophs**, organisms that make their own food—sugars—by harvesting energy directly from the environment (*auto*– means self; –*troph* refers to nourishment). All organisms need carbon; autotrophs obtain it from inorganic molecules such as carbon dioxide (CO_2). By contrast, **heterotrophs** get their carbon by breaking down organic molecules assembled by other organisms (*hetero*– means other). Heterotrophs are an ecosystem's consumers.

PROPERTIES OF LIGHT

Photosynthesizers make their own food by converting light energy to chemical energy. In order to understand how that happens, you have to know a little about the nature of light. Light is electromagnetic radiation, a type of energy that moves through space in waves, a bit like waves moving across an ocean. The distance between the crests of two successive waves is a **wavelength**, measured in nanometers (nm). Light that humans can see is a small part of the spectrum of electromagnetic radiation emitted by the sun (**FIGURE 6.1A**). Visible light travels in wavelengths between 380 and 750 nm, and this is the main form of energy that drives photosynthesis. Our eyes perceive all of these wavelengths combined as white light, and particular wavelengths in this range as different colors. White light

separates into its component colors when it passes through a prism, or raindrops that act as tiny prisms. A prism bends longer wavelengths more than it bends shorter ones, so a rainbow of colors forms.

Light travels in waves, but it is also organized in packets of energy called photons. A photon's energy and its wavelength are related, so all photons traveling at the same wavelength carry the same amount of energy. Photons that carry the least amount of energy travel in longer wavelengths; those that carry the most energy travel in shorter wavelengths (**FIGURE 6.1B**).

CAPTURING A RAINBOW

Photosynthesizers use pigments to capture light. A **pigment** is an organic molecule that selectively absorbs light of specific wavelengths. Wavelengths of light that are not absorbed are reflected, and that reflected light gives each pigment its characteristic color.

Chlorophyll *a* is the most common photosynthetic pigment in plants and photosynthetic protists. It also occurs in some bacteria. Chlorophyll *a* absorbs violet, red, and orange light, and it reflects green light, so it appears green to us. Accessory pigments, including other chlorophylls, collectively harvest a wide range of additional light wavelengths for photosynthesis (**FIGURE 6.2**).

A pigment molecule is a bit like an antenna specialized for receiving light. Each has a light-trapping part in which single bonds alternate with double bonds; electrons

A Electromagnetic radiation moves through space in waves that we measure in nanometers (nm). Visible light makes up a very small part of this energy. Raindrops or a prism can separate visible light's different wavelengths, which we see as different colors. About 25 million nanometers are equal to 1 inch.

B Light is organized as packets of energy called photons. The shorter a photon's wavelength, the greater its energy.

FIGURE 6.1 Properties of light.

Pigment	Color	Produced by			
		Plants	Protists	Bacteria	Archaea
Chlorophyll *a*	green	●	●	●	
Other chlorophylls	green	●	●	●	
Phycobilins					
phycocyanobilin	blue		●	●	
phycoerythrobilin	red		●	●	
phycoviolobilin	violet		●	●	
Carotenoids					
beta-carotene	orange	●	●	●	
lycopene	red	●	●		
lutein	yellow	●	●	●	
zeaxanthin	yellow	●	●	●	
fucoxanthin	brown	●	●		
Anthocyanins	red, blue	●●	●●	●●	
Retinal	violet				●

FIGURE 6.2 Examples of photosynthetic pigments. Photosynthetic pigments can collectively absorb almost all visible light wavelengths. *Left*, the light-catching part of a pigment (shown in color) is the region in which single bonds alternate with double bonds. These and many other pigments (including heme, Section 5.5) are derived from evolutionary remodeling of the same compound. Animals convert dietary beta-carotene into a similar pigment (retinal) that is the basis of vision.

populating the atoms in such arrays easily absorb a photon—but not just any photon. Only a photon with exactly enough energy to boost an electron to a higher energy level is absorbed (Section 2.2). This is why a pigment absorbs light of only certain wavelengths.

An excited electron (one that has been boosted to a higher energy level) quickly emits its extra energy and returns to a lower energy level. As you will see in Section 6.4, photosynthetic cells capture energy emitted from an electron returning to a lower energy level.

Most photosynthetic organisms use a combination of pigments to capture light for photosynthesis—and often for additional purposes. Many accessory pigments are antioxidants that protect cells from the damaging effects of UV light in the sun's rays (Section 5.5). Appealing colors attract animals to ripening fruit or pollinators to flowers. You may already be familiar with some of these molecules.

Carrots, for example, are orange because they contain beta-carotene (β-carotene); roses are red and violets are blue because of their anthocyanin content.

In green plants, chlorophylls are usually so abundant that they mask the colors of the other pigments. Plants that change color during autumn are preparing for a period of dormancy; they conserve resources by moving nutrients from tender parts that would be damaged by winter cold (such as leaves) to protected parts (such as roots). Chlorophylls are not needed during dormancy, so they are disassembled and their components recycled. Yellow and orange accessory pigments are also recycled, but not as quickly as chlorophylls. Their colors begin to show as the chlorophyll content declines in leaves. Anthocyanin synthesis also increases in some plants, adding red and purple tones to turning leaf colors. (Chapter 27 returns to the topic of dormancy in plants.)

autotroph Organism that makes its own food using energy from the environment and carbon from inorganic molecules such as CO_2.
chlorophyll *a* Main photosynthetic pigment in plants.
heterotroph Organism that obtains carbon from organic compounds assembled by other organisms.
pigment An organic molecule that can absorb light of certain wavelengths.
wavelength Distance between the crests of two successive waves.

TAKE-HOME MESSAGE 6.1

The sun emits electromagnetic radiation (light). Visible light is the main form of energy that drives photosynthesis.

Light travels in waves and is organized as photons. We see different wavelengths of visible light as different colors.

Pigments absorb light at specific wavelengths. Photosynthetic species use pigments such as chlorophyll *a* to harvest the energy of light for photosynthesis.

CREDITS: (2) photo, © Photobac/Shutterstock; art, © Cengage Learning.

A Light micrograph of a filament of green algae. Each strand is a stack of individual photosynthetic cells. Theodor Engelmann used several species of algae in a series of experiments to determine whether some colors of light are better for photosynthesis than others.

400 nm   500 nm   600 nm   700 nm

Wavelength

B Engelmann directed light through a prism so that bands of colors crossed a water droplet on a microscope slide. The water held a strand of photosynthetic algae, and also oxygen-requiring bacteria. The bacteria clustered around the algal cells that were releasing the most oxygen—the ones most actively engaged in photosynthesis. Those cells were under blue and red light.

phycoerythrobilin   phycocyanobilin

chlorophyll *b*

β-carotene

chlorophyll *a*

Amount of light absorbed

400 nm   500 nm   600 nm   700 nm

C Absorption spectra of chlorophylls *a* and *b*, β-carotene, and two phycobilins reveal the efficiency with which these pigments absorb different wavelengths of visible light. Line color indicates the characteristic color of each pigment.

FIGURE 6.3 {Animated} Discovery that photosynthesis is driven best by particular wavelengths of visible light.

FIGURE IT OUT: Which three pigments in **C** would you conclude are the main ones in the green algae tested in **B**?

Answer: Chlorophyll *a*, chlorophyll *b*, and β-carotene

In 1882, botanist Theodor Engelmann designed a set of experiments to test his hypothesis that the color of light affects the rate of photosynthesis. It had long been known that photosynthesis releases oxygen, so Engelmann used oxygen emission as an indirect measurement of photosynthetic activity. He directed a spectrum of light across individual strands of green algae suspended in water (**FIGURE 6.3A**). Oxygen-sensing equipment had not yet been invented, so Engelmann used motile, oxygen-requiring bacteria to show him where the oxygen concentration in the water was highest. The bacteria moved through the water and gathered mainly where blue and red light fell across the algal cells (**FIGURE 6.3B**). Engelmann concluded that photosynthetic cells illuminated by light of these colors were releasing the most oxygen—a sign that blue and red light are the best for driving photosynthesis in these algal cells.

Today we have equipment that can directly measure how efficiently a photosynthetic pigment absorbs different wavelengths of light. A graph that shows this efficiency is called an absorption spectrum. Peaks in the graph indicate wavelengths absorbed best (**FIGURE 6.3C**). Engelmann's results—where the bacteria clustered around the algal cells—represent the combined spectra of all the photosynthetic pigments present in the tested algae.

The combination of pigments used for photosynthesis differs among species. Why? Photosynthetic species are adapted to the environment in which they evolved, and light that reaches different environments varies in its proportions of wavelengths. Consider that seawater absorbs green and blue-green light less efficiently than other colors. Thus, more green and blue-green light penetrates deep ocean water. Algae that live in in this environment tend to have pigments—mainly phycobilins—that absorb green and blue-green light (*below*).

TAKE-HOME MESSAGE 6.2

A combination of pigments allows a photosynthetic organism to most efficiently capture the particular range of light wavelengths that reaches the habitat in which it evolved.

CREDITS: (3A) Jason Sonneman; (3B,C) © Cengage Learning; (in text) © Michael Davidson/The Florida State University.

6.3 WHAT HAPPENS DURING PHOTOSYNTHESIS?

All life is sustained by inputs of energy, but not all forms of energy can sustain life. Sunlight, for example, is abundant here on Earth, but it cannot be used to directly power protein synthesis or other energy-requiring reactions that keep organisms alive. Photosynthesis converts the energy of light into the energy of chemical bonds. Unlike light, chemical energy can power the reactions of life, and it can be stored for use at a later time.

In eukaryotes, photosynthesis takes place in chloroplasts (Section 4.8). Plant chloroplasts have two outer membranes, and they are filled with a thick, cytoplasm-like fluid called **stroma** (FIGURE 6.4). Suspended in the stroma are the chloroplast's own DNA, some ribosomes, and an inner, much-folded **thylakoid membrane**. The folds of a thylakoid membrane typically form stacks of interconnected disks called thylakoids. The space enclosed by the thylakoid membrane is a single, continuous compartment.

Photosynthesis is often summarized by this equation:

$$CO_2 + water \xrightarrow{\text{light energy}} sugars + O_2$$

CO_2 is carbon dioxide, and O_2 is oxygen; both are gases abundant in the atmosphere. Keep in mind that photosynthesis is not a single reaction. Rather, it is a metabolic pathway (Section 5.4), a series of many reactions that occur in two stages. Molecules embedded in the thylakoid membrane carry out the reactions of the first stage, which are driven by light and thus called the **light-dependent reactions**. The "photo" in photosynthesis means light, and it refers to the conversion of light energy to the chemical bond energy of ATP during this stage. In addition to making ATP, the main light-dependent pathway in chloroplasts splits water molecules and releases O_2. Hydrogen ions and electrons from the water molecules end up in the coenzyme NADPH:

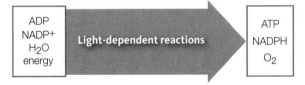

The "synthesis" part of photosynthesis refers to the reactions of the second stage, which build sugars from CO_2

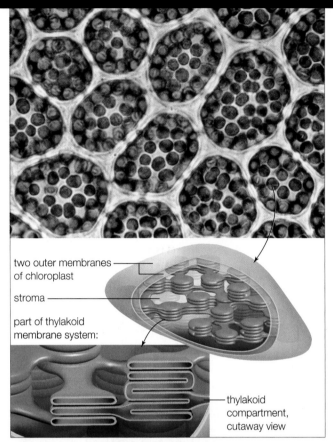

two outer membranes of chloroplast

stroma

part of thylakoid membrane system:

thylakoid compartment, cutaway view

FIGURE 6.4 {Animated} Zooming in on the site of photosynthesis in a plant cell. The micrograph shows chloroplasts in cells of a moss leaf.

and water. These sugar-building reactions run in the stroma. They are collectively called the **light-independent reactions** because light energy does not power them. Instead, they run on energy delivered by NADPH and ATP that formed during the first stage:

---

light-dependent reactions First stage of photosynthesis; convert light energy to chemical energy.
light-independent reactions Second stage of photosynthesis; use ATP and NADPH to assemble sugars from water and CO_2.
stroma The cytoplasm-like fluid between the thylakoid membrane and the two outer membranes of a chloroplast.
thylakoid membrane A chloroplast's highly folded inner membrane system; forms a continuous compartment in the stroma.

TAKE-HOME MESSAGE 6.3

In eukaryotic cells, the first stage of photosynthesis occurs at the thylakoid membrane of chloroplasts. During these light-dependent reactions, light energy drives the formation of ATP and NADPH.

In eukaryotic cells, the second stage of photosynthesis occurs in the stroma of chloroplasts. During these light-independent reactions, ATP and NADPH drive the synthesis of sugars from water and carbon dioxide.

A chloroplast's thylakoid membrane contains millions of light-harvesting complexes, which are circular arrays of chlorophylls, various accessory pigments, and proteins (**FIGURE 6.5**). When a chlorophyll or accessory pigment in a light-harvesting complex absorbs light, one of its electrons jumps to a higher energy level, or shell (Section 2.2). The electron quickly drops back down to a lower shell by emitting its extra energy. Light-harvesting complexes hold on to that emitted energy by passing it back and forth, a bit like volleyball players pass a ball among team members. The reactions of photosynthesis begin when energy being passed around the thylakoid membrane reaches a photosystem. A **photosystem** is a group of hundreds of chlorophylls, accessory pigments, and other molecules that work as a unit to begin the reactions of photosynthesis.

FIGURE 6.5 A view of some components of the thylakoid membrane as seen from the stroma. Molecules of electron transfer chains and ATP synthases are also present, but not shown for clarity.

photosystem   light-harvesting complex

FIGURE 6.6 Summary of the inputs and outputs of the two pathways of light-dependent reactions.

THE NONCYCLIC PATHWAY

Thylakoid membranes contain two kinds of photosystems, type I and type II, that were named in the order of their discovery. In cyanobacteria, plants, and all photosynthetic protists, both photosystem types work together in the noncyclic pathway of photosynthesis (**FIGURE 6.6A**). The pathway begins when energy being passed among light-harvesting complexes reaches a photosystem II (**FIGURE 6.7**). At the center of each photosystem are two very closely associated chlorophyll *a* molecules (a "special pair"). When a photosystem absorbs energy, electrons are ejected from its special pair ❶.

A photosystem that loses electrons must be restocked with more. Photosystem II restocks itself with electrons by pulling them off of water molecules in the thylakoid compartment. Pulling electrons off of water molecules causes them to split into hydrogen ions and oxygen atoms ❷. The oxygen atoms combine and diffuse out of the cell as oxygen gas (O_2). This and any other process by which a molecule is broken apart by light energy is called **photolysis**.

The actual conversion of light energy to chemical energy occurs when electrons ejected from photosystem II enter an electron transfer chain in the thylakoid membrane ❸. Remember that electron transfer chains can harvest the energy of electrons in a series of redox reactions, releasing a bit of their extra energy with each step (Section 5.4). In this case, molecules of the electron transfer chain use the released energy to actively transport hydrogen ions (H^+) across the membrane, from the stroma to the thylakoid compartment ❹. Thus, the flow of electrons through electron transfer chains sets up and maintains a hydrogen ion gradient across the thylakoid membrane.

The hydrogen ion gradient is a type of potential energy (Section 5.1) that can be tapped to make ATP. Hydrogen ions in the thylakoid compartment want to follow their concentration gradient by moving back into the stroma. However, ions cannot diffuse through lipid bilayers (Section 5.6). H^+ leaves the thylakoid compartment only by flowing through proteins called ATP synthases embedded in the thylakoid membrane ❼. An ATP synthase is both a transport protein and an enzyme. When hydrogen ions flow through its interior, the protein phosphorylates ADP, so ATP forms in the stroma ❽. The process by which the flow of electrons through electron transfer chains drives ATP formation is called **electron transfer phosphorylation**.

After the electrons have moved through the first electron transfer chain, they are accepted by a photosystem I. When this photosystem absorbs light energy, its special pair of chlorophylls emits electrons ❺. These electrons enter a second, different electron transfer chain. At the end of this

CREDIT: (5) From Starr/Taggart/Evers/Starr, Biology, 13E. © 2013 Cengage Learning; (6) © Cengage Learning.

1 light energy   **4** H+   **5** light energy   **8** ATP

photosystem II   **3** electron transfer chain   photosystem I   **6** electron transfer chain   ATP synthase   ADP, P$_i$

e− e− e−   e−   e− e−   NADPH

e−   e− e−   H+

thylakoid compartment   **2**   **7** H+

H$_2$O   H+ H+ H+ H+   H+   H+ H+ H+ H+

stroma

O$_2$

1 Light energy ejects electrons from a photosystem II.

2 The photosystem pulls replacement electrons from water molecules, which then break apart into oxygen and hydrogen ions. The oxygen leaves the cell as O$_2$.

3 The electrons enter an electron transfer chain in the thylakoid membrane.

4 Energy lost by the electrons as they move through the chain is used to actively transport hydrogen ions from the stroma into the thylakoid compartment. A hydrogen ion gradient forms across the thylakoid membrane.

5 Light energy ejects electrons from a photosystem I. Replacement electrons come from an electron transfer chain.

6 The ejected electrons move through a second electron transfer chain, then combine with NADP+ and H+, so NADPH forms.

7 Hydrogen ions in the thylakoid compartment are propelled through the interior of ATP synthases by their gradient across the thylakoid membrane.

8 Hydrogen ion flow causes ATP synthases to phosphorylate ADP, so ATP forms in the stroma.

 FIGURE 6.7 {Animated} Light-dependent reactions, noncyclic pathway. ATP and oxygen gas are produced in this pathway. Electrons that travel through two different electron transfer chains end up in NADPH.

chain, the coenzyme NADP+ accepts the electrons along with H+, so NADPH forms **6**:

$$NADP^+ + 2e^- + H^+ \longrightarrow \boxed{NADPH}$$

NADPH is a powerful reducing agent (electron donor).

THE CYCLIC PATHWAY

As you will see in the next section, ATP and NADPH produced in the light-dependent reactions are used to make sugars. On its own, the noncyclic pathway does not yield enough ATP to balance NADPH use in sugar production pathways. The cyclic pathway produces additional ATP for this purpose (**FIGURE 6.6B**).

In the cyclic pathway, electrons that are ejected from photosystem I enter an electron transfer chain, and then return to photosystem I. As in the noncyclic pathway, the electron transfer chain uses electron energy to move hydrogen ions into the thylakoid compartment, and the

resulting hydrogen ion gradient drives ATP formation. However, the cyclic pathway does not produce NADPH or oxygen gas.

The cyclic pathway also allows light-dependent reactions to continue when the noncyclic pathway stops, for example under intense illumination. Light energy in excess of what can be used for photosynthesis can result in the formation of dangerous free radicals (Section 2.2). A light-induced structural change in photosystem II prevents this from happening. The photosystem stops initiating the noncyclic pathway, and traps excess energy instead. At such times, the cyclic pathway predominates.

TAKE-HOME MESSAGE 6.4

Photosynthetic pigments in the thylakoid membrane transfer the energy of light to photosystems, which eject electrons that enter electron transfer chains.

In both noncyclic and cyclic pathways, the flow of electrons through the transfer chains sets up hydrogen ion gradients that drive ATP formation.

In the noncyclic pathway, water molecules are split, oxygen is released, and electrons end up in NADPH.

In the cyclic pathway, no NADPH forms, and no oxygen is released.

electron transfer phosphorylation Process in which electron flow through electron transfer chains sets up a hydrogen ion gradient that drives ATP formation.
photolysis Process by which light energy breaks down a molecule.
photosystem Cluster of pigments and proteins that converts light energy to chemical energy in photosynthesis.

CREDIT: (7) © Cengage Learning; (7 icon, in text) From Starr/Evers/Starr, Biology Today and Tomorrow with Physiology, 4E. © 2013 Cengage Learning.

6.5 HOW DO THE LIGHT-INDEPENDENT REACTIONS WORK?

THE CALVIN–BENSON CYCLE

The enzyme-mediated reactions of the **Calvin–Benson cycle** build sugars in the stroma of chloroplasts (**FIGURE 6.8**). These reactions are light-independent because light energy does not power them. Instead, they run on ATP and NADPH that formed in the light-dependent reactions.

Light-independent reactions use carbon atoms from CO_2 to make sugars. Extracting carbon atoms from an inorganic source and incorporating them into an organic molecule is a process called **carbon fixation**. In most plants, photosynthetic protists, and some bacteria, the enzyme **rubisco** fixes carbon by attaching CO_2 to RuBP (ribulose bisphosphate), a five-carbon molecule ❶.

FIGURE 6.8 {Animated} The Calvin–Benson cycle. This sketch shows a cross-section of a chloroplast with the reactions cycling in the stroma. The steps shown are a summary of six cycles of reactions (see Appendix III for details). Black balls are carbon atoms.

❶ Six CO_2 diffuse into a photosynthetic cell, and then into a chloroplast. Rubisco attaches each to a RuBP molecule. The resulting intermediates split, so twelve molecules of PGA form.

❷ Each PGA molecule gets a phosphate group from ATP, plus hydrogen and electrons from NADPH. Twelve PGAL form.

❸ Two PGAL may combine to form one six-carbon sugar (such as glucose).

❹ The remaining ten PGAL receive phosphate groups from ATP. The transfer primes them for endergonic reactions that regenerate the 6 RuBP.

The six-carbon intermediate that forms by this reaction is unstable, so it splits right away into two three-carbon molecules of PGA (phosphoglycerate). Each PGA receives a phosphate group from ATP, and hydrogen and electrons from NADPH ❷. Thus, ATP energy and the reducing power of NADPH convert each molecule of PGA into a molecule of PGAL (phosphoglyceraldehyde), a phosphorylated sugar.

In later reactions, two or more of the three-carbon PGAL molecules can be combined and rearranged to form larger carbohydrates. Glucose, remember, has six carbon atoms. To make one glucose molecule, six CO_2 must be attached to six RuBP molecules, so twelve PGAL form. Two PGAL may combine to form one six-carbon glucose ❸. The ten remaining PGAL regenerate the starting compound of the cycle, RuBP ❹. Most of the glucose that a plant makes is converted at once to sucrose or starch by other pathways.

ADAPTATIONS TO CLIMATE

Mechanisms that help a plant prevent water loss also limit the gas exchange needed for photosynthesis. Most plants have a thin, waterproof cuticle that limits evaporation of water from their aboveground parts. Gases cannot diffuse across the cuticle, so the surfaces of leaves and stems are studded with tiny, closable gaps called stomata. Stomata are tiny gateways for gases. When they are open, CO_2 can diffuse from the air into photosynthetic tissues, and O_2 can diffuse out of the tissues into the air. Stomata close to conserve water on hot, dry days. When that happens, gas exchange comes to a halt. Closed stomata limit the availability of CO_2 for the light-independent reactions, so sugar synthesis slows. This detrimental effect is greatest in **C3 plants**, which fix carbon only by the Calvin–Benson cycle. They are called C3 plants because a three-carbon molecule (PGA) is the first stable intermediate in their light-independent reactions. When the CO_2 concentration inside a C3 plant declines, rubisco uses oxygen as a substrate in **photorespiration**, an alternate pathway that produces carbon dioxide. Thus, when a C3 plant closes stomata during the day, it loses carbon instead of fixing it (**FIGURE 6.9A**). In addition, ATP and NADPH are used to convert the pathway's intermediates to a molecule that can enter the Calvin–Benson cycle, so extra energy is required to make sugars. C3 plants compensate for photorespiration by making a lot of rubisco: It is the most abundant protein on Earth.

In many plant lineages, an additional set of reactions compensates for rubisco's inefficiency. Plants that use

A When the CO_2 level declines in leaves of a C3 plant, rubisco uses oxygen as a substrate in photorespiration, and sugar production becomes inefficient.

B In a C3 plant (barley, *left*), chloroplasts—the sites of carbon fixation—occur mainly in mesophyll cells. In a C4 plant (millet, *right*), carbon fixation occurs first in mesophyll cells, then in bundle-sheath cells. C4 adaptations maintain a high CO_2/O_2 ratio near rubisco.

FIGURE 6.9 {Animated} Anatomical and biochemical specializations minimize photorespiration in C4 plants. Micrographs show leaf cross sections.

these reactions also close stomata on dry days, but their sugar production does not decline. Examples include corn, switchgrass, and bamboo. We call these **C4 plants** because the first stable intermediate to form in their light-independent reactions is a four-carbon compound. C4 plants fix carbon twice, in two kinds of cells (**FIGURE 6.9B**). The first set of reactions occurs in mesophyll cells, where carbon is fixed by an enzyme that does not use oxygen even when the carbon dioxide level is low. The resulting intermediate is transported to bundle-sheath cells, where it is converted to CO_2. Rubisco fixes carbon for the second time as the CO_2 enters the Calvin–Benson cycle.

Bundle-sheath cells of C4 plants have chloroplasts that carry out light-dependent reactions, but only in the cyclic pathway. No oxygen is released, so the O_2 level near rubisco stays low. This, along with the high CO_2 level provided by the C4 reactions, minimizes photorespiration, so sugar production stays efficient in these plants even in hot, dry weather (**FIGURE 6.10**).

Succulents, cacti, and other **CAM plants** use a carbon-fixing pathway that allows them to conserve water even in desert regions with extremely high daytime temperatures.

CAM stands for crassulacean acid metabolism, after the Crassulaceae family of plants in which this pathway was first studied. Like C4 plants, CAM plants fix carbon twice, but the reactions occur at different times rather than in different cells. Stomata on a CAM plant open at night, when typically lower temperatures minimize evaporative water loss. The plants fix carbon from CO_2 in the air at this time. The product of the cycle, a four-carbon acid, is stored in the cell's central vacuole. When the stomata close the next day, the acid moves out of the vacuole and becomes broken down to CO_2, which is fixed for the second time when it enters the Calvin–Benson cycle.

FIGURE 6.10 Crabgrass "weeds" overgrowing a lawn. Crabgrasses, which are C4 plants, thrive in hot, dry summers, when they easily outcompete Kentucky bluegrass and other fine-leaved C3 grasses commonly planted in residential lawns.

TAKE-HOME MESSAGE 6.5

The light-independent reactions build sugars using carbon fixed from CO_2. They run on ATP and electrons from NADPH.

C3 plants use only the Calvin–Benson cycle. In these plants, photorespiration on hot, dry days reduces the efficiency of sugar production, so it limits growth.

Plants adapted to hot, dry conditions minimize photorespiration by fixing carbon twice. C4 plants separate the two sets of reactions in space; CAM plants separate them in time.

C3 plant Type of plant that uses only the Calvin–Benson cycle to fix carbon.
C4 plant Type of plant that minimizes photorespiration by fixing carbon twice, in two cell types.
Calvin–Benson cycle Cyclic carbon-fixing pathway that builds sugars from CO_2; the light-independent reactions of photosynthesis.
CAM plant Type of plant that conserves water by fixing carbon twice, at different times of day.
carbon fixation Process by which carbon from an inorganic source such as carbon dioxide gets incorporated into an organic molecule.
photorespiration Reaction in which rubisco attaches oxygen instead of carbon dioxide to ribulose bisphosphate.
rubisco Ribulose bisphosphate carboxylase. Carbon-fixing enzyme of the Calvin–Benson cycle.

CREDITS: (9A) © Cengage Learning; (9B left) Masahiro Yamada, Michio Kawasaki, Tatsuo Sugiyama, Hiroshi Miyake, Mitsutaka Taniguchi; Differential Positioning of C4 Mesophyll and Bundle Sheath Chloroplasts: Aggregative Movement of C4 Mesophyll Chloroplasts in Response to Environmental Stresses: Plant and Cell Physiology; (2009) 50(10): 1736–1749; (9B right) Eri Maai, Shouu Shimada, Masahiro Yamada, Tatsuo Sugiyama, Hiroshi Miyake, Mitsutaka Taniguchi; The avoidance and aggregative movements of mesophyll chloroplasts in C4 monocots in response to blue light and abscisic acid; Journal of Experimental Botany, doi:10.1093/jxb/err008, by permission of Oxford University Press; (10) Image courtesy msuturfweeds.net.

Sustainability

FIGURE 6.11 Switchgrass growing wild in a North American prairie.

TODAY, THE EXPRESSION "FOOD IS FUEL" IS NOT JUST ABOUT EATING. With fossil fuel prices soaring, there is an increasing demand for biofuels, which are oils, gases, or alcohols made from organic matter that is not fossilized. Most materials we use for biofuel production today consist of food crops—mainly corn, soybeans, and sugarcane. Growing these crops in large quantities is typically damaging to the environment, and using them to make biofuel competes with our food supply.

How did we end up competing with our vehicles for food? We both run on the same fuel: energy that plants have stored in chemical bonds. Fossil fuels such as petroleum, coal, and natural gas formed from the remains of ancient swamp forests that decayed and compacted over millions of years. These fuels consist of molecules originally assembled by ancient plants. Biofuels—and foods—consist mainly of molecules originally assembled by modern plants.

A lot of energy is locked up in the chemical bonds of molecules made by plants. That energy can fuel heterotrophs, as when an animal cell powers ATP synthesis by breaking the bonds of sugars (a topic detailed in the next chapter). It can also fuel our cars, which run on energy released by burning biofuels or fossil fuels. Both processes are fundamentally the same: They release energy by breaking the bonds of organic molecules. Both use oxygen to break those bonds, and both produce carbon dioxide.

Photosynthesis removes carbon dioxide from the atmosphere, and fixes its carbon atoms in organic compounds. When we burn fossil fuels, the carbon that has been sequestered in them for hundreds of millions of years is released back into the atmosphere, mainly as CO_2 that reenters the atmosphere. Our extensive use of fossil fuels has put Earth's atmospheric cycle of carbon dioxide out of balance: We are adding far more CO_2 to the atmosphere than photosynthetic organisms are removing from it. Atmospheric carbon dioxide affects Earth's climate, so this increase in CO_2 is contributing to global climate change.

CREDIT: (11) Photo by Peggy Greb/USDA.

Ratna Sharma and Mari Chinn researching ways to reduce the cost of producing biofuel from renewable sources such as wild grasses and agricultural waste.

National Geographic Grantee
WILLIE SMITS

Unlike fossil fuels, biofuels are a renewable source of energy: We can always make more of them simply by growing more plants. Also unlike fossil fuels, biofuels do not contribute to global climate change, because growing plant matter for fuel recycles carbon that is already in the atmosphere.

Corn and other food crops are rich in oils, starches, and sugars that can be easily converted to biofuels. The starch in corn kernels, for example, can be enzymatically broken down to glucose, which is converted to ethanol by heterotrophic bacteria or yeast. Making biofuels from other types of plant matter requires additional steps, because these materials contain a higher proportion of cellulose. Breaking down this tough, insoluble carbohydrate to its glucose monomers adds a lot of cost to the biofuel product. Researchers are currently working on cost-effective ways to break down the abundant cellulose in fast-growing weeds such as switchgrass (FIGURE 6.11), and agricultural wastes such as wood chips, wheat straw, cotton stalks, and rice hulls.

One of Indonesia's most ardent rain forest protection activists is in what may seem an unlikely position: spearheading a project to produce biofuel from trees. But tropical forest scientist Willie Smits, after 30 years of studying fragile ecosystems in these Southeast Asian islands, wants to draw world attention to a powerhouse of a tree—the Arenga sugar palm, *Arenga pinnata*. Smits says that this deep-rooted palm could serve as the core of a waste-free system that produces a premium organic sugar as well as ethanol for fuel, providing food products and jobs to villagers while it helps preserve the existing native rain forest. Scientists who have studied the unique harvesting and production process developed by Smits agree the system would protect the atmosphere rather than add to Earth's growing carbon dioxide burden. "The palm juice chiefly consists of water and sugar—made from rain, sunshine, carbon dioxide, and nothing else," says Smits. "You are basically only harvesting sunshine." The project, being funded in part by a grant from National Geographic's Great Energy Challenge initiative, has the potential to disrupt a cycle of poverty and environmental devastation that has gripped one of the most vulnerable and remote areas of the planet, while providing a new source of sustainable fuel.

Summary

SECTIONS 6.1, 6.2   Plants and other **autotrophs** make their own food using energy from the environment and carbon from inorganic sources such as CO_2. **Heterotrophs** get carbon from molecules that other organisms have already assembled. Visible light drives photosynthesis, which begins when light is absorbed by photosynthetic pigments. **Pigments** absorb light of particular **wavelengths** only; wavelengths not captured are reflected as its characteristic color. The main photosynthetic pigment, **chlorophyll _a_**, absorbs violet and red light, so it appears green. Accessory pigments absorb additional wavelengths.

SECTION 6.3   In chloroplasts, the **light-dependent reactions** of photosynthesis occur at a much-folded **thylakoid membrane**. The membrane forms a compartment in the chloroplast's interior (**stroma**), in which the **light-independent reactions** occur:

SECTION 6.4   In the light-dependent reactions, light-harvesting complexes in the thylakoid membrane absorb photons and pass the energy to **photosystems**. Receiving energy causes photosystems to release electrons.

In the noncyclic pathway, electrons released from photosystem II flow through an electron transfer chain, then to photosystem I. Photosystem II replaces lost electrons by pulling them from water, which then splits into H^+ and O_2 (an example of **photolysis**). Electrons released from photosystem I end up in NADPH.

In the cyclic pathway, electrons released from photosystem I enter an electron transfer chain, then cycle back to photosystem I. NADPH does not form and O_2 is not released.

ATP forms by **electron transfer phosphorylation** in both pathways. Electrons flowing through electron transfer chains cause H^+ to accumulate in the thylakoid compartment. The H^+ follows its gradient back across the membrane through ATP synthases, driving ATP synthesis.

SECTION 6.5   **Carbon fixation** occurs in light-independent reactions. Inside the stroma, the enzyme **rubisco** attaches a carbon from CO_2 to RuBP to start the **Calvin–Benson cycle**. This cyclic pathway uses energy from ATP, carbon and oxygen from CO_2, and hydrogen and electrons from NADPH to make sugars.

On hot, dry days, plants conserve water by closing stomata, so CO_2 for light-independent reactions cannot enter their tissues. In **C3 plants**, the resulting low CO_2 level causes **photorespiration**, which reduces the efficiency of sugar production. Other types of plants minimize photorespiration by fixing carbon twice, thus keeping the CO_2 level high and the O_2 level low near rubisco. **C4 plants** carry out the two sets of reactions in different cell types; **CAM plants** carry them out at different times.

SECTION 6.6   Autotrophs remove CO_2 from the atmosphere; the metabolic activity of most organisms puts it back. Humans disrupt this cycle by burning fossil fuels, which adds extra CO_2 to the atmosphere. The resulting imbalance is contributing to global warming.

Self-Quiz   Answers in Appendix VII

1. A cat eats a bird, which ate a caterpillar that chewed on a weed. Which of these organisms are autotrophs? Which ones are heterotrophs?

2. Which of the following statements is incorrect?
   a. Pigments absorb light of certain wavelengths only.
   b. Many accessory pigments are multipurpose molecules.
   c. Chlorophyll is green because it absorbs green light.

3. In plants, the light-dependent reactions proceed at/in the _____ .
   a. thylakoid membrane   c. stroma
   b. plasma membrane   d. cytoplasm

4. When a photosystem absorbs light, _____ .
   a. sugar phosphates are produced
   b. electrons are transferred to ATP
   c. RuBP accepts electrons
   d. electrons are ejected from its special pair

5. In the light-dependent reactions, _____ .
   a. carbon dioxide is fixed   d. CO_2 accepts electrons
   b. ATP forms   e. b and c
   c. sugars form   f. a and c

6. What accumulates inside the thylakoid compartment during the light-dependent reactions?
   a. sugars   b. hydrogen ions   c. O_2 d. CO_2

7. The atoms in the molecular oxygen released during photosynthesis come from split _____ molecules.
   a. sugar   c. water
   b. CO_2 d. O_2

8. Light-independent reactions in plants proceed at/in the _____ of chloroplasts.
   a. thylakoid membrane   c. stroma
   b. plasma membrane   d. cytoplasm

CREDIT: (in text) © Cengage Learning 2014.

Data Analysis Activities

Energy Efficiency of Biofuel Production Most material currently used for biofuel production in the United States consists of food crops—mainly corn, soybeans, and sugarcane. In 2006, David Tilman and his colleagues published the results of a 10-year study comparing the net energy output of various biofuels. The researchers grew a mixture of native perennial grasses without irrigation, fertilizer, pesticides, or herbicides, in sandy soil that was so depleted by intensive agriculture that it had been abandoned. They measured the usable energy in biofuels made from the grasses, from corn, and from soy. They also measured the energy it took to grow and produce each kind of biofuel (**FIGURE 6.12**).

1. About how much energy did ethanol produced from one hectare of corn yield? How much energy did it take to grow the corn to make that ethanol?

2. Which of the biofuels tested had the highest ratio of energy output to energy input?

3. Which of the three crops would require the least amount of land to produce a given amount of biofuel energy?

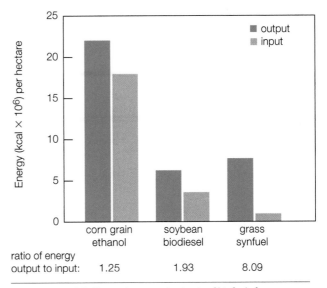

| ratio of energy output to input: | 1.25 | 1.93 | 8.09 |

FIGURE 6.12 Energy inputs and outputs of biofuels from different sources. One hectare is about 2.5 acres.

9. The Calvin–Benson cycle starts when _____ .
   a. light is available
   b. carbon dioxide is attached to RuBP
   c. electrons leave photosystem II

10. Which of the following substances does *not* participate in the Calvin–Benson cycle?
    a. ATP   c. NADPH   e. PGAL
    b. O_2 d. RuBP   f. CO_2

11. Plants use energy in _____ to drive photosynthesis.
    a. light   b. hydrogen ions   c. O_2 d. CO_2

12. Most of the carbon dioxide used in photosynthesis comes from _____ .
    a. glucose   c. rainwater
    b. the atmosphere   d. photolysis

13. Match each term with its most suitable description.
    ___ PGAL formation
    ___ CO_2 fixation
    ___ photolysis
    ___ ATP forms; NADPH does not
    ___ photorespiration
    ___ photosynthesis
    ___ pigment
    ___ autotroph

    a. absorbs light
    b. converts light to chemical energy
    c. self-feeder
    d. electrons cycle back to photosystem I
    e. problem in C3 plants
    f. ATP, NADPH needed
    g. water molecules split
    h. rubisco function

CENGAGE To access course materials, please visit
brain.com www.cengagebrain.com.

Critical Thinking

1. About 200 years ago, Jan Baptista van Helmont wanted to know where growing plants get the materials necessary for increases in size. He planted a tree seedling weighing 5 pounds in a barrel filled with 200 pounds of soil and then watered the tree regularly. After five years, the tree weighed 169 pounds, 3 ounces, and the soil weighed 199 pounds, 14 ounces. Because the tree had gained so much weight and the soil had lost so little, he concluded that the tree had gained all of its additional weight by absorbing the water he had added to the barrel, but of course he was incorrect. What really happened?

2. While gazing into an aquarium, you observe bubbles coming from an aquatic plant (*left*). What are the bubbles and where do they come from?

3. A C3 plant absorbs a carbon radioisotope (as part of $^{14}CO_2$). In which stable, organic compound does the labeled carbon appear first?

4. As you learned in this chapter, cell membranes are required for electron transfer phosphorylation. Thylakoid membranes in chloroplasts serve this purpose in photosynthetic eukaryotes. Prokaryotic cells do not have this organelle, but many are photosynthesizers. How do you think they carry out the light-dependent reactions, given that they have no chloroplasts?

Like you, a whale breathes air to provide its cells with a fresh supply of oxygen for aerobic respiration. Carbon dioxide released from aerobically respiring cells leaves the body in each exhalation.

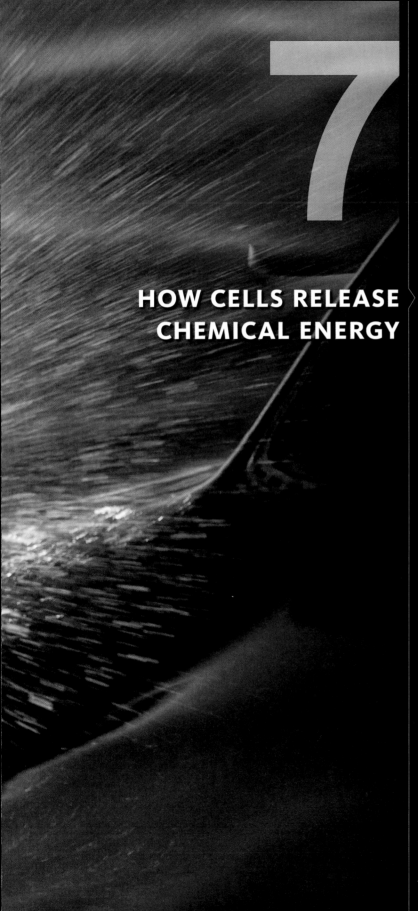

7

HOW CELLS RELEASE CHEMICAL ENERGY

Links to Earlier Concepts

This chapter focuses on metabolic pathways (Section 5.4) that harvest energy (5.1) stored in the chemical bonds of sugars (3.2). Some reactions (3.1) of these pathways occur in mitochondria (4.7). You will revisit free radicals (2.2), lipids (3.3), proteins (3.4), electron transfer chains (5.4), coenzymes (5.5), membrane transport (5.6, 5.7), and photosynthesis (6.4).

KEY CONCEPTS

ENERGY FROM SUGARS
Most cells can make ATP by breaking down sugars in either aerobic respiration or anaerobic fermentation pathways. Aerobic respiration yields the most ATP.

GLYCOLYSIS
Aerobic respiration and fermentation start in the cytoplasm with glycolysis, a pathway that splits glucose into two pyruvate molecules and yields two ATP.

AEROBIC RESPIRATION
Eukaryotes break down pyruvate to CO_2 in mitochondria. Many coenzymes are reduced; these deliver electrons and hydrogen ions to electron transfer chains that drive ATP formation.

FERMENTATION
Fermentation ends in the cytoplasm, where organic molecules accept electrons from pyruvate. The net yield of ATP is small compared with that from aerobic respiration.

OTHER METABOLIC PATHWAYS
Cells also make ATP by breaking down molecules other than sugars. Dietary lipids and proteins are converted to molecules that enter glycolysis or another step in the aerobic respiration pathway.

Photosynthetic organisms capture energy from the sun and store it in the form of sugars. They and most other organisms use energy stored in sugars to run the diverse reactions that sustain life. However, sugars rarely participate in such reactions, so how do cells harness their energy? In order to use the energy stored in sugars, cells must first transfer it to molecules—ATP in particular—that do participate in energy-requiring reactions. The energy transfer occurs when cells break the bonds of a sugar's carbon backbone. Energy released as those bonds are broken drives ATP synthesis. The two main mechanisms by which organisms break down sugars to make ATP are aerobic respiration and fermentation.

FIGURE 7.1 {Animated} Comparison of aerobic respiration and fermentation.

 FIGURE IT OUT: Which pathway produces more ATP?

Answer: Aerobic respiration

aerobic respiration Oxygen-requiring metabolic pathway that breaks down sugars to produce ATP.
fermentation A metabolic pathway that breaks down sugars to produce ATP and does not require oxygen.

AEROBIC RESPIRATION AND FERMENTATION COMPARED

Aerobic respiration is an oxygen-requiring metabolic pathway that breaks down sugars to make ATP. It is the main energy-releasing pathway in nearly all eukaryotes and some bacteria. Aerobic respiration occurs in three stages (**FIGURE 7.1A**). The first stage, glycolysis, is a linear pathway that occurs in cytoplasm. Glycolysis begins the breakdown of one sugar molecule for a net yield of 2 ATP. In eukaryotes, the next two stages occur in mitochondria. The second stage, the Krebs cycle, completes the breakdown of the sugar molecule to CO_2. This cyclic pathway produces 2 ATP and reduces many coenzymes. In the third stage, electron transfer phosphorylation (Section 6.4), coenzymes reduced during glycolysis and the Krebs cycle deliver electrons and hydrogen ions to electron transfer chains. Energy released by electrons as they move through the chains drives the formation of as many as 32 ATP. Water forms when oxygen accepts hydrogen ions and electrons at the end of the electron transfer chains. Aerobic respiration, which means "taking a breath of air," refers to this pathway's requirement for oxygen as the final acceptor of electrons.

Fermentation refers to sugar breakdown pathways that do not require oxygen to make ATP (**FIGURE 7.1B**). Like aerobic respiration, fermentation begins with glycolysis in cytoplasm. Unlike aerobic respiration, fermentation occurs entirely in cytoplasm, and does not include electron transfer chains. The reactions that conclude fermentation produce no additional ATP, and the final acceptor of electrons is an organic molecule (not oxygen).

Aerobic respiration produces about 36 ATP per sugar molecule; fermentation produces only 2. Fermentation provides enough ATP to sustain many single-celled species. It also helps cells of multicelled species produce ATP under anaerobic conditions, but aerobic respiration is a much more efficient way of harvesting energy from sugars. You and other large, multicelled organisms could not live without its higher yield.

TAKE-HOME MESSAGE 7.1

Most cells can make ATP by breaking down sugars, either in aerobic respiration or fermentation.

Aerobic respiration and fermentation begin in cytoplasm.

Fermentation does not require oxygen and ends in cytoplasm.

Aerobic respiration requires oxygen and, in eukaryotes, it ends in mitochondria. This pathway yields much more ATP than fermentation.

CREDIT: (1) © Cengage Learning.

7.2 HOW DID ENERGY-RELEASING PATHWAYS EVOLVE?

PEOPLE MATTER

National Geographic Grantee
DR. J. WILLIAM SCHOPF

For the first 85 percent of its history, Earth was populated by what was essentially pond scum. In 1987, National Geographic grantee J. William Schopf discovered what may be evidence of cells 3.465 billion years old, opening the floodgates to decades of controversy—and research that is filling in the holes in our understanding of how and when life evolved.

The first cells we know of appeared on Earth about 3.4 billion years ago. Like some modern prokaryotes, these ancient organisms did not tap into sunlight: They extracted the energy they needed from simple molecules such as methane and hydrogen sulfide. When the cyclic pathway of photosynthesis first evolved (Section 6.4), sunlight offered cells that used it an essentially unlimited supply of energy. Shortly afterward, this pathway became modified. The new noncyclic pathway split water molecules into hydrogen and oxygen. Cells that used the pathway were very successful. Oxygen gas (O_2) released from uncountable numbers of water molecules began seeping out of photosynthetic prokaryotes. The gas reacts easily with metals, so at first, most of it combined with metal atoms in exposed rocks. After the exposed minerals became saturated with oxygen, the gas began to accumulate in the ocean and the atmosphere. From that time on, the world of life would never be the same.

Before photosynthesis evolved, molecular oxygen had been a very small component of Earth's early atmosphere. In what may have been the earliest case of catastrophic pollution, the new abundance of this gas exerted tremendous pressure on all life at the time. Why? Then, like now, enzymes that require metal cofactors were a critical part of metabolism. Oxygen reacts with metal cofactors, and free radicals (Section 2.2) form during those reactions. Free radicals damage DNA and other biological molecules, so they are dangerous to life. Cells with no way to cope with them quickly died out. Only a few lineages persisted in deep water, muddy sediments, and other **anaerobic** (oxygen-free) habitats.

Antioxidants evolved in the survivors. Cells that made these molecules were the first **aerobic** organisms—they could live in the presence of oxygen. As they evolved, their antioxidant molecules became incorporated into new metabolic pathways that put oxygen's reactive properties to use. One of the new pathways was aerobic respiration. This pathway requires oxygen, and it produces carbon dioxide—the raw materials from which photosynthetic organisms make sugars. It also combines molecular oxygen with hydrogen ions and electrons—exactly the reverse of the reaction that splits water during photosynthesis:

$$O_2 + 4e^- + 4H^+ \longrightarrow 2H_2O$$

With this connection, the cycling of carbon, hydrogen, and oxygen through living things came full circle (*left*).

energy

PHOTOSYNTHESIS

CO_2
H_2O

sugar
O_2

AEROBIC RESPIRATION

energy

aerobic Involving or occurring in the presence of oxygen.
anaerobic Occurring in the absence of oxygen.

TAKE-HOME MESSAGE 7.2

Molecular oxygen produced by early photosynthetic prokaryotes put severe pressure on all life.

The evolution of antioxidants allowed the reactive properties of oxygen to be put to use in new metabolic pathways.

Today, carbon dioxide, water, sugar, and oxygen cycle through the world of life via photosynthesis (energy capture) and aerobic respiration (energy release).

GLYCOLYSIS

↓

KREBS CYCLE

↓

ELECTRON TRANSFER PHOSPHORYLATION

FIGURE 7.2 {Animated} Glycolysis (*opposite*).

For clarity, we track only the six carbon atoms (black balls) that enter the reactions as part of glucose. Cells invest two ATP to start glycolysis, so the net yield from one glucose molecule is two ATP. Two NADH also form, and two pyruvate molecules are the end products. Appendix III has more details for interested students.

Glycolysis is a series of reactions that begin the sugar breakdown pathways of aerobic respiration (*above*) and fermentation. The reactions of glycolysis, which occur with some variation in the cytoplasm of almost all cells, convert one six-carbon molecule of sugar (such as glucose) into two molecules of **pyruvate**, an organic compound with a three-carbon backbone:

glucose   *glycolysis* →   pyruvate (2)

The word glycolysis comes from two Greek words: *glyk–*, sweet, and *–lysis*, loosening; it refers to the release of chemical energy from sugars. Other six-carbon sugars such as fructose and galactose can enter glycolysis, but for clarity we focus here on glucose.

Glycolysis begins when a molecule of glucose enters a cell through a glucose transporter, a passive transport protein you encountered in Section 5.7. The cell invests two ATP in the endergonic reactions that begin the pathway (**FIGURE 7.2**). In the first reaction, a phosphate group is transferred from ATP to the glucose, thus forming glucose-6-phosphate ❶. A model of hexokinase, the enzyme that catalyzes this reaction, is pictured in Section 5.3.

Glycolysis continues as the glucose-6-phosphate accepts a phosphate group from another ATP, then splits ❷ to form two PGAL (phosphoglyceraldehyde). Remember from Section 6.5 that this phosphorylated sugar also forms during the Calvin–Benson cycle.

---

glycolysis Set of reactions in which a six-carbon sugar (such as glucose) is converted to two pyruvate for a net yield of two ATP.
pyruvate Three-carbon end product of glycolysis.
substrate-level phosphorylation The formation of ATP by the direct transfer of a phosphate group from a substrate to ADP.

In the next reaction, each PGAL receives a second phosphate group, and each gives up two electrons and a hydrogen ion. Two molecules of PGA (phosphoglycerate) form as products of this reaction ❸. The electrons and hydrogen ions are accepted by two NAD^+, which thereby become reduced to NADH. Aerobic respiration's third stage requires this NADH, as does fermentation.

Next, a phosphate group is transferred from each PGA to ADP, so two ATP form ❹. The direct transfer of a phosphate group from a substrate to ADP is called **substrate-level phosphorylation**. Substrate-level phosphorylation is a completely different process from the way ATP forms during electron transfer phosphorylation (Section 6.4).

Glycolysis ends with the formation of two more ATP by substrate-level phosphorylation ❺. Remember, two ATP were invested to begin the reactions of glycolysis. A total of four ATP form, so the net yield is two ATP per molecule of glucose ❻. The pathway also produces two three-carbon pyruvate molecules. Pyruvate is a substrate for the second-stage reactions of aerobic respiration, and also for fermentation reactions.

TAKE-HOME MESSAGE 7.3

Glycolysis is the first stage of sugar breakdown in both aerobic respiration and fermentation.

The reactions of glycolysis occur in the cytoplasm.

Glycolysis converts one molecule of glucose to two molecules of pyruvate, with a net yield of two ATP. Two NADH also form.

GLYCOLYSIS

glucose

ATP

① → ADP

glucose-6-phosphate

ATP

② → ADP

fructose-1,6-bisphosphate

2 PGAL

2 NAD⁺

③

e⁻ e⁻ e⁻ e⁻ ⟹ **NADH**

2 coenzymes reduced

2 PGA

2 ADP

④

ATP

2 ATP produced
by substrate-level
phosphorylation

2 PEP

2 ADP

⑤

ATP

2 ATP produced
by substrate-level
phosphorylation

2 pyruvate

⑥ Net 2 ATP + 2 NADH

*to second stage of aerobic respiration
or fermentation*

ATP-Requiring Steps

❶ A phosphate group is transferred from ATP to glucose, forming glucose-6-phosphate. (You learned about the enzyme that catalyzes this reaction, hexokinase, in **FIGURE 5.10** and Section 5.7).

❷ A phosphate group from a second ATP is transferred to the glucose-6-phosphate. The resulting molecule is unstable, and it splits into two three-carbon molecules. The molecules are interconvertible, so we will call them both PGAL (phosphoglyceraldehyde).

Two ATP have now been invested in the reactions.

ATP-Generating Steps

❸ An enzyme attaches a phosphate to the two PGAL, so two PGA (phosphoglycerate) form. Two electrons and a hydrogen ion (not shown) from each PGAL are accepted by NAD⁺, so two NADH form.

❹ An enzyme transfers a phosphate group from each PGA to ADP, forming two ATP and two intermediate molecules (PEP).

The original energy investment of two ATP has now been recovered.

❺ An enzyme transfers a phosphate group from each PEP to ADP, forming two more ATP and two molecules of pyruvate.

❻ Summing up, glycolysis yields two NADH, two ATP (net), and two pyruvate for each glucose molecule.

Depending on the type of cell and environmental conditions, the pyruvate may enter the second stage of aerobic respiration or it may be used in other ways, such as in fermentation.

7.4 WHAT HAPPENS DURING THE SECOND STAGE OF AEROBIC RESPIRATION?

The second stage of aerobic respiration (*above*) occurs inside mitochondria (**FIGURE 7.3**). It includes two sets of reactions, acetyl–CoA formation and the **Krebs cycle**, that break down pyruvate, the product of glycolysis. All of the carbon atoms that were once part of glucose end up in CO_2, which departs the cell. Only two ATP form, but the reactions reduce many coenzymes. The energy of electrons carried by these coenzymes will drive the reactions of the third stage of aerobic respiration.

ACETYL–CoA FORMATION

Aerobic respiration's second stage begins when the two pyruvate molecules that formed during glycolysis enter a mitochondrion. Pyruvate is transported across the mitochondrion's two membranes and into the inner compartment, which is called the mitochondrial matrix (**FIGURE 7.4**). There, an enzyme immediately splits each pyruvate into one molecule of CO_2 and a two-carbon acetyl group ($—COCH_3$). The CO_2 diffuses out of the cell, and the acetyl group combines with a molecule called coenzyme A (abbreviated CoA). The product of this reaction is acetyl–CoA ❶. Electrons and hydrogen ions released by the reaction combine with NAD^+, so NADH also forms.

THE KREBS CYCLE

Each molecule of acetyl–CoA now carries two carbons into the Krebs cycle. Remember from Section 5.4 that a cyclic pathway is not a physical object, such as a wheel. It is called a cycle because the last reaction in the pathway regenerates the substrate of the first. In this case, a substrate of the Krebs cycle's first reaction—and a product of the last—is four-carbon oxaloacetate.

During each cycle of Krebs reactions, two carbon atoms of acetyl–CoA are transferred to oxaloacetate, forming citrate, the ionized form of citric acid ❷. The Krebs cycle is also called the citric acid cycle after this first intermediate. In later reactions, two CO_2 form and depart the cell. Two NAD^+ are reduced when they accept hydrogen ions and electrons, so two NADH form ❸ and ❹. ATP forms by substrate-level phosphorylation ❺. Two coenzymes are reduced: an FAD (flavin adenine dinucleotide) ❻, and another NAD^+ ❼. The final steps of the pathway regenerate oxaloacetate ❽.

FIGURE 7.3 The second stage of aerobic respiration, acetyl–CoA formation and the Krebs cycle, occurs inside mitochondria. *Left,* an inner membrane divides a mitochondrion's interior into two fluid-filled compartments. *Right,* the second stage of aerobic respiration takes place in the mitochondrion's innermost compartment, or matrix.

ACETYL–CoA FORMATION AND THE KREBS CYCLE

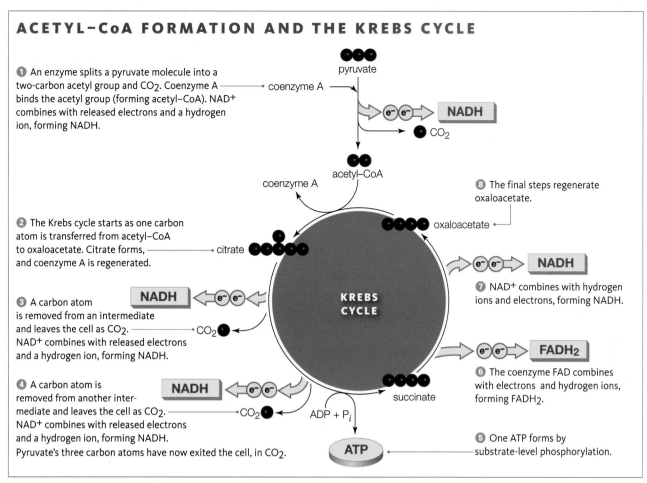

❶ An enzyme splits a pyruvate molecule into a two-carbon acetyl group and CO_2. Coenzyme A binds the acetyl group (forming acetyl–CoA). NAD^+ combines with released electrons and a hydrogen ion, forming NADH.

❷ The Krebs cycle starts as one carbon atom is transferred from acetyl–CoA to oxaloacetate. Citrate forms, and coenzyme A is regenerated.

❸ A carbon atom is removed from an intermediate and leaves the cell as CO_2. NAD^+ combines with released electrons and a hydrogen ion, forming NADH.

❹ A carbon atom is removed from another intermediate and leaves the cell as CO_2. NAD^+ combines with released electrons and a hydrogen ion, forming NADH. Pyruvate's three carbon atoms have now exited the cell, in CO_2.

❺ One ATP forms by substrate-level phosphorylation.

❻ The coenzyme FAD combines with electrons and hydrogen ions, forming $FADH_2$.

❼ NAD^+ combines with hydrogen ions and electrons, forming NADH.

❽ The final steps regenerate oxaloacetate.

pyruvate • coenzyme A • NADH • CO_2 • acetyl–CoA • coenzyme A • citrate • KREBS CYCLE • oxaloacetate • succinate • $ADP + P_i$ • ATP

FIGURE 7.4 {Animated} Acetyl–CoA formation and the Krebs cycle. It takes two cycles of Krebs reactions to break down two pyruvate molecules that formed during glycolysis of one glucose molecule. After two cycles, all six carbons that entered glycolysis in one glucose molecule have left the cell, in six CO_2. Electrons and hydrogen ions are released as each carbon is removed from the backbone of intermediate molecules; ten coenzymes will carry them to the third and final stage of aerobic respiration. Not all reactions are shown; see Appendix III for details.

After two cycles of Krebs reactions, the two carbon atoms carried by each acetyl–CoA end up in CO_2. Thus, the combined second-stage reactions of aerobic respiration break down two pyruvate to six CO_2:

pyruvate (2) → 2nd stage of aerobic respiration → carbon dioxide (6)

Remember, the two pyruvate were a product of glycolysis. So, at this point in aerobic respiration, the carbon backbone of one glucose molecule has been broken down completely, its six carbon atoms having exited the cell in CO_2.

Krebs cycle Cyclic pathway that, along with acetyl–CoA formation, breaks down pyruvate to carbon dioxide during aerobic respiration.

Two ATP that form during the second stage add to the small net yield of 2 ATP from glycolysis. However, ten coenzymes (eight NAD^+ and two FAD) are reduced during this stage. Add in the two NAD^+ that were reduced in glycolysis, and the full breakdown of each glucose molecule has a big potential payoff. Twelve reduced coenzymes will deliver electrons—and the energy they carry—to the third stage of aerobic respiration.

TAKE-HOME MESSAGE 7.4

The second stage of aerobic respiration, acetyl–CoA formation and the Krebs cycle, occurs in the inner compartment (matrix) of mitochondria.

The second-stage reactions convert the two pyruvate that formed in glycolysis to six CO_2. Two ATP form, and ten coenzymes (eight NAD^+ and two FAD) are reduced.

FIGURE 7.5 {Animated} The third and final stage of aerobic respiration, electron transfer phosphorylation.

1 NADH and FADH$_2$ deliver their cargo of electrons and hydrogen ions to electron transfer chains in the inner mitochondrial membrane.

2 Electron flow through the chains causes the hydrogen ions (H$^+$) to be pumped from the matrix to the intermembrane space. A hydrogen ion gradient forms across the inner mitochondrial membrane.

3 Hydrogen ion flow back to the matrix through ATP synthases drives the formation of ATP from ADP and phosphate (P$_i$).

4 Oxygen combines with electrons and hydrogen ions at the end of the electron transfer chains, so water forms.

The third stage of aerobic respiration occurs at the inner mitochondrial membrane (**FIGURE 7.5**). Electron transfer phosphorylation reactions begin with the coenzymes NADH and FADH$_2$, which became reduced during the first two stages of aerobic respiration. These coenzymes now deliver their cargo of electrons and hydrogen ions to electron transfer chains embedded in the inner mitochondrial membrane **1**.

As the electrons move through the chains, they give up energy little by little (Section 5.4). Some molecules of the transfer chains harness that energy to actively transport the hydrogen ions across the inner membrane, from the matrix to the intermembrane space **2**. The accumulating ions form a hydrogen ion gradient across the inner mitochondrial membrane. This gradient attracts the ions back toward the matrix. However, ions cannot diffuse through a lipid bilayer on their own (Section 5.7). Hydrogen ions cross the inner mitochondrial membrane only by flowing through ATP synthases embedded in the membrane. The flow of hydrogen ions through ATP synthases causes these proteins to attach phosphate groups to ADP, so ATP forms **3**.

Oxygen accepts electrons at the end of mitochondrial electron transfer chains **4**. When oxygen accepts electrons, it combines with hydrogen ions to form water, which is a product of the third-stage reactions.

CREDIT: (5) © Cengage Learning.

Stage 1

Glycolysis in cytoplasm splits a glucose molecule into 2 pyruvate; 2 NADH and 4 ATP also form. An investment of 2 ATP began the reactions, so the net yield is 2 ATP.

Stage 2

Acetyl–CoA formation and the Krebs cycle in the mitochondrial matrix break down the pyruvate to CO_2, which leaves the cell. Ten additional coenzymes are reduced. Two ATP form.

Stage 3

In electron transfer phosphorylation, the reduced coenzymes give up electrons and hydrogen ions to electron transfer chains in the inner mitochondrial membrane. Energy lost by the electrons as they move through the chains is used to move H^+ across the membrane. The resulting gradient causes H^+ to flow through ATP synthases, which drives ATP synthesis.

glucose

2 ATP → GLYCOLYSIS → 4 ATP (2 net)

2 NADH   2 pyruvate

2 NADH

2 NADH ← 2 CO_2

2 acetyl–CoA

4 CO_2

KREBS CYCLE

6 NADH ← 2 ATP
2 $FADH_2$

ATP ATP ATP ATP

ELECTRON TRANSFER PHOSPHORYLATION → 32

oxygen H_2O

FIGURE 7.6 Summary of the three stages of aerobic respiration in a mitochondrion.

For each glucose molecule that enters aerobic respiration, four ATP form in the first- and second-stage reactions. The twelve coenzymes reduced in these two stages deliver enough electrons to fuel synthesis of about thirty-two additional ATP during the third stage. Thus, the breakdown of one glucose molecule yields about thirty-six ATP (**FIGURE 7.6**). The ATP yield varies depending on cell type. For example, the typical yield of aerobic respiration in brain and skeletal muscle cells is thirty-eight ATP, not thirty-six.

Remember that some energy dissipates with every transfer (Section 5.2). Even though aerobic respiration is a very efficient way of retrieving energy from sugars, about 60 percent of the energy harvested in this pathway disperses as metabolic heat.

TAKE-HOME MESSAGE 7.5

In aerobic respiration's third stage, electron transfer phosphorylation, energy released by electrons moving through electron transfer chains is ultimately captured in the attachment of phosphate to ADP.

The third-stage reactions begin when coenzymes that were reduced in the first and second stages deliver electrons and hydrogen ions to electron transfer chains in the inner mitochondrial membrane.

Energy released by electrons as they pass through electron transfer chains is used to pump H^+ from the mitochondrial matrix to the intermembrane space. The H^+ gradient that forms across the inner mitochondrial membrane drives the flow of hydrogen ions through ATP synthases, which results in ATP formation.

About thirty-two ATP form during the third-stage reactions, so a typical net yield of all three stages of aerobic respiration is thirty-six ATP per glucose.

CREDIT: (6) © Cengage Learning.

GLYCOLYSIS

A Alcoholic fermentation begins with glycolysis, and the final steps regenerate NAD⁺. The net yield of these reactions is two ATP per molecule of glucose (from glycolysis).

B *Saccharomyces* cells (*top*). One product of alcoholic fermentation in these cells (ethanol) makes beer alcoholic; another (CO_2) makes it bubbly. Holes in bread are pockets where CO_2 released by fermenting *Saccharomyces* cells accumulated in the dough.

FIGURE 7.7 {Animated} Alcoholic fermentation.

TWO FERMENTATION PATHWAYS

Aerobic respiration and fermentation begin with the same set of glycolysis reactions in cytoplasm. After glycolysis, the two pathways differ. The final steps of fermentation occur in the cytoplasm and do not require oxygen. In these reactions, pyruvate is converted to other molecules, but it is not fully broken down to CO_2 (as occurs in aerobic respiration). Electrons do not move through electron transfer chains, so no additional ATP forms. However, electrons are removed from NADH, so NAD⁺ is regenerated. Regenerating this coenzyme allows glycolysis—and the small ATP yield it offers—to continue. Thus, the net ATP yield of fermentation consists of the two ATP that form in glycolysis.

Alcoholic Fermentation In **alcoholic fermentation**, the pyruvate from glycolysis is converted to ethanol (**FIGURE 7.7A**). First, 3-carbon pyruvate is split into carbon dioxide and 2-carbon acetaldehyde. Then, electrons and hydrogen are transferred from NADH to the acetaldehyde, forming NAD⁺ and ethanol:

pyruvate   carbon dioxide   acetaldehyde   ethanol

Alcoholic fermentation in a fungus, *Saccharomyces cerevisiae*, sustains these yeast cells as they grow and reproduce. It also helps us produce beer, wine, and bread (**FIGURE 7.7B**). Beer brewers typically use germinated, roasted, and crushed barley as a sugar source for *Saccharomyces* fermentation. Ethanol produced by the fermenting yeast cells makes the beer alcoholic, and CO_2 makes it bubbly. Flowers of the hop plant add flavor and help preserve the finished product. Winemakers start with crushed grapes for *Saccharomyces* fermentation. The yeast cells convert sugars in the grape juice to ethanol.

Bakers take advantage of alcoholic fermentation by *Saccharomyces* cells to make bread from flour, which contains starches and a protein called gluten. When flour is kneaded with water, the gluten forms polymers in long, interconnected strands that make the resulting dough stretchy and resilient. Yeast cells in the dough produce CO_2 as they ferment the starches. The gas accumulates in bubbles that are trapped by the mesh of gluten strands. As the bubbles expand, they cause the dough to rise. Ethanol produced by the fermentation reactions evaporates during baking.

Lactate Fermentation In **lactate fermentation**, the electrons and hydrogen ions carried by NADH are transferred directly to pyruvate (**FIGURE 7.8A**). This

CREDITS: (7A, in text) © Cengage Learning; (7B top) © Visuals Unlimited/Masterfile; (7B bottom left) © Elena Boshkovska/Shutterstock; (7B bottom right) © optimarc/Shutterstock.

reaction converts pyruvate to 3-carbon lactate (the ionized form of lactic acid), and also converts NADH to NAD^+:

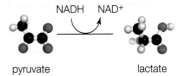

pyruvate   lactate

Some lactate fermenters spoil food, but we use others to preserve it. For instance, *Lactobacillus* bacteria break down lactose in milk by fermentation. We use this bacteria to produce dairy products such as buttermilk, cheese, and yogurt, and also to pickle vegetables and other foods.

Cells in animal skeletal muscles are fused as long fibers that carry out aerobic respiration, lactate fermentation, or both. Red fibers have many mitochondria and produce ATP mainly by aerobic respiration. These fibers sustain prolonged activity such as marathon runs. They are red because they have an abundance of myoglobin, a protein that stores oxygen for aerobic respiration (**FIGURE 7.8B**). White muscle fibers contain few mitochondria and no myoglobin, so they do not carry out a lot of aerobic respiration. Instead, they make most of their ATP by lactate fermentation. This pathway makes ATP quickly but not for long, so it is useful for quick, strenuous activities such as weight lifting or sprinting (**FIGURE 7.8C**). The low ATP yield does not support prolonged activity.

Most human muscles are a mixture of white and red fibers, but the proportions vary among muscles and among individuals. Great sprinters tend to have more white fibers. Great marathon runners tend to have more red fibers. Chickens cannot fly very far because their flight muscles consist mostly of white fibers (thus, the "white" breast meat). A chicken most often walks or runs. Its leg muscles consist mostly of red muscle fibers, the "dark meat." Section 32.5 returns to skeletal muscle fibers and how they work.

alcoholic fermentation Anaerobic sugar breakdown pathway that produces ATP, CO_2, and ethanol.
lactate fermentation Anaerobic sugar breakdown pathway that produces ATP and lactate.

TAKE-HOME MESSAGE 7.6

ATP can form by sugar breakdown in fermentation pathways, which are anaerobic.

The end product of lactate fermentation is lactate. The end product of alcoholic fermentation is ethanol.

Both pathways have a net yield of two ATP per glucose molecule. The ATP forms during glycolysis.

Fermentation reactions regenerate the coenzyme NAD^+, without which glycolysis (and ATP production) would stop.

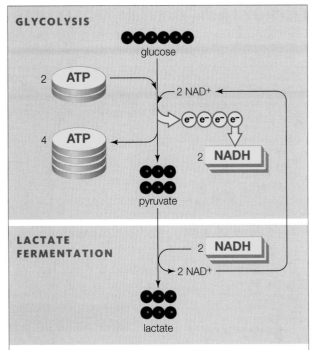

A Lactate fermentation begins with glycolysis, and the final steps regenerate NAD^+. The net yield of these reactions is two ATP per molecule of glucose (from glycolysis).

B Lactate fermentation occurs in white muscle fibers, visible in this cross-section of human thigh muscle. The red fibers, which make ATP by aerobic respiration, sustain endurance activities.

C Intense activity such as sprinting quickly depletes oxygen in muscles. Under anaerobic conditions, ATP is produced mainly by lactate fermentation in white muscle fibers. Fermentation does not make enough ATP to sustain this type of activity for long.

FIGURE 7.8 Lactate fermentation.

7.7 CAN THE BODY USE ANY ORGANIC MOLECULE FOR ENERGY?

ENERGY FROM DIETARY MOLECULES

Glycolysis converts glucose to pyruvate, and electrons are transferred from pyruvate to coenzymes during aerobic respiration's second stage. In other words, glucose becomes oxidized (it gives up electrons) and coenzymes become reduced (they accept electrons). Oxidizing an organic molecule can break the covalent bonds of its carbon backbone. Aerobic respiration generates a lot of ATP by fully oxidizing glucose, completely dismantling it carbon by carbon.

Cells also dismantle other organic molecules by oxidizing them. Complex carbohydrates, fats, and proteins in food can be converted to molecules that enter glycolysis or the Krebs cycle (FIGURE 7.9). As in glucose metabolism, many coenzymes are reduced, and the energy of the electrons they carry ultimately drives the synthesis of ATP in electron transfer phosphorylation.

A Complex carbohydrates are broken down to their monosaccharide subunits, which can enter glycolysis ❶.

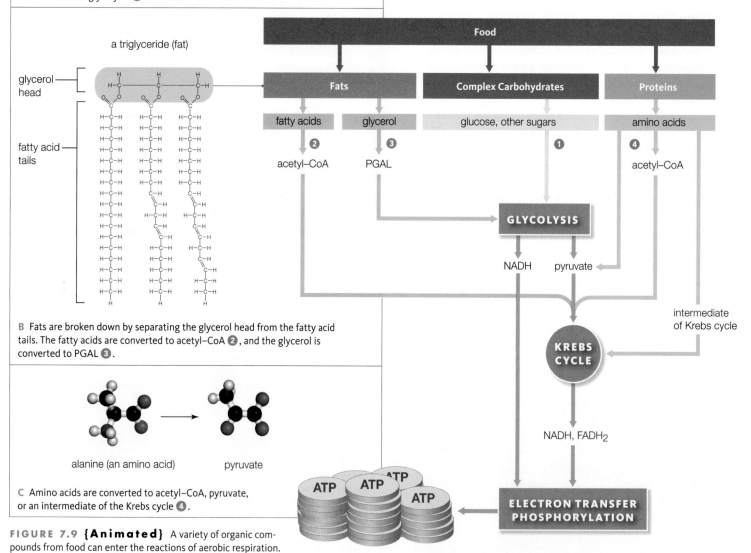

starch (a complex carbohydrate) → glucose

a triglyceride (fat)

glycerol head

fatty acid tails

B Fats are broken down by separating the glycerol head from the fatty acid tails. The fatty acids are converted to acetyl–CoA ❷, and the glycerol is converted to PGAL ❸.

alanine (an amino acid) → pyruvate

C Amino acids are converted to acetyl–CoA, pyruvate, or an intermediate of the Krebs cycle ❹.

Food

| Fats | Complex Carbohydrates | Proteins |

fatty acids | glycerol | glucose, other sugars | amino acids

❷ acetyl–CoA | ❸ PGAL | ❶ | ❹ acetyl–CoA

GLYCOLYSIS

NADH   pyruvate

intermediate of Krebs cycle

KREBS CYCLE

NADH, FADH₂

ATP ATP ATP ATP

ELECTRON TRANSFER PHOSPHORYLATION

FIGURE 7.9 {Animated} A variety of organic compounds from food can enter the reactions of aerobic respiration.

CREDITS: (9) From Starr/Taggart/Evers/Starr, Biology, 13E. © 2013 Cengage Learning; (top inset) ©shabaneiro/Shutterstock.

Complex Carbohydrates In humans and other mammals, the digestive system breaks down starch and other complex carbohydrates to monosaccharides (**FIGURE 7.9A**). These sugars are quickly taken up by cells and converted to glucose-6-phosphate for glycolysis ❶. When a cell produces more ATP than it uses, the concentration of ATP rises in the cytoplasm. A high concentration of ATP causes glucose-6-phosphate to be diverted away from glycolysis and into a pathway that forms glycogen. Liver and muscle cells especially favor the conversion of glucose to glycogen, and these cells contain the body's largest stores of it. Between meals, the liver maintains the glucose level in blood by converting the stored glycogen to glucose.

Fats A fat molecule has a glycerol head and one, two, or three fatty acid tails (Section 3.3). Cells dismantle these molecules by first breaking the bonds that connect the fatty acid tails to the glycerol head (**FIGURE 7.9B**). Nearly all cells in the body can oxidize free fatty acids by splitting their long backbones into two-carbon fragments. These fragments are converted to acetyl–CoA, which can enter the Krebs cycle ❷. Enzymes in liver cells convert the glycerol to PGAL, an intermediate of glycolysis ❸.

On a per carbon basis, fats are a richer source of energy than carbohydrates. Carbohydrate backbones have many oxygen atoms, so they are partially oxidized. A fat's long fatty acid tails are hydrocarbon chains that typically have no oxygen atoms bonded to them, so they have a longer way to go to become oxidized—more reactions are required to fully break them down. Coenzymes accept electrons in these oxidation reactions. The more reduced coenzymes that form, the more electrons can be delivered to the ATP-forming machinery of electron transfer phosphorylation.

What happens if you eat too many carbohydrates? When the blood level of glucose gets too high, acetyl–CoA is diverted away from the Krebs cycle and into a pathway that makes fatty acids. That is why excess dietary carbohydrate ends up as fat.

Proteins Enzymes in the digestive system split dietary proteins into their amino acid subunits, which are absorbed into the bloodstream. Cells use the amino acids to build proteins or other molecules. When you eat more protein than your body needs for this purpose, the amino acids are broken down. The amino (NH_3^+) group is removed, and it becomes ammonia (NH_3), a waste product that is eliminated in urine. The carbon backbone is split, and acetyl–CoA, pyruvate, or an intermediate of the Krebs cycle forms, depending on the amino acid (**FIGURE 7.9C**). These molecules enter aerobic respiration's second stage ❹.

PEOPLE MATTER

DR. BENJAMIN RAPOPORT

MIT engineers Benjamin Rapoport, Jakub Kedzierski, and Rahul Sarpeshkar have developed a tiny fuel cell that runs on the same sugar that powers human cells: glucose.

The fuel cell strips electrons from glucose molecules to create a small electric current. In this way, it mimics the activity of cellular enzymes that break down glucose to generate ATP.

The researchers fabricated the fuel cell on a silicon chip, so it can be integrated with other implantable circuits that could, for example, be implanted in the spinal cord to help paralyzed patients move their arms and legs again. Current devices can do this too, but they require an external power source. The new fuel cell can use glucose in the fluid that bathes the brain. Glucose is normally the brain's only fuel, and this fluid contains a lot of it. The fuel cell uses only a tiny amount of glucose, so it would have a minimal impact on brain function.

"It will be a few more years into the future before you see people with spinal-cord injuries receive such implantable systems in the context of standard medical care, but those are the sorts of devices you could envision powering from a glucose-based fuel cell," says Rapoport.

TAKE-HOME MESSAGE 7.7

Oxidizing organic molecules can break their carbon backbones, releasing electrons whose energy can be harnessed to drive ATP formation in aerobic respiration.

Fats, complex carbohydrates, and proteins can be oxidized in aerobic respiration to yield ATP. First the digestive system and then individual cells convert molecules in food into substrates of glycolysis or aerobic respiration's second-stage reactions.

Education

FIGURE 7.10 This cross-section of a nerve shows how these cells are packed with mitochondria. Mitochondria are powerhouses of all eukaryotic cells. When they malfunction, the lights go off in cellular businesses.

AEROBIC RESPIRATION IS A DANGEROUS OCCUPATION. When an oxygen molecule accepts electrons from an electron transfer chain in a mitochondrion, it dissociates into oxygen atoms. These atoms immediately combine with hydrogen ions and end up in water molecules. Occasionally, however, an oxygen atom escapes this final reaction. The atom has an unpaired electron, so it is a free radical. Free radicals can easily strip electrons from (oxidize) biological molecules and break their carbon backbones.

Mitochondria cannot detoxify free radicals, so they rely on antioxidant enzymes and vitamins in the cell's cytoplasm to do it for them. The system works well, at least most of the time. However, a genetic disorder or an unfortunate encounter with a toxin or pathogen can result in a missing antioxidant, or a defective component of the mitochondrial electron transfer chain. In either case, the normal cellular balance of aerobic respiration and free radical formation is tipped. Free radicals accumulate and destroy first the function of mitochondria, then the cell. The resulting tissue damage is called oxidative stress.

At least 83 proteins are directly involved in mitochondrial electron transfer chains. A defect in any one of them—or in any of the thousands of other

"Tom does not look sick, but inside his organs are all getting badly damaged," said Martine Martin, pictured here with her eight-year-old son. Tom was born with a mitochondrial disease. He eats with the help of a machine, suffers intense pain, and will soon be blind. Despite intensive medical intervention, he is not expected to reach his teens.

proteins used by mitochondria—can wreak havoc in the body. Hundreds of incurable disorders are associated with such defects (FIGURE 7.10), and more are being discovered all the time. Nerve and brain cells, which require a lot of ATP, are particularly affected. Symptoms range from mild to major progressive neurological deficits, blindness, deafness, diabetes, strokes, seizures, gastrointestinal malfunction, and disabling muscle weakness. New research is showing that mitochondrial malfunction is also involved in many other illnesses, including cancer, hypertension, and Alzheimer's and Parkinson's diseases.

Summary

SECTIONS 7.1, 7.2   Most organisms can make ATP by breaking down sugars in fermentation or aerobic respiration. Both pathways begin in cytoplasm. **Aerobic respiration** requires oxygen and, in eukaryotes, ends in mitochondria. It includes electron transfer chains, and ATP forms by electron transfer phosphorylation. **Fermentation** pathways end in cytoplasm and do not require oxygen. Aerobic respiration yields much more ATP per glucose molecule than fermentation.

Photosynthesis by early prokaryotes changed the composition of Earth's atmosphere, with profound effects on life's evolution. Organisms that could not tolerate the increased atmospheric oxygen persisted only in **anaerobic** habitats. The evolution of antioxidants allowed organisms to tolerate the increase in the atmospheric content of oxygen, and to thrive under **aerobic** conditions. Over time, the antioxidants became incorporated into aerobic respiration and other pathways that harnessed the reactive properties of oxygen.

SECTION 7.3   **Glycolysis**, the first stage of aerobic respiration and fermentation, occurs in cytoplasm. In the reactions, enzymes use two ATP to convert one molecule of glucose or another six-carbon sugar to two molecules of 3-carbon **pyruvate**. Electrons and hydrogen ions are transferred to two NAD^+, which are thereby reduced to NADH. Four ATP also form by **substrate-level phosphorylation**.

SECTION 7.4   In eukaryotes, aerobic respiration continues in mitochondria. The second stage of aerobic respiration, acetyl–CoA formation and the **Krebs cycle**, takes place in the inner compartment (matrix) of the mitochondrion. The first steps convert the two pyruvate from glycolysis to two acetyl–CoA and two CO_2. The acetyl–CoA delivers carbon atoms to the Krebs cycle. Electrons and hydrogen ions are transferred to NAD^+ and FAD, which are thereby reduced to NADH and $FADH_2$. ATP forms by substrate-level phosphorylation. Two cycles of Krebs reactions break down the two pyruvate from glycolysis. At this stage of aerobic respiration, the glucose molecule that entered glycolysis has been dismantled completely: All of its carbon atoms have exited the cell in CO_2.

SECTION 7.5   In the third and final stage of aerobic respiration, electron transfer phosphorylation, the many coenzymes that were reduced in the first two stages now deliver their cargo of electrons and hydrogen ions to electron transfer chains in the inner mitochondrial membrane. The electrons move through the chains, releasing energy bit by bit; molecules of the chain use that energy to move H^+ from the matrix to the intermembrane space. Hydrogen ions accumulate in the intermembrane space, forming a gradient across the inner

Summary continued

membrane. The ions follow the gradient back to the matrix through ATP synthases. H^+ flow through these transport proteins drives ATP synthesis.

Oxygen accepts electrons at the end of the chains and combines with hydrogen ions, so water forms.

The ATP yield of aerobic respiration varies, but typically it is about thirty-six ATP for each glucose molecule that enters glycolysis.

SECTION 7.6 Anaerobic fermentation pathways begin with glycolysis, and they run entirely in the cytoplasm. An organic molecule, rather than oxygen, accepts electrons at the end of these reactions. The end product of **alcoholic fermentation** is ethyl alcohol, or ethanol. The end product of **lactate fermentation** is lactate.

The final steps of fermentation regenerate NAD^+, which is required for glycolysis to continue, but they produce no ATP. Thus, the breakdown of one glucose molecule in either alcoholic or lactate fermentation yields only the two ATP from glycolysis.

Skeletal muscle consists of two types of fiber. ATP produced primarily by aerobic respiration in red fibers sustains activities that require endurance. Lactate fermentation in white fibers supports activities that occur in short, intense bursts.

SECTION 7.7 Oxidizing an organic molecule can break its carbon backbone. Aerobic respiration fully oxidizes glucose, dismantling its backbone carbon by carbon. Each carbon removed releases electrons that drive ATP formation in electron transfer phosphorylation. Organic molecules other than sugars are also broken down (oxidized) for energy. In humans and other mammals, first the digestive system and then individual cells convert fats, proteins, and complex carbohydrates in food to molecules that are substrates of glycolysis or the second-stage reactions of aerobic respiration.

SECTION 7.8 Free radicals that form during aerobic respiration are detoxified by antioxidant molecules in the cell's cytoplasm. Missing antioxidant molecules or heritable defects in mitochondrial electron transfer chain components can cause a buildup of free radicals that damage the cell—and ultimately, the individual. Symptoms can be lethal. Oxidative stress due to mitochondrial malfunction plays a role in many illnesses such as cancer, and Alzheimer's and Parkinson's diseases.

Self-Quiz Answers in Appendix VII

1. Is the following statement true or false? Unlike animals, which make many ATP by aerobic respiration, plants make all of their ATP by photosynthesis.

2. Glycolysis starts and ends in the _____ .
   a. nucleus   c. plasma membrane
   b. mitochondrion   d. cytoplasm

3. Which of the following metabolic pathways require(s) molecular oxygen (O_2)?
   a. aerobic respiration
   b. lactate fermentation
   c. alcoholic fermentation
   d. all of the above

4. Which molecule does not form during glycolysis?
   a. NADH   c. oxygen (O_2)
   b. pyruvate   d. ATP

5. In eukaryotes, aerobic respiration is completed in the _____ .
   a. nucleus   c. plasma membrane
   b. mitochondrion   d. cytoplasm

6. In eukaryotes, fermentation is completed in the _____ .
   a. nucleus   c. plasma membrane
   b. mitochondrion   d. cytoplasm

7. Which of the following reaction pathways is not part of the second stage of aerobic respiration?
   a. electron transfer   c. Krebs cycle
      phosphorylation   d. glycolysis
   b. acetyl–CoA formation   e. a and d

8. After the Krebs reactions run through _____ cycle(s), one glucose molecule has been completely broken down to CO_2.
   a. one   b. two   c. three   d. six

9. In the third stage of aerobic respiration, _____ is the final acceptor of electrons.
   a. water   c. oxygen (O_2)
   b. hydrogen   d. NADH

10. Most of the energy that is released by the full breakdown of glucose to CO_2 and water ends up in _____ .
    a. NADH   c. heat
    b. ATP   d. electrons

11. _____ accepts electrons in alcoholic fermentation.
    a. Oxygen   c. Acetaldehyde
    b. Pyruvate   d. Ethanol

12. Your body cells can break down _____ as a source of energy to fuel ATP production.
    a. fatty acids   c. amino acids
    b. glycerol   d. all of the above

13. Which of the following is *not* produced by an animal muscle cell operating under anaerobic conditions?

a. heat
c. ATP
e. pyruvate
b. lactate
d. NAD$^+$
f. all are produced

14. Hydrogen ion flow drives ATP synthesis during _____ .

a. glycolysis
b. the Krebs cycle
c. aerobic respiration
d. fermentation
e. a and c

15. Match the term with the best description.

___ mitochondrial matrix   a. needed for glycolysis
___ pyruvate   b. inner space
___ NAD$^+$ c. makes many ATP
___ mitochondrion   d. product of glycolysis
___ NADH   e. reduced coenzyme
___ anaerobic   f. no oxygen required

Critical Thinking

1. The higher the altitude, the lower the oxygen level in air. Climbers of very tall mountains risk altitude sickness, which is characterized by shortness of breath, weakness, dizziness, and confusion.

The early symptoms of cyanide poisoning are the same as those for altitude sickness. Cyanide binds tightly to cytochrome *c* oxidase, the protein that reduces oxygen molecules in the final step of mitochondrial electron transfer chains. Cytochrome *c* oxidase with bound cyanide can no longer transfer electrons. Explain why cyanide poisoning starts with the same symptoms as altitude sickness.

2. As you learned, membranes impermeable to hydrogen ions are required for electron transfer phosphorylation. Membranes in mitochondria serve this purpose in eukaryotes. Bacteria do not have this organelle, but they do make ATP by electron transfer phosphorylation. How do you think they do it, given that they have no mitochondria?

3. The bar-tailed godwit is a type of shorebird that makes an annual migration from Alaska to New Zealand and back. The birds make each 11,500-kilometer (7,145-mile) trip by flying over the Pacific Ocean in about nine days, depending on weather, wind speed, and direction of travel. One bird was observed to make the entire journey uninterrupted, a feat that is comparable to a human running a nonstop seven-day marathon at 70 kilometers per hour (43.5 miles per hour). Would you expect the flight (breast) muscles of bar-tailed godwits to be light or dark colored? Explain your answer.

Data Analysis Activities

Mitochondrial Abnormalities in Tetralogy of Fallot

Tetralogy of Fallot (TF) is a genetic disorder characterized by four major malformations of the heart. The circulation of blood is abnormal, so TF patients have too little oxygen in their blood. Inadequate oxygen levels result in damaged mitochondrial membranes, which in turn cause cells to self-destruct.

In 2004, Sarah Kuruvilla and her colleagues looked at abnormalities in the mitochondria of heart muscle in TF patients. Some of their results are shown in **FIGURE 7.11**.

1. Which abnormality was most strongly associated with tetralogy of Fallot?

2. Can you make any correlations between blood oxygen content and mitochondrial abnormalities in these TF patients?

FIGURE 7.11 Mitochondrial changes in tetralogy of Fallot (TF).

A Normal heart muscle. Many mitochondria between the fibers provide muscle cells with ATP for contraction.

B Heart muscle from a person with TF has swollen, broken mitochondria.

Patient (age)	SPO$_2$ (%)	Mitochondrial Abnormalities in TF			
		Number	Shape	Size	Broken
1 (5)	55	+	+	−	−
2 (3)	69	+	+	−	−
3 (22)	72	+	+	−	−
4 (2)	74	+	+	−	−
5 (3)	76	+	+	−	+
6 (2.5)	78	+	+	−	+
7 (1)	79	+	+	−	−
8 (12)	80	+	−	+	−
9 (4)	80	+	+	−	−
10 (8)	83	+	−	+	−
11 (20)	85	+	+	−	−
12 (2.5)	89	+	−	+	−

C Types of mitochondrial abnormalities in TF patients. SPO$_2$ is oxygen saturation of the blood. A normal value of SPO$_2$ is 96%. Abnormalities are marked +.

Information encoded in DNA is the basis of visible traits that define species and distinguish individuals. Identical twins are identical because they inherited copies of the same DNA.

8

DNA STRUCTURE AND FUNCTION

Links to Earlier Concepts

Radioisotope tracers (Section 2.1) were used in research that led to the discovery that DNA (3.6), not protein (3.4, 3.5), is the hereditary material (1.2) of all organisms. This chapter revisits free radicals (2.2), the cell nucleus (4.5), and metabolism (5.3–5.5).

KEY CONCEPTS

DISCOVERY OF DNA'S FUNCTION
The work of many scientists over nearly a century led to the discovery that DNA, not protein, stores hereditary information in all living things.

STRUCTURE OF DNA MOLECULES
A DNA molecule consists of two long chains of nucleotides coiled into a double helix. The order of the four types of nucleotides in a chain differs among individuals and species.

CHROMOSOMES
The DNA of eukaryotes is divided among a characteristic number of chromosomes. A living cell's chromosomes contain all of the information necessary to build a new individual.

DNA REPLICATION
Before a cell divides, it copies its DNA so both descendant cell's will inherit a full complement of chromosomes. Replication of each DNA molecule produces two duplicates.

MUTATIONS
DNA damage by environmental agents can cause replication errors. Newly forming DNA is monitored for errors, most of which are corrected. Uncorrected errors become mutations.

8.1 HOW WAS DNA'S FUNCTION DISCOVERED?

FIGURE 8.1 DNA extracted from human cells.

A Griffith's first experiment showed that R cells were harmless. When injected into mice, the bacteria multiplied, but the mice remained healthy.

B The second experiment showed that an injection of S cells caused mice to develop fatal pneumonia. Their blood contained live S cells.

C For a third experiment, Griffith killed S cells with heat before injecting them into mice. The mice remained healthy, indicating that the heat-killed S cells were harmless.

D In his fourth experiment, Griffith injected a mixture of heat-killed S cells and live R cells. To his surprise, the mice became fatally ill, and their blood contained live S cells.

FIGURE 8.2 {Animated} Fred Griffith's experiments with two strains (R and S) of *Streptococcus pneumoniae* bacteria.

The substance we now call DNA (**FIGURE 8.1**) was first described in 1869 by Johannes Miescher, a chemist who extracted it from cell nuclei. Miescher determined that DNA is not a protein, and that it is rich in nitrogen and phosphorus, but he never learned its function. That would take many more years and experiments by many scientists.

Sixty years after Miescher's work, Frederick Griffith unexpectedly uncovered a clue about DNA's function. Griffith was studying pneumonia-causing bacteria in the hope of creating a vaccine. He isolated two strains (types) of the bacteria, one harmless (R), the other lethal (S). Griffith used R and S cells in a series of experiments testing their ability to cause pneumonia in mice (**FIGURE 8.2**). He discovered that heat destroyed the ability of lethal S bacteria to cause pneumonia, but it did not destroy their hereditary material, including whatever specified "kill mice." That material could be transferred from the dead S cells to the live R cells, which put it to use. The transformation was permanent and heritable: Even after hundreds of generations, descendants of transformed R cells retained the ability to kill mice.

What substance had caused the transformation? In 1940, Oswald Avery and Maclyn McCarty set out to identify that substance, which they termed the "transforming principle," by a process of elimination. The researchers made an extract of S cells that contained only lipid, protein, and nucleic acids. The S cell extract could still transform R cells after it had been treated with lipid- and protein-destroying enzymes. Thus, the transforming principle could not be lipid or protein, and Avery and McCarty realized that the substance they were seeking must be nucleic acid—DNA or RNA. DNA-degrading enzymes destroyed the extract's ability to transform cells, but RNA-degrading enzymes did not. Thus, DNA had to be the transforming principle.

The result surprised Avery and McCarty, who, along with most other scientists, had assumed that proteins were the material of heredity. After all, traits are diverse, and proteins are the most diverse of all biological molecules. The two scientists were so skeptical that they published their results only after they had convinced themselves, by years of painstaking experimentation, that DNA was indeed hereditary material. They were also careful to point out that they had not proven DNA was the *only* hereditary material.

Avery and McCarty's tantalizing results prompted a stampede of other scientists into the field of DNA research. The resulting explosion of discovery confirmed the molecule's role as carrier of hereditary information. Key in this advance was the realization that any molecule—DNA or otherwise—had to have certain properties in order to function as the sole repository of hereditary material.

CREDITS: (1) Patrick Landmann/Science Source; (2) © Cengage Learning.

B In one experiment, bacteria were infected with virus particles that had been labeled with a radioisotope of sulfur (^{35}S). The sulfur had labeled mainly viral proteins. The viruses were dislodged from the bacteria by whirling the mixture in a kitchen blender. Most of the radioactive sulfur was detected in the viruses, not in the bacterial cells. The viruses had not injected protein into the bacteria.

A Top, a model of a bacterio-phage. Bottom, micrograph of three viruses injecting DNA into an *E. coli* cell.

C In another experiment, bacteria were infected with virus particles that had been labeled with a radioisotope of phosphorus (^{32}P). The phosphorus had labeled mainly viral DNA. When the viruses were dislodged from the bacteria, the radioactive phosphorus was detected mainly inside the bacterial cells. The viruses had injected DNA into the cells—evidence that DNA is the genetic material of this virus.

FIGURE 8.3 {Animated} The Hershey–Chase experiments. Alfred Hershey and Martha Chase carried out experiments to determine the composition of the hereditary material that bacteriophage inject into bacteria. The experiments were based on the knowledge that proteins contain more sulfur (S) than phosphorus (P), and DNA contains more phosphorus than sulfur.

First, a full complement of hereditary information must be transmitted along with the molecule; second, each cell of a given species should contain the same amount of it; third, because the molecule functions as a genetic bridge between generations, it has to be exempt from change; and fourth, it must be capable of encoding the almost unimaginably huge amount of information required to build a new individual.

In the late 1940s, Alfred Hershey and Martha Chase proved that DNA, and not protein, satisfies the first property of a hereditary molecule: It transmits a full complement of hereditary information. Hershey and Chase specialized in working with **bacteriophage**, a type of virus that infects bacteria (**FIGURE 8.3**). Like all viruses, these infectious particles carry information about how to make new viruses in their hereditary material. After one injects a cell with this material, the cell starts making new virus particles. Hershey and Chase carried out an elegant series of experiments proving that the material bacteriophage injects into bacteria is DNA, not protein (**FIGURE 8.3B,C**).

bacteriophage Virus that infects bacteria.

The second property expected of a hereditary molecule was pinned on DNA by André Boivin and Roger Vendrely, who meticulously measured the amount of DNA in cell nuclei from a number of species. In 1948, they proved that body cells of any individual of a species contain precisely the same amount of DNA. Daniel Mazia's laboratory discovered that the protein and RNA content of cells varies over time, but not the DNA content, demonstrating that DNA is not involved in metabolism (and proving DNA has the third property expected of a hereditary molecule). The fourth property—that a hereditary molecule must somehow encode a huge amount of information—would be proven along with the elucidation of DNA's structure, a topic we continue in the next section.

TAKE-HOME MESSAGE 8.1

DNA, the molecule of inheritance, was first discovered in the late 1800s. Its role as the carrier of hereditary information was uncovered over many years, as scientists built upon one another's discoveries.

ADENINE (A)
deoxyadenosine triphosphate

BASE
SUGAR

GUANINE (G)
deoxyguanosine triphosphate

THYMINE (T)
deoxythymidine triphosphate

CYTOSINE (C)
deoxycytidine triphosphate

FIGURE 8.4 {Animated} The four nucleotides in DNA. All four have three phosphate groups, a deoxyribose sugar (orange), and a nitrogen-containing base (blue) after which it is named. Biochemist Phoebus Levene identified the structure of these bases and how they are connected in nucleotides in the early 1900s. Levene worked with DNA for almost 40 years.

Adenine and guanine bases are purines; thymine and cytosine, pyrimidines. Numbering the carbons in the sugars allows us to keep track of the orientation of nucleotide chains (compare **FIGURE 8.6**).

BUILDING BLOCKS OF DNA

DNA is a polymer of nucleotides, each with a five-carbon sugar, three phosphate groups, and one of four nitrogen-containing bases (**FIGURE 8.4**). Just how those four nucleotides—adenine (A), guanine (G), thymine (T), and cytosine (C)—are arranged in a DNA molecule was a puzzle that took over 50 years to solve.

Clues about DNA's structure started coming together around 1950, when Erwin Chargaff, one of many researchers investigating DNA's function, made two important discoveries about the molecule. First, the amounts of thymine and adenine are identical, as are the amounts of cytosine and guanine (A = T and G = C). We call this discovery Chargaff's first rule. Chargaff's second discovery, or rule, is that the DNA of different species differs in its proportions of adenine and guanine.

Meanwhile, American biologist James Watson and British biophysicist Francis Crick had been sharing ideas about the structure of DNA. The helical (coiled) pattern of secondary structure that occurs in many proteins (Section 3.4) had just been discovered, and Watson and Crick suspected that the DNA molecule was also a helix. The two spent many hours arguing about the size, shape, and bonding requirements of the four kinds of nucleotides that make up DNA. They pestered chemists to help them identify bonds they might have overlooked, fiddled with cardboard cutouts, and made models from scraps of metal connected by suitably angled "bonds" of wire.

Biochemist Rosalind Franklin had also been working on the structure of DNA. Like Crick, Franklin specialized in x-ray crystallography, a technique in which x-rays are directed through a purified and crystallized substance. Atoms in the substance's molecules scatter the x-rays in a pattern that can be captured as an image. Researchers can use the pattern to calculate the size, shape, and spacing between any repeating elements of the molecules—all of which are details of molecular structure.

As molecules go, DNA is gigantic, and it was difficult to crystallize given the techniques of the time. Franklin made the first clear x-ray diffraction image (*left*) of DNA as it occurs in cells. From the information in this image, she calculated that DNA is very long compared to its 2-nanometer diameter. She also identified a repeating pattern every 0.34 nanometer along its length, and another every 3.4 nanometers.

Franklin's image and data came to the attention of Watson and Crick, who now had all the information they needed to build a model of the DNA helix (**FIGURE 8.5**), one with two sugar–phosphate chains running in opposite directions, and paired bases inside (**FIGURE 8.6**). Bonds between the sugar of one nucleotide and the phosphate of the next form the backbone of each chain (or strand). Hydrogen bonds between the internally positioned bases hold the two strands together. Only two kinds of base pairings form: A to T, and G to C, which explains the first of Chargaff's rules. Most scientists had assumed (incorrectly) that the bases had to be on the outside of the helix, because they would be more accessible to DNA-copying enzymes that way. You will see in Section 8.4 how DNA replication enzymes access the bases on the inside of the double helix.

DNA'S BASE SEQUENCE

A small piece of DNA from a tulip, a human, or any other organism might be:

T	G	A	G	G	A	C	T	C	C	T	C
A	C	T	C	C	T	G	A	G	G	A	G

one base pair

Notice how the two strands of DNA match. They are complementary—the base of each nucleotide on one strand pairs with a suitable partner base on the other. This base-pairing pattern (A to T, G to C) is the same in all molecules of DNA. How can just two kinds of base pairings give rise to the incredible diversity of traits we see among living things? Even though DNA is composed of only four nucleotides, the *order* in which one nucleotide follows the next along a strand—the **DNA sequence**—varies tremendously among species (which explains Chargaff's second rule). DNA molecules can be hundreds of millions of nucleotides long, so their sequence can encode a massive amount of information (we return to the nature of that information in the next chapter). DNA sequence variation is the basis of traits that define species and distinguish individuals. Thus DNA, the molecule of inheritance in every cell, is the basis of life's unity. Variations in its nucleotide sequence are the foundation of life's diversity.

DNA sequence Order of nucleotides in a strand of DNA.

TAKE-HOME MESSAGE 8.2

A DNA molecule consists of two nucleotide chains (strands) running in opposite directions and coiled into a double helix. Internally positioned nucleotide bases hydrogen-bond between the two strands. A pairs with T, and G with C.

The sequence of bases along a DNA strand varies among species and among individuals. This variation is the basis of life's diversity.

CREDITS: (in text, 6) © Cengage Learning; (5) A.C. Barrington Brown, © 1968 J. D. Watson.

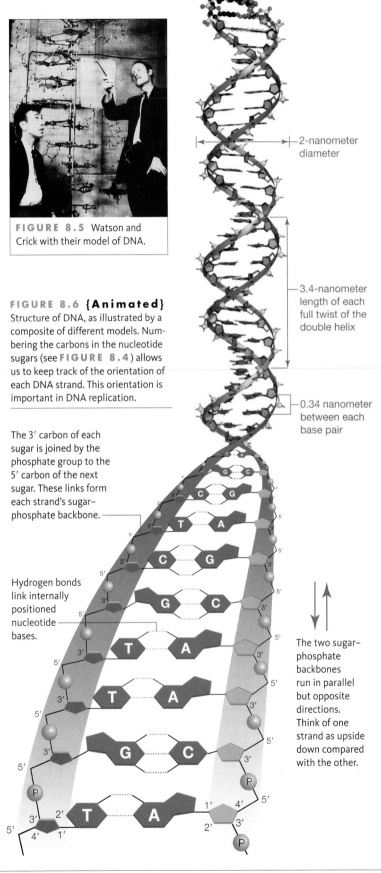

FIGURE 8.5 Watson and Crick with their model of DNA.

FIGURE 8.6 {Animated}
Structure of DNA, as illustrated by a composite of different models. Numbering the carbons in the nucleotide sugars (see **FIGURE 8.4**) allows us to keep track of the orientation of each DNA strand. This orientation is important in DNA replication.

The 3' carbon of each sugar is joined by the phosphate group to the 5' carbon of the next sugar. These links form each strand's sugar–phosphate backbone.

Hydrogen bonds link internally positioned nucleotide bases.

2-nanometer diameter

3.4-nanometer length of each full twist of the double helix

0.34 nanometer between each base pair

The two sugar–phosphate backbones run in parallel but opposite directions. Think of one strand as upside down compared with the other.

Stretched out end to end, the DNA in a single human cell would be about 2 meters (6.5 feet) long. How can that much DNA pack into a nucleus that is less than 10 micrometers in diameter? Such tight packing is possible because proteins associate with the DNA and help keep it organized. In cells, DNA molecules and their associated proteins form structures called **chromosomes** (FIGURE 8.7). In a chromosome of a eukaryotic cell, the DNA double helix ❶ wraps twice at regular intervals around "spools" of proteins called **histones** ❷. These DNA–histone spools, which are called **nucleosomes**, look like beads on a string in micrographs (*left*). Interactions among histones and other proteins twist the spooled DNA into a tight fiber ❸. This fiber coils, and then it coils again into a hollow cylinder, a bit like an old-style telephone cord ❹.

During most of the cell's life, each chromosome consists of one DNA molecule. When the cell prepares to divide,

it duplicates its chromosomes by DNA replication (more about this process in the next section). After replication, each chromosome consists of two DNA molecules, or **sister chromatids**, attached to one another at a constricted region called the **centromere**:

The chromosomes condense into their familiar "X" shapes ❺ just before the cell divides.

CHROMOSOME NUMBER AND TYPE

The DNA of a eukaryotic cell is divided among several chromosomes that differ in length and shape ❻. Each species has a characteristic **chromosome number**—the number of chromosomes in its cells. For example, the chromosome

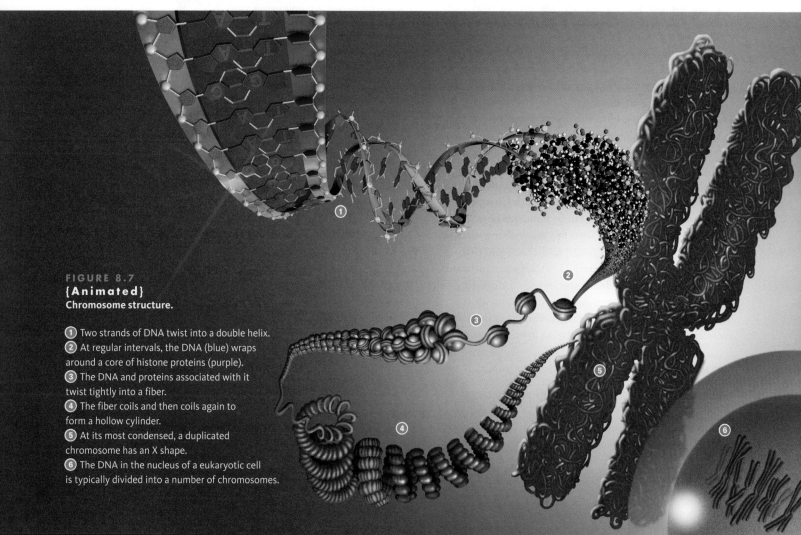

FIGURE 8.7
{Animated}
Chromosome structure.

❶ Two strands of DNA twist into a double helix.
❷ At regular intervals, the DNA (blue) wraps around a core of histone proteins (purple).
❸ The DNA and proteins associated with it twist tightly into a fiber.
❹ The fiber coils and then coils again to form a hollow cylinder.
❺ At its most condensed, a duplicated chromosome has an X shape.
❻ The DNA in the nucleus of a eukaryotic cell is typically divided into a number of chromosomes.

CREDITS: (in text left) O. L. Miller, Jr., Steve L. McKnight; (in text right) © Cengage Learning; (7) From Starr/Evers/Starr, Biology Today and Tomorrow with Physiology, 4E. © 2013 Cengage Learning.

FIGURE 8.8 {Animated} A karyotype of a human female, showing 22 pairs of autosomes and a pair of X chromosomes (XX).

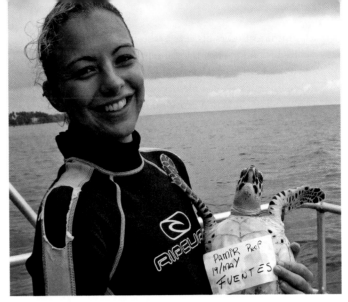

FIGURE 8.9 National Geographic Explorer Mariana Fuentes studies sea turtle populations. Climate change is an immediate, serious threat to these reptiles, in part because the temperature of the sand in which their eggs are buried—not sex chromosomes—determines the sex of the hatchlings. Fuentes predicts that rising global temperatures will soon skew the gender ratio of hatchlings toward all female, with disastrous results for sea turtle populations.

number of oak trees is 12, so the nucleus of a cell from an oak tree contains 12 chromosomes. The chromosome number of humans is 46, so our cells have 46 chromosomes.

Actually, human body cells have two sets of 23 chromosomes—two of each type. Having two sets of chromosomes means these cells are **diploid**, or 2*n*. A **karyotype** is an image of an individual's diploid set of chromosomes (**FIGURE 8.8**). To create a karyotype, cells taken from an individual are treated to make the chromosomes condense, and then stained so the chromosomes can be distinguished under a microscope. A micrograph of a single cell is digitally rearranged so the images of the chromosomes are lined up by centromere location, and arranged according to size, shape, and length.

In a human body cell, all but one pair of chromosomes are **autosomes**, which are the same in both females and males. The two autosomes of a pair have the same length, shape, and centromere location. They also hold information

about the same traits. Think of them as two sets of books on how to build a house. Your father gave you one set. Your mother had her own ideas about wiring, plumbing, and so on. She gave you an alternate set that says slightly different things about many of those tasks.

Members of a pair of **sex chromosomes** differ between females and males, and the differences determine an individual's sex. The sex chromosomes of humans are called X and Y. The body cells of typical human females have two X chromosomes (XX); those of typical human males have one X and one Y chromosome (XY). XX females and XY males are the rule among fruit flies, mammals, and many other animals, but there are other patterns. In butterflies, moths, birds, and certain fishes, males are the ones with identical sex chromosomes. Environmental factors (not sex chromosomes) determine sex in some invertebrates and reptiles (**FIGURE 8.9**).

---

autosome A chromosome that is the same in males and females.
centromere Of a duplicated eukaryotic chromosome, constricted region where sister chromatids attach to each other.
chromosome A structure that consists of DNA and associated proteins; carries part or all of a cell's genetic information.
chromosome number The total number of chromosomes in a cell of a given species.
diploid Having two of each type of chromosome characteristic of the species (2*n*).
histone Type of protein that structurally organizes eukaryotic chromosomes.
karyotype Image of an individual's set of chromosomes arranged by size, length, shape, and centromere location.
nucleosome A length of DNA wound twice around a spool of histone proteins.
sex chromosome Member of a pair of chromosomes that differs between males and females.
sister chromatids The two attached DNA molecules of a duplicated eukaryotic chromosome.

CREDITS: (8) © University of Washington Department of Pathology; (9) © Mariana Fuentes.

During most of its life, a typical cell contains one set of chromosomes. When the cell reproduces, it divides. The two descendant cells must inherit a full complement of chromosomes—a complete copy of genetic information—or they will not function properly. Thus, in preparation for division, the cell copies its chromosomes so that it contains two sets: one for each of its future offspring.

The process by which a cell copies its DNA is called **DNA replication**. During this energy-intensive metabolic pathway, enzymes and other molecules open the double helix of a DNA molecule to expose the internally positioned bases, then link nucleotides into new strands of DNA according to the sequence of those bases.

Each chromosome is replicated in its entirety. Two identical molecules of DNA are the result. In eukaryotes, these molecules are sister chromatids that remain attached at the centromere until cell division occurs.

SEMICONSERVATIVE REPLICATION

Before DNA replication, a chromosome consists of one molecule of DNA—one double helix (**FIGURE 8.10**). As replication begins, enzymes break the hydrogen bonds that hold the double helix together, so the two DNA strands unwind and separate ❶. Another enzyme constructs **primers**—short, single strands of nucleotides that serve as attachment points for **DNA polymerase**, the enzyme that assembles new strands of DNA. The nucleotide bases of a primer can form hydrogen bonds with exposed bases of a single strand of DNA ❷. Thus, a primer can base-pair with a complementary strand of DNA:

The establishment of base-pairing between two strands of DNA (or DNA and RNA) is called **nucleic acid hybridization**. Hybridization is spontaneous, driven by hydrogen bonding between bases of complementary strands.

DNA polymerases attach to the hybridized primers and begin DNA synthesis. As a DNA polymerase moves along a strand, it uses the sequence of exposed nucleotide bases as a template, or guide, to assemble a new strand of DNA from free nucleotides ❸.

Each nucleotide provides energy for its own attachment to the end of a growing strand of DNA. Remember from Section 5.5 that the bonds between a nucleotide's phosphate groups hold a lot of free energy. Two of the three phosphate groups are removed when the nucleotide is added to a DNA strand. Breaking those bonds releases enough free energy to drive the attachment.

A DNA polymerase follows base-pairing rules: It adds a T to the end of the new DNA strand when it reaches an A in the template strand; it adds a G when it reaches a C; and so on. Thus, the nucleotide sequence of each new strand of DNA is complementary to its template (parental) strand. The enzyme **DNA ligase** seals any gaps, so the new DNA strands are continuous ❹.

❶ As replication begins, enzymes begin to unwind and separate the two strands of DNA.

❷ Primers base-pair with the exposed single DNA strands.

❸ Starting at primers, DNA polymerases (green boxes) assemble new strands of DNA from nucleotides, using the parent strands as templates.

❹ DNA ligase seals any gaps that remain between bases of the "new" DNA, so a continuous strand forms.

❺ Each parental DNA strand serves as a template for assembly of a new strand of DNA. Both strands of the double helix serve as templates, so two double-stranded DNA molecules result. One strand of each is parental (old), and the other is new, so DNA replication is said to be semiconservative.

enzymes

primer

DNA polymerase

nucleotide

DNA ligase

FIGURE 8.10 {Animated} DNA replication, in which a double-stranded molecule of DNA is copied in entirety. The Y-shaped structure of a DNA molecule undergoing replication is called a replication fork.

Both of the two strands of the parent molecule are copied at the same time. As each new DNA strand lengthens, it winds up with its template strand into a double helix. So, after replication, two double-stranded molecules of DNA have formed ❺. One strand of each molecule is parental (old), and the other is new; hence the name of the process, **semiconservative replication.** Each new strand of DNA is complementary in sequence to one of the two parent strands, so both double-stranded molecules produced by DNA replication are duplicates of the parent molecule.

DIRECTIONAL SYNTHESIS

Numbering the carbons of the sugars in nucleotides allows us to keep track of the orientation of DNA strands in a double helix (see **FIGURES 8.4** and **8.6**). Each strand has two ends. The last carbon atom on one end of the strand is a 5′ (5 prime) carbon of a sugar; the last carbon atom on the other end is a 3′ (three prime) carbon of a sugar:

5′ ▬▬▬▬▬ 3′
3′ ▬▬▬▬▬ 5′

DNA polymerase can attach a nucleotide only to a 3′ end. Thus, during DNA replication, only one of two new strands of DNA can be constructed in a single piece (**FIGURE 8.11**). Synthesis of the other strand occurs in segments that must be joined by DNA ligase where they meet up. This is why we say that DNA synthesis proceeds only in the 5′ to 3′ direction.

DNA ligase Enzyme that seals gaps in double-stranded DNA.
DNA polymerase DNA replication enzyme. Uses one strand of DNA as a template to assemble a complementary strand of DNA from nucleotides.
DNA replication Process by which a cell duplicates its DNA before it divides.
nucleic acid hybridization Convergence of complementary nucleic acid strands. Arises because of base-pairing interactions.
primer Short, single strand of DNA that base-pairs with a targeted DNA sequence.
semiconservative replication Describes the process of DNA replication, which produces two copies of a DNA molecule: one strand of each copy is new, and the other is parental.

TAKE-HOME MESSAGE 8.4

DNA replication is an energy-intensive metabolic pathway by which a cell copies its chromosomes.

During replication of a molecule of DNA, each strand of its double helix serves as a template for synthesis of a new, complementary strand of DNA.

Replication of a molecule of DNA produces two double helices that are duplicates of the parent molecule. One strand of each is parental; the other is new.

A During DNA synthesis, only one of the two new strands can be assembled in a single piece. The other strand forms in short segments, which are called Okazaki fragments after the two scientists who discovered them. DNA ligase joins Okazaki fragments where they meet.

B DNA synthesis proceeds only in the 5′ to 3′ direction because DNA polymerase catalyzes only one reaction: the formation of a bond between the 3′ carbon on the end of a DNA strand and the phosphate on a nucleotide's 5′ carbon.

FIGURE 8.11 Discontinuous synthesis of DNA. This close-up of a replication fork shows that only one of the two new DNA strands is assembled in one piece.

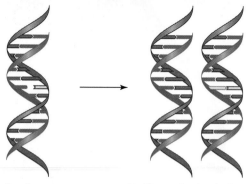

A Repair enzymes can recognize a mismatched base (yellow), but sometimes fail to correct it before DNA replication.

B After replication, both strands base-pair properly. Repair enzymes can no longer recognize the error, which has now become a mutation that will be passed on to the cell's descendants.

FIGURE 8.12 How a replication error can become a mutation.

A Major breaks (red arrows) in chromosomes of a human white blood cell after exposure to ionizing radiation. Pieces of broken chromosomes often become lost during DNA replication.

B These *Ranunculus* flowers were grown from plants harvested around Chernobyl, Ukraine, where in 1986 an accident at a nuclear power plant released huge amounts of radiation. A normal flower is shown for comparison, in the inset.

FIGURE 8.13 Exposure to ionizing radiation causes mutations.

REPLICATION ERRORS

Mistakes can and do occur during DNA replication. Sometimes, the wrong base is added to a growing DNA strand; at other times, a nucleotide gets lost, or an extra one slips in. Either way, the newly synthesized DNA strand will no longer be complementary to its parent strand. Most of these replication errors occur simply because DNA polymerases work very fast, copying about 50 nucleotides per second in eukaryotes, and up to 1,000 per second in bacteria. Mistakes are inevitable, and some types of DNA polymerases make a lot of them. Luckily, most DNA polymerases also proofread their work. They can correct a mismatch by reversing the synthesis reaction to remove the mispaired nucleotide, then resuming synthesis in the forward direction.

Replication errors also occur after the cell's DNA gets broken or otherwise damaged, because DNA polymerases do not copy damaged DNA very well. In most cases, repair enzymes and other proteins remove and replace damaged or mismatched bases in DNA before replication begins.

When proofreading and repair mechanisms fail, an error becomes a **mutation**, a permanent change in the DNA sequence of a cell's chromosome(s). Repair enzymes cannot fix a mutation after DNA replication has occurred, because they do not recognize correctly paired bases (**FIGURE 8.12**). Thus, a mutation is passed to the cell's descendants, their descendants, and so on.

Mutations can form in any type of cell. Those that occur during egg or sperm formation can be passed to offspring, and in fact each human child is born with an average of 36 new ones. Mutations that alter DNA's instructions may have a harmful or lethal outcome; most cancers begin with them (we return to this topic in Section 11.5). However, not all mutations are dangerous: As you will see in Chapter 17, they give rise to the variation in traits that is the raw material of evolution.

AGENTS OF DNA DAMAGE

Electromagnetic energy with a wavelength shorter than 320 nanometers, including x-rays, most ultraviolet (UV) light, and gamma rays, can knock electrons out of atoms. Such ionizing radiation damages DNA, breaking it into pieces that get lost during replication (**FIGURE 8.13A**). Ionizing radiation can also cause covalent bonds to form between bases on opposite strands of the double helix, an outcome that permanently blocks replication. (We consider cancer-causing effects of such cell cycle interruptions in Chapter 11.) High-energy radiation also fatally alters nucleotide bases. Repair enzymes can remove bases damaged in this way, but they leave an empty space in the double helix or

CREDITS: (12) © Cengage Learning 2015; (13A) Olga Shovman, Andrew C. Riches, Douglas Adamson, and Peter E. Bryant. An improved assay for radiation-induced chromatid breaks using a colcemid block and calyculin-induced PCC combination. *Mutagenesis* (2008) 23(4): 267–270 first published online March 6, 2008 doi:10.1093/mutage/gen009, by permission of Oxford University Press; (13B) main, Courtesy of Janis Ruksans; inset, Frank Sommariva/image/imagebroker.net/SuperStock.

even a strand break. Sometimes the enzymes cut out the entire nucleotide from the strand, leaving an unpaired nucleotide on the opposite strand. Any of these events can result in mutations (**FIGURE 8.13B**).

UV light in the range of 320–380 nanometers can boost electrons to a higher energy level, but not enough to knock them out of atoms. UV light in this range is still

a thymine dimer

dangerous, because it has enough energy to open up the double bond in the ring of a cytidine or thymine base. The open ring can form a covalent bond with the ring of an adjacent cytidine or thymine (*left*). The resulting dimer kinks the DNA strand. DNA polymerase tends to copy the kinked part incorrectly during replication, and mutations are the outcome. Mutations that arise as a result of nucleotide dimers are the primary cause of skin cancer. Exposing unprotected skin to sunlight increases the risk of cancer because its UV wavelengths cause dimers to form. For every second a skin cell spends in the sun, 50–100 of these dimers form in its DNA.

Exposure to some natural or synthetic chemicals also causes mutations. For instance, several of the fifty-five or more cancer-causing chemicals in tobacco smoke transfer methyl groups ($-CH_3$) to the nucleotide bases in DNA. Nucleotides altered in this way do not base-pair correctly. Other chemicals in the smoke are converted by the body to compounds that are easier to excrete, and the breakdown products bind irreversibly to DNA. Replication errors that can lead to mutation may be the outcome in both cases. Cigarette smoke also contains free radicals, which inflict the same damage on DNA as ionizing radiation.

---

mutation Permanent change in the nucleotide sequence of DNA.

TAKE-HOME MESSAGE 8.5

Proofreading and repair mechanisms usually maintain the integrity of a cell's genetic information by correcting mispaired bases and fixing damaged DNA before replication.

Mismatched or damaged nucleotides that are not repaired can become mutations—permanent changes in the DNA sequence of a chromosome.

DNA damage by environmental agents such as UV light and chemicals can result in mutations, because damaged DNA is not replicated very well.

PEOPLE MATTER

DR. ROSALIND FRANKLIN

Rosalind Franklin had been told she would be the only one in her department working on the structure of DNA, so she did not know that Maurice Wilkins was already doing the same thing just down the hall. Franklin's meticulous work yielded the first clear x-ray diffraction image of DNA as it occurs inside cells, and she gave a presentation on this work in 1952. DNA, she said, had two chains twisted into a double helix, with a backbone of phosphate groups on the outside, and bases arranged in an as-yet unknown way on the inside. She had calculated DNA's diameter, the distance between its chains and between its bases, the angle of the helix, and the number of bases in each coil. Francis Crick, with his crystallography background, would have recognized the significance of the work—if he had been there. James Watson was in the audience but he did not fully understand the implications of Franklin's x-ray diffraction image or her calculations.

Franklin started to write a research paper on her findings. Meanwhile, and perhaps without her knowledge, Watson reviewed Franklin's x-ray diffraction image with Wilkins, and Watson and Crick read Franklin's unpublished data. That data provided Watson and Crick with the last piece of the DNA puzzle. In 1953, they put together all of the clues that had been accumulating for fifty years and built the first accurate model of DNA structure. On April 25, 1953, Rosalind Franklin's work appeared third in a series of articles about the structure of DNA in the journal *Nature*. Wilkins's research paper was the second article in the series. The work of Franklin and Wilkins supported with experimental evidence Watson and Crick's theoretical model, which was presented in the first article.

Rosalind Franklin died in 1958 at the age of 37, of ovarian cancer probably caused by extensive exposure to x-rays during her work. At the time, the link between x-rays, mutations, and cancer was not understood. Because the Nobel Prize is not given posthumously, Franklin did not share in the 1962 honor that went to Watson, Crick, and Wilkins for the discovery of the structure of DNA.

The word "cloning" means making an identical copy of something, and it can refer to deliberate interventions in reproduction that produce an exact genetic copy of an organism. Genetically identical organisms occur all the time in nature, arising most often by the process of asexual reproduction (which we discuss in Chapter 11). Embryo splitting, another natural process, results in identical twins. The first few divisions of a fertilized egg form a ball of cells that sometimes splits spontaneously. If both halves of the ball continue to develop independently, identical twins result.

Artificial embryo splitting has been used in research and animal husbandry for decades. With this technique, a ball of cells is grown from a fertilized egg in a laboratory. The tiny ball is teased apart into two halves, each of which goes on to develop as a separate embryo. The embryos are implanted in surrogate mothers, who give birth to identical twins. Artificial twinning and any other technology that yields genetically identical individuals is called **reproductive cloning**.

Twins get their DNA from two parents that typically differ in their DNA sequence. Thus, although twins produced by embryo splitting are identical to one another, they are not identical to either parent. Animal breeders who want an exact copy of a specific individual may turn to a cloning method that starts with a somatic cell taken from an adult organism (a somatic cell is a body cell, as opposed to a reproductive cell; *soma* is a Greek word for body). All cells descended from a fertilized egg inherit the same DNA. Thus, the DNA in each living cell of an individual is like a master blueprint that contains enough information to build an entirely new individual. However, a somatic cell taken from an adult will not automatically start dividing to produce an embryo. It must first be tricked into rewinding its developmental clock. During development, cells in an embryo start using different subsets of their DNA. As they do, the cells become different in form and function, a process called **differentiation**. Differentiation is usually a one-way path in animal cells. Once a cell has become specialized, all of its descendant cells will be specialized the same way. By the time a liver cell, muscle cell, or other differentiated cell forms, most of its DNA has been turned off, and is no longer used. To clone an adult, scientists transform one of its differentiated cells into an undifferentiated cell by turning its unused DNA back on. One way to do this is **somatic cell nuclear transfer (SCNT)**, a laboratory procedure in which an unfertilized egg's nucleus is replaced with the nucleus of a donor's somatic cell (**FIGURE 8.14**). If all goes well, the egg's cytoplasm reprograms the transplanted DNA to direct the development of an embryo, which is then implanted into a surrogate mother. The animal that is born to the surrogate is genetically identical with the donor of the nucleus—a clone.

SCNT is now a common practice among people who breed prized livestock. Among other benefits, many more offspring can be produced in a given time frame by cloning than by traditional breeding methods. Cloned animals have the same championship features as their DNA donors

A A cow's egg is held in place by suction through a hollow glass tube called a micropipette. DNA is identified by a purple stain.

B Another micropipette punctures the egg and sucks out the DNA. All that remains inside the egg's plasma membrane is cytoplasm.

C A new micropipette prepares to enter the egg at the puncture site. The pipette contains a cell grown from the skin of a donor animal.

D The micropipette enters the egg and delivers the skin cell to a region between the cytoplasm and the plasma membrane.

E After the pipette is withdrawn, the donor's skin cell is visible next to the cytoplasm of the egg. The transfer is now complete.

F An electric current causes the foreign cell to fuse with and deposit its nucleus into the cytoplasm of the egg. The egg begins to divide, and an embryo forms.

FIGURE 8.14 {**Animated**} An example of somatic cell nuclear transfer, using cattle cells. This series of micrographs was taken at a company that specializes in cloning livestock.

CREDIT: (14) Courtesy of Cyagra, Inc., www.cyagra.com.

FIGURE 8.15 Champion Holstein dairy cow (*right*) and her clone (*left*), who was produced by somatic cell nuclear transfer in 2003.

(FIGURE 8.15). Offspring can also be produced from a donor animal that is castrated or even dead.

As the techniques become routine, cloning humans is no longer only within the realm of science fiction. SCNT is already being used to produce human embryos for medical purposes, a practice called **therapeutic cloning**. Undifferentiated (stem) cells taken from the cloned human embryos are used to treat human patients and to study human diseases. For example, embryos created using cells from people with genetic heart defects are allowing researchers to study how the defect causes developing heart cells to malfunction. Such research may ultimately lead to treatments for people who suffer from fatal diseases. (We return to the topic of stem cells and their potential medical benefits in Chapter 28.) Human cloning is not the intent of such research, but if it were, SCNT would indeed be the first step toward that end.

differentiation Process by which cells become specialized during development; occurs as different cells in an embryo begin to use different subsets of their DNA.
reproductive cloning Technology that produces genetically identical individuals.
somatic cell nuclear transfer (SCNT) Reproductive cloning method in which the DNA of an adult donor's body cell is transferred into an unfertilized egg.
therapeutic cloning The use of SCNT to produce human embryos for research purposes.

TAKE-HOME MESSAGE 8.6

Reproductive cloning technologies produce genetically identical individuals.

The DNA inside a living cell contains all the information necessary to build a new individual.

In somatic cell nuclear transfer (SCNT), the DNA of an adult donor's body cell is transferred to an egg with no nucleus. The hybrid cell may develop into an embryo that is genetically identical to the donor's.

CREDITS: (15) Courtesy of Cyagra, Inc., www.cyagra.com; (16) © James Symington.

Application: Get Involved

FIGURE 8.16 James Symington and his dog Trakr at Ground Zero, 9/11/2001.

WHY CLONE ANIMALS? **Consider the story of Canadian police officer James Symington and his search dog Trakr. On September 11, 2001, Symington drove Trakr from Nova Scotia to Manhattan. Within hours of arriving, the dog led rescuers to the area where the final survivor of the World Trade Center attacks was buried. She had been clinging to life, pinned under rubble from the building where she had worked. Symington and Trakr helped with the search and rescue efforts for three days nonstop, until Trakr collapsed from smoke and chemical inhalation, burns, and exhaustion (FIGURE 8.16).**

Trakr survived the ordeal, but later lost the use of his limbs, probably because of toxic smoke exposure at Ground Zero. The hero dog died in April 2009, but his DNA lives on—in his clones. Symington's essay about Trakr's superior nature and abilities as a search and rescue dog won the Golden Clone Giveaway, a contest to find the world's most clone-worthy dog. Trakr's DNA was inserted into donor dog eggs, which were then implanted into surrogate mother dogs. Five puppies, all clones of Trakr, were delivered to Symington in July 2009. Today, the clones are search and rescue dogs for Team Trakr Foundation, Symington's international humanitarian organization.

Cloning animals raises uncomfortable ethical questions about cloning humans. For example, if cloning a lost animal for a grieving owner is acceptable, why would it not be acceptable to clone a lost child for a grieving parent? Different people have very different answers to such questions, so controversy over cloning continues to rage even as techniques improve.

Summary

SECTION 8.1 Eighty years of experimentation with cells and **bacteriophage** offered solid evidence that deoxyribonucleic acid (DNA), not protein, is the hereditary material of all life.

SECTION 8.2 A DNA nucleotide has a five-carbon sugar (deoxyribose), three phosphate groups, and one of four nitrogen-containing bases after which the nucleotide is named: adenine, thymine, guanine, or cytosine. DNA is a polymer that consists of two strands of these nucleotides coiled into a double helix. Hydrogen bonding between the internally positioned bases holds the strands together. The bases pair in a consistent way: adenine with thymine (A–T), and guanine with cytosine (G–C). The order of bases along a strand of DNA—the **DNA sequence**—varies among species and among individuals, and this variation is the basis of life's diversity.

SECTION 8.3 The DNA of eukaryotes is typically divided among a number of **chromosomes** that differ in length and shape. In eukaryotic chromosomes, the DNA wraps around **histone** proteins to form **nucleosomes**. When duplicated, a eukaryotic chromosome consists of two **sister chromatids** attached at a **centromere**. **Diploid** cells have two of each type of chromosome. **Chromosome number** is the total number of chromosomes in a cell of a given species. A human body cell has twenty-three pairs of chromosomes. Members of a pair of **sex chromosomes** differ among males and females. Chromosomes that are the same in males and females are **autosomes**. Autosomes of a pair have the same length, shape, and centromere location. A **karyotype** is an individual's complete set of chromosomes.

SECTION 8.4 A cell copies its chromosomes before it divides so each of its offspring will inherit a complete set of genetic information. **DNA replication** is the energy-intensive metabolic pathway in which a cell copies its chromosomes. For each double-stranded molecule of DNA that is copied, two double-stranded DNA molecules that are duplicates of the parent are produced. One strand of each molecule is new, and the other is parental; thus the name **semiconservative replication**. During DNA replication, enzymes unwind the double helix. **Primers** base-pair with the exposed single strands of DNA, a process called **nucleic acid hybridization**. Starting at the primers, **DNA polymerase** enzymes use each strand as a template to assemble new, complementary strands of DNA from free nucleotides. Synthesis of one strand necessarily occurs discontinuously. **DNA ligase** seals any gaps to form continuous strands.

SECTION 8.5 Proofreading by DNA polymerases corrects most DNA replication errors as they occur. DNA damage by environmental agents, including ionizing and nonionizing radiation, free radicals, and some other natural and synthetic chemicals, can lead to replication errors because DNA polymerase does not copy damaged

DNA very well. Most types of DNA damage can be repaired before replication begins. Uncorrected replication errors become **mutations**, which are permanent changes in the nucleotide sequence of a cell's DNA. Cancer begins with mutations, but not all mutations are harmful.

SECTIONS 8.6, 8.7 **Somatic cell nuclear transfer (SCNT)** and other types of **reproductive cloning** technologies produce genetically identical individuals (clones). SCNT using human cells is called **therapeutic cloning**. The DNA in each living cell contains all the information necessary to build a new individual. During development, cells of an embryo become specialized as they begin to use different subsets of their DNA (a process called **differentiation**).

Self-Quiz   Answers in Appendix VII

1. Which is not a nucleotide base in DNA?
   a. adenine   c. glutamine   e. cytosine
   b. guanine   d. thymine   f. All are in DNA.

2. What are the base-pairing rules for DNA?
   a. A–G, T–C   b. A–C, T–G   c. A–T, G–C

3. Variation in _____ is the basis of variation in traits.
   a. karyotype   c. the double helix
   b. the DNA sequence   d. chromosome number

4. One species' DNA differs from others in its _____ .
   a. nucleotides   c. sugar–phosphate backbone
   b. DNA sequence   d. all of the above

5. In eukaryotic chromosomes, DNA wraps around _____ .
   a. histone proteins   c. centromeres
   b. nucleosomes   d. none of the above

6. Chromosome number _____ .
   a. refers to a particular chromosome in a cell
   b. is an identifiable feature of a species
   c. is the number of autosomes in cells of a given type

7. Human body cells are diploid, which means _____ .
   a. they are complete
   b. they have two sets of chromosomes
   c. they contain sex chromosomes

8. When DNA replication begins, _____ .
   a. the two DNA strands unwind from each other
   b. the two DNA strands condense for base transfers
   c. old strands move to find new strands

9. DNA replication requires _____ .
   a. DNA polymerase   c. primers
   b. nucleotides   d. all are required

10. Energy that drives DNA synthesis comes from _____ .
    a. ATP only   c. DNA nucleotides
    b. DNA polymerase   d. a and c

Data Analysis Activities

Hershey-Chase Experiments The graph in **FIGURE 8.17** is reproduced from Hershey and Chase's original publication. The data are from the two experiments described in Section 8.1, in which bacteriophage DNA and protein were labeled with radioactive tracers and allowed to infect bacteria. The virus–bacteria mixtures were whirled in a blender to dislodge the viruses, and the tracers were tracked inside and outside of the bacteria.

1. Before blending, what percentage of each isotope, ^{35}S and ^{32}P, was outside the bacteria?

2. After 4 minutes in the blender, what percentage of each isotope was outside the bacteria?

3. How did the researchers know that the radioisotopes in the fluid came from outside of the bacterial cells (extracellular) and not from bacteria that had been broken apart by whirling in the blender?

4. The extracellular concentration of which isotope increased the most with blending?

5. Do these results imply that viruses inject DNA or protein into bacteria? Why or why not?

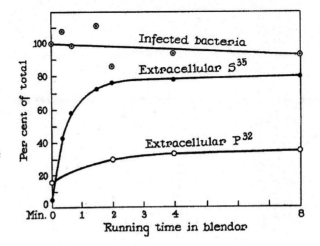

FIGURE 8.17 Detail of Alfred Hershey and Martha Chase's 1952 publication describing their experiments with bacteriophage. "Infected bacteria" refers to the percentage of bacteria that survived the blender.

11. The phrase "5′ to 3′" refers to the _____ .
    a. timing of DNA replication
    b. directionality of DNA synthesis
    c. number of phosphate groups

12. After DNA replication, a eukaryotic chromosome _____ .
    a. consists of two sister chromatids
    b has a characteristic X shape
    c. is constricted at the centromere
    d. all of the above

13. All mutations _____ .
    a. cause cancer   c. are caused by radiation
    b. lead to evolution   d. change the DNA sequence

14. _____ is an example of reproductive cloning.
    a. Somatic cell nuclear transfer (SCNT)
    b. Multiple offspring from the same pregnancy
    c. Artificial embryo splitting
    d. a and c

15. Match the terms appropriately.
    ___ bacteriophage   a. nitrogen-containing base, sugar, phosphate group(s)
    ___ clone
    ___ nucleotide   b. copy of an organism
    ___ diploid   c. does not determine sex
    ___ DNA ligase   d. only DNA and protein
    ___ DNA polymerase   e. seals breaks in a DNA strand
    ___ autosome   f. can cause cancer
    ___ mutation   g. two chromosomes of each type
                           h. adds nucleotides to a growing DNA strand

Critical Thinking

1. Show the complementary strand of DNA that forms on this template DNA fragment during replication:
   5′—GGTTTCTTCAAGAGA—3′

2. Woolly mammoths have been extinct for about 10,000 years, but we often find their well-preserved remains in Siberian permafrost. Research groups are now planning to use SCNT to resurrect these huge elephant-like mammals. No mammoth eggs have been recovered so far, so elephant eggs would be used instead. An elephant would also be the surrogate mother for the resulting embryo. The researchers may try a modified SCNT technique used to clone a mouse that had been dead and frozen for sixteen years. Ice crystals that form during freezing break up cell membranes, so cells from the frozen mouse were in bad shape. Their DNA was transferred into donor mouse eggs, and cells from the resulting embryos were fused with mouse stem cells. Four healthy clones were born from the hybrid embryos. What are some of the pros and cons of cloning an extinct animal?

3. Xeroderma pigmentosum is an inherited disorder characterized by rapid formation of skin sores that develop into cancers. All forms of radiation trigger these symptoms, including fluorescent light, which contains UV light in the range of 320–400 nm. What normal function has been compromised in affected individuals?

CENGAGE **brain**.com To access course materials, please visit www.cengagebrain.com.

CREDIT: (17) *Journal of General Physiology*, 36(1), Sept. 20, 1952.

CHAPTER 8 **145**
DNA STRUCTURE
AND FUNCTION

The hairless appearance of a sphynx cat arises from a single base-pair mutation in its DNA. The change results in an altered form of the keratin protein that makes up cat fur.

FROM DNA TO PROTEIN

Links to Earlier Concepts

Your knowledge of base pairing (Section 8.2) and chromosomes (8.3) will help you understand how cells use nucleic acids (3.6) to build proteins (3.4). You will revisit cell structure, including membrane proteins (4.3), the nucleus (4.5) and endomembrane system (4.6); as well as concepts of hydrophobicity (2.4), pathogenic bacteria (4.12), cofactors (5.5), enzyme function (5.3), DNA replication (8.4), and mutation (8.5).

KEY CONCEPTS

GENE EXPRESSION
The information encoded in DNA occurs in subsets called genes. The conversion of genetic information to a protein product occurs in two steps: transcription and translation.

DNA TO RNA: TRANSCRIPTION
During transcription, a gene region in one strand of DNA serves as a template for assembling a strand of RNA. In eukaryotes, a new RNA is modified before leaving the nucleus.

RNA
A messenger RNA carries a gene's protein-building instructions as a string of three-nucleotide codons. Transfer RNA and ribosomal RNA translate those instructions into a protein.

RNA TO PROTEIN: TRANSLATION
During translation, amino acids are assembled into a polypeptide in the order determined by the sequence of codons in an mRNA.

ALTERED PROTEINS
Mutations that change a gene's DNA sequence alter the instructions it encodes. A protein built using altered instructions may function improperly or not at all.

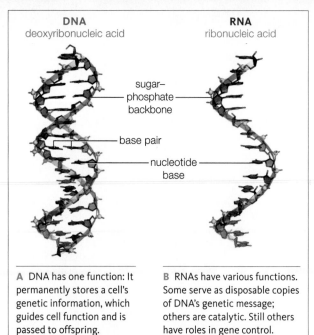

DNA	RNA
deoxyribonucleic acid	ribonucleic acid

sugar–phosphate backbone

base pair

nucleotide base

A DNA has one function: It permanently stores a cell's genetic information, which guides cell function and is passed to offspring.

B RNAs have various functions. Some serve as disposable copies of DNA's genetic message; others are catalytic. Still others have roles in gene control.

FIGURE 9.1 Comparing structure and function of DNA and RNA.

base (guanine)

3 phosphate groups

sugar (deoxyribose)

A **The DNA nucleotide guanine (G)**, or deoxyguanosine triphosphate, one of the four nucleotides in DNA. The other nucleotides—adenine, uracil, and cytosine—differ only in their component bases (blue). Three of the four bases in RNA nucleotides are identical to the bases in DNA nucleotides.

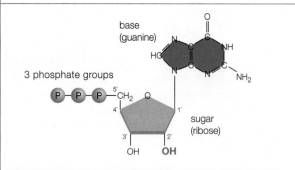

base (guanine)

3 phosphate groups

sugar (ribose)

B **The RNA nucleotide guanine (G)**, or guanosine triphosphate. The only difference between the DNA and RNA versions of guanine (or adenine, or cytosine) is that RNA has a hydroxyl group (shown in red) at the 2′ carbon of the sugar.

FIGURE 9.2 Comparing nucleotides of DNA and RNA.

You learned in Chapter 8 that an individual's chromosomes are like a set of books that provide building and operating instructions. You already know the alphabet used to write that book: the four letters A, T, G, and C, for the four nucleotides in DNA: adenine, thymine, guanine, and cytosine. In this chapter, we investigate the nature of information represented by the sequence of nucleotides in DNA, and how a cell uses that information.

DNA TO RNA

Information encoded within a chromosome's DNA sequence occurs in hundreds or thousands of units called genes. The DNA sequence of a **gene** encodes (contains instructions for building) an RNA or protein product. Converting the information encoded by a gene into a product starts with RNA synthesis, or transcription. During **transcription**, enzymes use the gene's DNA sequence as a template to assemble a strand of RNA:

$$DNA \xrightarrow{\textit{transcription}} RNA$$

Most of the RNA inside cells occurs as a single strand that is similar in structure to a single strand of DNA (**FIGURE 9.1**). Both RNA and DNA are chains of nucleotides. Like a DNA nucleotide, an RNA nucleotide has three phosphate groups, a sugar, and one of four bases. However, the sugar in an RNA nucleotide is a ribose, which differs just a bit from deoxyribose, the sugar in a DNA nucleotide (**FIGURE 9.2**). Three bases (adenine, cytosine, and guanine) occur in both RNA and DNA nucleotides, but the fourth base differs. In DNA, the fourth base is thymine (T); in RNA, it is uracil (U).

DNA's important but only role is to store a cell's genetic information. By contrast, a cell makes several kinds of RNAs, each with a different function. Three types of RNA have roles in protein synthesis. **Ribosomal RNA** (**rRNA**) is the main component of ribosomes (Section 4.4), which assemble amino acids into polypeptide chains (Section 3.4). **Transfer RNA** (**tRNA**) delivers the amino acids to ribosomes, one by one, in the order specified by a **messenger RNA** (**mRNA**).

RNA TO PROTEIN

Messenger RNA was named for its function as the "messenger" between DNA and protein. An mRNA's protein-building message is encoded by sets of three nucleotides, "genetic words" that occur one after another along its length. Like the words of a sentence, a series of these genetic words can form a meaningful parcel of information—in this case, the sequence of amino acids of a protein.

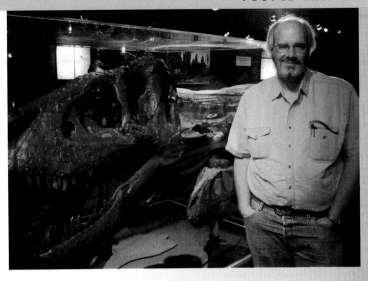

National Geographic Grantee
DR. JOHN "JACK" HORNER

xcavating a *Tyrannosaurus rex* proved even more exciting than legendary paleontologist Jack Horner and his colleagues had anticipated when they discovered branching blood vessels and bone matrix inside its thigh bone. The team had never expected to find unfossilized tissues in the 68-million-year-old remains, because the molecules of life tend to break down relatively quickly. The tightly wound, durable structure of collagen (the main protein component of bone) may hold the key to the seemingly inexplicable preservation of the ancient tissue.

Fragments of collagen protein isolated from the tissue have a primary structure very similar to that of chicken bone collagen, providing the first molecular support for the hypothesis that modern birds are descended from dinosaurs. Until this discovery, the dinosaur–bird connection had been entirely based on physical similarities in fossils' body structures.

Researchers often compare DNA sequences to investigate evolutionary relationships, but no one has found DNA in such an ancient fossil. The sequence of amino acids in a protein is encoded by a gene, so protein similarities can also be used as evidence of hereditary connection. "If we spend time getting as deep into the sediment as we can, I think we're going to find that many specimens are like this," Horner said.

By the process of **translation**, the protein-building information in an mRNA is decoded (translated) into a sequence of amino acids. The result is a polypeptide chain that twists and folds into a protein:

$$\text{mRNA} \xrightarrow{\textit{translation}} \text{protein}$$

Transcription and translation are part of **gene expression**, the multistep process by which information encoded in a gene guides the assembly of an RNA or protein product.

---

gene A part of a chromosome that encodes an RNA or protein product in its DNA sequence.
gene expression Process by which the information in a gene guides assembly of an RNA or protein product.
messenger RNA (mRNA) RNA that has a protein-building message.
ribosomal RNA (rRNA) RNA that becomes part of ribosomes.
transcription Process by which enzymes assemble an RNA using the nucleotide sequence of a gene as a template.
transfer RNA (tRNA) RNA that delivers amino acids to a ribosome during translation.
translation Process by which a polypeptide chain is assembled from amino acids in the order specified by an mRNA.

During gene expression, this information flows from DNA to RNA to protein:

$$\text{DNA} \xrightarrow{\textit{transcription}} \text{mRNA} \xrightarrow{\textit{translation}} \text{protein}$$

A cell's DNA sequence contains all the information it needs to make the molecules of life. Each gene encodes an RNA, and RNAs interact to assemble proteins from amino acids (Section 3.4). Proteins (enzymes, in particular) assemble lipids and carbohydrates, replicate DNA, make RNA, and perform many other functions that keep the cell alive.

TAKE-HOME MESSAGE 9.1

Information in a DNA sequence occurs in units called genes. A cell uses the information encoded in a gene to make an RNA or protein product, a process called gene expression.

The DNA sequence of a gene is transcribed into RNA.

Information carried by a messenger RNA (mRNA) is translated into a protein.

Remember that DNA replication begins with one DNA double helix and ends with two DNA double helices (Section 8.4). The two double helices are identical to the parent molecule because base-pairing rules are followed during DNA replication. A nucleotide can be added to a growing strand of DNA only if it base-pairs with the

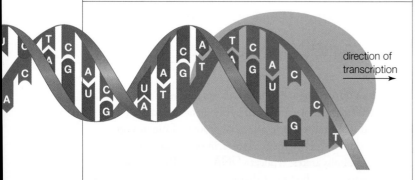

1 The enzyme RNA polymerase binds to a promoter in the DNA. The binding positions the polymerase near a gene. Only the DNA strand complementary to the gene sequence will be translated into RNA.

RNA — DNA winding up — DNA unwinding

2 RNA polymerase begins to move along the gene and unwind the DNA. As it does, it links RNA nucleotides in the order specified by the base sequence of the complementary (noncoding) DNA strand. The DNA winds up again after the polymerase passes.

direction of transcription

3 Zooming in on the site of transcription, we can see that RNA polymerase covalently bonds successive nucleotides into an RNA strand. The base sequence of the new RNA strand is complementary to the base sequence of its DNA template strand, so it is an RNA copy of the gene.

FIGURE 9.3 {Animated} Transcription. By this process, a strand of RNA is assembled from nucleotides. A gene region in the DNA serves as the template for RNA synthesis.

FIGURE IT OUT: After the guanine (G), what nucleotide will be added to this growing strand of RNA?
Answer: Another guanine

corresponding nucleotide of the parent strand: G pairs with C, and A pairs with T (Section 8.2):

The same base-pairing rules also govern RNA synthesis in transcription. An RNA strand is structurally so similar to a DNA strand that the two can base-pair if their nucleotide sequences are complementary. In such hybrid molecules, G pairs with C, and A pairs with U (uracil):

During transcription, a strand of DNA acts as a template upon which a strand of RNA is assembled from nucleotides. A nucleotide can be added to a growing RNA only if it is complementary to the corresponding nucleotide of the parent strand of DNA. Thus, a new RNA is complementary in sequence to the DNA strand that served as its template. As in DNA replication, each nucleotide provides the energy for its own attachment to the end of a growing strand.

Transcription is similar to DNA replication in that one strand of a nucleic acid serves as a template for synthesis of another. However, in contrast with DNA replication, only part of one DNA strand, not the whole molecule, is used as a template for transcription. The enzyme **RNA polymerase**, not DNA polymerase, adds nucleotides to the end of a growing RNA. Also, transcription produces a single strand of RNA, not two DNA double helices.

In eukaryotic cells, transcription occurs in the nucleus; in prokaryotes, it occurs in cytoplasm. The process begins when an RNA polymerase and regulatory proteins attach to the DNA at a site called a **promoter** (FIGURE 9.3 **1**). Binding positions the polymerase close to the gene that will be transcribed. The strand that is complementary to the gene sequence (the noncoding strand) is the one that serves as the template for transcription.

Like DNA polymerase, RNA polymerase moves along DNA (Section 8.4). As the RNA polymerase moves over a gene region, it unwinds the double helix just a bit so it can "read" the base sequence of the DNA strand **2**. The polymerase joins free RNA nucleotides into a chain, in the order dictated by that DNA sequence. As in

CREDITS: (3) © Cengage Learning; (in text) From Starr/Evers/Starr, Biology Today and Tomorrow with Physiology, 4E.
© 2013 Cengage Learning.

DNA molecule   RNA molecules   a "Christmas tree"

FIGURE 9.4 Typically, many RNA polymerases simultaneously transcribe the same gene, producing a structure often called a "Christmas tree" after its shape. Here, four genes next to one another on the same chromosome are being transcribed.

FIGURE IT OUT: Are the polymerases transcribing this DNA molecule moving from left to right or from right to left?

Answer: Left to right (the RNAs get longer as the polymerases move along the DNA)

DNA replication, the synthesis is directional: An RNA polymerase adds nucleotides only to the 3′ end of the growing strand of RNA.

When the polymerase reaches the end of the gene region, it releases the DNA and the new RNA. RNA polymerase follows base-pairing rules, so the new RNA strand is complementary in base sequence to the DNA strand from which it was transcribed ❸. It is an RNA copy of a gene, the same way that a paper transcript of a conversation carries the same information in a different format. Typically, many polymerases transcribe a particular gene region at the same time, so many new RNA strands can be produced very quickly (**FIGURE 9.4**).

POST-TRANSCRIPTIONAL MODIFICATIONS

Just as a dressmaker may snip off loose threads or add bows to a dress before it leaves the shop, so do eukaryotic cells tailor their RNA before it leaves the nucleus. Consider that most eukaryotic genes contain intervening sequences called **introns**. Introns are removed in chunks from a newly transcribed RNA before it leaves the nucleus. Sequences that stay in the RNA are called **exons** (**FIGURE 9.5**). Exons can be rearranged and spliced together in different combinations—a process called **alternative splicing**—so one gene may encode different proteins.

A newly transcribed RNA that will become an mRNA is further tailored after splicing. Enzymes attach a modified guanine "cap" to the 5′ end; later, this cap will help the finished mRNA bind to a ribosome. Between 50 and 300 adenines are also added to the 3′ end of a new mRNA. This poly-A tail is a signal that allows an mRNA to be exported from the nucleus, and as you will see in Chapter 10, it helps regulate the timing and duration of the mRNA's translation.

FIGURE 9.5 {Animated} Post-transcriptional modification of RNA. Introns are removed and exons spliced together. Messenger RNAs also get a poly-A tail and modified guanine "cap."

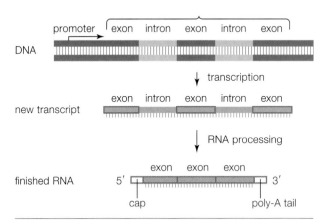

alternative splicing Post-translational RNA modification process in which some exons are removed or joined in various combinations.
exon Nucleotide sequence that remains in an RNA after post-transcriptional modification.
intron Nucleotide sequence that intervenes between exons and is removed during post-transcriptional modification.
promoter In DNA, a sequence to which RNA polymerase binds.
RNA polymerase Enzyme that carries out transcription.

CREDITS: (4) © O. L. Miller; (5) From Starr/Taggart/Evers/Starr, Biology, 13E. © 2013 Cengage Learning.

9.3 WHAT ROLES DO mRNA, rRNA, AND tRNA PLAY DURING TRANSLATION?

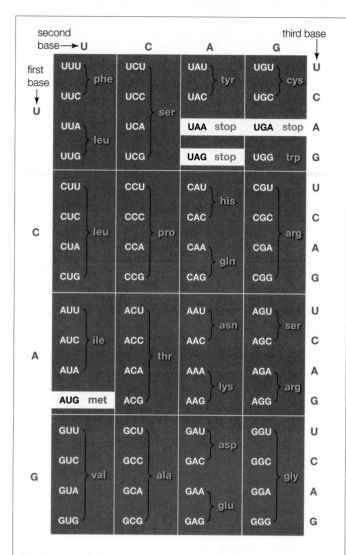

A codon table. Each codon in mRNA is a set of three nucleotide bases. Left column lists a codon's first base, the top row lists the second, and the right column lists the third. Sixty-one of the triplets encode amino acids; one of those, AUG, both codes for methionine and serves as a signal to start translation. Three codons are signals that stop translation.

ala alanine (A)	gly glycine (G)	pro proline (P)
arg arginine (R)	his histidine (H)	ser serine (S)
asn asparagine (N)	ile isoleucine (I)	thr threonine (T)
asp aspartic acid (D)	leu leucine (L)	trp tryptophan (W)
cys cysteine (C)	lys lysine (K)	tyr tyrosine (Y)
glu glutamic acid (E)	met methionine (M)	val valine (V)
gln glutamine (Q)	phe phenylalanine (F)	

Amino acid names and abbreviations.

FIGURE 9.6 The genetic code.

FIGURE IT OUT: Which codons specify the amino acid lysine (lys)?

Answer: AAA and AAG

DNA stores heritable information about proteins, but making those proteins requires messenger RNA (mRNA), transfer RNA (tRNA), and ribosomal RNA (rRNA). The three types of RNA interact to translate DNA's information into a protein.

THE MESSENGER: mRNA

An mRNA is essentially a disposable copy of a gene. Its job is to carry the gene's protein-building information to the other two types of RNA during translation. That protein-building information consists of a linear sequence of genetic "words" spelled with an alphabet of the four nucleotide bases A, C, G, and U. Each of the genetic "words" carried by an mRNA is three bases long, and each is a code—a **codon**—for a particular amino acid. With four possible nucleotides in each of the three positions of a codon, there are a total of sixty-four (or 4^3) mRNA codons. Collectively, the sixty-four codons constitute the **genetic code** (FIGURE 9.6). The sequence of bases in a triplet determines which amino acid the codon specifies. For instance, the codon UUU codes for the amino acid phenylalanine (phe), and UUA codes for leucine (leu).

Codons occur one after another along the length of an mRNA. When an mRNA is translated, the order of its codons determines the order of amino acids in the resulting polypeptide. Thus, the base sequence of a gene is transcribed into the base sequence of an mRNA, which is in turn translated into an amino acid sequence (FIGURE 9.7).

With a few exceptions, twenty naturally occurring amino acids are encoded by the sixty-four codons in the genetic

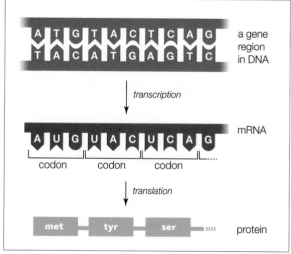

FIGURE 9.7 Example of the correspondence between DNA, RNA, and protein. A gene region in a strand of chromosomal DNA is transcribed into an mRNA, and the codons of the mRNA specify a chain of amino acids—a protein.

code. Sixty-four codons are more than are needed to specify twenty amino acids, so some amino acids are specified by more than one codon. For instance, the amino acid tyrosine (tyr) is specified by two codons: UAA and UAC.

Other codons signal the beginning and end of a protein-coding sequence. In most species, the first AUG in an mRNA serves as the signal to start translation. AUG is the codon for methionine, so methionine is always the first amino acid in new polypeptides of such organisms. The codons UAA, UAG, and UGA do not specify an amino acid. These are signals that stop translation, so they are called stop codons. A stop codon marks the end of the protein-coding sequence in an mRNA.

The genetic code is highly conserved, which means that most organisms use the same code and probably always have. Bacteria, archaea, and some protists have a few codons that differ from the eukaryotic code, as do mitochondria and chloroplasts—a clue that led to a theory of how these two organelles evolved (we return to this topic in Section 18.5).

THE TRANSLATORS: rRNA AND tRNA

Ribosomes interact with transfer RNAs (tRNAs) to translate the sequence of codons in an mRNA into a polypeptide. A ribosome has two subunits, one large and one small (FIGURE 9.8). Both subunits consist mainly of rRNA, with some associated structural proteins. During translation, a large and a small ribosomal subunit converge as an intact ribosome on an mRNA. Ribosomal RNA is one example of RNA with enzymatic activity: rRNA catalyzes formation of a peptide bond between amino acids as they are delivered to the ribosome.

Each tRNA has two attachment sites. The first is an **anticodon**, which is a triplet of nucleotides that base-pairs with an mRNA codon (FIGURE 9.9A). The other attachment site binds to an amino acid—the one specified by the codon. Transfer RNAs with different anticodons carry different amino acids.

During translation, tRNAs deliver amino acids to a ribosome, one after the next in the order specified by the codons in an mRNA (FIGURE 9.9B). As the amino acids are delivered, the ribosome joins them via peptide bonds into a new polypeptide (Section 3.4). Thus, the order of codons in an mRNA—DNA's protein-building message—becomes translated into a new protein.

---

anticodon In a tRNA, set of three nucleotides that base-pairs with an mRNA codon.
codon In an mRNA, a nucleotide base triplet that codes for an amino acid or stop signal during translation.
genetic code Complete set of sixty-four mRNA codons.

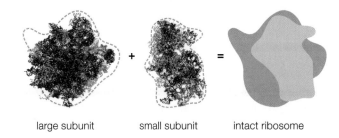

large subunit   small subunit   intact ribosome

FIGURE 9.8 {Animated} Ribosome structure. Each intact ribosome consists of a large and a small subunit. The structural protein components of the two subunits are shown in green; the catalytic rRNA components, in brown.

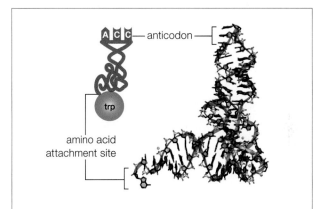

A Icon and model of the tRNA that carries the amino acid tryptophan. Each tRNA's anticodon is complementary to an mRNA codon. Each also carries the amino acid specified by that codon.

B During translation, tRNAs dock at an intact ribosome (for clarity, only the small subunit is shown, in tan). Here, the anticodons of two tRNAs have base-paired with complementary codons on an mRNA (red). The amino acids they carry are not shown, for clarity.

FIGURE 9.9 tRNA structure.

TAKE-HOME MESSAGE 9.3

The sequence of nucleotide triplets (codons) in an mRNA encode a gene's protein-building message.

The genetic code consists of sixty-four codons. Three are signals that stop translation; the remaining codons specify an amino acid. In most mRNAs, the first occurrence of the codon that specifies methionine is a signal to begin translation.

Ribosomes, which consist of two subunits of rRNA and proteins, assemble amino acids into polypeptide chains.

A tRNA has an anticodon complementary to an mRNA codon, and a binding site for the amino acid specified by that codon. During translation, tRNAs deliver amino acids to ribosomes.

CREDITS: (8) left & middle, From Starr/Taggart/Evers/Starr, Biology 13E. © 2013 Cengage Learning; right, From Starr/Evers/Starr, Biology Today and Tomorrow with Physiology, 3E. © 2010 Cengage Learning; (9A left) © Cengage Learning; (9A right, B) From Starr/Taggart/Evers/Starr, Biology, 13E. © 2013 Cengage Learning.

FIGURE 9.10 Overview of translation. In eukaryotes, RNA transcribed in the nucleus moves into the cytoplasm through nuclear pores. Translation occurs in the cytoplasm. Ribosomes simultaneously translating the same mRNA are called polysomes.

Translation, the second part of protein synthesis, occurs in the cytoplasm of all cells. Cytoplasm has many free amino acids, tRNAs, and ribosomal subunits available to participate in the process.

FIGURE 9.10 shows an overview of translation as it occurs in eukaryotes. An mRNA is transcribed in the nucleus ❶, and then transported through nuclear pores into the cytoplasm ❷. Translation begins when a small ribosomal subunit binds to the mRNA. Next, the anticodon of a special tRNA called an initiator base-pairs with the first AUG codon of the mRNA. Then, a large ribosomal subunit joins the small subunit ❸, and the intact ribosome begins to assemble a polypeptide chain as it moves along the mRNA ❹.

FIGURE 9.11 shows details of translation. Initiator tRNAs carry methionine, so the first amino acid of the new polypeptide chain is methionine. Another tRNA joins the complex when its anticodon base-pairs with the second codon in the mRNA ❺. This tRNA brings with it the second amino acid. The ribosome then catalyzes formation of a peptide bond between the first two amino acids ❻.

As the ribosome moves to the next codon, it releases the first tRNA. Another tRNA brings the third amino acid to the complex as its anticodon base-pairs with the third codon of the mRNA ❼. A peptide bond forms between the second and third amino acids ❽.

The second tRNA is released and the ribosome moves to the next codon. Another tRNA brings the fourth amino acid to the complex as its anticodon base-pairs with the fourth codon of the mRNA ❾. A peptide bond forms between the third and fourth amino acids. Elongation of the new polypeptide chain continues as the ribosome catalyzes peptide bonds between amino acids delivered by successive tRNAs.

CREDIT: (10) From Starr/Evers/Starr, Biology Today and Tomorrow with Physiology, 4E. © 2013 Cengage Learning.

Termination occurs when the ribosome reaches a stop codon in the mRNA ❿. The mRNA and the polypeptide detach from the ribosome, and the ribosomal subunits separate from each other. Translation is now complete. The new polypeptide either joins the pool of proteins in the cytoplasm, or it enters rough ER of the endomembrane system (Section 4.6).

In cells that are making a lot of protein, many ribosomes may simultaneously translate the same mRNA, in which case they are called polysomes:

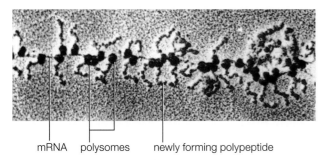

mRNA   polysomes   newly forming polypeptide

In bacteria and archaea, transcription and translation both occur in the cytoplasm, and these processes are closely linked in time and space. Translation begins before transcription ends, so a transcription "Christmas tree" is often decorated with polysome "balls."

Given that many polypeptides can be translated from one mRNA, why would any cell also make many copies of an mRNA? Compared with DNA, RNA is not very stable. An mRNA may last only a few minutes in cytoplasm before enzymes disassemble it. The fast turnover allows cells to adjust their protein synthesis quickly in response to changing needs.

Translation is energy intensive. That energy is provided mainly in the form of phosphate-group transfers from the RNA nucleotide GTP (shown in **FIGURE 9.2B**) to molecules involved in the process.

TAKE-HOME MESSAGE 9.4

Translation is an energy-requiring process that converts the protein-building information carried by an mRNA into a polypeptide.

Translation begins when an mRNA joins with an initiator tRNA and two ribosomal subunits.

Amino acids are delivered to the complex by tRNAs in the order dictated by successive mRNA codons. As amino acids arrive, the ribosome joins each to the end of the polypeptide.

Translation ends when the ribosome encounters a stop codon in the mRNA. The mRNA and the polypeptide are released, and the ribosome disassembles.

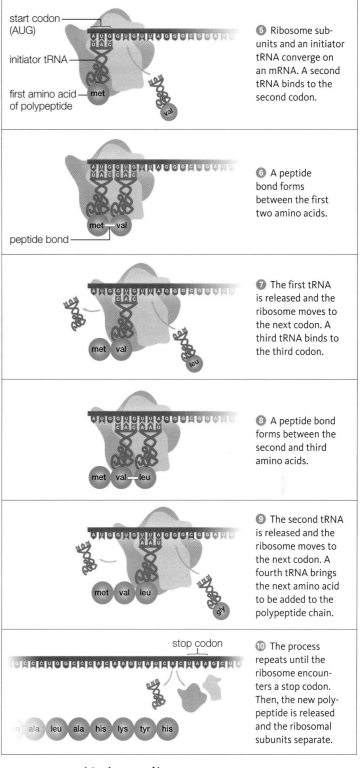

❺ Ribosome subunits and an initiator tRNA converge on an mRNA. A second tRNA binds to the second codon.

❻ A peptide bond forms between the first two amino acids.

❼ The first tRNA is released and the ribosome moves to the next codon. A third tRNA binds to the third codon.

❽ A peptide bond forms between the second and third amino acids.

❾ The second tRNA is released and the ribosome moves to the next codon. A fourth tRNA brings the next amino acid to be added to the polypeptide chain.

❿ The process repeats until the ribosome encounters a stop codon. Then, the new polypeptide is released and the ribosomal subunits separate.

FIGURE 9.11 {Animated} Translation. Translation begins when ribosomal subunits and an initiator tRNA converge on an mRNA. tRNAs deliver amino acids in the order dictated by successive codons in the mRNA. The ribosome links the amino acids together as it moves along the mRNA, so a polypeptide forms and elongates. Translation ends when the ribosome reaches a stop codon.

A Hemoglobin, an oxygen-binding protein in red blood cells. This protein consists of four polypeptides: two alpha globins (blue) and two beta globins (green). Each globin has a pocket that cradles a heme (red). Oxygen molecules bind to the iron atom at the center of each heme.

B Part of the DNA (blue), mRNA (brown), and amino acid sequence of human beta globin. Numbers indicate nucleotide position in the mRNA.

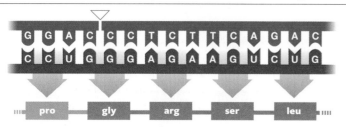

C A base-pair substitution replaces a thymine with an adenine. When the altered mRNA is translated, valine replaces glutamic acid as the sixth amino acid. Hemoglobin with this form of beta globin is called HbS, or sickle hemoglobin.

D A base-pair deletion shifts the reading frame for the rest of the mRNA, so a completely different protein product forms. The mutation shown results in a defective beta globin. The outcome is beta thalassemia, a genetic disorder in which a person has an abnormally low amount of hemoglobin.

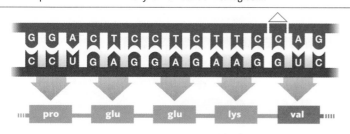

E An insertion of one nucleotide causes the reading frame for the rest of the mRNA to shift. The protein translated from this mRNA is too short and does not assemble correctly into hemoglobin molecules. As in D, the outcome is beta thalassemia.

FIGURE 9.12 {Animated} Examples of mutations.

Mutations, remember, are permanent changes in a DNA sequence (Section 8.5). A mutation in which one base pair is replaced by a different base pair is a **base-pair substitution**. Other mutations may involve the loss of one or more nucleotides (a **deletion**) or the addition of one or more extra nucleotides (an **insertion**).

Mutations are relatively uncommon events in a normal cell. Consider that the chromosomes in a diploid human cell collectively consist of about 6.5 billion nucleotides, any of which may become mutated each time that cell divides. On average, about 175 nucleotides do change during DNA replication. However, only about 3 percent of the cell's DNA encodes protein products, so there is a low probability that any of those mutations will be in a protein-coding region.

When a mutation does occur in a protein-coding region, the redundancy of the genetic code offers the cell a margin of safety. For example, a mutation that changes a CCC codon to CCG may not have further effects, because both of these codons specify serine. Other mutations may change an amino acid in a protein, or result in a premature stop codon that shortens it.

Mutations that alter a protein can have drastic effects on an organism. Consider the effects of mutations on hemoglobin, an oxygen-transporting protein in your red blood cells. Hemoglobin's structure allows it to bind and release oxygen. In adult humans, a hemoglobin molecule consists of four polypeptides called globins: two alpha globins and two beta globins (**FIGURE 9.12A**). Each globin folds around a heme, a cofactor with an iron atom at its center (Section 5.5). Oxygen molecules bind to hemoglobin at those iron atoms.

Mutations in the genes for alpha or beta globin cause a condition called anemia, in which a person's blood is deficient in red blood cells or in hemoglobin. Both outcomes limit the blood's ability to carry oxygen, and the resulting symptoms range from mild to life-threatening.

Sickle-cell anemia, a type of anemia that is most common in people of African ancestry, arises because of a base-pair substitution in the beta globin gene. The substitution causes the body to produce a version of beta globin in which the sixth amino acid is valine instead of glutamic acid (**FIGURE 9.12B,C**). Hemoglobin assembled with this altered beta globin chain is called sickle hemoglobin, or HbS.

Unlike glutamic acid, which carries a negative charge, valine carries no charge. As a result of that one base-pair substitution, a tiny patch of the beta globin polypeptide that is normally hydrophilic becomes hydrophobic. This change slightly alters the hemoglobin's behavior. Under certain

CREDITS: (12A) From Starr/Evers/Starr, Biology Today and Tomorrow with Physiology, 3E. © 2010 Cengage Learning; (12B–E) © Cengage Learning.

A base-pair substitution results in the abnormal beta globin chain of sickle hemoglobin (HbS). The sixth amino acid in such chains is valine, not glutamic acid. The difference causes HbS molecules to form rod-shaped clumps that distort normally round blood cells (red) into sickle shapes (tan).

FIGURE 9.13 An amino acid substitution results in abnormally shaped red blood cells characteristic of sickle-cell anemia.

conditions, HbS molecules stick together and form large, rodlike clumps. Red blood cells that contain the clumps become distorted into a crescent (sickle) shape (**FIGURE 9.13**). Sickled cells clog tiny blood vessels, thus disrupting blood circulation throughout the body. Over time, repeated episodes of sickling can damage organs and cause death.

A different type of anemia, beta thalassemia, is caused by the deletion of the twentieth nucleotide in the coding region of the beta globin gene (**FIGURE 9.12D**). Like many other deletions, this one causes the reading frame of the mRNA codons to shift. A frameshift usually has drastic consequences because it garbles the genetic message, just as incorrectly grouping a series of letters garbles the meaning of a sentence:

> The fat cat ate the sad rat
> T hef atc ata tet hes adr at

The frameshift caused by the beta globin deletion results in a polypeptide that differs drastically from normal beta globin in amino acid sequence and length. This outcome

is the source of the anemia. Beta thalassemia can also be caused by insertion mutations, which, like deletions, often result in frameshifts (**FIGURE 9.12E**).

Not all mutations that affect protein structure disrupt codons for amino acids. DNA also contains special nucleotide sequences that influence the expression of nearby genes (we return to this topic in the next chapter). A promoter is one example; an intron–exon splice site is another. Consider the mutation that causes hairlessness in cats (as shown in the chapter opening photo). In this case, a base-pair substitution disrupts an intron–exon splice site in the gene for keratin, a fibrous protein (Section 3.4). The intron, which is not correctly removed from the RNA, becomes an insertion in the mRNA. The altered protein translated from this mRNA cannot properly assemble into filaments that make up cat fur.

base-pair substitution Type of mutation in which a single base pair changes.
deletion Mutation in which one or more nucleotides are lost.
insertion Mutation in which one or more nucleotides become inserted into DNA.

TAKE-HOME MESSAGE 9.5

Mutations that result in an altered protein can have drastic consequences.

A base-pair substitution may change an amino acid in a protein, or it may introduce a premature stop codon.

Frameshifts that occur after an insertion or deletion can change an mRNA's codon reading frame, thus garbling its protein-building instructions.

Education

FIGURE 9.14 Bulgarian spy's weapon: an umbrella modified to fire a tiny pellet of ricin into a victim. An umbrella like this one was used to assassinate Georgi Markov on the streets of London in 1978.

A DOSE OF RICIN AS SMALL AS A FEW GRAINS OF SALT CAN KILL AN ADULT HUMAN, and there is no antidote. Ricin is a protein that deters beetles, birds, mammals, and other animals from eating seeds of the castor-oil plant (*Ricinus communis*), which grows wild in tropical regions worldwide and is widely cultivated. Castor-oil seeds are the source of castor oil, an ingredient in plastics, cosmetics, paints, soaps, polishes, and many other items. After the oil is extracted from the seeds, the ricin is typically discarded along with the leftover seed pulp.

Lethal effects of ricin were being exploited as long ago as 1888, but using ricin as a weapon is now banned by most countries under the Geneva Protocol. However, controlling its production is impossible, because it takes no special skills or equipment to manufacture the toxin from easily obtained raw materials. Thus, ricin appears periodically in the news as a tool of terrorists. For example, in June, 2013, a Texas actress was arrested for sending ricin-laced letters to President Obama

and the mayor of New York City. Perhaps the most famous example occurred in 1978, at the height of the Cold War when defectors from countries under Russian control were targets for assassination. Bulgarian journalist Georgi Markov had defected to England and was working for the BBC. As he made his way to a bus stop on a London street, an assassin used a modified umbrella (FIGURE 9.14) to fire a tiny, ricin-laced ball into Markov's leg. Markov died in agony three days later.

Ricin is called a ribosome-inactivating protein (RIP) because it inactivates ribosomes. RIPs are enzymes that remove a particular adenine base from one of the rRNAs in the ribosome's heavy subunit. The adenine is part of a binding site for proteins involved in GTP-requiring steps of elongation. After the base has been removed, the ribosome can no longer bind to these proteins, and elongation stops. If enough ribosomes are affected, protein synthesis grinds to a halt. Proteins are critical to all life processes, so cells that cannot make them die very quickly. Someone who inhales ricin can die from low

FIGURE 9.15 Lethal lineup: a few toxic ribosome-inactivating proteins (RIPs) and their sources. One of the two chains of a toxic RIP helps the molecule cross a cell's plasma membrane; the other is an enzyme that inactivates ribosomes.

blood pressure and respiratory failure within a few days of exposure.

Other RIPs are made by some bacteria, mushrooms, algae, and many plants (including food crops such as tomatoes, barley, and spinach). Most of these proteins are not particularly toxic in humans because they do not cross intact cell membranes very well. Those that do, including ricin, have a domain that binds tightly to glycolipids attached to proteins on our plasma membranes (**FIGURE 9.15**). Binding causes the cell to take up the RIP by endocytosis (Section 5.8). Once inside cytoplasm, the enzyme part of the molecule quickly goes to work: One molecule of ricin can inactivate more than 1,000 ribosomes per minute.

Fortunately, few people actually encounter ricin. Other RIPs are more prevalent. Bracelets made from beautiful seeds were recalled from stores in 2011 after a botanist recognized the seeds as jequirity beans. These beans contain abrin, an RIP even more toxic than ricin. Shiga toxin, an RIP made by *Shigella dysenteriae* bacteria, causes a severe bloody diarrhea (dysentery) that can be lethal. Some strains of *E. coli* bacteria make Shiga-like toxin, an RIP that is the source of intestinal illness (Section 4.12).

Despite their toxicity, the main function of RIPs may not be destroying ribosomes. Many are part of the immune system in plants, but it is their antiviral and anticancer activity that has researchers abuzz. Plants that make RIPs have been used as traditional medicines for many centuries. Western scientists are now investigating RIPs as potential weapons to combat HIV and cancer.

The unique properties of RIPs are proving particularly useful in drug design. For example, researchers who design drugs for cancer therapy have modified ricin's glycolipid-binding domain to recognize plasma membrane proteins (Section 4.3) especially abundant in cancer cells. The modified ricin preferentially enters—and kills—cancer cells. Ricin's toxic enzyme has also been attached to an antibody that can find cancer cells in a person's body. The intent of both strategies: to assassinate the cancer cells without harming normal ones.

Summary

SECTION 9.1 Information encoded within the nucleotide sequence of DNA occurs in subsets called **genes**. Converting the information in a gene to an RNA or protein product is called **gene expression**. RNA is produced during **transcription**. Ribosomal RNA (**rRNA**) and **transfer RNA** (**tRNA**) interact during **translation** of a **messenger RNA** (**mRNA**) into a protein product:

$$\text{DNA} \xrightarrow{\text{transcription}} \text{mRNA} \xrightarrow{\text{translation}} \text{protein}$$

SECTION 9.2 During transcription, the enzyme **RNA polymerase** binds to a **promoter** near a gene on a chromosome. The polymerase moves over the gene region, linking RNA nucleotides in the order dictated by the nucleotide sequence of the DNA. The new RNA strand is an RNA copy of the gene.

The RNA of eukaryotes is modified before it leaves the nucleus. **Introns** are removed, and the remaining **exons** may be rearranged and spliced in different combinations, a process called **alternative splicing**. A cap and poly-A tail are also added to a new mRNA.

SECTION 9.3 An mRNA carries DNA's protein-building information. The information consists of a series of **codons**, which are sets of three nucleotides. Sixty-four codons constitute the **genetic code**. Three codons function as signals that terminate translation. The remaining codons specify a particular amino acid. Some amino acids are specified by multiple codons.

Each tRNA has an **anticodon** that can base-pair with a codon, and it binds to the amino acid specified by that codon. Enzymatic rRNA and proteins make up the two subunits of ribosomes.

SECTION 9.4 During translation, protein-building information that is carried by an mRNA directs the synthesis of a polypeptide. First, an mRNA, an initiator tRNA, and two ribosomal subunits converge. Next, amino acids are delivered by tRNAs in the order specified by the codons in the mRNA. The intact ribosome catalyzes formation of a peptide bond between the successive amino acids, so a polypeptide forms. Translation ends when the ribosome encounters a stop codon in the mRNA.

SECTION 9.5 **Insertions**, **deletions**, and **base-pair substitutions** are mutations. A mutation that changes a gene's product may have harmful effects. Sickle-cell anemia, which is caused by a base-pair substitution in the gene for the beta globin chain of hemoglobin, is one example. Beta thalassemia is an outcome of frameshift mutations in the beta globin gene.

SECTION 9.6 The ability to make proteins is critical to all life processes. Ribosome-inactivating proteins (RIPs) have an enzyme domain that permanently disables ribosomes. Ricin and other toxic RIPs have an additional protein domain that triggers endocytosis. Once inside cytoplasm, the molecule's enzyme domain destroys the cell's ability to make proteins.

Self-Quiz   Answers in Appendix VII

1. A chromosome contains many different gene regions that are transcribed into different _____ .
   a. proteins   c. RNAs
   b. polypeptides   d. a and b

2. A binding site for RNA polymerase is called a _____ .
   a. gene   c. codon
   b. promoter   d. protein

3. An RNA molecule is typically _____ ; a DNA molecule is typically _____ .
   a. single-stranded; double-stranded
   b. double-stranded; single-stranded
   c. both are single-stranded
   d. both are double-stranded

4. RNAs form by _____ ; proteins form by _____ .
   a. replication; translation
   b. translation; transcription
   c. transcription; translation
   d. replication; transcription

5. The main function of a DNA molecule is to _____ .
   a. store heritable information
   b. carry RNA's message for translation
   c. form peptide bonds between amino acids
   d. carry amino acids to ribosomes

6. The main function of an mRNA molecule is to _____ .
   a. store heritable information
   b. carry DNA's genetic message for translation
   c. form peptide bonds between amino acids
   d. carry amino acids to ribosomes

7. Energy that drives transcription is provided mainly by _____ .
   a. ATP   c. GTP
   b. RNA nucleotides   d. all are correct

8. Most codons specify a(n) _____ .
   a. protein   c. amino acid
   b. polypeptide   d. mRNA

9. Anticodons pair with _____ .
   a. mRNA codons   c. RNA anticodons
   b. DNA codons   d. amino acids

10. Up to _____ amino acids can be encoded by an mRNA that consists of 45 nucleotides plus a stop codon.
    a. 15   c. 90
    b. 45   d. 135

Data Analysis Activities

RIPs as Cancer Drugs Researchers are taking a page from the structure–function relationship of RIPs in their quest for cancer treatments. The most toxic RIPs, remember, have one domain that interferes with ribosomes, and another that carries them into cells. Melissa Cheung and her colleagues incorporated a peptide that binds to skin cancer cells into the enzymatic part of an RIP, the *E. coli* Shiga-like toxin. The researchers created a new RIP that specifically kills skin cancer cells, which are notoriously resistant to established therapies. Some of their results are shown in **FIGURE 9.16**.

1. Which cells had the greatest response to an increase in concentration of the engineered RIP?
2. At what concentration of RIP did all of the different kinds of cells survive?
3. Which cells survived best at 10^{-6} grams per liter RIP?
4. On which type of cancer cells did the RIP have the least effect?

FIGURE 9.16 Effect of an engineered RIP on cancer cells.

The model on the *left* shows the enzyme portion of *E. coli* Shiga-like toxin that has been engineered to carry a small sequence of amino acids (in blue) that targets skin cancer cells. (Red indicates the active site.)

The graph on the *right* shows the effect of this engineered RIP on human cancer cells of the skin (●); breast (◆); liver (▲); and prostate (■).

11. _____ are removed from new mRNAs.
    a. Introns   c. Telomeres
    b. Exons   d. Amino acids

12. Where does transcription take place in a typical eukaryotic cell?
    a. the nucleus   c. the cytoplasm
    b. ribosomes   d. b and c are correct

13. Where does translation take place in a typical eukaryotic cell?
    a. the nucleus   c. a and b
    b. the cytoplasm   d. neither a nor b

14. Energy that drives translation is provided mainly by _____ .
    a. ATP   c. GTP
    b. amino acids   d. all are correct

15. Match the terms with the best description.
    ___ genetic message   a. protein-coding segment
    ___ promoter   b. RNA polymerase binding site
    ___ polysome   c. read as base triplets
    ___ exon   d. removed before translation
    ___ genetic code   e. occurs only in groups
    ___ intron   f. complete set of 64 codons

CENGAGE To access course materials, please visit
brain.com www.cengagebrain.com.

Critical Thinking

1. Researchers are designing and testing antisense drugs as therapies for a variety of diseases, including cancer, AIDS, diabetes, and muscular dystrophy. The drugs are also being tested to fight infection by deadly viruses such as Ebola. Antisense drugs consist of short mRNA strands that are complementary in base sequence to mRNAs linked to the diseases. Speculate on how these drugs work.

2. An anticodon has the sequence GCG. What amino acid does this tRNA carry? What would be the effect of a mutation that changed the C of the anticodon to a G?

3. Each position of a codon can be occupied by one of four (4) nucleotides. What is the minimum number of nucleotides per codon necessary to specify all 20 of the amino acids that are found in proteins?

4. Refer to **FIGURE 9.6**, then translate the following mRNA nucleotide sequence into an amino acid sequence, starting at the first base:

(5') UGUCAUGCUCGUCUUGAAUCUUGU
GAUGCUCGUUGGAUUAAUUGU (3')

5. Translate the sequence of bases in the previous question, starting at the second base.

6. Can you spell your name using the one-letter amino acid abbreviations shown in **FIGURE 9.6**? If so, construct an mRNA sequence that encodes your "protein" name.

CREDIT: Source: Cheung et al., *Molecular Cancer*, 9:28, 2010.

National Geographic Explorer Jane Goodall observes
the behavior of two chimpanzees. About 97 percent of
chimpanzee DNA is identical with human DNA, but how
that DNA is used differs between the two species. The
differences in gene expression patterns give rise to major
differences in biology and behavior.

10

CONTROL OF GENE EXPRESSION

Links to Earlier Concepts

This chapter explores metabolism (Sections 5.3, 5.4, 5.5) in the context of gene expression (9.1). You will be applying what you know about DNA: structure (8.2), chromosomes (8.3), replication and hybridization (8.4), mutations (8.5, 9.5), and differentiation (8.6), as well as transcription (9.2) and translation (9.4). You will also revisit functional groups (3.1), carbohydrates (3.2), active transport (5.7), glycolysis (7.1), and fermentation (7.6).

KEY CONCEPTS

MECHANISMS OF GENE CONTROL
Every step of gene expression is regulated. This control is critical for development, and it allows individual cells to respond to changes in extracellular conditions.

MASTER GENES
During development, the orderly, localized expression of master genes gives rise to the body plan of complex multicelled animals.

GENE CONTROL IN EUKARYOTES
Genes that govern X chromosome inactivation and male sex determination in mammals, and flower formation in plants, offer examples of gene control in eukaryotes.

GENE CONTROL IN PROKARYOTES
Most gene control in prokaryotes occurs at the level of transcription. Fast adjustment of transcription allows these cells to respond quickly to changes in external conditions.

EPIGENETICS
New research is revealing how gene expression patterns that arise during an individual's lifetime in response to environmental pressures can be passed to descendants.

A typical cell in your body uses only about 10 percent of its genes at one time. Some of the active genes affect structural features and metabolic pathways common to all of your cells; others are expressed only by certain subsets of cells. For example, most body cells express genes that encode the enzymes of glycolysis, but only immature red blood cells express genes that encode globin.

Control over which genes are expressed at a particular time is necessary for cell differentiation (Section 8.6), and for proper development of complex, multicelled bodies. Such control also allows individual cells—prokaryotic and eukaryotic types—to respond appropriately to changes in their external environment.

GENE EXPRESSION CONTROL

The "switches" that turn a gene on or off are molecules or processes that trigger or inhibit the individual steps of its expression (**FIGURE 10.1**).

❶ Transcription In prokaryotes, most control over gene expression occurs at the level of transcription, but eukaryotes regulate this step too. Proteins called **transcription factors** affect whether and how fast a gene is transcribed by binding directly to the DNA. Transcription of a eukaryotic gene is typically governed by many interacting transcription factors, giving eukaryotic cells a nuanced level of control over RNA production. A simpler level of control allows prokaryotes to adapt very quickly to changes in their environment.

There are many types of transcription factors. Those called **repressors** shut off transcription or slow it down, either by preventing RNA polymerase from accessing the promoter or by impeding its progress along the DNA strand. Eukaryotic repressors work by binding directly to a promotor, or to a silencer—a site in the DNA that may be thousands of base pairs away from the gene. Prokaryotic silencers are called **operators** (we discuss operators in Section 10.4). **Activators** are transcription factors that recruit RNA polymerase to a promoter or help

it bind, so they speed up transcription. Some eukaryotic activators work by binding to DNA sequences called **enhancers**, which, like silencers, may be far away from the gene they affect. Transcription factors that bind to regions of DNA called insulators prevent nearby genes from being affected by enhancers or silencers (**FIGURE 10.2**).

Chromatin structure also affects transcription. Almost all eukaryotic cells and some archaea have histones (Section 8.3). In these cells, only DNA regions that have been unwound from histones are accessible to RNA polymerase. Modifications to histone proteins change the way they interact with the DNA that wraps around them. Some modifications make histones release their grip on the DNA; others make them tighten it. For example, adding acetyl groups ($-COCH_3$) to a histone loosens the DNA, so enzymes that acetylate histones allow transcription to proceed in that region of DNA. Conversely, adding methyl groups ($-CH_3$) to a histone tightens the DNA, so enzymes that methylate histones shut down transcription.

In some specialized cells of eukaryotes, a very high level of gene expression can be achieved when DNA is copied repeatedly without cell division. The result is a set of polytene chromosomes, each consisting of hundreds or thousands of side-by-side copies of the same DNA molecule (the chromosome in **FIGURE 10.2** is polytene). Transcription of one gene occurs simultaneously on all of the DNA strands, quickly producing a lot of mRNA.

❷ mRNA Processing and Transport As you know, transcription in eukaryotes occurs in the nucleus, and translation occurs in cytoplasm (Section 9.2). An mRNA can pass through pores of a nuclear envelope only after it has been processed appropriately—spliced, capped, and finished with a poly-A tail. Mechanisms that delay these post-transcriptional modifications also delay the mRNA's appearance in cytoplasm for translation.

Control over post-transcriptional modification can also affect the form of a protein. Consider RNA transcribed from the gene for fibronectin, a protein produced by cells of vertebrate animals. Two cell types splice this RNA alternatively, so they produce different mRNAs—and different forms of fibronectin. Liver cells produce a soluble form that circulates in blood plasma. Fibroblasts produce an insoluble form that is a major protein component of extracellular matrix (Section 4.10).

The majority of eukaryotic mRNAs are delivered to organelles or specific regions of cytoplasm. This localization allows translation of an mRNA to occur close to where its protein product is being used. In an egg, mRNA localization is crucial for proper development of the future

FIGURE 10.1 {Animated}
Points of control over gene expression.

DNA

❶ Transcription

RNA

❷ mRNA Processing and Transport

mRNA

❸ Translation

polypeptide

❹ Post-Translational Modification

active protein

FIGURE 10.2 Part of a chromosome in a salivary gland cell of a fruit fly. DNA appears blue. Red and green show the locations of two transcription factors bound to insulator sequences (yellow shows where these two colors overlap). These proteins are restricting enhancer access to the DNA.

embryo. A short base sequence near an mRNA's poly-A tail is like a zip code that specifies a particular destination. Proteins that attach to the zip code drag the mRNA along cytoskeletal elements to that destination. Other proteins influence localization by interacting with mRNA-binding proteins. Researchers recently discovered that mRNA localization also occurs in prokaryotes, but the mechanism is not yet understood.

❸ **Translation** In eukaryotes, most control over gene expression occurs at the level of translation. Production of the many molecules that participate in translation is a major point of control in these cells. An mRNA's sequence also affects translation. For example, proteins that bind to a zip code region prevent transcription from occurring before the mRNA is delivered to its final destination. As another example, consider that the longer an mRNA lasts, the more protein can be made from it. Enzymes begin to disassemble a new mRNA as soon as it arrives in cytoplasm. The fast turnover allows a cell to adjust its protein synthesis quickly in response to changing needs. How long an mRNA persists depends on its base sequence, the length of its poly-A tail, and which proteins are attached to it.

In eukaryotes, translation of a particular mRNA can be shut down by tiny bits of noncoding RNA called microRNAs. A microRNA is complementary in sequence to part of an mRNA, and when the two show up together in cytoplasm they base-pair to form a small double-stranded region of RNA. By a process called RNA interference, any double-stranded RNA is cut up into small bits that are taken up by special enzyme complexes. These complexes then destroy every RNA in a cell that can base-pair with the bits. Thus, expression of a microRNA results in the destruction of all mRNA complementary to it.

Double-stranded RNA is also a factor in control over translation in prokaryotes. For example, bacteria can shut off translation of a particular mRNA by expressing an antisense RNA (one that is complementary in sequence to the mRNA). When the two molecules base-pair, ribosomes cannot initiate translation on the resulting double-stranded RNA. As another example, some bacterial mRNAs can loop back on themselves to form a small double-stranded region. Translation only occurs when this structure is unraveled, for example by heat.

❹ **Post-Translational Modification** Many newly synthesized polypeptide chains must be modified before they become functional. For example, some enzymes become active only after they have been phosphorylated (Section 5.5). Such post-translational modifications inhibit, activate, or stabilize many molecules, including enzymes that participate in transcription and translation.

activator Transcription factor that increases the rate of transcription.
enhancer In eukaryotic cells, a binding site in DNA for an activator.
operator In prokaryotes, a binding site in DNA for a repressor.
repressor Transcription factor that reduces the rate of transcription.
transcription factor Protein that influences transcription by binding directly to DNA; for example, an activator or repressor.

TAKE-HOME MESSAGE 10.1

Gene control is necessary for individual cells to respond to changes in their extracellular environment. It is also crucial for proper development of complex, multicelled eukaryotes.

Gene expression can be switched on or off, or speeded up or slowed down, by molecules and processes that operate at each step.

CREDIT: (2) *Journal of Biosciences*, Volume 36, Number 3, August 2011, Indian Academy of Sciences, Springer.

A The master gene *even-skipped* is expressed (in red) only where two maternal gene products (blue and green) overlap.

90 minutes

100 minutes

B By 165 minutes after fertilization, the products of several master genes, including the two shown here in green and blue, have confined the expression of *even-skipped* (red) to seven stripes. (Pink and yellow areas are regions in which red fluorescence has overlapped with blue or green.)

120 minutes

140 minutes

165 minutes

C One day later, seven segments have developed. The position of the segments corresponds to the position of the *even-skipped* stripes.

13 hours

FIGURE 10.3 How gene expression control makes a fly, as illuminated by the formation of segments in a *Drosophila* embryo.

Expression of different master genes is shown by different colors in fluorescence microscopy images of whole embryos at successive stages of development (time after fertilization is indicated). Bright dots are individual nuclei.

MASTER GENES

As an animal embryo develops, its cells differentiate and form tissues, organs, and body parts. The entire process is driven by cascades of master gene expression. The products of **master genes** affect the expression of many other genes. Expression of a master gene causes other genes to be expressed, which in turn cause other genes to be expressed, and so on. The final outcome is the completion of an intricate task such as the formation of an eye.

The orchestration of gene expression during development begins when maternal mRNAs are delivered to opposite ends of an unfertilized egg as it forms. These mRNAs are translated only after the egg is fertilized. Then, their protein products diffuse away, forming gradients that span the entire developing embryo. The position of a nucleus within the embryo determines how much of these proteins it is exposed to. This in turn determines which master genes it turns on. The products of those master genes also form in gradients that span the embryo. Still other master genes are transcribed depending on where a nucleus falls within these gradients, and so on. Eventually, the products of master genes cause undifferentiated cells to differentiate, and specialized structures form in specific regions of the embryo (**FIGURE 10.3**).

HOMEOTIC GENES

A **homeotic gene** is a type of master gene that governs the formation of a body part such as an eye, leg, or wing. Animal homeotic genes encode transcription factors with a homeodomain, which is a region of about sixty amino acids that can bind directly to a promoter or some other sequence of nucleotides in a chromosome (**FIGURE 10.4A**).

Homeotic genes are often named for what happens when a mutation alters their function. For example, fruit flies with a mutation that affects their *antennapedia* gene (*ped* means foot) have legs in place of antennae (**FIGURE 10.4B**). The *dunce* gene is required for learning and memory. *Wingless, wrinkled,* and *minibrain* are self-explanatory. *Tinman* is necessary for development of a heart. Flies with a mutated *groucho* gene have extra bristles above their eyes (**FIGURE 10.4C**). Flies with a mutated *eyeless* gene develop with no eyes (**FIGURE 10.5A,B**). One gene was named *toll,* after what its German discoverer exclaimed upon seeing the disastrous effects of the mutation (*toll* is German slang that means "cool!").

The function of many homeotic genes has been discovered by deliberately manipulating their expression. Researchers can inactivate a gene by introducing a mutation that prevents its expression, or by deleting it entirely, an experiment called a **knockout**. A knockout organism (one

CREDITS: (3A–B) © Maria Samsonova and John Reinitz; (3C) © Jim Langeland, Jim Williams, Julie Gates, Kathy Vorwerk, Steve Paddock, and Sean Carroll, HHMI, University of Wisconsin-Madison.

A The protein product (in gold) of the homeotic gene *antennapedia* attached to a promoter. The homeodomain is the region that binds to the DNA. Expression of *antennapedia* in embryonic tissues of the insect thorax causes legs to form.

B A mutation that triggers expression of the *antennapedia* gene in embryonic tissues of the head causes legs to form there too. Compare a normal fly, *right*.

C *Groucho* mutation *left*. Normal fly, *right*.

FIGURE 10.4 Effects of mutations in homeotic genes.

eye

A Normal fruit fly with large, round eyes.

B A fruit fly with a mutation in its *eyeless* gene develops with no eyes.

C Eyes form wherever the *eyeless* gene is expressed in fly embryos—here, on the head and wing.

The *PAX6* gene of humans, mice, squids, and some other animals is so similar to *eyeless* that it also triggers eye development in flies.

D Normal human eye with a colored iris surrounding the pupil (dark area where light enters).

E Eye that developed without an iris, a result of a mutation in *PAX6*. This condition is called aniridia.

FIGURE 10.5 Eyes and *eyeless*.

that has had a gene knocked out) may differ from normal individuals, and the differences are clues to the function of the missing gene product.

Homeotic genes affect development by the same mechanisms in all multicelled eukaryotes, and many are interchangeable among different species. Thus, we can infer that they evolved in the most ancient eukaryotic cells. Homeodomains often differ among species only in conservative substitutions (one amino acid has replaced another with similar chemical properties). Consider the *eyeless* gene. Eyes form in embryonic fruit flies wherever this gene is expressed, which, in normal flies, is only in tissues of the head. If the *eyeless* gene is expressed in another part of the developing embryo, eyes form there too (**FIGURE 10.5C**). Humans, squids, mice, fish, and many other animals have a gene called *PAX6*, which is very similar in DNA sequence to the *eyeless* gene in flies. In humans, mutations in *PAX6* cause eye disorders such as aniridia, in which a person's irises are underdeveloped

or missing (**FIGURE 10.5D,E**). If the *PAX6* gene from a human or mouse is inserted into a fly, it has the same effect as the *eyeless* gene: An eye forms wherever it is expressed. Such studies are evidence of shared ancestry among these evolutionarily distant animals.

homeotic gene Type of master gene; its expression controls formation of specific body parts during development.
knockout An experiment in which a gene is deliberately inactivated in a living organism; also, an organism that carries a knocked-out gene.
master gene Gene encoding a product that affects the expression of many other genes.

TAKE-HOME MESSAGE 10.2

Animal development is orchestrated by cascades of master gene expression in embryos.

The expression of homeotic genes during development governs the formation of specific body parts.

Homeotic genes that function in similar ways in evolutionarily distant animals are evidence of shared ancestry.

CREDITS: (4A) From Starr/Taggart/Evers/Starr, Biology, 13E. © 2013 Cengage Learning; (4B) left, © Visuals Unlimited; right, © Jürgen Berger, Max-Planck-Institut for Developmental Biology, Tübingen; (4C) Courtesy of Dr. Barbara Jennings, UCL Cancer Institute, www.ucl.ac.uk; (5A,B) David Scharf/Science Source; (5C) Eye of Science/Science Source; (5D) M. Bloch; (5E) Courtesy of the Aniridia Foundation International, www.aniridia.net.

Gene control influences many traits that are characteristic of humans and other eukaryotic organisms, as the following examples illustrate.

X MARKS THE SPOT

In humans and other mammals, a female's cells contain two X chromosomes, one inherited from her mother, the other one from her father. In each cell, one X chromosome is always tightly condensed (**FIGURE 10.6A**). We call the condensed X chromosomes **Barr bodies**, after Murray Barr, who discovered them. Condensation prevents transcription,

A Barr bodies are visible as red spots in the nucleus of the four XX cells on the *left*. Compare the nucleus of two XY cells to the *right*.

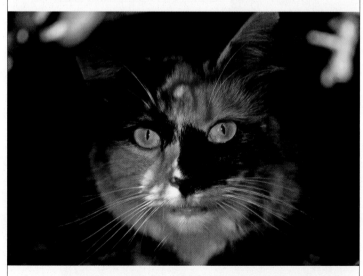

B When this cat was an embryo, one of the two X chromosomes was inactivated in each of her cells. The descendants of the cells formed her adult body, which is a mosaic for expression of X chromosome genes. Black fur arises in patches where genes on the X chromosome inherited from one parent are expressed; orange fur arises in patches where genes on the X chromosome inherited from the other parent are expressed.

FIGURE 10.6 {Animated} X chromosome inactivation.

so most of the genes on a Barr body are not expressed. This **X chromosome inactivation** ensures that only one of the two X chromosomes in a female's cells is active. According to a mechanism called **dosage compensation**, the inactivation equalizes expression of X chromosome genes between the sexes. The body cells of male mammals (XY) have one set of X chromosome genes. Body cells of female mammals (XX) have two sets, but female embryos do not develop properly when both sets are expressed.

X chromosome inactivation occurs when an embryo is a ball of about 200 cells. In humans and most other mammals, it occurs independently in every cell of a female embryo. The maternal X chromosome may get inactivated in one cell, and the paternal or maternal X chromosome may get inactivated in a cell next to it. Once the selection is made in a cell, all of that cell's descendants make the same selection as they continue dividing and forming tissues. As a result of random inactivation of maternal and paternal X chromosomes, an adult female mammal is a "mosaic" for the expression of X chromosome genes. She has patches of tissue in which genes of the maternal X chromosome are expressed, and patches in which genes of the paternal X chromosome are expressed (**FIGURE 10.6B**).

How does just one of two X chromosomes get inactivated? An X chromosome gene called *XIST* is transcribed on only one of the two X chromosomes. The gene's product, a long noncoding RNA, sticks to the chromosome that expresses the gene. The RNA coats the chromosome, and by an unknown mechanism causes it to condense into a Barr body. Thus, transcription of the *XIST* gene keeps the chromosome from transcribing other genes. The other chromosome does not express *XIST*, so it does not get coated with RNA; its genes remain available for transcription. How a cell "chooses" which X chromosome will express *XIST* is still unknown.

MALE SEX DETERMINATION IN HUMANS

The human X chromosome carries 1,336 genes. Some of those genes are associated with sexual traits, such as the distribution of body fat and hair. However, most of the genes on the X chromosome govern nonsexual traits such as blood clotting and color perception. Such genes are expressed in both males and females. Males, remember, also inherit one X chromosome.

The human Y chromosome carries only 307 genes, but one of them is *SRY*—the master gene for male sex determination in mammals. Its expression in XY embryos triggers the formation of testes, which are male gonads. Some of the cells in these primary male reproductive

CREDITS: (6A) © Dr. William Strauss; (6B) Stephen St. John/National Geographic Creative.

petals   carpel

sepals   stamens

1 2 3 4

B

A   C

A gene mutations cause carpels to form in whorl 1, and stamens to form in whorl 2.

B gene mutations cause sepals to form in whorl 2, and carpels to form in whorl 3.

C gene mutations cause petals to form in whorl 3, and sepals to form in whorl 4.

Sequential expression of *A*, *B*, and *C* floral identity genes gives rise to four whorls of tissue in a floral shoot. Each whorl produces one floral structure: sepals, petals, stamens, or carpels. Expression of the *A* gene triggers development of the outer whorl, which produces sepals. *A* and *B* gene products trigger petals to form in the second whorl. *B* and *C* gene products together trigger stamens to form in the third whorl, and the *C* gene product alone triggers carpel development in the inner whorl.

FIGURE 10.7 {Animated} Control of flower formation, as revealed by mutations in *Arabidopsis thaliana*.

 FIGURE IT OUT: What type of genes are the floral identity genes?

Answer: They are homeotic genes.

organs make testosterone, a sex hormone that controls the emergence of male secondary sexual traits such as facial hair, increased musculature, and a deep voice. We know that *SRY* is the master gene that controls emergence of male sexual traits because mutations in this gene cause XY individuals to develop external genitalia that appear female. An XX embryo has no Y chromosome, no *SRY* gene, and much less testosterone, so primary female reproductive organs (ovaries) form instead of testes. Ovaries make estrogens and other sex hormones that will govern the development of female secondary sexual traits, such as enlarged, functional breasts, and fat deposits around the hips and thighs.

FLOWER FORMATION

In flowering plants, populations of cells in a shoot tip may give rise to a flower instead of leaves. Studies of mutations in thale cress, *Arabidopsis thaliana*, revealed the gene control behind this switch in development. Transcription factors produced by three sets of floral identity genes (called *A*, *B*, and *C*) guide the process. These genes are switched on by

environmental cues such as seasonal changes in the length of night, as you will see in Section 27.11.

When a flower forms at the tip of a shoot, differentiating cells form whorls of tissue, one over the other like layers of an onion. Each whorl produces one type of floral structure— sepals, petals, stamens, or carpels. This pattern is dictated by sequential, overlapping expression of the *ABC* genes (**FIGURE 10.7**). The *A* genes are switched on first in a shoot tip, and their products trigger events that cause the outer whorl to form and give rise to sepals. *B* genes switch on before *A* genes turn off. Together, *A* and *B* gene products cause the second whorl to form and produce petals. Next, *A* genes turn off and the *C* gene switches on (there is only one *C* gene). Together, the products of the *B* and *C* genes trigger formation of the third whorl, which makes stamens. Finally, the *B* gene turns off, and the *C* gene product on its own gives rise to the fourth, inner whorl, which produces the carpel.

Barr body Inactivated X chromosome in a cell of a female mammal. The other X chromosome is active.

dosage compensation Mechanism in which X chromosome inactivation equalizes gene expression between males and females.

X chromosome inactivation Developmental shutdown of one of the two X chromosomes in the cells of female mammals.

TAKE-HOME MESSAGE 10.3

X chromosome inactivation balances expression of X chromosome genes between female (XX) and male (XY) mammals.

SRY gene expression triggers the development of male traits in mammals.

In plants, expression of *ABC* floral identity genes governs development of the specialized parts of a flower.

CREDITS: (7) top left, © Cengage Learning; bottom left, Jürgen Berger, Max Planck Institute for Developmental Biology, Tübingen, Germany, (7A–B) © Jose Luis Riechmann; (7C) Image by Marty Yanofsky.

Prokaryotes do not undergo development, so these cells have no need of master genes. However, they do respond to environmental fluctuations by adjusting gene expression. For example, when a preferred nutrient becomes available, a bacterium begins transcribing genes whose products allow the cell to use that nutrient. When the nutrient is no longer available, transcription of those genes stops. Thus, the cell does not waste energy and resources producing gene products that are not needed at a particular moment.

Bacteria control gene expression mainly by adjusting the rate of transcription. Genes that are used together often occur together on the chromosome, one after the other. A single promoter precedes the genes, so all are transcribed together into a single RNA strand. Thus, their transcription is controllable in a single step that typically involves repressor binding to an operator. A group of genes together with a promoter and one or more operators that control their transcription are collectively called an **operon**. Operons were discovered in bacteria, but they also occur in archaea and eukaryotes.

THE *lac* OPERON

Escherichia coli lives in the gut of mammals, where it dines on nutrients traveling past. Its carbohydrate of choice is glucose, but it can make use of other sugars such as the lactose in milk. An operon called *lac* allows *E. coli* cells to metabolize lactose (**FIGURE 10.8**). The *lac* operon includes three genes and a promoter flanked by two operators ❶. One gene encodes an active transport protein (Section 5.7) that brings lactose across the plasma membrane into the cell. Another encodes an enzyme that breaks the bond between lactose's two monosaccharide monomers, glucose and galactose. (The third gene encodes an enzyme whose function is still being investigated.)

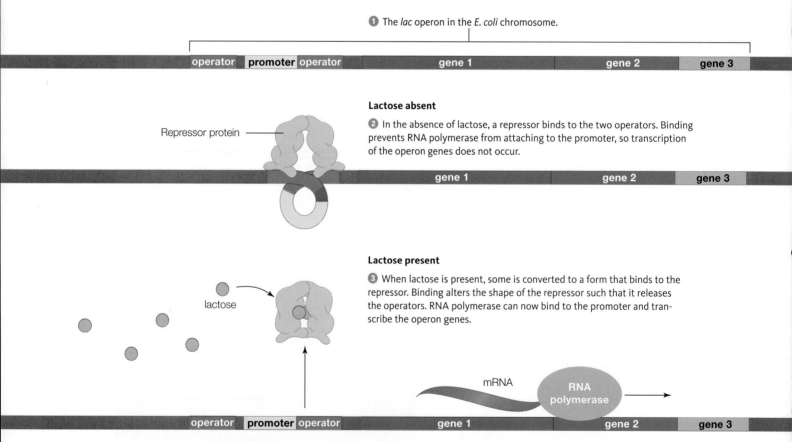

❶ The *lac* operon in the *E. coli* chromosome.

| operator | promoter | operator | gene 1 | gene 2 | gene 3 |

Lactose absent

❷ In the absence of lactose, a repressor binds to the two operators. Binding prevents RNA polymerase from attaching to the promoter, so transcription of the operon genes does not occur.

Repressor protein

| gene 1 | gene 2 | gene 3 |

Lactose present

❸ When lactose is present, some is converted to a form that binds to the repressor. Binding alters the shape of the repressor such that it releases the operators. RNA polymerase can now bind to the promoter and transcribe the operon genes.

lactose

mRNA

RNA polymerase

| operator | promoter | operator | gene 1 | gene 2 | gene 3 |

FIGURE 10.8 {Animated} Example of gene control in bacteria: the lactose (*lac*) operon on a bacterial chromosome. The operon consists of a promoter flanked by two operators, and three genes that allow lactose to be metabolized.

FIGURE IT OUT: What portion of the operon binds RNA polymerase when lactose is present?

Answer: The promoter

got lactase?

Recent analyses of DNA from well-preserved skeletons shows that the vast majority of adult humans living about 8,000 years ago in Europe were lactose intolerant. Around that time, a mutation appeared in the DNA of prehistoric people inhabiting a region between what is now central Europe and the Balkans. This mutation allowed its bearers to continue digesting milk as adults, and it spread rapidly to the rest of the continent along with the practice of dairy farming.

Today, most adults of northern and central European ancestry are able to digest milk because they carry this mutation, a single base-pair substitution in an enhancer that controls the lactase gene promoter. Other mutations in the same enhancer arose independently in North Africa, southern Asia, and the Middle East. Some people descended from these populations can continue to digest milk as adults.

FIGURE 10.9 Milk wasn't on the Stone Age menu.

Bacteria conserve resources by making these proteins only when lactose is present. When lactose is not present, a repressor binds to the two operators and twists the region of DNA with the promoter into a loop ❷. RNA polymerase cannot bind to the twisted-up promoter, so the *lac* operon's genes cannot be transcribed. When lactose is present, some of it is converted to another sugar that binds to the repressor and changes its shape. The altered repressor releases the operators and the looped DNA unwinds. The promoter is now accessible to RNA polymerase, and transcription of lactose-metabolizing genes begins ❸.

LACTOSE INTOLERANCE

Like *E. coli*, humans and other mammals break down lactose into monosaccharide subunits, but most do so only when they are young. An individual's ability to digest lactose declines at a species-specific age. In the majority of humans worldwide, the switch occurs at about age five, when expression of the gene for lactase shuts off. The resulting decline in production of this lactose-metabolizing enzyme results in a common condition known as lactose intolerance.

Cells in the intestinal lining secrete lactase into the small intestine, where the enzyme cleaves lactose into its

operon Group of genes together with a promoter–operator DNA sequence that controls their transcription.

glucose and galactose monomers. The monosaccharides are absorbed directly by the small intestine, but lactose and other disaccharides are not. Thus, when lactase production slows, lactose passes undigested through the small intestine. The lactose ends up in the large intestine, which hosts huge numbers of *E. coli* and a variety of other bacteria. These resident organisms respond to the abundant supply of this sugar by switching on their *lac* operons. Carbon dioxide, methane, hydrogen, and other gaseous products of their various fermentation reactions accumulate quickly in the large intestine, distending its wall and causing pain. Other products of their metabolism disrupt the solute–water balance inside the large intestine, and diarrhea results.

Not everybody is lactose intolerant. About one-third of human adults carry a mutation that allows them to digest milk; this mutation is more common in some populations than in others (**FIGURE 10.9**).

TAKE-HOME MESSAGE 10.4

The bacterial *lac* operon allows expression of lactose-metabolizing proteins only when lactose is present.

Most adult humans do not produce the enzyme that breaks down lactose. When undigested lactose enters the large intestine, resident bacteria give rise to symptoms of lactose intolerance.

You learned in Section 10.1 that methylation of histone proteins silences DNA transcription. Direct methylation of DNA also suppresses gene expression, but in a way that is often more permanent than histone modification. Once a particular nucleotide has become methylated in a cell's DNA, it will usually stay methylated in all of the cell's descendants. Methylation and other heritable modifications to DNA that affect its function but do not involve changes in the nucleotide sequence are said to be **epigenetic**.

DNA methylation is a necessary part of differentiation, so it begins early in embryonic development: Genes actively expressed in cells of a zygote become silenced as their promoters get methylated. An individual's DNA continues to acquire methylations during its lifetime.

In eukaryotes, methyl groups are usually added to a cytosine that is followed by a guanine (**FIGURE 10.10A**), but which of these cytosines are methylated varies by the individual. This is because methylation is influenced by environmental factors. For instance, humans conceived during a famine end up with an unusually low number of methyl groups attached to the nucleotides of certain genes. The product of one of those genes is a hormone that fosters prenatal growth and development. The resulting increase in expression of this gene may offer a survival advantage in a poor nutritional environment.

Methyl groups are added to nucleotides by chance during DNA replication, so cells that divide a lot tend to have more methyl groups in their DNA than inactive cells. Free radicals and toxic chemicals add more methyl groups. These and other factors that influence DNA methylation can have intergenerational effects. When an organism reproduces, it passes its DNA to offspring. Methylation of parental DNA is normally "reset" in the first cell of the new individual, with new methyl groups being added and old ones being removed. This reprogramming does not remove all of the parental methyl groups, however, so methylations acquired during an individual's lifetime can be passed to future offspring.

Inheritance of epigenetic modifications can adapt offspring to an environmental challenge much more quickly than evolution (we return to evolutionary processes in Chapter 17). Such modifications are not considered to be evolutionary because the underlying DNA sequence does not change. Even so, they may persist for generations after an environmental challenge has faded. For example, a recent study showed that grandsons of boys who endured a winter of famine tend to outlive—by far—grandsons of boys who overate at the same age (**FIGURE 10.10B**). The effect is presumed to be due to epigenetic modification because these results were corrected for socioeconomic and genetic factors. In a similar study, nine-year-old boys whose fathers smoked cigarettes before age 11 were overweight compared with boys whose fathers did not smoke in childhood. In these and other studies, the effect was sex-limited: Boys were affected by lifestyle of individuals in the paternal line; girls, by individuals in the maternal line.

A With DNA methylation, a methyl group (red) is most often attached to a cytosine that is followed by a guanine. The model on the *right* shows methyl groups attached to a cytosine–guanine pair on complementary DNA strands. When the cytosine on one strand is methylated, enzymes methylate the cytosine on the other strand. This is why a methylation tends to persist in a cell's descendants.

B DNA methylation and other epigenetic changes can be heritable. In 1944, a supply blockade followed by a very harsh winter caused a severe famine in the Nazi-occupied Netherlands. Grandsons of boys who endured the famine (such as the one pictured here) lived about 32 years longer than grandsons of boys who ate well during the same winter. These results were corrected for other factors so the effect is thought to be epigenetic.

FIGURE 10.10 DNA methylation.

epigenetic Refers to heritable changes in gene expression that are not the result of changes in DNA sequence.

TAKE-HOME MESSAGE 10.5

Epigenetic modifications of chromosomal DNA, including DNA methylations acquired during an individual's lifetime, can be passed to offspring.

CREDITS: (10A) From Starr/Taggart/Evers/Starr, Biology, 13E. © 2013 Cengage Learning; (10B) © Marius Meijboom/ Nederlands Fotomuseum, all rights reserved.

Education

FIGURE 10.11 Pink Steel, a dragon boat team composed of breast cancer survivors.

"THERE IS A MOMENT WHEN EVERYTHING CHANGES—WHEN THE WIDTH OF TWO FINGERS CAN SUDDENLY BE THE TOTAL DISTANCE BETWEEN YOU AND ETERNITY." Seventeen-year-old Robin Shoulla wrote those words after being diagnosed with breast cancer. At an age when most young women are thinking about school, friends, parties, and potential careers, Robin was dealing with radical mastectomy: the removal of a breast, all lymph nodes under the arm, and skeletal muscles in the chest wall under the breast. She was pleading with her oncologist not to use her jugular vein for chemotherapy and wondering if she would survive to see the next year.

Cancer typically begins with a mutation in a gene whose product is part of a system of stringent control over cell growth and division. Two examples are *BRCA1* and *BRCA2*: A mutated version of one or both of these genes is often found in breast and ovarian cancer cells. Because such mutations can be inherited, cancer is not only a disease of the elderly (FIGURE 10.11).

BRCA1 and *BRCA2* are master genes whose protein products help maintain the structure and

number of chromosomes in a dividing cell. They also participate directly in DNA repair, so any mutations that alter this function also alter the cell's capacity to repair damaged DNA. Other mutations are likely to accumulate, and that sets the stage for cancer.

Researchers recently found that the RNA product of the *XIST* gene does not properly coat one of the two X chromosomes in breast cancer cells. In these cells, both X chromosomes are active. It makes sense that two active X chromosomes would have something to do with abnormal gene expression, but why the RNA product of an unmutated *XIST* gene does not properly coat an X chromosome in cancer cells remains a mystery. Mutations in the *BRCA1* gene may be part of the answer. The protein product of this gene physically associates with the RNA product of the *XIST* gene. Researchers were able to restore proper *XIST* RNA coating—and proper X chromosome inactivation—by restoring the function of the *BRCA1* gene product in breast cancer cells.

Robin Shoulla is one of the unlucky people who carry mutations in both *BRCA1* and *BRCA2*, but she survived. Now, she has what she calls a normal life: career, husband, children. Her goal as a cancer survivor: "To grow very old with gray hair and spreading hips, smiling."

Summary

SECTION 10.1 Which genes a cell uses depends on the type of organism, the type of cell, conditions inside and outside the cell, and, in complex multicelled species, the organism's stage of development.

All organisms control gene expression. The control is necessary for cell differentiation during development in multicelled eukaryotes, and it also allows individual cells to respond appropriately to changes in their environment.

Different molecules and processes govern every step between transcription of a gene and delivery of the gene's product to its final destination. **Transcription factors** such as **activators** and **repressors** influence transcription by binding to chromosomal DNA at sites such as promoters, **enhancers**, **operators**, and silencers.

SECTION 10.2 Control over gene expression governs embryonic development of complex, multicelled animal bodies. Various **master genes** are expressed locally in different parts of an embryo as it develops. Their products, which diffuse through the embryo in gradients, affect expression of other master genes, which in turn affect the expression of others, and so on. Cells differentiate according to their exposure to these gradients. Eventually, master gene expression induces the expression of **homeotic genes**, the products of which govern the development of body parts. The function of many homeotic genes was revealed by **knockouts** in fruit flies.

SECTION 10.3 In cells of female mammals, one of the two X chromosomes is condensed as a **Barr body**, rendering most of its genes permanently inaccessible. By the theory of **dosage compensation**, this **X chromosome inactivation** balances gene expression between the sexes. The inactivation occurs because the *XIST* gene's RNA product shuts down the one X chromosome that transcribes it. The *SRY* gene determines male sex in humans.

Overlapping expression of master genes guides expression of flower formation in plants. Cells differentiate and form sepals, petals, stamens, or carpels depending on which floral identity gene products they are exposed to.

SECTION 10.4 Prokaryotes do not undergo development. Most of their gene control reversibly adjusts transcription rates in response to environmental conditions, especially nutrient availability. The *lac* **operon** governs expression of three genes, the three products of which allow a bacterial cell to metabolize lactose. Two operators that flank the promoter are binding sites for a repressor that blocks transcription. In most humans, the ability to break down lactose ends in early childhood.

SECTION 10.5 **Epigenetic** refers to heritable modifications of DNA that affect gene expression but do not involve changes to the DNA sequence. DNA methylations and other epigenetic modifications acquired during an individual's lifetime can persist for generations.

SECTION 10.6 A complex interplay of gene expression is a critical part of normal functioning of a multicelled body. Cancer typically begins with mutations in master genes that govern cell division.

Self-Quiz Answers in Appendix VII

1. The expression of a gene may depend on _____ .
   a. the type of organism   c. the type of cell
   b. environmental conditions d. all of the above

2. Gene expression in multicelled eukaryotic organisms changes in response to _____ .
   a. extracellular conditions c. operons
   b. master gene products   d. a and b

3. Binding of _____ to _____ in DNA can increase the rate of transcription of specific genes.
   a. activators; repressors   c. repressors; operators
   b. activators; enhancers   d. both a and b

4. Proteins that influence RNA synthesis by binding directly to DNA are called _____ .
   a. promoters   c. operators
   b. transcription factors   d. enhancers

5. Eukaryotic gene control governs _____ .
   a. transcription   e. translation
   b. RNA processing   f. protein modification
   c. RNA transport   g. a through e
   d. mRNA degradation   h. all of the above

6. Muscle cells differ from bone cells because _____ .
   a. they carry different genes
   b. they use different genes
   c. both a and b

7. Control over eukaryotic gene expression guides _____ .
   a. natural selection   c. development
   b. nutrient availability   d. all of the above

8. Homeotic gene products _____ .
   a. flank a bacterial operon
   b. map out the overall body plan in embryos
   c. control the formation of specific body parts

9. A gene that is knocked out is _____ .
   a. deleted   c. expressed
   b. inactivated   d. either a or b

10. Which of the following includes all of the others?
    a. homeotic genes   c. *SRY* gene
    b. master genes   d. *PAX6*

11. The expression of *ABC* genes _____ .
    a. occurs in layers of an onion
    b. controls flower formation
    c. causes mutations in flowers

Data Analysis Activities

Effect of Paternal Grandmother's Food Supply on Infant Mortality Researchers are investigating long-reaching epigenetic effects of starvation, in part because historical data on periods of famine are widely available. Before the industrial revolution, a failed harvest in one autumn typically led to severe food shortages the following winter. A retrospective study has correlated female infant mortality at certain ages with the abundance of food during the paternal grandmother's childhood. **FIGURE 10.12** shows some of the results of this study.

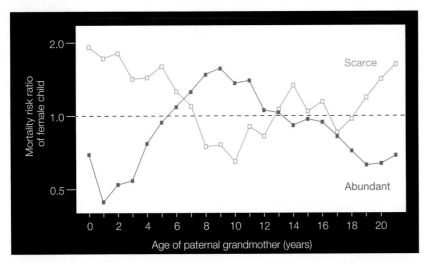

FIGURE 10.12 Graph showing the relative risk of early death of a female child, correlated with the age at which her paternal grandmother experienced a winter with a food supply that was scarce (blue) or abundant (red) during childhood. The dotted line represents no difference in risk of mortality. A value above the line means an increased risk; one below the line indicates a reduced risk.

1. Compare the mortality of girls whose paternal grandmothers ate well at age 2 with that of those who experienced famine at the same age. Which girl was more likely to die early? How much more likely was she to die?

2. Children have a period of slow growth around age 9. What trend in this data can you see around that age?

3. There was no correlation between early death of a male child and eating habits of his paternal grandmother, but there was a strong correlation with the eating habits of his paternal grandfather. What does this tell you about the probable location of epigenetic changes that gave rise to these data?

---

12. During X chromosome inactivation, _____ .
    a. female cells shut down
    b. RNA coats a chromosome
    c. pigments form
    d. both a and b

13. A cell with a Barr body is _____ .
    a. a bacterium   c. from a female mammal
    b. a sex cell   d. infected by the Barr virus

14. Operons _____ .
    a. only occur in bacteria
    b. have multiple genes
    c. involve selective gene expression

15. Match the terms with the most suitable description.
    ___ knockout   a. makes a man out of you
    ___ *SRY* gene   b. binding site for repressor
    ___ operator   c. requires gene expression control
    ___ Barr body   d. may have epigenetic effects
    ___ differentiation   e. inactivated X chromosome
    ___ methylation   f. gene deleted

Critical Thinking

1. Why are some genes expressed and some not?

2. Do the same types of gene control operate in bacterial cells and eukaryotic cells?

3. Suppose a breeder decides to separate baby guinea pigs from their mothers three weeks after they were born. However, he has trouble identifying the sex of young guinea pigs. Suggest how a quick look through a microscope can help him identify the females.

wild-type

mutant

4. Almost all calico cats are female. Why?

5. The photos on the *left* show flowers from *Arabidopsis* plants. One plant is wild-type (unmutated); the other carries a mutation in one of its *ABC* floral identity genes. This mutation causes sepals and petals to form instead of stamens and carpels. Refer to **FIGURE 10.7** to decide which gene (*A*, *B*, or *C*) has been inactivated by the mutation.

A multicelled eukaryote develops by repeated cell divisions. These are early frog embryos, each a product of three divisions of one fertilized egg.

11

HOW CELLS REPRODUCE

Links to Earlier Concepts

Before beginning this chapter, be sure you understand cell structure (Sections 4.1, 4.5, 4.9, 4.10); chromosomes (8.3); and DNA replication (8.4) and repair (8.5). What you know about receptors and recognition proteins (4.3), free radicals (5.5) and mutations (9.5), fermentation (7.6), and eukaryotic gene control (10.1) will help you understand how cancer develops.

KEY CONCEPTS

THE CELL CYCLE

A cell cycle starts when a new cell forms by division of a parent cell, and ends when the cell completes its own division. Built-in checkpoints control the timing and rate of the cycle.

MITOSIS

Mitosis, a mechanism by which a cell's nucleus divides, maintains the chromosome number. Four sequential stages parcel the cell's duplicated chromosomes into two new nuclei.

CYTOPLASMIC DIVISION

After nuclear division, the cytoplasm may divide, so one nucleus ends up in each of two new cells. The division proceeds by different mechanisms in animal and plant cells.

MITOTIC CLOCKS

Built into eukaryotic chromosomes are DNA sequences that protect the cell's genetic information. Degradation of these sequences is associated with cell death and aging.

THE CELL CYCLE GONE AWRY

On rare occasions, checkpoint mechanisms fail, and cell division becomes uncontrollable. Tumor formation and cancer are outcomes.

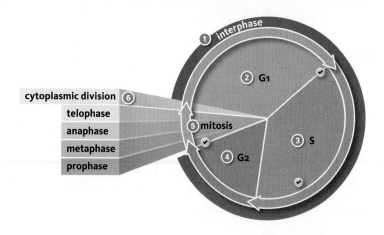

① A cell spends most of its life in interphase, which includes three stages: G1, S, and G2.

② G1 is the interval of growth before DNA replication. The cell's chromosomes are unduplicated.

③ S is the time of synthesis, during which the cell copies its DNA (duplicates its chromosomes).

④ G2 is the interval after DNA replication and before mitosis. The cell prepares to divide during this stage.

⑤ The nucleus divides during mitosis, the four stages of which are detailed in the next section. After mitosis, the cytoplasm may divide. Each descendant cell begins the cycle anew, in interphase.

☑ Built-in checkpoints stop the cycle from proceeding until certain conditions are met.

FIGURE 11.1 **{Animated}** The eukaryotic cell cycle. The length of the intervals differs among cells. G1, S, and G2 are part of interphase.

MULTIPLICATION BY DIVISION

A life cycle is the collective series of events that an organism passes through during its lifetime. Multicelled organisms and free-living cells have life cycles, but what about cells that make up a multicelled body? Biologists consider such cells to be individually alive, each with its own life that passes through a series of recognizable stages. The events that occur from the time a cell forms until the time it divides are collectively called the **cell cycle** (**FIGURE 11.1**).

A typical cell spends most of its life in **interphase** ①. During this phase, the cell increases its mass, roughly doubles the number of its cytoplasmic components, and replicates its DNA in preparation for division. Interphase is typically the longest part of the cycle, and it consists of three stages: G1, S, and G2. G1 and G2 were named "Gap" intervals because outwardly they seem to be periods of inactivity, but they are not.

Most cells going about their metabolic business are in G1 ②. Cells preparing to divide enter S ③, the time of DNA synthesis, when they duplicate their chromosomes (Section 8.4). During G2 ④, the cell prepares to divide by making the proteins that will drive the process of division. Once S begins, DNA replication usually proceeds at a predictable rate until division begins.

The remainder of the cycle consists of the division process itself. When a cell divides, both of its cellular offspring end up with DNA and a blob of cytoplasm. Each of the offspring of a eukaryotic cell inherits its DNA packaged inside a nucleus. Thus, a eukaryotic cell's nucleus has to divide before its cytoplasm does.

Mitosis is a nuclear division mechanism that maintains the chromosome number ⑤. In multicelled organisms, mitosis and cytoplasmic division ⑥ are the basis of

increases in body size and tissue remodeling during development (**FIGURE 11.2**), as well as ongoing replacements of damaged or dead cells. Mitosis and cytoplasmic division are also part of **asexual reproduction**, a reproductive mode by which offspring are produced by one parent only. This mode of reproduction is used by some multicelled eukaryotes and many single-celled ones. (Prokaryotes do not have a nucleus and do not undergo mitosis. We discuss their reproduction in Section 19.4.)

When a cell divides by mitosis, it produces two descendant cells, each with the chromosome number of the parent. However, if only the total number of chromosomes mattered, then one of the descendant cells might get, say, two pairs of chromosome 22 and no chromosome 9. A cell cannot function properly without a full complement of DNA, which means it needs to have *a copy of each*

FIGURE 11.2 A tadpole develops from repeated mitotic divisions of an egg. After it hatches, the individual will grow and undergo metamorphosis to develop into a frog.

chromosome. Thus, the two cells produced by mitosis have the same number and types of chromosomes as the parent.

Remember from Section 8.3 that your body's cells are diploid, which means their nuclei contain pairs of chromosomes—two of each type. One chromosome of a pair was inherited from your father; the other, from your mother. Except for a pairing of nonidentical sex chromosomes (XY) in males, the chromosomes of each pair are homologous. **Homologous chromosomes** have the same length, shape, and genes (*hom–* means alike).

FIGURE 11.3 shows how homologous chromosomes are distributed to descendant cells when a diploid cell divides by mitosis. When a cell is in G1, each of its chromosomes consists of one double-stranded DNA molecule. The cell replicates its DNA in S, so by G2, each of its chromosomes consists of two double-stranded DNA molecules. These molecules stay attached to one another at the centromere as sister chromatids until mitosis is almost over, and then they are pulled apart and packaged into two separate nuclei. The next section details this process.

When sister chromatids are pulled apart, each becomes an individual chromosome that consists of one double-stranded DNA molecule. Thus, each of the two new nuclei that form in mitosis contains a full complement of (unduplicated) chromosomes. When the cytoplasm divides, these nuclei are packaged into separate cells. Each new cell starts the cell cycle over again in G1 of interphase.

CONTROL OVER THE CELL CYCLE

When a cell divides—and when it does not—is determined by mechanisms of gene expression control (Section 10.1). Like the accelerator of a car, some of these mechanisms cause the cell cycle to advance. Others are like brakes, preventing the cycle from proceeding. In the adult body, brakes on the cell cycle normally keep the vast majority of cells in G1. Most of your nerve cells, skeletal muscle cells, heart muscle cells, and fat-storing cells have been in G1 since you were born, for example.

Control over the cell cycle also ensures that a dividing cell's descendants receive intact copies of its chromosomes.

---

asexual reproduction Reproductive mode of eukaryotes by which offspring arise from a single parent only.
cell cycle A series of events from the time a cell forms until its cytoplasm divides.
homologous chromosomes Chromosomes with the same length, shape, and genes.
interphase In a eukaryotic cell cycle, the interval between mitotic divisions when a cell grows, roughly doubles the number of its cytoplasmic components, and replicates its DNA.
mitosis Nuclear division mechanism that maintains the chromosome number.

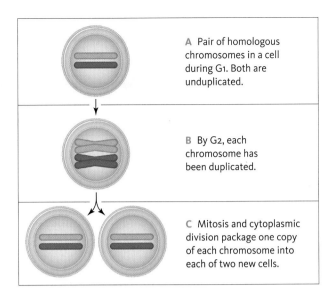

A Pair of homologous chromosomes in a cell during G1. Both are unduplicated.

B By G2, each chromosome has been duplicated.

C Mitosis and cytoplasmic division package one copy of each chromosome into each of two new cells.

FIGURE 11.3 How mitosis maintains chromosome number in a diploid cell. For clarity, only one homologous pair is shown. The maternal chromosome is shown in pink, the paternal one in blue.

Built-in checkpoints monitor whether the cell's DNA has been copied completely, whether it is damaged, or even whether enough nutrients to support division are available. Protein products of "checkpoint genes" interact to carry out this type of control. For example, a checkpoint that operates in S puts the brakes on the cycle if the cell's chromosomes are damaged during DNA replication (Section 8.5). Checkpoint proteins that function as sensors recognize damaged DNA and bind to it. Upon binding, they trigger other events that stall the cell cycle, and also enhance expression of genes involved in DNA repair. After the problem has been corrected, the brakes are lifted and the cell cycle proceeds. If the problem remains uncorrected, other checkpoint proteins may initiate a series of events that eventually cause the cell to self-destruct.

TAKE-HOME MESSAGE 11.1

A cell cycle is the sequence of stages through which a cell passes during its lifetime (interphase, mitosis, and cytoplasmic division).

A eukaryotic cell reproduces by division: nucleus first, then cytoplasm. Each descendant cell receives a set of chromosomes and some cytoplasm.

When a nucleus divides by mitosis, each new nucleus has the same chromosome number as the parent cell.

Mechanisms of gene expression control can advance, delay, or block the cell cycle in response to internal and external conditions. Checkpoints built into the cycle allow problems to be corrected before the cycle proceeds.

11.2 WHAT IS THE SEQUENCE OF EVENTS DURING MITOSIS?

Plant nucleus   **Animal nucleus**

① Interphase
Interphase cells are shown for comparison, but interphase is not part of mitosis. The nuclear envelope is intact.

centrosome

② Early Prophase
Mitosis begins. Transcription stops, and the DNA begins to appear grainy as it starts to condense. The nuclear envelope begins to break up and the centrosome gets duplicated.

③ Prophase
The duplicated chromosomes become visible as they condense. One of the two centrosomes moves to the opposite side of the cell as the nuclear envelope breaks up completely. Spindle microtubules assemble and bind to chromosomes at the centromere. Sister chromatids become attached to opposite centrosomes.

spindle
microtubule

④ Metaphase
All of the chromosomes are aligned midway between the spindle poles.

⑤ Anaphase
Spindle microtubules separate the sister chromatids and move them toward opposite spindle poles. Each sister chromatid has now become an individual, unduplicated chromosome.

⑥ Telophase
The chromosomes reach opposite sides of the cell and loosen up. Mitosis ends when a new nuclear envelope forms around each cluster of chromosomes.

FIGURE 11.4 {Animated}   Mitosis. Micrographs show nuclei of plant cells (onion root, *left*), and animal cells (fertilized eggs of a round-worm, *right*). A diploid (2*n*) animal cell with two chromosome pairs is illustrated.

CREDITS: (4) Art, © Cengage Learning; plant cell photos, Michael Clayton/ University of Wisconsin, Department of Botany; animal cell photos, ISM/Phototake.

During interphase, a cell's chromosomes are loosened to allow transcription and DNA replication. Loosened chromosomes are spread out, so they are not easily visible under a light microscope (**FIGURE 11.4 ❶**). In preparation for nuclear division, the chromosomes begin to pack tightly ❷. Transcription and DNA replication stop as the chromosomes condense into their most compact "X" forms (Section 8.3). Tight condensation keeps the chromosomes from getting tangled and breaking during nuclear division.

Just before prophase, the centrosome becomes duplicated. Most animal cells have these structures, which typically consist of a pair of centrioles surrounded by a region of dense cytoplasm. (Remember from Section 4.9 that barrel-shaped centrioles help microtubules assemble.)

A cell reaches **prophase**, the first stage of mitosis, when its chromosomes have condensed so much that they are visible under a light microscope ❸. "Mitosis" is from *mitos*, the Greek word for thread, after the threadlike appearance of the chromosomes during nuclear division. If the cell has centrosomes, one of them now moves to the opposite side of the cell. Microtubules begin to assemble and lengthen from the centrosomes (or from other structures in cells with no centrosomes). The lengthening microtubules form a **spindle**, which is a temporary structure for moving chromosomes during nuclear division (**FIGURE 11.5**). The general area from which the spindle forms on each side of the cell is now called a spindle pole.

Spindle microtubules penetrate the nuclear region as the nuclear envelope breaks up. Some of the microtubules stop lengthening when they reach the middle of the cell. Others lengthen until they reach a chromosome and attach to it at the centromere. By the end of prophase, one sister chromatid of each chromosome has become attached to microtubules extending from one spindle pole, and the other sister has become attached to microtubules extending from the other spindle pole.

The opposing sets of microtubules then begin a tug-of-war by adding and losing tubulin subunits. As the microtubules lengthen and shorten, they push and pull

FIGURE 11.5 The spindle in a dividing cell of an amphibian. Microtubules (green) have extended from two centrosomes to form the spindle, which has attached to and aligned the chromosomes (blue) midway between its two poles. Red shows actin microfilaments.

the chromosomes. When all the microtubules are the same length, the chromosomes are aligned midway between spindle poles ❹. The alignment marks **metaphase** (from *meta*, the ancient Greek word for between).

During **anaphase**, the spindle pulls the sister chromatids of each duplicated chromosome apart and moves them toward opposite spindle poles ❺. Each DNA molecule has now become a separate chromosome.

Telophase begins when two clusters of chromosomes reach the spindle poles ❻. Each cluster has the same number and kinds of chromosomes as the parent cell nucleus had: two of each type of chromosome, if the parent cell was diploid. A new nuclear envelope forms around each set of chromosomes as they loosen up again. At this point, telophase—and mitosis—are finished.

---

anaphase Stage of mitosis during which sister chromatids separate and move toward opposite spindle poles.
metaphase Stage of mitosis at which all chromosomes are aligned midway between spindle poles.
prophase Stage of mitosis during which chromosomes condense and become attached to a newly forming spindle.
spindle Temporary structure that moves chromosomes during nuclear division; consists of microtubules.
telophase Stage of mitosis during which chromosomes arrive at opposite spindle poles and decondense, and two new nuclei form.

TAKE-HOME MESSAGE 11.2

Chromosomes are duplicated before mitosis begins. Each now consists of two DNA molecules attached as sister chromatids.

In prophase, the chromosomes condense and a spindle forms. Spindle microtubules attach to the chromosomes as the nuclear envelope breaks up.

At metaphase, the spindle has aligned all of the (still duplicated) chromosomes in the middle of the cell.

In anaphase, sister chromatids separate and move toward opposite spindle poles. Each DNA molecule is now an individual chromosome.

In telophase, two clusters of chromosomes reach opposite spindle poles. A new nuclear envelope forms around each cluster, so two new nuclei form.

At the end of mitosis, each new nucleus has the same number and types of chromosomes as the parent cell's nucleus.

In most eukaryotes, the cell cytoplasm divides between late anaphase and the end of telophase, so two cells form, each with their own nucleus. The mechanism of cytoplasmic division, which is called **cytokinesis**, differs between plants and animals.

Typical animal cells pinch themselves in two after nuclear division ends (**FIGURE 11.6**). How? The spindle begins to disassemble during telophase ❶. The cell cortex, which is the mesh of cytoskeletal elements just under the plasma membrane (Section 4.9), includes a band of actin and myosin filaments that wraps around the cell's midsection. The band is called a contractile ring because it contracts when its component proteins are energized by phosphate-group transfers from ATP. When the ring contracts, it drags the attached plasma membrane inward ❷. The sinking plasma membrane becomes visible on the outside of the cell as an indentation between the former spindle poles ❸. The indentation, which is called a **cleavage furrow**, advances around the cell and deepens until the cytoplasm (and the cell) is pinched in two ❹. Each of the two cells formed by this division has its own nucleus and some of the parent cell's cytoplasm, and each is enclosed by a plasma membrane.

Dividing plant cells face a particular challenge because a stiff cell wall surrounds their plasma membrane (Section 4.10). Accordingly, plant cells have their own mechanism of cytokinesis. By the end of anaphase, a set of short microtubules has formed on either side of the future plane of division. These microtubules guide vesicles from Golgi bodies and the cell surface to the division plane ❺. After mitosis, the vesicles start to fuse into a disk-shaped **cell plate** ❻. The plate expands at its edges until it reaches the plasma membrane and attaches to it, thus partitioning the cytoplasm ❼. In time, the cell plate will develop into two new cell walls, so each of the descendant cells will be enclosed by its own plasma membrane and wall ❽.

Animal cell

❶ In a dividing animal cell, the spindle begins to disassemble after mitosis is completed.

❷ At the midpoint of the former spindle, a ring of actin and myosin filaments attached to the plasma membrane contracts.

❸ This contractile ring pulls the cell surface inward as it shrinks.

❹ The ring contracts until it pinches the cell in two.

Plant cell

❺ In a dividing plant cell, vesicles cluster at the future plane of division before mitosis ends.

❻ The vesicles fuse with each other, forming a cell plate along the plane of division.

❼ The cell plate expands outward along the plane of division. When it reaches the plasma membrane, it attaches to the membrane and partitions the cytoplasm.

❽ The cell plate matures as two new cell walls. These walls join with the parent cell wall, so each descendant cell becomes enclosed by its own wall.

FIGURE 11.6 {Animated} Cytoplasmic division of animal cells (*top*) and plant cells (*bottom*).

cell plate A disk-shaped structure that forms during cytokinesis in a plant cell; matures as a cross-wall between the two new nuclei.
cleavage furrow In a dividing animal cell, the indentation where cytoplasmic division will occur.
cytokinesis Cytoplasmic division.

TAKE-HOME MESSAGE 11.3

In most eukaryotes, the cell cytoplasm divides between late anaphase and the end of telophase. Two descendant cells form, each with its own nucleus.

The mechanism of cell division differs between plants and animals.

In animal cells, a contractile ring pinches the cytoplasm in two. In plant cells, a cell plate that forms in the middle of the cell partitions the cytoplasm when it reaches and connects to the parent cell wall.

CREDIT: (6) From Starr/Taggart/Evers/Starr, Biology, 13E. © 2013 Cengage Learning.

11.4 WHAT IS THE FUNCTION OF TELOMERES?

FIGURE 11.7 Telomeres. The bright dots at the end of each DNA strand in these duplicated chromosomes show telomere sequences.

In 1997, Scottish geneticist Ian Wilmut made worldwide headlines after his team cloned the first mammal from an adult somatic cell (SCNT, Section 8.6). The animal, a lamb named Dolly, was genetically identical to the sheep that had donated an udder cell. At first, Dolly looked and acted like a normal sheep, but she died early. By the time Dolly was five, she was as fat and arthritic as a twelve-year-old sheep. The following year, she contracted a lung disease that is typical of geriatric sheep, and had to be euthanized.

Dolly's early demise may have been the result of abnormally short telomeres. **Telomeres** are noncoding DNA sequences that occur at the ends of eukaryotic chromosomes (**FIGURE 11.7**). Vertebrate telomeres consist of a short DNA sequence, 5′-TTAGGG-3′, repeated perhaps thousands of times. These "junk" repeats provide a buffer against the loss of more valuable DNA internal to the chromosomes.

A telomere buffer is particularly important because, under normal circumstances, a eukaryotic chromosome shortens by about 100 nucleotides with each DNA replication. When a cell's offspring receive chromosomes with too-short telomeres, checkpoint gene products halt the cell cycle, and the descendant cells die shortly thereafter. Most body cells can divide only a certain number of times before this happens. This cell division limit may be a fail-safe mechanism in case a cell loses control over the cell cycle and begins to divide again and again. A limit on the number of divisions keeps such cells from overrunning the body (an outcome that, as you will see in the next section, has dangerous consequences to health). The cell division limit varies by species, and it may be part of the mechanism

that sets an organism's life span. When Dolly was only two years old, her telomeres were as short as those of a six-year-old sheep—the exact age of the adult animal that had been her genetic donor. Scientists are careful to point out that shortening telomeres could be an effect of aging rather than a cause.

A few normal cells in an adult retain the ability to divide indefinitely. Their descendants replace cell lineages that eventually die out when they reach their division limit. These cells, which are called stem cells, are immortal because they continue to make an enzyme called telomerase. Telomerase reverses the telomere shortening that normally occurs after DNA replication.

Mice that have had their telomerase enzyme knocked out age prematurely. Their tissues degenerate much more quickly than those of normal mice, and their life expectancy declines to about half that of a normal mouse. When one of these knockout mice is close to the end of its shortened life span, rescuing the function of its telomerase enzyme results in lengthened telomeres. The rescued mouse also regains vitality: Decrepit tissue in its brain and other organs repairs itself and begins to function normally, and the once-geriatric individual even begins to reproduce again. While telomerase holds therapeutic promise for rejuvenation of aged tissues, it can also be dangerous: Cancer cells characteristically express high levels of the molecule.

TAKE-HOME MESSAGE 11.4

Telomeres protect eukaryotic chromosomes from losing genetic information at their ends.

Telomeres shorten with every cell division in normal body cells. When they are too short, the cell stops dividing and dies. Thus, telomeres are associated with aging.

telomere Noncoding, repetitive DNA sequence at the end of chromosomes; protects the coding sequences from degradation.

11.5 WHAT HAPPENS WHEN CONTROL OVER THE CELL CYCLE IS LOST?

THE ROLE OF MUTATIONS

Sometimes a checkpoint gene mutates so that its protein product no longer works properly. In other cases, the controls that regulate its expression fail, and a cell makes too much or too little of its product. When enough checkpoint mechanisms fail, a cell loses control over its cell cycle. Interphase may be skipped, so division occurs over and over with no resting period. Signaling mechanisms that cause abnormal cells to die may stop working. The problem is compounded because checkpoint malfunctions are passed along to the cell's descendants, which form a **neoplasm**, an accumulation of cells that lost control over how they grow and divide.

A neoplasm that forms a lump in the body is called a **tumor**, but the two terms are sometimes used interchangeably. Once a tumor-causing mutation has

FIGURE 11.8 Effects of an oncogene. In this section of human breast tissue, a brown-colored tracer shows the active form of the EGF receptor. Normal cells are lighter in color. The dark cells have an overactive EGF receptor that is constantly stimulating mitosis; these cells have formed a neoplasm.

A Red dots show the location of the *BRCA1* gene product.   B Green dots pinpoint the location of another checkpoint gene product.

FIGURE 11.9 Checkpoint genes in action. Radiation damaged the DNA inside this nucleus. Two proteins have clustered around the same chromosome breaks in the same nucleus; both function to recruit DNA repair enzymes. The integrated action of these and other checkpoint gene products blocks mitosis until the DNA breaks are fixed.

occurred, the gene it affects is called an oncogene. An **oncogene** is any gene that can transform a normal cell into a tumor cell (Greek *onkos*, or bulging mass). Oncogene mutations in reproductive cells can be passed to offspring, which is a reason that some types of tumors run in families.

Genes encoding proteins that promote mitosis are called **proto-oncogenes** because mutations can turn them into oncogenes. A gene that encodes the epidermal growth factor (EGF) receptor is an example of a proto-oncogene. **Growth factors** are molecules that stimulate a cell to divide and differentiate. The EGF receptor is a plasma membrane protein; when it binds to EGF, it becomes activated and triggers the cell to begin mitosis. Mutations can result in an EGF receptor that stimulates mitosis even when EGF is not present. Most neoplasms carry mutations resulting in an overactivity or overabundance of this particular receptor (**FIGURE 11.8**).

Checkpoint gene products that inhibit mitosis are called tumor suppressors because tumors form when they are missing. The products of the *BRCA1* and *BRCA2* genes (Section 10.6) are examples of tumor suppressors. These proteins regulate, among other things, the expression of DNA repair enzymes (**FIGURE 11.9**). Tumor cells often have mutations in their *BRCA* genes.

Viruses such as HPV (human papillomavirus) cause a cell to make proteins that interfere with its own tumor suppressors. Infection with HPV causes skin growths called warts, and some kinds are associated with neoplasms that form on the cervix.

CANCER

Benign neoplasms such as warts are not usually dangerous (**FIGURE 11.10**). They grow very slowly, and their cells retain the plasma membrane adhesion proteins that keep them properly anchored to the other cells in their home tissue ❶.

A malignant neoplasm is one that gets progressively worse, and is dangerous to health. Malignant cells typically display the following three characteristics:

First, like cells of all neoplasms, malignant cells grow and divide abnormally. Controls that usually keep cells from

cancer Disease that occurs when a malignant neoplasm physically and metabolically disrupts body tissues.
growth factor Molecule that stimulates mitosis and differentiation.
metastasis The process in which malignant cells spread from one part of the body to another.
neoplasm An accumulation of abnormally dividing cells.
oncogene Gene that helps transform a normal cell into a tumor cell.
proto-oncogene Gene that, by mutation, can become an oncogene.
tumor A neoplasm that forms a lump.

CREDITS: (8) © From Expression of the epidermal growth factor receptor (EGFR) and the phosphorylated EGFR in invasive breast carcinomas. http://breast-cancer research.com/content/10/3/R49; (9) © Phillip B. Carpenter, Department of Biochemistry and Molecular Biology, University of Texas–Houston Medical School.

① Benign neoplasms grow slowly and stay in their home tissue.

② Cells of a malignant neoplasm can break away from their home tissue.

③ The malignant cells become attached to the wall of a lymph vessel or blood vessel (as shown here). They release digestive enzymes that create an opening in the wall, then enter the vessel.

④ The cells creep or tumble along inside vessels, then exit the same way they got in. Migrating cells may start growing in other tissues, a process called metastasis.

FIGURE 11.10 {**Animated**} Neoplasms and malignancy.

A Basal cell carcinoma is the most common type of skin cancer. This slow-growing, raised lump may be uncolored, reddish-brown, or black.

B Squamous cell carcinoma is the second most common form of skin cancer. This pink growth, firm to the touch, grows under the surface of skin.

C Melanoma spreads fastest. Cells form dark, encrusted lumps that may itch or bleed easily.

FIGURE 11.11 Skin cancer can be detected with early screening.

getting overcrowded in tissues are lost in malignant cells, so their populations may reach extremely high densities with cell division occurring very rapidly. The number of small blood vessels that transport blood to the growing cell mass also increases abnormally.

Second, the cytoplasm and plasma membrane of malignant cells are altered. The cytoskeleton may be shrunken, disorganized, or both. Malignant cells typically have an abnormal chromosome number, with some chromosomes present in multiple copies, and others missing or damaged. The balance of metabolism is often shifted, as in an amplified reliance on ATP formation by fermentation rather than aerobic respiration.

Altered or missing proteins impair the function of the plasma membrane of malignant cells. For example, these cells do not stay anchored properly in tissues because their plasma membrane adhesion proteins are defective or missing ②. Malignant cells can slip easily into and out of vessels of the circulatory and lymphatic systems ③. By migrating through these vessels, the cells can establish neoplasms elsewhere in the body ④. The process in which malignant cells break loose from their home tissue and invade other parts of the body is called **metastasis**. Metastasis is the third hallmark of malignant cells.

The disease called **cancer** occurs when the abnormally dividing cells of a malignant neoplasm disrupt body tissues,

both physically and metabolically. Unless chemotherapy, surgery, or another procedure eliminates malignant cells from the body, they can put an individual on a painful road to death. Each year, cancer causes 15 to 20 percent of all human deaths in developed countries. The good news is that mutations in multiple checkpoint genes are required to transform a normal cell into a malignant one, and such mutations may take a lifetime to accumulate. Lifestyle choices such as not smoking and avoiding exposure of unprotected skin to sunlight can reduce one's risk of acquiring mutations in the first place. Some neoplasms can be detected with periodic screening such as gynecology or dermatology exams (**FIGURE 11.11**). If detected early enough, many types of malignant neoplasms can be removed before metastasis occurs.

TAKE-HOME MESSAGE 11.5

Neoplasms form when cells lose control over their cell cycle and begin dividing abnormally.

Mutations in multiple checkpoint genes can give rise to a malignant neoplasm that gets progressively worse.

Cancer is a disease that occurs when the abnormally dividing cells of a malignant neoplasm physically and metabolically disrupt body tissues.

Although some mutations are inherited, lifestyle choices and early intervention can reduce one's risk of cancer.

CREDITS: (10) From Starr/Taggart/Evers/Starr, Biology, 13E. © 2013 Cengage Learning; (11A) © Ken Greer/Visuals Unlimited; (11B) Biophoto Associates/Photo Researchers, Inc.; (11C) James Stevenson/Photo Researchers, Inc.

Application: HENRIETTA'S IMMORTAL CELLS

Exploration

FIGURE 11.12 HeLa cells, a legacy of cancer victim Henrietta Lacks. The cells in this fluorescent micrograph are undergoing mitosis.

FINDING HUMAN CELLS THAT GROW IN A LABORATORY TOOK GEORGE AND MARGARET GEY NEARLY 30 YEARS. In 1951, their assistant Mary Kubicek prepared yet another sample of human cancer cells. Mary named the cells HeLa, after the first and last names of the patient from whom the cells had been taken. The HeLa cells began to divide, again and again. The cells were astonishingly vigorous, quickly coating the inside of their test tube and consuming their nutrient broth. Four days later, there were so many cells that the researchers had to transfer them to more tubes. The cell populations increased at a phenomenal rate. The cells were dividing every twenty-four hours and coating the inside of the tubes within days.

Sadly, cancer cells in the patient were dividing just as fast. Only six months after she had been diagnosed with cervical cancer, malignant cells had invaded tissues throughout her body. Two months after that, Henrietta Lacks, a young African American woman from Baltimore, was dead.

Although Henrietta passed away, her cells lived on in the Geys' laboratory. The Geys were able to grow poliovirus in HeLa cells, a practice that enabled them to determine which strains of the virus cause polio. That work was a critical step in the development of polio vaccines, which have since saved millions of lives.

Henrietta Lacks was just thirty-one, a wife and mother of five, when runaway cell divisions of cancer killed her. Her cells, however, are still dividing, again and again, more than fifty years after she died. Frozen away in tiny tubes and packed in Styrofoam boxes, HeLa cells continue to be shipped among laboratories all over the world. They are still widely used to investigate cancer (FIGURE 11.12), viral growth, protein synthesis, the effects of radiation, and countless other processes important in medicine and research. HeLa cells helped several researchers win Nobel Prizes, and some even traveled into space for experiments on satellites.

CREDIT: (12) main, Dr. Paul D. Andrews/ University of Dundee.

In these mitotic HeLa cells, chromosomes appear white and the spindle is red. Green identifies an enzyme that helps attach spindle microtubules to centromeres. Blue pinpoints a protein that helps sister chromatids stay attached to one another at the centromere. At this stage of telophase, the blue and green proteins should be closely associated midway between the two clusters of chromosomes. The abnormal distribution means that the spindle microtubules are not properly attached to the centromeres.

Henrietta Lacks

These days, physicians and researchers are required to obtain a signed consent form before they take tissue samples from a patient. No such requirement existed in the 1950s. It was common at that time for doctors to experiment on patients without their knowledge or consent. Thus, the young resident who was treating Henrietta Lacks's cancerous cervix probably never even thought about asking permission before he took a sample of it. That sample was the one that the Geys used to establish the HeLa cell line. No one in Henrietta's family knew about the cells until 25 years after her death. HeLa cells are still being sold worldwide, but her family has not received any share of profits.

Ongoing research with HeLa cells may one day allow researchers to identify drugs that target and destroy malignant cells or stop them from dividing. The research is far too late to have saved Henrietta Lacks, but it may one day yield drugs that put the brakes on cancer.

PEOPLE MATTER

National Geographic Explorer
DR. IAIN COUZIN

Can a million migrating wildebeests help explain why cancer spreads? Ask Iain Couzin. He is exploring how collective behavior in animals can be quantified and analyzed to give us new insights into the patterns of nature—and ourselves.

"We're realizing that animals have highly coordinated social systems and make decisions together," Couzin says. "They can do things collectively that no individual could do alone. It's still a very unexplored area of animal behavior." Couzin blends fieldwork, lab experiments, computer simulations, and complex mathematical models to test theories about how and why cells, animals, and humans organize and work together.

Couzin recently coauthored a paper hypothesizing that cancer cells migrating during metastasis—when the cells leave the primary tumor and journey elsewhere in the body—may have some parallels to animal swarms. As animals do in swarms, metastatic cells collectively can sense the environment and make decisions in response to it. It is very early theoretical work, but it does point to a new angle for cancer research: trying to knock out the mechanisms behind such collective migration.

Summary

SECTION 11.1 A **cell cycle** includes all the stages through which a eukaryotic cell passes during its lifetime; it starts when a new cell forms, and ends when the cell reproduces. Most of a cell's activities, including replication of the cell's **homologous chromosomes**, occur during **interphase**.

A eukaryotic cell reproduces by dividing: nucleus first, then cytoplasm. **Mitosis** is a mechanism of nuclear division that maintains the chromosome number. It is the basis of growth, cell replacements, and tissue repair in multicelled species, and **asexual reproduction** in many species.

SECTION 11.2 Mitosis proceeds in four stages. In **prophase**, the duplicated chromosomes start to condense. Microtubules assemble and form a **spindle**, and the nuclear envelope breaks up. Some microtubules that extend from one spindle pole attach to one chromatid of each chromosome; some that extend from the opposite spindle pole attach to its sister chromatid. These microtubules drag each chromosome toward the center of the cell.

At **metaphase**, all chromosomes are aligned at the spindle's midpoint.

During **anaphase**, the sister chromatids of each chromosome detach from each other, and the spindle microtubules move them toward opposite spindle poles.

During **telophase**, a complete set of chromosomes reaches each spindle pole. A nuclear envelope forms around each cluster. Two new nuclei, each with the parental chromosome number, are the result.

SECTION 11.3 **Cytokinesis** typically follows nuclear division. In animal cells, a contractile ring of microfilaments pulls the plasma membrane inward, forming a **cleavage furrow** that pinches the cytoplasm in two. In plant cells, vesicles guided by microtubules to the future plane of division merge as a **cell plate**. The plate expands until it fuses with the parent cell wall, thus becoming a cross-wall that partitions the cytoplasm.

SECTION 11.4 **Telomeres** that protect the ends of eukaryotic chromosomes shorten with every DNA replication. Cells that inherit too-short telomeres die, and in most cells this limits the number of divisions that can occur.

SECTION 11.5 The products of checkpoint genes, including receptors for **growth factors**, work together to control the cell cycle. These molecules monitor the integrity of the cell's DNA, and can pause the cycle until breaks or other problems are fixed. When checkpoint mechanisms fail, a cell loses control over its cell cycle, and the cell's descendants form a **neoplasm**. Neoplasms may form lumps called **tumors**.

Checkpoint genes are examples of **proto-oncogenes**, which means mutations can turn them into tumor-causing **oncogenes**. Mutations in multiple checkpoint genes can transform benign neoplasms into malignant ones. Cells of malignant neoplasms can break loose from their home tissues and colonize other parts of the body, a process called **metastasis**. **Cancer** occurs when malignant neoplasms physically and metabolically disrupt normal body tissues.

SECTION 11.6 An immortal line of human cells (HeLa) is a legacy of cancer victim Henrietta Lacks. Researchers all over the world continue to work with these cells as they try to unravel the mechanisms of cancer.

Self-Quiz   Answers in Appendix VII

1. Mitosis and cytoplasmic division function in _____ .
   a. asexual reproduction of single-celled eukaryotes
   b. growth and tissue repair in multicelled species
   c. gamete formation in bacteria and archaea
   d. sexual reproduction in plants and animals
   e. both a and b

2. A duplicated chromosome has _____ chromatid(s).
   a. one   c. three
   b. two   d. four

3. Homologous chromosomes _____ .
   a. carry the same genes   c. are the same length
   b. are the same shape   d. all of the above

4. Most cells spend the majority of their lives in _____ .
   a. prophase   d. telophase
   b. metaphase   e. interphase
   c. anaphase   f. d and e

5. The spindle attaches to chromosomes at the _____ .
   a. centriole   c. centromere
   b. contractile ring   d. centrosome

6. Only _____ is not a stage of mitosis.
   a. prophase   c. interphase
   b. metaphase   d. anaphase

7. In intervals of interphase, G stands for _____ .
   a. gap   b. growth   c. Gey   d. gene

8. Interphase is the part of the cell cycle when _____ .
   a. a cell ceases to function
   b. a cell forms its spindle apparatus
   c. a cell grows and duplicates its DNA
   d. mitosis proceeds

9. After mitosis, the chromosome number of a descendant cell is _____ the parent cell's.
   a. the same as   c. rearranged compared to
   b. one-half of   d. doubled compared to

10. A plant cell divides by the process of _____ .
    a. telekinesis   c. fission
    b. nuclear division   d. cytokinesis

Data Analysis Activities

HeLa Cells Are a Genetic Mess HeLa cells continue to be an extremely useful tool in cancer research. One early finding was that HeLa cells can vary in chromosome number. Defects in proteins that orchestrate cell division result in descendant cells with too many or too few chromosomes, an outcome that is one of the hallmarks of cancer cells.

The panel of chromosomes in **FIGURE 11.13**, originally published in 1989 by Nicholas Popescu and Joseph DiPaolo, shows all of the chromosomes in a single metaphase HeLa cell.

FIGURE 11.13 Chromosomes in a HeLa cell.

1. What is the chromosome number of this HeLa cell?
2. How many extra chromosomes does this cell have, compared to a normal human body cell?
3. Can you tell that this cell came from a female? How?

11. In the diagram of the nucleus *below*, fill in the blanks with the name of each interval.

_____   _____   _____   _____   _____

12. *BRCA1* and *BRCA2* _____ .
   a. are checkpoint genes   c. encode tumor suppressors
   b. are proto-oncogenes   d. all of the above

13. _____ are characteristic of cancer.
   a. Malignant cells   b. Neoplasms   c. Tumors

14. Match each term with its best description.
   ___ cell plate   a. lump of cells
   ___ spindle   b. made of microfilaments
   ___ tumor   c. divides plant cells
   ___ cleavage furrow   d. organize(s) the spindle
   ___ contractile ring   e. caused by metastatic cells
   ___ cancer   f. made of microtubules
   ___ centrosomes   g. indentation
   ___ telomere   h. shortens with age

15. Match each stage with the events listed.
   ___ metaphase   a. sister chromatids move apart
   ___ prophase   b. chromosomes start to condense
   ___ telophase   c. new nuclei form
   ___ interphase   d. all duplicated chromosomes are
   ___ anaphase   aligned at the spindle equator
   ___ cytokinesis   e. DNA replication
                       f. cytoplasmic division

Critical Thinking

1. When a cell reproduces by mitosis and cytoplasmic division, does its life end?

 2. The eukaryotic cell in the photo on the *left* is in the process of cytoplasmic division. Is this cell from a plant or an animal? How do you know?

3. Exposure to radioisotopes or other sources of radiation can damage DNA. Humans exposed to high levels of radiation face a condition called radiation poisoning. Why do you think that hair loss and damage to the lining of the gut are early symptoms of radiation poisoning? Speculate about why exposure to radiation is used as a therapy to treat some kinds of cancers.

4. Suppose you have a way to measure the amount of DNA in one cell during the cell cycle. You first measure the amount at the G1 phase. At what points in the rest of the cycle will you see a change in the amount of DNA per cell?

CENGAGE To access course materials, please visit
brain.com www.cengagebrain.com.

CREDITS: (13) © Dr. Thomas Ried, NIH and the American Association for Cancer Research. (S-Q11) © Cengage Learning; (CT2) D. M. Phillips/Visuals Unlimited.

New Zealand mud snails can reproduce on their own (asexually) or with a partner (sexually). Natural populations of this species vary in the frequency of sexual and asexual individuals.

12

MEIOSIS AND SEXUAL REPRODUCTION

Links to Earlier Concepts

Before you begin this chapter, be sure you understand how eukaryotic chromosomes are organized (Section 8.3) and how genes work (9.1). You will draw on your knowledge of DNA replication (8.4), cytoplasmic division (11.3), and cell cycle controls (11.5) as we compare meiosis with mitosis (11.2). This chapter also revisits clones (8.6), the effects of mutation (9.5), and the function of telomeres (11.4).

KEY CONCEPTS

SEX AND ALLELES
In asexual reproduction, one parent transmits its genes to offspring. In sexual reproduction, offspring inherit genes from two parents who usually differ in some number of alleles.

MEIOSIS IN REPRODUCTION
Meiosis is a nuclear division process that reduces the chromosome number. It occurs only in cells that play a role in sexual reproduction in eukaryotes.

STAGES OF MEIOSIS
The chromosome number becomes reduced by the two nuclear divisions of meiosis. During this process, the chromosomes are sorted into four new nuclei.

SHUFFLING PARENTAL DNA
During meiosis, homologous chromosomes swap segments, then are randomly sorted into separate nuclei. Both processes lead to novel combinations of alleles among offspring.

MITOSIS AND MEIOSIS COMPARED
Similarities between mitosis and meiosis suggest meiosis originated by evolutionary remodeling of mechanisms that already existed for mitosis and, before that, for repairing damaged DNA.

FIGURE 12.1 **A moment in sexual reproduction.**
Sex mixes up the genetic material of two individuals. In flowering plants, pollen grains (orange) germinate on flower carpels (yellow). Pollen tubes with male gametes inside grow from the grains down into tissues of the ovary, which house the flower's female gametes.

INTRODUCING ALLELES

In asexual reproduction, a single individual gives rise to offspring that are identical to itself and to one another. By contrast, **sexual reproduction** involves two individuals and mixes their genetic material (**FIGURE 12.1**).

In your somatic (body) cells and in those of many other sexually reproducing eukaryotes, one chromosome of each homologous pair is maternal, and the other is paternal (Section 8.3). Homologous chromosomes carry the same genes (**FIGURE 12.2A**). However, the corresponding genes on maternal and paternal chromosomes often vary—just a bit—in DNA sequence. Over evolutionary time, unique mutations accumulate in separate lines of descent, and some of those mutations occur in genes. Thus, the DNA sequence of any gene may differ from the corresponding gene on the homologous chromosome (**FIGURE 12.2B**). Different forms of the same gene are called **alleles**.

Alleles may encode slightly different forms of the gene's product. Such differences influence the details of traits shared by a species. Consider that one of the approximately 20,000 genes in human chromosomes encodes beta globin (Section 9.5). Like most human genes, the beta globin gene has multiple alleles—more than 700 in this case. A few beta

globin alleles cause sickle-cell anemia, several cause beta thalassemia, and so on. Allele differences among individuals are one reason that the members of a sexually reproducing species are not identical. Offspring of sexual reproducers inherit new combinations of alleles, which is the basis of new combinations of traits.

ON THE ADVANTAGES OF SEX

If the function of reproduction is the perpetuation of one's genes, then an organism that reproduces only by mitosis would seem to win the evolutionary race. When it reproduces, it passes all of its genes to every one of its offspring. Only about half of a sexual reproducer's genes are passed to each offspring. Yet most eukaryotes reproduce sexually, at least some of the time. Why?

Consider that all offspring of an asexual reproducer are clones. They have the same alleles—and the same traits—as their parent. Consistency is a good thing if an organism lives in a favorable, unchanging environment. Alleles that help it survive and reproduce do the same for its descendants. However, most environments are constantly changing. Offspring of asexual reproducers are equally vulnerable to unfavorable environmental change. In changing environments, sexual reproducers have the evolutionary edge. Their offspring inherit different combinations of alleles, so they vary in the details of their shared traits. Some may have a particular combination of traits that suits them perfectly to a change. As a group, their diversity offers them a better chance of surviving an environmental challenge than clones.

Perhaps the most important advantage of sexual reproduction involves the inevitable occurrence of harmful mutations. A population of sexual reproducers has a better chance of weathering the effects of such mutations. With asexual reproduction, individuals bearing a harmful mutation necessarily pass it to all of their offspring. This outcome would be rare in sexual reproduction, because each offspring of a sexual union has a 50 percent chance of inheriting a parent's mutation. Thus, all else being equal, harmful mutations accumulate in an asexually reproducing population more quickly than in a sexually reproducing one.

Environmental change is the norm. Consider, for example, the interaction between a predatory species and its prey. In each generation, prey individuals with traits that allow them to hide from, fend off, or escape the predator will leave the most young. However, the predator is constantly changing too: In each generation, predators best able to find, capture, and overcome prey leave the most descendants. Thus predators and prey are locked in a constant race, with each genetic improvement in one species

A Corresponding colored patches in this fluorescence micrograph indicate corresponding DNA sequences in a homologous chromosome pair. These chromosomes carry the same set of genes.

Genes occur in pairs on homologous chromosomes.

The members of each pair of genes may be identical, or they may differ slightly, as alleles.

B Homologous chromosomes carry the same series of genes, but the DNA sequence of any one of those genes might differ just a bit from that of its partner on the homologous chromosome.

FIGURE 12.2 Genes on chromosomes. Different forms of a gene are called alleles.

countered by an improvement in the other. The Red Queen hypothesis holds that sexual reproduction is widespread because of the pressure for constant change resulting from such species interactions. The name of the hypothesis is a reference to Lewis Carroll's book *Through the Looking Glass.* In the book, the Queen of Hearts tells Alice, "It takes all the running you can do, to keep in the same place."

alleles Forms of a gene with slightly different DNA sequences; may encode slightly different versions of the gene's product.
sexual reproduction Reproductive mode by which offspring arise from two parents and inherit genes from both.

TAKE-HOME MESSAGE 12.1

Paired genes on homologous chromosomes may vary in DNA sequence as alleles. Alleles arise by mutation.

Alleles are the basis of differences in shared traits. Offspring of sexual reproducers inherit new combinations of parental alleles—thus new combinations of such traits.

National Geographic Grantee
MAURINE NEIMAN

nimals that reproduce solely by asexual means are very rare. However, some populations of the New Zealand freshwater snail pictured in the chapter opener do just that. Maurine Neiman compares sexually reproducing and asexual populations of these snails to determine the costs and benefits of sex. Neiman and her collaborators Amy Krist and Adam Kay have discovered that sexual and asexual snails might differ in their need for phosphorus. Like most sexual organisms, the sexual snails have two chromosome sets; like most animals that cannot reproduce sexually, the asexual snails have at least three. DNA has a high phosphorus content, so having the extra sets of chromosomes multiplies each organism's requirement for this nutrient, which could add up to a big minus in the cost-of-asexuality equation.

Neiman's research has shown that extra chromosome sets translate into a disadvantage in low-phosphorus environments for the asexual snails, setting the stage for the possibility that the sexual snails—with the fewest chromosome sets of all—are likely to beat out asexuals when phosphorus is scarce. Follow-up experiments will extend beyond explaining the predominance of sex. These tiny snails have spread far beyond their native New Zealand, and huge populations of them are now disrupting ecosystems all over the world. The invasive populations are always asexual (and in fact many other invasive species have three or more sets of chromosomes). Fertilizers and detergents contain a high level of phosphorus, so agricultural runoff and other types of water pollution may be fueling population explosions of these species.

CREDITS: (2A) Image courtesy of Carl Zeiss MicroImaging, Thornwood, NY; (2B) © Cengage Learning; (in text) © Maurine Neiman.

FIGURE 12.3 **Gametes.** This illustration shows a human egg (female gamete) surrounded by sperm (male gametes).

MEIOSIS HALVES THE CHROMOSOME NUMBER

Sexual reproduction involves the fusion of mature reproductive cells—**gametes**—from two parents (**FIGURE 12.3**). Gametes have a single set of chromosomes, so they are **haploid** (n): Their chromosome number is half of the diploid ($2n$) number (Section 8.3). **Meiosis**, the nuclear division mechanism that halves the chromosome number, is necessary for gamete formation. Meiosis also gives rise to new combinations of parental alleles.

Gametes arise by division of **germ cells**, which are immature reproductive cells that form in special reproductive organs (**FIGURE 12.4**). Animals and plants make gametes somewhat differently. In animals, meiosis in diploid germ cells gives rise to eggs (female gametes) or sperm (male gametes). In plants, haploid germ cells form by meiosis. Gametes form when these cells divide by mitosis.

The first part of meiosis is similar to mitosis. A cell duplicates its DNA before either nuclear division process begins. As in mitosis, a spindle forms, and its microtubules move the duplicated chromosomes to opposite spindle poles.

However, meiosis sorts the chromosomes into new nuclei not once, but twice, so it results in the formation of four haploid nuclei. The two consecutive nuclear divisions are called meiosis I and meiosis II:

In some cells, meiosis II occurs immediately after meiosis I. In others, a period of protein synthesis—but no DNA replication—intervenes between the divisions.

During meiosis I, every duplicated chromosome aligns with its homologous partner (**FIGURE 12.5 ❶**). Then the homologous chromosomes are pulled away from one another and packaged into separate nuclei ❷. At this stage of meiosis, the chromosome number has been reduced. Each

CREDITS: (3) Francis Leroy, Biocosmos/Science Photo Library/Science Source; (in text) © Cengage Learning 2015.

testis   ovary

A Reproductive organs of humans. Meiosis in germ cells inside testes and ovaries produces gametes (sperm and eggs).

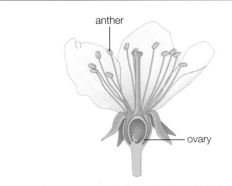

anther

ovary

B Reproductive organs of a flowering plant. Meiosis produces haploid germ cells inside anthers and ovaries. These cells divide by mitosis to give rise to gametes (sperm and eggs).

FIGURE 12.4 {**Animated**} Examples of reproductive organs in **A** animals and **B** plants.

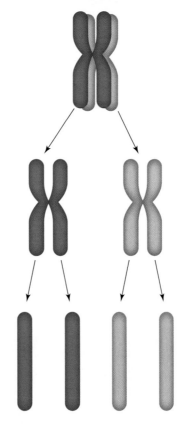

❶ Chromosomes are duplicated before meiosis begins. During meiosis I, each chromosome in the nucleus pairs with its homologous partner. The nucleus contains two of each chromosome, so it is diploid (2*n*).

❷ Homologous partners separate and are packaged into two new nuclei. Each new nucleus contains one of each chromosome, so it is haploid (*n*). The chromosomes are still duplicated.

❸ Sister chromatids separate in meiosis II and are packaged into four new nuclei. Each new nucleus contains one of each chromosome, so it is haploid (*n*). The chromosomes are now unduplicated.

FIGURE 12.5 How meiosis halves the chromosome number.

of the two new nuclei has one copy of each chromosome, so it is haploid (*n*). The chromosomes are still duplicated (the sister chromatids remain attached to one another).

During meiosis II, the sister chromatids are pulled apart, and each becomes an individual, unduplicated chromosome ❸. The chromosomes are sorted into four new nuclei. Each new nucleus still has one copy of each chromosome, so it is haploid (*n*).

Thus, meiosis partitions the chromosomes of one diploid nucleus (2*n*) into four haploid (*n*) nuclei. The next section zooms in on the details of this process.

FERTILIZATION RESTORES THE CHROMOSOME NUMBER

Haploid gametes form by meiosis. The diploid chromosome number is restored at **fertilization**, when two haploid gametes fuse to form a **zygote**, the first cell of a new individual. Thus, meiosis halves the chromosome number, and fertilization restores it.

If meiosis did not precede fertilization, the chromosome number would double with every generation. As you will see in Chapter 14, chromosome number changes can have

drastic consequences, particularly in animals. An individual's set of chromosomes is like a fine-tuned blueprint that must be followed exactly, page by page, in order to build a body that functions normally.

fertilization Fusion of two gametes to form a zygote.
gamete Mature, haploid reproductive cell; e.g., an egg or a sperm.
germ cell Immature reproductive cell that gives rise to haploid gametes when it divides.
haploid Having one of each type of chromosome characteristic of the species.
meiosis Nuclear division process that halves the chromosome number. Basis of sexual reproduction.
zygote Cell formed by fusion of two gametes at fertilization; the first cell of a new individual.

TAKE-HOME MESSAGE 12.2

The nuclear division process of meiosis is the basis of sexual reproduction in plants and animals.

Meiosis halves the diploid (2*n*) chromosome number, to the haploid number (*n*), for forthcoming gametes.

When two gametes fuse at fertilization, the diploid chromosome number is restored in the resulting zygote.

CREDITS: (4A) From Starr, Biology, 7E. © 2008 Cengage Learning; (4B) From Starr/Taggart/Evers/Starr, Biology, 13E. © 2013 Cengage Learning; (5) © Cengage Learning 2015.

FIGURE 12.6 shows the stages of meiosis in a diploid (2*n*) cell, which contains two sets of chromosomes. DNA replication occurs before meiosis I, so each chromosome has two sister chromatids.

Meiosis I The first stage of meiosis I is prophase I ❶. During this phase, the chromosomes condense, and homologous chromosomes align tightly and swap segments (more about segment-swapping in the next section). The

nuclear envelope breaks up. A spindle forms, and by the end of prophase I, microtubules attach one chromosome of each homologous pair to one spindle pole, and the other to the opposite spindle pole. These microtubules grow and shrink, pushing and pulling the chromosomes as they do. At metaphase I ❷, all of the microtubules are the same length, and the chromosomes are aligned in the middle of the cell. In anaphase I ❸, the spindle pulls the homologous chromosomes of each pair apart and toward opposite spindle poles. The two sets of chromosomes reach the spindle poles during telophase I ❹, and a new nuclear envelope forms around each cluster of chromosomes as the DNA loosens up. The two new nuclei are haploid (*n*); each contains one set of (duplicated) chromosomes. The

---

FIGURE 12.6 {Animated} Meiosis. Two pairs of chromosomes are illustrated in a diploid (2*n*) cell. Homologous chromosomes are indicated in blue and pink. Micrographs show meiosis in a lily plant cell (*Lilium regale*).

 FIGURE IT OUT: During which stage of meiosis does the chromosome number become reduced?   Answer: Anaphase I

MEIOSIS I: ONE DIPLOID NUCLEUS TO TWO HAPLOID NUCLEI

❶ Prophase I
Homologous chromosomes condense, pair up, and swap segments. Spindle microtubules attach to them as the nuclear envelope breaks up.

❷ Metaphase I
Homologous chromosome pairs are aligned between spindle poles. Spindle microtubules attach the two chromosomes of each pair to opposite spindle poles.

❸ Anaphase I
All of the homologous chromosomes separate and begin heading toward the spindle poles.

❹ Telophase I
A complete set of chromosomes clusters at both ends of the cell. A nuclear envelope forms around each set, so two haploid (*n*) nuclei form.

plasma membrane   spindle

nuclear envelope breaking up

pair of homologous chromosomes

cytoplasm often divides at this point. Each chromosome is still duplicated (it consists of two sister chromatids).

Meiosis II DNA replication does not occur before meiosis II, which proceeds simultaneously in both nuclei that formed in meiosis I. In prophase II ❺, the chromosomes condense and the nuclear envelope breaks up. A new spindle forms. By the end of prophase II, spindle microtubules attach each chromatid to one spindle pole, and its sister chromatid to the opposite spindle pole. These microtubules push and pull the chromosomes, aligning them in the middle of the cell at metaphase II ❻. In anaphase II ❼, the spindle microtubules pull the sister chromatids apart and toward opposite spindle

poles. Each chromosome is now unduplicated (it consists of one molecule of DNA). During telophase II ❽, these chromosomes reach the spindle poles. New nuclear envelopes form around the four clusters of chromosomes as the DNA loosens up. The cytoplasm often divides at this point to form four haploid (n) cells whose nuclei contain one set of (unduplicated) chromosomes.

TAKE-HOME MESSAGE 12.3

During meiosis, the nucleus of a diploid ($2n$) cell divides twice. Four haploid (n) nuclei form, each with a full set of chromosomes—one of each type.

MEIOSIS II: TWO HAPLOID NUCLEI TO FOUR HAPLOID NUCLEI

❺ **Prophase II**
The chromosomes condense. Spindle microtubules attach to each sister chromatid as the nuclear envelope breaks up.

❻ **Metaphase II**
The (still duplicated) chromosomes are aligned midway between spindle poles.

❼ **Anaphase II**
Sister chromatids separate. The now unduplicated chromosomes head to the spindle poles.

❽ **Telophase II**
A complete set of chromosomes clusters at both ends of the cell. A new nuclear envelope forms around each set, so four haploid (n) nuclei form.

No DNA replication

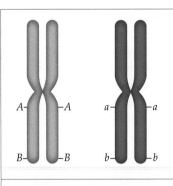

A Here, we focus on only two of the many genes on a chromosome. In this example, one gene has alleles *A* and *a*; the other has alleles *B* and *b*.

B Close contact between homologous chromosomes promotes crossing over between nonsister chromatids. Paternal and maternal chromatids exchange corresponding pieces.

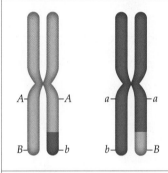

C Crossing over mixes up paternal and maternal alleles on homologous chromosomes.

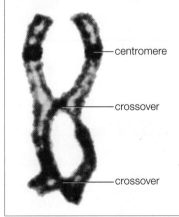

centromere

crossover

D Each pair of homologous chromosomes can cross over multiple times. This is a normal and common process of meiosis.

crossover

FIGURE 12.7 {Animated} Crossing over. Blue signifies a paternal chromosome, and pink, its maternal homologue. For clarity, we show only one pair of homologous chromosomes.

 FIGURE IT OUT: In how many places is the chromosome pictured in **D** crossing over?

Answer: Two

The previous section mentioned briefly that duplicated chromosomes swap segments with their homologous partners during prophase I. It also showed how spindle microtubules align and then separate homologous chromosomes during anaphase I. These events, along with fertilization, contribute to the variation in combinations of traits among the offspring of sexually reproducing species.

CROSSING OVER IN PROPHASE I

Early in prophase I of meiosis, all chromosomes in the cell condense. When they do, each is drawn close to its homologous partner, so that the chromatids align along their length:

This tight, parallel orientation favors **crossing over**, a process by which a chromosome and its homologous partner exchange corresponding pieces of DNA during meiosis (**FIGURE 12.7**). Homologous chromosomes may swap any segment of DNA along their length, although crossovers tend to occur more frequently in certain regions.

Swapping segments of DNA shuffles alleles between homologous chromosomes. It breaks up the particular combinations of alleles that occurred on the parental chromosomes, and makes new ones on the chromosomes that end up in gametes. Thus, crossing over introduces novel combinations of traits among offspring. It is a normal and frequent process in meiosis, but the rate of crossing over varies among species and among chromosomes. In humans, between 46 and 95 crossovers occur per meiosis, so on average each chromosome crosses over at least once.

CHROMOSOME SEGREGATION

Normally, all of the new nuclei that form in meiosis I receive a complete set of chromosomes. However, whether a new nucleus ends up with the maternal or paternal version of a chromosome is entirely random. The chance that the maternal or the paternal version of any chromosome will end up in a particular nucleus is 50 percent. Why? The answer has to do with the way the spindle segregates the homologous chromosomes during meiosis I.

The process of chromosome segregation begins in prophase I. Imagine one of your own germ cells undergoing meiosis. Crossovers have already made genetic mosaics of

❶ The four possible alignments of three pairs of chromosomes in a nucleus at metaphase I.

❷ Resulting combinations of maternal and paternal chromosomes in the two nuclei that form at telophase I.

❸ Resulting combinations of maternal and paternal chromosomes in the four nuclei that form at telophase II. Eight different combinations are possible.

FIGURE 12.8 {Animated} Hypothetical segregation of three pairs of chromosomes in meiosis I. Maternal chromosomes are pink; paternal, blue. Which chromosome of each pair gets packaged into which of the two new nuclei that form at telophase I is random. For simplicity, no crossing over occurs in this example, so all sister chromatids are identical.

its chromosomes, but for simplicity let's put crossing over aside for a moment. Just call the twenty-three chromosomes you inherited from your mother the maternal ones, and the twenty-three from your father the paternal ones.

During prophase I, microtubules fasten your cell's chromosomes to the spindle poles. Chances are very low that all of the maternal chromosomes get attached to one pole and all of the paternal chromosomes get attached to the other. Microtubules extending from a spindle pole bind to the centromere of the first chromosome they contact, regardless of whether it is maternal or paternal. Though each homologous partner becomes attached to the opposite spindle pole, there is no pattern to the attachment of the maternal or paternal chromosomes to a particular pole.

Now imagine that your germ cell has just three pairs of chromosomes (**FIGURE 12.8**). By metaphase I, those three pairs of maternal and paternal chromosomes have been divided up between the two spindle poles in one of four ways ❶. In anaphase I, homologous chromosomes separate and are pulled toward opposite spindle poles. In telophase I, a new nucleus forms around the chromosomes that cluster at each spindle pole. Each nucleus contains one of eight possible combinations of maternal and paternal chromosomes ❷.

In telophase II, each of the two nuclei divides and gives rise to two new haploid nuclei. The two new nuclei are identical because no crossing over occurred in our hypothetical example, so all of the sister chromatids were identical. Thus, at the end of meiosis in this cell, two (2) spindle poles have divvied up three (3) chromosome pairs. The resulting four nuclei have one of eight (2^3) possible combinations of maternal and paternal chromosomes ❸.

Cells that give rise to human gametes have twenty-three pairs of homologous chromosomes, not three. Each time a human germ cell undergoes meiosis, the four gametes that form end up with one of 8,388,608 (or 2^{23}) possible combinations of homologous chromosomes. That number does not even take into account crossing over, which mixes up the alleles on maternal and paternal chromosomes, or fusion with another gamete at fertilization.

crossing over Process by which homologous chromosomes exchange corresponding segments of DNA during prophase I of meiosis.

TAKE-HOME MESSAGE 12.4

Crossing over—recombination between nonsister chromatids of homologous chromosomes—occurs during prophase I.

Homologous chromosomes can get attached to either spindle pole in prophase I, so each chromosome of a homologous pair can end up in either one of the two new nuclei.

Crossing over and random sorting of chromosomes into gametes give rise to new combinations of alleles—thus new combinations of traits—among offspring of sexual reproducers.

12.5 ARE THE PROCESSES OF MITOSIS AND MEIOSIS RELATED?

This chapter opened with hypotheses about evolutionary advantages of asexual and sexual reproduction. It seems like a giant evolutionary step from producing clones to producing genetically varied offspring, but was it really?

By mitosis and cytoplasmic division, one cell becomes two new cells that have the parental chromosomes. Mitotic (asexual) reproduction results in clones of the parent. Meiosis results in the formation of haploid gametes. Gametes of two parents fuse to form a zygote, which is a cell of mixed parentage. Meiotic (sexual) reproduction

results in offspring that differ genetically from the parent, and from one another.

Though the end results differ, there are striking parallels between the four stages of mitosis and meiosis II (**FIGURE 12.9**). As one example, a spindle forms and separates chromosomes during both processes. There are many more similarities at the molecular level.

Long ago, the molecular machinery of mitosis may have been remodeled into meiosis. Evidence for this hypothesis includes a host of shared molecules, including the products

FIGURE 12.9 {Animated} Comparing meiosis II with mitosis.

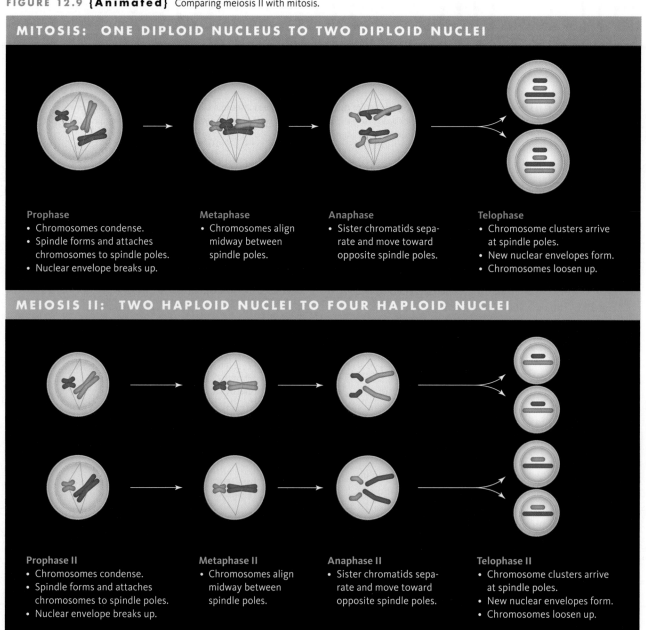

MITOSIS: ONE DIPLOID NUCLEUS TO TWO DIPLOID NUCLEI

Prophase
- Chromosomes condense.
- Spindle forms and attaches chromosomes to spindle poles.
- Nuclear envelope breaks up.

Metaphase
- Chromosomes align midway between spindle poles.

Anaphase
- Sister chromatids separate and move toward opposite spindle poles.

Telophase
- Chromosome clusters arrive at spindle poles.
- New nuclear envelopes form.
- Chromosomes loosen up.

MEIOSIS II: TWO HAPLOID NUCLEI TO FOUR HAPLOID NUCLEI

Prophase II
- Chromosomes condense.
- Spindle forms and attaches chromosomes to spindle poles.
- Nuclear envelope breaks up.

Metaphase II
- Chromosomes align midway between spindle poles.

Anaphase II
- Sister chromatids separate and move toward opposite spindle poles.

Telophase II
- Chromosome clusters arrive at spindle poles.
- New nuclear envelopes form.
- Chromosomes loosen up.

of the *BRCA* genes (Sections 10.6 and 11.5) that are made by all modern eukaryotes. By monitoring and fixing problems with the DNA—such as damaged or mismatched bases (Section 8.5)—these molecules actively maintain the integrity of a cell's chromosomes. It turns out that many of the same molecules help homologous chromosomes cross over in prophase I of meiosis (**FIGURE 12.10**). Some proteins function as part of checkpoints in both mitosis and meiosis, so mutations that affect them or the rate at which they are made can affect the outcomes of both nuclear division processes.

In anaphase of mitosis, sister chromatids are pulled apart. What would happen if the connections between the sisters did not break? Each duplicated chromosome would be pulled to one or the other spindle pole—which is exactly what happens in anaphase I of meiosis.

The shared molecules and mechanisms imply a shared evolutionary history; sexual reproduction probably originated with mutations that affected processes of mitosis. As you will see in later chapters, the remodeling of existing processes into new ones is a common evolutionary theme.

FIGURE 12.10 Example of a molecule that functions in mitosis and meiosis. This fluorescence micrograph shows homologous chromosome pairs (red) in the nucleus of a human cell during prophase I of meiosis. Centromeres are blue. Yellow pinpoints the location of a protein called MLH1 assisting with crossovers. MLH1 also helps repair mismatched bases during mitosis.

TAKE-HOME MESSAGE 12.5

Meiosis may have evolved by the remodeling of existing mechanisms of mitosis.

Application: Exploration

FIGURE 12.11 A bdelloid rotifer. All of these tiny animals are female.

WHY DO MALES EXIST? No male has ever been found among the tiny freshwater creatures called bdelloid rotifers (**FIGURE 12.11**). Females have been reproducing for 80 million years solely through cloning themselves. Bdelloids are one of the few groups of animals to have completely abandoned sex.

Compared to sex, asexual reproduction is often seen as a poor long-term strategy because it lacks crossing over—the chromosomal shuffling that brings about genetic diversity thought to give species an adaptive edge in the face of new challenges. Bdelloids have contradicted this theory by being very successful; over 360 species are alive today.

A newly discovered ability may help to explain the success of the bdelloids despite their rejection of sex. These rotifers can apparently import genes from bacteria, fungi, protists, and even plants. If the main advantage of sex is that it promotes genetic diversity, why worry about it when you have the genes of entire kingdoms available to you?

The direct swapping of genetic material is incredibly rare in animals, but bdelloids are bringing in external genes to an extent completely unheard of in complex organisms. Each rotifer is a genetic mosaic whose DNA spans almost all the major kingdoms of life: About 10 percent of its active genes have been pilfered from other organisms.

CREDITS: (10) © 2007 American Society for Reproductive Medicine. Published by Elsevier Inc. All rights reserved, Image supplied by Renée H. Martin, Ph.D.; (11) © Wim van Egmond/Visuals Unlimited/Corbis.

Summary

SECTION 12.1 **Sexual reproduction** mixes up the genetic information of two parents. The offspring of sexual reproducers typically vary in shared, inherited traits. This variation in traits can offer an evolutionary advantage over genetically identical offspring produced by asexual reproduction.

Sexual reproduction produces offspring with pairs of chromosomes, one of each homologous pair from the mother and the other from the father. The two chromosomes of a pair carry the same genes. The DNA sequence of paired genes often varies slightly, in which case they are called **alleles**. Alleles are the basis of differences in shared, heritable traits. They arise by mutation.

SECTION 12.2 **Meiosis**, the basis of sexual reproduction in eukaryotes, is a nuclear division mechanism that halves the chromosome number for forthcoming **gametes**. **Haploid** (*n*) gametes are mature reproductive cells that form from **germ cells.** The fusion of two haploid gametes during **fertilization** restores the diploid parental chromosome number in the **zygote**, the first cell of the new individual.

SECTION 12.3 DNA replication occurs before meiosis, so each chromosome consists of two molecules of DNA (sister chromatids). Two nuclear divisions (I and II) occur during meiosis. Meiosis I begins when the chromosomes condense and align tightly with their homologous partners during prophase I. Microtubules then extend from the spindle poles, penetrate the nuclear region, and attach to one or the other chromosome of each homologous pair. At metaphase I, all chromosomes are lined up at the spindle equator. During anaphase I, homologous chromosomes separate and move to opposite spindle poles. Two nuclear envelopes form around the two sets of chromosomes during telophase I. The cytoplasm may divide at this point. There may be a resting period before meiosis resumes, but DNA replication does not occur.

The second nuclear division, meiosis II, occurs in both haploid nuclei that formed in meiosis I. The chromosomes are still duplicated; each still consists of two sister chromatids. The chromosomes condense in prophase II, and align in metaphase II. Sister chromatids of each chromosome are pulled apart from each other in anaphase II, so at the end of meiosis each chromosome consists of one molecule of DNA. By the end of telophase II, four haploid nuclei have typically formed, each with a complete set of (unduplicated) chromosomes.

SECTION 12.4 Meiosis shuffles parental alleles, so offspring inherit non-parental combinations of them. During prophase I, homologous chromosomes exchange corresponding segments. This **crossing over** mixes up the alleles on maternal and paternal chromosomes, thus giving rise to combinations of alleles not present in either parental chromosome. The random segregation of maternal and paternal chromosomes into gametes also contributes to variation in traits among offspring of sexual reproducers. Microtubules can attach the maternal or the paternal chromosome of each pair to one or the other spindle pole. Either chromosome may end up in any new nucleus, and in any gamete.

SECTION 12.5 Like mitosis, meiosis requires a spindle to move and sort duplicated chromosomes, but meiosis occurs only in cells that are involved in sexual reproduction. The process of meiosis resembles that of mitosis, and may have evolved from it. Many of the same molecules function the same way in both processes.

SECTION 12.6 A few groups of animals have survived for millions of years by reproducing only asexually, despite the lack of chromosome shufflings that bring about genetic diversity in offspring. Bdelloid rotifers may have offset this disadvantage by picking up new genes from organisms in other kingdoms.

Self-Quiz   Answers in Appendix VII

1. The main evolutionary advantage of sexual over asexual reproduction is that it produces _____ .
   a. more offspring per individual
   b. more variation among offspring
   c. healthier offspring

2. Meiosis is a necessary part of sexual reproduction because it _____ .
   a. divides two nuclei into four new nuclei
   b. reduces the chromosome number for gametes
   c. produces clones that can cross over

3. Meiosis _____ .
   a. occurs in all eukaryotes
   b. supports growth and tissue repair in multicelled species
   c. gives rise to genetic diversity among offspring
   d. is part of the life cycle of all cells

4. Sexual reproduction in animals requires _____ .
   a. meiosis   c. germ cells
   b. fertilization   d. all of the above

5. Meiosis _____ the parental chromosome number.
   a. doubles   c. maintains
   b. halves   d. mixes up

6. Dogs have a diploid chromosome number of 78. How many chromosomes do their gametes have?
   a. 39   c. 156
   b. 78   d. 234

7. The cell in the diagram to the *right* is in anaphase I, not anaphase II. I know this because _____ .

Data Analysis Activities

BPA and Abnormal Meiosis In 1998, researchers at Case Western University were studying meiosis in mouse oocytes when they saw an unexpected and dramatic increase of abnormal meiosis events (**FIGURE 12.12**). Improper segregation of chromosomes during meiosis is one of the main causes of human genetic disorders, which we will discuss in Chapter 14.

The researchers discovered that the spike in meiotic abnormalities began immediately after the mouse facility started washing the animals' plastic cages and water bottles in a new, alkaline detergent. The detergent had damaged the plastic, which as a result was leaching bisphenol A (BPA). BPA is a synthetic chemical that mimics estrogen, the main female sex hormone in animals. BPA is still widely used to manufacture polycarbonate plastic items (including water bottles) and epoxies (including the coating on the inside of metal cans of food).

Caging materials	Total number of oocytes	Abnormalities
Control: New cages with glass bottles	271	5 (1.8%)
Damaged cages with glass bottles		
Mild damage	401	35 (8.7%)
Severe damage	149	30 (20.1%)
Damaged bottles	197	53 (26.9%)
Damaged cages with damaged bottles	58	24 (41.4%)

FIGURE 12.12 Meiotic abnormalities associated with exposure to damaged plastic caging. Fluorescent micrographs show nuclei of single mouse oocytes in metaphase I. **A** Normal metaphase; **B–D** examples of abnormal metaphase. Chromosomes appear red; spindle fibers, green.

1. What percentage of mouse oocytes displayed abnormalities of meiosis with no exposure to damaged caging?

2. Which group of mice showed the most meiotic abnormalities in their oocytes?

3. What is abnormal about metaphase I as it is occurring in the oocytes shown in the micrographs in **FIGURE 12.12B, C**, and **D**?

8. The cell pictured to the *right* is in which stage of nuclear division?
   a. anaphase   c. anaphase II
   b. anaphase I   d. none of the above

9. Crossing over mixes up _____ .
   a. chromosomes   c. zygotes
   b. alleles   d. gametes

10. Crossing over happens during which phase of meiosis?
   a. prophase I   c. anaphase I
   b. prophase II   d. anaphase II

11. _____ contributes to variation in traits among the offspring of sexual reproducers.
   a. Crossing over
   b. Random attachment of chromosomes to spindle poles
   c. Fertilization
   d. both a and b
   e. all are factors

12. Which of the following is one of the very important differences between mitosis and meiosis?
   a. Chromosomes align midway between spindle poles only in meiosis.
   b. Homologous chromosomes pair up only in meiosis.
   c. DNA is replicated only in mitosis.
   d. Sister chromatids separate only in meiosis.
   e. Interphase occurs only in mitosis.

13. Match each term with its description.
   ____ interphase   a. different forms of a gene
   ____ metaphase I   b. useful for varied offspring
   ____ alleles   c. may be none between meiosis I and meiosis II
   ____ zygotes   d. chromosomes lined up
   ____ gametes   e. haploid
   ____ males   f. form at fertilization
   ____ prophase I   g. mash-up time

Critical Thinking

1. In your own words, explain why sexual reproduction tends to give rise to greater genetic diversity among offspring in fewer generations than asexual reproduction.

2. Make a simple sketch of meiosis in a cell with a diploid chromosome number of 4. Now try it when the chromosome number is 3.

3. The diploid chromosome number for the body cells of a frog is 26. What would the frog chromosome number be after three generations if meiosis did not occur before gamete formation?

CENGAGE To access course materials, please visit
brain www.cengagebrain.com.
.com

CREDITS: (12) Reprinted from *Current Biology*, Vol 13, (Apr 03), Authors Hunt, Koehler, Susiarjo, Hodges, Ilagan, Voigt, Thomas, Thomas and Hassold, Bisphenol A Exposure Causes Meiotic Aneuploidy in the Female Mouse, pp. 546–553, © 2003 Cell Press. Published by Elsevier Ltd. With permission from Elsevier; (in text S-Q 8) Michael Clayton/University of Wisconsin, Department of Botany.

Eye color, like many other human traits, does not occur in discrete forms. The continuous range of variation in color among individuals is the result of interactions among several genes involved in making and distributing melanins.

13

OBSERVING PATTERNS IN INHERITED TRAITS

Links to Earlier Concepts

You may want to review what you know about traits (Section 1.4), chromosomes (8.3), genes and gene expression (9.1), mutation (9.5), sexual reproduction and alleles (12.1), and meiosis (12.2–12.4). You will revisit probability and sampling error (1.7), laws of nature (1.8), protein structure (3.4,3.5), pigments (6.1), clones (8.6), gene control (10.1, 10.2, 11.5), and epigenetics (10.5).

KEY CONCEPTS

WHERE MODERN GENETICS STARTED

Gregor Mendel discovered that inherited traits are specified in units. The units, which are distributed into gametes in predictable patterns, were later identified as genes.

MONOHYBRID CROSSES

Tracking inheritance patterns of single traits led to the discovery that during meiosis, pairs of genes on homologous chromosomes separate and end up in different gametes.

DIHYBRID CROSSES

Tracking inheritance patterns of two unrelated traits led to the discovery that in most cases, genes of a pair segregate into gametes independently of other gene pairs.

NON-MENDELIAN INHERITANCE

An allele may be partly dominant over a nonidentical partner, or codominant with it. Multiple genes may influence a trait; some genes influence many traits.

COMPLEX VARIATIONS IN TRAITS

Environmental factors can alter the expression of genes that influence a trait. Many traits appear in a continuous range of forms.

In the nineteenth century, people thought that hereditary material must be some type of fluid, with fluids from both parents blending at fertilization like milk into coffee. However, the idea of "blending inheritance" failed to explain what people could see with their own eyes. Children sometimes have traits such as freckles that do not appear in either parent. A cross between a black horse and a white one does not produce gray offspring.

The naturalist Charles Darwin did not accept the idea of blending inheritance, but he could not come up with an alternative hypothesis even though inheritance was central to his theory of natural selection. (We return to Darwin and his

theory of natural selection in Chapter 16.) At the time, no one knew that hereditary information (DNA) is divided into discrete units (genes), an insight that is critical to understanding how traits are inherited. However, even before Darwin presented his theory, someone had been gathering evidence that would support it. Gregor Mendel (*above*), an Austrian monk, had been carefully breeding thousands of pea plants. By keeping detailed records of how traits passed from one generation to the next, Mendel had been collecting evidence of how inheritance works.

MENDEL'S EXPERIMENTS

Mendel cultivated the garden pea plant (**FIGURE 13.1**). This species is naturally self-fertilizing, which means its flowers produce male and female gametes ❶ that form viable embryos when they meet up. In order to study inheritance, Mendel had to carry out controlled matings between individuals with specific traits, then observe and document the traits of their offspring. To keep an individual pea plant from self-fertilizing, Mendel removed the pollen-bearing anthers from its flowers. He then cross-fertilized the plant by brushing its egg-bearing carpels with pollen from another plant ❷. He collected the seeds ❸ from the cross-fertilized individual, and recorded the traits of the new pea plants that grew from them ❹.

Many of Mendel's experiments started with plants that "breed true" for particular traits such as white flowers or purple flowers. Breeding true for a trait means that, new mutations aside, all offspring have the same form of the trait as the parent(s), generation after generation. For example, all offspring of pea plants that breed true for white flowers also have white flowers. As you will see in the next section, Mendel cross-fertilized pea plants that breed true for different forms of a trait, and discovered that the traits of the offspring often appear in predictable patterns. Mendel's meticulous work tracking pea plant traits led him to conclude (correctly) that hereditary information passes from one generation to the next in discrete units.

INHERITANCE IN MODERN TERMS

DNA was not proven to be hereditary material until the 1950s (Section 8.1), but Mendel discovered its units, which we now call genes, almost a century before then. Today, we know that individuals of a species share certain traits because their chromosomes carry the same genes.

Each gene occurs at a specific location, or **locus** (plural, loci), on a particular chromosome (**FIGURE 13.2**). The somatic cells of humans and other animals are diploid,

❶ In the flowers of garden pea plants, pollen grains that form in anthers produce male gametes; female gametes form in carpels.

❷ Experimenters can control the transfer of hereditary material from one pea plant to another by snipping off a flower's anthers (to prevent the flower from self-fertilizing), and then brushing pollen from another flower onto its carpel.

In this example, pollen from a plant that has purple flowers is brushed onto the carpel of a white-flowered plant.

❸ Later, seeds develop inside pods of the cross-fertilized plant. An embryo in each seed develops into a mature pea plant.

❹ Every plant that arises from the cross has purple flowers. Predictable patterns such as this are evidence of how inheritance works.

FIGURE 13.1 {Animated} Breeding garden pea plants.

FIGURE 13.2 {Animated} Loci of a few human genes. Genetic disorders that result from mutations in the genes are shown in parentheses. The number or letter below each chromosome is its name; the characteristic banding patterns appear after staining. A similar map of all 23 human chromosomes is in Appendix IV.

so they have pairs of genes, on pairs of homologous chromosomes. In most cases, both genes of a pair are expressed. Genes at the same locus on a pair of homologous chromosomes may be identical, or they may vary as alleles (Section 12.1). Organisms breed true for a trait because they carry identical alleles of genes governing that trait. An individual with two identical alleles of a gene is **homozygous** for the allele. By contrast, an individual with two different alleles of a gene is **heterozygous** (*hetero*– means mixed).

FIGURE 13.3 Genotype gives rise to phenotype. In this example, the dominant allele *P* specifies purple flowers; the recessive allele *p*, white flowers.

dominant Refers to an allele that masks the effect of a recessive allele paired with it in heterozygous individuals.
genotype The particular set of alleles that is carried by an individual's chromosomes.
heterozygous Having two different alleles of a gene.
homozygous Having identical alleles of a gene.
hybrid The heterozygous offspring of a cross or mating between two individuals that breed true for different forms of a trait.
locus Location of a gene on a chromosome.
phenotype An individual's observable traits.
recessive Refers to an allele with an effect that is masked by a dominant allele on the homologous chromosome.

Hybrids are heterozygous offspring of a cross or mating between individuals that breed true for different forms of a trait.

When we say that an individual is homozygous or heterozygous, we are discussing its **genotype**, the particular set of alleles it carries. Genotype is the basis of **phenotype**, which refers to the individual's observable traits. "White-flowered" and "purple-flowered" are examples of pea plant phenotypes that arise from differences in genotype.

The phenotype of a heterozygous individual depends on how the products of its two different alleles interact. In many cases, the effect of one allele influences the effect of the other, and the outcome of this interaction is reflected in the individual's phenotype. An allele is **dominant** when its effect masks that of a **recessive** allele paired with it. Usually, a dominant allele is represented by an italic capital letter such as *A*; a recessive allele, with a lowercase italic letter such as *a*. Consider the purple- and white-flowered pea plants that Mendel studied. In these plants, the allele that specifies purple flowers (let's call it *P*) is dominant over the allele that specifies white flowers (*p*). Thus, a pea plant homozygous for the dominant allele (*PP*) has purple flowers; one homozygous for the recessive allele (*pp*) has white flowers (**FIGURE 13.3**). A heterozygous plant (*Pp*) has purple flowers.

When homologous chromosomes separate during meiosis (Section 12.3), the gene pairs on those chromosomes separate too. Each gamete that forms carries only one of the two genes of a pair (**FIGURE 13.4**). Thus, plants homozygous for the dominant allele (*PP*) can only make gametes that carry the dominant allele *P* **❶**. Plants homozygous for the recessive allele (*pp*) can only make gametes that carry the recessive allele *p* **❷**. If these homozygous plants are crossed (*PP* × *pp*), only one outcome is possible: A gamete carrying allele *P* meets up with a gamete carrying allele *p* **❸**. All offspring of this cross will have both alleles—they will be heterozygous (*Pp*).

A grid called a **Punnett square** is helpful for predicting the outcomes of such crosses (**FIGURE 13.5**).

Our example illustrated a pattern so predictable that it can be used as evidence of a dominance relationship between alleles. In a **testcross**, an individual that has a dominant trait (but an unknown genotype) is crossed with an individual known to be homozygous for the recessive allele. The pattern of traits among the offspring of the cross can reveal whether the tested individual is heterozygous or homozygous. If all of the offspring of the testcross have the dominant trait, then the parent with the unknown genotype is homozygous for the dominant allele. If any of the offspring have the recessive trait, then it is heterozygous.

Dominance relationships between alleles determine the phenotypic outcome of a **monohybrid cross**, in which individuals that are identically heterozygous for one gene—*Pp* for example—are bred together or self-fertilized. The frequency at which traits associated with the alleles appear among the offspring depends on whether one of the alleles is dominant over the other.

To perform a monohybrid cross, we would start with two individuals that breed true for two different forms of a trait. In garden pea plants, flower color (purple and white) is one example of a trait with two distinct forms, but there are many others. Mendel investigated seven of them: stem length (tall and short), seed color (yellow and green), pod texture (smooth and wrinkled), and so on (**TABLE 13.1**). A cross between individuals that breed true for two forms of a trait yields offspring identically heterozygous for the alleles that govern the trait. When these F_1 (first generation) hybrids are crossed, the frequency at which the two traits appear in the F_2 (second generation) offspring offers information about a dominance relationship between the alleles. F is an abbreviation for filial, which means offspring.

A cross between two purple-flowered heterozygous individuals (*Pp*) is an example of a monohybrid cross. Each of these plants can make two types of gametes: ones that carry a *P* allele, and ones that carry a *p* allele (**FIGURE 13.6A**). So, in a monohybrid cross between two *Pp* plants (*Pp* × *Pp*), the two types of gametes can meet up in four possible ways at fertilization:

Possible Event		Probable Outcome
Sperm *P* meets egg *P*	→	zygote genotype is *PP*
Sperm *P* meets egg *p*	→	zygote genotype is *Pp*
Sperm *p* meets egg *P*	→	zygote genotype is *Pp*
Sperm *p* meets egg *p*	→	zygote genotype is *pp*

Three out of four possible outcomes of this cross include at least one copy of the dominant allele *P*. Each time

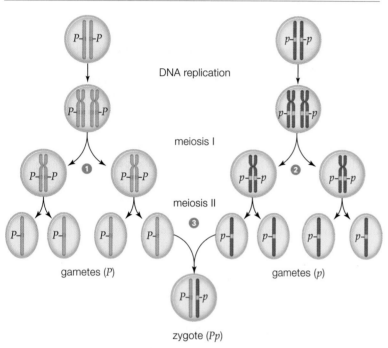

FIGURE 13.4 Segregation of genes on homologous chromosomes into gametes. Homologous chromosomes separate during meiosis, so the pairs of genes they carry separate too. Each of the resulting gametes carries one of the two members of each gene pair. For clarity, only one set of chromosomes is illustrated.

❶ All gametes made by a parent homozygous for a dominant allele carry that allele.

❷ All gametes made by a parent homozygous for a recessive allele carry that allele.

❸ If these two parents are crossed, the union of any of their gametes at fertilization produces a zygote with both alleles. All offspring of this cross will be heterozygous.

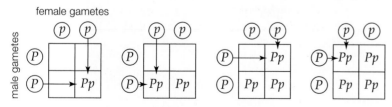

FIGURE 13.5 Making a Punnett square. Parental gametes are listed in circles on the top and left sides of a grid. Each square is filled with the combination of alleles that would result if the gametes in the corresponding row and column met up.

CREDIT: (4, 5) From Starr/Taggart/Evers/Starr, Biology, 13E. © 2013 Cengage Learning.

TABLE 13.1

Mendel's Seven Pea Plant Traits

Trait	Dominant Form	Recessive Form
Seed Shape	Round	Wrinkled
Seed Color	Yellow	Green
Pod Texture	Smooth	Wrinkled
Pod Color	Green	Yellow
Flower Color	Purple	White
Flower Position	Along Stem	At Tip
Stem Length	Tall	Short

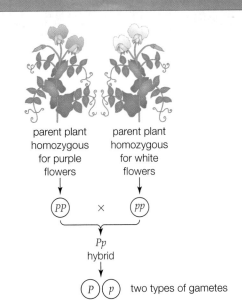

parent plant homozygous for purple flowers   parent plant homozygous for white flowers

PP × pp

Pp hybrid

P p two types of gametes

A All of the F$_1$ offspring of a cross between two plants that breed true for different forms of a trait are identically heterozygous (Pp). These offspring make two types of gametes: P and p.

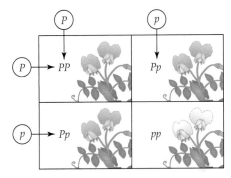

	P	p
P	PP	Pp
p	Pp	pp

B A monohybrid cross is a cross between these F$_1$ offspring. In this example, the phenotype ratio in F$_2$ offspring is 3:1 (3 purple to 1 white).

FIGURE 13.6 {Animated} A monohybrid cross.

 FIGURE IT OUT: How many genotypes are possible in the F$_2$ generation?

Answer: Three: PP, Pp, and pp

fertilization occurs, there are 3 chances in 4 that the resulting offspring will inherit a P allele, and have purple flowers. There is 1 chance in 4 that it will inherit two recessive p alleles, and have white flowers. Thus, the probability that a particular offspring of this cross will have purple or white flowers is 3 purple to 1 white, which we represent as a ratio of 3:1 (**FIGURE 13.6B**). The 3:1 pattern is an indication that purple and white flower color are specified by alleles with a clear dominance relationship: Purple is dominant; white, recessive. If the probability of one individual inheriting a particular genotype is difficult to imagine, think about probability in terms phenotypes of many offspring. In this example, there will be roughly three purple-flowered plants for every white-flowered one.

---

law of segregation The two members of each pair of genes on homologous chromosomes end up in different gametes during meiosis.
monohybrid cross Cross between two individuals identically heterozygous for one gene; for example $Aa × Aa$.
Punnett square Diagram used to predict the genetic and phenotypic outcome of a cross.
testcross Method of determining genotype by tracking a trait in the offspring of a cross between an individual of unknown genotype and an individual known to be homozygous recessive.

The phenotype ratios in the F$_2$ offspring of Mendel's monohybrid crosses were all close to 3:1. These results became the basis of his **law of segregation**, which we state here in modern terms: Diploid cells carry pairs of genes, on pairs of homologous chromosomes. The two genes of each pair are separated from each other during meiosis, so they end up in different gametes.

TAKE-HOME MESSAGE 13.2

Homologous chromosomes carry pairs of genes. The two genes of each pair are separated from each other during meiosis, so they end up in different gametes.

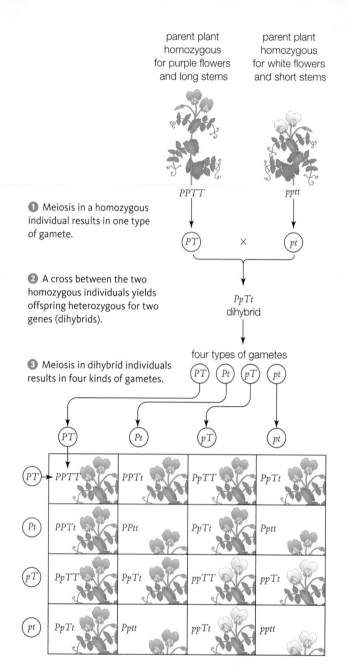

parent plant homozygous for purple flowers and long stems

parent plant homozygous for white flowers and short stems

PPTT

pptt

1 Meiosis in a homozygous individual results in one type of gamete.

(PT) × (pt)

2 A cross between the two homozygous individuals yields offspring heterozygous for two genes (dihybrids).

PpTt dihybrid

four types of gametes

3 Meiosis in dihybrid individuals results in four kinds of gametes.

(PT) (Pt) (pT) (pt)

	(PT)	(Pt)	(pT)	(pt)
(PT)	*PPTT*	*PPTt*	*PpTT*	*PpTt*
(Pt)	*PPTt*	*PPtt*	*PpTt*	*Pptt*
(pT)	*PpTT*	*PpTt*	*ppTT*	*ppTt*
(pt)	*PpTt*	*Pptt*	*ppTt*	*pptt*

4 If two of the dihybrid individuals are crossed, the four types of gametes can meet up in 16 possible ways. Of 16 possible offspring genotypes, 9 will result in plants that are purple-flowered and tall; 3, purple-flowered and short; 3, white-flowered and tall; and 1, white-flowered and short. Thus, the ratio of phenotypes is 9:3:3:1.

FIGURE 13.7 {Animated} A dihybrid cross between plants that differ in flower color and plant height. In this example, *P* and *p* are dominant and recessive alleles for flower color; *T* and *t* are dominant and recessive alleles for height.

 FIGURE IT OUT: What do the flowers inside the boxes represent?

Answer: Phenotypes of the F₂ offspring

A monohybrid cross allows us to track alleles of one gene pair. What about alleles of two gene pairs? In a **dihybrid cross**, individuals identically heterozygous for alleles of two genes (dihybrids) are crossed. As with a monohybrid cross, the pattern of traits seen in the offspring of the cross depends on the dominance relationships between alleles of the genes.

Let's use a gene for flower color (*P*, purple; *p*, white) and one for plant height (*T*, tall; *t*, short) in an example. **FIGURE 13.7** shows a dihybrid cross starting with one parent plant that breeds true for purple flowers and tall stems (*PPTT*), and one that breeds true for white flowers and short stems (*pptt*). The *PPTT* plant only makes gametes with the dominant alleles (*PT*); the *pptt* plant only makes gametes with the recessive alleles (*pt*) **1**. So, all offspring from a cross between these parent plants (*PPTT* × *pptt*) will be dihybrids (*PpTt*) with purple flowers and tall stems **2**.

Four combinations of alleles are possible in the gametes of *PpTt* dihybrids **3**. If two *PpTt* plants are crossed (a dihybrid cross, *PpTt* × *PpTt*), the four types of gametes can combine in sixteen possible ways at fertilization **4**. Nine of the sixteen genotypes would give rise to tall plants with purple flowers; three, to short plants with purple flowers; three, to tall plants with white flowers; and one, to short plants with white flowers. Thus, the ratio of phenotypes among the offspring of this dihybrid cross would be 9:3:3:1.

Mendel discovered the 9:3:3:1 ratio of phenotypes among the offspring of his dihybrid crosses, but he had no idea what it meant. He could only say that "units" specifying one trait (such as flower color) are inherited independently of "units" specifying other traits (such as plant height). In time, Mendel's hypothesis became known as the **law of independent assortment**, which we state here in modern terms: During meiosis, the two genes of a pair tend to be sorted into gametes independently of how other gene pairs are sorted into gametes.

Mendel published his results in 1866, but apparently his work was read by few and understood by no one at the time. In 1871 he was promoted, and his pioneering experiments ended. When he died in 1884, he did not know that his work with pea plants would be the starting point for modern genetics.

CONTRIBUTION OF CROSSOVERS

How two genes get sorted into gametes depends partly on whether they are on the same chromosome. When homologous chromosomes separate during meiosis, either member of the pair can end up in either of the two new nuclei that form. This random assortment happens

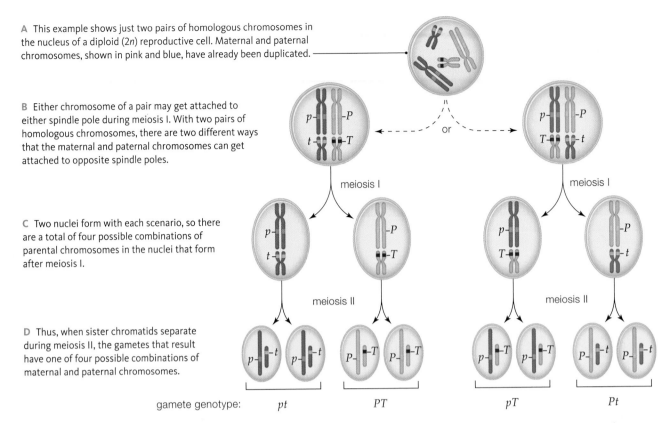

A This example shows just two pairs of homologous chromosomes in the nucleus of a diploid (2n) reproductive cell. Maternal and paternal chromosomes, shown in pink and blue, have already been duplicated.

B Either chromosome of a pair may get attached to either spindle pole during meiosis I. With two pairs of homologous chromosomes, there are two different ways that the maternal and paternal chromosomes can get attached to opposite spindle poles.

C Two nuclei form with each scenario, so there are a total of four possible combinations of parental chromosomes in the nuclei that form after meiosis I.

D Thus, when sister chromatids separate during meiosis II, the gametes that result have one of four possible combinations of maternal and paternal chromosomes.

gamete genotype: *pt*   *PT*   *pT*   *Pt*

FIGURE 13.8 {Animated} Independent assortment of genes on different chromosomes. Genes that are far apart on the same chromosome usually assort independently too, because crossovers typically separate them.

independently for each pair of homologous chromosomes in the cell. Thus, genes on one chromosome assort into gametes independently of genes on the other chromosomes (**FIGURE 13.8**).

Pea plants have seven chromosomes. Mendel studied seven pea genes, and all of them assorted into gametes independently of one another. Was he lucky enough to choose one gene on each of those chromosomes? As it turns out, some of the genes Mendel studied *are* on the same chromosome. These genes are far enough apart that crossing over occurs between them very frequently—so frequently that they tend to assort into gametes independently, just as if they were on different chromosomes. By contrast, genes that are very close together on a chromosome usually do not

assort independently into gametes, because crossing over does not happen between them very often. Thus, gametes usually end up with parental combinations of alleles of these genes.

Genes that do not assort independently into gametes are said to be linked. Linked genes were identified by tracking inheritance in human families over several generations. All of the genes on a chromosome are called a **linkage group**. Peas have 7 different chromosomes, so they have 7 linkage groups. Humans have 23 different chromosomes, so they have 23 linkage groups.

dihybrid cross Cross between two individuals identically heterozygous for two genes; for example *AaBb × AaBb*.
law of independent assortment During meiosis, members of a pair of genes on homologous chromosomes tend to be distributed into gametes independently of other gene pairs.
linkage group All genes on a chromosome.

> **TAKE-HOME MESSAGE 13.3**
>
> During meiosis, gene pairs on homologous chromosomes tend to be distributed into gametes independently of how other gene pairs are distributed.
>
> Independent assortment depends on proximity. Genes that are closer together on a chromosome get separated less frequently by crossovers, so gametes often receive parental combinations of alleles of these genes.

Genotype: AA or AO | AB | BB or BO | OO

Phenotype: A | AB | B | O

FIGURE 13.9 Combinations of alleles (genotype) that are the basis of human blood type (phenotype).

homozygous parent (RR) × homozygous parent (rr) ⟶ heterozygous offspring (Rr)

A Cross a red-flowered with a white-flowered snapdragon plant, and all of the offspring will have pink flowers.

B If two of the pink-flowered snapdragons are crossed, the phenotypes of their offspring will occur in a 1:2:1 ratio.

	R	r
R	RR	Rr
r	Rr	rr

FIGURE 13.10 {Animated} Incomplete dominance in heterozygous (pink) snapdragons. One allele (R) results in the production of a red pigment; the other (r) results in no pigment.

 FIGURE IT OUT: Is the experiment in **B** a monohybrid cross or a dihybrid cross?

Answer: A monohybrid cross

In the Mendelian inheritance patterns discussed in the last two sections, the effect of a dominant allele on a trait fully masks that of a recessive one. Other inheritance patterns are more common, but also more complex.

CODOMINANCE

With **codominance**, traits associated with two nonidentical alleles of a gene are equally apparent in heterozygotes; neither allele is dominant or recessive. Codominance may occur in **multiple allele systems**, in which three or more alleles of a gene persist at relatively high frequency among individuals of a population. Consider the *ABO* gene, which encodes an enzyme that modifies a carbohydrate on the surface of human red blood cells. The *A* and *B* alleles encode slightly different versions of this enzyme, which in turn modify the carbohydrate differently. The *O* allele has a mutation that prevents its enzyme product from becoming active at all.

The two alleles you carry for the *ABO* gene determine the form of the carbohydrate on your blood cells, so they are the basis of your blood type. The *A* and the *B* allele are codominant when paired. If your genotype is *AB*, then you have both versions of the enzyme, and your blood type is AB. The *O* allele is recessive when paired with either the *A* or *B* allele. If your genotype is *AA* or *AO*, your blood type is A. If your genotype is *BB* or *BO*, it is type B. If you are *OO*, it is type O (**FIGURE 13.9**).

Receiving incompatible blood in a transfusion is dangerous because the immune system attacks red blood cells bearing molecules that do not occur in one's own body. The attack can cause the blood cells to clump or burst, with potentially fatal consequences. The blood cells of people with type O blood do not carry the carbohydrate that can trigger this immune response. Thus, people with type O blood can donate blood to anyone; they are called universal donors. However, because their body is unfamiliar with the carbohydrates made by people with type A or B blood, they can receive type O blood only. People with type AB blood can receive a transfusion of any blood type, so they are called universal recipients.

INCOMPLETE DOMINANCE

With **incomplete dominance**, one allele is not fully dominant over the other, so the heterozygous phenotype is an intermediate blend of the two homozygous phenotypes. A gene that affects flower color in snapdragon plants is an example. One allele of the gene (*R*) encodes an enzyme that makes a red pigment. The enzyme encoded by a mutated allele (*r*) cannot make any pigment. Plants homozygous for the *R* allele (*RR*) make a lot of red pigment, so they have red flowers. Plants homozygous for the *r* allele (*rr*) make no pigment, so their flowers are white. Heterozygous plants (*Rr*) make only

CREDITS: (9) photo, Annie Cavanagh/Wellcome Images; art, © Cengage Learning; (10A) © JupiterImages Corporation; (10B) From Starr/Evers/Starr, Biology Today and Tomorrow with Physiology, 4E. © 2013 Cengage Learning.

enough red pigment to color their flowers pink (**FIGURE 13.10**). A cross between two heterozygous plants yields red-, pink-, and white-flowered offspring in a 1:2:1 ratio.

EPISTASIS

Some traits are affected by multiple genes, an effect called polygenic inheritance or **epistasis**. Consider fur color in dogs, which depends on pigments called melanins. A dark brown melanin gives rise to brown or black fur; a reddish melanin is responsible for yellow fur. The production and deposition of melanin pigments in fur depends on several genes. The product of one gene (*TYRP1*) helps make the brown melanin. A dominant allele (*B*) of this gene results in a higher production of this melanin than the recessive allele (*b*). A different gene (*MC1R*) affects which type of melanin is produced. A dominant allele (*E*) of this gene triggers production of the brown melanin; its recessive partner (*e*) carries a mutation that results in production of the reddish form. Dogs homozygous for the *e* allele are yellow because they produce only the reddish melanin (**FIGURE 13.11**).

PLEIOTROPY

In many cases, a single gene influences multiple traits, an effect called **pleiotropy**. Mutations that alter the gene affect all of the traits at once. Many complex genetic disorders, including sickle-cell anemia (Section 9.5) and Marfan syndrome, arise as a result of mutations in pleiotropic genes. Marfan syndrome is caused by mutations that affect fibrillin. Long fibers of this protein impart elasticity to tissues of the heart, skin, blood vessels, tendons, and other body parts. Mutations cause tissues to form with defective fibrillin or none at all. The largest blood vessel leading from the heart, the aorta, is particularly affected. The aorta's thick wall is not as elastic as it should be, and it eventually stretches and becomes leaky. Thinned and weakened, the aorta can rupture during exercise—an abruptly fatal outcome.

About 1 in 5,000 people have Marfan syndrome, and there is no cure. Its effects—and risks—are manageable with early diagnosis, but symptoms are often missed. Many affected people die suddenly and early without ever knowing they had the disorder (**FIGURE 13.12**).

codominance Effect in which the full and separate phenotypic effects of two alleles are apparent in heterozygous individuals.
epistasis Polygenic inheritance, in which a trait is influenced by multiple genes.
incomplete dominance Effect in which one allele is not fully dominant over another, so the heterozygous phenotype is an intermediate blend between the two homozygous phenotypes.
multiple allele system Gene for which three or more alleles persist in a population at relatively high frequency.
pleiotropy Effect in which a single gene affects multiple traits.

CREDITS: (11) photo, © John Daniels/ardea.com; art, © Cengage Learning; (12) Courtesy of The Family of Haris Charalambous and the University of Toledo.

FIGURE 13.11 {Animated} An example of epistasis. Interactions among products of two gene pairs affect coat color in Labrador retrievers. Dogs with alleles *E* and *B* have black fur. Those with an *E* and two recessive *b* alleles have brown fur. Dogs homozygous for the recessive *e* allele have yellow fur.

FIGURE 13.12
A heartbreaker: Marfan syndrome. In 2006, 21-year-old basketball star Haris Charalambous collapsed and died suddenly during warm-up exercises. An autopsy revealed that his aorta had burst, an effect of the Marfan syndrome that Charalambous did not realize he had. Assistant trainer Brian Jones says, "Haris was just the nicest, funniest kid in the world. With his size, he was sort of lovably goofy. He was everybody's best friend."

TAKE-HOME MESSAGE 13.4

Some alleles are not dominant or recessive when paired.

With incomplete dominance, one allele is not fully dominant over another, so the heterozygous phenotype is an intermediate blend of the two homozygous phenotypes.

In codominance, two alleles have full and separate effect, so the phenotype of a heterozygous individual comprises both homozygous phenotypes.

In some cases, one gene influences multiple traits. In other cases, multiple genes influence the same trait.

A The color of the snowshoe hare's fur varies by season. In summer, the fur is brown (*left*); in winter, white (*right*). Both forms offer seasonally appropriate camouflage from predators.

B The height of a mature yarrow plant depends on the elevation at which it grows.

C The body form of the water flea on the top develops in environments with few predators. A longer tail spine and a pointy head (*bottom*) develop in response to chemicals emitted by insects that prey on the fleas.

FIGURE 13.13 {Animated} Examples of environmental effects on phenotype.

The phrase "nature versus nurture" refers to a centuries-old debate about whether human behavioral traits arise from one's genetics (nature) or from environmental factors (nurture). It turns out that both play a role. The environment affects the expression of many genes, which in turn affects phenotype—including human behavioral traits. We can summarize this thinking with an equation:

$$\text{genotype} + \text{environment} \longrightarrow \text{phenotype}$$

Epigenetics research is revealing that the environment makes an even greater contribution to this equation than most biologists had suspected (Section 10.5).

Environmentally driven changes in gene expression patterns involve gene control (Section 10.1). For example, environmental cues trigger some cell-signaling pathways that end with methyl groups being removed from or added to particular regions of DNA. The change in methylation enhances or suppresses gene expression in those regions.

SOME ENVIRONMENTAL EFFECTS

Mechanisms that adjust phenotype in response to external cues are part of an individual's normal ability to adapt to its environment, as the following examples illustrate.

Seasonal Changes in Coat Color Seasonal changes in temperature and the length of day affect the production of melanin and other pigments that color the skin and fur of many animals. These species have different color phases in different seasons (**FIGURE 13.13A**). Hormonal signals triggered by the seasonal changes cause fur to be shed, and new fur grows back with different types and amounts of pigments deposited in it. The resulting change in phenotype provides these animals with seasonally appropriate camouflage from predators.

Effect of Altitude on Yarrow In plants, a flexible phenotype gives immobile individuals an ability to thrive in diverse habitats. For example, genetically identical yarrow plants grow to different heights at different altitudes (**FIGURE 13.13B**). More challenging temperature, soil, and water conditions are typically encountered at higher altitudes. Differences in altitude are also correlated with changes in the reproductive mode of yarrow: Plants at higher altitude tend to reproduce asexually, and those at lower altitude tend to reproduce sexually.

Alternative Phenotypes in Water Fleas Water fleas have different phenotypes depending on whether the aquatic insects that prey on them are present (**FIGURE 13.13C**). Individuals also switch between asexual and sexual modes of reproduction depending on environmental conditions. During the early spring, competition is scarce in their freshwater pond habitats. At that time, the fleas reproduce rapidly by asexual means, giving birth to large numbers of female offspring that quickly fill the ponds. Later in the season, competition for resources intensifies as the pond water becomes warmer, saltier, and more crowded. Under these conditions, some of the water fleas start giving birth to males, and then reproducing sexually. The increased genetic diversity of sexually produced offspring may offer the population an advantage in a more challenging environment.

Psychiatric Disorders Does the environment affect human genes? Researchers recently discovered that mutations in four human gene regions are associated with five psychiatric disorders: autism, depression, schizophrenia, bipolar disorder, and attention deficit hyperactivity disorder (ADHD). However, there must be an environmental component too, because one person with the mutations might get one type of disorder, while a relative with the same mutations might get another—two different results from the same genetic underpinnings. Moreover, the majority of people who carry these mutations never end up with a psychiatric disorder.

Recent discoveries in animal models are beginning to unravel some of the mechanisms by which environment can influence mental state in humans. For example, we now know that learning and memory are associated with dynamic and rapid DNA modifications in brain cells. Mood is, too. Stress-induced depression causes methylation-based silencing of a particular nerve growth factor gene; some antidepressants work by reversing this methylation. As another example, rats whose mothers are not very nurturing end up anxious and having a reduced resilience for stress as adults. The difference between these rats and ones who had nurturing maternal care is traceable to epigenetic DNA modifications that result in a lower than normal level of another nerve growth factor. Drugs can reverse these modifications—and their effects. We do not yet know all of the genes that influence human mental state, but the implication of such research is that future treatments for many disorders will involve deliberate modification of methylation patterns in an individual's DNA.

PEOPLE MATTER

DR. GAY BRADSHAW

The air explodes with the sound of high-powered rifles and the startled infant watches his family fall to the ground, the image seared into his memory. He and other orphans are then transported to distant locales to start new lives. Ten years later, the teenaged orphans begin a killing rampage, leaving more than a hundred victims.

A scene describing post-traumatic stress disorder (PTSD) in Kosovo or Rwanda? The similarities are striking—but the teenagers are young elephants, and the victims, rhinoceroses.

Gay Bradshaw, a psychologist and the director of the Kerulos Center in Oregon, has brought the latest insights from human neuroscience and psychology to bear on startling field observations of elephant behavior. She suspects that some threatened elephant populations might be suffering from chronic stress and trauma brought on by human encroachment and killing. "The loss of older elephants," says Bradshaw, "and the extreme psychological and physical trauma of witnessing the massacres of their family members interferes with a young elephant's normal development."

Under normal conditions, an early and healthy emotional relationship between an infant and its mother fosters the development of self-regulatory structures in the brain's right hemisphere. All mammals share this developmental attachment mechanism. With trauma, a malfunction can develop that makes the individual vulnerable to PTSD and predisposed to violence as an adult. Individuals who survive trauma often face a lifelong struggle with depression, suicide, or behavioral dysfunctions. In addition, children of trauma survivors can exhibit similar symptoms, an effect that is likely to be epigenetic at least in part.

As with humans, an intact, functioning social order helps buffer the effects of trauma in elephants. When park rangers introduced older males into the herd of marauding adolescent orphans, the orphans' violent behavior abruptly stopped.

TAKE-HOME MESSAGE 13.5

The environment influences gene expression, and therefore can alter phenotype.

Cell-signaling pathways link environmental cues with changes in gene expression.

FIGURE 13.14 Face length varies continuously in dogs. A gene with 12 alleles influences this trait.

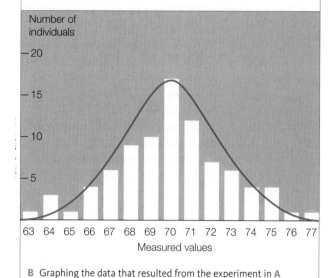

63 64 65 66 67 68 69 70 71 72 73 74 75 76 77

A To see if human height varies continuously, male biology students at the University of Florida were divided into categories of one-inch increments in height and counted.

Number of individuals

—20

—15

—10

—5

63 64 65 66 67 68 69 70 71 72 73 74 75 76 77
Measured values

B Graphing the data that resulted from the experiment in **A** produces a bell-shaped curve, an indication that height does vary continuously in humans.

FIGURE 13.15 {Animated} Continuous variation.

The pea plant phenotypes that Mendel studied appeared in two or three forms, which made them easy to track through generations. However, many other traits do not appear in distinct forms. Such traits are often the result of complex genetic interactions—multiple genes, multiple alleles, or both—with added environmental influences (we return to this topic in Chapter 17, as we consider some evolutionary consequences of variation in phenotype). Tracking traits with complex variation presents a special challenge, which is why the genetic basis of many of them has not yet been completely unraveled.

Some traits occur in a range of small differences that is called **continuous variation**. Continuous variation can be an outcome of epistasis, in which multiple genes affect a single trait. The more genes that influence a trait, the more continuous is its variation. Traits that arise from genes with a lot of alleles may also vary continuously. Some genes have regions of DNA in which a series of 2 to 6 nucleotides is repeated hundreds or thousands of times in a row. These **short tandem repeats** can spontaneously expand or contract very quickly compared with the rate of mutation, and the resulting changes in the gene's DNA sequence may be preserved as alleles. For example, short tandem repeats have given rise to 12 alleles of a homeotic gene that influences the length of the face in dogs, with longer repeats associated with longer faces (**FIGURE 13.14**).

Human skin color varies continuously (a topic that we return to in Chapter 14), as does human eye color (shown in the chapter opener). How do we determine whether a particular trait varies continuously? Let's use another human trait, height, as an example. First, the total range of phenotypes is divided into measurable categories—inches, in this case (**FIGURE 13.15A**). Next, the individuals in each category are counted; these counts reveal the relative frequencies of phenotypes across the range of values. Finally, the data is plotted as a bar chart (**FIGURE 13.15B**). A graph line around the top of the bars shows the distribution of values for the trait. If the line is a bell-shaped curve, or **bell curve**, the trait varies continuously.

bell curve Bell-shaped curve; typically results from graphing frequency versus distribution for a trait that varies continuously.
continuous variation Range of small differences in a shared trait.
short tandem repeat In chromosomal DNA, sequences of a few nucleotides repeated multiple times in a row.

TAKE-HOME MESSAGE 13.6

The more genes and other factors that influence a trait, the more continuous is its range of variation.

13.7 Application: MENACING MUCUS

Lindsay, 22   Savannah, 19   Ben, 23   Jeff, 21   Brandon, 18   Cody, 23

FIGURE 13.16 Cystic fibrosis. These are a few of the many young victims of cystic fibrosis, which occurs most often in people of northern European ancestry. At least one young person dies every day in the United States from complications of this disease.

CYSTIC FIBROSIS (CF) IS THE MOST COMMON FATAL GENETIC DISORDER IN THE UNITED STATES. It occurs in people homozygous for a mutated allele of the *CFTR* gene. This gene encodes an active transport protein that moves chloride ions out of epithelial cells. Sheets of these cells line the passageways and ducts of the lungs, liver, pancreas, intestines, reproductive system, and skin. When chloride ions leave these cells, water follows by osmosis. The process maintains a thin film of water on the surface of the epithelial sheets.

The allele most commonly associated with CF has a 3 base pair deletion. It is called *ΔF508* because the protein it encodes is missing the normal 508th amino acid, a phenylalanine (F). The deletion prevents proper membrane trafficking of newly assembled polypeptides, which are left stranded in endoplasmic reticulum. The altered protein can function properly, but it never reaches the cell surface to do its job.

Epithelial cell membranes that lack the CFTR protein cannot transport chloride ions. Too few chloride ions leave these cells. Not enough water leaves them either, so the surfaces of epithelial cell sheets are too dry. Mucus that normally slips through the body's tubes sticks to the walls of the tubes instead. This outcome has pleiotropic effects because thick globs of mucus accumulate and clog passageways and ducts throughout the body. Breathing becomes difficult as the mucus obstructs the smaller airways of the lungs. Digestive problems arise as ducts that lead to the gut get clogged with mucus. Males are typically infertile because their sperm flow is hampered.

CFTR also helps alert the immune system to the presence of disease-causing bacteria in the lungs. The CFTR protein functions as a receptor: It binds directly to bacteria and triggers endocytosis. Endocytosis of bacteria into epithelial cells lining the respiratory tract initiates an immune response. When the cells lack CFTR, this early alert system fails, so bacteria have time to multiply before being detected by the immune system. Thus, chronic bacterial infections of the lungs are a hallmark of cystic fibrosis. Antibiotics help control infections, but there is no cure. Most affected people die before age thirty, when their tormented lungs fail (**FIGURE 13.16**).

The *ΔF508* allele is at least 50,000 years old and very common: in some populations, 1 in 25 people are heterozygous for it. Why does the allele persist if it is so harmful? *ΔF508* is codominant with the normal allele. Heterozygous individuals typically have no symptoms of cystic fibrosis; their cells have plasma membranes with enough CFTR to transport chloride ions normally. The *ΔF508* allele may offer these individuals an advantage in surviving certain deadly infectious diseases. CFTR's receptor function is an essential part of the immune response to bacteria in the respiratory tract. However, the same function allows bacteria to enter cells of the gastrointestinal tract, where they can be deadly. For example, endocytosis of *Salmonella typhi* bacteria into epithelial cells lining the gut results in a dangerous infection called typhoid fever. Cells lacking CFTR do not take up these bacteria. Thus, people who carry *ΔF508* are probably less susceptible to typhoid fever and other bacterial diseases that begin in the intestinal tract.

Summary

SECTION 13.1 Gregor Mendel indirectly discovered the role of alleles in inheritance by breeding pea plants and tracking traits of the offspring. Each gene occurs at a **locus**, or location, on a chromosome. Individuals with identical alleles are **homozygous** for the allele. **Heterozygous** individuals, or **hybrids**, have two nonidentical alleles. A **dominant** allele masks the effect of a **recessive** allele on the homologous chromosome. **Genotype** (an individual's particular set of alleles) gives rise to **phenotype**, which refers to an individual's observable traits.

SECTION 13.2 Crossing individuals that breed true for two forms of a trait yields identically heterozygous offspring. A cross between such offspring is a **monohybrid cross**. The frequency at which the traits appear in offspring of such **testcrosses** can reveal dominance relationships among the alleles associated with those traits.

Punnett squares are useful for determining the probability of offspring genotype and phenotype. Mendel's monohybrid cross results led to his **law of segregation** (stated here in modern terms): Diploid cells have pairs of genes on homologous chromosomes. The two genes of a pair separate from each other during meiosis, so they end up in different gametes.

SECTION 13.3 Crossing individuals that breed true for two forms of two traits yields F_1 offspring identically heterozygous for alleles governing those traits. A cross between such offspring is a **dihybrid cross**. The frequency at which the two traits appear in F_2 offspring can reveal dominance relationships between alleles associated with those traits. Mendel's dihybrid cross results led to his **law of independent assortment** (stated here in modern terms): Paired genes on homologous chromosomes tend to sort into gametes independently of other gene pairs during meiosis. Crossovers can break up **linkage groups**.

SECTION 13.4 With **incomplete dominance**, the phenotype of heterozygous individuals is an intermediate blend of the two homozygous phenotypes. With **codominant** alleles, heterozygous individuals have both homozygous phenotypes. Codominance may occur in **multiple allele systems** such as the one underlying ABO blood typing. With **epistasis**, two or more genes affect the same trait. A **pleiotropic** gene affects two or more traits.

SECTION 13.5 An individual's phenotype is influenced by environmental factors. Environmental cues alter gene expression by way of cell signaling pathways that ultimately affect gene controls.

SECTION 13.6 A trait that is influenced by multiple genes often occurs in a range of small increments of phenotype called **continuous variation**. Continuous variation typically occurs as a **bell curve** in the range of values. Multiple alleles such as those that arise in regions of **short tandem repeats** can give rise to continuous variation.

SECTION 13.7 Cystic fibrosis occurs in people homozygous for a mutated allele of the *CFTR* gene. The allele persists at high frequency despite its devastating effects. Carrying the allele may offer heterozygous individuals protection from dangerous gastrointestinal tract infections.

Self-Quiz Answers in Appendix VII

1. A heterozygous individual has a _____ for a trait being studied.
   a. pair of identical alleles
   b. pair of nonidentical alleles
   c. haploid condition, in genetic terms

2. An organism's observable traits constitute its _____ .
   a. phenotype   c. genotype
   b. variation   d. pedigree

3. In genetics, F stands for filial, which means _____ .
   a. friendly   c. final
   b. offspring   d. hairlike

4. The second-generation offspring of a cross between individuals who are homozygous for different alleles of a gene are called the _____ .
   a. F_1 generation   c. hybrid generation
   b. F_2 generation   d. none of the above

5. F_1 offspring of the cross $AA \times aa$ are _____ .
   a. all AA c. all Aa
   b. all aa d. 1/2 AA and 1/2 aa

6. Refer to question 5. Assuming complete dominance, the F_2 generation will show a phenotypic ratio of _____ .
   a. 3:1   b. 9:1   c. 1:2:1   d. 9:3:3:1

7. A testcross is a way to determine _____ .
   a. phenotype   b. genotype   c. both a and b

8. Assuming complete dominance, crosses between two dihybrid F_1 pea plants, which are offspring from a cross $AABB \times aabb$, result in F_2 phenotype ratios of _____ .
   a. 1:2:1   b. 3:1   c. 1:1:1:1   d. 9:3:3:1

9. The probability of a crossover occurring between two genes on the same chromosome _____ .
   a. is unrelated to the distance between them
   b. decreases with the distance between them
   c. increases with the distance between them

10. A gene that affects three traits is _____ .
    a. epistatic   c. pleiotropic
    b. a multiple allele system d. dominant

11. The phenotype of individuals heterozygous for _____ alleles comprises both homozygous phenotypes.
    a. epistatic   c. pleiotropic
    b. codominant   d. hybrid

Data Analysis Activities

Carrying the Cystic Fibrosis Allele Offers Protection from Typhoid Fever Epithelial cells that lack the CFTR protein cannot take up bacteria by endocytosis. Endocytosis is an important part of the respiratory tract's immune defenses against common *Pseudomonas* bacteria, which is why *Pseudomonas* infections of the lungs are a chronic problem in cystic fibrosis patients. Endocytosis is also the way that *Salmonella typhi* enter cells of the gastrointestinal tract, where internalization of this bacteria can result in typhoid fever.

Typhoid fever is a common worldwide disease. Its symptoms include extreme fever and diarrhea, and the resulting dehydration causes delirium that may last several weeks. If untreated, it kills up to 30 percent of those infected. Around 600,000 people die annually from typhoid fever. Most of them are children.

In 1998, Gerald Pier and his colleagues compared the uptake of *S. typhi* by different types of epithelial cells: those homozygous for the normal allele, and those heterozygous for the ΔF508 allele associated with CF. (Cells that are homozygous for the mutation do not take up any *S. typhi* bacteria.) Some of the results are shown in **FIGURE 13.17**.

FIGURE 13.17 Effect of the ΔF508 mutation on the uptake of three different strains of *Salmonella typhi* bacteria by epithelial cells.

1. Regarding the Ty2 strain of *S. typhi*, about how many more bacteria were able to enter normal cells (those heterozygous for the normal allele) than cells heterozygous for the ΔF508 allele?
2. Which strain of bacteria entered normal epithelial cells most easily?
3. Entry of all three *S. typhi* strains into the heterozygous epithelial cells was inhibited. Is it possible to tell which strain was most inhibited?

---

12. _____ in a trait is indicated by a bell curve.

13. Match the terms with the best description.
    ___ dihybrid cross   a. *bb*
    ___ monohybrid cross   b. *AaBb* × *AaBb*
    ___ homozygous condition   c. *Aa*
    ___ heterozygous condition   d. *Aa* × *Aa*

Genetics Problems Answers in Appendix VII

1. Mendel crossed a true-breeding pea plant with green pods and a true-breeding pea plant with yellow pods. All offspring had green pods. Which color is recessive?

2. Assuming that independent assortment occurs during meiosis, what type(s) of gametes will form in individuals with the following genotypes?
    a. *AABB*   b. *AaBB*   c. *Aabb*   d. *AaBb*

3. Determine the predicted genotype frequencies among the offspring of an *AABB* × *aaBB* mating.

4. Heterozygous individuals perpetuate some alleles that have lethal effects in homozygous individuals. A mutated allele (M^L) associated with taillessness in Manx cats (*left*) is an example. Cats homozygous for this allele ($M^L M^L$) typically die before birth due to severe spinal cord defects. In a case of incomplete dominance, cats heterozygous for the M^L allele and the normal, unmutated allele (M) have a short, stumpy tail or none at all. Two $M^L M$ heterozygous cats mate. What is the probability that any of their kittens will be heterozygous ($M^L M$)?

5. People homozygous for a base-pair substitution in the beta-globin gene have sickle-cell anemia (Section 9.5). A couple who are planning to have children discover that both of the individuals are heterozygous for the mutated allele (Hb^S) and the normal allele (Hb^A). Calculate the probability that any one of their children will be born with sickle-cell anemia.

6. In sweet pea plants, an allele for purple flowers (*P*) is dominant to an allele for red flowers (*p*). An allele for long pollen grains (*L*) is dominant to an allele for round pollen grains (*l*). Bateson and Punnett crossed a plant having purple flowers/long pollen grains with one having white flowers/round pollen grains. All F$_1$ offspring had purple flowers and long pollen grains. Among the F$_2$ generation, the researchers observed the following phenotypes:
    296 purple flowers/long pollen grains
    19 purple flowers/round pollen grains
    27 red flowers/long pollen grains
    85 red flowers/round pollen grains
    What is the best explanation for these results?

CENGAGE **brain** To access course materials, please visit www.cengagebrain.com.

This family lives in Tanzania, where exposure to intense sunlight is responsible for the skin cancer that kills almost everyone with the albino phenotype. An abnormally low amount of melanin leaves people with this trait defenseless against UV radiation in the sun's rays. Recessive alleles on an autosome give rise to albinism.

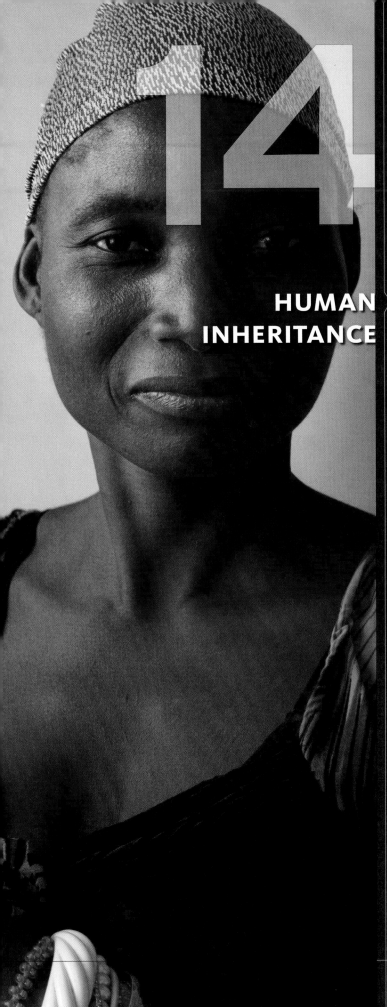

HUMAN INHERITANCE

AP Photo/Jacquelyn Martin.

Links to Earlier Concepts

Be sure you understand dominance relationships (Sections 13.1, 13.4, and 13.5), gene expression (9.1, 9.2), and mutations (9.5). You will use your knowledge of chromosomes (8.3), DNA replication and repair (8.4, 8.5), meiosis (12.2, 12.3), and sex determination (10.3). Sampling error (1.7), proteins (3.4), cell components (4.5, 4.9, 4.10), metabolism (5.4), pigments (6.1), telomeres (11.4), and oncogenes (11.5) will turn up in the context of genetic disorders.

KEY CONCEPTS

TRACKING TRAITS IN HUMANS

Inheritance patterns in humans are revealed by following traits through generations of a family. Tracked traits are often genetic abnormalities or syndromes associated with a genetic disorder.

AUTOSOMAL INHERITANCE

Traits associated with dominant alleles on autosomes appear in every generation. Traits associated with recessive alleles on autosomes can skip generations.

SEX-LINKED INHERITANCE

Traits associated with alleles on the X chromosome tend to affect more men than women. Men cannot pass such alleles to a son; carrier mothers bridge affected generations.

CHROMOSOME CHANGES

Some genetic disorders arise after large-scale change in chromosome structure. With few exceptions, a change in the number of autosomes is fatal in humans.

GENETIC TESTING

Genetic testing provides information about the risk of passing a harmful allele to offspring. Prenatal testing can reveal a genetic abnormality or disorder in a developing fetus.

TABLE 14.1

Examples of Genetic Abnormalities and Disorders in Humans

Disorder or Abnormality	Main Symptoms
Autosomal dominant inheritance pattern	
Achondroplasia	One form of dwarfism
Aniridia	Defects of the eyes
Camptodactyly	Rigid, bent fingers
Familial hypercholesterolemia	High cholesterol level; clogged arteries
Huntington's disease	Degeneration of the nervous system
Marfan syndrome	Abnormal or missing connective tissue
Polydactyly	Extra fingers, toes, or both
Progeria	Drastic premature aging
Neurofibromatosis	Tumors of nervous system, skin
Autosomal recessive inheritance pattern	
Albinism	Absence of pigmentation
Hereditary methemoglobinemia	Blue skin coloration
Cystic fibrosis	Difficulty breathing; chronic lung infections
Ellis–van Creveld syndrome	Dwarfism, heart defects, polydactyly
Fanconi anemia	Physical abnormalities, marrow failure
Galactosemia	Brain, liver, eye damage
Hereditary hemochromatosis	Joints, organs damaged by iron overload
Phenylketonuria (PKU)	Mental impairment
Sickle-cell anemia	Anemia, pain, swelling, frequent infections
Tay–Sachs disease	Deterioration of mental and physical abilities; early death
X-linked recessive inheritance pattern	
Androgen insensitivity syndrome	XY individual but having some female traits; sterility
Red–green color blindness	Inability to distinguish red from green
Hemophilia	Impaired blood clotting ability
Muscular dystrophies	Progressive loss of muscle function
X-linked anhidrotic dysplasia	Mosaic skin (patches with or without sweat glands); other ill effects
X-linked dominant inheritance pattern	
Fragile X syndrome	Intellectual, emotional disability
Incontinentia pigmenti	Abnormalities of skin, hair, teeth, nails, eyes; neurological problems
Changes in chromosome number	
Down syndrome	Mental impairment; heart defects
Turner syndrome (XO)	Sterility; abnormal ovaries, sexual traits
Klinefelter syndrome	Sterility; mild mental impairment
XXX syndrome	Minimal abnormalities
XYY condition	Mild mental impairment or no effect
Changes in chromosome structure	
Chronic myelogenous leukemia (CML)	Overproduction of white blood cells; organ malfunctions
Cri-du-chat syndrome	Mental impairment; abnormal larynx

Some organisms, including pea plants and fruit flies, are ideal for genetic analysis. They have relatively few chromosomes, they reproduce quickly under controlled conditions, and breeding them poses few ethical problems. It does not take long to follow a trait through many generations. Humans, however, are a different story. Unlike flies grown in laboratories, we humans live under variable conditions, in different places, and we live as long as the geneticists who study us. Most of us select our own mates and reproduce if and when we want to. Our families tend to be on the small side, so sampling error (Section 1.7) is a major factor in studying them.

Because of these and other challenges, geneticists often use historical records to track traits through many generations of a family. These researchers make standardized charts of genetic connections called **pedigrees** (**FIGURE 14.1**). Analysis of a pedigree can reveal whether a trait is associated with a dominant or recessive allele, and whether the allele is on an autosome or a sex chromosome. Pedigree analysis also allows geneticists to determine the probability that a trait will recur in future generations of a family or a population.

TYPES OF GENETIC VARIATION

Some easily observed human traits follow Mendelian inheritance patterns. Like the flower color of pea plants, these traits are controlled by a single gene with alleles that have a clear dominance relationship. (Appendix IV shows a map of human chromosomes with the locations of some of these alleles.) Consider how someone who is homozygous for two recessive alleles of the *MC1R* gene (Section 13.4) makes the reddish melanin but not the brown melanin, so this person has red hair.

Single genes on autosomes or sex chromosomes also govern more than 6,000 genetic abnormalities and disorders. **TABLE 14.1** lists a few examples. A genetic abnormality is a rare or uncommon version of a trait, such as having six fingers on a hand. By contrast, a genetic disorder sooner or later causes medical problems that may be severe. A genetic disorder is often characterized by a specific set of symptoms (a syndrome). Most research in the field of human genetics focuses on disorders, because what we learn may help us develop treatments for affected people.

The next two sections of this chapter focus on inheritance patterns of human single-gene disorders, which affect about 1 in 200 people. Keep in mind that these patterns are the least common. Most human traits are

pedigree Chart showing the pattern of inheritance of a trait through generations in a family.

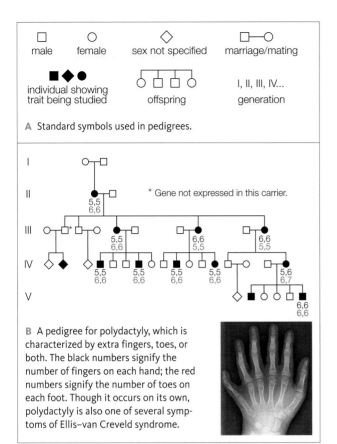

male   female   sex not specified   marriage/mating

individual showing trait being studied   offspring   I, II, III, IV... generation

A Standard symbols used in pedigrees.

I

II
5,5
6,6

* Gene not expressed in this carrier.

III
5,5
6,6   6,6
5,5   6,6
5,5

IV
5,5
6,6   5,5
6,6   5,5
6,6   5,5
6,6   5,6
6,7

V
6,6
6,6

B A pedigree for polydactyly, which is characterized by extra fingers, toes, or both. The black numbers signify the number of fingers on each hand; the red numbers signify the number of toes on each foot. Though it occurs on its own, polydactyly is also one of several symptoms of Ellis–van Creveld syndrome.

FIGURE 14.1 {Animated} Pedigrees.

polygenic (Section 13.4) and have epigenetic contributions (Section 13.5). Many genetic disorders are like this, including diabetes, asthma, obesity, cancers, heart disease, and multiple sclerosis. The inheritance patterns of these disorders are complex, and despite intense research our understanding of the genetics behind them remains incomplete.

Sections 14.4 and 14.5 explore some causes and effects of major changes in chromosomes—alterations in chromosome number or structure. Such changes occur in about 1 of every 100 births worldwide, and in many cases they have drastic consequences on health.

TAKE-HOME MESSAGE 14.1

Human inheritance patterns are often studied by tracking genetic abnormalities or disorders through family trees.

A genetic disorder is an inherited condition that causes medical problems. A genetic abnormality is a rare version of an inherited trait.

Some human genetic traits are governed by single genes and are inherited in a Mendelian fashion. Many others are influenced by multiple genes and epigenetics.

PEOPLE MATTER

DR. NANCY WEXLER

The village of Barranquitas, Venezuela, has the highest incidence of Huntington's disease in the world. A person with this incurable, fatal hereditary disorder gradually loses muscle control. Eventually, serious problems with swallowing cause many patients to die from choking or malnutrition. Beyond the physical symptoms, deep depression can often take hold.

Huntington's affects 1 in 10,000 people worldwide, but in Barranquitas the rate is more like 1 in 10. Some 1,000 villagers already have full-blown Huntington's; many more carry the gene. Such a high concentration of Huntington's patients made this region the backbone of Nancy Wexler's research. Wexler has been coming here for more than 30 years to study the genetics behind the disorder.

This is more than an academic pursuit or a career goal for her. "My mother died of Huntington's and she was a scientist. My father was a scientist too, and so we said 'Let's find a cure.' And we still say that. You can't get up in the morning without having hope and confidence that the cure is just around the corner."

Wexler and her colleagues collected DNA from and compiled an extended pedigree for nearly 10,000 Venezuelans. Her research was critical to the discovery that a dominant allele on human chromosome 4 causes Huntington's. As the daughter of a Huntington's sufferer, she has a one-in-two chance of carrying the fatal genetic flaw herself.

In 1999, Wexler cofounded a care home for Huntington's sufferers near Lake Maracaibo in Venezuela. The home, Casa Hogar, is a haven for more than 50 people whose families can no longer cope. Casa Hogar is facing a chronic lack of funding, possibly even closure. Still, Wexler remains confident that one day it won't be needed. "We never know when some miraculous discovery is going to be made," she said. "There are science breakthroughs on the horizon and happening now so I am very hopeful about the cure in the near future."

CREDITS: (1) art, © Cengage Learning 2015; photo, Courtesy of Irving Buchbinder, DPM, DABPS, Community Health Services, Hartford CT; (in text) Acey Harper/Time & Life Pictures/Getty Images.

14.2 HOW DO WE KNOW WHEN A TRAIT IS AFFECTED BY AN ALLELE ON AN AUTOSOME?

THE AUTOSOMAL DOMINANT PATTERN

A trait associated with a dominant allele on an autosome appears in people who are heterozygous for it as well as those who are homozygous. Such traits appear in every generation of a family, and they occur with equal frequency in both sexes. When one parent is heterozygous, and the other is homozygous for the recessive allele, each of their children has a 50 percent chance of inheriting the dominant allele and having the associated trait (**FIGURE 14.2A**).

Achondroplasia A form of hereditary dwarfism called achondroplasia offers an example of an autosomal dominant disorder (one caused by a dominant allele on an autosome). Mutations associated with achondroplasia occur in a gene for a growth hormone receptor. The mutations cause the receptor, a regulatory molecule that slows bone development, to be overly active. About 1 in 10,000 people is heterozygous for one of these mutations. As adults, affected people are, on average, about four feet, four inches (1.3 meters) tall, with arms and legs that are short relative to torso size (**FIGURE 14.2B**). An allele that causes achondroplasia can be passed to children because its expression does not interfere with reproduction, at least in heterozygous people. The homozygous condition results in severe skeletal malformations that cause early death.

Huntington's Disease Alleles that cause Huntington's disease are also inherited in an autosomal dominant pattern. Mutations associated with this disorder alter a gene for a cytoplasmic protein whose function is still unknown. The mutations are insertions caused by expansion of a short tandem repeat (Section 13.6), in which the same three nucleotides become repeated many, many times in the gene's sequence. The altered gene encodes an oversized protein product that gets chopped into pieces inside nerve cells of the brain. The pieces accumulate in cytoplasm as large clumps that eventually prevent the cells from functioning properly. Brain cells involved in movement, thinking, and emotion are particularly affected. In the most common form of Huntington's, symptoms do not start until after the age of thirty, and affected people die during their forties or fifties. With this and other late-onset disorders, people tend to reproduce before symptoms appear, so the allele is often passed unknowingly to children.

Hutchinson–Gilford Progeria Hutchinson–Gilford progeria is an autosomal dominant disorder characterized by drastically accelerated aging. It is usually caused by a mutation in the gene for lamin A, a protein subunit of intermediate filaments that support the nuclear envelope (Section 4.9). Lamins also have roles in mitosis, DNA synthesis and repair, and transcriptional regulation. The

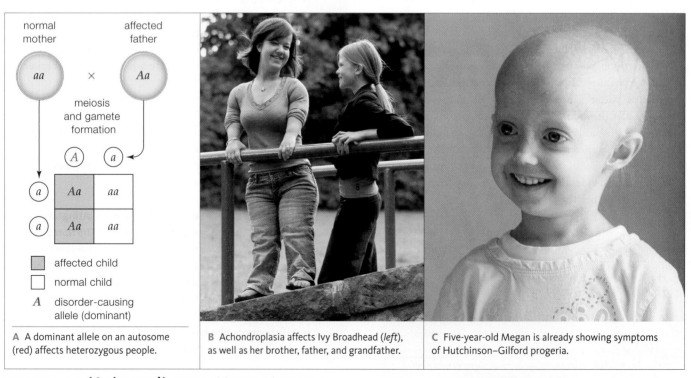

A A dominant allele on an autosome (red) affects heterozygous people.

B Achondroplasia affects Ivy Broadhead (*left*), as well as her brother, father, and grandfather.

C Five-year-old Megan is already showing symptoms of Hutchinson–Gilford progeria.

FIGURE 14.2 {Animated} Autosomal dominant inheritance.

CREDITS: (2A) From Starr/Taggart/Evers/Starr, Biology, 13E. © 2013 Cengage Learning; (2B) © Newcastle Photos and Ivy & Violet Broadhead and family; (2C) Photo courtesy of The Progeria Research Foundation.

mutation, a base-pair substitution, adds a signal for a splice site (Section 9.2). The resulting lamin A protein is too short and cannot be processed correctly after translation. Cells that carry this mutation have a nucleus that is grossly abnormal, with nuclear pore complexes that do not assemble properly and membrane proteins localized to the wrong side of the nuclear envelope. The function of the nucleus as protector of chromosomes and gateway of transcription is severely impaired, so DNA damage accumulates quickly. The effects are pleiotropic. Outward symptoms begin to appear before age two, as skin that should be plump and resilient starts to thin, muscles weaken, and bones soften. Premature baldness is inevitable (**FIGURE 14.2C**). Most people with the disorder die in their early teens as a result of a stroke or heart attack brought on by hardened arteries, a condition typical of advanced age. Progeria does not run in families because affected people do not live long enough to reproduce.

THE AUTOSOMAL RECESSIVE PATTERN

A recessive allele on an autosome is expressed only in homozygous people, so traits associated with the allele tend to skip generations. Both sexes are equally affected. People heterozygous for the allele are carriers, which means that they have the allele but not the trait. Any child of two carriers has a 25 percent chance of inheriting the allele from both parents (**FIGURE 14.3A**). Being homozygous for the allele, such children would have the trait.

Tay–Sachs Disease Alleles associated with Tay–Sachs disease are inherited in an autosomal recessive pattern. In the general population, about 1 in 300 people is a carrier for one of these allele, but the incidence is ten times higher in some groups, such as Jews of eastern European descent. The gene altered in Tay–Sachs encodes a lysosomal enzyme responsible for breaking down a particular type of lipid. Mutations cause this enzyme to misfold and become destroyed, so cells make the lipid but cannot break it down. Typically, newborns homozygous for a Tay–Sachs allele seem normal, but within three to six months they become irritable, listless, and may have seizures as the lipid accumulates in their nerve cells. Blindness, deafness, and paralysis follow. Affected children usually die by age five (**FIGURE 14.3B**).

Albinism Albinism, a genetic abnormality characterized by an abnormally low level of the pigment melanin, is also inherited in an autosomal recessive pattern. Mutations associated with the albino phenotype occur in genes involved in melanin synthesis. Skin, hair, or eye pigmentation may be reduced or missing, as shown in the chapter opening

A Only people homozygous for a recessive allele on an autosome have the associated trait. In this example, both parents are carriers. Each of their children has a 25 percent chance of inheriting two alleles, and being affected by the trait.

B Conner Hopf was diagnosed with Tay–Sachs disease at age 7½ months. He died before his second birthday.

FIGURE 14.3 {Animated} Autosomal recessive inheritance.

photo. In the most dramatic form of the phenotype, the skin is very white and does not tan, and the hair is white. The lack of pigment in the irises of the eyes allows underlying blood vessels to show through, so the irises appear red. Melanin plays a role in the retina, so people with the albino phenotype tend to have vision problems.

TAKE-HOME MESSAGE 14.2

With an autosomal dominant inheritance pattern, anyone with the allele, homozygous or heterozygous, has the associated trait. The trait tends to appear in every generation.

With an autosomal recessive inheritance pattern, only persons who are homozygous for an allele have the associated trait. The trait tends to skip generations.

CREDITS: (3A) From Starr/Taggart/Evers/Starr, Biology, 13E. © 2013 Cengage Learning; (3B) Courtesy of © Conner's Way Foundation, www.connersway.com.

Many genetic disorders are associated with alleles on the X chromosome (**FIGURE 14.4**). Almost all of them are inherited in a recessive pattern, probably because those caused by dominant X chromosome alleles tend to be lethal in male embryos.

THE X-LINKED RECESSIVE PATTERN

A recessive allele on the X chromosome (an X-linked recessive allele) leaves two clues when it causes a genetic disorder. First, an affected father never passes an X-linked recessive allele to a son, because all children who inherit their father's X chromosome are female (**FIGURE 14.5A**). Thus, a heterozygous female is always the bridge between an affected male and his affected grandson. Second, the disorder appears in males more often than in females. This is because all males who carry the allele have the disorder, but not all heterozygous females do. Remember that one of the two X chromosomes in each cell of a female is inactivated as a Barr body (Section 10.3). As a result, only about half of a heterozygous female's cells express the recessive allele. The other half of her cells express the dominant, normal allele that she carries on her other X chromosome, and this expression can mask the phenotypic effects of the recessive allele.

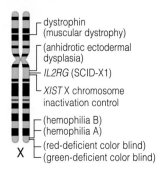

FIGURE 14.4 The human X chromosome. This chromosome carries about 2,000 genes—almost 10 percent of the total. Most X chromosome alleles that cause genetic disorders are inherited in a recessive pattern. A few disorders are listed (in parentheses).

Red–Green Color Blindness   Color blindness refers to a range of conditions in which an individual cannot distinguish among some or all colors in the spectrum of visible light. These conditions are typically inherited in an X-linked recessive pattern, because most of the genes involved in color vision are on the X chromosome.

Humans can sense the differences among 150 colors, and this perception depends on pigment-containing receptors

A In this example of X-linked inheritance, the mother carries a recessive allele on one of her two X chromosomes (red).

B A view of color blindness. The photo on the *left* shows how a person with red–green color blindness sees the photo on the *right*. The perception of blues and yellows is normal; red and green appear similar. The circles are part of a standardized test for color blindness. A set of 38 of these circles is commonly used to diagnose deficiencies in color perception.

You may have one form of red–green color blindness if you see a 7 in this circle instead of a 29.

You may have another form of red–green color blindness if you see a 3 instead of an 8 in this circle.

FIGURE 14.5 {Animated}   X-linked recessive inheritance.

CREDITS: (4) © Cengage Learning; (5A) From Starr/Taggart/Evers/Starr, Biology, 13E. © 2013 Cengage Learning; (5B) left, Gary L. Friedman, www.FriedmanArchives.com.; right, Life Nature Library, The Primates, 1965, Sarel Eimerl and Irven DeVore.

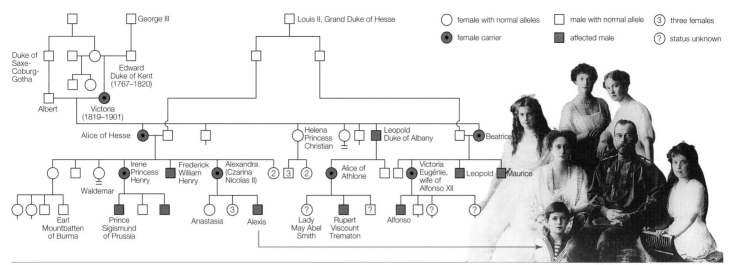

FIGURE 14.6 {Animated} A classic case of X-linked recessive inheritance: a partial pedigree of the descendants of Queen Victoria of England. At one time, the recessive X-linked allele that resulted in hemophilia was present in eighteen of Victoria's sixty-nine descendants, who sometimes intermarried. Of the Russian royal family members shown, the mother (Alexandra Czarina Nicolas II) was a carrier.

 FIGURE IT OUT: How many of Alexis's siblings were affected by hemophilia A?

Answer: None

in the eyes. Mutations that result in altered or missing receptors affect color vision. For example, people who have red–green color blindness see fewer than 25 colors because receptors that respond to red and green wavelengths are weakened or absent (**FIGURE 14.5B**). Some confuse red and green; others see green as gray.

Duchenne Muscular Dystrophy

An X-linked recessive disorder, Duchenne muscular dystrophy (DMD), is characterized by muscle degeneration. It is caused by mutations in the X chromosome gene for dystrophin, a cytoskeletal protein that links actin microfilaments in cytoplasm to a complex of proteins in the plasma membrane. This complex structurally and functionally links the cell to extracellular matrix. When dystrophin is absent, the entire protein complex is unstable. Muscle cells, which are subject to stretching, are particularly affected. Their plasma membrane is easily damaged, and they become flooded with calcium ions. Eventually, the muscle cells die and become replaced by fat cells and connective tissue.

DMD affects about 1 in 3,500 people, almost all of them boys. Symptoms begin between ages three and seven. Anti-inflammatory drugs can slow the progression of DMD, but there is no cure. When an affected boy is about twelve years old, he will begin to use a wheelchair and his heart muscle will start to fail. Even with the best care, he will probably die before the age of thirty, from a heart disorder or respiratory failure (suffocation).

Hemophilia A

Hemophilia A is an X-linked recessive disorder that interferes with blood clotting. Most of us have a blood clotting mechanism that quickly stops bleeding from minor injuries. That mechanism involves factor VIII, a protein product of a gene on the X chromosome. Bleeding can be prolonged in males who carry a mutation in this gene. Females who have two mutated alleles are also affected (heterozygous females make enough factor VIII to have a clotting time that is close to normal). Affected people tend to bruise very easily, but internal bleeding is their most serious problem. Repeated bleeding inside the joints disfigures them and causes chronic arthritis.

In the nineteenth century, the incidence of hemophilia A was relatively high in royal families of Europe and Russia, probably because the common practice of inbreeding kept the allele in their family trees (**FIGURE 14.6**). Today, about 1 in 7,500 people in the general population is affected. That number may be rising because the disorder is now a treatable one. More affected people are living long enough to transmit the mutated allele to children.

TAKE-HOME MESSAGE 14.3

Men who have an X-linked allele have the associated trait, but not all heterozygous women do. Thus, the trait appears more often in men.

Men transmit an X-linked allele to their daughters, but not to their sons.

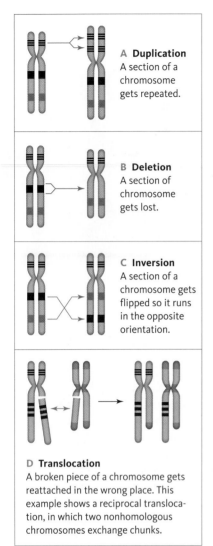

A Duplication
A section of a chromosome gets repeated.

B Deletion
A section of chromosome gets lost.

C Inversion
A section of a chromosome gets flipped so it runs in the opposite orientation.

D Translocation
A broken piece of a chromosome gets reattached in the wrong place. This example shows a reciprocal translocation, in which two nonhomologous chromosomes exchange chunks.

FIGURE 14.7 {Animated}
Major changes in chromosome structure.

Mutation is a term that generally refers to small-scale changes in DNA sequence—one or a few nucleotides. Chromosome changes on a larger scale also occur. Like mutations, these changes may be induced by exposure to chemicals or radiation. Others are an outcome of faulty crossing over during prophase I of meiosis. For example, nonhomologous chromosomes may align and swap segments at spots where the DNA sequence is similar. Homologous chromosomes sometimes misalign along their length. In both cases, crossing over results in the exchange of segments that are not equivalent.

Chromosome structural changes also result from the activity of **transposable elements**, which are segments of DNA, hundreds to thousands of nucleotides long, that can move spontaneously within or between chromosomes. Repeated DNA sequences at their ends allow the segments to move during mitosis or meiosis. Transposable elements are common in the DNA of all species; about 45 percent of human DNA consists of them or their remnants.

TYPES OF CHROMOSOMAL CHANGE

Regardless of the cause, large-scale changes in chromosome structure can be categorized into several groups (**FIGURE 14.7**). In most cases, these changes have drastic effects on health; about half of all miscarriages are due to chromosome abnormalities of the developing embryo.

Duplication Even normal chromosomes have DNA sequences that are repeated two or more times. These

repetitions are called **duplications** (**FIGURE 14.7A**). Some newly occurring duplications, such as the expansion mutations that cause Huntington's disease, cause genetic abnormalities or disorders. Others, as you will see shortly, have been evolutionarily important.

Deletion Large-scale deletions in a chromosome (**FIGURE 14.7B**) often have severe consequences. Duchenne muscular dystrophy most often arises from deletions in the X chromosome. A different deletion in chromosome 5 shortens life span, impairs mental functioning, and results in an abnormally shaped larynx. This disorder, cri-du-chat (French for "cat's cry"), is named for the sound that affected infants make when they cry.

Inversion With an **inversion**, a segment of chromosomal DNA becomes oriented in the reverse direction, with no molecular loss (**FIGURE 14.7C**). An inversion may not affect a carrier's health if it does not interrupt a gene or gene control region, because the individual's cells still contain their full complement of genetic material. However, fertility may be compromised because a chromosome with an inversion does not pair properly with its homologous partner during meiosis. Crossovers between these mispaired chromosomes can produce other chromosome abnormalities that reduce the viability of forthcoming embryos. People who carry an inversion may not know about it until they are diagnosed with infertility and their karyotype is checked.

Translocation If a chromosome breaks, the broken part may get attached to a different chromosome, or to a different part of the same one. This type of structural change is called a **translocation**. Most translocations are reciprocal, in which two nonhomologous chromosomes exchange broken parts (**FIGURE 14.7D**). A reciprocal translocation between chromosomes 8 and 14 is the usual cause of Burkitt's lymphoma, an aggressive cancer of the immune system. This translocation moves a proto-oncogene to a region that is vigorously transcribed in immune cells, with the result being uncontrolled cell divisions that are characteristic of cancer (Section 11.5). Many other reciprocal translocations have no adverse effects on health, but, like inversions, they can compromise fertility. During meiosis, translocated chromosomes pair abnormally and segregate improperly; about half of the resulting gametes carry major duplications or deletions. If one of these gametes unites with a normal gamete at fertilization, the resulting embryo almost always dies. As with inversions, people who carry a translocation may not know about it until they have difficulty with fertility.

(autosome pair)	Y X	Y X	Y X	Y X	Y X
Ancestral reptiles >350 mya	Ancestral reptiles 350 mya	Monotremes 320–240 mya	Marsupials 170–130 mya	Monkeys 130–80 mya	Humans 50–30 mya

SRY — (labels)

area that cannot cross over

A Before 350 mya, sex was determined by temperature, not by chromosome differences.

B The *SRY* gene begins to evolve 350 mya. The DNA sequences of the chromosomes diverge as other mutations accumulate.

C By 320–240 mya, the DNA sequences of the chromosomes are so different that the pair can no longer cross over in one region. The Y chromosome begins to shorten.

D Three more times, the pair stops crossing over in yet another region. Each time, the DNA sequences of the chromosomes diverge, and the Y chromosome shortens. Today, the pair crosses over only at a small region near the ends.

FIGURE 14.8 Evolution of the Y chromosome. Today, the *SRY* gene determines male sex. Homologous regions of the chromosomes are shown in pink; mya, million years ago. Monotremes are egg-laying mammals; marsupials are pouched mammals.

CHROMOSOME CHANGES IN EVOLUTION

There is evidence of major structural alterations in the chromosomes of all known species. For example, duplications have often allowed a copy of a gene to mutate while the original carried out its unaltered function. The multiple and strikingly similar globin chain genes of mammals apparently evolved by this process. Globin chains, remember, associate to form molecules of hemoglobin (Section 9.5). Two identical genes for the alpha chain—and five other slightly different versions of it—form a cluster on chromosome 16. The gene for the beta chain clusters with four other slightly different versions on chromosome 11.

As another example, X and Y chromosomes were once homologous autosomes in ancient, reptilelike ancestors of mammals (**FIGURE 14.8**). Ambient temperature probably determined the gender of those organisms, as it still does in turtles and some other modern reptiles. About 350 million years ago, a gene on one of the two homologous chromosomes mutated. The change, which was the beginning of the male sex determination gene *SRY*, interfered with crossing over during meiosis. A reduced frequency of crossing over allowed the chromosomes to diverge around the changed region as mutations began to accumulate separately in the two chromosomes. Over evolutionary time, the chromosomes became so different that they no longer crossed over at all in the changed region, so they diverged even more. Today, the Y chromosome is much smaller than the X, and is homologous with it only in a tiny part. The Y crosses over mainly with itself—by translocating duplicated regions of its own DNA.

Some chromosome structure changes contributed to differences among closely related organisms, such as apes

and humans. Human somatic cells have twenty-three pairs of chromosomes, but cells of chimpanzees, gorillas, and orangutans have twenty-four. Thirteen human chromosomes are almost identical with chimpanzee chromosomes. Nine more are similar, except for some inversions. One human chromosome matches up with two in chimpanzees and the other great apes (**FIGURE 14.9**). During human evolution, two chromosomes evidently fused end to end and formed our chromosome 2. How do we know? The region where the fusion occurred contains remnants of a telomere (Section 11.4).

telomere sequence

human   chimpanzee

FIGURE 14.9
Human chromosome 2 compared with chimpanzee chromosomes 2A and 2B.

duplication Repeated section of a chromosome.
inversion Structural rearrangement of a chromosome in which part of the DNA becomes oriented in the reverse direction.
translocation Structural change of a chromosome in which a broken piece gets reattached in the wrong location.
transposable element Segment of DNA that can move spontaneously within or between chromosomes.

TAKE-HOME MESSAGE 14.4

A segment of a chromosome may be duplicated, deleted, inverted, or translocated. Any of these changes are usually harmful or lethal, but may be conserved in the rare circumstance that it has a neutral or beneficial effect.

14.5 WHAT ARE THE EFFECTS OF CHROMOSOME NUMBER CHANGES IN HUMANS?

About 70 percent of flowering plant species, and some insects, fishes, and other animals, are **polyploid**, which means that they have three or more complete sets of chromosomes. Cells in some adult human tissues are normally polyploid, but inheriting more than two full sets of chromosomes is invariably fatal in humans.

An **aneuploid** individual inherited too many or too few copies of a particular chromosome. Less than 1 percent of children are born with a diploid chromosome number that differs from the normal 46.

Changes in chromosome number are usually the outcome of **nondisjunction**, the failure of chromosomes to separate properly during nuclear division—mitosis or meiosis. Nondisjunction during meiosis (**FIGURE 14.10**) can affect chromosome number at fertilization. For example, if a normal gamete (*n*) fuses with another gamete that has an extra chromosome (*n*+1), the resulting zygote will have three copies of one type of chromosome and two of every other type (2*n*+1), a type of aneuploidy called trisomy. If an *n*−1 gamete fuses with a normal *n* gamete, the new individual will be 2*n*−1, a condition called monosomy.

AUTOSOMAL ANEUPLOIDY AND DOWN SYNDROME

In most cases, autosomal aneuploidy in humans is fatal before birth or shortly thereafter. An important exception is trisomy 21. A person born with three chromosomes 21 has a high likelihood of surviving infancy, and will develop Down syndrome. Mild to moderate mental impairment and health problems such as heart disease are hallmarks of this disorder. Other effects may include a somewhat flattened facial profile, a fold of skin that starts at the inner corner of

each eyelid, white spots on the iris (**FIGURE 14.11**), and one deep crease (instead of two shallow creases) across each palm. The skeleton grows and develops abnormally, so older children have short body parts, loose joints, and misaligned bones of the fingers, toes, and hips. The muscles and reflexes are weak, and motor skills such as speech develop slowly. With medical care, affected individuals live about fifty-five years. Early training can help these individuals learn to care for themselves and to take part in normal activities. Down syndrome occurs once in about 700 births, and the risk increases with maternal age.

SEX CHROMOSOME ANEUPLOIDY

Nondisjunction also causes alterations in the number of X and Y chromosomes, with a frequency of about 1 in 400 live births. Most often, such alterations lead to mild difficulties in learning and impaired motor skills such as a speech delay. These problems may be very subtle.

Turner Syndrome Individuals with Turner syndrome have an X chromosome and no corresponding X or Y chromosome (XO). The syndrome is thought to arise most frequently as an outcome of inheriting an unstable Y chromosome from the father. The zygote starts out being genetically male, with an X and a Y chromosome. Sometime during early development, the Y chromosome breaks up and is lost, so the embryo continues to develop as a female.

There are fewer people affected by Turner syndrome than other chromosome abnormalities: Only about 1 in 2,500 newborn girls has it. XO individuals grow up well proportioned but short, with an average height of four feet, eight inches (1.4 meters). Their ovaries do not develop

---

FIGURE 14.10 {**Animated**} An example of nondisjunction during meiosis. Of the two pairs of homologous chromosomes shown here, one fails to separate during anaphase I. The chromosome number is altered in the resulting gametes.

| Metaphase I | Anaphase I | Telophase I | Metaphase II | Anaphase II | Telophase II |

FIGURE 14.11 A Down syndrome phenotype. Excess tissue deposits on the colored part of the eye give rise to a ring of starlike white speckles, a lovely phenotypic effect of the chromosome number change that causes Down syndrome.

properly, so they do not make enough sex hormones to become sexually mature and do not develop secondary sexual traits such as enlarged breasts.

XXX Syndrome A female may inherit multiple X chromosomes, a condition called XXX syndrome. XXX syndrome occurs in about 1 of 1,000 births. As with Down syndrome, risk increases with maternal age. Only one X chromosome is typically active in female cells, so having extra X chromosomes usually does not cause physical or medical problems, but mild mental impairment may occur.

Klinefelter Syndrome About 1 out of every 500 males has an extra X chromosome (XXY). The resulting disorder, Klinefelter syndrome, develops at puberty. XXY males tend to be overweight, tall, and have mild mental impairment. They make more estrogen and less testosterone than normal males. This hormone imbalance causes affected men to have small testes and a small prostate gland, a low sperm count, sparse facial and body hair, a high-pitched voice, and enlarged breasts. Testosterone injections during puberty can minimize some of these traits.

XYY Syndrome About 1 in 1,000 males is born with an extra Y chromosome (XYY), a result of nondisjunction of the Y chromosome during sperm formation. Adults tend to be taller than average and have mild mental impairment, but most are otherwise normal. XYY men were once thought to be predisposed to a life of crime. This misguided view was based on sampling error (too few cases in narrowly chosen groups such as prison inmates) and bias (the researchers who gathered the karyotypes also took the personal histories of the participants). That view has since been disproven: Men with XYY syndrome are only slightly more likely to be convicted for crimes than unaffected men. Researchers now believe this slight increase can be explained by poor socioeconomic conditions related to the effects of the syndrome.

aneuploid Having too many or too few copies of a particular chromosome.
nondisjunction Failure of sister chromatids or homologous chromosomes to separate during nuclear division.
polyploid Having three or more of each type of chromosome characteristic of the species.

TAKE-HOME MESSAGE 14.5

Polyploidy is fatal in humans, but not in flowering plants and some other organisms.

Aneuploidy can arise from nondisjunction during meiosis. In humans, most cases of aneuploidy are associated with some degree of mental impairment.

Studying human inheritance patterns has given us many insights into how genetic disorders arise and progress, and how to treat them. Some disorders can be detected early enough to start countermeasures before symptoms develop. For this reason, most hospitals in the United States now screen newborns for mutations that cause phenylketonuria, or PKU. The mutations affect an enzyme that converts the amino acid phenylalanine to tyrosine. Without this enzyme, the body becomes deficient in tyrosine, and phenylalanine accumulates to high levels. The imbalance inhibits protein synthesis in the brain, which in turn results in severe neurological symptoms. Restricting all intake of phenylalanine can slow the progression of PKU, so routine early screening has resulted in fewer individuals suffering from the symptoms of the disorder.

The probability that a child will inherit a genetic disorder can often be estimated by testing prospective parents for alleles known to be associated with genetic disorders. Karyotypes and pedigrees are also useful in this type of screening, which can help the parents make decisions about family planning. Genetic screening can also be done post-conception, in which case it is called prenatal diagnosis (prenatal means before birth). Prenatal diagnosis checks for physical and genetic abnormalities in an embryo or fetus. More than 30 conditions are detectable prenatally, including aneuploidy, hemophilia, Tay–Sachs disease, sickle-cell anemia, muscular dystrophy, and cystic fibrosis. If the disorder is treatable, early detection allows the newborn to receive prompt and appropriate treatment. A few defects are even surgically correctable before birth. Prenatal diagnosis also gives parents time to prepare for the birth of an affected child, and an opportunity to decide whether to continue with the pregnancy or terminate it.

As an example of how prenatal diagnosis works, consider a woman who becomes pregnant at age thirty-five. Her doctor will probably perform a procedure called obstetric sonography, in which ultrasound waves directed across the woman's abdomen form images of the fetus's limbs and internal organs. If the images reveal a physical defect that may be the result of a genetic disorder, a more invasive technique would be recommended for further diagnosis. With fetoscopy, sound waves pulsed from inside the mother's uterus yield images much higher in resolution than ultrasound. Samples of tissue or blood are often taken at the same time, and some corrective surgeries can be performed.

Human genetics studies show that our thirty-five-year-old woman has about a 1 in 80 chance that her baby will be born with a chromosomal abnormality, a risk more than six times greater than when she was twenty years old. Thus, even if no abnormalities are detected by ultrasound, she probably will be offered a more thorough diagnostic procedure, amniocentesis, in which a small sample of fluid is drawn from the amniotic sac enclosing the fetus (FIGURE 14.12). The fluid contains cells shed by the fetus, and those cells can be tested for genetic disorders. Chorionic villus sampling (CVS) can be performed earlier than amniocentesis. With this technique, a few cells from the chorion are removed and tested for genetic disorders. (The chorion is a membrane that surrounds the amniotic sac and helps form the placenta, an organ that allows substances to be exchanged between mother and embryo.)

An invasive procedure often carries a risk to the fetus. The risks vary by the procedure. Amniocentesis has improved so much that, in the hands of a skilled physician, the procedure no longer increases the risk of miscarriage. CVS occasionally disrupts the placenta's development and thus causes underdeveloped or missing fingers and toes in 0.3 percent of newborns. Fetoscopy raises the miscarriage risk by a whopping 2 to 10 percent.

FIGURE 14.12 {Animated} An 8-week-old fetus. With amniocentesis, fetal cells shed into the fluid inside the amniotic sac are tested for genetic disorders. Chorionic villus sampling tests cells of the chorion, which is part of the placenta.

placenta   amniotic sac

TAKE-HOME MESSAGE 14.6

Studying inheritance patterns for genetic disorders has helped researchers develop treatments for some of them.

Genetic testing can provide prospective parents with information about the health of their future children.

14.7 Application: SHADES OF SKIN

FIGURE 14.13 Fraternal twins Kian and Remee. Both of the children's grandmothers are of European descent, and have pale skin. Both of their grandfathers are of African descent, and have dark skin. The twins inherited different alleles of some genes that affect skin color from their parents, who, given the appearance of their children, must be heterozygous for those alleles.

SKIN COLOR, LIKE MOST OTHER HUMAN TRAITS, HAS A GENETIC BASIS. The color of human skin begins with melanosomes, which are organelles that make melanin pigments. Most people have about the same number of melanosomes in their skin cells. Variations in skin color arise from differences in formation and deposition of melanosomes in the skin, as well as in the kinds and amounts of melanins they make. More than 100 genes are involved in these processes.

Human skin color variation may have evolved as a balance between vitamin production and protection against harmful UV radiation in the sun's rays. Dark skin would have been beneficial under the intense sunlight of African savannas where humans first evolved. Melanin is a natural sunscreen: It prevents UV radiation from breaking down folate, a vitamin essential for normal sperm formation and embryonic development.

Early human groups that migrated to regions with cold climates were exposed to less sunlight. In these regions, lighter skin color is beneficial. Why? UV radiation stimulates skin cells to make a molecule the body converts to vitamin D. Where sunlight exposure is minimal, UV radiation is less of a risk than vitamin D deficiency, which has serious health consequences for developing fetuses and children.

The evolution of regional variations in human skin color began with mutations. Consider a gene on chromosome 15 that encodes a transport protein in melanosome membranes. Nearly all people of African, Native American, or east Asian descent carry the same allele of this gene. Between 6,000 and 10,000 years ago, a mutation gave rise to a different allele. The mutation, a single base-pair substitution, changed the 111th amino acid of the transport protein from alanine to threonine. The change results in less melanin—and lighter skin color—than the original African allele does. Today, nearly all people of European descent carry this mutated allele.

A person of mixed ethnicity may make gametes that contain different combinations of alleles for dark and light skin. It is fairly rare that one of those gametes contains mainly alleles for dark skin, or mainly alleles for light skin, but it happens (FIGURE 14.13). Skin color is only one of many human traits that vary as a result of single nucleotide mutations. The small scale of such changes offers a reminder that all of us share the genetic legacy of common ancestry.

Summary

SECTION 14.1 Geneticists study inheritance patterns in humans by tracking genetic disorders and abnormalities through families. A genetic abnormality is an uncommon version of a heritable trait that does not result in medical problems. A genetic disorder is a heritable condition that sooner or later results in mild or severe medical problems. Geneticists make **pedigrees** to reveal inheritance patterns for alleles that can be predictably associated with specific phenotypes.

SECTION 14.2 An allele is inherited in an autosomal dominant pattern if the trait it specifies appears in everyone who carries it, and both sexes are affected with equal frequency. Such traits appear in every generation of families that carry the allele. An allele is inherited in an autosomal recessive pattern if the trait it specifies appears only in homozygous people. Such traits also appear in both sexes equally, but they can skip generations.

SECTION 14.3 An allele is inherited in an X-linked pattern when it occurs on the X chromosome. Most X-linked disorders are inherited in a recessive pattern, and these tend to appear in men more often than in women. Heterozygous women have a dominant, normal allele that can mask the effects of the recessive one; men do not. Men can transmit an X-linked allele to their daughters, but not to their sons. Only a woman can pass an X-linked allele to a son.

SECTION 14.4 Faulty crossovers and the activity of **transposable elements** can give rise to major changes in chromosome structure, including **duplications**, **inversions**, and **translocations**. Some of these changes are harmful or lethal in humans; others affect fertility. Even so, major structural changes have accumulated in the chromosomes of all species over evolutionary time.

SECTION 14.5 Occasionally, abnormal events occur before or during meiosis, and new individuals end up with the wrong chromosome number. Consequences range from minor to lethal changes in form and function.

Chromosome number change is usually an outcome of **nondisjunction**, in which chromosomes fail to separate properly during meiosis. **Polyploid** individuals have three or more of each type of chromosome. Polyploidy is lethal in humans, but not in flowering plants, and some insects, fishes, and other animals.

Aneuploid individuals have too many or too few copies of a chromosome. In humans, most cases of autosomal aneuploidy are lethal. Trisomy 21, which causes Down syndrome, is an exception. A change in the number of sex chromosomes usually results in some degree of impairment in learning and motor skills.

SECTION 14.6 Prospective parents can estimate their risk of transmitting a harmful allele to offspring with genetic screening, in which their pedigrees and genotype are analyzed by a genetic counselor. Prenatal genetic testing can reveal a genetic disorder before birth.

SECTION 14.7 Like most other human traits, skin color has a genetic basis. Minor differences in the alleles that govern melanin production and the deposition of melanosomes affect skin color. The differences probably evolved as a balance between vitamin production and protection against harmful UV radiation.

Self-Quiz Answers in Appendix VII

1. Constructing a family pedigree is particularly useful when studying inheritance patterns in organisms that _____ .
   a. produce many offspring per generation
   b. produce few offspring per generation
   c. have a very large chromosome number
   d. reproduce asexually
   e. have a fast life cycle

2. Pedigree analysis is necessary when studying human inheritance patterns because _____ .
   a. humans have more than 20,000 genes
   b. of ethical problems with human experimentation
   c. inheritance in humans is more complicated than in other organisms
   d. genetic disorders occur in humans
   e. all of the above

3. A recognized set of symptoms that characterize a genetic disorder is a(n) _____ .
   a. syndrome   b. disease   c. abnormality

4. If one parent is heterozygous for a dominant allele on an autosome and the other parent does not carry the allele, any child of theirs has a _____ chance of having the associated trait.
   a. 25 percent   c. 75 percent
   b. 50 percent   d. no chance; it will die

5. Is this statement true or false? A son can inherit an X-linked recessive allele from his father.

6. A trait that is present in a male child but not in either of his parents is characteristic of _____ inheritance.
   a. autosomal dominant   d. It is not possible to
   b. autosomal recessive   answer this question
   c. X-linked recessive   without more information.

7. Color blindness is inherited in an _____ pattern.
   a. autosomal dominant   c. X-linked dominant
   b. autosomal recessive   d. X-linked recessive

8. A female child inherits one X chromosome from her mother and one from her father. What sex chromosome does a male child inherit from each of his parents?

Data Analysis Activities

Skin Color Survey of Native Peoples In 2000, researchers measured the average amount of UV radiation received in more than fifty regions of the world, and correlated it with the average skin reflectance of people native to those regions (reflectance is a way to measure the amount of melanin pigment in skin). Some of the results of this study are shown in **FIGURE 14.14**.

1. Which country receives the most UV radiation?
2. Which country receives the least UV radiation?
3. People native to which country have the darkest skin?
4. People native to which country have the lightest skin?
5. According to these data, how does the skin color of indigenous peoples correlate with the amount of UV radiation incident in their native regions?

Country	Skin Reflectance	UVMED
Australia	19.30	335.55
Kenya	32.40	354.21
India	44.60	219.65
Cambodia	54.00	310.28
Japan	55.42	130.87
Afghanistan	55.70	249.98
China	59.17	204.57
Ireland	65.00	52.92
Germany	66.90	69.29
Netherlands	67.37	62.58

FIGURE 14.14 Skin color of indigenous peoples and regional incident UV radiation. Skin reflectance measures how much light of 685-nanometer wavelength is reflected from skin; UVMED is the annual average UV radiation received at Earth's surface.

9. Alleles for Tay–Sachs disease are inherited in an autosomal recessive pattern. Why would two parents with a normal phenotype have a child with Tay–Sachs?
   a. Both parents are homozygous for a Tay–Sachs allele.
   b. Both parents are heterozygous for a Tay–Sachs allele.
   c. A new mutation gave rise to Tay–Sachs in the child.
   d. b or c

10. The *SRY* gene gives rise to the male phenotype in humans (Sections 10.3 and 14.4). What do you think the inheritance pattern of *SRY* alleles is called?

11. Nondisjunction may occur during _____ .
   a. mitosis
   b. meiosis
   c. fertilization
   d. both a and b

12. Nondisjunction can result in _____ .
   a. duplications
   b. aneuploidy
   c. crossing over
   d. pleiotropy

13. Is this statement true or false? Inheriting three or more of each type of chromosome characteristic of the species results in a condition called polyploidy.

14. Klinefelter syndrome (XXY) can be easily diagnosed by _____ .
   a. pedigree analysis
   b. aneuploidy
   c. karyotyping
   d. phenotypic treatment

15. Match the chromosome terms appropriately.
   ___ polyploidy
   ___ deletion
   ___ aneuploidy
   ___ translocation
   ___ syndrome
   ___ transposable element

   a. symptoms of a genetic disorder
   b. segment of a chromosome moves to a nonhomologous chromosome
   c. extra sets of chromosomes
   d. gets around
   e. a chromosome segment lost
   f. one extra chromosome

Genetics Problems Answers in Appendix VII

1. Does the phenotype indicated by the red circles and squares in this pedigree show an inheritance pattern that is autosomal dominant, autosomal recessive, or X-linked?

2. Human females have two X chromosomes (XX); males have one X and one Y chromosome (XY).
   a. Does a male inherit an X chromosome from his mother or his father?
   b. With respect to X-linked alleles, how many different types of gametes can a male produce?
   c. A female homozygous for an X-linked allele can produce how many types of gametes with respect to that allele?
   d. A female heterozygous for an X-linked allele can produce how many types of gametes with respect to that allele?

3. Somatic cells of individuals with Down syndrome usually have an extra chromosome 21; they contain forty-seven chromosomes. A few individuals with Down syndrome have forty-six chromosomes: two normal-appearing chromosomes 21, and a longer-than-normal chromosome 14. Speculate on how this chromosome abnormality arises.

4. An allele responsible for Marfan syndrome (Section 13.4) is inherited in an autosomal dominant pattern. What is the chance that a child will inherit the allele if one parent does not carry it and the other is heterozygous?

CENGAGE brain.com To access course materials, please visit www.cengagebrain.com.

Fluorescent pigments illuminate individual nerve cells in the brain stem of a "brainbow" mouse. Brainbow mice, which are transgenic for multiple pigments, are allowing researchers to map the complex neural circuitry of the brain.

15

BIOTECHNOLOGY

Links to Earlier Concepts

This chapter builds on your understanding of DNA (Sections 8.2, 8.3, 13.1, 14.6) and DNA replication (8.4). Clones (8.6), gene expression (9.1, 9.2), and knockouts (10.2) are important in genetic engineering, particularly in research on human traits (13.6) and genetic disorders (Chapter 14). You will revisit tracers (2.1), triglycerides (3.3), denaturation (3.5), bacteria (4.4), β-carotene (6.1), mutations (9.5), the *lac* operon (10.4), cancer (11.5), and alleles (12.1).

KEY CONCEPTS

DNA CLONING

Researchers make recombinant DNA by cutting and pasting together DNA from different species. Plasmids and other vectors can carry foreign DNA into host cells.

FINDING NEEDLES IN HAYSTACKS

Genetic engineering, the directed modification of an organism's genes, relies on laboratory techniques for isolating and identifying particular fragments of DNA.

DNA SEQUENCING

Sequencing reveals the linear order of nucleotides in DNA. Comparing genomes offers insights into human genes and evolution. DNA sequence can be used to identify individuals.

GENETIC ENGINEERING

Genetic engineering is now a routine part of research and industrial applications. Genetically modified organisms are used to produce food, medicines, and other products.

GENE THERAPY

The directed modification of human DNA continues to be tested in medical applications. It also continues to raise ethical questions about modifying the human genome.

Photograph courtesy of © Dr. Jean Levit. The Brainbow technique was developed in the laboratories of Jeff W. Lichtman and Joshua R. Sanes at Harvard University. This image has received the Bioscape imaging competition 2007 prize.

5′   3′

1 The restriction enzyme *Eco* RI (named after *E. coli*, the bacteria from which it was isolated) recognizes a specific base sequence (GAATTC) in DNA from two different sources.

2 The enzyme cuts the DNA into fragments. *Eco* RI leaves single-stranded tails ("sticky ends") where it cuts DNA.

3 When the DNA fragments from the two sources are mixed together, matching sticky ends base-pair with each other.

4 DNA ligase joins the base-paired DNA fragments. Molecules of recombinant DNA are the result.

FIGURE 15.1 {Animated} Making recombinant DNA.

FIGURE IT OUT: Why did the enzyme cut both strands of DNA?

Answer: Because the recognition sequence occurs on both strands.

CUT AND PASTE

In the 1950s, excitement over the discovery of DNA's structure (Section 8.2) gave way to frustration: No one could determine the order of nucleotides in a molecule of DNA. Identifying a single base among thousands or millions of others turned out to be a huge technical challenge.

Research in a seemingly unrelated field yielded a solution when Werner Arber, Hamilton Smith, and their coworkers discovered how some bacteria resist infection by bacteriophage (Section 8.1). These bacteria have enzymes that chop up any injected viral DNA before it has a chance to integrate into the bacterial chromosome. The enzymes restrict viral growth; hence their name, restriction enzymes. A **restriction enzyme** cuts DNA wherever a specific nucleotide sequence occurs (**FIGURE 15.1 1**). The discovery of restriction enzymes allowed researchers to cut chromosomal DNA into manageable chunks. It also allowed them to combine DNA fragments from different organisms. How? Many restriction enzymes leave single-stranded tails on DNA fragments **2**. Researchers realized that complementary tails will base-pair, regardless of the source of DNA **3**. The tails are called "sticky ends," because two DNA fragments stick together when their matching tails base-pair. The enzyme DNA ligase (Section 8.4) can be used to seal the gaps between base-paired sticky ends, so continuous DNA strands form **4**. Thus, using appropriate restriction enzymes and DNA ligase, researchers can cut and paste DNA from different sources. The result, a hybrid molecule that consists of genetic material from two or more organisms, is called **recombinant DNA**.

Making recombinant DNA is the first step in **DNA cloning**, a set of laboratory methods that uses living cells to

FIGURE 15.2 Plasmid cloning vectors. **A** Micrograph of a plasmid. **B** A commercial plasmid cloning vector. Restriction enzyme recognition sequences are indicated on the right by the name of the enzyme that cuts them. Researchers insert foreign DNA into the vector at these sequences. Bacterial genes (gold) help researchers identify host cells that take up a vector with inserted DNA. This vector carries two antibiotic resistance genes and the *lac* operon (Section 10.4).

Kanamycin
P_{lac} lacZ
pDrive Cloning Vector
Ampicillin

- KpnI
- SphI
- PstI
- BamHI
- EcoRI
- SalI
- AccI
- XhoI
- XbaI
- BstXI
- SacI
- NotI

CREDITS: (1) © Cengage Learning; (2A) Professor Stanley Cohen/Science Source; (2B) With permission of © QIAGEN, Showing a reduced pDrive Cloning Vector.

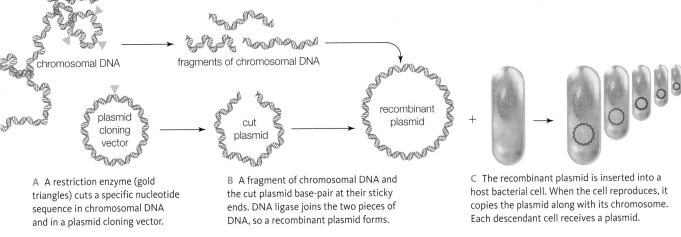

A A restriction enzyme (gold triangles) cuts a specific nucleotide sequence in chromosomal DNA and in a plasmid cloning vector.

B A fragment of chromosomal DNA and the cut plasmid base-pair at their sticky ends. DNA ligase joins the two pieces of DNA, so a recombinant plasmid forms.

C The recombinant plasmid is inserted into a host bacterial cell. When the cell reproduces, it copies the plasmid along with its chromosome. Each descendant cell receives a plasmid.

FIGURE 15.3 {Animated} An example of cloning. Here, a fragment of chromosomal DNA is inserted into a bacterial plasmid.

mass-produce specific DNA fragments. Researchers clone a fragment of DNA by inserting it into a **cloning vector**, which is a molecule that can carry foreign DNA into host cells. Bacterial plasmids (Section 4.4) may be used as cloning vectors (**FIGURE 15.2**). A bacterium copies all of its DNA before it divides, so its offspring inherit plasmids along with chromosomes. If a plasmid carries a fragment of foreign DNA, that fragment gets copied and distributed to descendant cells along with the plasmid (**FIGURE 15.3**).

A host cell into which a cloning vector has been inserted can be grown in the laboratory (cultured) to yield a huge population of genetically identical cells, or clones (Section 8.6). Each clone contains a copy of the vector and the inserted DNA fragment. The hosted DNA fragment can be harvested in large quantities from the clones.

cDNA CLONING

Remember from Section 9.2 that eukaryotic DNA contains introns. Unless you are a eukaryotic cell, it is not very easy to determine which parts of eukaryotic DNA encode gene products. Thus, researchers who study gene expression in eukaryotes often start with mature mRNA, because introns are removed during post-transcriptional processing.

cDNA Complementary strand of DNA synthesized from an RNA template by the enzyme reverse transcriptase.
cloning vector A DNA molecule that can accept foreign DNA and be replicated inside a host cell.
DNA cloning Set of methods that uses living cells to make many identical copies of a DNA fragment.
recombinant DNA A DNA molecule that contains genetic material from more than one organism.
restriction enzyme Type of enzyme that cuts DNA at a specific nucleotide sequence.
reverse transcriptase An enzyme that uses mRNA as a template to make a strand of cDNA.

An mRNA cannot be cut with restriction enzymes or pasted with DNA ligase, because these enzymes work only on double-stranded DNA. Thus, cloning with mRNA requires **reverse transcriptase**, a replication enzyme that uses an RNA template to assemble a strand of complementary DNA, or **cDNA**:

DNA polymerase is used to copy the cDNA into a second strand of DNA. The outcome is a double-stranded DNA version of the original mRNA:

*Eco*RI recognition site

Like any other double-stranded DNA, this fragment may be cut with restriction enzymes and pasted into a cloning vector using DNA ligase.

A Individual bacterial cells from a DNA library are spread over the surface of a solid growth medium. The cells divide repeatedly and form colonies—clusters of millions of genetically identical descendant cells.

B Special paper is pressed onto the surface of the growth medium. Some cells from each colony stick to the paper.

C The paper is soaked in a solution that ruptures the cells and makes the released DNA single-stranded. The DNA clings to the paper in spots mirroring the distribution of colonies.

D A radioactive probe is added to the liquid bathing the paper. The probe hybridizes with any spot of DNA that contains a complementary sequence.

E The paper is pressed against x-ray film. The radioactive probe darkens the film in a spot where it has hybridized. The spot's position is compared to the positions of the original bacterial colonies. Cells from the colony that corresponds to the spot are cultured, and their DNA is harvested.

FIGURE 15.4 {Animated} Nucleic acid hybridization. In this example, a radioactive probe helps identify a bacterial colony that contains a targeted sequence of DNA.

DNA LIBRARIES

The entire set of genetic material—the **genome**—of most organisms consists of thousands of genes. To study or manipulate a single gene, researchers must first separate it from all of the other genes in a genome. They often begin by cutting an organism's DNA into pieces, and then cloning all the pieces. The result is a genomic library, a set of clones that collectively contain all of the DNA in a genome. Researchers may also harvest mRNA, make cDNA copies of it, and then clone the cDNA. The resulting cDNA library represents only those genes being expressed at the time the mRNA was harvested.

Genomic and cDNA libraries are **DNA libraries**, sets of cells that host various cloned DNA fragments. In such libraries, a cell that contains a particular DNA fragment of interest is mixed up with thousands or millions of others that do not—a needle in a genetic haystack. One way to find that clone among the others involves the use of a **probe**, which is a fragment of DNA or RNA labeled with a tracer (Section 2.1). For example, to find a particular gene, researchers may use radioactive nucleotides to synthesize a short strand of DNA complementary in sequence to a similar gene. Because the nucleotide sequences of the probe and the gene are complementary, the two can hybridize. (Remember from Section 8.4 that nucleic acid hybridization is the establishment of base pairing between nucleic acid strands.) When the probe is mixed with DNA from a library, it will hybridize with the gene, but not with other DNA (**FIGURE 15.4**). Researchers can pinpoint a clone that hosts the gene by detecting the label on the probe. That clone is isolated and cultured, and DNA can be extracted in bulk from the cultured cells for research or other purposes.

PCR

The **polymerase chain reaction** (**PCR**) is a technique used to mass-produce copies of a particular section of DNA without having to clone it in living cells (**FIGURE 15.5**). The reaction can transform a needle in a haystack—that one-in-a-million fragment of DNA— into a huge stack of needles with a little hay in it.

The starting material for PCR is any sample of DNA with at least one molecule of a targeted sequence. It might be DNA from a mixture of 10 million different clones, a sperm, a hair left at a crime scene, or a mummy—essentially any sample that has DNA in it.

The PCR reaction is similar to DNA replication (Section 8.4). It requires two primers. Each base-pairs with one end of the section of DNA to be amplified,

targeted section

FIGURE 15.5 {Animated} Two rounds of PCR. Each cycle of this reaction can double the number of copies of a targeted section of DNA. Thirty cycles can make a billion copies.

❶ DNA template (blue) is mixed with primers (pink), nucleotides, and heat-tolerant *Taq* DNA polymerase.

or mass-produced ❶. Researchers mix these primers with the starting (template) DNA, nucleotides, and DNA polymerase, then expose the reaction mixture to repeated cycles of high and low temperatures. A few seconds at high temperature disrupts the hydrogen bonds that hold the two strands of a DNA double helix together (Section 8.2), so every molecule of DNA unwinds and becomes single-stranded. As the temperature of the reaction mixture is lowered, the single DNA strands hybridize with the primers ❷.

❷ When the mixture is heated, the double-stranded DNA separates into single strands. When the mixture is cooled, some of the primers base-pair with the DNA at opposite ends of the targeted sequence.

The DNA polymerases of most organisms denature at the high temperature required to separate DNA strands. The kind that is used in PCR reactions, *Taq* polymerase, is from *Thermus aquaticus*. This bacterial species lives in hot springs and hydrothermal vents, so its DNA polymerase necessarily tolerates heat. *Taq* polymerase, like other DNA polymerases, recognizes hybridized primers as places to start DNA synthesis ❸. Synthesis proceeds along the template strand until the temperature rises and the DNA separates into single strands ❹. The newly synthesized DNA is a copy of the targeted section. When the mixture is cooled, the primers rehybridize, and DNA synthesis begins again. Each cycle of heating and cooling takes only a few minutes, but it can double the number of copies of the targeted section of DNA ❺. Thirty PCR cycles may amplify that number a billionfold.

❸ *Taq* polymerase begins DNA synthesis at the primers, so it produces complementary strands of the targeted DNA sequence.

❹ The mixture is heated again, so all double-stranded DNA separates into single strands. When it is cooled, primers base-pair with the targeted sequence in the original template DNA and in the new DNA strands.

DNA library Collection of cells that host different fragments of foreign DNA, often representing an organism's entire genome.
genome An organism's complete set of genetic material.
polymerase chain reaction (PCR) Method that rapidly generates many copies of a specific section of DNA.
probe Short fragment of DNA labeled with a tracer; designed to hybridize with a nucleotide sequence of interest.

❺ Each cycle of heating and cooling can double the number of copies of the targeted DNA section.

CREDIT: (5) © Cengage Learning.

Researchers use a technique called **sequencing** to determine the order of nucleotides in a fragment of DNA that has been isolated by cloning or PCR. The most common method is similar to DNA replication (Section 8.4). The DNA to be sequenced (the template) is mixed with nucleotides, a primer, and DNA polymerase. Starting at the primer, the polymerase joins the nucleotides into a new strand of DNA, in the order dictated by the sequence of the template (**FIGURE 15.6**).

Remember that DNA polymerase can add a nucleotide only to the hydroxyl group on the 3′ carbon of a DNA strand. The sequencing reaction mixture includes four kinds of modified nucleotides that lack the hydroxyl group on their 3′ carbon ❶. Each kind (A, C, G, or T) is labeled with a different colored pigment. During the reaction, the polymerase randomly adds either a regular nucleotide or a modified nucleotide to the end of a growing DNA strand. If it adds a modified nucleotide, the 3′ carbon of the strand will not have a hydroxyl group, so synthesis of the strand ends there ❷. The reaction produces millions of DNA

fragments of different lengths—incomplete, complementary copies of the starting DNA ❸. Each fragment of a given length ends with the same modified nucleotide. For example, if the tenth base in the template DNA was thymine, then any newly synthesized fragment that is 10 bases long ends with a modified adenine.

The DNA fragments are then separated by length. Using a technique called **electrophoresis**, an electric field pulls the fragments through a semisolid gel. Fragments of different sizes move through the gel at different rates. The shorter the fragment, the faster it moves, because shorter fragments slip through the tangled molecules of the gel faster than longer fragments do. All fragments of the same length move through the gel at the same speed, so they gather into bands. All fragments in a given band have the same modified nucleotide at their ends, and the pigment labels now impart distinct colors to the bands ❹. Each color designates one of the four modified nucleotides, so the order of colored bands in the gel represents the DNA sequence ❺.

FIGURE 15.6 {Animated} DNA sequencing, in which DNA polymerase is used to incompletely replicate a section of DNA.

DNA template strand

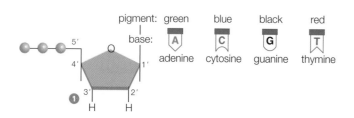

pigment: green   blue   black   red

base: A   C   G   T
   adenine cytosine guanine thymine

❶ Sequencing depends on modified nucleotides that have a hydrogen atom instead of a hydroxyl group on the 3′ carbon (compare the structure with those in **FIGURE 8.4**). Each is labeled with a colored pigment.

❷ DNA polymerase uses a section of DNA as a template to synthesize new strands of DNA. Synthesis of each new strand stops when a modified nucleotide is added.

❸ At the end of the reaction, there are many incomplete copies of the template DNA in the mixture.

❹ Electrophoresis separates the copied DNA fragments into bands according to their length. All of the DNA strands in each band end with the same nucleotide; thus, each band is the color of that nucleotide's tracer pigment.

❺ A computer detects and records the color of successive bands on the gel (see **FIGURE 15.7** for an example). The order of colors of the bands represents the sequence of the template DNA.

CREDIT: (6A) From Starr/Taggart/Evers/Starr, Biology, 13E. © 2013 Cengage Learning; (6B) © Cengage Learning.

FIGURE 15.7 Human DNA sequence data. The order of colors in each vertical lane reveals one part of the DNA sequence.

THE HUMAN GENOME PROJECT

The sequencing method we have just described was invented in 1975. Ten years later, it had become so routine that scientists began to consider sequencing the entire human genome—all 3 billion nucleotides. Proponents of the idea said it could provide huge payoffs for medicine and research. Opponents said this daunting task would divert attention and funding from more urgent research. It would require 50 years to sequence the human genome given the techniques of the time. However, the techniques continued to improve rapidly, and with each improvement more nucleotides could be sequenced in less time. Automated (robotic) DNA sequencing and PCR had just been invented. Both were still too cumbersome and expensive to be useful in routine applications, but they would not be so for long. Waiting for faster technologies seemed the most efficient way to sequence the genome, but just how fast did they need to be before the project should begin?

A few privately owned companies decided not to wait, and started sequencing. One of them intended to determine the genome sequence in order to patent it. The idea of patenting the human genome provoked widespread outrage, but it also spurred commitments in the public sector. In 1988, the National Institutes of Health (NIH) essentially took over the project by hiring James Watson (of DNA structure fame) to head an official Human Genome Project, and providing $200 million per year to fund it.

A partnership formed between the NIH and international institutions that were sequencing different parts of the genome. Watson set aside 3 percent of the funding for studies of ethical and social issues arising from the work. He later resigned over a patent disagreement, and geneticist Francis Collins took his place.

Amid ongoing squabbles over patent issues, Celera Genomics formed in 1998. With biologist Craig Venter at its helm, the company intended to commercialize human genetic information. Celera invented faster techniques for sequencing genomic DNA, because the first to have the complete sequence had a legal basis for patenting it. The competition motivated the international partnership to accelerate its efforts. Then, in 2000, U.S. President Bill Clinton and British Prime Minister Tony Blair jointly declared that the sequence of the human genome could not be patented. Celera kept sequencing anyway, and, in 2001, the competing governmental and corporate teams published about 90 percent of the sequence. In 2003, fifty years after the discovery of the structure of DNA, the sequence of the human genome was officially completed (**FIGURE 15.7**).

> **TAKE-HOME MESSAGE 15.3**
>
> With DNA sequencing, a strand of DNA is partially replicated. Electrophoresis is used to separate the resulting fragments by length.
>
> Improved sequencing techniques and worldwide efforts allowed the human genome sequence to be determined.

electrophoresis Technique that separates DNA fragments by size.
sequencing Method of determining the order of nucleotides in DNA.

CREDIT: (7) Patrick Landmann/Science Source.

15.4 HOW DO WE USE WHAT RESEARCHERS DISCOVER ABOUT GENOMES?

It took 15 years to sequence the human genome for the first time, but the techniques have improved so much that sequencing an entire genome now takes about a day. Anyone can now pay to have their genome sequenced (a cost of $5,000 to $8,000, at this writing).

Despite our ability to determine the sequence of an individual's genome, however, it will be a long time before we understand all the information coded within that sequence. The human genome contains a massive amount of seemingly cryptic data. One way to decipher it is by comparing it to the genomes of other species, the premise being that all organisms are descended from shared ancestors, so all genomes are related to some extent. We see evidence of such genetic relationships simply by comparing the raw sequence data, which, in some regions, is extremely similar across many species (FIGURE 15.8).

The study of genomes is called **genomics**, a broad field that encompasses whole-genome comparisons, structural analysis of gene products, and surveys of small-scale variations in sequence. Genomics is providing powerful insights into evolution, and it has many medical benefits. We have learned the function of many human genes by studying their counterpart genes in other species. For instance, researchers comparing human and mouse genomes discovered a human version of a mouse gene, *APOA5*, that encodes a lipoprotein (Section 3.4). Mice with an *APOA5* knockout have four times the normal level of triglycerides in their blood. The researchers then looked for—and found—a correlation between *APOA5* mutations and high triglyceride levels in humans. High triglycerides are a risk factor for coronary artery disease.

DNA PROFILING

About 99 percent of your DNA is exactly the same as everyone else's. The shared part is what makes you human; the differences make you a unique member of the species. If you compared your DNA with your neighbor's, about 2.97 billion nucleotides of the two sequences would be identical; the remaining 30 million or so nonidentical nucleotides are sprinkled throughout your chromosomes. The sprinkling

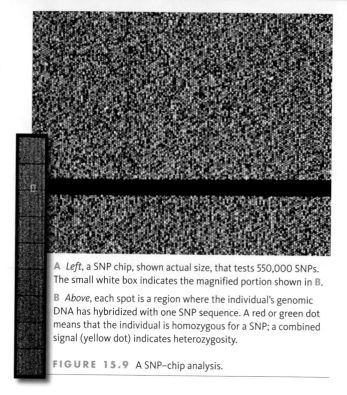

A *Left*, a SNP chip, shown actual size, that tests 550,000 SNPs. The small white box indicates the magnified portion shown in **B**.

B *Above*, each spot is a region where the individual's genomic DNA has hybridized with one SNP sequence. A red or green dot means that the individual is homozygous for a SNP; a combined signal (yellow dot) indicates heterozygosity.

FIGURE 15.9 A SNP–chip analysis.

is not entirely random because some regions of DNA vary less than others. Such conserved regions are of particular interest to researchers because they are the ones most likely to have an essential function. When a conserved sequence does vary among people, the variation tends to be in nucleotides at a particular location. A base-pair substitution carried by a measurable percentage of a population, usually above 1 percent, is called a **single-nucleotide polymorphism**, or **SNP** (pronounced "snip").

Alleles of most genes differ by single nucleotides, and differences in alleles are the basis of the variation in human traits that makes each individual unique (Section 12.1). In fact, those differences are so unique that they can be used to identify you. Identifying an individual by his or her DNA is called **DNA profiling**.

One type of DNA profiling involves SNP-chips (FIGURE 15.9). A SNP-chip is a tiny glass plate with

---

FIGURE 15.8 Genomic DNA alignment. This is a region of the gene for a DNA polymerase. Nucleotides that differ from those in the human sequence are highlighted. The chance that any two of these sequences would randomly match is about 1 in 10^{46}.

```
758 GATAATCCTGTTTTGAACAAAAGGTCAAATTGCTGAATAGAAA-GTCTTGATTAACTAAAAGATGTACAAAGTGGAATTA 836  Human
752 GATAATCCTGTTTTGAACAAAAGGTCAAATTGCTGAATAGAAA-GTCTTGATTAACTAAAAGATGTACAAAGTGGAATTA 830  Mouse
751 GATAATCCTGTTTTGAACAAAAGGTCAAATTGCTGAATAGAAA-GTCTTGATTAACTAAAAGATGTACAAAGTGGAATTA 829  Rat
754 GATAATCCTGTTTTGAACAAAAGGTCAAATTGCTGAATAGAAA-GTCTTGATTAACTAAAAGATGTACAAAGTGGAATTA 832  Dog
782 GATAATCCTGTTTTGAACAAAAGGTCAAATTGCTGAATAGAAA-GTCTTGATTAACTAAAAGATGTACAAAGTGGAATTA 860  Chicken
758 GATAATCCTGTTTTGAACAAAAGGTCAAATTGCTGAATAGAAA-GTCTTGATTAAGTAAAAGATGTACAAAGTGGAATTA 836  Frog
823 GATAATCCTGTTTTGAACAAAAGGTCAGATTGCTGAATAGAAAAGGCTTGATTAAAGCAGAGATGTACAAAGTGGACGCA 902  Zebrafish
763 GATAATCCTGTTTTGAACAAAAGGTCAAATTGTTGAATAGAGACGCTTTGATAAAGCGGAGGAGGTACAAAGTGGGACC- 841  Pufferfish
```

CREDITS: (8) © Cengage Learning; (9A) The Sanger Institute. Wellcome Images; (9B) Wellcome Trust Sanger Institute.

A Gray boxes indicate which regions of the individual's DNA were tested.

| D5S818 | D13S317 | D7S820 | D16S539 | CSF1PO | Penta D |

B The number of repeats is shown in a box below each peak. A peak's location on the x-axis corresponds to the length of the DNA fragment amplified (a measure of the number of repeats). Peak size reflects the amount of DNA.

FIGURE 15.10 {Animated} An individual's (partial) short tandem repeat profile. Remember, human body cells are diploid. Double peaks appear on a profile when the two members of a chromosome pair carry a different number of repeats.

 FIGURE IT OUT: How many repeats does this individual have at the Penta D region? Answer: 12 on one chromosome; 14 on the other

microscopic spots of DNA stamped on it. The DNA sample in each spot is a short, synthetic single strand with a unique SNP sequence. When an individual's genomic DNA is washed over a SNP-chip, it hybridizes only with DNA spots that have a matching SNP sequence. Probes reveal where the genomic DNA has hybridized—and which SNPs are carried by the individual.

Another method of DNA profiling involves analysis of short tandem repeats in an individual's chromosomes (Section 13.6). Short tandem repeats tend to occur in predictable spots, but the number of times a sequence is repeated in each spot differs among individuals. For example, one person's DNA may have fifteen repeats of the nucleotides TTTTC at a certain spot on one chromosome. Another person's DNA may have this sequence repeated only twice in the same location. Such repeats slip spontaneously into DNA during replication, and their numbers grow or shrink over generations. Unless two people are identical twins, the chance that they have identical short tandem repeats in even three regions of DNA is 1 in a quintillion (10^{18}), which is far more than the number of people who have ever lived. Thus, an individual's array of short tandem repeats is, for all practical purposes, unique.

Analyzing a person's short tandem repeats begins with PCR, which is used to copy ten to thirteen particular regions of chromosomal DNA known to have repeats. The lengths of the copied DNA fragments differ among most individuals, because the number of tandem repeats in those regions also differs. Thus, electrophoresis can be used to reveal an individual's unique array of short tandem repeats (**FIGURE 15.10**).

Short tandem repeat analysis will soon be replaced by full genome sequencing, but for now it continues to be a common DNA profiling method. Geneticists compare short tandem repeats on Y chromosomes to determine relationships among male relatives, and to trace an individual's ethnic heritage. They also track mutations that accumulate in populations over time by comparing DNA profiles of living humans with those of ancient ones. Such studies are allowing us to reconstruct population dispersals that happened in the ancient past.

Short tandem repeat profiles are routinely used to resolve kinship disputes, and as evidence in criminal cases. Within the context of a criminal or forensic investigation, DNA profiling is called DNA fingerprinting. As of January 2013, the database of DNA fingerprints maintained by the Federal Bureau of Investigation (the FBI) contained the short tandem repeat profiles of 10.1 million convicted offenders, and had been used in over 190,000 criminal investigations. DNA fingerprints have also been used to identify the remains of over 470,000 people, including the individuals who died in the World Trade Center on September 11, 2001.

DNA profiling Identifying an individual by analyzing the unique parts of his or her DNA.
genomics The study of genomes.
single-nucleotide polymorphism (SNP) One-nucleotide DNA sequence variation carried by a measurable percentage of a population.

TAKE-HOME MESSAGE 15.4

Analysis of the human genome sequence is yielding new information about our genes and how they work.

DNA profiling identifies individuals by the unique parts of their DNA.

A *E. coli* bacteria transgenic for a fluorescent jellyfish protein. Variation in fluorescence among the genetically identical cells reveals differences in gene expression that may help us understand why some bacteria become dangerously resistant to antibiotics, and others do not.

B Zebrafish engineered to glow in places where BPA, an endocrine-disrupting chemical, is present. The fish are literally illuminating where this pollutant acts in the body—and helping researchers discover what it does when it gets there.

C Transgenic goats produce human antithrombin, an anti-clotting protein. Antithrombin harvested from their milk is used as a drug during surgery or childbirth to prevent blood clotting in people with hereditary antithrombin deficiency. This genetic disorder carries a high risk of life-threatening clots.

FIGURE 15.11 Examples of GMOs.

Genetic engineering is a process by which an individual's genome is deliberately modified. A gene from one species may be transferred to another to produce an organism that is **transgenic**, or a gene may be altered and reinserted into an individual of the same species. Both methods result in a **genetically modified organism**, or **GMO**.

The most common GMOs are bacteria (**FIGURE 15.11A**) and yeast. These cells have the metabolic machinery to make complex organic molecules, and they are easily modified to produce, for example, medically important proteins. People with diabetes were among the first beneficiaries of such organisms. Insulin for their injections was once extracted from animals, but it provoked an allergic reaction in some people. Human insulin, which does not provoke allergic reactions, has been produced by transgenic *E. coli* since 1982. Slight modifications of the gene have yielded fast-acting and slow-release forms of human insulin.

Genetically engineered microorganisms also produce proteins used in foods. For example, cheese is traditionally made with an extract of calf stomachs, which contain the enzyme chymotrypsin. Most cheese manufacturers now use chymotrypsin produced by genetically engineered bacteria. Other enzymes produced by GMOs improve the taste and clarity of beer and fruit juice, slow bread staling, or modify certain fats.

The first genetically modified animals were mice. Today, engineered mice are commonplace, and they are invaluable in research (an example is shown in the chapter opener). We have discovered the function of human genes (including the *APOA5* gene discussed in Section 15.4) by inactivating their counterparts in mice. Genetically modified mice are also used as models of human diseases. For example, researchers inactivated the molecules involved in the control of glucose metabolism, one by one. Studying the effects of the knockouts in mice has resulted in much of our current understanding of how diabetes works in humans.

Other genetically modified animals are useful in research (**FIGURE 15.11B**), and some make molecules that have medical and industrial applications. Various transgenic goats produce proteins used to treat cystic fibrosis, heart attacks, blood clotting disorders (**FIGURE 15.11C**), and even nerve gas exposure. Goats transgenic for a spider silk gene produce the silk protein in their milk; researchers can spin this protein into nanofibers that are useful in medical and electronics applications. Rabbits make human interleukin-2, a protein that triggers divisions of immune cells. Genetic engineering has also given us pigs with heart-healthy fat and environmentally friendly low-phosphate feces, muscle-bound trout, chickens that do not transmit bird flu, and cows that do not get mad cow disease.

As crop production expands to keep pace with human population growth, many farmers have begun to rely on genetically modified crop plants. Genes are often introduced into plant cells by way *Agrobacterium tumefaciens*. These bacteria carry a plasmid with genes that cause tumors to form on infected plants; hence the name Ti plasmid (for

CREDITS: (11A) Courtesy of Systems Biodynamics Lab, P. I. Jeff Hasty, UCSD Department of Bioengineering, and Scott Cookson; (11B) © Charles Taylor/University of Exeter; (11C) © GTC Biotherapeutics, Inc.

Tumor-inducing). Researchers replace the tumor-inducing genes with foreign or modified genes, then use the plasmid as a vector to deliver the genes into plant cells. Whole plants can be grown from cells that integrate a recombinant plasmid into their chromosomes (**FIGURE 15.12**).

Many genetically modified crops carry genes that impart resistance to devastating plant diseases. Others offer improved yields. GMO crops such as Bt corn and soy help farmers use smaller amounts of toxic pesticides (**FIGURE 15.13**). Organic farmers often spray their crops with spores of Bt (*Bacillus thuringiensis*), a bacterial species that makes a protein toxic only to some insect larvae. Researchers transferred the gene encoding the Bt protein into plants. The engineered plants produce the Bt protein, and larvae die shortly after eating their first and only GMO meal.

Transgenic crop plants are also being developed for impoverished regions of the world. Genes that confer drought tolerance, insect resistance, and enhanced nutritional value are being introduced into plants such as corn, rice, beans, sugarcane, cassava, cowpeas, banana, and wheat. The resulting GMO crops may help people who rely on agriculture for food and income.

At this writing, ninety-two crops have been approved for unrestricted use in the United States. Worldwide, more than 330 million acres are currently planted in GMO crops, the majority of which are corn, sorghum, cotton, soy, canola, and alfalfa engineered for resistance to the herbicide glyphosate. Rather than tilling the soil to control weeds, farmers spray their fields with glyphosate, which kills the weeds but not the engineered crops.

Many people worry that our ability to tinker with genetics has surpassed our ability to understand the impact of the tinkering. Controversy raised by GMO use invites you to read the research and form your own opinions. The alternative is to be swayed by media hype (the term "Frankenfood," for instance), or by reports from potentially biased sources (such as herbicide manufacturers).

genetic engineering Process by which deliberate changes are introduced into an individual's genome.
genetically modified organism (GMO) Organism whose genome has been modified by genetic engineering.
transgenic Refers to a genetically modified organism that carries a gene from a different species.

TAKE-HOME MESSAGE 15.5

Genetic engineering is the deliberate alteration of an individual's genome, and it results in a genetically modified organism (GMO).

A transgenic organism carries a gene from a different species.

A A Ti plasmid carrying a foreign gene is inserted into an *Agrobacterium tumefaciens* bacterium.

B The bacterium infects a plant cell and transfers the Ti plasmid into it. The plasmid DNA, along with the foreign gene, becomes integrated into one of the cell's chromosomes.

C The infected plant cell divides, and its descendants form an embryo, then a plant (left). Cells of the transgenic plant carry and express the foreign gene.

FIGURE 15.12 {Animated} Using the Ti plasmid to make transgenic plants.

FIGURE 15.13 Farmers can use much less pesticide on crops that make their own. The genetically modified plants that produced the row of corn on the *top* carry a gene from the bacteria *Bacillus thuringensis* (Bt) that conferred insect resistance. Compare the corn from unmodified plants, *bottom*. No pesticides were used on either crop.

CREDITS: (12A–B) © Cengage Learning; (12C) Pascal Goetgheluck/Science Source; (13) The Bt and Non-Bt corn photos were taken as part of field trial conducted on the main campus of Tennessee State University at the Institute of Agriculture and Environmental Research. The work was supported by a competitive grant from the CSREES, USDA titled "Southern Agricultural Biotechnology Consortium for Underserved Communities," (2000–2005). Dr. Fisseha Tegegne and D. Ahmad Aziz served as Principal and Co-principal Investigators respectively to conduct the portion of the study in the State of Tennessee.

15.6 CAN WE GENETICALLY MODIFY PEOPLE?

GENE THERAPY

We know of more than 15,000 serious genetic disorders. Collectively, they cause 20 to 30 percent of infant deaths each year, and account for half of all mentally impaired patients and a fourth of all hospital admissions. They also contribute to many age-related disorders, including cancer, Parkinson's disease, and diabetes. Drugs and other treatments can minimize the symptoms of some genetic disorders, but gene therapy is the only cure. **Gene therapy** is the transfer of recombinant DNA into an individual's body cells, with the intent to correct a genetic defect or treat a disease. The transfer, which occurs by way of lipid clusters or genetically engineered viruses, inserts an unmutated gene into an individual's chromosomes.

Human gene therapy is a compelling reason to embrace genetic engineering research. It is now being tested as a treatment for AIDS, muscular dystrophy, heart attack, sickle-cell anemia, cystic fibrosis, hemophilia A, Parkinson's disease, Alzheimer's disease, several types of cancer, and inherited diseases of the eye, the ear, and the immune system. Results have been encouraging. For example, gene therapy has recently been used to treat acute lymphoblastic leukemia, a typically fatal cancer of bone marrow cells. A viral vector was used to insert a gene into immune cells extracted from patients. When the engineered cells were reintroduced into the patients' bodies, the inserted gene directed the destruction of the cancer cells. The therapy worked astonishingly well: In one patient, all traces of the leukemia vanished in eight days. However, the outcome of manipulating a gene in a living individual can be unpredictable. In an early trial, for example, twenty boys were treated with gene therapy for a severe X-linked genetic disorder called SCID-X1. Five of them developed leukemia, and one died. The researchers had wrongly predicted that cancer related to the therapy would be rare. Research now implicates the gene targeted for repair, especially when combined with the virus that delivered it. Integration of the modified viral DNA activated nearby proto-oncogenes (Section 11.5) in the children's chromosomes.

EUGENICS

The idea of selecting the most desirable human traits, **eugenics**, is an old one. It has been used as a justification for some of the most horrific episodes in human history, including the genocide of 6 million Jews during World War II. Thus, it continues to be a hotly debated social issue. For example, using gene therapy to cure human genetic disorders seems like a socially acceptable goal to most people, but imagine taking this idea a bit further. Would it also be acceptable to engineer the genome of an individual who is within a normal range of phenotype in order to

modify a particular trait? Researchers have already produced mice that have improved memory, enhanced learning ability, bigger muscles, and longer lives. Why not people?

Given the pace of genetics research, the debate is no longer about how we would engineer desirable traits, but how we would choose the traits that are desirable. Realistically, cures for many severe but rare genetic disorders will not be found, because the financial return would not cover the cost of the research. Eugenics, however, may be profitable. How much would potential parents pay to be sure that their child will be tall or blue-eyed? Would it be okay to engineer "superhumans" with breathtaking strength or intelligence? How about a treatment that can help you lose that extra weight, and keep it off permanently? The gray area between interesting and abhorrent can be very different depending on who is asked. In a survey conducted in the United States, more than 40 percent of those interviewed said it would be fine to use gene therapy to make smarter and cuter babies. In one poll of British parents, 18 percent would be willing to use it to keep a child from being aggressive, and 10 percent would use it to keep a child from growing up to be homosexual.

Some people are concerned that gene therapy puts us on a slippery slope that may result in irreversible damage to ourselves and to the biosphere. We as a society may not have the wisdom to know how to stop once we set foot on that slope; one is reminded of our peculiar human tendency to leap before we look. And yet, something about the human experience allows us to dream of such things as wings of our own making, a capacity that carried us into space. In this brave new world, the questions before you are these: What do we stand to lose if serious risks are not taken? And, do we have the right to impose the potential consequences on people who would choose not to take those risks?

---

eugenics Idea of deliberately improving the genetic qualities of the human race.

gene therapy Treating a genetic defect or disorder by transferring a normal or modified gene into the affected individual.

TAKE-HOME MESSAGE 15.6

Genes can be transferred into a person's cells to correct a genetic defect or treat a disease. However, the outcome of altering a person's genome has been unpredictable.

We as a society must continue to work our way through the ethical implications of applying DNA technologies.

15.7 Application: PERSONAL GENETIC TESTING

Actress Angelina Jolie discovered via genetic testing that she carries a *BRCA1* mutation associated with an 87% lifetime risk of developing breast cancer. Even though she did not yet have cancer, Jolie underwent a double mastectomy. By doing so, she reduced her risk of breast cancer to 5%.

Education

FIGURE 15.14 Celebrity Angelina Jolie chose preventive treatment after genetic testing showed she had a very high risk of breast cancer.

DO YOU WANT TO KNOW YOUR SNP PROFILE? Finding out which of about 1 million SNPs you carry has never been easier. Genetic testing companies can extract your DNA from a few drops of spit, then analyze it using a SNP-chip. Results typically include estimated risks of developing conditions associated with your particular set of SNPs. For example, the test will probably determine whether you are homozygous for one allele of the *MC1R* gene (Section 13.4). If you are, the company's report will tell you that you have red hair. Few SNPs have such a clear effect, however. Consider the lipoprotein particles that carry fats and cholesterol through our bloodstreams. These particles consist of variable amounts and types of lipids and proteins, one of which is specified by the gene *APOE*. About one in four people carries an allele of this gene, $\varepsilon 4$, that increases one's risk of developing Alzheimer's disease later in life. If you are heterozygous for this allele, a DNA testing company will report that your lifetime risk of developing the disease is about 29 percent, as compared with about 9 percent for someone who has no $\varepsilon 4$ allele.

What, exactly, does a 29 percent lifetime risk of Alzheimer's disease mean? The number is a probability statistic; it means, on average, 29 of every 100 people who have the $\varepsilon 4$ allele eventually get the disease. However, a risk is just that. Not everyone who has the $\varepsilon 4$ allele develops Alzheimer's, and not everyone who develops the disease has the allele. Other unknown factors, including epigenetic modifications of DNA, contribute to the disease. We still have a limited understanding of how genes contribute to many health conditions, particularly age-related ones such as Alzheimer's disease

Geneticists believe that it will be at least five to ten more years before genotyping can be used to accurately predict an individual's future health problems. Nonetheless, we are at a tipping point; personalized genetic testing is already beginning to revolutionize medicine. Cancer treatments are now being tailored to fit the genetic makeup of individual patients. People who discover they carry alleles associated with a heightened risk of a medical condition are being encouraged to make lifestyle changes that could delay the condition's onset or prevent it entirely. Preventive treatments based on personal genetics are becoming more common—and more mainstream (FIGURE 15.14).

Summary

SECTION 15.1 In **DNA cloning**, researchers use **restriction enzymes** to cut a sample of DNA into pieces, and then use DNA ligase to splice the fragments into plasmids or other **cloning vectors**. The resulting molecules of **recombinant DNA** are inserted into host cells such as bacteria. Division of host cells produces huge populations of genetically identical descendant cells (clones), each with a copy of the cloned DNA fragment.

The enzyme **reverse transcriptase** is used to transcribe RNA into **cDNA** for cloning.

SECTION 15.2 A **DNA library** is a collection of cells that host different fragments of DNA, often representing an organism's entire **genome**. Researchers can use **probes** to identify cells in a library that carry a specific fragment of DNA. The **polymerase chain reaction** (**PCR**) uses primers and a heat-resistant DNA polymerase to rapidly increase the number of copies of a targeted section of DNA.

SECTION 15.3 Advances in **sequencing**, which reveals the order of nucleotides in DNA, allowed the DNA sequence of the entire human genome to be determined. DNA polymerase is used to partially replicate a DNA template. The reaction produces a mixture of DNA fragments of all different lengths; **electrophoresis** separates the fragments by length into bands.

SECTION 15.4 **Genomics** provides insights into the function of the human genome. Similarities between genomes of different organisms are evidence of evolutionary relationships, and can be used as a predictive tool in research.

DNA profiling identifies a person by the unique parts of his or her DNA. An example is the determination of an individual's array of short tandem repeats or **single-nucleotide polymorphisms** (**SNPs**). Within the context of a criminal investigation, a DNA profile is called a DNA fingerprint.

SECTION 15.5 Recombinant DNA technology is the basis of **genetic engineering**, the directed modification of an organism's genetic makeup with the intent to modify its phenotype. A gene from one species is inserted into an individual of a different species to make a **transgenic** organism, or a gene is modified and reinserted into an individual of the same species. The result of either process is a **genetically modified organism** (**GMO**).

Bacteria and yeast, the most common genetically engineered organisms, produce proteins that have medical value. The majority of the animals that are being created by genetic engineering are used for medical applications or research. Most transgenic crop plants, which are now in widespread use worldwide, were created to help farmers produce food more efficiently. Some have enhanced nutritional value.

SECTION 15.6 With **gene therapy**, a gene is transferred into body cells to correct a genetic defect or treat a disease. Potential benefits of genetically modifying humans must be weighed against potential risks. The practice raises ethical issues such as whether **eugenics** is desirable in some circumstances.

SECTION 15.7 Personal genetic testing, which reveals a person's unique array of SNPs, is beginning to revolutionize the way medicine is practiced.

Self-Quiz   Answers in Appendix VII

1. _____ cut(s) DNA molecules at specific sites.
   a. DNA polymerase   c. Restriction enzymes
   b. DNA probes   d. DNA ligase

2. A _____ is a molecule that can be used to carry a fragment of DNA into a host organism.
   a. cloning vector   c. GMO
   b. chromosome   d. cDNA

3. Reverse transcriptase assembles a(n) _____ on a(n) _____ template.
   a. mRNA; DNA   c. DNA; ribosome
   b. cDNA; mRNA   d. protein; mRNA

4. For each species, all _____ in the complete set of chromosomes is/are the _____ .
   a. genomes; phenotype   c. mRNA; start of cDNA
   b. DNA; genome   d. cDNA; start of mRNA

5. A set of cells that host various DNA fragments collectively representing an organism's entire set of genetic information is a _____ .
   a. genome   c. genomic library
   b. clone   d. GMO

6. _____ is a technique to determine the order of nucleotide bases in a fragment of DNA.
   a. PCR   c. Electrophoresis
   b. Sequencing   d. Nucleic acid hybridization

7. Fragments of DNA can be separated by electrophoresis according to _____ .
   a. sequence   b. length   c. species

8. PCR can be used _____ .
   a. to increase the number of specific DNA fragments
   b. in DNA fingerprinting
   c. to modify a human genome
   d. a and b are correct

9. An individual's set of unique _____ can be used as a DNA profile.
   a. DNA sequences   c. SNPs
   b. short tandem repeats d. all of the above

10. True or false? Some humans are genetically modified.

Data Analysis Activities

Enhanced Spatial Learning Ability in Mice with an Autism Mutation Autism is a neurobiological disorder with symptoms that include impaired social interactions and stereotyped patterns of behavior. Around 10 percent of autistic people have an extraordinary skill or talent such as greatly enhanced memory.

Mutations in neuroligin 3, an adhesion protein that connects brain cells to one another, have been associated with autism. One mutation changes amino acid 451 from arginine to cysteine. In 2007, Katsuhiko Tabuchi and his colleagues genetically modified mice to carry the same arginine-to-cysteine substitution in their neuroligin 3. Mice with the mutation had impaired social behavior. Spatial learning ability was tested in a water maze, in which a platform is submerged a few millimeters below the surface of a deep pool of warm water. The platform is not visible to swimming mice. Mice do not particularly enjoy swimming, so they locate a hidden platform as fast as they can. When tested again, they can remember its location by checking visual cues around the edge of the pool. How quickly they remember the platform's location is a measure of spatial learning ability (**FIGURE 15.15**).

a water maze

FIGURE 15.15 Spatial learning ability in mice with a mutation in neuroligin 3 (*R451C*), compared with unmodified (wild-type) mice.

1. In the first test, how many days did unmodified mice need to learn to find the location of a hidden platform within 10 seconds?
2. Did the modified or the unmodified mice learn the location of the platform faster in the first test?
3. Which mice learned faster the second time around?
4. Which mice showed the greatest improvement in memory between the first and the second test?

---

11. Which of the following can be used to carry foreign DNA into host cells? Choose all correct answers.
    - a. RNA
    - b. viruses
    - c. PCR
    - d. lipid clusters
    - e. bacteria
    - f. plasmids

12. Transgenic _____ can pass a foreign gene to offspring.
    - a. plants
    - b. animals
    - c. bacteria
    - d. all of the above

13. _____ can correct a genetic defect in an individual.
    - a. Cloning vectors
    - b. Gene therapy
    - c. Eugenics
    - d. a and b

14. Match the recombinant DNA method with the appropriate enzyme.
    - ___ PCR
    - ___ cutting DNA
    - ___ cDNA synthesis
    - ___ DNA sequencing
    - ___ pasting DNA
    - a. *Taq* polymerase
    - b. DNA ligase
    - c. reverse transcriptase
    - d. restriction enzyme
    - e. DNA polymerase (not *Taq*)

15. Match each term with the most suitable description.
    - ___ DNA profile
    - ___ Ti plasmid
    - ___ eugenics
    - ___ SNP
    - ___ transgenic
    - ___ GMO
    - a. GMO with a foreign gene
    - b. alleles commonly contain them
    - c. a person's unique collection of short tandem repeats
    - d. selecting "desirable" traits
    - e. genetically modified
    - f. used in plant gene transfers

Critical Thinking

1. The results of a paternity test using short tandem repeats are shown in the table below. Who's the daddy? How sure are you?

	Mother	Baby	Alleged Father #1	Alleged Father #2
D3S1358	15, 17	17, 23	23, 27	17, 15
TH01	9, 9	9, 9	9, 12	12, 12
D21S11	29, 29	29, 27	27, 28	29, 28
D18S51	14, 18	18, 20	15, 20	17, 22
Penta E	14, 14	14, 14	14, 14	15, 16
D5D818	11, 14	14, 16	12, 16	14, 20
D13S317	11, 13	10, 13	8, 10	18, 18
D7S820	7, 13	13, 13	13, 19	13, 13
D16S539	13, 13	13, 15	12, 15	10, 12
CSF1PO	12, 12	10, 12	8, 10	12, 17
Penta D	12, 14	5, 12	14, 14	18, 25
amelogenin	X, X	X,Y	X,Y	X,Y
vWa	15, 17	17, 22	15, 22	22, 22
D8S1179	13, 13	8, 13	8, 13	15, 15
TPOX	11, 11	11, 11	10, 11	17, 22
FGA	23, 23	23, 25	18, 25	23, 23

CENGAGE brain .com To access course materials, please visit www.cengagebrain.com.

High in the Andes, a scientist infers the stride of an extinct dinosaur by measuring the distance between its fossilized footprints. We often reconstruct history by studying physical evidence of events that took place long ago. This practice relies on a foundational premise of science: Natural phenomena that occurred in the past can be explained by the same physical, chemical, and biological processes operating today.

16

EVIDENCE OF EVOLUTION

Links to Earlier Concepts

You may wish to review critical thinking (Section 1.5) before reading this chapter, which explores a clash between belief and science (1.7). What you know about alleles (12.1) will help you understand natural selection. The chapter revisits radioisotopes (2.1), the effect of photosynthesis on Earth's early atmosphere (7.2), the genetic code and mutations (9.3, 9.5), master genes (10.2, 10.3), and evolution by gene duplication (14.4).

KEY CONCEPTS

EMERGENCE OF EVOLUTIONARY THOUGHT
Nineteenth-century naturalists investigating the global distribution of species discovered patterns that could not be explained within the framework of traditional belief systems.

A THEORY TAKES FORM
Evidence of evolution, or change in lines of descent, led Charles Darwin and Alfred Wallace to develop a theory of how traits that define each species change over time.

EVIDENCE FROM FOSSILS
The fossil record provides physical evidence of past changes in many lines of descent. We use the property of radioisotope decay to determine the age of rocks and fossils.

INFLUENTIAL GEOLOGIC FORCES
By studying rock layers and fossils in them, we can correlate geologic events with evolutionary events. Such correlations help explain the distribution of species, past and present.

EVIDENCE IN BODY FORM
Comparisons of genes, developmental patterns, and body form provide information about how organisms are related to one another. Lineages with recent common ancestry are most similar.

A Emu, native to Australia.   B Rhea, native to South America.   C Ostrich, native to Africa.

FIGURE 16.1 Similar-looking, related species native to distant geographic realms. These birds are unlike most others in several unusual features, including long, muscular legs and an inability to fly. All are native to open grassland regions about the same distance from the equator.

People have long been curious about the natural world and our place in it. About 2,300 years ago, the Greek philosopher Aristotle described nature as a continuum of organization, from lifeless matter through complex plants and animals. Aristotle's work greatly influenced later European thinkers, who adopted his view of nature and modified it in light of their own beliefs. By the fourteenth century, Europeans generally believed that a "great chain of being" extended from the lowest form (snakes), up through humans, to spiritual beings. Each link in the chain was a species, and each was said to have been forged at the same time, in one place and in a perfect state. The chain itself was complete and continuous. Because everything that needed to exist already did, there was no room for change.

European naturalists who embarked on globe-spanning survey expeditions brought back tens of thousands of plants and animals from Asia, Africa, North and South America, and the Pacific Islands. Each newly discovered species was carefully catalogued as another link in the chain of being. By the late 1800s, naturalists were seeing patterns in where species live and similarities in body plans, and had started to think about the natural forces that shape life. These naturalists were pioneers in **biogeography**, the study of patterns in the geographic distribution of species and communities. Some of the patterns raised questions that could not be answered within the framework of prevailing belief systems. For example, globe-trotting explorers had discovered plants and animals living in extremely isolated places. The isolated species looked suspiciously similar to species living across vast expanses of open ocean, or on the other side of impassable mountain ranges. The three birds in **FIGURE 16.1** live on different continents, but

they share a set of unusual features. These flightless birds sprint about on long, muscular legs in flat, open grasslands about the same distance from the equator. All raise their long necks to watch for predators. Alfred Wallace, an explorer who was particularly interested in the geographical distribution of animals, thought that the shared set of unusual traits might mean that these three birds descended from a common ancestor (and he was right), but he had no idea how they could have ended up on different continents.

Naturalists of the time also had trouble classifying organisms that are very similar in some features, but different in others. For example, the plants in **FIGURE 16.2** are native to different continents. Both live in hot

FIGURE 16.2 Similar-looking, unrelated species. On the *left*, an African milk barrel cactus (*Euphorbia horrida*), native to the Great Karoo desert of South Africa. On the *right*, saguaro cactus (*Carnegiea gigantea*), native to the Sonoran Desert of Arizona.

deserts where water is seasonally scarce. Both have rows of sharp spines that deter herbivores, and both store water in their thick, fleshy stems. However, their reproductive parts are very different, so these plants cannot be as closely related as their outward appearance might suggest.

Observations such as these are examples of **comparative morphology**, the study of anatomical patterns—similarities and differences among the body plans of organisms. Today, comparative morphology is part of taxonomy (Section 1.4), but in the nineteenth century it was the only way to distinguish species. In some cases, comparative morphology revealed anatomical details—body parts with no apparent function, for example—that added to the mounting confusion. If every species had been created in a perfect state, then why were there useless parts such as wings in birds that do not fly, eyes in moles that are blind, or remnants of a tail in humans (**FIGURE 16.3**)?

Fossils were puzzling too. A **fossil** is physical evidence—remains or traces—of an organism that lived in the ancient past. Geologists mapping rock formations exposed by erosion or quarrying had discovered identical sequences of rock layers in different parts of the world. Deeper layers held fossils of simple marine life. Layers above those held similar but more complex fossils (**FIGURE 16.4**). In higher layers, fossils that were similar but even more complex resembled modern species. What did these sequences mean?

Fossils of many animals unlike any living ones were also being unearthed. If these animals had been perfect at the time of creation, then why had they become extinct?

Taken as a whole, the accumulating findings from biogeography, comparative morphology, and geology did not fit with prevailing beliefs of the nineteenth century. If species had not been created in a perfect state (and extinct species, fossil sequences, and "useless" body parts implied that they had not), then perhaps species had indeed changed over time.

---

biogeography Study of patterns in the geographic distribution of species and communities.
comparative morphology The scientific study of similarities and differences in body plans.
fossil Physical evidence of an organism that lived in the ancient past.

FIGURE 16.3 A vestigial structure: human tailbones. Nineteenth-century naturalists were well aware of—but had trouble explaining—body structures such as human tailbones that had apparently lost most or all function.

coccyx (tailbones)

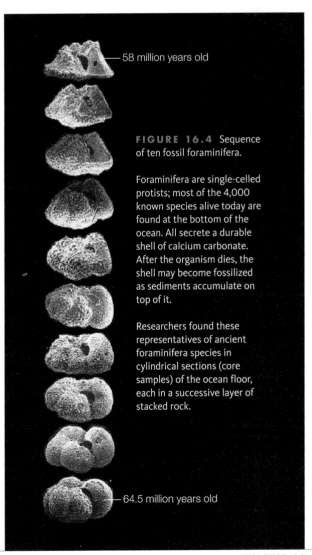

58 million years old

FIGURE 16.4 Sequence of ten fossil foraminifera.

Foraminifera are single-celled protists; most of the 4,000 known species alive today are found at the bottom of the ocean. All secrete a durable shell of calcium carbonate. After the organism dies, the shell may become fossilized as sediments accumulate on top of it.

Researchers found these representatives of ancient foraminifera species in cylindrical sections (core samples) of the ocean floor, each in a successive layer of stacked rock.

64.5 million years old

CREDITS: (3) © Zephyr/Science Photo Library/Science Source; (4) Courtesy of Daniel C. Kelley, Anthony J. Arnold, and William C. Parker, Florida State University Department of Geological Science.

Around 1800, naturalists were trying to explain the mounting evidence that life on Earth, and even Earth itself, had changed over time. Georges Cuvier (*left*), an expert in zoology and paleontology, proposed an idea startling for the time: Many species that had once existed were now extinct. Cuvier knew about evidence that Earth's surface had changed. For example, he had seen fossilized seashells on mountainsides far from modern seas. Like most others of his time, he assumed Earth's age to be in the thousands, not billions, of years. He reasoned that geologic forces unlike any known at the time would have been necessary to raise seafloors to mountaintops in this short time span. Catastrophic geological events would have caused extinctions, after which surviving species repopulated Earth.

 Jean-Baptiste Lamarck (*left*) was thinking about processes that drive **evolution**, or change in a line of descent. A line of descent is also called a **lineage**. Lamarck thought that a species gradually improved over generations because of an inherent drive toward perfection, up the chain of being. By Lamarck's hypothesis, environmental pressures cause an internal need for change in an individual's body, and the resulting change is inherited by offspring. (Lamarck was correct in thinking that environmental factors affect traits, but his understanding of how traits are passed to offspring was incomplete.)

 Charles Darwin (*left*) had earned a theology degree from Cambridge after an attempt to study medicine. All through school, however, he had spent most of his time with faculty members and other students who embraced natural history. In 1831, when he was 22, Darwin joined a 5-year survey expedition to South America on the ship *Beagle*, and he quickly became an enthusiastic naturalist. During the *Beagle*'s voyage, Darwin found many unusual fossils, and saw diverse species living in environments that ranged from the sandy shores of remote islands to plains high in the Andes. Along the way, he read the first volume of a new and popular book, Charles Lyell's *Principles of Geology*. Lyell (*left*) was a proponent of what became known as the theory of uniformity, the idea that gradual, everyday geological processes such as erosion could have sculpted Earth's current landscape over great spans of time. The theory challenged the prevailing belief that Earth was 6,000 years old. By Lyell's calculations, it must have taken millions of years to sculpt Earth's surface. Darwin's exposure to Lyell's ideas gave him insights into the history of the regions he would encounter on his journey.

A Fossil of a glyptodon, an automobile-sized mammal that existed from 2 million to 15,000 years ago.

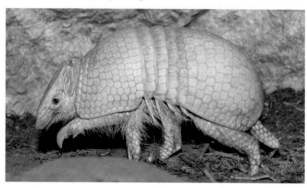

B A modern armadillo, about a foot long.

FIGURE 16.5 Ancient relatives: glyptodon and armadillo. Though widely separated in time, these animals share a restricted distribution and unusual traits, including a shell and helmet of keratin-covered bony plates—a material similar to crocodile and lizard skin. (The fossil in **A** is missing its helmet.)

Among the thousands of specimens Darwin collected during the *Beagle*'s voyage were fossil glyptodons. These armored mammals are extinct, but they have many unusual traits in common with modern armadillos (**FIGURE 16.5**). Armadillos also live only in places where glyptodons once lived. Could the odd shared traits and restricted distribution mean that glyptodons were ancient relatives of armadillos? If so, perhaps traits of their common ancestor had changed in the line of descent that led to armadillos. But why would such changes occur?

 Economist Thomas Malthus (*left*) had correlated increases in the size of human populations with episodes of famine, disease, and war. He proposed the idea that humans run out of food, living space, and other resources because they tend to reproduce beyond the capacity of their environment to sustain them. When that happens, the individuals of a population must either compete with one another for the limited resources, or develop technology to increase productivity. Darwin realized that Malthus's ideas had wider application: All populations, not just human ones, must have the capacity to produce more individuals than their environment can support.

Darwin started thinking about how individuals of a species often vary a bit in the details of shared traits such as size, coloration, and so on. He saw such variation among finch species on isolated islands of the Galápagos archipelago. This island chain is separated from South America by 900 kilometers (550 miles) of open ocean, so most species living on the islands did not have the opportunity for interbreeding with mainland populations. The Galápagos island finches resembled finch species in South America, but many of them had unique traits that suited them to their particular island habitat.

Darwin was familiar with dramatic variations in traits of pigeons, dogs, and horses produced through selective breeding. He recognized that a natural environment could similarly select traits that make individuals of a population suited to it. It dawned on Darwin that having a particular form of a shared trait might give an individual an advantage over competing members of its species. In any population, some individuals have forms of shared traits that make them better suited to their environment than others. In other words, individuals of a natural population vary in fitness. Today, we define **fitness** as the degree of adaptation to a specific environment, and measure it by relative genetic contribution to future generations. A trait that enhances an individual's fitness is called an evolutionary **adaptation**, or **adaptive trait**.

Over many generations, individuals with the most adaptive traits tend to survive longer and reproduce more than their less fit rivals. Darwin understood that this process, which he called **natural selection**, could be a mechanism by which evolution occurs. If an individual has a form of a trait that makes it better suited to an environment, then it is better able to survive. If an individual is better able to survive, then it has a better chance of living long enough to produce offspring. If individuals with an adaptive, heritable trait produce more offspring than those that do not, then the frequency of that trait will tend to increase in the population over successive generations. **TABLE 16.1** summarizes this reasoning.

Darwin wrote out his ideas about natural selection, but let ten years pass without publishing them. In the meantime, Alfred Wallace (*left*), who had been studying wildlife in the Amazon basin and the Malay Archipelago, sent an essay to Darwin for advice. Wallace's essay outlined evolution by natural selection—the very same hypothesis as Darwin's. Wallace had written earlier letters to Darwin and Lyell about patterns in the geographic distribution of species, and had come to the same

conclusion. In 1858, the idea of evolution by natural selection was presented at a scientific meeting, with Darwin and Wallace credited as authors. Wallace was in the field and knew nothing about the meeting, which Darwin did not attend. The next year, Darwin published *On the Origin of Species*, which laid out detailed evidence in support of natural selection. Many people had already accepted the idea of descent with modification (evolution). However, there was a fierce debate over the idea that evolution occurs by natural selection. Decades would pass before experimental evidence from the field of genetics led to its widespread acceptance as a theory by the scientific community.

As you will see in the remainder of this chapter, the theory of evolution by natural selection is supported by and helps explain the fossil record as well as similarities in the form, function, and biochemistry of living things.

TABLE 16.1

Principles of Natural Selection, in Modern Terms

Observations About Populations

〉 Natural populations have an inherent capacity to increase in size over time.

〉 As population size increases, resources that are used by its individuals (such as food and living space) eventually become limited.

〉 When resources are limited, individuals of a population compete for them.

Observations About Genetics

〉 Individuals of a species share certain traits.

〉 Individuals of a natural population vary in the details of those shared traits.

〉 Shared traits have a heritable basis, in genes. Slightly different forms of those genes (alleles) give rise to variation in shared traits.

Inferences

〉 A certain form of a shared trait may make its bearer better able to survive.

〉 Individuals of a population that are better able to survive tend to leave more offspring.

〉 Thus, an allele associated with an adaptive trait tends to become more common in a population over time.

adaptation (adaptive trait) A heritable trait that enhances an individual's fitness in a particular environment.
evolution Change in a line of descent.
fitness Degree of adaptation to an environment, as measured by an individual's relative genetic contribution to future generations.
lineage Line of descent.
natural selection Differential survival and reproduction of individuals of a population based on differences in shared, heritable traits. Driven by environmental pressures.

TAKE-HOME MESSAGE 16.2

Evidence that Earth and the species on it had changed over very long spans of time led to the theory of evolution by natural selection.

Natural selection is a process in which individuals of a population survive and reproduce with differing success depending on the details of their shared, heritable traits.

Traits favored in a particular environment are adaptive.

16.3 WHY DO BIOLOGISTS STUDY ROCKS AND FOSSILS?

A Fossil skeleton of an ichthyosaur that lived about 200 million years ago. These marine reptiles were about the same size as modern porpoises, breathed air like them, and probably swam as fast, but the two groups are not closely related.

B Extinct wasp encased in amber, which is ancient tree sap. This 9-mm-long insect lived about 20 million years ago.

C Fossilized imprint of a leaf from a 260-million-year-old *Glossopteris*, a type of plant called a seed fern.

D Fossilized footprint of a theropod, a name that means "beast foot." This group of carnivorous dinosaurs, which includes the familiar *Tyrannosaurus rex*, arose about 250 million years ago.

E Coprolite (fossilized feces). Fossilized food remains and parasitic worms inside coprolites offer clues about the diet and health of extinct species. A foxlike animal excreted this one.

FIGURE 16.6 Examples of fossils.

Even before Darwin's time, fossils were recognized as stone-hard evidence of earlier forms of life (**FIGURE 16.6**). Most fossils consist of mineralized bones, teeth, shells, seeds, spores, or other hard body parts. Trace fossils such as footprints and other impressions, nests, burrows, trails, eggshells, or feces are evidence of an organism's activities.

The process of fossilization typically begins when an organism or its traces become covered by sediments, mud, or ash. Groundwater then seeps into the remains, filling spaces around and inside of them. Minerals dissolved in the water gradually replace minerals in bones and other hard tissues. Mineral particles that crystallize and settle out of the groundwater inside cavities and impressions form detailed imprints of internal and external structures. Sediments that slowly accumulate on top of the site exert increasing pressure, and, after a very long time, extreme pressure transforms the mineralized remains into rock.

Most fossils are found in layers of sedimentary rock that forms as rivers wash silt, sand, volcanic ash, and other materials from land to sea. Mineral particles in the materials settle on the seafloor in horizontal layers that vary in thickness and composition. After many millions of years, the layers of sediments become compacted into layered sedimentary rock. Even though most sedimentary rock forms at the bottom of a sea, geologic processes can tilt the rock and lift it far above sea level, where the layers may become exposed by the erosive forces of water and wind (the chapter opening photo shows an example).

Biologists study sedimentary rock formations in order to understand life's historical context. Features of the formations can provide information about conditions in

the environment in which they formed. Consider banded iron, a unique formation named after its distinctive striped appearance (*left*). Huge deposits of this sedimentary rock are the source of most iron we mine for steel today, but they also hold a record of how the evolution of the noncyclic pathway of photosynthesis changed the chemistry of Earth. Banded iron started forming about 2.4 billion years ago, right after photosynthesis evolved (Section 7.2). At that time, Earth's atmosphere and ocean contained very little oxygen, so almost all of the iron on Earth was in a reduced form (Section 5.4). Reduced iron dissolves in water, and ocean water contained a lot of it. Oxygen released into the ocean by early photosynthetic bacteria quickly combined with the dissolved iron. The resulting oxidized iron compounds are completely insoluble in water, and they began to rain down on the ocean floor in massive quantities. These compounds

CREDITS: (6A) © Jonathan Blair; (6B) © Dr. Michael Engel, University of Kansas; (6C) © Martin Land/Science Source; (6D) © Louie Psihoyos/Getty Images; (6E) Courtesy of Stan Celestian/Glendale Community College Earth Science Image Archive; (in text) Natural History Museum, London/Science Photo Library/Science Source.

accumulated in sediments that would eventually become compacted into banded iron formations.

The massive sedimentation of oxidized iron continued for about 600 million years. After that, ocean water no longer contained very much dissolved iron, and oxygen gas bubbling out of it had oxidized the iron in rocks exposed to the atmosphere.

THE FOSSIL RECORD

We have fossils for more than 250,000 known species. Considering the current range of biodiversity, there must have been many millions more, but we will never know all of them. Why not? The odds are against finding evidence of an extinct species, because fossils are relatively rare. When an organism dies, its remains are often obliterated quickly by scavengers. Organic materials decompose in the presence of moisture and oxygen, so remains that escape scavenging can endure only if they dry out, freeze, or become encased in an air-excluding material such as sap, tar, or mud. Remains that do become fossilized are often deformed, crushed, or scattered by erosion and other geologic assaults.

In order for us to know about an extinct species that existed long ago, we have to find a fossil of it. At least one specimen had to be buried before it decomposed or something ate it. The burial site had to escape destructive geologic events, and it had to be accessible for us to find.

Most ancient species had no hard parts to fossilize, so we do not find much evidence of them. For example, there are many fossils of bony fishes and mollusks with hard shells, but few fossils of the jellyfishes and soft worms that were probably much more common. Also think about relative numbers of organisms. Fungal spores and pollen grains are typically released by the billions. By contrast, the earliest humans lived in small bands and few of their offspring survived. The odds of finding even one fossilized human bone are much smaller than the odds of finding a fossilized fungal spore. Finally, imagine two species, one that existed only briefly and the other for billions of years. Which is more likely to be represented in the fossil record? Despite these challenges, the fossil record is substantial enough to help us reconstruct large-scale patterns in the history of life.

TAKE-HOME MESSAGE 16.3

Fossils are evidence of organisms that lived in the remote past, a stone-hard historical record of life.

The fossil record will never be complete. Geologic events have obliterated much of it. The rest of the record is slanted toward species that had hard parts, lived in dense populations with wide distribution, and persisted for a long time.

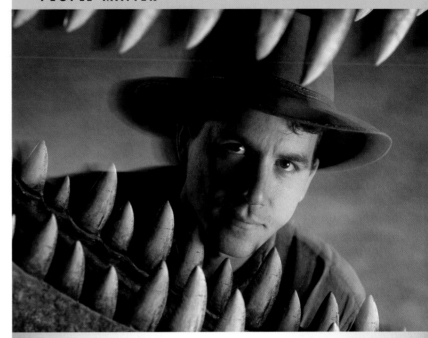

National Geographic Explorer-in-Residence
DR. PAUL SERENO

A real-life Indiana Jones, paleontologist Paul Sereno blends his background as an artist with a love for science and history. Sereno's passion carries him to the remote corners of the world to discover new species under the harshest of conditions.

Sereno's fieldwork began in 1988 in the Andes, where his team discovered the first dinosaurs to roam the Earth, including the most primitive of all: *Eoraptor*. This work culminated in the most complete picture yet of the dawn of the dinosaur era, some 225 million years ago. In the 1990s, Sereno's expeditions shifted to the Sahara. There, his teams have since excavated more than 70 tons of fossils representing organisms such as the huge-clawed fish-eater *Suchomimus*, the gigantic *Carcharodontosaurus* (its jaws pictured above, with Sereno), and a series of crocs including the 40-foot-long "SuperCroc" *Sarcosuchus*, the world's largest crocodile. In 2001, a trip to India yielded the Asian continent's first dinosaur skull—a new species of predator, *Rajasaurus*. Also in 2001, Sereno began an ongoing series of expeditions to China, first exploring remote areas of the Gobi in Inner Mongolia and discovering a herd of more than 20 dinosaurs that had died in their tracks. In 2012, he reported the discovery of *Pegomastax*, a bizarre, cat-sized dinosaur with a parrotlike beak and sharp fangs.

16.4 HOW IS THE AGE OF ROCKS AND FOSSILS MEASURED?

FIGURE 16.7 {Animated} Half-life.

FIGURE IT OUT: How much of any radioisotope remains after two of its half-lives have passed?

Answer: 25 percent

A Long ago, ^{14}C and ^{12}C were incorporated into the tissues of a nautilus. The carbon atoms were part of organic molecules in the animal's food. ^{12}C is stable and ^{14}C decays, but the proportion of the two isotopes in the nautilus's tissues remained the same. Why? The nautilus continued to gain both types of carbon atoms in the same proportions from its food.

B The nautilus stopped eating when it died, so its body stopped gaining carbon. The ^{12}C atoms in its tissues were stable, but the ^{14}C atoms (represented as red dots) were decaying into nitrogen atoms. Thus, over time, the amount of ^{14}C decreased relative to the amount of ^{12}C. After 5,730 years, half of the ^{14}C had decayed; after another 5,730 years, half of what was left had decayed, and so on.

C Fossil hunters discover the fossil and measure its content of ^{14}C and ^{12}C. They use the ratio of these isotopes to calculate how many half-lives passed since the organism died. For example, if its ^{14}C to ^{12}C ratio is one-eighth of the ratio in living organisms, then three half-lives $(\frac{1}{2})^3$ must have passed since it died. Three half-lives of ^{14}C is 17,190 years.

FIGURE 16.8 {Animated} Example of how radiometric dating is used to find the age of a carbon-containing fossil. Carbon 14 (^{14}C) is a radioisotope of carbon that decays into nitrogen. It forms in the atmosphere and combines with oxygen to become CO_2, which enters food chains by way of photosynthesis.

Remember from Section 2.1 that a radioisotope is a form of an element with an unstable nucleus. Atoms of a radioisotope become atoms of other elements—daughter elements—as their nucleus disintegrates. This radioactive decay is not influenced by temperature, pressure, chemical bonding state, or moisture; it is influenced only by time. Thus, like the ticking of a perfect clock, each type of radioisotope decays at a constant rate. The time it takes for half of the atoms in a sample of radioisotope to decay is called a **half-life** (**FIGURE 16.7**).

Half-life is a characteristic of each radioisotope. For example, radioactive uranium 238 decays into thorium 234, which decays into something else, and so on until it becomes lead 206. The half-life of the decay of uranium 238 to lead 206 is 4.5 billion years.

The predictability of radioactive decay can be used to find the age of a volcanic rock (the date it solidified). Rock deep inside Earth is hot and molten, so atoms swirl and mix in it. Rock that reaches the surface cools and hardens. As the rock cools, minerals crystallize in it. Each kind of mineral has a characteristic structure and composition. For example, the mineral zircon (*left*) consists mainly of ordered arrays of zirconium silicate molecules ($ZrSiO_4$). Some of the molecules in a newly formed zircon crystal have uranium atoms substituted for zirconium atoms, but never lead atoms. However, uranium decays into lead at a predictable rate. Thus, over time, uranium atoms disappear from a zircon crystal, and lead atoms accumulate in it. The ratio of uranium atoms to lead atoms in a zircon crystal can be measured precisely. That ratio can be used to calculate how long ago the crystal formed (its age).

zircon

We have just described **radiometric dating**, a method that can reveal the age of a material by measuring its content of a radioisotope and daughter elements. The oldest known terrestrial rock, a tiny zircon crystal from the Jack Hills in Western Australia, is 4.404 billion years old.

Recent fossils that still contain carbon can be dated by measuring their carbon 14 content (**FIGURE 16.8**). Most of the ^{14}C in a fossil will have decayed after about 60,000 years. The age of fossils older than that can be estimated by dating volcanic rocks in lava flows above and below the fossil-containing layer of sedimentary rock.

FINDING A MISSING LINK

The discovery of intermediate forms of cetaceans (an order of animals that includes whales, dolphins, and porpoises) provides an example of how scientists use fossil finds and radiometric dating to piece together evolutionary history. For some time, evolutionary biologists predicted that the

CREDITS: (7) © Cengage Learning; (8A) © PhotoDisc/Getty Images; (in text) Courtesy of Stan Celestian/Glendale Community College Earth Science Image Archive; (8B, C) © Cengage Learning 2015.

ancestors of modern cetaceans walked on land, then took up life in the water. Evidence in support of this line of thinking includes a set of distinctive features of the skull and lower jaw that cetaceans share with some kinds of ancient carnivorous land animals. DNA sequence comparisons indicate that the ancient land animals were probably artiodactyls, hooved mammals with an even number of toes (two or four) on each foot (**FIGURE 16.9A**). Modern representatives of the artiodactyl lineage include camels, hippopotamuses, pigs, deer, sheep, and cows.

Until recently, we had no fossils demonstrating gradual changes in skeletal features that accompanied a transition of whale lineages from terrestrial to aquatic life. Researchers knew there were intermediate forms because they had found a representative fossil skull of an ancient whalelike animal, but without a complete skeleton the rest of the story remained speculative.

Then, in 2000, Philip Gingerich and his colleagues unearthed complete skeletons of two ancient whales: a fossil *Rodhocetus kasrani* excavated from a 47-million-year-old rock formation in Pakistan, and a fossil *Dorudon atrox*, from 37-million-year-old rock in Egypt (**FIGURE 16.9B,C**). Both fossil skeletons had whalelike skull bones, as well as intact ankle bones. The ankle bones of both fossils have distinctive features in common with those of extinct and modern artiodactyls. Modern cetaceans do not have even a remnant of an ankle bone (**FIGURE 16.9D**).

Rodhocetus and *Dorudon* were not direct ancestors of modern whales, but their telltale ankle bones mean they are long-lost relatives. Both whales were offshoots of the ancient artiodactyl-to-modern-whale lineage as it transitioned from life on land to life in water. The proportions of limbs, skull, neck, and thorax indicate *Rodhocetus* swam with its feet, not its tail. Like modern whales, the 5-meter (16-foot) *Dorudon* was clearly a fully aquatic tail-swimmer: The entire hindlimb was only about 12 centimeters (5 inches) long, much too small to have supported the animal's tremendous body out of water.

half-life Characteristic time it takes for half of a quantity of a radioisotope to decay.
radiometric dating Method of estimating the age of a rock or fossil by measuring the content and proportions of a radioisotope and its daughter elements.

TAKE-HOME MESSAGE 16.4

The predictability of radioisotope decay can be used to estimate the age of rock layers and fossils in them.

Radiometric dating helps evolutionary biologists retrace changes in ancient lineages.

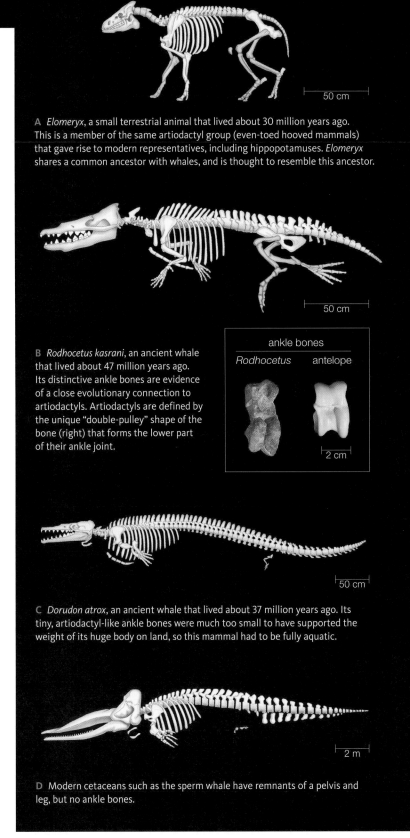

A *Elomeryx*, a small terrestrial animal that lived about 30 million years ago. This is a member of the same artiodactyl group (even-toed hooved mammals) that gave rise to modern representatives, including hippopotamuses. *Elomeryx* shares a common ancestor with whales, and is thought to resemble this ancestor.

B *Rodhocetus kasrani*, an ancient whale that lived about 47 million years ago. Its distinctive ankle bones are evidence of a close evolutionary connection to artiodactyls. Artiodactyls are defined by the unique "double-pulley" shape of the bone (right) that forms the lower part of their ankle joint.

ankle bones
Rodhocetus   antelope

C *Dorudon atrox*, an ancient whale that lived about 37 million years ago. Its tiny, artiodactyl-like ankle bones were much too small to have supported the weight of its huge body on land, so this mammal had to be fully aquatic.

D Modern cetaceans such as the sperm whale have remnants of a pelvis and leg, but no ankle bones.

FIGURE 16.9 Ancient relatives of whales. The ancestor of whales and other cetaceans was an artiodactyl that walked on land. The lineage transitioned from life on land to life in water over millions of years, and as it did, the animals' limb bones became smaller and smaller. Comparable hindlimb bones are highlighted in blue.

Wind, water, and other forces continuously sculpt Earth's surface, but they are only part of a much bigger picture of geological change. All continents that exist today were once part of a supercontinent—**Pangea**—that split into fragments and drifted apart.

The idea that continents move around, originally called continental drift, was proposed in the early 1900s to explain why the Atlantic coasts of South America and Africa seem to "fit" like jigsaw puzzle pieces, and why the same types of fossils occur in identical rock formations on both sides of the Atlantic Ocean. It also explained why the magnetic poles of gigantic rock formations point in different directions on different continents. Rock forms when molten lava solidifies on Earth's surface. Some iron-rich minerals become magnetic as they solidify, and their magnetic poles align with Earth's poles when they do. If the continents never moved, then all of these ancient rocky magnets should be aligned north-to-south, like compass needles. Indeed, the magnetic poles of each rock formation are aligned—but they do not always point north-to-south. Either Earth's magnetic poles veer dramatically from their north–south axis, or the continents must wander.

The concept of moving continents was initially greeted with skepticism because there was no known mechanism capable of causing such movements. Then, in the late 1950s, deep-sea explorers found immense ridges and trenches stretching thousands of kilometers across the seafloor (**FIGURE 16.10**). The discovery led to the **plate tectonics theory**, which explains how continents move: Earth's outer layer of rock is cracked into immense plates, like a huge cracked eggshell. Molten rock streaming from an undersea ridge ❶ or continental rift at one edge of a plate pushes old rock at the opposite edge into a trench ❷. The movement is like that of a colossal conveyor belt that transports continents on top of it to new locations. The plates move no more than 10 centimeters (4 inches) a year—about half as fast as your toenails grow—but it is enough to carry a continent all the way around the world after 40 million years or so (**FIGURE 16.11**).

The San Andreas Fault, which extends 800 miles through California, marks the boundary between two tectonic plates.

FIGURE 16.10 **Plate tectonics.** Huge pieces of Earth's outer layer of rock slowly drift apart and collide. As these plates move, they convey continents around the globe.

❶ At oceanic ridges, plumes of molten rock welling up from Earth's interior drive the movement of tectonic plates. New crust spreads outward as it forms on the surface, forcing adjacent tectonic plates away from the ridge and into trenches elsewhere.

❷ At trenches, the advancing edge of one plate plows under an adjacent plate and buckles it.

❸ Faults are ruptures in Earth's crust where plates meet. The diagram shows a rift fault, in which plates move apart. The photo above shows a strike-slip fault, in which two abutting plates slip against one another in opposite directions.

❹ Plumes of molten rock rupture a tectonic plate at what are called "hot spots." The Hawaiian Islands have been forming from molten rock that continues to erupt from a hot spot under the Pacific Plate. This and other tectonic plates are shown in Appendix V.

❸ fault	❷ trench	❶ ridge	❹ hot spot	trench

600 mya

430 mya

Gondwana

340 mya

240 mya

Pangea

200 mya

150 mya

65 mya

present

FIGURE 16.11 A series of reconstructions of the drifting continents. mya: million years ago.

Evidence of tectonic movement is all around us, in faults ❸ and other geological features of our landscapes. For example, volcanic island chains (archipelagos) form as a plate moves across an undersea hot spot. These hot spots are places where a plume of molten rock wells up from deep inside Earth and ruptures a tectonic plate ❹.

The fossil record also provides evidence in support of plate tectonics. Consider an unusual rock formation that exists in a huge belt across Africa. The sequence of rock layers in this formation is so complex that it is quite unlikely to have formed more than once, but identical sequences of layers also occur in huge belts that span India, South America, Madagascar, Australia, and Antarctica. Across all of these continents, the layers are the same ages. They also hold fossils found nowhere else, including imprints of the seed fern *Glossopteris* (pictured in **FIGURE 16.6C**). The most probable explanation for these observations is that the layered rock formed in one long belt on a single continent, which later broke up.

We now know that at least five times since Earth's outer layer of rock solidified 4.55 billion years ago, supercontinents formed and then split up again. One called **Gondwana** formed about 500 million years ago. Over the next 230 million years, this supercontinent wandered across the South Pole, then drifted north until it merged with other landmasses to form Pangea (**FIGURE 16.11**). Most of the landmasses currently in the Southern Hemisphere as well as India and Arabia were once part of Gondwana. Many modern species, including the birds pictured in **FIGURE 16.1**, live only in these places.

As you will see in later chapters, the changes brought on by plate tectonics have had a profound impact on life. Colliding continents have physically separated organisms living in oceans, and brought together those that had been living apart on land. As continents broke up, they separated organisms living on land, and brought together ones that had been living in separate oceans. Such changes have been a major driving force of evolution, a topic that we return to in the next chapter.

Gondwana Supercontinent that existed before Pangea, more than 500 million years ago.
Pangea Supercontinent that formed about 270 million years ago.
plate tectonics theory Theory that Earth's outer layer of rock is cracked into plates, the slow movement of which rafts continents to new locations over geologic time.

TAKE-HOME MESSAGE 16.5
Over geologic time, movements of Earth's crust have caused dramatic changes in continents and oceans. These changes profoundly influenced the course of life's evolution.

Eon	Era	Period	Epoch	mya	Major Geologic and Biological Events
Phanerozoic	Cenozoic	Quaternary	Recent	0.01	Modern humans evolve. Major extinction event is now under way.
			Pleistocene	2.5	
		Neogene	Pliocene	5.3	Tropics, subtropics extend poleward. Climate cools; dry woodlands and grasslands emerge. Adaptive radiations of mammals, insects, birds.
			Miocene	23.0	
		Paleogene	Oligocene	33.9	
			Eocene	56.0	
			Paleocene	66.0 ◄	Major extinction event
	Mesozoic	Cretaceous	Upper		Flowering plants diversify; sharks evolve. All dinosaurs and many marine organisms disappear at the end of this epoch.
				100.5	
			Lower		Climate very warm. Dinosaurs continue to dominate. Important modern insect groups appear (bees, butterflies, termites, ants, and herbivorous insects including aphids and grasshoppers). Flowering plants originate and become dominant land plants.
				145.0	
		Jurassic			Age of dinosaurs. Lush vegetation; abundant gymnosperms and ferns. Birds appear. Pangea breaks up.
				201.3 ◄	Major extinction event
		Triassic			Recovery from the major extinction at end of Permian. Many new groups appear, including turtles, dinosaurs, pterosaurs, and mammals.
				252 ◄	Major extinction event
	Paleozoic	Permian			Supercontinent Pangea and world ocean form. Adaptive radiation of conifers. Cycads and ginkgos appear. Relatively dry climate leads to drought-adapted gymnosperms and insects such as beetles and flies.
				299	
		Carboniferous			High atmospheric oxygen level fosters giant arthropods. Spore-releasing plants dominate. Age of great lycophyte trees; vast coal forests form. Ears evolve in amphibians; penises evolve in early reptiles (vaginas evolve later, in mammals only).
				359 ◄	Major extinction event
		Devonian			Land tetrapods appear. Explosion of plant diversity leads to tree forms, forests, and many new plant groups including lycophytes, ferns with complex leaves, seed plants.
				419	
		Silurian			Radiations of marine invertebrates. First appearances of land fungi, vascular plants, bony fishes, and perhaps terrestrial animals (millipedes, spiders).
				443 ◄	Major extinction event
		Ordovician			Major period for first appearances. The first land plants, fishes, and reef-forming corals appear. Gondwana moves toward the South Pole and becomes frigid.
				485	
		Cambrian			Earth thaws. Explosion of animal diversity. Most major groups of animals appear (in the oceans). Trilobites and shelled organisms evolve.
				541	
Proterozoic					Oxygen accumulates in atmosphere. Origin of aerobic metabolism. Origin of eukaryotic cells, then protists, fungi, plants, animals. Evidence that Earth mostly freezes over in a series of global ice ages between 750 and 600 mya.
				2,500	
Archaean and earlier					3,800–2,500 mya. Origin of bacteria and archaea.
					4,600–3,800 mya. Origin of Earth's crust, first atmosphere, first seas. Chemical, molecular evolution leads to origin of life (from protocells to anaerobic single cells).

FIGURE 16.12 {**Animated**} The geologic time scale (above) correlated with sedimentary rock exposed by erosion in the Grand Canyon (opposite). Orange triangles mark times of great mass extinctions. "First appearance" refers to appearance in the fossil record, not necessarily the first appearance on Earth. mya: million years ago. Dates are from the International Commission on Stratigraphy, 2013.

Similar sequences of sedimentary rock layers occur around the world. Transitions between the layers mark boundaries between great intervals of time in the **geologic time scale**, which is a chronology of Earth's history (**FIGURE 16.12**). Each layer's composition offers clues about conditions on

Earth during the time the layer was deposited. Fossils in the layers are a record of life during that period of time.

TAKE-HOME MESSAGE 16.6

The geologic time scale correlates geological and evolutionary events of the ancient past.

geologic time scale Chronology of Earth's history.

CREDITS: (12) art, © Cengage Learning; photo, © Michael Pancier.

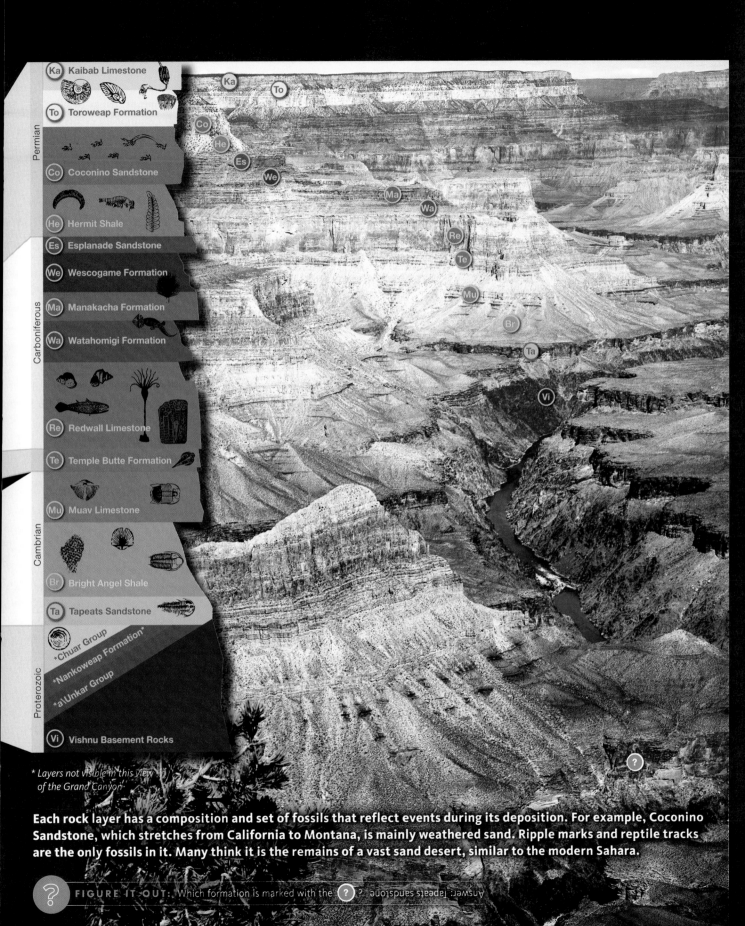

Ka Kaibab Limestone

To Toroweap Formation

Permian

Co Coconino Sandstone

He Hermit Shale

Es Esplanade Sandstone

We Wescogame Formation

Ma Manakacha Formation

Carboniferous

Wa Watahomigi Formation

Re Redwall Limestone

Te Temple Butte Formation

Mu Muav Limestone

Cambrian

Br Bright Angel Shale

Ta Tapeats Sandstone

Ca *Chuar Group*

Nankoweap Formation

a\Unkar Group

Proterozoic

Vi Vishnu Basement Rocks

* Layers not visible in this view of the Grand Canyon

Each rock layer has a composition and set of fossils that reflect events during its deposition. For example, Coconino Sandstone, which stretches from California to Montana, is mainly weathered sand. Ripple marks and reptile tracks are the only fossils in it. Many think it is the remains of a vast sand desert, similar to the modern Sahara.

FIGURE IT OUT: Which formation is marked with the **?** ? Answer: Tapeats sandstone

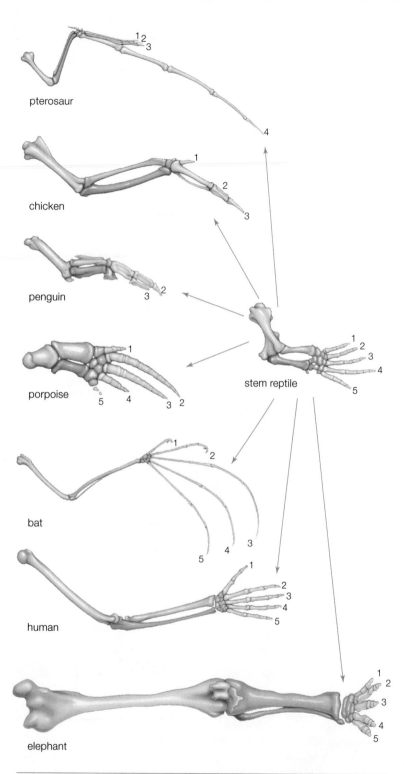

pterosaur

chicken

penguin

porpoise

stem reptile

bat

human

elephant

FIGURE 16.13 {**Animated**} Morphological divergence among vertebrate forelimbs, starting with the bones of an ancient stem reptile. The number and position of many skeletal elements were preserved when these diverse forms evolved; notice the bones of the forearms. Certain bones were lost over time in some of the lineages (compare the digits numbered 1 through 5). Drawings are not to scale.

To biologists, remember, evolution means change in a line of descent. How do they reconstruct evolutionary events that occurred in the ancient past? Evolutionary biologists are a bit like detectives, using clues to piece together a history that they did not witness in person. Fossils provide some clues. The body form and function of organisms that are alive today provide others.

MORPHOLOGICAL DIVERGENCE

Body parts that appear similar in separate lineages because they evolved in a common ancestor are called **homologous structures** (*hom–* means "the same"). Homologous structures may be used for different purposes in different groups, but the very same genes direct their development.

A body part that outwardly appears very different in separate lineages may be homologous in underlying form. Vertebrate forelimbs, for example, vary in size, shape, and function. However, they clearly are alike in the structure and positioning of bony elements, and in their internal patterns of nerves, blood vessels, and muscles.

As you will see in the next chapter, populations that are not interbreeding diverge genetically, and in time these divergences give rise to changes in body form. Change from the body form of a common ancestor is an evolutionary pattern called **morphological divergence**. Consider the limb bones of modern vertebrate animals. Fossil evidence suggests that many vertebrates are descended from a family of ancient "stem reptiles" that crouched low to the ground on five-toed limbs. Descendants of this ancestral group diversified over millions of years, and eventually gave rise to modern reptiles, birds, and mammals. A few lineages that had become adapted to walking on land even returned to life in the seas. During this time, the limbs became adapted for many different purposes (**FIGURE 16.13**). They became modified for flight in extinct reptiles called pterosaurs and in bats and most birds. In penguins and porpoises, the limbs are now flippers useful for swimming. In humans, five-toed forelimbs became arms and hands with four fingers and an opposable thumb. Among elephants, the limbs are now strong and pillarlike, capable of supporting a great deal of weight. Limbs degenerated to nubs in pythons and boa constrictors, and they disappeared entirely in other snakes.

MORPHOLOGICAL CONVERGENCE

Body parts that appear similar in different species are not always homologous; they sometimes evolve independently in lineages subject to the same environmental pressures. The independent evolution of similar body parts in different lineages is **morphological convergence**. Structures that are similar as a result of morphological convergence are

CREDIT: (13) From Starr/Evers/Starr, Biology Today and Tomorrow with Physiology, 4E. © 2013 Cengage Learning.

called **analogous structures**. Analogous structures look alike but did not evolve in a shared ancestor; they evolved independently after the lineages diverged.

For example, bird, bat, and insect wings all perform the same function, which is flight. However, several clues tell us that the wing surfaces are not homologous. All of the wings are adapted to the same physical constraints that govern flight, but each is adapted in a different way. In the case of birds and bats, the limbs themselves are homologous, but the adaptations that make those limbs useful for flight differ. The surface of a bat wing is a thin, membranous extension of the animal's skin. By contrast, the surface of a bird wing is a sweep of feathers, which are specialized structures derived from skin. Insect wings differ even more. An insect wing forms as a saclike extension of the body wall. Except at forked veins, the sac flattens and fuses into a thin membrane. The sturdy, chitin-reinforced veins structurally support the wing. Unique adaptations for flight are evidence that wing surfaces of birds, bats, and insects are analogous structures that evolved after the ancestors of these modern groups diverged (**FIGURE 16.14**).

As another example of morphological convergence, the similar external structures of American cacti and African euphorbias (see **FIGURE 16.2**) are adaptations to similarly harsh desert environments where rain is scarce. Distinctive accordion-like pleats allow the plant body to swell with water when rain does come. Water stored in the plants' tissues allows them to survive long dry periods. As the stored water is used, the plant body shrinks, and the folded pleats provide it with some shade in an environment that typically has none. Despite these similarities, a closer look reveals many differences that indicate the two types of plants are not closely related. For example, cactus spines have a simple fibrous structure; they are modified leaves that arise from dimples on the plant's surface. Euphorbia spines project smoothly from the plant surface, and they are not modified leaves: In many species the spines are actually dried flower stalks (*below*).

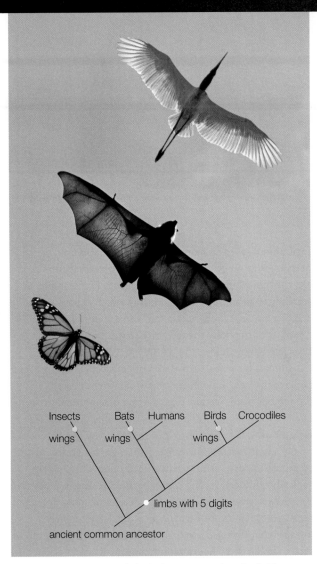

FIGURE 16.14 Morphological convergence in animals. The surfaces of an insect wing, a bat wing, and a bird wing are analogous structures. The diagram shows how the evolution of wings (yellow dots) occurred independently in the three separate lineages that led to bats, birds, and insects. You will read more about diagrams that show evolutionary relationships in Section 17.12.

---

analogous structures Similar body structures that evolved separately in different lineages.
homologous structures Body structures that are similar in different lineages because they evolved in a common ancestor.
morphological convergence Evolutionary pattern in which similar body parts evolve separately in different lineages.
morphological divergence Evolutionary pattern in which a body part of an ancestor changes in its descendants.

TAKE-HOME MESSAGE 16.7

Body parts are often modified differently in different lines of descent.

Some body parts that appear alike evolved independently in different lineages.

CREDITS: (in text) © James C. Gaither, www.flickr.com/photos/jim-sf; (14) top, © Panoramic Images/Getty Images; middle, © Taro Taylor, www.flickr.com/photos/tjt195; bottom, © Alberto J. Espiñeira Francés - Alesfra/Getty Images; art, © Cengage Learning.

16.8 HOW DO SIMILARITIES IN DNA AND PROTEIN REFLECT EVOLUTION?

FIGURE 16.15 Visual comparison of vertebrate embryos. All vertebrates go through an embryonic stage in which they have four limb buds, a tail, and divisions called somites along their back. From *left* to *right*: human, mouse, bat, chicken, alligator.

Evolution also leaves clues in patterns of embryonic development: In general, the more closely related animals are, the more similar is their development. For example, all vertebrates go through a stage during which a developing embryo has four limb buds, a tail, and a series of somites— divisions of the body that give rise to the backbone and associated skin and muscle (**FIGURE 16.15**).

Animals have similar patterns of embryonic development because the very same master genes direct the process. Remember from Section 10.2 that the development of an embryo into the body of a plant or animal is orchestrated by layer after layer of master gene expression. The failure of any single master gene to participate in this symphony of expression can result in a drastically altered body plan, typically with devastating consequences. Because a mutation in a master gene typically unravels development completely, these genes tend to be highly conserved. Even among lineages that diverged a very long time ago, such genes often retain similar sequences and functions.

Consider homeotic genes called *Hox*. Like other homeotic genes, *Hox* gene expression helps sculpt details of the body's form during embryonic development. Vertebrate animals have multiple sets of the same ten *Hox* genes that

FIGURE 16.16 How differences in body form arise from differences in master gene expression. Expression of the *Hoxc6* gene is indicated by purple stain in two vertebrate embryos, chicken (*left*) and garter snake (*right*). Expression of this gene causes a vertebra to develop ribs as part of the back. Chickens have 7 vertebrae in their back and 14 to 17 vertebrae in their neck; snakes have upwards of 450 back vertebrae and essentially no neck.

occur in insects and other arthropods. You have already read about one of these genes, *antennapedia*, which determines the identity of the thorax (the body part with legs) in fruit flies. One vertebrate version of *antennapedia* is called *Hoxc6*,

FIGURE 16.17 Example of a protein comparison. Here, part of the amino acid sequence of mitochondrial cytochrome *b* from 20 species is aligned. This protein is a crucial component of mitochondrial electron transfer chains. The honeycreeper sequence is identical in ten species of honeycreeper; amino acids that differ in the other species are shown in red. Dashes are gaps in the alignment.

 FIGURE IT OUT: Based on this comparison, which species is the most closely related to the honeycreepers?   Answer: The song sparrow

```
honeycreepers (10) . . . CRDVQFGWLIRNLHANGASFFFICIYLHIGRGIYYGSYLNK--ETWNIGVILLLTLMATAFVGYVLPWGQMSFWG . . .
      song sparrow . . . CRDVQFGWLIRNLHANGASFFFICIYLHIGRGIYYGSYLNK--ETWNVGIIILLLALMATAFVGYVLPWGQMSFWG . . .
  Gough Island finch . . . CRDVQFGWLIRNIHANGASFFFICIYLHIGRGIYYGSYLYK--ETWNVGVILLLTLMATAFVGYVLPWGQMSFWG . . .
        deer mouse . . . CRDVNYGWLIRYMHANGASMFFICLFLHVGRGMYYGSYTFT--ETWNIGIVLLFAVMATAFMGYVLPWGQMSFWG . . .
  Asiatic black bear . . . CRDVHYGWIIRYMHANGASMFFICLFMHVGRGLYYGSYLLS--ETWNIGIILLFTVMATAFMGYVLPWGQMSFWG . . .
     bogue (a fish) . . . CRDVNYGWLIRNLHANGASFFFICIYLHIGRGLYYGSYLYK--ETWNIGVVLLLLVMGTAFVGYVLPWGQMSFWG . . .
            human . . . TRDVNYGWIIRYLHANGASMFFICLFLHIGRGLYYGSFLYS--ETWNIGIILLLATMATAFMGYVLPWGQMSFWG . . .
thale cress (a plant) . . . MRDVEGGWLLRYMHANGASMFLIVVYLHIFRGLYHASYSSPREFVWCLGVVIFLLMIVTAFIGYVLPWGQMSFWG . . .
       baboon louse . . . ETDVMNGWMVRSIHANGASWFFIMLYSHIFRGLWVSSFTQP--LVWLSGVIILFLSMATAFLGYVLPWGQMSFWG . . .
       baker's yeast . . . MRDVHNGYILRYLHANGASFFFMVMFMHMAKGLYYGSYRSPRVTLWNVGVIIFTLTIATAFLGYCCVYGQMSHWG . . .
```

CREDITS: (15) From left: © Lennart Nilsson/Bonnierforlagen AB; Courtesy of Anna Bigas, IDIBELL-Institut de Recerca Oncologica, Spain; From "Embryonic staging system for the short-tailed fruit bat, *Carollia perspicillata*, a model organism for the mammalian order Chiroptera, based upon timed pregnancies in captive-bred animals" C.J. Cretekos et al., *Developmental Dynamics* Volume 233, Issue 3, July 2005, Pages: 721–738. Reprinted with permission of Wiley-Liss, Inc. a subsidiary of John Wiley & Sons, Inc.; Courtesy of Prof. Dr. G. Elisabeth Pollerberg, Institut für Zoologie, Universität Heidelberg, Germany; USGS; (16) Courtesy of Ann C. Burke, Wesleyan University; (17) From Starr/Evers/Starr, Biology Today and Tomorrow with Physiology, 4E. © 2013 Cengage Learning.

and it determines the identity of the back (as opposed to the neck or tail). Expression of the *Hoxc6* gene causes ribs to develop on a vertebra. Vertebrae of the neck and tail normally develop with no *Hoxc6* expression, and no ribs (FIGURE 16.16).

Given that the very same genes direct development in all of the vertebrate lineages, how do the adult forms end up so different? Part of the answer is that there are differences in the onset, rate, or completion of early steps in development brought about by variations in master gene expression. The variation has arisen at least in part as a result of gene duplications followed by mutation, the same way that multiple globin genes evolved in primates (Section 14.4).

Genes that are not conserved are the basis of major phenotypic differences that define species. Over time, inevitable mutations change the DNA sequence of a lineage's genome. The more recently two lineages diverged, the less time there has been for unique mutations to accumulate in the DNA of each one. That is why the genomes of closely related species tend to be more similar than those of distantly related ones—a general rule that can be used to estimate relative times of divergence. Two species with very few similar genes probably have not shared an ancestor for a long time—long enough for many mutations to have accumulated in the DNA of their separate lineages. Consider that about 88 percent of the mouse genome sequence is identical with the human genome, as is 73 percent of the zebrafish genome, 47 percent of the fruit fly genome, and 25 percent of the rice genome.

Getting useful information from comparing DNA requires a lot more data than comparing proteins. This is because coincidental homologies are statistically more likely to occur with DNA comparisons—there are only four nucleotides in DNA versus twenty amino acids in proteins. Thus, proteins are more commonly compared. By comparing the amino acid sequence of a protein among several species, the number of amino acid differences can be used as a measure of relative relatedness (FIGURE 16.17).

TAKE-HOME MESSAGE 16.8

Similarities in patterns of animal development occur because the same genes direct the process. Similar developmental patterns—and shared genes—are evidence of common ancestry, which can be ancient.

Mutations change the nucleotide sequence of each lineage's DNA over time. There are generally fewer differences between the DNA of more closely related lineages.

Similar genes give rise to similar proteins. Fewer differences occur among the proteins of more closely related lineages.

Application: Exploration

FIGURE 16.18 The K–Pg boundary sequence, an unusual, worldwide sedimentary rock formation that formed 66 million years ago.

WHAT KILLED THE DINOSAURS? Most scientists now think that the dinosaurs perished in the aftermath of a catastrophic meteorite impact. No human witnesses were around at the time, so how do they know what happened? The event is marked by an unusual, worldwide formation of sedimentary rock (FIGURE 16.18). There are plenty of dinosaur fossils below this formation, which is called the K–Pg boundary sequence (formerly known as the K–T boundary). Above it, there are none, anywhere. The rock consists of an unusual clay rich in iridium, an element much

 more abundant in asteroids than in Earth's crust. It also contains shocked quartz (*left*) and small glass spheres called tektites, minerals that form when quartz or sand undergoes a sudden, violent application of extreme pressure. The only processes on Earth that produce these minerals are atomic bomb explosions and meteorite impacts.

Geologists concluded that the K–Pg boundary layer must have originated with extraterrestrial material, and began looking for evidence of a meteorite that hit Earth 66 million years ago—one big enough to cover the entire planet with its debris. Twenty years later, they found it: an impact crater the size of Ireland off the coast of the Yucatán Peninsula. To make a crater this big, a meteorite 20 km (12 miles) wide would have slammed into Earth with the force of 100 trillion tons of dynamite—enough to cause an ecological disaster of sufficient scale to wipe out almost all life on Earth.

Summary

SECTION 16.1 Expeditions by nineteenth-century explorers yielded increasingly detailed observations of nature. Geology, **biogeography**, and **comparative morphology** of organisms and their **fossils** led to new ways of thinking about the natural world.

SECTION 16.2 Prevailing belief systems may influence interpretation of the underlying cause of a natural event. Nineteenth-century naturalists tried to reconcile traditional belief systems with physical evidence of **evolution**, or change in a **lineage** over time.

Humans select desirable traits in animals by selective breeding. Charles Darwin and Alfred Wallace independently came up with a theory of how environments also select traits, stated here in modern terms: A population tends to grow until it exhausts environmental resources. As that happens, competition for those resources intensifies among the population's members. Individuals with forms of shared, heritable traits that give them an advantage in this competition tend to produce more offspring. Thus, **adaptive traits** (**adaptations**) that impart greater **fitness** to an individual become more common in a population over generations. The process in which environmental pressures result in the differential survival and reproduction of individuals of a population is called **natural selection**. It is one of the processes that drives evolution.

SECTION 16.3 Fossils are typically found in stacked layers of sedimentary rock. Younger fossils usually occur in layers deposited more recently, on top of older fossils in older layers. Fossils are relatively scarce, so the fossil record will always be incomplete.

SECTION 16.4 A radioisotope's characteristic **half-life** can be used to determine the age of rocks and fossils. This technique, **radiometric dating**, helps us understand the ancient history of many lineages.

SECTION 16.5 According to the **plate tectonics theory**, Earth's crust is cracked into giant plates that carry landmasses to new positions as they move. Earth's landmasses have periodically converged as supercontinents such as **Gondwana** and **Pangea**.

SECTION 16.6 Transitions in the fossil record are the boundaries of great intervals of the **geologic time scale**, a chronology of Earth's history that correlates geologic and evolutionary events.

SECTION 16.7 Comparative morphology is one way to study evolutionary connections among lineages. **Homologous structures** are similar body parts that, by **morphological divergence**, became modified differently in different lineages. Such parts are evidence of a common ancestor. **Analogous structures** are body parts that look alike in different lineages but did not evolve in a common ancestor. By the process of **morphological convergence**, they evolved separately after the lineages diverged.

SECTION 16.8 We can discover and clarify evolutionary relationships through comparisons of DNA and protein sequences, because lineages that diverged recently tend to share more sequences than ones that diverged long ago. Master genes that affect development tend to be highly conserved, so similarities in patterns of embryonic development reflect shared ancestry that can be evolutionarily ancient.

SECTION 16.9 A mass extinction 66 million years ago may have been caused by an asteroid impact that left traces in a worldwide sedimentary rock formation.

Self-Quiz   Answers in Appendix VII

1. The number of species on an island usually depends on the size of the island and its distance from a mainland. This statement would most likely be made by _____ .
   a. an explorer   c. a geologist
   b. a biogeographer   d. a philosopher

2. The bones of a bird's wing are similar to the bones in a bat's wing. This observation is an example of _____ .
   a. uniformity   c. comparative morphology
   b. evolution   d. a lineage

3. Evolution _____ .
   a. is natural selection
   b. is change in a line of descent
   c. can occur by natural selection
   d. b and c are correct

4. A trait is adaptive if it _____ .
   a. arises by mutation   c. is passed to offspring
   b. increases fitness   d. occurs in fossils

5. In which type of rock are you more likely to find a fossil?
   a. basalt, a dark, fine-grained volcanic rock
   b. limestone, composed of calcium carbonate sediments
   c. slate, a volcanically melted and cooled shale
   d. granite, which forms by crystallization of molten rock below Earth's surface

6. If the half-life of a radioisotope is 20,000 years, then a sample in which three-quarters of that radioisotope has decayed is _____ years old.
   a. 15,000   b. 26,667   c. 30,000   d. 40,000

7. Did Pangea or Gondwana form first?

8. Forces that cause geologic change include _____ (select all that are correct).
   a. erosion   d. tectonic plate movement
   b. natural selection   e. wind
   c. volcanic activity   f. meteorite impacts

9. Through _____ , a body part of an ancestor is modified differently in different lines of descent.

Data Analysis Activities

Discovery of Iridium in the K–Pg Boundary Layer In the late 1970s, geologist Walter Alvarez was investigating the composition of the K–Pg boundary sequence in different parts of the world. He asked his father, Nobel Prize–winning physicist Luis Alvarez, to help him analyze the elemental composition of the layer (*right*, Luis and Walter Alvarez with a section of the boundary sequence).

The Alvarezes and their colleagues tested the K–Pg boundary sequence in Italy and Denmark. They discovered that it contains a much higher iridium content than the surrounding rock layers. Some of their results are shown in **FIGURE 16.19**.

1. What was the iridium content of the K–Pg boundary sequence?
2. How much higher was the iridium content of the boundary layer than the sample taken 0.7 meter above the sequence?

Sample Depth	Average Abundance of Iridium (ppb)
+ 2.7 m	< 0.3
+ 1.2 m	< 0.3
+ 0.7 m	0.36
boundary layer	41.6
− 0.5 m	0.25
− 5.4 m	0.30

FIGURE 16.19 Abundance of iridium in and near the K–Pg boundary sequence in Stevns Klint, Denmark. Many rock samples taken from above, below, and at the boundary were tested for iridium content. Depths are given as meters above or below the boundary.

The iridium content of an average Earth rock is 0.4 parts per billion (ppb) of iridium. An average meteorite contains about 550 parts per billion of iridium.

---

10. Homologous structures among major groups of organisms may differ in _____ .
    a. size   b. shape   c. function   d. all of the above

11. By altering steps in the program by which embryos develop, a mutation in a _____ may lead to major differences in body form between related lineages.
    a. derived trait   c. homologous structure
    b. homeotic gene   d. all of the above

12. The dinosaurs died _____ million years ago.

13. All of the following data types can be used as evidence of shared ancestry except similarities in _____ .
    a. amino acid sequence   d. embryonic development
    b. DNA sequence   e. form due to convergence
    c. fossil morphology   f. all are appropriate

14. Match the terms with the most suitable description.
    ___ fitness
    ___ fossils
    ___ natural
        selection
    ___ half-life
    ___ homologous
        structures
    ___ analogous
        structures
    ___ lineage
    ___ sedimentary rock

    a. line of descent
    b. measured by relative genetic contribution to future generations
    c. human arm and bird wing
    d. evidence of ancient life
    e. characteristic of radioisotope
    f. insect wing and bird wing
    g. survival of the fittest
    h. good for finding fossils

Critical Thinking

1. Radiometric dating does not measure the age of an individual atom. It is a measure of the age of a quantity of atoms—a statistic. As with any statistical measure, its values may deviate around an average (see sampling error, Section 1.7). Imagine that one sample of rock is dated ten different ways. Nine of the tests yield an age close to 225,000 years. One test yields an age of 3.2 million years. Do the nine consistent results imply that the one that deviates is incorrect, or does the one odd result invalidate the nine that are consistent?

2. If you think of geologic time spans as minutes, life's history might be plotted on a clock such as the one shown *below*. According to this clock, the most recent epoch started in the last 0.1 second before noon. Where does that put you?

CREDITS: (19) left, © Lawrence Berkeley National Laboratory; right, © Cengage Learning; (in text) From Starr/Evers/ Starr, Biology Today and Tomorrow with Physiology, 4E. © 2013 Cengage Learning.

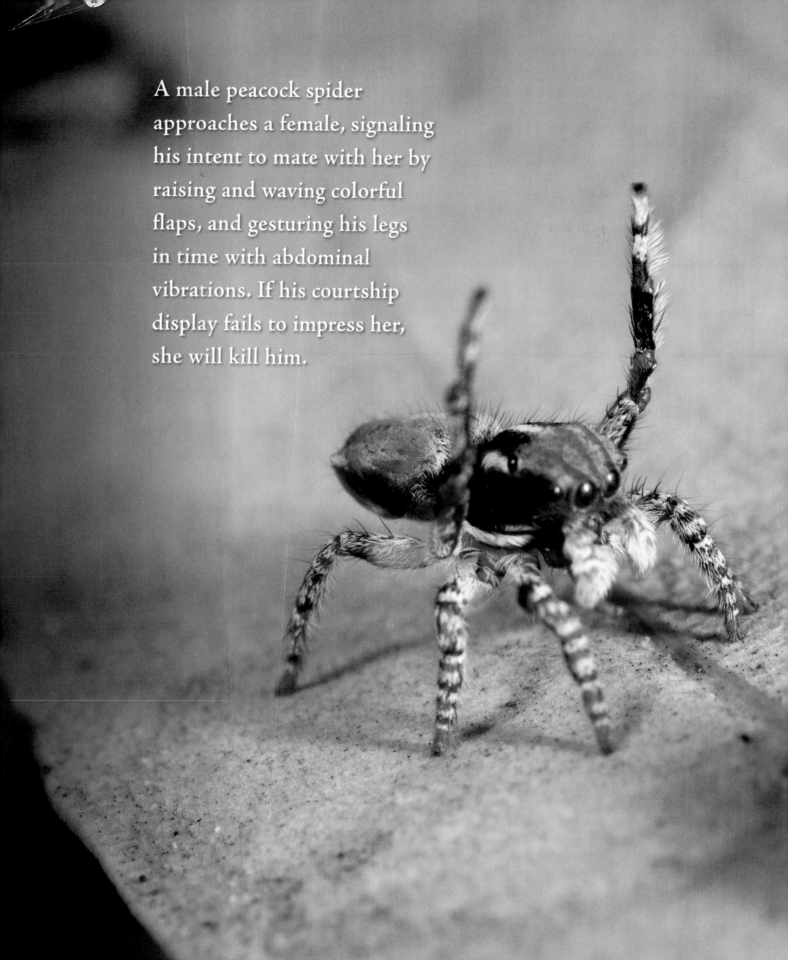

A male peacock spider approaches a female, signaling his intent to mate with her by raising and waving colorful flaps, and gesturing his legs in time with abdominal vibrations. If his courtship display fails to impress her, she will kill him.

17

PROCESSES OF EVOLUTION

Links to Earlier Concepts

A review of species (Section 1.4), mutations (8.5, 9.5), sexual reproduction (12.1, 12.2), inheritance (13.1, 13.2), traits (13.4–13.6, 14.1), and natural selection (16.2) will be helpful. This chapter also revisits populations (1.1), experiments (1.5), sampling error (1.7), homeotic genes (10.2), *BRCA* genes (10.6, 15.7), phenotype (13.1), polyploidy (14.5), genetic screening (14.6), transgenic plants (15.5), plate tectonics (16.5), and the geologic time scale (16.6).

KEY CONCEPTS

MICROEVOLUTION
Members of a population inherit different alleles, which are the basis of differences in phenotype. An allele may increase or decrease in frequency in a population, a change called microevolution.

PROCESSES OF MICROEVOLUTION
Natural selection can shift or maintain the range of variation in heritable traits. Change in allele frequency can occur by chance alone. Gene flow between populations keeps them similar.

HOW SPECIES ARISE
Speciation typically starts after gene flow ends. Microevolution leads to genetic divergences, which are reinforced as mechanisms evolve that prevent interbreeding.

MACROEVOLUTION
Macroevolutionary patterns include the origin of major groups, one species giving rise to many, two species evolving jointly, and mass extinctions.

PHYLOGENY
Understanding a group's evolutionary history can help us protect endangered species. It also helps us understand the origin and transmission of infectious diseases.

VARIATION IN SHARED TRAITS

Section 1.1 introduced a **population** as a group of interbreeding individuals of the same species in some specified area. The individuals of a population (and a species) share morphological, physiological, and behavioral traits because they have the same genes. Almost every shared trait varies a bit among members of a sexually reproducing species (**FIGURE 17.1**); this variation arises mainly because different individuals inherit different combinations of alleles (Sections 13.1 and 13.2).

Some traits occur in distinct forms, or morphs. A trait with only two forms is dimorphic (*di–* means two). The pea plants that Gregor Mendel studied are dimorphic for flower color—their flowers are either white or purple. In this case, dimorphic flower color arises from two alleles with a clear dominance relationship. Traits with more than two distinct forms are polymorphic (*poly–*, many). Human blood type, which is determined by the codominant *ABO* alleles, is an example (Section 13.4). The genetic basis of traits that vary continuously (Section 13.6) is often quite complex. Any of the genes that influence such traits may have multiple alleles.

In earlier chapters, you learned about the processes that introduce and maintain variation in traits among individuals of a species (**TABLE 17.1**). Mutation is the original source of new alleles. Other events shuffle alleles into different combinations, and what a shuffle that is! There are $10^{116,446,000}$ possible combinations of human alleles. Not even 10^{10} people are living today. Unless you have an identical twin, it is unlikely that another person with your precise genetic makeup has ever lived, or ever will.

AN EVOLUTIONARY VIEW OF MUTATIONS

Being the original source of new alleles, mutations are worth another look, this time in context of their impact on populations. We cannot predict when or in which individual a particular gene will mutate. We can, however, predict the average mutation rate of a species, which is the probability that a mutation will occur in a given interval. In the human species, that rate is about 2.2×10^{-9} mutations per base pair per year. In other words, what we define as the human genome sequence changes by about 70 nucleotides every decade.

Many mutations give rise to structural, functional, or behavioral alterations that reduce an individual's chances of surviving and reproducing. Even one biochemical change may be devastating. Consider collagen, a fibrous protein that structurally supports tissues that compose skin, bones, tendons, lungs, blood vessels, and other parts of the vertebrate body. If one of the genes for collagen mutates in a

---

TABLE 17.1

Sources of Variation in Traits Among Individuals of a Species

Genetic Event	Effect
Mutation	Source of new alleles
Crossing over at meiosis I	Introduces new combinations of alleles into chromosomes
Independent assortment at meiosis I	Mixes maternal and paternal chromosomes
Fertilization	Combines alleles from two parents
Changes in chromosome number or structure	Often dramatic changes in structure and function

---

way that changes the protein's structure, the entire body may be affected. A mutation such as this can change phenotype (Section 13.1) so drastically that it results in death, in which case it is called a **lethal mutation**.

A **neutral mutation** is one that has no effect on survival or reproduction. For instance, a mutation that results in your earlobes being attached to your head instead of swinging freely should not in itself stop you from surviving and reproducing as well as anybody else. So, natural selection does not affect the frequency of this particular mutation in a population.

Occasionally, a change in the environment favors a mutation that had previously been neutral or even somewhat harmful. Even if a beneficial mutation bestows only a slight advantage, its frequency tends to increase in a population over time. This is because natural selection operates on traits with a genetic basis.

Mutations have been altering genomes for billions of years, and they are still at it. Cumulatively, they have given rise to Earth's staggering biodiversity. Think about it: The

---

allele frequency Abundance of a particular allele among members of a population.

gene pool All the alleles of all the genes in a population; a pool of genetic resources.

lethal mutation Mutation that alters phenotype so drastically that it causes death.

microevolution Change in an allele's frequency in a population.

neutral mutation A mutation that has no effect on survival or reproduction.

population A group of organisms of the same species who live in a specific location and breed with one another more often than they breed with members of other populations.

Variation in shared traits among individuals is mainly an outcome of variations in alleles that influence those traits.

FIGURE 17.1 Sampling morphological variation among zigzag Nerite snails and (insets) humans.

reason you do not look like an apple or an earthworm or even your next-door neighbor began with mutations that occurred in different lines of descent.

ALLELE FREQUENCIES

Together, all the alleles of all the genes of a population comprise a pool of genetic resources—a **gene pool**. The members of a population breed with one another more often than they breed with members of other populations, so their gene pool is more or less isolated.

We refer to the abundance of any particular allele among members of a population as its **allele frequency**. Any change in allele frequency in the gene pool of a population (or a species) is called **microevolution**. Microevolution is always occurring in natural populations because, as you will see in the next sections, processes that drive it—mutation,

natural selection, and genetic drift—are always operating. Remember, even though we can recognize patterns of evolution, none of them are purposeful. Evolution simply fills the nooks and crannies of opportunity.

TAKE-HOME MESSAGE 17.1

Individuals of a natural population share morphological, physiological, and behavioral traits characteristic of the species. Alleles are the main basis of differences in the details of those shared traits.

All alleles of all individuals in a population make up the population's gene pool. An allele's abundance in the gene pool is called its allele frequency.

Microevolution is change in allele frequency. It is always occurring in natural populations because processes that drive it are always operating.

GENETIC EQUILIBRIUM

Early in the twentieth century, Godfrey Hardy (a mathematician) and Wilhelm Weinberg (a physician) independently applied the rules of probability to population genetics. They realized that, under certain theoretical conditions, allele frequencies in a sexually reproducing population's gene pool would remain stable from one

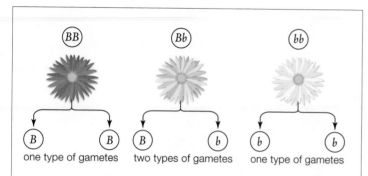

A In this two-allele system, *B* specifies dark blue flowers; *b*, white. Plants that are homozygous (*B* or *b*) make one kind of gamete. Heterozygous plants (*Bb*) have light blue flowers and make two kinds of gametes (*B* and *b*).

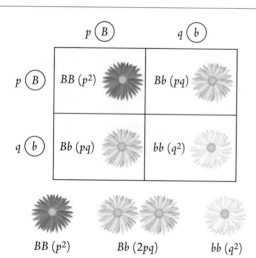

B Say *p* is the proportion of *B* alleles in the gene pool, and *q* is the proportion of *b* alleles. This Punnett square shows that in each generation, the predicted proportion of offspring that will inherit two *B* alleles is *p* × *p*, or p^2. Likewise, the proportion that will inherit both alleles is $2pq$, and the proportion that will inherit two *b* alleles is q^2.

FIGURE 17.2 {Animated} Calculating Hardy–Weinberg frequencies. In this example, two alleles of a gene show incomplete dominance over flower color.

FIGURE IT OUT: If ¼ of this population has dark blue flowers and ¼ has white flowers, what proportion of the next generation will have light blue flowers (assuming genetic equilibrium)?

Answer: Half of the gametes have a *B* allele; the other half have a *b* allele. Both *p* and *q* = 0.5, so $2pq$ = 50 percent.

generation to the next. The population would remain in this stable state, called **genetic equilibrium**, as long as all of the following five conditions are met:

1. Mutations never occur.
2. The population is infinitely large.
3. The population is isolated from all other populations of the species—no individual enters or leaves.
4. Mating is random.
5. All individuals survive and produce the same number of offspring.

Thus, if we see an allele's frequency change in a shared gene pool, at least one of the five conditions is not being met. As you can imagine, all five of these conditions never occur in natural populations.

APPLYING THE HARDY–WEINBERG LAW

The concept of genetic equilibrium under ideal conditions is called the Hardy–Weinberg law. To see how it works, consider a hypothetical gene that encodes a blue pigment in daisies. A plant homozygous for one allele (*BB*) has dark blue flowers. A plant homozygous for the other allele (*bb*) has white flowers. These two alleles are inherited in a pattern of incomplete dominance, so a heterozygous plant (*Bb*) has medium-blue flowers (**FIGURE 17.2A**).

Start with the concept that allele frequencies always add up to one. For a gene with two alleles, the following equation is true:

$$p + q = 1.0$$

where *p* is the frequency of one allele in the population, and *q* is the frequency of the other. Remember from Section 13.2 that paired alleles assort into different gametes during meiosis. **FIGURE 17.2B** shows the predictable proportions in which those gametes meet up at fertilization in our example. The predicted fraction of offspring that inherit two *B* alleles (*BB*) is *p* × *p*, or p^2; the fraction that inherit two *b* alleles (*bb*) is q^2; and the fraction that inherit one *B* allele and one *b* allele (*Bb*) is $2pq$. Note that the frequencies of the three genotypes, whatever they may be, add up to 1.0:

$$p^2 + 2pq + q^2 = 1.0$$

Suppose our hypothetical population consists of 1,000 plants: 490 homozygous (*BB*), 420 heterozygous (*Bb*), and 90 homozygous (*bb*), and each of these individuals

genetic equilibrium Theoretical state in which an allele's frequency never changes in a population's gene pool.

makes just two gametes. All 980 gametes made by the *BB* individuals will have the *B* allele, as will half of the gametes made by the 420 *Bb* individuals. Thus, the frequency of the *B* allele among the pool of gametes is:

$$B\,(p) = \frac{980 + 420}{2,000 \text{ alleles}} = \frac{1,400}{2,000} = 0.7$$

$$b\,(q) = \frac{180 + 420}{2,000 \text{ alleles}} = \frac{600}{2,000} = 0.3$$

Using our equation, the proportion of individuals in the next generation is predicted to be:

$$BB \quad (p^2) \quad = \quad (0.7)^2 \quad = 0.49$$
$$Bb \quad (2pq) \quad = \quad 2\,(0.7 \times 0.3) \quad = 0.42$$
$$bb \quad (q^2) \quad = \quad (0.3)^2 \quad = 0.09$$

These proportions are the same as the ones in the parent population. As long as the five conditions required for genetic equilibrium are met, traits specified by the alleles should show up in the same proportions in each generation. If they do not, the population is evolving.

REAL-WORLD SITUATIONS

Genetic equilibrium is often used as a benchmark. As an example, researchers used it to determine the carrier frequency of an allele that causes hereditary hemochromatosis (HH), the most common genetic disorder among people of Irish ancestry. This autosomal recessive disorder causes affected individuals to absorb too much iron from food. As a result, they can have liver problems, fatigue, and arthritis. The recessive allele's frequency (q) was found to be 0.14. If $q = 0.14$, then p, the frequency of the normal allele, must be 0.86. Thus, the carrier frequency, $2pq$, was calculated to be 0.24 (24 percent of the population).

As another example, consider that mutations in the *BRCA* genes have been linked to breast cancer in adults (Sections 10.6 and 15.7). A deviation from predicted allele frequencies suggested that these mutations also have effects even before birth, so researchers investigated the frequency of mutated alleles of these genes among newborn girls. They found fewer individuals homozygous for these alleles than expected, based on the number of heterozygous individuals. Thus, in homozygous form, *BRCA* mutations impair the survival of female embryos.

FIGURE 17.3
Overview of three modes of natural selection.

The remainder of this chapter explores the mechanisms and effects of processes that drive evolution, including natural selection. Remember from Section 16.2 that natural selection is a process in which environmental pressures result in the differential survival and reproduction of individuals of a population. It influences the frequency of alleles in a population by operating on phenotypes with a heritable, genetic basis.

We observe different patterns of natural selection, depending on the selection pressures and the organisms involved. Sometimes, individuals with a trait at one extreme of a range of variation are selected against, and those at the other extreme are adaptive. We call this pattern directional selection. With stabilizing selection, midrange forms of a trait are adaptive, and the extremes are selected against. With disruptive selection, forms at the extremes of the range of variation are adaptive, and the intermediate forms are selected against. We will discuss these three modes of natural selection, which **FIGURE 17.3** summarizes, in the following two sections.

Section 17.6 explores sexual selection, a mode of natural selection that operates on a population by influencing mating success. This section also discusses balanced polymorphism, a particular case in which natural selection maintains a relatively high frequency of multiple alleles in a population.

Natural selection and other processes of evolution can alter a population so much that it becomes a new species. We discuss mechanisms of speciation in the final sections.

TAKE-HOME MESSAGE 17.2

Researchers measure genetic change by comparing it with a theoretical baseline of genetic equilibrium.

TAKE-HOME MESSAGE 17.3

Natural selection, one of the most influential processes of evolution, can increase, decrease, or maintain the frequency of specific traits in a population.

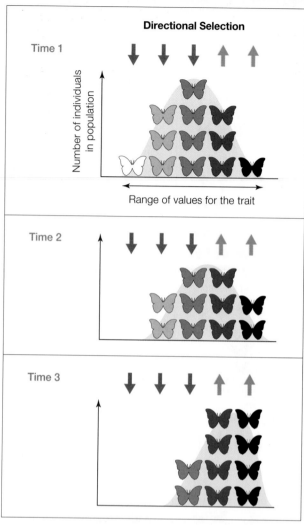

Directional Selection

Time 1

Number of individuals in population

Range of values for the trait

Time 2

Time 3

FIGURE 17.4 {Animated} With directional selection, a form of a trait at one end of a range of variation is adaptive. Bell-shaped curves indicate continuous variation. Red arrows indicate which forms are being selected against; green, forms that are adaptive.

A Light-colored moths on a nonsooty tree trunk (*top*) are hidden from predators; dark ones (*bottom*) stand out.	B In places where soot darkens tree trunks, the dark color (*bottom*) provides more camouflage than the light color (*top*).

FIGURE 17.5 {Animated} Adaptive value of two color forms of the peppered moth.

Directional selection shifts allele frequencies in a consistent direction, so forms at one end of a range of phenotypic variation become more common over time (**FIGURE 17.4**). The following examples show how field observations provide evidence of directional selection.

THE PEPPERED MOTH

A well-documented change in the coloration of peppered moths illustrates how environmental change influences directional selection. Peppered moths feed and mate at night, then rest on trees during the day. In preindustrial England, the vast majority of peppered moths were white with black speckles, and a small number were much darker. At this time, the air was clean, and light-gray lichens grew on the trunks and branches of most trees. When light-colored moths rested on lichen-covered trees, they were well camouflaged, whereas darker moths were not (**FIGURE 17.5A**). By the 1850s, dark moths had become much more common than light moths. The industrial revolution had begun, and smoke emitted by coal-burning factories was killing lichens. Dark moths were better camouflaged on lichen-free, soot-darkened trees (**FIGURE 17.5B**).

Scientists suspected that predation by birds was the selective pressure that shaped moth coloration, and in the 1950s, H. B. Kettlewell set out to test this hypothesis. He bred dark and light moths in captivity, marked them for easy identification, then released them in several areas. His team recaptured more of the dark moths in the polluted areas and more light ones in the less polluted ones. The researchers also observed predatory birds eating more light-colored moths in soot-darkened forests, and more dark-colored moths in cleaner, lichen-rich forests. Dark-colored moths were clearly at a selective advantage in industrialized areas.

Pollution controls went into effect in 1952. As a result of improved environmental standards, tree trunks gradually became free of soot, and lichens made a comeback. Kettlewell observed that moth phenotypes shifted too: Wherever pollution decreased, the frequency of dark moths decreased as well. Recent research has confirmed Kettlewell's results implicating birds and soot as selective agents of peppered moth coloration. It has also shown that coloration in peppered moths is determined by a single gene. Individuals that carry a dominant allele of this gene are black; those homozygous for a recessive allele are lighter.

WARFARIN-RESISTANT RATS

Human attempts to control the environment can result in directional selection. Consider that the average city in the United States sustains about one rat for every ten people. Rats thrive in urban centers, where garbage is plentiful and

FIGURE 17.6 Rats thrive wherever people do. Spreading poisons around buildings and soil does not usually exterminate rat populations, which recover quickly. Rather, the practice exerts directional selection favoring resistant rats.

natural predators are not (**FIGURE 17.6**). Part of their success stems from an ability to reproduce very quickly: Rat populations can expand within weeks to match the amount of garbage available for them to eat.

For decades, people have been fighting back with dogs, traps, ratproof storage facilities, and poisons that include arsenic and cyanide. Baits laced with warfarin, an organic compound that interferes with blood clotting, became popular in the 1950s. Rats that ate the poisoned baits died within days after bleeding internally or losing blood through cuts or scrapes. Warfarin was extremely effective, and its impact on harmless species was much lower than that of other rat poisons. It quickly became the rat poison of choice. By 1980, however, about 10 percent of rats in urban areas were resistant to warfarin. What happened?

Warfarin exposure had exerted directional selection on rat populations, favoring a particular allele in the rats' gene pool. Warfarin inhibits the gene's product, an enzyme that recycles vitamin K after it has been used to activate blood

clotting factors (we return to this topic in Section 33.4). A mutation had made the enzyme less active, but also insensitive to warfarin. "What happened" was evolution by natural selection. Rats with the normal allele died after eating warfarin. The lucky ones with a warfarin-resistance allele survived and passed it to their offspring. The rat populations recovered quickly, and a higher proportion of rats in the next generation carried the mutated allele. With each onslaught of warfarin, the frequency of this allele in the rat populations increased.

When warfarin resistance increased in rat populations, people stopped using this poison. The frequency of the warfarin-resistance allele in rat populations declined, probably because rats that carry the allele are not as healthy as ones that do not. Now, savvy exterminators in urban areas know that the best way to control a rat infestation is to exert another kind of selection pressure: Remove their source of food, which is usually garbage. Then the rats will eat each other.

directional selection Mode of natural selection in which phenotypes at one end of a range of variation are favored.

TAKE-HOME MESSAGE 17.4

Directional selection causes allele frequencies underlying a range of variation to shift in a consistent direction.

17.5 WHAT TYPES OF NATURAL SELECTION FAVOR INTERMEDIATE OR EXTREME FORMS OF TRAITS?

Natural selection does not always result in a directional shift in a population's range of phenotypes. In some cases, a midrange form of a trait is adaptive; in others, a midrange form is eliminated and the most extreme forms are adaptive.

STABILIZING SELECTION

Stabilizing selection tends to preserve midrange phenotypes in a population. With this mode of natural selection, an intermediate form of a trait is adaptive, and extreme forms are not (**FIGURE 17.7**).

Stabilizing selection maintains an intermediate body mass in populations of sociable weavers (**FIGURE 17.8**). These birds live in the African savanna, where they build

large communal nests (*left*), and their body mass has a genetic basis. Between 1993 and 2000, Rita Covas and her colleagues investigated selection pressures that operate on sociable weaver body mass by capturing and weighing thousands of birds before and after the breeding seasons. The results indicated that optimal body mass in sociable weavers is a trade-off between the risks of starvation and predation. Birds that carry less fat are more likely to starve than fatter birds. However, birds that carry more fat spend more time eating,

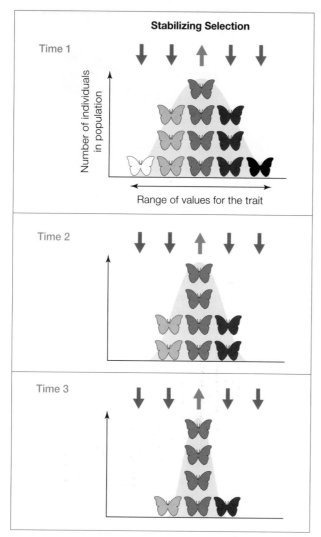

FIGURE 17.7 {Animated} Stabilizing selection eliminates extreme forms of a trait, and maintains an intermediate form. Red arrows indicate which forms are being selected against; green, the form that is adaptive. Compare the data set from a field experiment in **FIGURE 17.8**.

FIGURE 17.8 Stabilizing selection in sociable weavers (*top*). The graph (*bottom*) shows the number of birds (out of 977) that survived a breeding season.

 FIGURE IT OUT: What is the optimal mass of a sociable weaver?

Answer: About 29 grams

UNIT 3
PRINCIPLES OF EVOLUTION

CREDITS: (7, 8 bottom) © Cengage Learning; (8 top) Peter Chadwick/Science Source; (inset) Courtesy © Rui Omelas.

which in this species means foraging in open areas where they are easily accessible to predators. Fatter birds are also more attractive to predators, and not as agile when escaping. Thus, predators are agents of selection that eliminate the fattest individuals. Birds of intermediate weight have the selective advantage, and they make up the bulk of sociable weaver populations.

DISRUPTIVE SELECTION

With **disruptive selection**, forms of a trait at both ends of a range of variation are adaptive, and intermediate forms are not (**FIGURE 17.9**).

Consider the black-bellied seedcracker, a colorful finch species native to Cameroon, Africa. In these birds, there is a genetic basis for bill size. The bill of a typical black-bellied seedcracker, male or female, is either 12 millimeters wide, or wider than 15 millimeters (**FIGURE 17.10**). Birds with a bill size between 12 and 15 millimeters are uncommon. It is as if every human adult were 4 feet or 6 feet tall, with no one of intermediate height. Seedcrackers with the large and small bill forms inhabit the same geographic range, and they breed randomly with respect to bill size.

Environmental factors that affect feeding performance maintain the dimorphism in seedcracker bill size. The finches feed mainly on the seeds of two types of sedge, a grasslike plant. One sedge produces hard seeds; the other, soft seeds. Small-billed birds are better at opening the soft seeds, but large-billed birds are better at cracking the hard ones. During Cameroon's semiannual wet seasons, when both hard and soft sedge seeds are abundant, all seedcrackers feed on both types. During the region's dry seasons, when seeds become scarce and competition for food intensifies, each bird focuses on eating the seeds that it opens most efficiently: Small-billed birds feed mainly on soft seeds, and large-billed birds feed mainly on hard seeds. Birds with intermediate-sized bills cannot open either type of seed as efficiently as the other birds, so they are less likely to survive the dry seasons.

disruptive selection Mode of natural selection in which traits at the extremes of a range of variation are adaptive, and intermediate forms are not.
stabilizing selection Mode of natural selection in which an intermediate form of a trait is adaptive, and extreme forms are not.

TAKE-HOME MESSAGE 17.5

With stabilizing selection, an intermediate phenotype is adaptive, and extreme forms are selected against.

With disruptive selection, an intermediate form of a trait is selected against, and extreme phenotypes are adaptive.

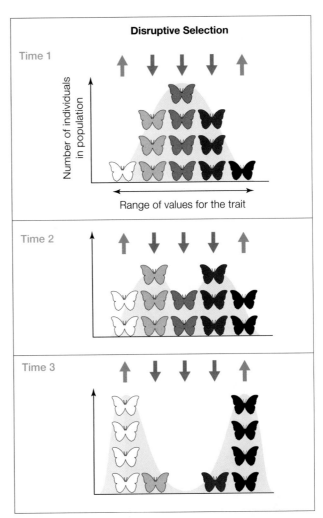

FIGURE 17.9 {**Animated**} Disruptive selection eliminates midrange forms of a trait, and maintains extreme forms. Red arrows indicate which forms are being selected against; green, the form that is adaptive.

FIGURE 17.10 {**Animated**} Disruptive selection in African seedcracker populations maintains a distinct dimorphism in bill size. Competition for scarce food during dry seasons favors birds with bills that are either 12 millimeters wide (*left*) or 15 to 20 millimeters wide (*right*). Birds with bills of intermediate size are selected against.

A Male elephant seals fight for sexual access to a cluster of females. Males of this species typically compete for access to the clusters of females.

B A male bird of paradise engaged in a flashy court-ship display has caught the eye (and, perhaps, the sexual interest) of a female. Female birds of paradise are choosy; a male mates with any female that accepts him.

C Female stalk-eyed flies prefer to mate with males that have the longest eyestalks, a trait that provides no obvious selec-tive advantage other than sexual attractiveness.

FIGURE 17.11 Sexual selection in action.

Selection pressures that operate on natural populations are often not as clear-cut as the examples in the previous sections might suggest. A particular form of a trait may be adaptive in one circumstance but harmful in another. Even individuals of the same species can play a role.

SURVIVAL OF THE SEXIEST

Not all evolution is driven by selection for traits that influence survival. Competition for mates is a selective pressure that shapes form and behavior in many species. Consider how males and females of many sexually reproducing species are different in size or another aspect of their appearance—a **sexual dimorphism**. Individuals of one sex (often males) are more colorful, larger, or more aggressive than individuals of the other sex. These traits can seem puzzling because they take energy and time away from activities that enhance survival, and some actually hinder an individual's ability to survive. Why, then, do they persist?

The answer is **sexual selection**, in which the evolutionary winners outreproduce others of a population because they are better at securing mates. With this mode of natural selection, the most adaptive forms of a trait are those that help individuals defeat rivals for mates, or are most attractive to the opposite sex.

For example, the females of some species cluster in defensible groups when they are sexually receptive, and males compete for sole access to the groups. Competition for the ready-made harems favors brawny, combative males (**FIGURE 17.11A**).

As another example, males or females that are choosy about mates act as selective agents on their own species. The females of some species shop for a mate among males that display species-specific cues such as a highly specialized appearance or courtship behavior (**FIGURE 17.11B**). The cues often include flashy body parts or movements, traits that tend to attract predators and in some cases are a physical hindrance. However, to a female member of the species, a flashy male's survival despite his obvious handicap may imply health and vigor, two traits that are likely to improve her chances of bearing healthy, vigorous offspring. Selected males pass alleles for their attractive traits to the

balanced polymorphism Maintenance of two or more alleles of a gene at high frequency in a population.
frequency-dependent selection Natural selection in which a trait's adaptive value depends on its frequency in a population.
sexual dimorphism Difference in appearance between males and females of a species.
sexual selection Mode of natural selection in which some individuals outreproduce others of a population because they are better at securing mates.

☐ 0%–2%
☐ 2%–4%
☐ 4%–6%
☐ 6%–8%
☐ 8%–10%
☐ 10%–12%
☐ 12%–14%
☐ >14%

A Distribution (by percentage) of people who carry the sickle-cell allele.

B Distribution of malaria cases (orange) in Africa, Asia, and the Middle East in the 1920s, before the start of programs to control mosquitoes, which transmit the parasitic protist that causes the disease. Notice the correlation with the distribution of the sickle-cell allele in **A**. The photo shows a physician searching for mosquito larvae in Southeast Asia.

FIGURE 17.12 Malaria and sickle-cell anemia.

next generation of males, and females pass alleles that influence mate preference to the next generation of females. This type of sexual selection can result in highly exaggerated traits (**FIGURE 17.11C**).

MAINTAINING MULTIPLE ALLELES

Any mode of natural selection may keep two or more alleles of a gene circulating at relatively high frequency in a population's gene pool, a state called **balanced polymorphism**. For example, sexual selection maintains multiple alleles that govern eye color in populations of *Drosophila* fruit flies. Female flies prefer to mate with rare white-eyed males, until the white-eyed males become more common than red-eyed males, at which point the red-eyed flies are again preferred. This is also an example of **frequency-dependent selection**, in which the adaptive value of a particular form of a trait depends on its frequency in a population.

Balanced polymorphism can also arise in environments that favor heterozygous individuals (Section 13.1). Consider the gene that encodes the beta globin chain of hemoglobin. *HbA* is the normal allele; the codominant *HbS* allele carries a mutation that causes sickle-cell anemia (Section 9.5). Even with medical care, about 15 percent of individuals homozygous for the *HbS* allele die by age 18 from complications of the disorder.

Despite being so harmful, the *HbS* allele persists at very high frequency among the human populations in tropical and subtropical regions of Asia, Africa, and the Middle East. Why? Populations with the highest frequency of the *HbS* allele also have the highest incidence of malaria (**FIGURE 17.12**). Mosquitoes transmit the parasitic protist that causes malaria, *Plasmodium*, to human hosts (more about this in Section 20.5). *Plasmodium* multiplies in the liver and

then in red blood cells. The cells rupture and release new parasites during recurring bouts of severe illness.

It turns out that people who make both normal and sickle hemoglobin are more likely to survive malaria than people who make only normal hemoglobin. In *HbA/HbS* heterozygous individuals, *Plasmodium*-infected red blood cells sometimes sickle. The abnormal shape brings the cells to the attention of the immune system, which destroys them along with the parasites they harbor. By contrast, *Plasmodium*-infected red blood cells of individuals homozygous for the normal *HbA* allele do not sickle, so the parasite may remain hidden from the immune system.

In areas where malaria is common, the persistence of the *HbS* allele is a matter of relative evils. Malaria and sickle-cell anemia are both potentially deadly. Heterozygous individuals are not completely healthy, but they do have a better chance of surviving malaria than those who carry two normal alleles. With or without malaria, people with both alleles are more likely to live long enough to reproduce than individuals who are homozygous for the *HbS* allele. The result is that nearly one-third of the people living in the most malaria-ridden regions of the world are heterozygous for the *HbS* allele.

TAKE-HOME MESSAGE 17.6

With sexual selection, adaptive forms of a trait are those that give an individual an advantage in securing mates.

Sexual selection can reinforce phenotypic differences between males and females, and sometimes it results in exaggerated traits.

Balanced polymorphism can be an outcome of frequency-dependent selection, or of environmental pressures that favor heterozygous individuals.

17.7 WHAT MECHANISMS OTHER THAN NATURAL SELECTION AFFECT ALLELE FREQUENCIES?

GENETIC DRIFT

Genetic drift is random change in an allele's frequency over time, brought about by chance alone. We explain genetic drift in terms of probability—the chance that some event will occur. Sample size is important in probability. Remember from Section 1.7 that each time you flip a coin, there is a 50 percent chance it will land heads up. With 10 flips, the proportion of times heads actually land up may be very far from 50 percent. With 1,000 flips, that proportion is more likely to be near 50 percent.

A The flour beetle (*Tribolium castaneum*), shown here on a flake of cereal.

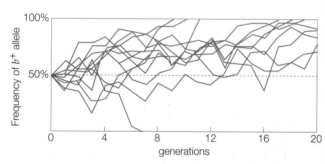

B The size of these populations was maintained at 10 breeding individuals. Allele b^+ was lost in one population (one graph line ends at 0).

C The size of these populations was maintained at 100 individuals. Drift in these populations was less than the small populations in **B**.

FIGURE 17.13 {Animated} Genetic drift experiment in flour beetles (shown in **A**). Beetles heterozygous for alleles b^+ and b were maintained in populations of **B** 10 individuals or **C** 100 individuals for 20 generations. Graph lines in **C** are smoother than in **B**, indicating that drift was greatest in the sets of 10 beetles and least in the sets of 100. Notice that the average frequency of allele b^+ rose at the same rate in both groups, an indication that natural selection was at work too: Allele b^+ was weakly favored.

FIGURE IT OUT: In how many populations did allele b^+ become fixed?

Answer: Six

The same rule holds for populations: the larger the population, the smaller the impact of random changes in allele frequencies. Imagine two populations, one with 10 individuals, the other with 100. If allele X occurs in both populations at a 10 percent frequency, then only one person carries the allele in the small population. If that individual dies without reproducing, then the population's gene pool will lose allele X. However, ten individuals in the large population carry the allele. All ten would have to die without reproducing for the allele to be lost. Thus, the chance that the small population will lose allele X is greater than that for the large population. This is a general effect: The loss of genetic diversity is possible in all populations, but it is more likely in small ones (**FIGURE 17.13**). When all individuals of a population are homozygous for an allele, we say that the allele is **fixed**. The frequency of a fixed allele will not change unless a new mutation occurs, or an individual bearing another allele enters the population.

BOTTLENECKS AND THE FOUNDER EFFECT

A drastic reduction in population size, which is called a **bottleneck**, can greatly reduce genetic diversity. For example, northern elephant seals (shown in **FIGURE 17.11A**) underwent a bottleneck during the late 1890s, when hunting reduced their population size to about twenty individuals. Hunting restrictions have since allowed the population to recover, but genetic diversity among its members has been greatly reduced. The bottleneck and subsequent genetic drift eliminated many alleles that had been previously present in the population.

A loss of genetic diversity can also occur when a small group of individuals establishes a new population. If the founding group is not representative of the original population in terms of allele frequencies, then the new population will not be representative of it either. This outcome is called the **founder effect** (**FIGURE 17.14A**). Consider that all three *ABO* alleles for blood type (Section 13.4) are common in most human populations. Native Americans are an exception, with the majority of individuals

---

bottleneck Reduction in population size so severe that it reduces genetic diversity.
fixed Refers to an allele for which all members of a population are homozygous.
founder effect After a small group of individuals found a new population, allele frequencies in the new population differ from those in the original population.
gene flow The movement of alleles into and out of a population.
genetic drift Change in allele frequency due to chance alone.
inbreeding Mating among close relatives.

CREDITS: (13A) Photo by Peggy Greb/ USDA; (13B,C) Adapted from S. S. Rich, A. E. Bell, and S. P. Wilson, "Genetic drift in small populations of Tribolium," Evolution 33:579–584, Fig. 1, p. 580, © 1979 by John Wiley and Sons. Used by permission of the publisher.

original population

founding group

new population

A The founder effect: a group that founds a new population is not representative of the original population. so allele frequencies differ between the new and the old populations.

B A high frequency of an allele that causes Ellis–van Creveld syndrome among the Lancaster Amish began with the founder effect.

FIGURE 17.14 The founder effect: mechanism and example.

being homozygous for the *O* allele. Native Americans are descendants of early humans who migrated from Asia between 14,000 and 21,000 years ago, across a narrow land bridge that once connected Siberia and Alaska. Analysis of DNA from ancient skeletal remains reveals that most early Americans were also homozygous for the *O* allele. Modern Siberian populations have all three alleles. Thus, the first humans in the Americas were probably members of a small group that had reduced genetic diversity compared with the general population.

Founding populations are often necessarily inbred. **Inbreeding** is breeding between close relatives. Closely related individuals tend to share more alleles than nonrelatives do, so inbred populations often have unusually high numbers of individuals homozygous for recessive alleles, some of which are harmful. This outcome is minimized in human populations where incest (mating between parents and children or between siblings) is discouraged or forbidden.

The Old Order Amish in Lancaster County, Pennsylvania, offer an example of the effects of inbreeding within human populations. Amish people marry only within their community. Intermarriage with other groups is not permitted, and no "outsiders" are allowed to join the community. As a result, Amish populations are moderately inbred, and many of their individuals are homozygous for harmful recessive alleles. The Lancaster population

has an unusually high frequency of a recessive allele that causes Ellis–van Creveld syndrome, a genetic disorder characterized by dwarfism, polydactyly, and heart defects, among other symptoms. This allele has been traced to a man and his wife, two of a group of 400 Amish people who immigrated to the United States in the mid-1700s. As a result of the founder effect and inbreeding since then, about 1 of 8 people in the Lancaster population is now heterozygous for the allele, and 1 in 200 is homozygous for it (**FIGURE 17.14B**).

GENE FLOW

Individuals of natural populations tend to mate or breed most frequently with other members of their own population. However, not all populations of a species are completely isolated from one another, and nearby populations may occasionally interbreed. Also, individuals sometimes leave one population and join another. **Gene flow**, the movement of alleles between populations, occurs in both cases. Gene flow can change or stabilize allele frequencies, thus countering the evolutionary effects of mutation, natural selection, and genetic drift.

Gene flow is typical among populations of animals, but it also occurs in less mobile organisms. Consider the acorns that jays disperse when they gather nuts for the winter (*left*). Every fall, these birds visit acorn-bearing oak trees repeatedly, then bury the acorns in the soil of territories that may be as much as a mile away. The jays transfer acorns (and the alleles carried by these seeds) among populations of oak trees that may otherwise be genetically isolated.

Gene flow also occurs when wind or animals transfer pollen from one plant to another, often over great distances (more about this in Chapter 27). Many opponents of genetic engineering cite gene flow from transgenic crop plants into wild populations via pollen transfer. For example, herbicide-resistance genes and the *Bt* gene (Section 15.5) are now commonly found in weeds and unmodified crop plants. Long-term effects of this gene flow are currently unknown.

CREDITS: (14A) © Cengage Learning 2015; (14B) © Dr. Victor A. McKusick; (inset) © Ashok Khosla, www.seeingbirds.com.

Mutation, natural selection, and genetic drift operate on all natural populations, and they do so independently in populations that are not interbreeding. When gene flow does not keep two populations alike, different genetic changes accumulate in each one. Over time, the populations may become so different that we call them different species. The evolutionary process in which new species arise is called **speciation.**

Evolution is a dynamic, extravagant, messy, and ongoing process that can be challenging for people who like their categories neat. Speciation offers a perfect example, because it rarely occurs at a precise moment in time: Individuals often continue to interbreed even as populations are diverging, and populations that have already diverged may come together and interbreed again.

FIGURE 17.15 {Animated} Reproductive isolating mechanisms that can prevent interbreeding.

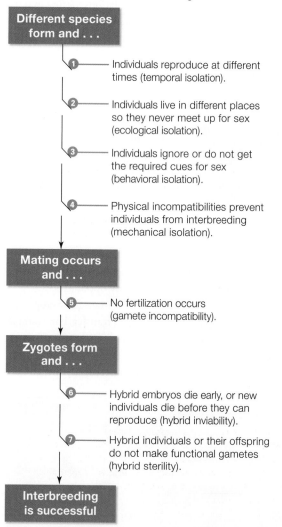

Every time speciation happens, it happens in a unique way, and each species is a product of its own unique evolutionary history. However, there are recurring patterns. For example, reproductive isolation is always part of speciation. **Reproductive isolation,** the end of gene flow between populations, is part of the process by which sexually reproducing species attain and maintain their separate identities. Mechanisms that prevent successful interbreeding reinforce differences between diverging populations (**FIGURE 17.15**).

MECHANISMS OF REPRODUCTIVE ISOLATION

❶ **Temporal Isolation** Some closely related species cannot interbreed because the timing of their reproduction differs. The periodical cicada (*left*) offers an example. Cicada larvae feed on roots as they mature underground, then the adults emerge to reproduce. Three cicada species reproduce every 17 years. Each has a sibling species with nearly identical form and behavior, except that the siblings emerge on a 13-year cycle instead of a 17-year cycle. Sibling species have the potential to interbreed, but they can only get together once every 221 years!

❷ **Ecological Isolation** Closely related species that are adapted to different microenvironments in the same region may be ecologically isolated. For example, two species of manzanita, a plant native to the Sierra Nevada mountain range, rarely hybridize. One species that lives high up on dry, rocky hillsides is better adapted for conserving water. The other, less drought-adapted species lives on lower slopes where water stress is not as intense. The physical separation makes cross-pollination unlikely.

❸ **Behavioral Isolation** In animals, behavioral differences can stop gene flow between related species. Males and females of many species engage in courtship displays before sex (the chapter opener photo shows an example). In a typical pattern, the female recognizes the sounds and movements of a male of her species as an overture to sex, but females of different species do not.

❹ Mechanical Isolation The size or shape of an individual's reproductive parts may prevent it from mating with members of closely related species. For example, plants called black sage and white sage grow in the same areas, but hybrids rarely form because the flowers of these two related species have become specialized for different pollinators (**FIGURE 17.16**).

❺ Gamete Incompatibility Even if gametes of different species do meet up, they often have molecular incompatibilities that prevent a zygote from forming. For example, the molecular signals that trigger pollen germination in flowering plants are species-specific (we return to pollen germination and other aspects of flowering plant reproduction in Section 27.2). Gamete incompatibility may be the primary speciation route among animals that release their eggs and free-swimming sperm into water.

❻ Hybrid Inviability Genetic changes are the basis of divergences in form, function, and behavior. Even chromosomes of species that diverged relatively recently may be different enough that a hybrid zygote ends up with extra or missing genes, or genes with incompatible products. Such outcomes typically disrupt embryonic development. Hybrids that do survive embryonic development often have reduced fitness. For example, hybrid offspring of lions and tigers have more health problems and a shorter life expectancy than individuals of either parent species.

❼ Hybrid Sterility Some interspecies crosses produce robust but sterile offspring. For example, mating between a female horse (64 chromosomes) and a male donkey (62 chromosomes) produces a mule. Mules are healthy, but their 63 chromosomes cannot pair up evenly during meiosis, so this animal makes few viable gametes.

If hybrids are fertile, their offspring usually have lower and lower fitness with each successive generation. Incompatible nuclear and mitochondrial DNA may be the cause (mitochondrial DNA is inherited from the mother only).

---

reproductive isolation The end of gene flow between populations.
speciation Evolutionary process in which new species arise.

TAKE-HOME MESSAGE 17.8

Speciation is an evolutionary process in which new species form. It varies in its details and duration.

Reproductive isolation, which occurs by one of several mechanisms, is always a part of speciation.

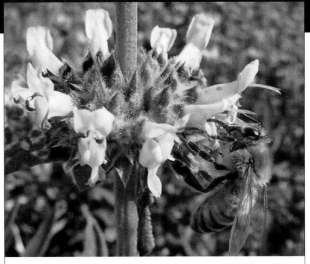

A Black sage is pollinated mainly by honeybees and other small insects.

B The flowers of black sage are too delicate to support larger insects. Big insects access the nectar of small sage flowers only by piercing from the outside, as this carpenter bee is doing. When they do so, they avoid touching the flower's reproductive parts.

anthers

stigma

C The reproductive parts (anthers and stigma) of white sage flowers are too far away from the petals to be brushed by honeybees, so honeybees are not efficient pollinators of this species. White sage is pollinated mainly by larger bees and hawkmoths, which brush the flower's stigma and anthers as they pry apart the petals to access nectar.

FIGURE 17.16 Mechanical isolation in sage.

CREDITS: (16A) Courtesy of Dr. James French; (16B) Courtesy of © Ron Brinkmann, www.flickr.com/photos/ronbrinkmann; (16C) © David Goodin.

17.9 WHAT IS ALLOPATRIC SPECIATION?

Genetic changes that lead to a new species can begin with physical separation between populations. With **allopatric speciation**, a physical barrier arises and separates two populations, ending gene flow between them (*allo*– means different; *patria*, fatherland). Then, reproductive isolating mechanisms evolve that prevent interbreeding even if the diverging populations do meet up again later.

Gene flow between populations separated by distance is often inconsistent. Whether a geographic barrier can completely block that gene flow depends on how the species travels (such as by swimming, walking, or flying), and how it reproduces (for example, by internal fertilization or by pollen dispersal).

A geographic barrier can arise in an instant, or over an eon. The Great Wall of China is an example of a barrier that arose abruptly. As it was being built, the wall interrupted gene flow among nearby populations of insect-pollinated plants; DNA sequence comparisons show that trees, shrubs, and herbs on either side of the wall are diverging genetically. Geographic isolation usually occurs much more slowly. For example, it took millions of years of tectonic plate movements (Section 16.5) to bring the two continents of North and South America close enough to collide. The land bridge where the two continents now connect is called the Isthmus of Panama. When this isthmus formed about 4 million years ago, it cut off the flow of water—and gene flow among populations of aquatic organisms—as it separated one large ocean into what are now the Pacific and Atlantic Oceans (**FIGURE 17.17**).

SPECIATION IN ARCHIPELAGOS

New species rarely form on island chains such as the Florida Keys that are in close proximity to a mainland. Being close to a mainland means gene flow is essentially unimpeded between island and mainland populations. By contrast, allopatric speciation is common on archipelagos (island chains) such as the Hawaiian and Galápagos Islands. These island chains are so geographically isolated that, for most species, gene flow does not occur between island and mainland populations.

The Hawaiian archipelago includes 19 islands and more than 100 atolls stretching 1,500 miles in the Pacific Ocean. These islands arose from hot spots on the ocean floor (Section 16.5). Because they were the tops of volcanoes, we can assume that their fiery surfaces were initially barren and inhospitable to life. Later, winds and currents carried a few individuals of mainland species to them. The individuals reproduced, and their descendants established populations. The lack of gene flow with mainland populations allowed the island populations to diverge. Today, thousands of

FIGURE 17.17 An example of allopatric speciation. When the Isthmus of Panama formed 4 million years ago, it cut off gene flow among ocean-dwelling populations of snapping shrimp. Today, shrimp species on opposite sides of the isthmus are so similar that they might interbreed, but they are behaviorally isolated: Instead of mating when they are brought together, they snap their claws at one another aggressively. The photos show two of the many closely related species that live on opposite sides of the isthmus.

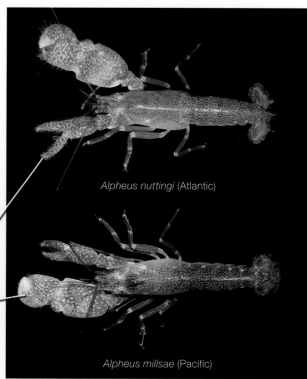

Alpheus nuttingi (Atlantic)

Alpheus millsae (Pacific)

Mexico · Atlantic Ocean · Pacific Ocean · Isthmus of Panama · Columbia · 0 (km) 1500 · 0 (mi) 1000

Akepa (*Loxops coccineus*) — Akekee (*Loxops caeruleirostris*) — Nihoa finch (*Telespiza ultima*) — Palila (*Loxioides bailleui*)

Iiwi (*Vestiaria coccinea*) — Akohekohe (*Palmeria dolei*) — Apapane (*Himatione sanguinea*) — Akiapolaau (*Hemignathus munroi*)

Maui parrotbill (*Pseudonestor xanthophrys*) — Maui Alauahio (*Paroreomyza montana*) — Kauai Amakihi (*Hemignathus kauaiensis*) — Hawaii Amakihi (*Hemignathus virens*)

FIGURE 17.18 {Animated}
Allopatric speciation gave rise to the Hawaiian honeycreepers. The Hawaiian Islands (*right*) are separated from mainland continents by thousands of miles of open ocean—a geographic barrier that prevented gene flow between island colonizers and mainland populations. DNA sequence comparisons suggest that the ancestor of all Hawaiian honeycreepers resembled the housefinch (*Carpodacus*, *left*).

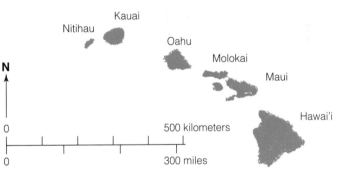

species are unique to this island chain. Consider Hawaiian honeycreepers, birds that are descendants of a mainland finch species that arrived on the islands about 3.5 million years ago. A buffet of fruits, seeds, nectars, tasty insects, and the near absence of competitors and predators allowed the finch's descendants to thrive. In the absence of gene flow, the island finch population diverged from the ancestral mainland species. Further divergences occurred because habitats on the landmasses of the Hawaiian archipelago vary

dramatically—from lava beds, rain forests, and grasslands to dry woodlands and snow-capped peaks. Selection pressures differ within and between these habitats. The cumulative result of all these divergences is a spectacular array of honeycreeper species (**FIGURE 17.18**).

allopatric speciation Speciation pattern in which a physical barrier ends gene flow between populations.

TAKE-HOME MESSAGE 17.9

A physical barrier that intervenes between populations or subpopulations of a species prevents gene flow among them. When gene flow ends, genetic divergences give rise to new species. This process is allopatric speciation.

17.10 CAN SPECIATION OCCUR WITHOUT A PHYSICAL BARRIER TO GENE FLOW?

SYMPATRIC SPECIATION

In **sympatric speciation**, populations inhabiting the same geographic region speciate in the absence of a physical barrier between them (*sym–* means together).

Sympatric speciation can occur in a single generation when the chromosome number multiplies. Polyploidy (having three or more sets of chromosomes, Section 14.5) typically arises when an abnormal nuclear division during meiosis or mitosis doubles the chromosome number. For example, if the nucleus of a somatic cell in a flowering plant fails to divide during mitosis, the resulting polyploid cell may proliferate and give rise to shoots and flowers. If the flowers can self-fertilize, a new polyploid species may be the result. Common bread wheat originated after related species hybridized, and then the chromosome number of the hybrid offspring doubled (**FIGURE 17.19**). Today, about 95 percent of ferns and 70 percent of flowering plant species are polyploid, as well as a few conifers, insects and other arthropods, mollusks, fishes, amphibians, and reptiles.

Sympatric speciation can also occur with no change in chromosome number. The mechanically isolated sage plants you just learned about speciated with no physical barrier to gene flow. As another example, more than 500 species of cichlid fishes arose by sympatric speciation in the shallow waters of Lake Victoria. This large freshwater lake sits isolated from river inflow on an elevated plain in Africa's Great Rift Valley. Since Lake Victoria formed about 400,000 years ago, it has dried up three times. DNA sequence comparisons indicate that almost all of the cichlid species in this lake arose since the last dry spell, which was 12,400 years ago. How could hundreds of species arise so quickly? In this case, the answer begins with differences in the water—color of ambient light and clarity—in different parts of the lake. The light in the lake's shallower, clear water is mainly blue; the light that penetrates the deeper, muddier water is mainly red. The cichlids vary in color and in patterning (**FIGURE 17.20**). Outside of captivity, female cichlids rarely mate with males of other species. Given a choice, they prefer to mate with brightly colored males of their own species. Their preference has a basis in genes that encode light-sensitive pigments of the retina (part of the eye). Retinal pigments made by species that live mainly in shallow areas of the lake are more sensitive to blue light. The males of these species are also the bluest. Retinal pigments made by species that live mainly in deeper areas of the lake are more sensitive to red light. Males of these species are redder. In other words, the colors that a female cichlid sees best are the same colors displayed by males of her species. Thus, mutations in genes that affect color perception are likely to affect a female's choice of mates. Such mutations are probably the way sympatric speciation occurs in these fish.

FIGURE 17.19 {Animated} Sympatric speciation in wheat. The wheat genome, which consists of seven chromosomes, occurs in slightly different forms called A, B, C, D, and so on. Many wheat species are polyploid, carrying more than two copies of the genome. For example, modern bread wheat (*Triticum aestivum*) is hexaploid, with six copies of the wheat genome: two each of genomes A, B, and D (or 42 AABBDD).

Triticum urartu (wild einkorn)	*Aegilops* (wild goatgrass, unknown species)	*Triticum* (hybrid)	*Triticum turgidum* (emmer)	*Aegilops tauschii* (goatgrass)	*Triticum aestivum* (bread wheat)
14 AA ×	14 BB →	14 AB →	28 AABB ×	14 DD →	42 AABBDD

A About 11,000 years ago, a diploid wheat (einkorn) hybridized with a diploid species of wild goatgrass.

B Tetraploid (4*n*) emmer arose when the chromosome number of the resulting hybrid doubled.

C Common bread wheat is the result of a hybridization between emmer and a diploid goatgrass.

FIGURE 17.20 Red fish, blue fish: Males of four closely related species of cichlid native to Lake Victoria, Africa. Hundreds of cichlid species arose by sympatric speciation in this lake. Mutations in genes that affect females' perception of the color of ambient light in deeper or shallower regions of the lake also affect their choice of mates. Female cichlids prefer to mate with brightly colored males of their own species.

 FIGURE IT OUT: What form of natural selection has been driving sympatric speciation in Lake Victoria cichlids?

Answer: Sexual selection

PARAPATRIC SPECIATION

With **parapatric speciation**, adjacent populations speciate despite being in contact across a common border. Divergences spurred by local selection pressures are reinforced because hybrids that form in the contact zone are less fit than individuals on either side of it.

Consider velvet walking worms, which resemble caterpillars but may be more related to spiders: They are predatory, and shoot streams of glue from their head to entangle insect prey. Two rare species of velvet walking worm are native to the island of Tasmania. The giant velvet walking worm and the blind velvet walking worm can interbreed, but they only do so in a tiny area where their habitats overlap. Hybrid offspring are sterile, which may be the main reason the two species are maintaining separate identities in the absence of a physical barrier between their adjacent populations.

parapatric speciation Speciation pattern in which populations speciate while in contact along a common border.
sympatric speciation Speciation pattern in which speciation occurs within a population, in the absence of a physical barrier to gene flow.

TAKE-HOME MESSAGE 17.10

With sympatric speciation, divergence within an interbreeding population leads to new species that inhabit the same area, with no physical barrier to gene flow.

With parapatric speciation, populations maintaining contact along a common border evolve into distinct species.

PEOPLE MATTER

National Geographic Grantee
DR. JULIA J. DAY

U nderstanding processes that lead to speciation is fundamental to explaining the diversity of life. National Geographic grantee Julia Day studies why some environments give rise to and maintain higher species richness than others. Her research focuses on comparing the staggering biodiversity of three East African great lakes: Tanganyika, Victoria, and Malawi. Cichlid fishes in these lakes evolved into "flocks" of many hundred species, most of which are close relatives. Each species flock displays astonishing levels of ecological, phenotypic, and behavioral diversity. In addition to being generally very colorful, these fish have a stunning variety of adaptations: unusual dietary habits, clever feeding behaviors, and sophisticated reproductive behaviors and parental care strategies.

Lake Tanganyika, despite being larger and older than Lakes Victoria and Malawi, harbors only about one-third the number of cichlid species in the other two lakes. Why the difference? Day and her team analyzed mitochondrial DNA samples from almost all of the Lake Tanganyika cichlids. Her results indicate that species in this lake diversified from several distinct lineages, rather than from a single ancestor (as occurred in Lakes Victoria and Malawi). Cichlid diversifications in Lake Tanganyika occurred several times, possibly coinciding with periods of changing water levels in the lake, or with successive invasions of new ancestral cichlid species. Speciation also occurred about six times more slowly than in the other lakes—a rate more in line with typical speciation rates of plants and animals in other environments.

Something about Lake Tanganyika was less conducive for cichlid speciation than the other lakes. Day thinks that diversification may have been relatively inhibited by the presence of older species already filling Lake Tanganyika's niches. Unlike Lakes Victoria and Malawi, Lake Tanganyika has not completely dried up in the past.

As these unique ecosystems are threatened from increasing populations and climate change, understanding and assessing the origins and maintenance of their biodiversity are of high priority.

CREDITS: (20) Kevin Bauman, www.african-cichlid.com; (in text) Courtesy of Julia J. Day.

CHAPTER 17 291
PROCESSES OF
EVOLUTION

Notochord
This tough, elastic tube, which is partially hollow and filled with fluid, is ancestral to the spinal cord.

Lobed fins
These fleshy fins retain a few of the ancestral bones that gave rise to legs and arms in other lineages.

Long gestation
Coelacanths give birth to litters of up to 26 fully developed "pups" after gestation of more than a year.

Rostral organ
A sensory organ that perceives electrical impulses in water, it probably helps the fish locate prey in dark ocean depths.

FIGURE 17.21 An example of stasis. *Left*, compare a 320-million-year-old coelacanth fossil found in Montana with a live coelacanth. *Right*, a few of the coelacanth's unusual ancestral features that have been lost in almost all other fish lineages over evolutionary time.

Microevolution is change in allele frequencies within a single species or population. **Macroevolution** is our name for evolutionary patterns on a larger scale: trends such as land plants evolving from green algae, the dinosaurs disappearing in a mass extinction, a burst of divergences from a single species, and so on.

PATTERNS OF MACROEVOLUTION

Stasis With the simplest macroevolutionary pattern, **stasis**, a lineage persists for millions of years with little evolutionary change. Consider coelacanths, an order of ancient lobe-finned fish that had been assumed extinct for at least 70 million years until a fisherman caught one in 1938. The modern coelacanth species are very similar to fossil specimens hundreds of millions of years old (**FIGURE 17.21**).

Exaptation Major evolutionary novelties often stem from the adaptation of an existing structure for a completely new purpose. This macroevolutionary pattern is called **exaptation**. For example, the feathers that allow modern birds to fly are derived from feathers that first evolved in some dinosaurs. Those dinosaurs could not have used their feathers for flight, but they probably did use them for insulation. Thus, we say that flight feathers in birds are an exaptation of insulating feathers in dinosaurs.

Mass Extinctions By current estimates, more than 99 percent of all species that ever lived are now **extinct**, which means they no longer have living members. In addition to continuing small-scale extinctions, the fossil record indicates that there have been more than twenty mass extinctions, which are simultaneous losses of many lineages. These

include five catastrophic events in which the majority of species on Earth disappeared (Section 16.6).

Adaptive Radiation With **adaptive radiation**, one lineage rapidly diversifies into several new species. Adaptive radiation can occur after individuals colonize a new environment that has a variety of different habitats with few or no competitors. The adaptation of populations to different regions of the new environment produces many new species. The Hawaiian honeycreepers arose this way, as did the Lake Victoria cichlids.

Adaptive radiation may also occur after a key innovation evolves. A **key innovation** is a new trait that allows its bearer to exploit a habitat more efficiently or in a novel way. The evolution of lungs offers an example, because lungs were a key innovation that opened the way for an adaptive radiation of vertebrates on land.

Adaptive radiation can also occur after geologic or climatic events eliminate some species from a habitat. The surviving species then have access to resources from

adaptive radiation A burst of genetic divergences from a lineage gives rise to many new species.
coevolution The joint evolution of two closely interacting species; each species is a selective agent for traits of the other.
exaptation Evolutionary adaptation of an existing structure for a completely new purpose.
extinct Refers to a species that no longer has living members.
key innovation An evolutionary adaptation that gives its bearer the opportunity to exploit a particular environment much more efficiently or in a new way.
macroevolution Large-scale evolutionary patterns and trends.
stasis Evolutionary pattern in which a lineage persists with little or no change over evolutionary time.

which they had previously been excluded. This is the way mammals were able to undergo an adaptive radiation after the dinosaurs disappeared.

Coevolution The process by which close ecological interactions between two species cause them to evolve jointly is called **coevolution**. One species acts as an agent of selection on the other, and each adapts to changes in the other. Over evolutionary time, the two species may become so interdependent that they can no longer survive without one another.

Relationships between coevolved species can be quite intricate. Consider the large blue butterfly (*Maculinea arion*), a parasite of ants (**FIGURE 17.22**). After hatching, the larvae (caterpillars) feed on wild thyme flowers and then drop to the ground. An ant that finds a caterpillar strokes it, which makes the caterpillar exude honey. The ant eats the honey and continues to stroke the caterpillar, which secretes more honey. This interaction continues for hours, until the caterpillar suddenly hunches itself up into a shape that appears (to an ant) very much like an ant larva. The deceived ant then picks up the caterpillar and carries it back to the ant nest, where, in most cases, other ants kill it—except, however, if the ants are of the species *Myrmica sabuleti*. Secretions of the caterpillar fool these ants into treating it just like a larva of their own. For the next 10 months, the caterpillar lives in the nest and grows to gigantic proportions by feeding on ant larvae. After it metamorphoses into a butterfly, the insect emerges from the ground to mate. Eggs are deposited on wild thyme near another *M. sabuleti* nest, and the cycle starts anew. This relationship between ant and butterfly is typical of coevolved relationships in that it is extremely specific. Any increase in the ants' ability to identify a caterpillar in their nest selects for caterpillars that better deceive the ants, which in turn select for ants that can better identify the caterpillars. Each species exerts directional selection on the other.

EVOLUTIONARY THEORY

Biologists do not doubt that macroevolution occurs, but many disagree about how it occurs. However we choose to categorize evolutionary processes, the very same genetic change may be at the root of all evolution—fast or slow, large-scale or small-scale. Dramatic jumps in morphology, if they are not artifacts of gaps in the fossil record, may be the result of mutations in homeotic or other regulatory genes. Macroevolution may include more processes than microevolution, or it may not. It may be an accumulation of many microevolutionary events, or it may be an entirely

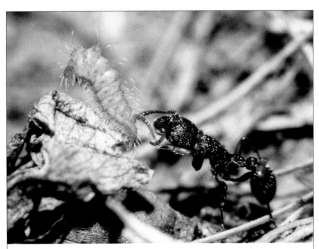

A To a *Myrmica sabuleti* ant, a honey-exuding, hunched-up *Maculinea arion* caterpillar appears to be an ant larva. This deceived ant is preparing to carry the caterpillar back to its nest, where the caterpillar will eat ant larvae for the next 10 months until it pupates.

B A *Maculinea arion* butterfly emerges from the pupa and lays its eggs on wild thyme flowers. Larvae that emerge from the eggs will survive only if a colony of *Myrmica sabuleti* ants adopts them.

FIGURE 17.22 An example of coevolved species.

different process. Evolutionary biologists may disagree about these and other hypotheses, but all of them are trying to explain the same thing: how all species are related by descent from common ancestors.

TAKE-HOME MESSAGE 17.11

Macroevolution comprises large-scale patterns of evolutionary change such as adaptive radiation, the origin of major groups, and mass extinctions.

TABLE 17.2

Examples of Characters

	Bird	Bat	Lion
Warm-blooded	Y	Y	Y
Hair	N	Y	Y
Milk	N	Y	Y
Teeth	N	Y	Y
Wings	Y	Y	N
Feathers	Y	N	N

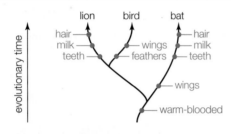

A If the bird and lion are most closely related, the derived traits would have evolved ten times in total.

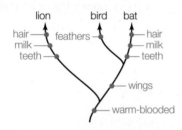

B If the bird and bat are most closely related, the derived traits would have evolved nine times in total.

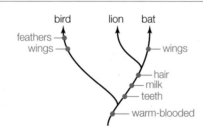

C If the lion and bat are most closely related, the derived traits would have evolved seven times in total.

FIGURE 17.23 An example of cladistics, using parsimony analysis with characters in **TABLE 17.2**.

A, **B**, and **C** show the three possible evolutionary pathways that could connect birds, bats, and lions; red indicates the evolution of a derived trait. The pathway most likely to be correct (**C**) is the simplest—the one in which the derived traits would have had to evolve the fewest number of times in total.

Classifying life's tremendous diversity into a series of taxonomic ranks (Section 1.4) is a useful endeavor, in the same way that it is useful to organize a telephone book or contact list in alphabetical order. Today, however, reconstructing evolutionary relationships among organisms has become at least as important as classifying them. Thus, biologists often focus on unraveling **phylogeny**, the evolutionary history of a species or a group of species. Phylogeny is a kind of genealogy that follows a lineage's evolutionary relationships through time.

Humans were not around to witness the evolution of most species, but we can use evidence to understand events in the ancient past (Chapter 16). For example, each species bears traces of its own unique evolutionary history in its characters. A **character** is a quantifiable, heritable trait, such as the nucleotide sequence of ribosomal RNA or the presence of wings (**TABLE 17.2**).

Traditional classification schemes group organisms based on shared characters: Birds have feathers, cacti have spines, and so on. By contrast, evolutionary biology tries to fit each species into a bigger picture of evolution: Every living thing is related if you just go back far enough in time. Evolutionary biologists pinpoint what makes the organisms share the characters in the first place: a common ancestor. They determine common ancestry by identifying derived traits. A **derived trait** is a character present in a group under consideration, but not in any of the group's ancestors. A group whose members share one or more defining derived traits is called a **clade**. By definition, a clade is a **monophyletic group**: one that consists of an ancestor (in which a derived trait evolved) together with any and all of its descendants.

Each species is a clade. Many higher taxonomic rankings are also equivalent to clades—flowering plants, for example, are both a phylum and a clade—but some are not. For example, the traditional Linnaean class Reptilia ("reptiles") includes crocodiles, alligators, tuataras, snakes, lizards, turtles, and tortoises. While it is convenient to classify these animals together, they would not constitute a clade unless birds are also included, as you will see in Chapter 24.

It is the recent nature of a derived trait that defines a clade. Consider how alligators look a lot more like lizards than birds. In this case, the similarity in appearance does indicate shared ancestry, but it is a more distant relationship than alligators have with birds. Evolutionary biologists discovered that alligators and birds share a more recent common ancestor than alligators and lizards do. Derived traits—a gizzard and a four-chambered heart—evolved in the lineage that gave rise to alligators and birds, but not in the one that gave rise to lizards.

CREDIT: (23) From Starr/Evers/Starr, Biology Today and Tomorrow with Physiology, 4E. © 2013 Cengage Learning.

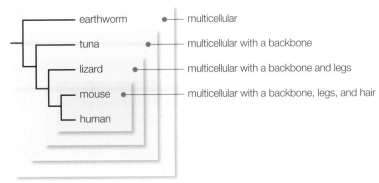

A Evolutionary connections among clades are represented as lines on a cladogram. Sister groups emerge from a node, which represents a common ancestor.

B A cladogram can be viewed as "sets within sets" of derived traits. Each set (an ancestor together with all of its descendants) is a clade.

FIGURE 17.24 {**Animated**} An example of a cladogram.

A species' ancestry remains the same no matter how it evolves. However, as with traditional taxonomy, we can make mistakes grouping organisms into clades if the information we have is incomplete. A clade is necessarily a hypothesis, and which organisms it includes may change when new discoveries are made. As with all hypotheses, the more data that support a cladistic grouping, the less likely it is to require revision.

CLADISTICS

In the big picture of evolution, all clades are interconnected; an evolutionary biologist's job is to figure out where the connections are. Making hypotheses about evolutionary relationships among clades is called **cladistics**. One way of doing this involves the logical rule of simplicity: When there are several possible ways that a group of clades can be connected, the simplest evolutionary pathway is probably the correct one. By comparing all of the possible connections among the clades, we can identify the simplest—the one in which the defining derived traits evolved the fewest number of times. The process of finding the simplest pathway is called parsimony analysis (**FIGURE 17.23**).

The result of a cladistic analysis is an **evolutionary tree**—a diagram of evolutionary connections—called a cladogram. **Cladograms** visually summarize our best data-supported hypotheses about how a group of clades are related (**FIGURE 17.24**). Data from an outgroup (a species not closely related to any member of the group under study) may be included in order to "root" the tree. Each line in a cladogram represents a lineage, which may branch into two lineages at a node. The node represents a common ancestor of two lineages. Every branch of a cladogram is a clade; the two lineages that emerge from a node on a cladogram are called **sister groups**.

character Quantifiable, heritable characteristic or trait.
clade A group whose members share one or more defining derived traits.
cladistics Making hypotheses about evolutionary relationships among clades.
cladogram Evolutionary tree diagram that shows evolutionary connections among a group of clades.
derived trait A novel trait present in a clade but not in the clade's ancestors.
evolutionary tree Diagram showing evolutionary connections.
monophyletic group An ancestor in which a derived trait evolved, together with all of its descendants.
phylogeny Evolutionary history of a species or group of species.
sister groups The two lineages that emerge from a node on a cladogram.

TAKE-HOME MESSAGE 17.12

Evolutionary biologists study phylogeny in order to understand how all species are connected by shared ancestry.

A clade is a monophyletic group whose members share one or more derived traits. Cladistics is a method of making hypotheses about evolutionary relationships among clades.

Cladograms and other evolutionary tree diagrams are hypotheses based on our best understanding of the evolutionary history of a group of organisms.

Researchers often study the evolution of viruses and other infectious agents by grouping them into clades based on biochemical characters. Even though viruses are not alive, they can mutate every time they infect a host, so their genetic material changes over time. Consider the H5N1 strain of influenza (flu) virus, which infects birds and other animals. H5N1 has a very high mortality rate in humans, but human-to-human transmission has been rare to date. However, the virus replicates in pigs without causing symptoms. Pigs transmit the virus to other pigs—and apparently to humans too. A phylogenetic analysis of H5N1 isolated from pigs showed that the virus "jumped" from birds to pigs at least three times since 2005, and that one of the isolates had acquired the potential to be transmitted among humans. An increased understanding of how this virus adapts to new hosts is helping researchers design more effective vaccines for it.

The story of the Hawaiian honeycreepers offers an example of how finding ancestral connections can help species that are still living. The first Polynesians arrived on the Hawaiian Islands sometime before 1000 A.D., and Europeans followed in 1778. Hawaii's rich ecosystem was hospitable to these newcomers and their domestic animals and crops. Escaped livestock began to eat and trample rain forest plants that had provided honeycreepers with food and shelter. Entire forests were cleared to grow imported crops, and plants that escaped cultivation began to crowd out native plants. Mosquitoes accidentally introduced in 1826 spread diseases such as avian malaria from imported chickens to native bird species. Stowaway rats and snakes ate their way through populations of native birds and their eggs. Mongooses deliberately imported to eat the rats and snakes preferred to eat birds and bird eggs.

The very isolation that had spurred adaptive radiations also made honeycreepers vulnerable to extinction. Divergence from the ancestral species had led to the loss of unnecessary traits such as defenses against mainland predators and diseases. Specializations such as extravagantly elongated beaks became hindrances when the birds' habitats suddenly changed or disappeared. Thus, at least 43 honeycreeper species that had thrived on the islands before humans arrived were extinct by 1778. Conservation efforts began in the 1960s, but 26 more species have since disappeared. Today, 35 of the remaining 68 species are endangered (**FIGURE 17.25**). They are still pressured by established populations of invasive, nonnative species of plants and animals. Rising global temperatures are also allowing mosquitoes to invade high-altitude habitats that had previously been too cold for the insects, so honeycreeper species remaining in these habitats are now succumbing to avian malaria and other mosquito-borne diseases.

A The palila has an adaptation that allows it to feed on the seeds of a native Hawaiian plant, which are toxic to most other birds. The one remaining palila population is declining because these plants are being trampled by cows and gnawed to death by goats and sheep. Only about 1,200 palila remained in 2010.

B The unusual lower bill of the akekee points to one side, allowing this bird to pry open buds that harbor insects. Avian malaria carried by mosquitoes to higher altitudes is decimating the last population of this species. Between 2000 and 2007, the number of akekee plummeted from 7,839 birds to 3,536.

C This poouli—rare, old, and missing an eye—died in 2004 from avian malaria. There were two other poouli alive at the time, but neither has been seen since then.

FIGURE 17.25 Three honeycreeper species: going, going, gone.

As more and more honeycreeper species become extinct, the group's reservoir of genetic diversity dwindles. The lowered diversity means the group as a whole is less resilient to change, and more likely to suffer catastrophic losses. Deciphering their phylogeny can tell us which honeycreeper species are most different from the others—and those are the ones most valuable in terms of preserving the group's genetic diversity. Such research allows us to concentrate our resources and conservation efforts on those species that hold the best hope for the survival of the entire group. For example, we now know the poouli (**FIGURE 17.25C**) to be the most distant relative in the honeycreeper family. Unfortunately, the knowledge came too late; the poouli is probably extinct. Its extinction means the loss of a large part of evolutionary history of the group: One of the longest branches of the honeycreeper family tree is gone forever.

TAKE-HOME MESSAGE 17.13

Among other applications, phylogeny research can help us understand the spread of infectious diseases, and also to focus our conservation efforts.

Sustainability

FIGURE 17.26 Abundant use of antibiotics in livestock has contributed to the worldwide prevalence of resistant bacteria.

WE ARE NOW PAYING THE PRICE FOR OVERUSE OF ANTIBIOTICS. Prior to the 1940s, scarlet fever, tuberculosis, and pneumonia caused one-fourth of the annual deaths in the United States. Since the 1940s, we have been relying on antibiotics such as penicillin to fight these and other dangerous bacterial diseases. We have also been using antibiotics in other, less dire circumstances. For an as-yet unknown reason, antibiotics promote growth in cattle, pigs, poultry (**FIGURE 17.26**), and even fish. The agricultural industry uses antibiotics mainly for this purpose. In addition, antibiotics that are used to prevent or treat infection are given to entire flocks or herds at once. In 2011, the U.S. agricultural industry used 13.7 million kilograms of antibiotics—more than four times the amount used to treat people.

Bacteria evolve at a much accelerated rate compared with humans, in part because they reproduce much more quickly. The common intestinal bacteria *E. coli* can divide every 17 minutes. Each new generation is an opportunity for mutation, so a bacterial gene pool can diversify very fast. Different species of bacteria can also share DNA, further adding to the diversity of their respective gene pools.

As you learned in Section 12.1, having a diverse gene pool is an advantage in a changing environment. When a natural bacterial population is exposed to an antibiotic, some cells in it are likely to survive because they carry an allele that offers resistance. As susceptible cells die and the survivors reproduce, the frequency of these antibiotic-resistance alleles increases in the population (an example of directional selection). A typical two-week course of antibiotics can potentially exert selection pressure on over a thousand generations of bacteria, and antibiotic-resistant strains are the outcome.

Antibiotic-resistant bacteria bred inside treated animals and humans end up in the environment, where they can easily spread to other individuals. These bacteria have plagued hospitals for years, and now we find them everywhere. They are common in day-care centers, schools, gyms, prisons, and other places where people are in close contact. We find them in pets and wildlife such as rabbits, mongooses, sharks, rodents, reptiles, and even in Arctic penguins. Drinking water supplies and Antarctic seawater contain them. A recent report found antibiotic-resistant bacteria in more than half of the samples of supermarket ground beef and pork chops, and over 80 percent of ground turkey. Some of these bacteria are resistant to most available antibiotics.

In humans, an infection with antibiotic resistant bacteria tends to be longer, more severe, and more likely to be deadly. The Centers for Disease Control and Prevention says that these "superbugs" contribute to death in up to 50 percent of patients who become infected.

Summary

SECTIONS 17.1, 17.2 All alleles of all genes in a **population** constitute a **gene pool**. Mutations may be **neutral, lethal**, or adaptive. **Microevolution** is change in **allele frequency** of a population. Deviations from **genetic equilibrium** indicate that a population is evolving.

SECTIONS 17.3–17.6 In **directional selection**, a phenotype at one end of a range of variation is adaptive. An intermediate form of a trait is adaptive in **stabilizing selection**; extreme forms are adaptive in **disruptive selection**. **Sexual dimorphism** is one outcome of **sexual selection**. **Frequency-dependent selection** or any other mode of natural selection can give rise to a **balanced polymorphism**.

SECTION 17.7 **Genetic drift**, which is most pronounced in small or **inbreeding** populations, can cause alleles to be **fixed**. The **founder effect** may occur after an evolutionary **bottleneck**. **Gene flow** can counter the effects of mutation, natural selection, and genetic drift.

SECTIONS 17.8–17.10 **Reproductive isolation** is always a part of **speciation** (**TABLE 17.3**). With **allopatric speciation**, a geographic barrier arises and ends gene flow between populations. **Sympatric speciation** occurs with no barrier to gene flow. With **parapatric speciation**, populations in contact along a common border speciate.

SECTION 17.11 **Macroevolution** refers to large-scale patterns of evolution. In **exaptation**, a lineage uses a structure for a different purpose than its ancestor. With **stasis**, a lineage changes little over evolutionary time. A **key innovation** can result in an **adaptive radiation**. **Coevolution** occurs when two species act as agents of selection upon one another. A lineage with no more living members is **extinct**.

SECTION 17.12 Evolutionary biologists reconstruct evolutionary history (**phylogeny**) by comparing physical, behavioral, and biochemical traits, or **characters**, among species. A **clade** is a **monophyletic group** that consists of an ancestor in which one or more **derived traits** evolved, together with all of its descendants. Making hypotheses about the evolutionary history of a group of clades is called **cladistics**. In **evolutionary tree** diagrams such as **cladograms**, each line represents a lineage. A lineage branches into two **sister groups** at a node, which represents a shared ancestor.

SECTION 17.13 Reconstructing phylogeny is part of our efforts to preserve endangered species. It also allows us to understand the spread of some infectious diseases.

SECTION 17.14 Overuse of antibiotics has resulted in directional selection for dangerous antibiotic-resistant bacteria that are now common in the environment.

Self-Quiz   Answers in Appendix VII

1. _____ is the original source of new alleles.
   a. Mutation   d. Gene flow
   b. Natural selection   e. All are original sources of
   c. Genetic drift   new alleles

2. Evolution can only occur in a population when _____ .
   a. mating is random
   b. there is selection pressure
   c. (neither is necessary)

3. Match the modes of natural selection with their best descriptions.
   ___ stabilizing   a. eliminates extreme forms of a trait
   ___ directional   b. eliminates midrange forms of a trait
   ___ disruptive   c. shifts allele frequency in one direction

4. Sexual selection frequently influences aspects of body form and can lead to _____ .
   a. sexual dimorphism   c. exaggerated traits
   b. male aggression   d. all of the above

5. The persistence of the sickle allele at high frequency in a population is an example of _____ .
   a. bottlenecking   c. natural selection
   b. inbreeding   d. balanced polymorphism

6. _____ tends to keep populations of a species similar to one another.
   a. Genetic drift   c. Mutation
   b. Gene flow   d. Natural selection

7. The theory of natural selection does not explain _____ .
   a. genetic drift   d. how mutations arise
   b. the founder effect e. inheritance
   c. gene flow   f. any of the above

8. A fire devastates all trees in a wide swath of forest. Populations of a species of tree-dwelling frog on either side of the burned area diverge to become separate species. This is an example of _____ .

TABLE 17.3

Comparison of Speciation Models

	Allopatric	Parapatric	Sympatric
Original population(s)			
Initiating event:	physical barrier arises	selection pressures differ	genetic change
Reproductive isolation occurs			
New species arises:	in isolation	in contact along common border	within existing population

Data Analysis Activities

Resistance to Rodenticides in Wild Rat Populations Beginning in 1990, rat infestations in northwestern Germany started to intensify despite continuing use of rat poisons. In 2000, Michael H. Kohn and his colleagues analyzed the genetics of wild rat populations around Munich. For part of their research, they trapped wild rats in five towns, and tested those rats for resistance to warfarin and the more recently developed poison bromadiolone. The results are shown in **FIGURE 17.27**.

1. In which of the five towns were most of the rats susceptible to warfarin?
2. Which town had the highest percentage of poison-resistant wild rats?
3. What percentage of rats in Olfen were resistant to warfarin?
4. In which town do you think the application of bromadiolone was most intensive?

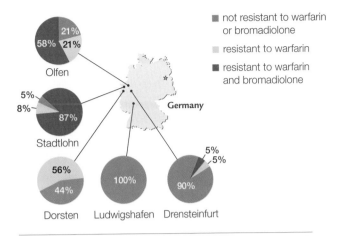

■ not resistant to warfarin or bromadiolone
■ resistant to warfarin
■ resistant to warfarin and bromadiolone

FIGURE 17.27 Resistance to rat poisons in wild populations of rats in Germany, 2000.

9. Sex in many birds is typically preceded by an elaborate courtship dance. If a male's movements are unrecognized by the female, she will not mate with him. This is an example of _____ .
   a. reproductive isolation   c. sexual selection
   b. behavioral isolation   d. all of the above

10. Cladistics _____ .
   a. is a way of reconstructing evolutionary history
   b. may involve parsimony analysis
   c. is based on derived traits
   d. all of the above are correct

11. In cladistics, the only taxon that is always correct as a clade is the _____ .
   a. genus   b. family   c. species   d. kingdom

12. In evolutionary trees, each node represents a(n) _____ .
   a. single lineage   c. point of divergence
   b. extinction   d. adaptive radiation

13. In cladograms, sister groups are _____ .
   a. inbred   c. represented by nodes
   b. the same age   d. in the same family

14. Match the evolutionary concepts.
   ____ gene flow   a. can lead to interdependent species
   ____ sexual   b. changes in a population's allele
        selection   frequencies due to chance alone
   ____ extinct   c. alleles enter or leave a population
   ____ genetic drift   d. evolutionary history
   ____ phylogeny   e. genetic winners are the sexiest
   ____ adaptive   f. burst of divergences
        radiation   g. no more living members
   ____ coevolution   h. evolutionary diagram
   ____ cladogram

Critical Thinking

1. Species have been traditionally characterized as "primitive" and "advanced." For example, mosses were considered to be primitive, and flowering plants advanced; crocodiles were primitive and mammals were advanced. Why do most biologists of today think it is incorrect to refer to any modern species as primitive?

2. Rama the cama, a llama–camel hybrid, was born in 1997. The idea was to breed an animal that has the camel's strength and endurance, and the llama's gentle disposition. However, instead of being large, strong, and sweet, Rama is smaller than expected and has a camel's short temper. The breeders plan to mate him with Kamilah, a female cama. What potential problems with this mating should the breeders anticipate?

3. Two species of antelope, one from Africa, the other from Asia, are put into the same enclosure in a zoo. To the zookeeper's surprise, individuals of the different species begin to mate and produce healthy, hybrid baby antelopes. Explain why a biologist might not view these offspring as evidence that the two species of antelope are in fact one.

4. Some people think that many of our uniquely human traits arose by sexual selection. Over thousands of years, women attracted to charming, witty men perhaps prompted the development of human intellect beyond what was necessary for mere survival. Men attracted to women with juvenile features may have shifted the species as a whole to be less hairy and softer featured than any of our simian relatives. Can you think of a way to test these hypotheses?

CENGAGE To access course materials, please visit
brain.com www.cengagebrain.com.

A low tide exposes rocky structures called stromatolites in Australia's Shark Bay. Bacteria have been building structures like these for billions of years. Fossil stromatolites are among our earliest evidence of life on Earth.

18

LIFE'S ORIGIN AND EARLY EVOLUTION

Links to Earlier Concepts

This chapter explains how scientists investigate life's origin and lays out what we know about life's early history. It draws on your knowledge of scientific method (Section 1.5), plate tectonics (16.5), and the geologic time scale (16.6). We discuss the origin of archaea and bacteria (4.4), and of eukaryotic organelles (4.5). We also return to the link between photosynthesis and aerobic respiration (7.2).

KEY CONCEPTS

BUILDING BLOCKS OF LIFE

Simulations show how organic monomers could have formed on the early Earth. Such compounds also form in space and could have been delivered by meteorites.

THE FIRST CELLS FORM

Experiments provide insight into how cells could have arisen from nonliving material through known physical and chemical processes.

LIFE'S EARLY EVOLUTION

The first cells were anaerobic and prokaryotic. Evolution of oxygen-producing photosynthesis altered Earth's atmosphere, creating selection pressure that favored aerobic organisms.

EUKARYOTIC ORGANELLES

The nucleus and endomembrane system are likely derived from infoldings of the plasma membrane. Bacteria are the ancestors of mitochondria and chloroplasts.

Photograph by Frans Lanting, National Geographic Creative.

CONDITIONS ON THE EARLY EARTH

To understand how life on Earth could have begun, it helps to know a bit about our planet's history. Scientists estimate that Earth formed by about 4.6 billion years ago through the aggregation of dust and rock bits that were orbiting our sun. Although no one has yet discovered rocks that date that far back, geologists have discovered crystals of zircon (a type of mineral) that formed about 4.3 billion years ago. As Section 16.4 explains, zircon crystals form when molten rock cools, and the timing of their formation can be determined by radiometric dating.

Geologists can learn what conditions were like on the early Earth by analyzing ancient crystals and rocks. For example, the composition of some 4.3-billion-year-old zircon crystals indicates that they formed in the presence of water. This suggests that water had begun to pool on Earth's surface by 4.3 billion years ago. The presence of water is important because water is essential to life. All metabolic reactions that take place in cells require water.

We know that Earth's early atmosphere contained little or no oxygen gas, because the oldest existing rocks show no evidence of iron oxidation (rusting). If oxygen had been present, it would have interfered with assembly of simple organic compounds.

FORMATION OF SIMPLE ORGANIC COMPOUNDS

All life consists of the same simple organic compounds (amino acids, fatty acids, nucleotides, and simple sugars). Thus, reactions that formed these compounds were probably the first step on the road to life. There are several ways in which this initial step could have taken place.

In the early 1950s, Stanley Miller and Harold Urey showed that lightning-fueled atmospheric reactions can produce simple organic compounds. They simulated Earth's early atmosphere by filling a reaction chamber with a mix of gases and water vapor, then zapped it with sparks to simulate lightning (**FIGURE 18.1**). Within a week, amino acids and other organic molecules formed. We now know that the mix of gases in the Miller–Urey experiment probably did not accurately represent those present on the early Earth. However, later experiments carried out using more accurate gas mixtures also produced amino acids.

Discovery of organic compounds inside meteorites that fell to Earth suggests another source for life's building blocks. Organic materials that formed in interstellar clouds of ice, dust, and gases could been carried to Earth on

FIGURE 18.1 {Animated} Diagram of an apparatus designed by Stanley Miller and Harold Urey to test whether organic compounds could have formed by chemical interactions in Earth's early atmosphere. Water, hydrogen gas (H_2), methane (CH_4), and ammonia (NH_3) circulated through the apparatus as sparks from an electrode simulated lightning.

 FIGURE IT OUT: Which gas in this mixture provided the nitrogen for the amino group in the amino acids?

Answer: Ammonia

meteorites. Keep in mind that during Earth's early years, meteorites fell to Earth thousands of times more frequently than they do today.

Reactions deep in the sea near hydrothermal vents could also have produced simple organic compounds. A **hydrothermal vent** is an underwater hot spring—a place where superheated, mineral-rich water streams out through a rocky opening. Scientists have simulated conditions near a hydrothermal vent by combining hot water with carbon monoxide (CO), potassium cyanide (KCN), and metal ions like those in rocks near the vents. Under these conditions, amino acids form within a week.

Note that the three mechanisms of organic compound formation discussed above are not mutually exclusive. Most likely all three operated simultaneously and contributed to an accumulation of simple organic compounds in Earth's early seas. It was in these seas that life first began.

TAKE-HOME MESSAGE 18.1

Earth formed by 4.6 billion years ago. By 4.3 billion years ago, it had seas and an atmosphere with little or no oxygen.

Simulations of conditions on the early Earth show organic compounds could have formed in the atmosphere or seas.

Organic compounds also form in space and could have been delivered to Earth by meteorites.

---

hydrothermal vent Underwater opening where hot, mineral-rich water streams out.

National Geographic
Explorer-in-Residence
DR. ROBERT BALLARD

Undersea explorer Bob Ballard is best known for finding wrecks of historic ships such as the RMS *Titanic*. His proudest accomplishment, however, is discovering that life thrives in the deep, dark ocean depths near hydrothermal vents. In 1977, Ballard led a team that used a submersible vehicle to explore a region of the seafloor where tectonic plates are moving apart (as described in Section 16.5). As Ballard and others had predicted, the team found openings (vents) in the seafloor. Mineral-rich water heated by geothermal energy streamed from the vents into the frigid waters of the deep ocean. To Ballard's astonishment, the team also found a wealth of previously unknown life. He says, "We discovered that this whole life system was living not off the energy from the sun, but from the energy of the Earth." Dr. Ballard's discovery led other scientists to reconsider life's origins. Many scientists now think that Earth's earliest life arose deep in the sea near hydrothermal vents.

Left, a black smoker, a type of hydrothermal vent.

CREDITS: From the IMAX film "Volcanoes of the Deep Sea" produced by The Stephen Low Company in association with Rutgers University; (top) O. Louis Mazzatenta/National Geographic Creative.

ON THE ROAD TO LIFE

In addition to sharing the same molecular components, all cells have a plasma membrane with a lipid bilayer. As Chapter 9 explained, cells have a genome of DNA that enzymes transcribe into RNA, and ribosomes that translate RNA into proteins. All cells replicate, and pass on copies of their genetic material to their descendants. The similarities in structure, metabolism, and replication processes among all known organisms are considered evidence that they all are descendants of the same cellular ancestor.

Time has erased all evidence of the earliest cells, but scientists can still investigate this first chapter in life's history. They use their knowledge of chemistry to design experiments that test whether a particular hypothesis about how life began is plausible. Results of such studies support the hypothesis that cells arose as a result of a stepwise process, beginning with inorganic materials (**FIGURE 18.2**). Each step on the road to life can be explained by chemical and physical mechanisms that still operate today.

ORIGIN OF METABOLISM

Modern cells take up organic subunits, concentrate them, and assemble them into organic polymers (Section 3.1). Before there were cells, a nonbiological process that concentrated organic subunits in one place would have increased the chance that the subunits would combine.

By one hypothesis, this process occurred on clay-rich tidal flats. Clay particles have a slight negative charge, so positively charged molecules in seawater stick to them. At low tide, evaporation would have concentrated the subunits even more, and energy from the sun could have caused them to bond together as polymers. In simulations of tidal flat conditions, amino acids assemble in short chains.

By another hypothesis, metabolic reactions began in the high-temperature, high-pressure environment near a hydrothermal vent. Rocks around the vents contain iron sulfide (pyrite) and are porous, with many tiny chambers about the size of cells (**FIGURE 18.3**). Metabolism may have begun when iron sulfide in the rocks donated electrons

FIGURE 18.2 {Animated} Proposed sequence for the evolution of cells. Scientists investigate this process by carrying out experiments and simulations that test hypotheses about feasibility of individual steps.

to dissolved carbon monoxide (CO), forming organic compounds. Under simulated vent conditions, organic compounds such as pyruvate do form and accumulate in rocky chambers. In addition, all modern organisms have proteins that use iron–sulfur clusters as cofactors (Section 5.5). The universal requirement for these cofactors may be a legacy of life's rocky beginnings.

ORIGIN OF THE CELL MEMBRANE

Molecules formed by early synthetic reactions would have floated away from one another unless something enclosed them. In modern cells, a plasma membrane serves this role. If the first reactions took place in tiny rock chambers, the rock would have acted as a boundary. Over time, lipids produced by reactions in a chamber could have accumulated and lined the chamber wall. Such lipid-enclosed collections of interacting molecules may have been the first protocells. A **protocell** is a membrane-enclosed collection of molecules that takes up material and replicates itself.

Experiments by Jack Szostak and others have shown that rock chambers are not necessary for protocell formation. **FIGURE 18.4A** is a computer model of one type of protocell that Szostak investigates. **FIGURE 18.4B** is a photo of a protocell that formed in his laboratory. It has a lipid bilayer membrane enclosing strands of RNA. Such a protocell "grows" by incorporating additional fatty acids

FIGURE 18.3 Cell-sized chambers in iron-sulfide-rich rocks formed by simulations of conditions near hydrothermal vents. Similar chambers could have served as protected environments in which the first metabolic reactions took place.

⊢——⊣ 20 µm

CREDITS: (2) © Cengage Learning; (3) The Geological Society Publishing House Michael J. Russell.

A Computer model of a protocell with a bilayer membrane of fatty acids around strands of RNA.

B Laboratory-formed protocell consisting of RNA-coated clay (red) surrounded by fatty acids and alcohols.

C Field-testing a hypothesis about protocell formation. David Deamer pours a mix of small organic molecules and phosphates into a hot acidic pool in Russia.

FIGURE 18.4 Protocells. Scientists test hypotheses about protocell formation through laboratory simulations and field experiments.

into its membrane and additional nucleotides into its RNA. Mechanical force causes division.

David Deamer studies protocell formation in both the laboratory and the field. In the lab, he has shown that the small organic molecules carried to Earth on meteorites can react with minerals and seawater to form vesicles with a lipid bilayer membrane. In the field, he tests whether specific environmental conditions can facilitate this process. In one experiment, he added a mix of organic subunits to the acidic waters of a clay-rich volcanic pool in Russia (**FIGURE 18.4C**). Although organic subunits bound tightly to the clay, no vesicle-like structures formed. Deamer concluded that hot acidic waters of volcanic springs do not provide conditions that favor protocell formation. He continues to carry out experiments to determine what naturally occurring conditions do favor this process.

ORIGIN OF THE GENOME

All modern cells have a genome of DNA. They pass copies of their DNA to descendant cells, which use instructions encoded in the DNA to build proteins. Some of these proteins are enzymes that synthesize new DNA, which is passed along to descendant cells, and so on. Thus, protein synthesis depends on DNA, which is built by proteins. How did this cycle begin?

In the 1960s, Francis Crick and Leslie Orgel addressed this dilemma by suggesting that RNA may have been the first molecule to encode genetic information. Since then, evidence for an early **RNA world**—a time when RNA both stored genetic information and functioned like an enzyme in protein synthesis—has accumulated. Scientists discovered **ribozymes**, RNAs that function as enzymes, in living cells. For example, the rRNA in ribosomes speeds formation of peptide bonds during protein synthesis (Section 9.3). Other ribozymes cut noncoding bits (introns) out of newly formed RNAs (Section 9.2). In addition, researchers have produced self-replicating ribozymes that copy themselves by assembling free nucleotides.

If the earliest self-replicating genetic systems were RNA-based, then why do all organisms have a genome of DNA? The structure of DNA may hold the answer. Compared to a double-stranded DNA molecule, single-stranded RNA breaks apart more easily and mutates more often. Thus, a switch from RNA to DNA would make larger, more stable genomes possible.

protocell Membranous sac that contains interacting organic molecules; hypothesized to have formed prior to the earliest life forms.
ribozyme RNA that functions as an enzyme.
RNA world Hypothetical early interval when RNA served as the genetic information.

TAKE-HOME MESSAGE 18.2

All living cells carry out metabolic reactions, are enclosed within a plasma membrane, and can replicate themselves.

Concentration of molecules on clay particles or in tiny rock chambers near hydrothermal vents may have helped start metabolic reactions.

Vesicle-like structures with outer membranes can form spontaneously.

An RNA-based system of inheritance may have preceded DNA-based systems.

CREDITS: (4A) © Janet Iwasa; (4B) From Hanczyc, Fujikawa, and Szostak, "Experimental Models of Primitive Cellular Compartments: Encapsulation, Growth, and Division"; www.sciencemag.org, Science 24 October 2003; 302;529, Fig. 2, p. 619. Reprinted with permission of the authors and AAAS, Section 19.5, Chase Studios/Photo Researchers, Inc., Section 19.6–7; (4C) Photo by Tony Hoffman, courtesy of David Deamer.

18.3 WHAT DO WE KNOW ABOUT EARLY CELLS?

TRAITS OF THE UNIVERSAL COMMON ANCESTOR

The processes described in Section 18.2 may have produced cellular life more than once. If so, all but one of those early cell lineages became extinct. We know from analysis of modern genomes that all species on Earth today are descended from a cell that lived as early as 4 billion years ago.

Given what scientists know about relationships among modern species, most assume that this common ancestor was prokaryotic, meaning it did not have a nucleus. Oxygen was scarce on the early Earth, so the ancestral cell must also have been anaerobic (capable of living without oxygen). Other aspects of this cell's metabolism are less clear. It may have been a heterotroph that fermented organic compounds. Alternatively, it may have been an autotroph that stripped electrons from inorganic material and assembled its own food from carbon dioxide. It was most likely not photosynthetic. Photosynthesis is a complicated process that requires the evolution of much specialized metabolic machinery.

A Micrograph of a filament that may be a 3.5-billion-year-old fossilized chain of photosynthetic bacteria.

B Micrograph showing structures that may be fossilized 3.4-billion-year-old sulfur-reducing bacteria.

FIGURE 18.5 Possible microfossils from western Australia.

FIGURE 18.6 Fossil stromatolite. It consists of layered remains of countless photosynthetic bacteria and sediment they captured.

Finding and identifying signs of early cells is a challenge. Cells are microscopic and most have no hard parts to fossilize. In addition, few ancient rocks that might hold early fossils still exist. Tectonic plate movements have destroyed nearly all rocks older than about 4 billion years, and slightly younger rocks have often been subject to heating and other processes that destroy traces of biological material. To add to the difficulty, structures formed by nonbiological processes sometimes resemble fossils. To avoid mistakenly accepting such material as a genuine fossil, scientists constantly reanalyze purported fossil finds and they often question one another's conclusions.

EVIDENCE OF EARLY PROKARYOTIC CELLS

The divergence that led to domains Bacteria and Archaea occurred very early in the history of life, and we have no fossils from before this divergence. At present, the oldest proposed cell microfossils (microscopic fossils) come from rock formations in Western Australia. In 1993, William Schopf proposed that 3.5-billion-year-old filaments in these rocks are fossilized chains of photosynthetic bacteria (**FIGURE 18.5A**). This interpretation has been challenged by other scientists, including Martin Brasier, who notes that mineral deposits that resemble these "fossil" filaments can form by geologic processes.

Brasier has put forward his own proposed contender for the title of oldest fossil cells (**FIGURE 18.5B**). Like Schopf's find, Brasier's cells come from Western Australia, but they are a bit younger, dating back 3.4 billion years. Pyrite in and around these cells suggests they may have been similar to the sulfate-reducing bacteria that live in present-day mud flats. These anaerobic bacteria use sulfur in the same way aerobic organisms use oxygen, that is, as the final electron acceptor in an energy-producing pathway. As a by-product of their metabolism, the bacteria produce hydrogen sulfide gas that combines with iron to form pyrite.

CREDITS: (5A) Courtesy of John Fuerst, University of Queensland, originally published in Archives of Microbiology vol 175, p 413–429 (Lindsay MR, Webb RI, Strous M, Jetten MS, Butler MK, Forde RS, Fuerst JA, Cell compartmentalisation in planctomycetes: novel types of structural organization for the bacteria cell, Arch Microbiol, 2001 Jun, 175(6): 413–29) (5B) Courtesy of David Wacey; (6) © Dr. J. Bret Bennington/Hofstra University.

Additional evidence of early cellular life comes from fossil stromatolites (**FIGURE 18.6**). A **stromatolite** is a rocky conical or dome-shaped structure composed of layers of cells, cell remains, and sediment. It forms when photosynthetic bacteria living in shallow sunlit water form a mat that traps sediments. Once a layer of sediment covers the bacteria, they grow up through it and trap more sediment. Scientists can observe this process in modern stromatolites such as those of Australia's Shark Bay, shown in the chapter's opening photo. The stromatolites in Shark Bay began growing an estimated 2,000 years ago and now stand up to 1.5 meters high. They consist of sediments and cyanobacteria, a group of bacteria that produce oxygen as a by-product of photosynthesis.

The oldest structures that might be fossil stromatolites date to 3.5 billion years ago. They are, however, highly degraded and may have formed by geologic rather than biological processes. Fossils that are undisputed stromatolites first appear about 2.8 billion years ago. Stromatolites reached their peak abundance about 1.25 billion years ago, when they were common worldwide.

EVIDENCE OF EARLY EUKARYOTES

It is difficult to find a nucleus in a fossilized cell, but other traits can indicate that the cell was probably eukaryotic. Eukaryotic cells are generally larger than prokaryotic ones. A cell wall with complex patterns, spines, or spikes likely housed a eukaryote. Researchers also look for biomarkers specific to eukaryotes. A **biomarker** is a substance that occurs only in or predominantly in cells of a specific type. For example, steroids are mainly found in eukaryotes, so traces of steroids are biomarkers for this group.

At present, the oldest widely accepted eukaryote microfossils date to about 1.8 billion years ago. The fossils resemble resting stage cells (cysts) that form during the life cycle of some present-day marine protists. However, we do not know whether these early fossil eukaryotes are related to any modern groups.

---

biomarker Substance found only or mainly in cells of one type.
stromatolite Rocky structures composed of layers of bacterial cells and sediments.

Many types of bacteria carry out photosynthesis, but only cyanobacteria do so by an oxygen-producing pathway (**FIGURE 18.7**). Evolution of oxygen-producing photosynthesis had a dramatic effect on early life. By about 2.5 billion years ago, oxygen released by cyanobacteria began to accumulate in Earth's seas and air (Section 7.2).

FIGURE 18.7 Fossilized chain of cyanobacteria from about 850 million years ago. Such cells produce oxygen as a by-product of photosynthesis. Activity of such cells added oxygen to Earth's seas and air.

In the seas, increased oxygen created a new selective pressure. Oxygen was toxic to many species that had evolved in its absence. It reacted with metal ions in their cells, forming free radicals (Section 2.2) that damaged essential cell components. Species that could not detoxify free radicals either went extinct or became restricted to the low-oxygen environments that remained.

By contrast, species with metabolic machinery capable of detoxifying oxygen thrived. Some cells began to carry out aerobic respiration, in which oxygen serves as the final electron acceptor (Section 7.5). As you will learn, one group of aerobic bacteria later evolved into mitochondria, the organelles that power eukaryotic cells.

An increase in atmospheric oxygen also led to formation of the **ozone layer**, a region of the upper atmosphere that contains a high concentration of ozone gas (O_3). The ozone layer absorbs ultraviolet (UV) radiation from the sun, preventing it from reaching Earth's surface. As Section 8.5 explained, such radiation is a dangerous mutation. Before the ozone layer formed, life existed only in the seas, where water shielded organisms from incoming UV radiation. Without an ozone layer to screen out some of this radiation, life could not have moved onto land.

---

ozone layer Atmospheric region with a high concentration of ozone (O_3) that screens out incoming UV radiation.

TAKE-HOME MESSAGE 18.3

All present-day life descended from the same anaerobic prokaryotic cell.

Microfossils show prokaryotic cells were present by 3.4 billion years ago and eukaryotic cells by 1.8 billion years ago.

Fossil stromatolites provide evidence of photosynthetic prokaryotes.

TAKE-HOME MESSAGE 18.4

Oxygen released by photosynthetic cyanobacteria began accumulating in the air and seas about 2.5 billion years ago.

As oxygen levels rose, species capable of detoxifying oxygen had a selective advantage.

Oxygen reacted in the upper atmosphere to form an ozone layer that shielded Earth's surface from UV radiation, making life on land possible.

ORIGIN OF THE NUCLEUS

The DNA of most prokaryotes lies unenclosed in the cell's cytoplasm. By contrast, the DNA of a eukaryotic cell is always enclosed within a nucleus and associated with an endomembrane system. The nucleus and endomembrane system probably evolved when the plasma membrane of an ancestral prokaryote folded inward (FIGURE 18.8).

Studies of the few types of bacteria that have internal membranes illustrates that such infolding does occur and how it can be advantageous. For example, some modern marine bacteria have membrane infoldings that increase the surface area available to hold membrane-associated enzymes.

Internal membranes also protect a genome from physical or biological threats. Consider *Gemmata obscuriglobus*, one of the few bacteria that houses its DNA inside a membrane (FIGURE 18.9). Like a eukaryotic nuclear envelope (Section 4.5), this membrane consists of a two lipid bilayer, but it does not have the equivalent nuclear pores. Compared to typical bacteria, *Gemmata obscuriglobus* withstands much higher levels of mutation-causing radiation. Researchers attribute this species' radiation resistance to the tighter packing, and therefore higher shielding, of its DNA within the membrane-enclosed compartment. The DNA of other bacteria is more vulnerable to radiation because it is more spread out. The membrane also helps prevent the cells' DNA from integrating any foreign genetic material. For example, it provides protection from viruses that inject their genetic material into bacterial cells.

ORIGIN OF MITOCHONDRIA AND CHLOROPLASTS

The **endosymbiont hypothesis** proposes that mitochondria and chloroplasts are descendants of aerobic bacteria that entered and replicated inside a host cell. Whether this host was a prokaryotic cell or an early eukaryote remains unclear. When the host cell divided, it passed some "guest" cells, referred to as endosymbionts, along to its offspring. As the two species lived together over many generations, genes that both partners carried were free to mutate. A gene could lose its function in one partner if the duplicate gene carried by the other partner still worked. Eventually, the host and endosymbiont became incapable of living independently. The endosymbionts had evolved into organelles.

FIGURE 18.8 {Animated} One hypothesis for the steps in organelle evolution.

Membrane infolding produced the endomembrane system. Then, an early endosymbiosis produced mitochondria, which occur in almost all eukaryotes. Later, photosynthetic bacteria entered a eukaryotic cell and, over many generations, evolved into chloroplasts.

ancestral prokaryote — DNA

aerobic bacteria are engulfed or infect the cell

infoldings of the plasma membrane

infoldings evolve into the nuclear envelope and endomembrane system

aerobic bacteria evolve into mitochondria

photosynthetic bacteria

engulfed photosynthetic bacteria evolve into chloroplasts

Eukaryotic cells: animals, fungi, some protists

Eukaryotic cells: plants, some protists

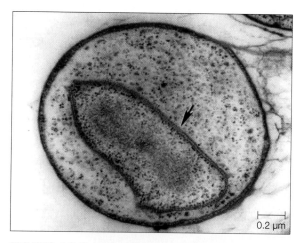

0.2 μm

FIGURE 18.9 Nucleus-like structure in a prokaryote. The DNA of *Gemmata obscuriglobus*, a species of bacteria, is enclosed by a double lipid bilayer membrane (indicated by the arrow).

CREDITS: (8) From RUSSELL/WORLFE/HERTZ/STARR, *Biology*, 2E, © 2011 Cengage Learning Inc. Reproduced by permission. www.cengage.com/permissions. (9) Courtesy of John Fuerst, University of Queensland. originally published in Archives of *Microbiology* vol 175, p 413–429 (Lindsay MR, Webb RI, Strous M, Jetten MS, Butler MK, Forde RJ, Fuerst JA. Cell compartmentalisation in planctomycetes: novel types of structural organisation for the bacterial cell. *Arch Microbiol*. 2001 Jun;175(6):413–29).

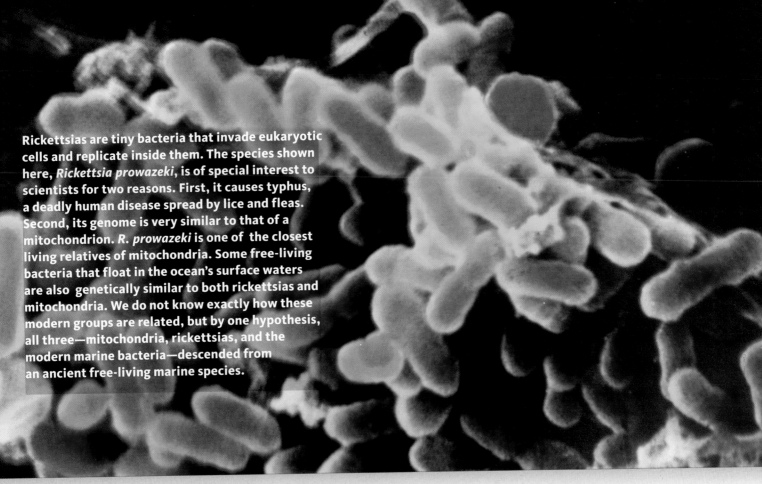

Rickettsias are tiny bacteria that invade eukaryotic cells and replicate inside them. The species shown here, *Rickettsia prowazeki*, is of special interest to scientists for two reasons. First, it causes typhus, a deadly human disease spread by lice and fleas. Second, its genome is very similar to that of a mitochondrion. *R. prowazeki* is one of the closest living relatives of mitochondria. Some free-living bacteria that float in the ocean's surface waters are also genetically similar to both rickettsias and mitochondria. We do not know exactly how these modern groups are related, but by one hypothesis, all three—mitochondria, rickettsias, and the modern marine bacteria—descended from an ancient free-living marine species.

FIGURE 18.10 Modern relatives of mitochondria.

As evidence in support of the endosymbiont hypothesis, mitochondria and chloroplasts resemble bacteria in their size and shape, and they replicate independently of the cell that holds them. Like bacteria, they have their own DNA in the form of a single circular chromosome. They also have at least two outer membranes, with the innermost membrane structurally similar to a bacterial plasma membrane.

Metabolic and genetic similarities between organelles and specific bacterial groups are taken as evidence of shared ancestry. So far, two groups of bacteria have been identified as possible close relatives of mitochondria (**FIGURE 18.10**). Chloroplasts are thought to have evolved from cyanobacteria. Cyanobacteria are the only modern bacteria that, like chloroplasts, carry out photosynthesis by a pathway that produces oxygen.

Nearly all eukaryotic lineages have mitochondria or mitochondria-like organelles, but only some have chloroplasts. Thus, biologists postulate that the two types of organelles were acquired independently in the sequence illustrated in **FIGURE 18.8**.

The endosymbiont hypothesis assumes that cells can enter and live inside other cells. It also assumes that such a relationship can, over time, become essential to the partners. Studies of modern-day cell partnerships lend support to both assumptions. One such study was carried out by microbiologist Kwang Jeon. In 1966, Jeon was studying *Amoeba proteus*, a species of single-celled protist. By accident, his amoebas became infected by a rod-shaped bacterium. Most infected amoebas died right away. A few, however, survived and reproduced despite their infection. Intrigued, Jeon maintained these infected cultures to see what would happen. Five years later, the descendant amoebas were host to many bacterial cells, yet they seemed healthy. In fact, when these amoebas were treated with bacteria-killing drugs that usually do not harm amoebas, they died. Apparently the amoebas had come to require the bacteria for some life-sustaining function. Further investigations revealed that the amoebas had lost the ability to make an essential enzyme. They now depended on their bacterial partners to make that enzyme for them.

TAKE-HOME MESSAGE 18.5

The nucleus and endomembrane system may have evolved from infoldings of the plasma membrane.

Mitochondria and chloroplasts may have evolved when bacterial endosymbionts and their hosts became mutually dependent.

endosymbiont hypothesis Theory that mitochondria and chloroplasts evolved from bacteria that entered and lived in a host cell.

The evolutionary events discussed in earlier sections of this chapter took place during a very long interval of time commonly called the Precambrian (**FIGURE 18.11**). The **Precambrian** encompasses almost all of Earth's history, from its origin 4.6 billion years ago to the beginning of the Cambrian period (542 million years ago). The Cambrian was the first period in our current geologic eon.

The Precambrian opened on a lifeless planet. By 4.3 billion years ago, water had pooled in seas and allowed protocells to form ❶. Cells may have evolved more than once, but all present-day life descends from the same single-celled prokaryotic anaerobe ❷. An early divergence separated the domains Bacteria and Archaea ❸. Later, an evolutionary branching from the Archaea became the domain Eukarya ❹. As oxygen released by cyanobacteria began to accumulate, aerobic cells thrived. One type of aerobic bacteria evolved into the mitochondria of early eukaryotes ❺. Similarly, cyanobacteria that partnered with one lineage of eukaryotes evolved into chloroplasts ❻.

Multicellularity evolved in several eukaryotic lineages ❼. A **multicellular organism** consists of interdependent cells that differ in their structure and function. The oldest fossil of a multicellular organism that we can assign to a modern group is a filamentous red alga that lived in the ocean about 1.2 billion years ago.

Two of the most familiar eukaryotic groups, fungi and animals, arose in the sea during the late Precambrian. The oldest fossil fungi are single celled flagellates. One group of modern fungi (chytrids) retains this form. The oldest animal fossils that scientists can assign to a modern group are sponges.

multicellular organism Organism that consists of interdependent cells of multiple types.
Precambrian Period from 4.6 billion to 542 million years ago.

TAKE-HOME MESSAGE 18.6

Life arose and diversified during the Precambrian. By the close of this period, bacteria, archaea, and eukaryotes—including early fungi and animals—lived in the seas.

FIGURE 18.11 {Animated} Important Precambrian events.

❶ The first protocells form in Earth's seas.

❷ Single-celled prokaryotic ancestor of all modern life evolves.

❸ Bacteria and Archaea diverge.
❹ Eukarya diverge from Archaea.

❺ Aerobic bacteria enter an early eukaryotic cell and evolve into mitochondria.

❻ Oxygen-producing photosynthetic bacteria enter a eukaryotic cell, evolve into chloroplasts.

❼ Multicellularity evolves independently in several eukaryotic lineages.

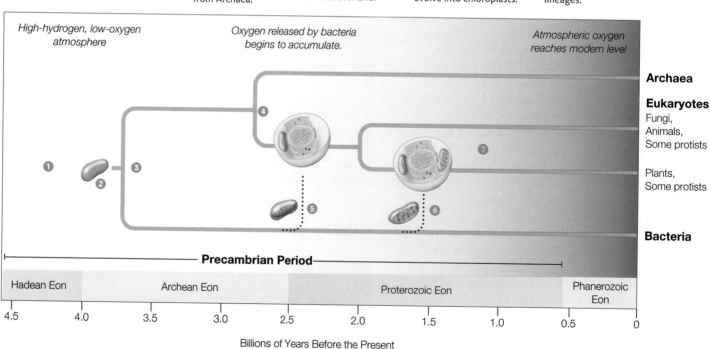

CREDITS: (11) © Cengage Learning.

FIGURE 18.12 Mars-like landscape of Chile's Atacama Desert. Scientist Jay Quade, visible in the distance at the right, was a member of a team that found bacteria living beneath this desert soil. The inset photo shows the relative sizes of Earth and Mars.

WE LIVE IN A VAST UNIVERSE THAT WE HAVE ONLY BEGUN TO EXPLORE. So far, we know of only one planet that has life—Earth. In addition, biochemical, genetic, and metabolic similarities among Earth's species imply that all evolved from a common ancestor that lived billions of years ago. What properties of the ancient Earth allowed life to arise, survive, and diversify? Could similar processes occur on other planets? These are some of the questions posed by astrobiology, the study of life's origins and distribution in the universe.

Astrobiologists study Earth's extreme habitats to determine the range of conditions that living things can tolerate. One group found bacteria living about 30 centimeters (1 foot) below the soil surface of Chile's Atacama Desert, a place said to be the driest on Earth (**FIGURE 18.12**). Another group drilled 3 kilometers (almost 2 miles) beneath the soil surface in Virginia, and found bacteria thriving at high pressure and temperature. They named their find *Bacillus infernus*, or "bacterium from hell."

Knowledge gained from studies of life on Earth inform the search for extraterrestrial life. On Earth, all metabolic reactions involve interactions among molecules in aqueous solution (dissolved in water). We assume that the same physical and chemical laws operate throughout the universe, so liquid water is considered an essential requirement for life. Thus, scientists were excited when a robotic lander discovered ice in the soil of Mars, our closest planetary neighbor. If there is life on Mars, it is likely to be underground. Mars has no ozone layer, so ultraviolet radiation would fry organisms at the planet's surface. However, Martian life may exist in deep rock layers just as it does on Earth.

Any Martian life is also almost certainly anaerobic. Mars is only about half the size of Earth. As a result of its smaller size, Mars has less gravity than Earth and is less able to keep atmospheric gases from drifting off into space. The relatively small amount of atmosphere that remains consists mainly of carbon dioxide, some nitrogen, and only traces of oxygen.

Suppose scientists do find evidence of microbial life on Mars or another planet. Why would it matter? Such a discovery would support the hypothesis that life on Earth arose as a consequence of physical and chemical processes that occur throughout the universe. The discovery of extraterrestrial microbes would also make the possibility of nonhuman intelligent life in the universe more likely. The more places life exists, the more likely it is that complex, intelligent life evolved on other planets in the same manner that it did on Earth.

Summary

SECTION 18.1   Earth formed by about 4.6 billion years ago, and by 4.3 billion years ago water had begun to pool in shallow seas. Earth's early seas and atmosphere were free of oxygen gas, as demonstrated by the lack of rust in the oldest remaining rocks.

Laboratory simulations demonstrate that the simple organic building blocks of life could have formed by lightning-fueled reactions in the atmosphere or as a result of reactions in hot, mineral-rich water around **hydrothermal vents**. Such compounds also form in deep space and can be carried to Earth by meteorites.

SECTION 18.2   Researchers carry out experiments to determine whether their hypotheses about steps on the road to life are plausible. Such experiments show that metabolic reactions could have begun after proteins formed spontaneously on an clay-rich tidal flat. Clay attracts amino acids that can bond under the heat of the sun. Metabolic reactions could also have begun in tiny cavities in rocks near deep-sea hydrothermal vents.

Laboratory-produced vesicles serve as a model for the **protocells** that likely preceded cells.

DNA now serves as the molecule of inheritance for all life. However, an **RNA world** may have preceded the current DNA-based system. RNA still is a part of ribosomes that carry out protein synthesis in all organisms. Existence of **ribozymes**, RNAs that act as enzymes, lends support to the RNA world hypothesis. A later switch from RNA to DNA would have made the genome more stable.

SECTION 18.3   Genetic studies indicate that all modern life descended from an anaerobic prokaryotic cell that lived about 4 billion years ago. The divergence of bacteria and archaea occurred soon thereafter.

The small size of cells, lack of hard parts, and destruction and alteration of rocks by geologic processes make it difficult to find and identify evidence of very early life. The oldest microfossils of prokaryotic cells date to about 3.5 billion years ago. The oldest stromatolite fossils date to about the same time. **Stromatolites** are dome-shaped rocky structures that form over thousands of years as colonies of photosynthetic bacteria trap sediment. In some locations, stromatolites are still forming as a result of the activity of oxygen-releasing cyanobacteria.

Fossils of large cells and cells with elaborate cell walls are considered likely eukaryotes, as are fossils associated with certain **biomarkers**. The earliest such fossil cells date to about 1.8 billion years ago.

SECTION 18.4   After photosynthesis evolved, oxygen released by cyanobacteria accumulated in Earth's air and seas. The increased oxygen in air and water favored cells that carried out aerobic respiration. This ATP-forming metabolic pathway was a key innovation in the evolution of eukaryotic cells.

Oxygen molecules react in Earth's upper atmosphere to form an **ozone layer**. Formation of the ozone layer provided protection from UV radiation and may have opened the way for life to move onto land.

SECTION 18.5   Internal membranes typical of eukaryotic cells may have evolved through infoldings of the plasma membrane of prokaryotic ancestors. The existence of internal membranes in some present-day bacteria supports this hypothesis.

Mitochondria and chloroplasts resemble bacteria in their size, shape, genome, and membrane structure. The **endosymbiont hypothesis** holds that these organelles are in fact modified bacteria. Presumably, bacteria entered a host cell and, over generations, host and guest cells came to depend on one another for essential metabolic processes. Mitochondria are descended from aerobic bacteria similar to modern rickettsias; chloroplasts, from cyanobacteria.

Support for the endosymbiont hypothesis comes from observation of modern instances in which bacterial cells have taken up permanent residence inside eukaryotes.

SECTION 18.6   The interval from 4.6 billion years ago to 542 million years ago is called the **Precambrian**. All three domains of life (Bacteria, Archaea, and Eukarya) evolved during the Precambrian. By the close of the Precambrian, **multicellular organisms** such as red algae and sponges lived in the seas.

SECTION 18.7   Astrobiology is the study of life's origin and distribution in the universe. The discovery of cells in deserts and deep below Earth's surface suggests that life may exist in similar settings on other planets. If life exists on Mars, it must be anaerobic, because the thin Martian atmosphere contains little oxygen.

Self-Quiz   Answers in Appendix VII

1. An abundance of _____ in Earth's early atmosphere would have prevented the spontaneous assembly of organic compounds on early Earth.
   a. hydrogen   b. methane   c. oxygen   d. nitrogen

2. Miller and Urey created a reaction chamber that simulated conditions in Earth's early atmosphere to test the hypothesis that _____ .
   a. lightning-fueled atmoheric reactions could have produced organic compounds
   b. meteorites contain organic compounds
   c. organic compounds form at hydrothermal vents
   d. oxygen prevents formation of organic compounds

3. The prevalence of iron–sulfur cofactors in organisms supports the hypothesis that life arose _____ .
   a. in outer space   c. near deep-sea vents
   b. on tidal flats   d. in the upper atmosphere

Data Analysis Activities

A Changing Earth Modern conditions on Earth are unlike those when life first evolved. **FIGURE 18.13** shows how the frequency of asteroid impacts and the composition of the atmosphere have changed over time. Use this figure and information in the chapter to answer the following questions.

1. Which occurred first a decline in asteroid impacts, or a rise in the atmospheric level of oxygen?
2. How do modern levels of carbon dioxide and oxygen compare to those at the time when the first cells arose?
3. Which is now more abundant, oxygen or carbon dioxide?

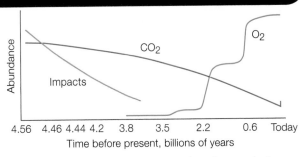

FIGURE 18.13 How asteroid impacts (green), atmospheric carbon dioxide concentration (pink), and oxygen concentration (blue) changed over geologic time.

4. RNA in ribosomes catalyzes formation of peptide bonds in all organisms. This supports the hypothesis that _____ .
   a. an RNA world existed prior to the rise of DNA
   b. RNA can hold more information than DNA
   c. only protists use RNA as their genetic material
   d. all of the above

5. By one hypothesis, clay _____ .
   a. facilitated assembly of early polypeptides
   b. was present at hydrothermal vents
   c. provided energy for early metabolism
   d. served as an early genome

6. The evolution of _____ resulted in an increase in the levels of atmospheric oxygen.
   a. protocells
   b. the ozone layer
   c. oxygen-producing photosynthesis
   d. multicellular eukaryotes

7. Mitochondria most resemble _____ .
   a. archaea   c. cyanobacteria
   b. aerobic bacteria   d. early eukaryotes

8. The presence of ozone in the upper atmosphere protects life from _____ .
   a. free radicals   c. viruses
   b. ultraviolet (UV) radiation   d. ionizing radiation

9. A ribozyme consists of _____ .
   a. clay   b. DNA   c. RNA   d. lipids

10. A rise in oxygen in Earth's air and seas put organisms that engaged in _____ at a selective advantage.
    a. aerobic respiration   c. photosynthesis
    b. fermentation   d. sexual reproduction

11. Which of the following was not present on Earth when chloroplasts first evolved?
    a. archaea   c. protists
    b. bacteria   d. animals

12. Chloroplasts most resemble _____ .
    a. archaea   c. cyanobacteria
    b. aerobic bacteria   d. early eukaryotes

13. During the Precambrian, _____ .
    a. protocells formed
    b. some bacteria evolved into mitochondria
    c. multicellular eukaryotes evolved
    d. all of the above

14. Arrange these events in order of occurrence, with 1 being the earliest and 6 the most recent.
    ___ 1   a. water pools to form
    ___ 2   Earth's first seas
    ___ 3   b. origin of mitochondria
    ___ 4   c. first protocells form
    ___ 5   d. Precambrian ends
    ___ 6   e. origin of chloroplasts
                 f. first animals appear

Critical Thinking

1. Researchers looking for fossils of the earliest life forms face many hurdles. For example, few sedimentary rocks date back more than 3 billion years. Review what you learned about plate tectonics (Section 16.5). Explain why so few remaining samples of these early rocks remain.

2. Rickettsias always live as parasites inside eukaryotic cells, and their genomes are much smaller than those of free-living bacteria. Organisms that live only as parasites often have reduced genomes compared to their free-living relatives. How could a parasitic lifestyle contribute to a reduction in genome size?

CENGAGE To access course materials, please visit
brain   www.cengagebrain.com.
.com

A population explosion of photosynthetic cyanobacteria colors water of California's Klamath River green.

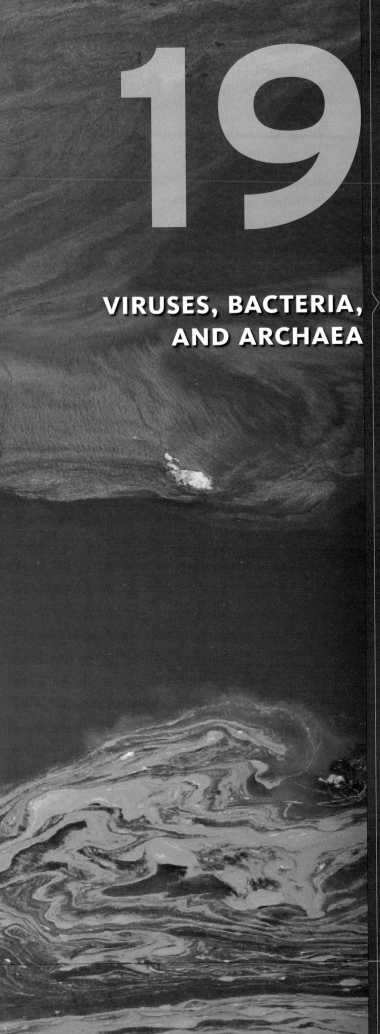

19

VIRUSES, BACTERIA, AND ARCHAEA

Links to Earlier Concepts

This chapter's discussion of viruses and viroids touches on reverse transcription (Section 15.1), ribozymes (18.2), DNA repair (8.5), and cancer (11.5). The chapter also covers bacteria and archaea (4.4). You will learn more about the three-domain classification system (1.4), bacteria that gave rise to organelles (18.5), and antibiotic resistance (17.14).

KEY CONCEPTS

VIRUSES AND VIROIDS

Viruses are noncellular, with a protein coat and a genome of nucleic acid. They must infect cells to replicate. Viroids are RNAs that infect plants.

FEATURES OF "PROKARYOTES"

Bacteria and archaea are small, structurally simple, and metabolically diverse. They divide by binary fission and can exchange genes among existing individuals.

BACTERIAL DIVERSITY

Bacteria put oxygen into the air, supply plants with essential nitrogen, and decompose materials. Some that live in or on our body benefit us, but others are pathogens.

ARCHAEAL DIVERSITY

The archaea were discovered relatively recently. Some species live in very hot or very salty places; others live in human or animal bodies. Few contribute to human disease.

VIRAL CHARACTERISTICS

A **virus** is a noncellular infectious particle that can replicate only in a living cell. A typical virus is so tiny that you would need an electron microscope to see it. A virus does not have ribosomes or other metabolic machinery, but it does have a genome of RNA or DNA. By many definitions, viruses are not alive. However, because they are replicators with a genome that can mutate, they do evolve by natural selection.

A free viral particle (a virus outside a cell) always has a genome enclosed within a protein coat. In some cases, the coat also encloses viral enzymes. Coat proteins protect the viral genome and facilitate its delivery into a host cell. In all viruses, some proteins of the viral coat must bind to proteins at the surface of a host cell during infection.

Viruses are either enveloped or nonenveloped. Most plant viruses are non-enveloped, meaning their protein coat is their outermost layer (**FIGURE 19.1A**). By contrast, most animal viruses have an envelope, a layer of cell membrane derived from the cell in which the virus formed (**FIGURE 19.1B**).

VIRAL REPLICATION

Viral replication begins when a virus attaches to membrane proteins of an appropriate host cell. After attachment, viral genetic material enters the cell. The result is a cellular hijacking. An infected cell puts aside normal tasks and instead produces viral components. These components self-assemble as new viral particles and are released from the cell.

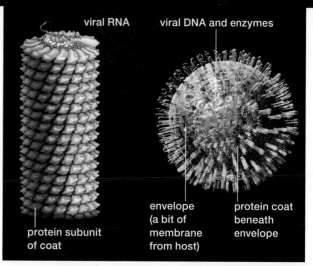

viral RNA   viral DNA and enzymes

envelope (a bit of membrane from host)   protein coat beneath envelope

protein subunit of coat

A Tobacco mosaic virus, a nonenveloped plant virus.

B Herpesvirus, an enveloped animal virus.

FIGURE 19.1 {Animated} Examples of viral structure.

Bacteriophage replication Viruses known as **bacteriophages** (or phages for short) infect bacteria and archaea. Phages have two replication pathways (**FIGURE 19.2**). Both begin when the phage attaches to a bacterium and injects DNA. In the **lytic pathway** (steps A–E), this DNA is put to use immediately, causing the host cell to produce new viral DNA and proteins. The viral components assemble as virus particles, which escape when the cell breaks open (lyses) and dies.

FIGURE IT OUT: What does the blue circle in A represent?

Answer: The bacterial chromosome

FIGURE 19.2 {Animated} Bacteriophage replication pathways.

E Lysis of the host cell releases phages.

A Phage binds to bacterial cell, inserts viral DNA (red).

A1 Phage DNA inserts into host chromosome (blue).

A2 Chromosome with integrated viral DNA is replicated.

Lytic Pathway

Lysogenic Pathway

D New phage particles form inside the host cell.

B Host replicates viral DNA, builds viral proteins.

A3 During cell division, new cells inherit a chromosome with viral DNA.

C Viral components meet up and self-assemble.

A4 Viral DNA is excised from chromosome and becomes active.

CREDITS: (1A) After Stephen L. Wolfe; (1B) © Russell Knightly/Science Source; (2) photo, Science Photo Library/Science Source; art, © Cengage Learning.

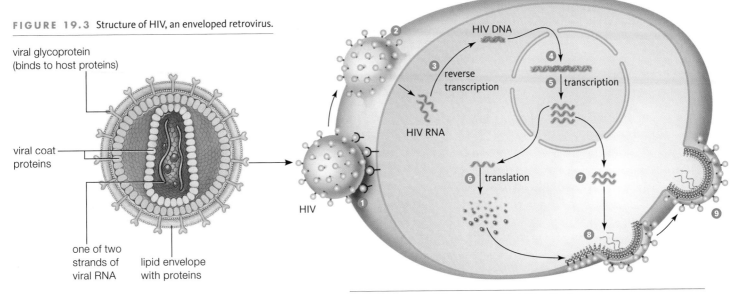

FIGURE 19.3 Structure of HIV, an enveloped retrovirus.

viral glycoprotein
(binds to host proteins)

viral coat
proteins

one of two
strands of
viral RNA

lipid envelope
with proteins

HIV DNA

reverse
transcription

transcription

HIV RNA

translation

HIV

FIGURE 19.4 {Animated} HIV replication.

❶ Viral protein binds to proteins at the surface of a white blood cell.
❷ Viral RNA and enzymes enter the cell.
❸ Viral reverse transcriptase uses viral RNA to make double-stranded viral DNA.
❹ Viral DNA enters the nucleus and is integrated into the host genome.
❺ Transcription produces viral RNA.
❻ Some viral RNA is translated to produce viral proteins.
❼ Other viral RNA forms the new viral genome.
❽ Viral proteins and viral RNA self-assemble at the host plasma membrane.
❾ New virus buds from the host cell, with an envelope of host plasma membrane.

Viral DNA also becomes integrated into the host cell's genome in the **lysogenic pathway** (steps A1–A4). However, viral genes are not expressed, so the host cell remains healthy. When this cell reproduces, a copy of the viral DNA is passed on along with the host's genome. Like miniature time bombs, the viral DNA in descendant cells awaits a signal to enter the lytic pathway.

Some bacteriophages always replicate by the lytic pathway. They kill their host cell quickly and are not passed from one bacterial generation to the next. Others replicate by either the lytic or lysogenic pathway, depending on conditions in the host cell.

HIV replication **HIV (human immunodeficiency virus)** (**FIGURE 19.3**) is an enveloped RNA virus that causes the disease known as AIDS (acquired immunodeficiency syndrome). HIV replicates inside human white blood cells (**FIGURE 19.4**). During infection, spikes of viral protein attach to proteins in the cell's plasma membrane ❶. The viral envelope and the membrane fuse, allowing viral enzymes and RNA to enter the cell ❷. One of these enzymes, reverse transcriptase, converts viral RNA into double-stranded DNA that the cell can transcribe ❸. RNA

viruses that use reverse transcriptase to produce viral DNA in a host are called **retroviruses**. Once viral DNA is made, it is moved into the nucleus, along with another viral enzyme that integrates it into a host chromosome ❹. The viral DNA is then transcribed along with host genes ❺. Some of the resulting viral RNA is translated into viral proteins ❻, and some becomes the genetic material of new HIV particles ❼. These particles self-assemble at the plasma membrane ❽ and a bit of the blood cell's plasma membrane becomes their viral envelope ❾.

Drugs that fight HIV interfere with viral binding to the host, reverse transcription, integration of DNA, or processing of viral polypeptides to form viral proteins.

bacteriophage Virus that infects bacteria.
HIV (human immunodeficiency virus) Virus that causes AIDS.
lysogenic pathway Bacteriophage replication path in which viral DNA becomes integrated into the host's chromosome and is passed to the host's descendants.
lytic pathway Bacteriophage replication pathway in which a virus immediately replicates in its host and kills it.
retrovirus RNA virus that uses the enzyme reverse transcriptase to produce viral DNA in a host cell.
virus Noncellular, infectious particle of protein and nucleic acid; replicates only in a host cell.

CREDITS: (3, 4) © Cengage Learning.

PEOPLE MATTER

Virologist
DR. NATHAN WOLFE

Where will the next global health threat arise and what can we do to head it off? National Geographic Explorer Dr. Nathan Wolfe is working to create an early warning system that can forecast and contain new plagues before they kill millions. He says, "The way that pandemics come to us is through our interaction with animals. That's true whether it's swine flu (H1N1), bird flu, Ebola, or HIV. These are all animal diseases that jumped to humans." Wolfe monitors hunters and other individuals who have high levels of contact with wild animals. When these individuals butcher an animal, they collect a spot of the animal's blood that is analyzed for viruses. "We watch as the viruses are pinging at us, and when something takes hold in humans, we sound the alarm." Wolfe recalls, "When I started this work in 1999, we were particularly interested in retroviruses because we knew they had the potential to cause devastating pandemics like HIV. But we didn't have a good idea of the frequency with which they were crossing over from animals to humans. Our results were shocking. We discovered that cross-species transmission wasn't rare; it was happening on a regular basis." Despite the many threats, Wolfe remains optimistic. "It's really the dawn of a new scientific era. As we try to detect viruses that can do great harm, we could also discover the next generation of vaccines and cures. If we can provide even a few months of early warning for just one pandemic, the benefits will outweigh all the time and energy we're devoting. Imagine preventing health crises, not just responding to them."

COMMON VIRAL DISEASES

Some viruses live in our body without any ill effects, but other are **pathogens**, meaning they cause disease. Viral diseases usually produce mild symptoms and sicken us only briefly. For example, some viruses infect cells in our upper respiratory system and cause common colds. Viruses that infect cells in the lining of our gut often cause a brief bout of vomiting and diarrhea.

Other viral pathogens persist in our body for long periods. Typically, an initial infection causes symptoms that subside quickly. However, the virus remains present in a latent state and can reawaken later on. For example, herpes simplex virus 1 (HSV-1) remains dormant in nerve cells for years. When activated, it replicates and causes painful "cold sores" at the edge of the lips (**FIGURE 19.5**). Another herpesvirus causes similar sores on the genitals.

A few types of viral infections increase the risk of cancer. Infection by certain strains of sexually transmitted human papillomaviruses (HPV) is the main cause of cervical cancer. Similarly, infection by some hepatitis viruses raises the risk of liver cancer.

EMERGING VIRAL DISEASES

An **emerging disease** is a disease that has only recently been detected in humans, or has recently expanded its range. AIDS is an emerging viral disease that was first identified in humans in 1981. Since then, it has caused about 30 million deaths. AIDS is a communicable disease, meaning HIV spreads from one infected person to another. Currently, about 34 million people are infected by HIV.

By contrast, the virus that causes West Nile fever cannot spread directly from person to person. Mosquitoes carry the virus from host to host, so we say they are the **vector** for this virus. Birds serve as a "reservoir" for West Nile virus, which means the virus can replicate in birds and birds serve as a source of virus for new human infections. West Nile virus was unknown in North America until 1999, when it emerged in New York. It has since spread across the continent. In 2012, there were more than 4,000 cases of West Nile fever in the United States and 163 deaths.

Ebola virus causes the emerging disease Ebola hemorrhagic fever. Symptoms of this incurable disease include fever, muscle pain, and massive internal and external bleeding. The death rate is close to 90 percent. Ebola virus

emerging disease A disease that was previously unknown or has recently begun spreading to a new region.
pathogen Disease-causing agent.
vector Animal that carries a pathogen from one host to the next.
viral recombination Multiple strains of virus infect a host simultaneously and swap genes.

FIGURE 19.5 Sign of an active herpes simplex virus 1 infection. Fluid rich in viral particles leaks from the open sore.

is highly contagious in humans, but so far it has been seen only in Africa, where fruit bats are its most likely reservoir.

VIRAL RECOMBINATION

Like living organisms, viruses have genomes that can mutate. RNA viruses such as HIV and influenza viruses (the viruses that cause the flu) mutate especially quickly. Viral genomes can also change when two viruses infect a host at the same time and exchange genes, a common process called **viral recombination**. A new subtype of H1N1 influenza virus that appeared in Asia in 2009 arose by recombination. The media called this virus a "swine flu," but it had a composite genome, with genes from a human flu virus, bird flu virus, and two different swine flu viruses. Fortunately, H1N1 proved less deadly than anticipated and rapid development of a vaccine put a stop to its spread by August 2010.

Another strain of influenza, H5N1, occasionally infects people who have direct contact with birds. From 2003 to 2012, there have been 608 reported human cases of influenza H5N1, mainly in Asia. Of these, 359 (about 60 percent) were fatal. Fortunately, person-to-person transmission of the H5N1 virus is exceedingly rare.

Health officials continue to carefully monitor H5N1 and H1N1 influenza. Either virus could mutate, and their coexistence raises the possibility of a potentially disastrous gene exchange. If H1N1 picked up genes from avian H5N1, the result could be a flu virus that is both easily transmissible and deadly.

Plant viruses usually enter a plant through a wound made by an insect or by pruning. Symptoms of viral infection typically include stunting and curling, yellowing, or spotting of leaves (FIGURE 19.6A). Viral infections can dramatically decrease crop yields, so plant viruses are of great commercial importance. Infected plants cannot be rid of a virus, so farmers focus on preventing viral infections. They grow plants that have been bred for viral resistance and try to fend off insects that transmit viral diseases.

Viroids, another type of plant pathogen, also enter plants through wounds. They consist solely of single-stranded RNA. Viroids are remarkably small, with a genome comprising fewer than 400 nucleotides. By comparison, even the smallest viral genome has thousands of nucleotides. Unlike the genetic material of a virus, viroid RNA does not encode proteins. The viroid causes disease by interfering with normal gene expression within the plant cell. A viroid infection typically stunts a plant and deforms its parts (FIGURE 19.6B). The viroid replicates with assistance of a plant enzyme (RNA polymerase) that normally transcribes the plant's DNA to RNA.

FIGURE 19.6 Symptoms of virus or viroid infection in plants.

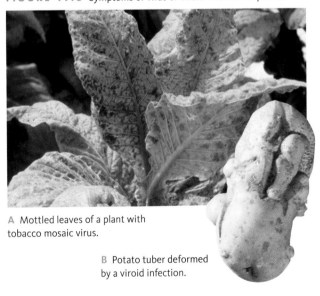

A Mottled leaves of a plant with tobacco mosaic virus.

B Potato tuber deformed by a viroid infection.

viroid Small noncoding RNA that can infect plants.

TAKE-HOME MESSAGE 19.2

Viruses cause many widespread, familiar diseases such as the common cold and cold sores, and some cause cancers.

Other viruses cause emerging diseases such as AIDS and West Nile virus that have only recently become global threats.

TAKE-HOME MESSAGE 19.3

Viruses and viroids (small RNAs) can enter a plant through a wound and cause disease.

The two lineages of prokaryotes (cells without a nucleus) belong to the domains Bacteria and Archaea. Later sections in this chapter describe unique features of each of these lineages. In this section, we focus on the structural and functional traits they have in common (**TABLE 19.1**).

CELL SIZE AND STRUCTURE

All bacteria and archaea are single-celled and nearly all are too small to be observed without a light microscope. Three cell shapes are common. Spherical cells are referred to as cocci (singular, coccus); rod-shaped cells as bacilli (singular, bacillus); and spiral cells as spirilli (singular, spirillum). **FIGURE 19.7** shows the typical structure of a prokaryotic cell. Most bacteria and archaea secrete a porous cell wall around their plasma membrane. Many also secrete a layer of slime or a capsule onto this wall. Within

FIGURE 19.7 **{Animated}** Structural features of a prokaryote.

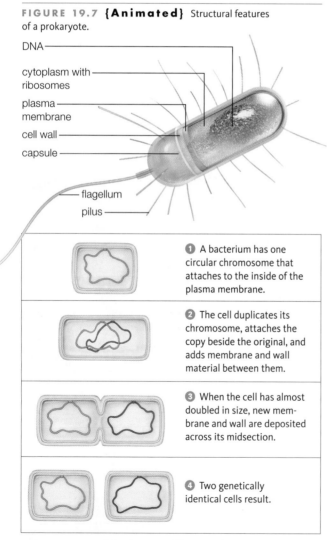

DNA
cytoplasm with ribosomes
plasma membrane
cell wall
capsule
flagellum
pilus

❶ A bacterium has one circular chromosome that attaches to the inside of the plasma membrane.

❷ The cell duplicates its chromosome, attaches the copy beside the original, and adds membrane and wall material between them.

❸ When the cell has almost doubled in size, new membrane and wall are deposited across its midsection.

❹ Two genetically identical cells result.

FIGURE 19.8 **{Animated}** Binary fission in bacteria.

TABLE 19.1

Prokaryotic Traits

1. No nucleus, endoplasmic reticulum, Golgi bodies
2. Single chromosome (a circular DNA molecule); many species also contain plasmids
3. Cell wall (in most species)
4. Ribosomes distributed in the cytoplasm
5. Asexual reproduction by binary fission
6. Capacity for gene exchange among existing cells through conjugation, transduction, and transformation

the cell, a single circular chromosome (a ring of double-stranded DNA) typically lies exposed in the cytoplasm. Some bacteria have internal membranes, but no known prokaryote has mitochondria, a nuclear envelope, or an endomembrane system like that of eukaryotes. Ribosomes scattered through the cytoplasm assemble proteins.

Bacteria and archaea often have one or more flagella that rotate like a propeller. By contrast, a eukaryotic flagellum whips from side to side. Many bacteria and archaea also have hairlike projections called pili that function in adhesion or locomotion. A type of retractable pilus can draw cells together for gene exchanges.

REPRODUCTION AND GENE EXCHANGE

Bacteria and archaea usually reproduce by **binary fission**, a type of asexual reproduction (**FIGURE 19.8**). The process begins when the cell replicates its single chromosome, which is attached to the inside of the plasma membrane ❶. The DNA replica attaches to the plasma membrane adjacent to the parent molecule. Addition of new membrane and wall material elongates the cell and moves the two DNA molecules apart ❷. Then, membrane and cell wall material is deposited across the cell's midsection ❸. This material partitions the cell, yielding two identical descendant cells ❹.

In addition to inheriting DNA "vertically" from a parent cell, prokaryotes engage in **horizontal gene transfer**: a transfer of genetic material between existing individuals. **Conjugation** involves transfer of genes on a plasmid. Recall that a plasmid is a small circle of DNA separate from the chromosome (Section 15.2). During conjugation, a cell that contains a plasmid extends a special sex pilus to another cell, draws it close, then puts a copy of the plasmid into its partner (**FIGURE 19.9**). Both bacteria and archaea have plasmids and conjugation can sometimes transfer genes between the two groups.

FIGURE IT OUT: Does conjugation increase the number of cells?

Answer: No. It is not a mode of reproduction.

CARBON SOURCE	ENERGY SOURCE	
	Light	Chemicals
Inorganic source such as CO_2	**Photoautotrophs** bacteria, archaea, photosynthetic protists, plants	**Chemoautotrophs** bacteria, archaea
Organic source such as glucose	**Photoheterotrophs** bacteria, archaea	**Chemoheterotrophs** bacteria, archaea, fungi, animals, nonphotosynthetic protists

FIGURE 19.10 {**Animated**} Modes of obtaining energy and carbon, and the groups that can use them.

 FIGURE IT OUT: Which group of organisms can build their own food from CO_2 in the dark?

Answer: Chemoautotrophs

Genes also move between prokaryotes by transduction and tranformation. Transduction occurs when a virus picks up a bit of DNA from one prokaryotic host cell, then transfers the DNA to its next host. Transformation occurs when bacteria or archaea take up DNA from their environment and integrate it into their genome.

METABOLIC DIVERSITY

Collectively, prokaryotes use all four possible mechanisms of obtaining energy and nutrients (**FIGURE 19.10**). Metabolic diversity gives these cells the ability to thrive in a vast variety of environments. Many bacteria and most archaea are anaerobic: They can (or must) live where there is no oxygen. Others are aerobic, which means they require (or at least tolerate) oxygen.

As Section 6.1 explained, autotrophs build their own food from an inorganic source of carbon such as carbon dioxide (CO_2). Many bacteria and some archaea are

photoautotrophs, which carry out photosynthesis. Like plants and photosynthetic protists, these organisms use light energy to fuel assembly of their food. No eukaryotes are **chemoautotrophs**, organisms that fuel the assembly of their food by oxidizing (removing electrons from) inorganic substances such as hydrogen sulfide or methane. Chemoautotrophic bacteria and archaea are the main producers in dark places such as the seafloor.

Heterotrophs obtain carbon by breaking down organic molecules from their environment. Some bacteria and archaea are **photoheterotrophs** that use light energy to fuel this process. No eukaryotes are photoheterotrophs. **Chemoheterotrophs** obtain both energy and carbon through the breakdown of organic compounds. This group includes fungi, animals, and nonphotosynthetic protists, as well as some archaea and most bacteria. All pathogenic bacteria are chemoheterotrophs that extract the organic compounds they need to live from their host. Other bacterial chemoheterotrophs serve as decomposers.

binary fission Method of asexual reproduction that divides one bacterial or archaeal cell into two identical descendant cells.
chemoautotroph Organism that uses carbon dioxide as its carbon source and obtains energy by oxidizing inorganic molecules.
chemoheterotroph Organism that obtains energy and carbon by breaking down organic compounds.
conjugation Mechanism of horizontal gene transfer in which one prokaryote passes a plasmid to another.
horizontal gene transfer Transfer of genetic material between existing individuals.
photoautotroph Organism that obtains carbon from carbon dioxide and energy from light.
photoheterotroph Organism that obtains its carbon from organic compounds and its energy from light.

TAKE-HOME MESSAGE 19.4

Prokaryotes (bacteria and archaea) are small, typically walled cells with no nuclear membrane, mitochondria, or endomembrane system.

Both groups of prokaryotes reproduce asexually by binary fission. They exchange genes by conjugation and other means of horizontal gene transfer.

Prokaryotes are metabolically diverse, collectively making use of all four modes of obtaining energy and nutrients. Many are anaerobic.

19.5 WHAT ARE SOME MAJOR BACTERIAL LINEAGES?

There are many bacterial lineages and new ones are constantly being discovered. Here we consider a few major groups to provide insight into bacterial diversity.

OXYGEN-PRODUCING CYANOBACTERIA

Photosynthesis evolved in many bacterial lineages, but only **cyanobacteria** release oxygen as a by-product. If, as evidence suggests, chloroplasts evolved from ancient cyanobacteria, we have cyanobacteria and their chloroplast descendants to thank for nearly all the oxygen in Earth's air.

Some cyanobacteria also carry out **nitrogen fixation**: They incorporate nitrogen from the air into ammonia (NH_3). Nitrogen fixation is an important ecological service. Photosynthetic eukaryotes need nitrogen but they cannot use the gaseous form ($N \equiv N$) because they do not have an enzyme that can break the molecule's triple bond. Plants and photosynthetic protists can, however, take up ammonia released by nitrogen-fixing bacteria.

Cyanobacteria can partner with fungi to form lichens (which we discuss in Section 22.3) and can grow on the surface of soils, but most are aquatic. The photo that opens this chapter shows a river tinted green by cyanobacteria. Aquatic cyanobacteria grow as single cells or as long filaments of cells arranged end to end (**FIGURE 19.11**). When conditions become unfavorable for growth, some filamentous cyanobacteria produce thick-walled resting cells. These cells are easily dispersed and remain dormant until environmental conditions improve.

HIGHLY DIVERSE PROTEOBACTERIA

Proteobacteria, the most diverse bacterial group, are defined on the basis of their ribosomal RNA sequence rather than any structural or metabolic feature. Most are aerobic. Some, such as the purple bacteria, carry out photosynthesis but do not produce oxygen as a by-product. Other proteobacteria are chemoautotrophs or chemoheterotrophs. One chemoautotrophic species, *Thiomargarita namibiensis*, is among the largest prokaryotes and can be seen even without a microscope (**FIGURE 19.12A**). A giant vacuole containing nitrate and sulfur makes up the bulk of the cell. The cell uses nitrate in its energy-releasing reactions and forms sulfur as a by-product of these reactions.

Many chemoheterotrophic proteobacteria live in other organisms. For example, members of the genus *Rhizobium* live inside the roots of legumes such as peas and beans. The bacteria receive sugars from the plant, and in turn provide the plant with ammonia from nitrogen fixation. Rickettsias live as parasites inside animals and are considered close relatives of mitochondria (Section 18.5).

Scientists use some proteobacteria in biological research and biotechnology. The most well-studied prokaryote is *Escherichia coli*, a rod-shaped species of proteobacteria that normally lives in the mammalian gut (**FIGURE 19.12B**). It is easily grown in the laboratory, so researchers often investigate genetic and metabolic processes by studying *E. coli*. It is also widely used in industrial biotechnology. Recombinant *E. coli* now produce many synthetic hormones and other proteins for medical use.

When biotechnologists want to alter a plant's genome, they may turn to *Agrobacterium*. These soil proteobacteria have a plasmid that gives them the capacity to infect plants and cause a tumor. As Section 15.5 explained, scientists can produce recombinant plants by inserting the foreign genes into the tumor-inducing plasmid, then infecting a plant with recombinant bacteria.

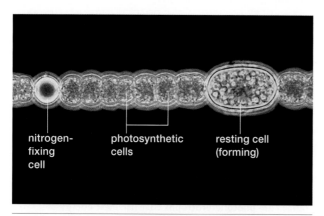

FIGURE 19.11 Chain of aquatic cyanobacterial cells.

nitrogen-fixing cell   photosynthetic cells   resting cell (forming)

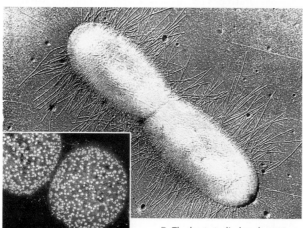

A The largest prokaryote, *Thiomargarita namibiensis*. Cells can be up to 0.75 mm wide.

B The best studied prokaryote, *E. coli*, can divide by binary fission every 20 minutes.

FIGURE 19.12 **Proteobacteria.**

CREDITS: (11) © P. W. Johnson and J. MeN. Sieburth, Univ. Rhode Island/BPS; (12A) © Dr. Manfred Schloesser, Max Planck Institute for Marine Microbiology; (12B) Courtesy James Evarts.

FIGURE 19.13 Lactobacilli in yogurt. The cells ferment milk sugars to produce lactate that gives yogurt its tangy taste.

THICK-WALLED GRAM POSITIVES

Gram-positive bacteria have thick cell walls that stain purple when prepared for microscopy by a process known as Gram staining. Most are chemoheterotrophs and many serve as decomposers. **Decomposers** break down complex organic molecules in wastes and remains into inorganic components that plants can take up and use. Decomposers also break down pesticides and pollutants, thus improving the environment for other organisms.

Actinomycetes are Gram-positive decomposers that grow through soil as long, branching chains of cells. Their presence gives freshly exposed soil its distinctive "earthy" smell. Many antibiotics, including streptomycin and vancomycin, were first isolated from actinomycetes.

Soil also contains members of the Gram-positive genus *Lactobacillus*. These cells ferment sugars and produce lactate. Lactobacilli sometimes spoil milk, but they are also used to produce sour foods such as sauerkraut and yogurt (**FIGURE 19.13**). Streptococci, which are close relatives of lactobacilli, include species that cause strep throat and the skin disease impetigo. Streptococci are also the usual cause of bacterial pneumonias.

Soil bacteria in the genera *Clostridium* and *Bacillus* form endospores when conditions are unfavorable. An **endospore** contains the cell's DNA and a bit of cytoplasm in a protective coat. It is functionally similar to a cyanobacterial resting cell, but much tougher. Endospores survive drying, boiling, and radiation. If they enter a human body and germinate, the result can be deadly. In 2001, distribution of *Bacillus anthracis* endospores through the United States mail resulted in five deaths from the disease anthrax.

SPIRAL-SHAPED SPIROCHETES

Spirochetes are very small bacteria with a shape like a stretched-out spring (**FIGURE 19.14**). Some live in the cattle gut and help their host by breaking down cellulose. Others are aquatic decomposers and some fix nitrogen. Still others are pathogens. One pathogenic spirochete causes the sexually transmitted disease syphilis, and another causes Lyme disease, which we discuss in the next section.

FIGURE 19.14 A spirochete.

---

cyanobacteria Photosynthetic, oxygen-producing bacteria.
decomposer Organism that breaks down organic compounds in wastes and remains into their inorganic subunits.
endospore Resistant resting stage of some soil bacteria.
Gram-positive bacteria Bacteria with thick cell walls that are colored purple when prepared for microscopy by Gram staining.
nitrogen fixation Incorporation of nitrogen gas into ammonia.
proteobacteria Most diverse bacterial lineage.
spirochetes Bacteria that resemble a stretched-out spring.

TAKE-HOME MESSAGE 19.5

Bacteria play important ecological roles. They put oxygen into the air, fix nitrogen, and act as decomposers.

Bacteria play an important role in scientific research, biotechnology, and food production.

Many bacterial groups include species that adversely affect human health.

19.6 HOW DO BACTERIA AFFECT HUMAN HEALTH?

NORMAL FLORA

Bacteria and other microorganisms that normally live in or on our body are our **normal flora**. The normal flora serves as a first defense against pathogens. For example, lactobacilli that normally live in the human mouth, gut, and vagina produce lactate, an acid that helps keep acid-intolerant pathogenic bacteria from becoming established. Some side effects of antibiotics result from the effects of these drugs on our normal flora. Antibiotics kill beneficial bacteria as well as harmful ones. When this disruption takes place in the gut, it causes diarrhea. When it happens in the vagina, the resulting overgrowth of yeast (fungal cells) can cause vaginitis.

In addition to their protective role, gut bacteria also benefit us by producing some essential vitamins. Our intestines are home to lactobacilli that synthesize some B vitamins and to *E. coli* that produce vitamin K.

TOXINS AND DISEASE

Pathogenic bacteria produce toxins that cause the symptoms of disease. A bacterial toxin may be a substance that bacteria release into their environment (an exotoxin), or a molecule integral to the cell's wall (an endotoxin). Exotoxins directly harm human cells. For example, botulinum toxin released

by *Clostridium botulinum* causes a dangerous paralyzing food poisoning by disrupting nerve cell function. Another bacterial exotoxin, Shiga toxin, is a ribosome-inhibiting protein (Section 9.6) that interferes with protein synthesis by intestinal cells. Endotoxins do not directly harm cells. Rather, they elicit an immune response that typically includes fever and aches. If this immune response spirals out of control, the resulting loss of blood pressure and organ failure can be deadly.

Bacteria in our normal skin flora can act as pathogens when a cut, scrape, or other wound allows them into our body. For example, *Staphylococcus aureus* that can live harmlessly on the skin sometimes infects deep skin layers. An antibiotic-resistant strain—methicillin-resistant *Staphylococcus aureus* (MRSA)—is especially dangerous, because it does not respond to most commonly used drugs.

Bacterial pathogens also enter the body in tainted food or water. In the United States, most cases of bacterial food poisoning involve *Salmonella* or *Campylobacter*, both proteobacteria. These bacteria live in the gut of animals such as chickens, and bacteria-rich animal feces sometimes get into food. Symptoms of food poisoning typically include fever, diarrhea, and abdominal cramps. Usually an affected

FIGURE 19.15 Signs of tuberculosis. A doctor at an Ethiopian hospital points out signs of TB on a chest x-ray.

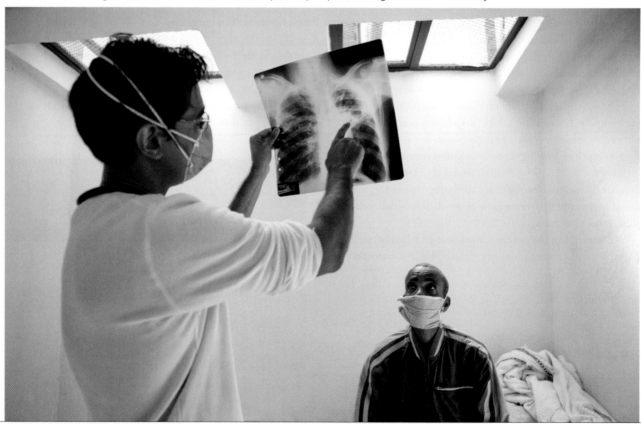

person's immune system rids the body of bacteria and recovery occurs within a few days to a week.

In regions where safe drinking water is not readily available, cholera sickens millions of people each year and kills about 100,000. Cholera-causing bacteria (*Vibrio cholerae*) produce an exotoxin that poisons intestinal cells. The resulting massive diarrhea causes solute and water losses that can be fatal. Tainted water also spreads *Helicobacter pylori*, the only bacterial species known to cause cancer. A long-term *H. pylori* infection increases the risk of ulcers and stomach cancer.

Communicable diseases caused by bacteria include strep throat, whooping cough, bacterial pneumonia, and the sexually transmitted diseases gonorrhea and syphilis. *Mycobacterium tuberculosis* causes the communicable disease tuberculosis (TB), which infects an estimated one-third of the world population. Fortunately, in most otherwise healthy people, a TB infection remains inactive; bacteria survive, but the immune system keeps them in check and the affected person cannot infect others. In a minority of people, the infection becomes active; bacteria grow in the lungs and cause coughing, chest pain, fever, and weight loss (FIGURE 19.15). A person with active TB spreads the disease by expelling tiny bacteria-laden droplets in coughs and sneezes. In 2011, about 2 million people died as a result of active TB. Both active and inactive TB infections can be cured by antibiotics, but killing all the bacteria in the body requires months of treatment. To further complicate matters, strains of *M. tuberculosis* resistant to most commonly used antibiotics are increasingly prevalent.

The most common vector-borne bacterial disease in the United States is Lyme disease. It occurs most frequently in northeastern and upper midwestern states. Ticks transmit the spirochete (*Borrelia burgdorferi*) that causes this disease and mice serve as its reservoir. Some infected people develop a rash at the site where the tick bite introduced the bacteria. More often, flulike symptoms and fever are the first indications of disease. Untreated, Lyme disease can damage joints, the heart, and the nervous system.

normal flora Normally harmless or beneficial microorganisms that typically live in or on a body.

TAKE-HOME MESSAGE 19.6

Bacteria of our normal flora protect us against infections and provide us with vitamins.

Pathogenic bacteria release toxins or have toxins in their cell wall.

Bacteria cause wound infections, food poisoning, and communicable diseases, and one species causes cancer.

Science is a self-correcting process in which new discoveries can overturn even long-held ways of thinking. For example, biologists historically divided all life into two domains, prokaryotes and eukaryotes. These groups were very different in size and structure, so scientists thought they represented distinct lineages (clades) that parted ways early in the history of life (FIGURE 19.16A).

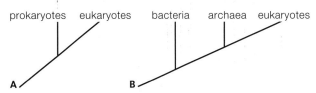

prokaryotes   eukaryotes   bacteria   archaea   eukaryotes

A   B

FIGURE 19.16 The A two-domain and B three-domain trees of life. The two-domain model was widely accepted until new evidence revealed previously unknown differences between bacteria and archaea. The three-domain model is now in wide use.

In the late 1970s Carl Woese began investigating evolutionary relationships among prokaryotes. By comparing ribosomal RNA gene sequences, Woese found that some methane-making cells were as similar to eukaryotes as they were to typical bacteria. Woese proposed that the methane makers were not bacteria but rather a previously unrecognized branch on the tree of life. To accommodate this branch, he proposed a new classification system with three domains of life: bacteria, archaea, eukaryotes (FIGURE 19.16B).

Woese's ideas were initially greeted with skepticism, but as years went by, evidence in support of them mounted. Archaea and bacteria have different cell wall and membrane components. Archaea and eukaryotes organize their DNA around histone proteins, which bacteria do not have. Sequencing the genome of the archaeon *Methanococcus jannaschii* (FIGURE 19.17) provided definitive support for Woese's proposal. Most of this archaeon's genes have no counterpart in bacteria. Today, the hypothesis that bacteria and archaea constitute a single lineage has been discarded, and the three-domain classification system is in widespread use. Woese compares discovery of archaea to the discovery of a new continent, which he and others are exploring.

0.5 μm

FIGURE 19.17
An archaeon, *Methanococcus jannaschii*.

TAKE-HOME MESSAGE 19.7

Genetic studies of prokaryotes revealed that the cells now known as archaea constitute a lineage distinct from bacteria.

Many archaea live in places where few or no other cells survive. Archaea were first discovered in hot springs, and many are **extreme thermophiles**, meaning they grow only at a very high temperature (**FIGURE 19.18A**). Some archaea that live near deep-sea hydrothermal vents grow even at 110°C (230°F). These organisms are chemoautotrophs that reduce sulfur to obtain energy.

Other archaea are **extreme halophiles**, organisms that live in highly salty water. Salt-loving archaea live in the Dead Sea, the Great Salt Lake, and smaller brine-filled lakes (**FIGURE 19.18B**). Most are photoheterotrophs that capture light energy with a red pigment (bacteriorhodopsin).

Many archaea, including some extreme thermophiles and extreme halophiles, are **methanogens**, or methane makers. These chemoautotrophs form ATP by pulling electrons from hydrogen gas or acetate. The reactions produce methane (CH_4), an odorless gas. Methanogenic archaea are strict anaerobes, meaning they cannot live in the presence of oxygen. They abound in sewage, marsh sediments, and the animal gut (**FIGURE 19.18C**). Cattle have methanogens in their stomach and release methane gas by belching.

About a third of people have significant numbers of methanogens in their intestine, so their flatulence (farts) contains methane. Archaea have also been discovered in the human mouth and vagina. So far, no archaea have been proven to be human pathogens. However, some methanogens that live in the mouth contribute to gum disease. By their presence, they may improve the environment for pathogenic bacteria that cause this disease.

Researchers continue to investigate the diversity of and evolutionary relationships among the archaea. Two major lineages have been identified. Most of the extreme thermophiles belong to the lineage Crenarchaeota, and most methanogenic and salt-loving archaea belong to the lineage Euryarchaeota.

extreme halophile Organism adapted to life in a highly salty environment.
extreme thermophile Organism adapted to life in a very high-temperature environment.
methanogen Organism that produces methane gas (CH_4) as a metabolic by-product.

TAKE-HOME MESSAGE 19.8

Archaea live in extremely salty and extremely high-temperature environments, as well as in oxygen-free sediments and the animal gut.

Few archaea contribute to human disease.

A Thermally heated waters. Archaeal extreme thermophiles live in the waters of this hot spring in Nevada.

B Highly salty waters. Pigmented extreme halophiles color the brine in this California lake.

C The gut of many animals. Cows belch frequently to release the methane produced by archaea in their stomach.

FIGURE 19.18 Examples of archaeal habitats.

CREDITS: (18A) © Savannah River Ecology Laboratory; (18B) Courtesy of Benjamin Brunner; (18C) Dr. John Brackenbury/Science Source.

19.9 Application: SHARING VIRUSES

Sustainability

FIGURE 19.19 Wild chimpanzees from a population infected by SIV, the chimpanzee equivalent of HIV.

WE SHARE MANY TRAITS WITH CHIMPANZEES, INCLUDING SUSCEPTIBILITY TO SOME VIRUSES. HIV is similar to simian immunodeficiency virus (SIV), which infects wild chimpanzees in Africa (FIGURE 19.19). In chimpanzees, as in humans, the virus harms the immune system. Researchers think HIV evolved after SIV entered and survived inside a human. Most likely, the person was exposed to the virus while butchering an infected animal. Chimpanzees and other primates are hunted and butchered as "bushmeat" in many parts of Africa.

To find out when HIV first infected humans, researchers looked for HIV in old tissue samples stored at hospitals. The earliest HIV samples known date to about 1960 and come from two people who lived in Africa's Democratic Republic of the Congo. Given what scientists know about the mutation rates for viruses, they estimate that HIV first infected humans in the early 1900s.

Comparing genes of HIV in stored and modern blood samples has allowed researchers to trace the movement of the virus out of Africa. In 1966, HIV was introduced from Africa to Haiti, where new mutations arose. In about 1969, someone infected by HIV with those new mutations introduced the virus to the United States. From there, it spread quietly for 12 years until AIDS was identified as a threat in 1981. Two years later, scientists showed that HIV causes AIDS.

Could other viruses also make their way from nonhuman primates into the human population? Some already are trickling in. For example, people exposed to the blood or saliva of a wild Old World primate can become infected by simian foamy virus (SFV). So far as we know, SFV infection has no adverse effect on human health. However, some viruses, such as HIV, often do not cause symptoms until years after an initial infection. There is also no evidence that SFV can currently spread from person to person. However, viruses can evolve. In addition, opportunities for SFV and other currently unknown viruses to infect humans are likely to increase as human populations expand into previously remote areas of primate habitat.

Summary

SECTION 19.1 A **virus** is a noncellular infectious agent with a protein coat around a core of DNA or RNA. In enveloped viruses, the coat is enclosed by a bit of plasma membrane derived from a previous host. A virus lacks ribosomes and other metabolic machinery, so it must replicate inside a host cell. Viruses attach to a host cell, then viral genes and enzymes direct the host to replicate viral genetic material and make viral proteins. New viral particles self-assemble and are released.

Bacteriophages can replicate in bacteria by two different pathways. Replication by the **lytic pathway** is rapid, and the new viral particles are released by lysis. During the **lysogenic pathway**, the virus enters a latent state that extends the cycle.

HIV (human immunodeficiency virus), the virus that causes AIDS, is an enveloped **retrovirus**. Its RNA must be reverse transcribed to DNA to begin the process of viral replication. The virus acquires its envelope as it buds from the plasma membrane of a host cell.

SECTION 19.2 Some viruses are human **pathogens**, meaning they cause disease. Viruses cause common colds, flus, and some cancers. Many viral diseases are communicable, but others require a **vector**, an animal that carries them between hosts. An **emerging disease** is newly recognized in humans (like Ebola) or is spreading to a new region (like West Nile virus). Changes to viral genomes occur as a result of mutation and **viral recombination**.

SECTION 19.3 Plants can be infected by viruses or **viroids**, which are tiny bits of RNA. Unlike a viral genome, viroid RNA does not encode proteins. A viral infection can stunt plants and deform plant parts.

SECTION 19.4 Bacteria and archaea are small, structurally simple cells. They do not have a nucleus or cytoplasmic organelles typical of eukaryotes. The single circular chromosome of double-stranded DNA resides in the cytoplasm. Most have a cell wall and many have flagella and hairlike pili.

Bacteria and archaea reproduce by **binary fission**: replication of a single, circular chromosome and division of a parent cell into two genetically equivalent descendants. **Horizontal gene transfers** move genes between existing cells, as when **conjugation** moves a plasmid with a few genes from one cell into another.

As a group, prokaryotes are metabolically diverse, with both anaerobes and aerobes. Some are **photoautotrophs** like plants and others are **chemoheterotrophs** like fungi and animals. Two modes of nutrition occur only among prokaryotes: **chemoautotrophs** extract energy from inorganic chemicals, and **photoheterotrophs** capture light energy but get their carbon from organic compounds.

SECTIONS 19.5, 19.6 Bacteria have essential ecological roles. **Cyanobacteria** produce oxygen during photosynthesis and are relatives of chloroplasts. Some also carry out **nitrogen fixation**, producing ammonia that algae and plants require. **Proteobacteria**, the most diverse bacterial lineage, also include nitrogen-fixers, as well as relatives of mitochondria. **Gram-positive bacteria** have thick walls and many live in soil, where they act as **decomposers**. Formation of **endospores** allows some Gram-positive bacteria to survive adverse conditions. **Spirochetes** resemble a stretched-out spring. They may be free-living or pathogens.

Bacteria that normally live in or on our body are part of our protective **normal flora**. Pathogenic bacteria cause disease by producing toxins.

SECTIONS 19.7, 19.8 Archaea are now recognized as members of a domain distinct from bacteria. They include **methanogens** (methane makers), **extreme halophiles** (salt lovers), and **extreme thermophiles** (heat lovers). Archaea coexist with bacteria in many habitats, including human and animal bodies. Few are pathogens.

SECTION 19.9 Scientists use their knowledge of evolution to investigate how pathogens such as HIV arise, function, and spread. HIV is a descendant of a virus that infects wild chimpanzees. Other viruses that infect wild primates have also been detected in humans.

Self-Quiz   Answers in Appendix VII

1. _____ can have a genome of either RNA or DNA.
   a. Bacteria   b. Viroids   c. Viruses   d. Archaea

2. Which is smallest?
   a. bacterium   b. viroid   c. virus   d. archaeon

3. In _____ , viral DNA becomes integrated into a bacterial chromosome and is passed to descendant cells.
   a. binary fission   c. the lysogenic pathway
   b. the lytic pathway   d. both b and c

4. During HIV replication, reverse trancriptase reads viral _____ to produce viral _____ .
   a. DNA; RNA   c. RNA; proteins
   b. RNA; DNA   d. DNA; proteins

5. Viral genomes can be altered by _____ .
   a. binary fission   c. mutation
   b. recombination   d. both b and c

6. Prokaryotic conjugation is a type of _____ .
   a. sexual reproduction   c. horizontal gene transfer
   b. asexual reproduction   d. both b and c

7. How many chromosomes do bacteria have?

8. _____ are oxygen-releasing photoautotrophs.
   a. Spirochetes   c. Cyanobacteria
   b. Archaeans   d. Viroids

Data Analysis Activities

Maternal Transmission of HIV Since the AIDS pandemic began, there have been more than 8,000 cases of mother-to-child HIV transmission in the United States. In 1993, American physicians began giving antiretroviral drugs to HIV-positive women during pregnancy and treating both mother and infant in the months after birth. Only about 10 percent of mothers were treated in 1993, but by 1999 more than 80 percent got antiviral drugs.

FIGURE 19.20 shows the number of AIDS diagnoses among children in the United States. Use the information in this graph to answer the following questions.

1. How did the number of children diagnosed with AIDS change during the late 1980s?
2. What year did new AIDS diagnoses in children peak, and how many children were diagnosed that year?
3. How did the number of AIDS diagnoses change as the use of antiretrovirals in mothers and infants increased?

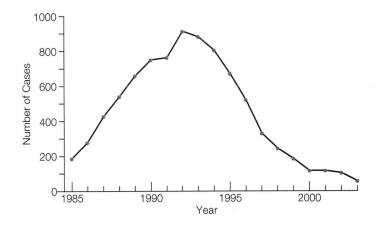

FIGURE 19.20 Number of new AIDS diagnoses in the United States per year among children exposed to HIV during pregnancy, birth, or by breast-feeding.

---

9. Nitrogen-fixation by bacteria produces _____ .
   a. nitrogen gas   b. methane   c. oxygen   d. ammonia

10. Vitamin-producing *E. coli* cells in your gut are _____ .
    a. normal flora   c. proteobacteria
    b. chemoheterotrophs   d. all of the above

11. A chemical that is released into the environment by bacteria and causes symptoms of disease is a(n) _____ .
    a. endospore   b. endotoxin   c. exotoxin   d. vector

12. Infection by some _____ can cause cancer.
    a. viruses   c. archaea
    b. bacteria   d. both a and b

13. A Gram-positive coccus is _____ .
    a. spherical   b. rod-shaped   c. spiral-shaped

14. Match each disease with the type of pathogen that causes it. Choices may be used more than once.
    ___ tuberculosis   a. virus
    ___ AIDS   b. bacteria
    ___ influenza (flu)
    ___ Lyme disease
    ___ cholera

15. Match each group with the most suitable description.
    ___ cyanobacteria   a. contain no protein
    ___ methanogens   b. live in salty places
    ___ viroids   c. live in hot places
    ___ retroviruses   d. release oxygen
    ___ extreme   e. release methane
        halophiles   f. RNA genome inside
    ___ extreme   a protein coat
        thermophiles

Critical Thinking

1. Rhinoviruses, the most common cause of colds, do not have a lipid envelope. Compared to enveloped viruses, such nonenveloped viruses tend to remain infectious outside the body longer, are more likely to be spread by contact with surfaces, and are less likely to be rendered harmless by exposure to hand sanitizer or handwashing. Explain how the lack of an envelope contributes to these characteristics.

2. Methanogens have been found in the human gut and deep-sea sediments, but not on human skin or in the surface waters of the ocean. What physiological trait of methanogens could explain this distribution?

3. Review the description of Fred Griffith's experiments with *Streptococcus pneumoniae* in Section 8.1. Using your knowledge of bacterial biology, explain the process by which the harmless bacteria became dangerous after being exposed to components of harmful bacterial cells.

4. The antibiotic penicillin acts by interfering with the production of new bacterial cell wall. Cells treated with penicillin do not die immediately, but they cannot reproduce. Explain how penicillin halts binary fission.

5. Many compounds secreted by soil bacteria have been isolated and are now produced synthetically for use as antibiotics. What function do you think these compounds play in the bacteria themselves? Devise an experiment that will test your hypothesis about the natural function of these substances.

CENGAGE **brain**.com   To access course materials, please visit www.cengagebrain.com.

A stand of giant kelp, the largest protists, off the coast of California. Like trees in a forest, kelp shelter and feed a wide variety of organisms.

20

THE PROTISTS

Links to Earlier Concepts

This chapter describes protists, a collection of eukaryotic lineages introduced in Section 1.3. We reexamine cell structures such as chloroplasts (6.3,6.4), pseudopods, and flagella (4.9); reconsider the effects of osmosis on cells (5.6); and return to photosynthetic pigments (6.1). We also delve again into how organelles evolve by endosymbiosis (18.5).

KEY CONCEPTS

A COLLECTION OF LINEAGES
The protist lineages include single-celled, colonial, and multicelled organisms. Photosynthetic protists have chloroplasts derived from either bacteria or other protists.

SINGLE-CELLED LINEAGES
Most protist lineages are entirely single-celled. Such groups include flagellated protozoans, shelled cells called foraminifera and radiolaria, and ciliates, dinoflagellates, and apicomplexans.

BROWN ALGAE AND RELATIVES
Multicellular brown algae and single-celled photosynthetic diatoms belong to the same lineage as filamentous heterotrophs called water molds.

RED ALGAE, GREEN ALGAE
Red algae and green algae include single-celled and multicelled aquatic producers. Red algae have pigments that allow them to live in deep waters. Green algae are the closest relatives of land plants.

AMOEBAS, SLIME MOLDS, AND CHOANOFLAGELLATES
Shape-shifting heterotrophic amoebas live in aquatic habitats. The related slime molds feed on forest floors. Choanoflagellates are the closest living protist relatives of animals.

A **protist** is a eukaryotic organism that is not a fungus, plant, or animal. Protists are not a clade (Section 17.12), because they include all members of some lineages, plus some members of other lineages. As **FIGURE 20.1** illustrates, some protists are more closely related to plants, fungi, or animals than to other protists. Like other eukaryotes, protists undergo mitosis and, if they reproduce sexually, meiosis.

Most protists live as single cells, but some lineages include colonial or multicellular members. Cells of a **colonial organism** live together, but remain self-sufficient. Each cell retains the traits required to survive and reproduce on its own. By contrast, cells of a **multicellular organism** have a division of labor and are interdependent.

Though typically small, protists have a huge ecological impact. Heterotrophic protists decompose organic material, prey on smaller organisms such as bacteria, or live inside the bodies of larger species. Photosynthetic protists use the same oxygen-producing photosynthetic pathway as cyanobacteria, and their activity produces much of the oxygen we breathe. They also take up huge amounts of carbon dioxide, and build organic compounds that are the basis for aquatic food chains.

All protist chloroplasts evolved by endosymbiosis (Section 18.5 and **FIGURE 20.2**). **Primary endosymbiosis** occurs when a bacterium enters a cell and its descendants evolve into an organelle ❶. Red algae, green algae, and land plants share an ancestor in which chloroplasts evolved by primary endosymbiosis. Their chloroplasts have two membranes, one from the bacteria, and one from the vacuole in which it was engulfed. **Secondary endosymbiosis** occurs when a photosynthetic protist engulfed by a heterotrophic protist evolves into a chloroplast ❷. In this case, the chloroplast often has more than two membranes. For example, some red algae evolved into chloroplasts in other protists.

colonial organism Organism composed of many similar cells, each capable of living and reproducing on its own.
multicellular organism Organism composed of interdependent cells that vary in their structure and function.
primary endosymbiosis Evolution of an organelle from bacteria that entered a host cell and lived inside it.
protist Eukaryote that is not a plant, fungus, or animal.
secondary endosymbiosis Evolution of an organelle from a protist that itself contains organelles that arose by primary endosymbiosis.

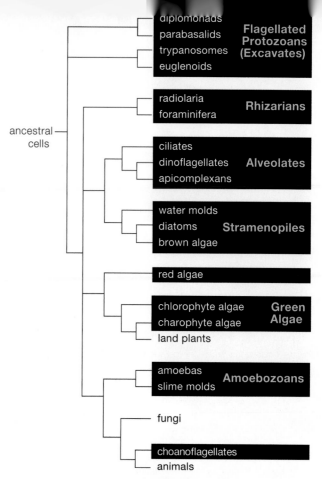

FIGURE 20.1 Phylogenetic tree for the eukaryotes discussed in this book. Like all such trees, it is a hypothesis. Protist groups are indicated by black boxes.

 FIGURE IT OUT: Are land plants more closely related to red algae or brown algae?

Answer: Red algae

TAKE-HOME MESSAGE 20.1

Protists include members of multiple eukaryotic lineages.

Most protists are single-celled, but multicellular and colonial forms evolved in some lineages.

Some protists are heterotrophs; others are photosynthetic with chloroplasts that evolve from bacteria or other protists.

Eukaryotic cell engulfs a cyanobacterium.

The resulting chloroplast has two membranes.

Heterotrophic protist engulfs an autotrophic one with chloroplasts that evolved by primary endosymbiosis.

The resulting chloroplast has four membranes.

FIGURE 20.2 Primary and secondary endosymbiosis.

20.2 WHAT ARE FLAGELLATED PROTOZOANS?

Single-celled, unwalled heterotrophic protists are commonly called protozoans. **Flagellated protozoans** (clade Excavata) have one or more flagella and a flagellated feeding groove. Food that enters this groove is taken up by phagocytosis. A **pellicle**, a layer of elastic proteins beneath the plasma membrane, helps these unwalled cells retain their shape.

ANAEROBIC FLAGELLATES

Diplomonads and parabasalids are two closely related groups of flagellates. Both can live where oxygen is low because they have modified mitochondria that make ATP anaerobically.

Diplomonads are unusual in that they have two nuclei. Most are parasitic. One species attaches to the human intestinal lining and causes the waterborne disease giardiasis (**FIGURE 20.3A**). Symptoms of giardiasis include cramps, nausea, and severe diarrhea. Infected people or animals excrete cysts (a hardy resting stage) of the protist in feces.

Parabasalids have a single nucleus and four flagella. One species causes trichomoniasis, a sexually transmitted disease. This parasite does not make cysts, so it cannot survive very long outside the human body. Fortunately for the parasite, sexual intercourse delivers it directly into hosts.

TRYPANOSOMES AND EUGLENOIDS

Trypanosomes are tapered cells that have a single large mitochondrion. Their flagellum is attached to the cell body by a membrane (**FIGURE 20.3B**). All trypanosomes are parasites. Biting insects transmit trypanosomes that cause human diseases such as sleeping sickness.

Euglenoids are a group of primarily freshwater protists closely related to trypanosomes. They have multiple mitochondria and a pellicle composed of protein strips (**FIGURE 20.4**). The interior of a euglenoid is saltier than its freshwater habitat, so water tends to diffuse into the cell. Like many other freshwater protists, euglenoids have one or more **contractile vacuoles**, organelles that collect excess water, then contract and expel it to the outside through a pore. Many euglenoids have chloroplasts descended from a green alga. They can carry out photosynthesis in the light, but become heterotrophs in the dark. An eyespot near the base of a long flagellum helps these cells detect light.

contractile vacuole In freshwater protists, an organelle that collects and expels excess water.
euglenoid Flagellated protozoan with multiple mitochondria; may be heterotrophic or have chloroplasts descended from green algae.
flagellated protozoan Protist belonging to an entirely or mostly heterotrophic lineage with no cell wall and one or more flagella.
pellicle Layer of proteins that gives shape to many unwalled, single-celled protists.
trypanosome Parasitic flagellated protist with a single mitochondrion and a flagellum that runs along the back of the cell.

A Diplomonad (*Giardia lamblia*) attached to the lining of the human intestine.

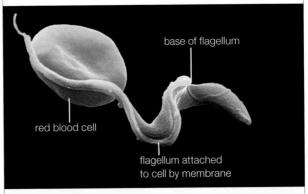

base of flagellum

red blood cell

flagellum attached to cell by membrane

B Trypanosome with a human red blood cell. Wavelike movement of the membrane-enclosed flagellum propels the trypanosome.

FIGURE 20.3 Examples of flagellated protozoans. "Protozoan" is a general term used to describe members of the primarily heterotrophic groups of unicellular protists.

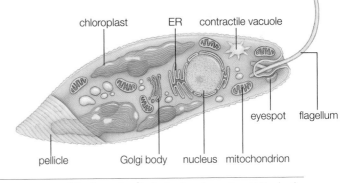

chloroplast   ER   contractile vacuole

eyespot   flagellum

pellicle   Golgi body   nucleus   mitochondrion

FIGURE 20.4 **{Animated}** Body plan of a euglenoid (*Euglena*), a freshwater species with chloroplasts that evolved from a green alga.

TAKE-HOME MESSAGE 20.2

Flagellated protozoans are unwalled unicellular organisms with one or more flagella.

Parabasalids and diplomonads are heterotrophs that have modified mitochondria and can live in anaerobic habitats. Some are important human pathogens.

Trypanosomes are parasites with one large mitochondrion. Some cause human disease.

Euglenoids are freshwater protists. They feed as heterotrophs or use chloroplasts that evolved from a green alga.

Rhizarians include two groups of single-celled marine protists—foraminifera and radiolaria—that secrete a sievelike shell. Like amoebas, which we discuss in Section 20.8, rhizarians are heterotrophs that use cytoplasmic extensions to capture prey. However, this mechanism of feeding evolved independently in the two groups; genetic comparisons show rhizarians and amoebas are not close relatives.

FIGURE 20.5 **Living foraminiferan.** This is one of the planktonic species, and the tiny gold specks are algae that live in its cytoplasm.

200 μm

CHALKY OR SILICA-SHELLED CELLS

Foraminifera secrete a calcium carbonate ($CaCO_3$) shell. Including its shell, an individual foraminiferal cell can be as big as a grain of sand. Most species live on the seafloor, where they probe the water and sediments for prey. Others are members of the marine plankton. **Plankton** is a community of mostly microscopic organisms that drift or swim in open waters. Planktonic foraminifera often have smaller photosynthetic protists such as diatoms or algae living inside them (**FIGURE 20.5**).

By taking up carbon dioxide (CO_2) and incorporating it into their calcium carbonate shells, foraminifera help the sea to absorb more carbon dioxide from the air. Lowering the concentration of CO_2 in the air is important because excess atmospheric CO_2 is one cause of global climate change.

Radiolaria secrete a glassy silica (SiO_2) shell (**FIGURE 20.6**) and have two cytoplasmic layers. The inner layer holds all the typical eukaryotic organelles and the outer one contains numerous gas-filled vacuoles that keep the cell afloat. Radiolaria are planktonic and they are most abundant in nutrient-rich tropical waters.

A Living radiolarian. B Radiolarian shell.

FIGURE 20.6 **Two silica-shelled radiolarians.**

RHIZARIAN REMAINS

Foraminifera and radiolaria have lived and died in the oceans for more than 500 million years, so remains of countless cells have fallen to the seafloor. Over time, geologic processes transformed some accumulations of foraminiferal shells into chalk and limestone, two types of calcium carbonate–rich sedimentary rock. The giant blocks of limestone used to build the great pyramids of Egypt consist largely of the shells of foraminifera that fell to the seafloor about 50 million years ago. Similarly, geologic processes transformed silica-rich deposits of radiolarian shells into a rock called chert.

Fossil foraminifera and radiolaria help geologists locate deposits of oil (petroleum). Oil forms over millions of years from lipids in the remains of marine protists. To locate rock layers likely to contain oil deposits, geologists drill into rock and look for fossil foraminifera or radiolaria. Observing which fossil species are present allows the geologists to determine how old the rocks are and whether they were laid down in an environment likely to favor oil formation.

foraminifera Heterotrophic single-celled protists with a porous calcium carbonate shell and long cytoplasmic extensions.
plankton Community of tiny drifting or swimming organisms.
radiolaria Heterotrophic single-celled protists with a porous shell of silica and long cytoplasmic extensions.

TAKE-HOME MESSAGE 20.3

Two related lineages of heterotrophic marine cells have porous secreted shells. Foraminifera have chalk shells and live in sediments or drift as part of plankton. Radiolarians have silica shells and are planktonic.

CREDITS: (5) Courtesy of Allen W. H. Bé & David A. Caron; (6A) © Franz Neidl; (6B) Wim van Egmond/Visuals Unlimited.

Ciliates, dinoflagellates, and apicomplexans belong to the clade Alveolata. "Alveolus" means sac, and the defining trait of alveolates is a layer of sacs beneath the plasma membrane. In this section, we discuss alveolates that are primarily aquatic: the ciliates and dinoflagellates. The section that follows covers apicomplexans, which are parasites.

CILIATED CELLS

Ciliates, or ciliated protozoans, are unwalled heterotrophic cells that use their many cilia to move and feed. Most are predators in seawater, fresh water, or damp soil. Members of the genus *Paramecium* are common in ponds (**FIGURE 20.7**). Their cilia sweep food into an oral groove, from which the particles are taken up by phagocytosis, then digested in food vacuoles. Exocytosis expels digestive waste, and contractile vacuoles squirt out excess water.

A few types of ciliates have adapted to life in the animal gut. Some gut ciliates help cattle, sheep, and related grazers break down cellulose in plant material. Others help termites digest wood. Only one ciliate (*Balantidium coli*) is a known human pathogen. It lives in the pig gut; human infections occur when pig feces get into drinking water.

WHIRLING DINOFLAGELLATES

Dinoflagellates are single-celled protists that typically have two flagella, one at the cell's tip and the other running through a groove around the cell's middle like a belt (**FIGURE 20.8**). Dinoflagellate means "whirling flagellate," and the combined actions of the two flagella cause the cell to spin as it moves forward. Many dinoflagellates deposit cellulose in the sacs beneath their plasma membrane, and these deposits form thick protective plates.

The vast majority of dinoflagellates are part of the marine plankton, and they are especially abundant in warm climates. In tropical seas, dinoflagellates are the most common source of **bioluminescence**, light produced by a living organism. When disturbed, dinoflagellates produce a blue glow by an oxidation reduction reaction (Section 5.4).

Some planktonic dinoflagellates prey on bacteria; others are photosynthetic, with chloroplasts that evolved from a red alga. Photosynthetic dinoflagellates that live in the tissues of reef-building corals help maintain coral reefs. The protists receive shelter within the coral, which is a type of invertebrate animal. In return, they provide the coral with sugars and oxygen. Without its dinoflagellate partners, a reef-building coral will die.

bioluminescence Light emitted by a living organism.
ciliate Single-celled, heterotrophic protist with many cilia.
dinoflagellate Single-celled, aquatic protist that moves with a whirling motion; may be heterotrophic or photosynthetic.

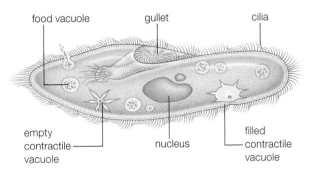

FIGURE 20.7 Structure of *Paramecium*, a freshwater ciliate.

Many free-living dinoflagellates are an important food source for marine animals, but others make toxins that poison animals that eat them. These toxins can move up food chains, so animals and people who eat fish or shellfish that ate toxic dinoflagellates can also be poisoned.

A few types of dinoflagellates are parasites of aquatic animals. For example, some dinoflagellates infect and sicken crabs and other crustaceans.

FIGURE 20.8 A photosynthetic dinoflagellate (*Karenia brevis*).

TAKE-HOME MESSAGE 20.4

Ciliates and dinoflagellates are two closely related lineages of single-celled, primarily aquatic protists.

Most ciliates are predators, but some live inside animals. Cilia on the cell's surface are used in locomotion and feeding.

Dinoflagellates have two flagella and move with a whirling motion. Most are planktonic predators or producers, but some are animal parasites. Some photosynthetic species live as partners inside reef-building corals.

20.5 HOW DOES MALARIA AFFECT HUMAN HEALTH?

Apicomplexans are parasitic alveolates that reproduce only inside cells of their hosts. Their name refers to a complex of microtubules at their apical (upper) end that allows them to pierce and enter a host cell.

Malaria is a deadly disease caused by apicomplexans of the genus *Plasmodium*. A bite from a female mosquito introduces the parasite into a human body, where it reproduces in the liver and in red blood cells (**FIGURE 20.9**). Malaria symptoms usually start a week or two after a mosquito bite, when infected liver cells rupture and release *Plasmodium* cells, metabolic wastes, and cellular debris into the blood. Shaking, chills, a burning fever, and sweats result. After the initial episode, symptoms may subside for weeks or even months. However, an ongoing infection damages the liver, spleen, kidneys, and brain. If untreated, malaria nearly always results in death.

Plasmodium cannot survive at low temperatures, so malaria is mainly a tropical disease. Today, it remains a threat in parts of Mexico, Central America, South America, Asia, and most especially in Africa. In 2011, 91 percent of the 670,000 malarial deaths reported to the World Health Organization occurred in Africa.

FIGURE 20.9 {Animated} Artist's depiction of a *Plasmodium*, the apicomplexan protist that causes malaria, emerging from a human red blood cell.

apicomplexan Parasitic protist that reproduces in cells of its host.

TAKE-HOME MESSAGE 20.5

Malaria, a disease caused by an apicomplexan protist, causes many human deaths in the tropics, especially in Africa.

PEOPLE MATTER

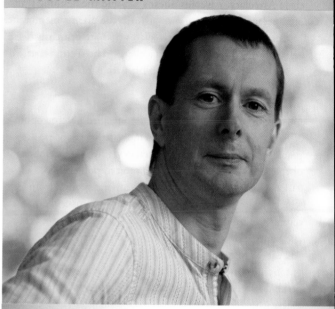

National Geographic Explorer
KEN BANKS

Ken Banks develops low-cost, low-tech innovations that improve the lives of people in developing nations. While involved in conservation work in Africa, Banks saw a huge unmet need for technology that could send information between groups in remote areas with no Internet access. Banks created a text messaging application called FrontlineSMS, which does just that. It is now used to deliver vital information in more than 130 nations.

In Cambodia, health officials use the system to pinpoint and contain malaria outbreaks. Community volunteers in rural areas are trained to diagnose malaria and are given a cell phone to report their findings. A volunteer who diagnoses a new malaria case gives the affected person an antimalarial drug, and reports the case to health officials via a text message. Three days later, the volunteer rechecks the patient's blood to be sure the drug has worked and the parasites are gone. If parasites remain, the person probably has a drug-resistant strain of malaria. If so, this too is immediately reported to health officials. By monitoring incoming reports from hundreds of volunteers, health officials can deploy antimalarial drugs and insecticide-treated nets where they will have the greatest impact.

CREDITS: (9) Malaria illustration by Drew Berry, The Walter and Eliza Hall Institute of Medical Research. (in text) Photograph by James Bedford, National Geographic Creative.

DIATOMS AND BROWN ALGAE

Diatoms and brown algae are photosynthetic members of the clade Stramenopila. Their chloroplasts, which evolved from a red alga, contain chlorophylls *a* and *c*. An accessory pigment (fucoxanthin) gives them a brown color.

Brown algae are multicelled "seaweeds" of temperate or cool seas (**FIGURE 20.10A**). Most grow along rocky seashores. They range in size from microscopic filaments to the largest protists—giant kelp that can reach 30 meters (100 feet) in height. The photo that opened this chapter shows a stand of giant kelp off the coast of California. Like trees in a forest, kelp shelter a wide variety of other organisms. Kelp are also the source of alginates, polysaccharides commonly used to thicken foods, beverages, cosmetics, and body lotions.

Diatoms (**FIGURE 20.10B,C**) are cells with a two-part silica shell. The upper part of the shell overlaps the lower part, like a shoe box. Diatoms live in lakes, seas, and damp soils. When marine diatoms die, their shells accumulate on the seafloor. In places where deposits of diatom shells have been lifted onto land by geological processes, people mine the resulting "diatomaceous earth." This silica-rich material is used in filters and cleaners, and as an insecticide that is nontoxic to vertebrates. Diatoms also contributed the bulk of the organic material to the seafloor deposits from which most oil formed. Like dinoflagellates, diatoms serve as food for many animals. Also like dinoflagellates, some diatoms produce a toxin that accumulates in fish, crabs, and shellfish. Eating seafood tainted by this toxin (domoic acid) can cause a potentially life-threatening form of food poisoning.

WATER MOLDS

Colorless water molds are also among the stramenopiles. **Water molds** are heterotrophic protists that grow as a mesh of nutrient-absorbing filaments. Fungi have a similar growth pattern, and water molds were once considered a type of fungus. More recently, genetic studies revealed their close relationship to the brown algae and diatoms.

Most water molds are decomposers in aquatic habitats or moist soil, but some are important plant pathogens. For example, in the mid-1800s, an outbreak of the water mold *Phytophthora infestans* destroyed Ireland's potato crop. The resulting famine led to hundreds of thousands of human deaths. In recent years, the spread of a related water mold (*P. ramorum*) has decimated oak forests in California and southern Oregon (**FIGURE 20.11A**). Water molds also infect animals. Freshwater fish serve as hosts for *Saprolegnia*, and infections often break out on fish farms and in aquariums. Affected fish develop cottony patches on their body (**FIGURE 20.11B**) and few survive infection.

A A brown alga (*Fucus*), common along rocky shores.

B Scanning electron micrograph of a diatom shell.

C Light micrograph of a live diatom with its brownish chloroplasts.

FIGURE 20.10 Photosynthetic stramenopiles.

A Trunk of an oak infected by *Phytophthora ramorum*.

B *Saprolegnia* growing on a fish.

FIGURE 20.11 Pathogenic water molds.

brown alga Multicelled marine protist with a brown accessory pigment in its chloroplasts.
diatom Single-celled photosynthetic protist with a brown accessory pigment in its chloroplasts and a two-part silica shell.
water mold Heterotrophic protist that grows as a mesh of nutrient-absorbing filaments.

TAKE-HOME MESSAGE 20.6

Brown algae are multicellular seaweeds. Diatoms are silica-shelled cells. Both stramenopile groups have chloroplasts that contain a brown accessory pigment.

Water molds are filamentous heterotrophs. Most are decomposers, but some are parasites of plants or animals.

CREDITS: (10A) Garo/ Science Source; (10B) Science Museum of Minnesota; (10C) © Wim van Egmond/ Visuals Unlimited; (11A) Pavel Svihra; (11B) Heather Angel.

Archaeplastids are organisms whose cellulose-walled cells contain chloroplasts with two membranes. Scientists think these chloroplasts evolved from cyanobacteria by primary endosymbiosis. Archaeplastids include two protist groups (red algae and green algae) that we discuss here, as well as land plants, which we consider in detail in the next chapter.

RED ALGAE

Red algae (clade Rhodophyta) are photosynthetic, generally multicelled protists that live in clear, warm seas. Most grow either as thin sheets or in a branching pattern (**FIGURE 20.12**). One subgroup, the coralline algae, deposits calcium carbonate in its cells. The rigid material produced by these algae contributes bulk to some tropical reefs.

Chloroplasts of red algae contain chlorophyll *a*, as well as red accessory pigments (phycobilins). Phycobilins absorb blue–green light, which penetrates deeper into water than light of other wavelengths. Thus, red algae can thrive at greater depths than other algae.

Two gelatinous polysaccharides, agar and carrageenan, are extracted from red algae for use as thickeners or stabilizers in foods, cosmetics, and personal care products. Agar is also important in microbiology. When mixed with appropriate nutrients, it forms a semisolid culture medium for growing bacteria or fungi.

Nori, the edible seaweed used to wrap sushi, is a red alga (*Porphyra*). Like many multicelled algae and all plants, *Porphyra* has a life cycle that alternates between haploid and diploid bodies—an **alternation of generations** (**FIGURE 20.13**). The nori **gametophyte**, or haploid body, is a sheetlike seaweed ❶ that forms gametes by mitosis ❷. When gametes join at fertilization, they form a diploid zygote ❸ that grows and develops into the diploid body, or **sporophyte** ❹. The nori sporophyte is a tiny, branching filament. The sporophyte produces haploid spores by meiosis ❺. The spore germinates, then grows and develops into a new gametophyte to complete the cycle ❻.

GREEN ALGAE

Green algae are single-celled, colonial, or multicellular autotrophs whose chloroplasts contain chlorophylls *a* and *b*. Some single-celled green algae live in the soil, others in

FIGURE 20.12 Branching and sheetlike red algae growing 75 meters (250 ft) beneath the sea surface in the Gulf of Mexico.

❹ sporophyte (2*n*)

zygote ❸

diploid stage

haploid stage

Fertilization

Meiosis

❷ male gametes

germinating spore (*n*)

female gametes

❺

❻

❶ gametophyte (*n*)

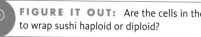

FIGURE 20.13 {**Animated**} Life cycle of a red alga (*Porphyra*), commonly known as nori.
❶ The haploid gametophyte is sheetlike.
❷ Gametes form at its edges.
❸ Fertilization produces a diploid zygote.
❹ The zygote develops into a diploid sporophyte.
❺ Haploid spores form by meiosis on the sporophyte, and are released.
❻ Spores germinate and develop into a new gametophyte.

FIGURE IT OUT: Are the cells in the sheets of algae used to wrap sushi haploid or diploid?

Answer: Haploid

CREDITS: (12) Image courtesy of FGB-NMS/UNCW-NURC; (13) art, © Cengage Learning; photo, © PhotoDisc/Getty Images.

the sea, and still others partner with a fungus to form a composite organism known as a lichen. However, the vast majority of green algae live in fresh water.

Chlamydomonas is a single-celled green alga common in ponds. Flagellated haploid cells (**FIGURE 20.14A**) reproduce asexually when conditions favor growth. If nutrients become scarce, gametes form by mitosis and fuse to form a diploid zygote with a thick wall. When conditions once again become favorable, the zygote undergoes meiosis, yielding four haploid, flagellated cells.

Volvox is a colonial freshwater species (**FIGURE 20.14B**). A colony consists of hundreds to thousands of flagellated cells that resemble *Chlamydomonas*. Thin cytoplasmic strands join the cells together as a whirling sphere. Daughter colonies form inside the parental colony, which eventually ruptures and releases them.

Wispy sheets of the multicelled green alga *Ulva* cling to coastal rocks worldwide. In some species, these sheets grow longer than your arm, but are less than 40 microns thick (**FIGURE 20.14C**). *Ulva* is commonly known as sea lettuce and is harvested for use in salads and soups.

Like the chloroplasts of green algae, those of land plants have two membranes and contain chlorophylls *a* and *c*. This and other similarities indicate that plants descended from a green alga. More specifically, land plants descended from a lineage of mostly freshwater green algae known as the charophyte algae (clade Charophyta). Modern members of this clade share unique structural and functional features with land plants (**FIGURE 20.15**).

A Single celled organism. *Chlamydomonas*, a single celled freshwater alga, uses its two flagella to swim.

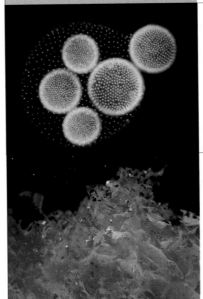

B Colony. *Volvox* colonies consist of flagellated cells connected by thin strands of cytoplasm. New colonies form inside a parent colony and are released.

C Multicellular organism. Long, thin sheets of sea lettuce (*Ulva*) are common along coasts where there is little wave action.

FIGURE 20.14 Three levels of organization among green algae.

alternation of generations Of land plants and some algae, a life cycle that includes haploid and diploid multicelled bodies.
gametophyte Gamete-producing haploid body that forms in the life cycle of land plants and some multicelled algae.
green alga Single-celled, colonial, or multicelled photosynthetic protist that has chloroplasts containing chlorophylls *a* and *b*.
red alga Photosynthetic protist; typically multicelled, with chloroplasts containing red accessory pigments (phycobilins).
sporophyte Spore-forming diploid body that forms in the life cycle of land plants and some multicelled algae.

TAKE-HOME MESSAGE 20.7

Red algae and green algae are protists that belong to the same clade as the land plants. All members of this clade deposit cellulose in their cell wall.

Red algae are mostly multicellular and marine. They have red accessory pigments that allow them to live at greater depths than other algae.

Green algae include single-celled, colonial, and multicelled species. One subgroup, the charophyte algae, includes the closest living relatives of land plants.

A *Coleochaete orbicularis* grows as a multicellular disk attached to a surface.

B *Chara*, commonly known as musk-grass or stinkweed for its strong odor.

FIGURE 20.15 Charophyte algae. Like plants, and unlike most other green algae, charophyte cells divide their cytoplasm by cell plate formation (Section 11.3) and have plasmodesmata (cytoplasmic connections between neighboring cells, Section 4.10).

Amoebozoans are shape-shifting heterotrophic cells that typically lack a wall or pellicle. They move about and capture smaller cells by extending lobes of cytoplasm called pseudopods (Section 4.9).

AMOEBAS

FIGURE 20.16 Freshwater amoeba.

Amoebas spend their entire lives as single cells (**FIGURE 20.16**). Most live in marine or freshwater sediments or in damp soil, where they are important predators of bacteria. A few affect human health. *Entamoeba* infects the human gut, causing cramps, aches, and bloody diarrhea. Infections are most common in developing nations where amoebic cysts contaminate drinking water. Another freshwater amoeba, *Naegleria fowleri*, can enter the nose and cause a rare but deadly brain infection. Most people become infected while swimming in a warm pond or lake, but people have also died after using tap water to irrigate their sinuses.

SLIME MOLDS

Slime molds are sometimes described as "social amoebas." Two types are common on the floor of temperate forests.

Cellular slime molds spend most of their existence as individual amoeba-like cells (**FIGURE 20.17**). Each cell eats bacteria and reproduces by mitosis ❶. If food runs out, thousands of cells stream together ❷ to form a cohesive multicelled unit referred to as a "slug" ❸. The slug moves to a suitable spot, where its component cells differentiate, forming a fruiting body with resting spores atop a stalk ❹. After disperal, each spore will release an amoeba-like cell.

Plasmodial slime molds spend most of their life cycle as a plasmodium, a multinucleated mass that forms when a diploid cell undergoes mitosis many times without cytoplasmic division. A plasmodium streams along surfaces, feeding on microbes and organic matter (**FIGURE 20.18**). When food runs out, the plasmodium develops into many spore-bearing fruiting bodies.

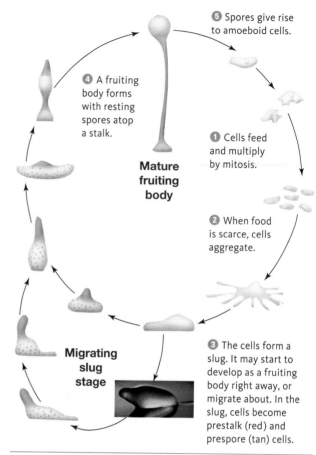

❺ Spores give rise to amoeboid cells.

❹ A fruiting body forms with resting spores atop a stalk.

Mature fruiting body

❶ Cells feed and multiply by mitosis.

❷ When food is scarce, cells aggregate.

Migrating slug stage

❸ The cells form a slug. It may start to develop as a fruiting body right away, or migrate about. In the slug, cells become prestalk (red) and prespore (tan) cells.

FIGURE 20.17 {Animated} Life cycle of *Dictyostelium discoideum*, a cellular slime mold.

FIGURE 20.18 Plasmodial slime mold streaming across a log.

---

amoeba Single-celled protist that extends pseudopods to move and to capture prey.
amoebozoan Shape-shifting heterotrophic protist with no pellicle or cell wall; an amoeba or slime mold.
cellular slime mold Amoeba-like protist that feeds as a single predatory cell; joins with others to form a multicellular spore-bearing structure under unfavorable conditions.
plasmodial slime mold Protist that feeds as a multinucleated mass; forms a spore-bearing structure when environmental conditions become unfavorable.

TAKE-HOME MESSAGE 20.8

Amoebozoans are heterotrophic protists with cells that lack a wall or pellicle, so they can constantly change shape.

Amoebas live as single cells, usually in fresh water.

Slime molds live on forest floors. Plasmodial slime molds feed as a big multinucleated mass. Cellular slime molds feed as single cells, but come together as a multicelled mass when conditions are unfavorable. Both types of slime molds form fruiting bodies that release spores.

20.9 WHICH PROTISTS ARE CLOSEST TO ANIMALS?

Aquatic, heterotrophic protists called **choanoflagellates** are the closest known protistan relatives of animals. A choanoflagellate cell has a flagellum surrounded by a "collar" of threadlike projections (FIGURE 20.19). Movement of the flagellum sets up a current that draws food-laden water through the collar. As you will learn in Chapter 23, some sponge cells have a similar structure and function.

Most choanoflagellates live as single cells, but some form colonies. The colonies arise by mitosis, when descendant cells do not separate after division. Instead, cellular offspring stick together with the help of adhesion proteins. Choanoflagellate adhesion proteins are similar to those of animals, and researchers have discovered that even solitary choanoflagellates have these proteins. By one hypothesis, the common ancestor of animals and choanoflagellates was a single-celled protist with adhesion proteins that helped it capture prey. Later, these proteins were put to use in a new context, helping choanoflagellates stick together to form multicelled colonies. Later still, the proteins allowed animal cells to adhere to one another in multicelled bodies. This modification in the use of adhesion proteins is an example of exaptation, an evolutionary process by which a trait that evolves with one function later takes on a different function (Section 17.11).

FIGURE 20.19 Choanoflagellate colony. It is composed of genetically identical cells like that illustrated at right.

collar
flagellum

choanoflagellate Heterotrophic freshwater protist with a flagellum and a food-capturing "collar." May be solitary or colonial.

TAKE-HOME MESSAGE 20.9

Choanoflagellates are close relatives of animals. Studies of colonial choanoflagellates may help us discover how the first animals evolved.

CREDITS: (19) photo, Courtesy of Damian Zanette; art, From Starr/Evers/Starr, Biology Today and Tomorrow with Physiology, 4E. © Cengage Learning; (20) © Peter M. Johnson/ www.flickr.com/photos/pmjohnso.

20.10 ALGAL BLOOMS

Application: Sustainability

FIGURE 20.20 A bloom of dinoflagellate cells colors seawater along Florida's Gulf coast red.

LIKE LAND PLANTS, ALGAE GROW FASTER WITH THE ADDITION OF CERTAIN NUTRIENTS. Fertilizing a houseplant or a lawn results in a spurt of growth. Similarly, adding nutrients to an aquatic habitat encourages photosynthetic protists to reproduce. We do not fertilize our waters on purpose, but fertilizers drain from croplands and lawns, and sewage and animal wastes from factory farms get into rivers and flow to the sea. The result is an "algal bloom," a population explosion of aquatic protists.

If the protist involved secretes toxins, the bloom can poison other species, including humans. Even nontoxic algal blooms can have negative environmental effects. The huge number of cells eventually die. Bacteria that decompose the remains deplete the water of oxygen, causing fish and other aquatic animals to smother.

Toxic algal blooms affect every coastal region of the United States. Blooms of toxin-producing dinoflagellates are common in the Gulf of Mexico and along the Atlantic coast (FIGURE 20.20). Along the Pacific coast, population explosions of toxic diatoms are most common.

Keeping harmful algal toxins out of the human food supply requires constant vigilance. These toxins have no color or odor, and are unaffected by heating or freezing. Government agencies use laboratory tests to detect algal toxins in water samples and shellfish. When the toxins reach a threatening level, a shore is closed to shellfishing.

Summary

SECTION 20.1 **Protists** are a diverse collection that includes members of many eukaryotic groups, some only distantly related to one another. Most protists are single cells, but some are **colonial organisms** or **multicellular organisms**. Some protists are heterotrophs and others have chloroplasts that evolved from cyanobacteria by **primary endosymbiosis**. Still others have chloroplasts that evolved from a red or green alga by **secondary endosymbiosis**.

SECTION 20.2 **Flagellated protozoans** are single unwalled cells. A protein covering, or **pellicle**, helps maintain the cell's shape. Diplomonads and parabasalids have modified mitochondria and are anaerobic. Members of both groups include species that infect humans.

Trypanosomes are parasites with a single mitochondrion and a flagellum that attaches to the side of the body. The related **euglenoids** typically live in fresh water. They have a **contractile vacuole** that squirts out excess water. Some have chloroplasts that evolved from a green alga.

SECTION 20.3 **Foraminifera** are single cells with a calcium carbonate shell. **Radiolaria** are single-celled and have a silica shell. Both groups are marine heterotrophs and part of **plankton**. Cytoplasmic extensions that stick out through their porous shell capture prey.

SECTIONS 20.4, 20.5 Tiny sacs (alveoli) beneath the plasma membrane characterize alveolates. All are single-celled. **Dinoflagellates** are whirling aquatic cells. They may be autotrophs or heterotrophs. Some are capable of **bioluminescence**. The **ciliates** have many cilia. They include aquatic predators and parasites. **Apicomplexans** live as parasites in the cells of animals. Mosquitoes transmit the apicomplexan that causes malaria.

SECTION 20.6 Stramenopiles include two photosynthetic groups and the colorless water molds. **Diatoms** are silica-shelled photosynthetic cells. Deposits of ancient diatom shells are mined as diatomaceous earth. **Brown algae** include microscopic strands and giant kelp, the largest protists. Brown algae are the source of algins, compounds used as thickeners and emulsifiers. Diatoms and brown algae share a brown accessory pigment. **Water molds** grow as a mesh of absorptive filaments. They include decomposers and parasites.

SECTION 20.7 Most **red algae** are multicelled and marine. Accessory pigments called phycobilins allow them to capture light even in deep waters. Red algae are commercially important as the source of agar, carrageenan, and as dry sheets (nori) used for wrapping sushi. **Green algae** may be single cells, colonial, or multicelled. They are the closest relatives of land plants.

Like land plants, some algae have an **alternation of generations**, a life cycle in which two kinds of multicelled bodies form: a diploid, spore-producing **sporophyte** and a haploid, gamete-producing **gametophyte**.

SECTION 20.8 **Amoebozoans** include solitary **amoebas** and slime molds, both heterotrophic. The **plasmodial slime molds** feed as a multinucleated mass. Amoeba-like cells of **cellular slime molds** aggregate when food is scarce. Both types of slime molds form multicelled fruiting bodies that disperse resting spores.

SECTION 20.9 **Choanoflagellates** are heterotrophic solitary or colonial protists that are close relatives of the animals.

SECTION 20.10 An algal bloom is a population explosion of aquatic protists that results from nutrient enrichment of an aquatic habitat. Algal blooms endanger other organisms.

Self-Quiz   Answers in Appendix VII

1. All flagellated protozoans _____ .
   a. lack mitochondria   c. live as single cells
   b. are photosynthetic   d. cause disease

2. Deposits of shells from ancient _____ are mined as chalk and limestone.
   a. dinoflagellates   c. radiolaria
   b. diatoms   d. foraminifera

3. The presence of a contractile vacuole indicates that a single-celled protist _____ .
   a. is marine   c. is photosynthetic
   b. lives in fresh water   d. secretes a toxin

4. Cattle benefit when _____ in their gut help them digest plant material.
   a. red algae   c. ciliates
   b. diatoms   d. foraminifera

5. An insect bite can transmit a malaria-causing _____ to a human host.
   a. trypanosome   c. ciliate
   b. apicomplexan   d. diplomonad

6. _____ are the closest relatives of the land plants.
   a. Green algae   c. Brown algae
   b. Red algae   d. Euglenoids

7. Accessory pigments of _____ allow them to carry out photosynthesis at greater depths than other algae.
   a. euglenoids   c. brown algae
   b. green algae   d. red algae

8. The most common bioluminescent protists in tropical seas are _____ .
   a. red algae   b. diatoms   c. dinoflagellates   d. radiolaria

9. The _____ are important plant pathogens.
   a. dinoflagellates   c. water molds
   b. ciliates   d. slime molds

Data Analysis Activities

Tracking Changes in Algal Blooms Reports of fish kills along Florida's southwest coast date to the mid-1800s, suggesting algal blooms are a natural phenomenon in this region. However, University of Miami researchers suspected that increased nutrient delivery from land contributed to an increase in the abundance of the dinoflagellates. Since the 1950s, the population of coastal cities in southwestern Florida has soared and the amount of agriculture increased. To find out if nearshore nutrients are affecting dinoflagellate numbers, the researchers looked at records for coastal waters that have been monitored for more than 50 years. **FIGURE 20.21** shows the average abundance and distribution of dinoflagellates during two time periods.

1. How did the average concentration of dinoflagellates in waters less than 5 kilometers from shore change between the two time periods?

2. How did the average concentration of dinoflagellates in waters more than 25 kilometers from shore change between the two time periods?

3. Do these data support the hypothesis that human activity increased the abundance of dinoflagellates by adding nutrients to coastal waters?

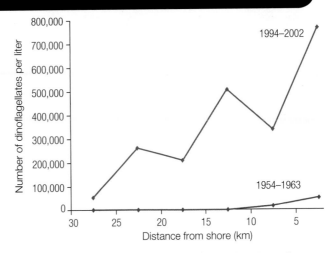

FIGURE 20.21 Average concentration of dinoflagellate cells detected at various distances from the shore during two time periods: 1954–1963 (blue line) and 1994–2002 (red line). Samples were collected from offshore waters between Tampa Bay and Sanibel Island.

4. If the two graph lines became farther apart as distance from the shore increased, what would that suggest about the nutrient source?

10. Silica-rich shells of ancient diatoms are the source of diatomaceous earth that can be used _____ .
    a. to thicken foods   c. as a fertilizer
    b. as a gelatin substitute   d. as an insecticide

11. The sporophyte of a multicellular alga _____ .
    a. is haploid   c. produces spores
    b. is a single cell   d. produces gametes

12. Cellular slime molds most often live _____ .
    a. on the forest floor   c. in an animal gut
    b. in a tropical sea   d. in a mountain lake

13. The protist that causes the sexually transmitted disease trichomoniasis is a(n) _____ .
    a. flagellated protozoan   c. ciliate
    b. radiolaria   d. apicomplexan

14. All green algae _____ .
    a. have a cell wall   c. are multicellular
    b. are marine   d. all of the above

15. Match each item with its description.
    ____ choanoflagellate   a. chalky-shelled heterotroph
    ____ apicomplexan   b. silica-shelled autotroph
    ____ foraminiferan   c. deep dweller with phycobilins
    ____ diatom   d. close relative of animals
    ____ brown alga   e. close relative of land plants
    ____ red alga   f. multicelled, with fucoxanthin
    ____ green alga   g. cause of malaria

Critical Thinking

1. Imagine you are in a developing country where sanitation is poor. Having read about parasitic flagellates in water and damp soil, what would you consider safe to drink? What foods might be best to avoid or which food preparation methods might make them safe to eat?

2. Water in abandoned swimming pools often turns green. If you examined a drop of this water with a microscope, how could you tell whether the water contains protists and, if so, which group they might belong to?

3. The "snow alga" *Chlamydomonas nivalis* (*right*) lives on glaciers. It is a green alga, but it has so many carotenoid pigments that it appears red. Besides their role in photosynthesis, what other function might these light-absorbing carotenoids serve in the alga's bright, arctic environment?

4. The protist that causes malaria evolved from a photosynthetic ancestor and has the remnant of a chloroplast. The organelle no longer functions in photosynthesis, but it remains essential to the protist. Why might targeting this organelle yield an antimalarial drug that produces minimal side effects in humans?

CENGAGE **brain** .com To access course materials, please visit www.cengagebrain.com.

Ancient bristlecone pines in
California's White Mountains.
These plants can live more than
4,500 years.

21 PLANT EVOLUTION

Links to Earlier Concepts

Section 20.7 **introduced the algae that are the closest relative of plants.** Section 12.2 **introduced gamete formation in plants and here you will see specific examples. You will learn about evolution of cell walls strengthened with lignin (4.10) and a waxy cuticle perforated by stomata (6.5). We also discuss plant fossils (16.3) and coevolution with pollinators (17.11).**

KEY CONCEPTS

ADAPTIVE TRENDS AMONG PLANTS

Plants evolved from a green alga. Over time, changes in structure, life cycle, and reproductive processes adapted plants to life in increasingly drier climates.

THE BRYOPHYTES

Bryophytes include the oldest plant lineages such as mosses. All are low-growing plants that disperse by releasing spores, and have flagellated sperm that swim to eggs.

SEEDLESS VASCULAR PLANTS

Internal pipelines that characterize vascular plants allow them to stand taller than bryophytes. Seedless vascular plants such as ferns release spores. Their sperm swim through water to eggs.

GYMNOSPERMS

Gymnosperms are seed plants—vascular plants that make pollen and release seeds, rather than spores. They do not require water for sperm to reach eggs. Gymnosperm seeds are not enclosed within a fruit.

ANGIOSPERMS

Angiosperms are seed plants that make flowers and form seeds inside fruits. They are the most widely dispersed and diverse plant group. Many enlist animals to move pollen or disperse seeds.

Photograph by Marc Moritsch, National Geographic Creative.

Plants are multicelled, photosynthetic eukaryotes that typically live on land. They first appeared about 500 million years ago. Green algae grew at the water's edge, and one lineage, the charophytes, gave rise to the first land plants. Like green algae, plants have cells with walls made of cellulose and chloroplasts that contain chlorophylls *a* and *b*.

A developmental trait defines plants. Their clade is called the embryophytes (meaning embryo-bearing plants), because their embryos form inside a chamber of parental tissues and receive nourishment from the parent during early development.

STRUCTURAL ADAPTATIONS

Moving onto land posed challenges to a previously aquatic lineage. A multicelled green alga absorbs all the water, dissolved nutrients, and gases it needs across its body surface. Water also buoys algal parts, helping an alga stand upright. By contrast, land plants face the threat of drying out, must take up water and nutrients from soil, and have to stand upright on their own.

A variety of structural features allow land plants to meet these challenges. Most secrete a waxy **cuticle** that reduces water loss (**FIGURE 21.1**). Closable pores called **stomata** (singular, stoma) extend across the cuticle. Depending on conditions in the environment and inside the plant, stomata can open to allow gas exchange or close to conserve water.

Early plants were held in place by threadlike structures, but these structures did not deliver water or dissolved

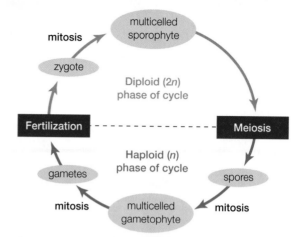

FIGURE 21.2 {Animated} Generalized plant life cycle.

minerals to the rest of the plant body. True roots contain vascular tissue: internal pipelines that transport water and nutrients among plant parts. **Xylem** is the vascular tissue that distributes water and mineral ions taken up by roots. **Phloem** is the vascular tissue that distributes sugars made by photosynthetic cells. Of the 295,000 or so modern plant species, more than 90 percent are **vascular plants**, meaning plants that have xylem and phloem. Mosses and other ancient plant lineages are referred to as **nonvascular plants**, meaning they do not have these vascular tissues.

An organic compound called **lignin** stiffens cell walls in vascular tissue. Lignin-reinforced vascular tissue not only distributes materials, it also helps vascular land plants stand upright and supports their branches. Most vascular plants have branches with many leaves that increase the surface area for capturing light and for gas exchange.

LIFE CYCLE CHANGES

Adapting to life in dry habitats also involved life cycle changes. Like some algae, land plants have an alternation of generations (**FIGURE 21.2**). Meiosis of cells in a diploid, multicelled **sporophyte** produces spores, which in plants are walled haploid cells. A spore germinates, divides by mitosis, and develops into a haploid, multicelled **gametophyte**. Mitosis of cells in a gametophyte produces gametes that combine at fertilization to form a diploid zygote. The zygote grows and develops into a new sporophyte.

In nonvascular plants, the gametophyte is the largest and longest-lived part of the life cycle. By contrast, the sporophyte dominates the life cycle of vascular plants. Living in dry conditions favors an increased emphasis on spore production, because spores withstand drying out better than gametes do.

FIGURE 21.1 Diagram of a vascular plant leaf in cross-section, showing some traits that contribute to the success of this group. The micrograph shows a stoma, a pore at the surface of a squash plant's leaf. Photosynthetic cells on either side of the stoma control its opening and closing to regulate water loss and gas exchange.

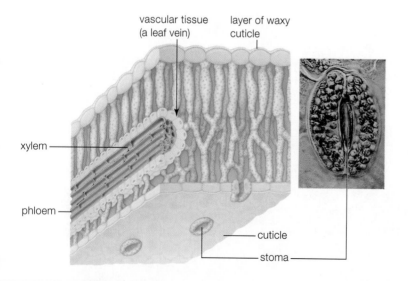

vascular tissue
(a leaf vein)

layer of waxy
cuticle

xylem

phloem

cuticle

stoma

Nonvascular plants	**Seedless vascular plants**	**Gymnosperms**	**Angiosperms**
• No xylem or phloem	• Vascular tissue present	• Vascular tissue present	• Vascular tissue present
• Gametophyte predominant	• Sporophyte predominant	• Sporophyte predominant	• Sporophyte predominant
• Water required for fertilization	• Water required for fertilization	• Pollen grains; water not required for fertilization	• Pollen grains; water not required for fertilization
• Seedless	• Seedless	• "Naked" seeds	• Seeds form in a floral ovary that becomes a fruit

liverworts   hornworts   mosses

club mosses, spike mosses

whisk ferns, horsetails, ferns

gnetophytes, ginkgos, conifers, cycads

monocots, eudicots, and relatives

ancestral alga

POLLEN AND SEEDS

Evolution of new reproductive traits in seed plants gave this vascular plant lineage a competitive edge in dry habitats. Seed plants do not release spores. Instead, their spores give rise to gametophytes inside specialized structures on the sporophyte body.

A **pollen grain** is a walled, immature male gametophyte of a seed plant. Once released, it can be transported to another plant by wind or animals even in the driest of times. By contrast, plants that do not make pollen (nonvascular plants and seedless vascular plants) can only reproduce when a film of water allows their sperm to swim to eggs.

Fertilization of a seed plant takes place on the sporophyte body. It results in development of a **seed**— an embryo sporophyte packaged with a supply of nutritive tissue inside a protective seed coat. Seed plants disperse a new generation by releasing seeds.

There are two modern seed plant lineages. Gymnosperms include nonflowering seed producers such as pine trees. Angiosperms, which make flowers and package their seeds inside a fruit, are the most widely distributed and diverse plant group.

FIGURE 21.3 summarizes the relationships among the major plant groups and the traits of each group.

cuticle Secreted covering at a body surface.
gametophyte Multicelled, haploid, gamete-producing body.
lignin Material that stiffens cell walls of vascular plants.
nonvascular plant Plant that does not have xylem and phloem; a bryophyte such as a moss.
phloem Plant vascular tissue that distributes sugars.
plant Multicelled photosynthetic organism in which embryos form on and are nurtured by the parent.
pollen grain Walled, immature male gametophyte of a seed plant.
seed Embryo sporophyte of a seed plant packaged with nutritive tissue inside a protective coat.
sporophyte Multicelled, diploid, spore-producing body.
stoma Opening across a plant's cuticle and epidermis; can be opened for gas exchange or closed to prevent water loss.
vascular plant Plant with xylem and phloem.
xylem Plant vascular tissue that distributes water and dissolved mineral ions.

> **TAKE-HOME MESSAGE 21.1**
>
> Nonvascular plants such as mosses have a life cycle dominated by a haploid gametophyte.
>
> Vascular plants have a life cycle dominated by a diploid sporophyte with vascular tissue. Like nonvascular plants, the oldest vascular plant lineages disperse by releasing spores.
>
> Seed plants, the most recently evolved plant lineage, can reproduce even in dry times because they make pollen. They disperse by releasing seeds, not spores.

Nonvascular plants, also known as **bryophytes**, include three modern lineages: mosses, hornworts, and liverworts. These are the only modern plants in which the gametophyte is larger and longer-lived than the sporophyte. All nonvascular plants produce flagellated sperm that require a film of water to swim to eggs, and all disperse by releasing spores, rather than seeds.

Nonvascular plants absorb nutrients across their surface, rather than withdrawing them from soil, so they can colonize rocky sites where vascular plants cannot become rooted. They also withstand drought and cold better than vascular plants. In some parts of the Arctic and Antarctic, nonvascular plants are the only plant life.

MOSSES

Mosses are the most diverse and familiar nonvascular plants. Like other nonvascular plants, mosses do not have true leaves or roots. However, their gametophytes have leaflike photosynthetic parts arranged around a central stalk (**FIGURE 21.4 ❶**). Threadlike **rhizoids** anchor the gametophyte, but do not take up water and nutrients as the roots of vascular plants do.

The moss sporophyte is not photosynthetic, so it depends on the gametophyte for nourishment even when mature. The sporophyte consists of a spore-producing structure (a sporangium) atop a stalk ❷. Meiosis of cells inside the sporangium produces haploid spores ❸. After dispersal by the wind, a spore germinates and grows into a gametophyte. Multicellular gamete-producing structures (gametangia) develop in or on the gametophyte. The moss we are using as our example has separate sexes, with each gametophyte producing either eggs or sperm ❹, but in some species, a gametophyte produces both. In either case, rain causes the gametophyte to release flagellated sperm that swim through a film of water to eggs ❺. Fertilization inside the egg chamber produces a zygote ❻ that grows and develops into a new sporophyte ❼.

Peat mosses (*Sphagnum*) are the most economically important nonvascular plants. They grow in peat bogs that cover hundreds of millions of acres in high-latitude

FIGURE 21.4 {Animated} Life cycle of a common moss (*Polytrichum*).

❶ The moss gametophyte has photosynthetic leaflike parts. Rhizoids hold it in place.
❷ The nonphotosynthetic moss sporophyte consists of a stalk and a capsule.
❸ Spores form by meiosis in the capsule, are released, and drift with the winds.
❹ Spores develop into gametophytes that produce eggs or sperm in gametangia at their tips.
❺ Sperm released from tips of sperm-producing gametophytes swim through water to eggs at tips of egg-producing gametophytes.
❻ Fertilization produces a zygote.
❼ The zygote grows and develops into a sporophyte while remaining attached to and nourished by its egg-producing parent.

CREDITS: (4) photo, Jane Burton/ Bruce Coleman Ltd.; art, From Starr/Evers/Starr, Biology Today and Tomorrow with Physiology, 4E. © 2013 Cengage Learning.

regions of Europe, Asia, and North America. Many peat bogs have persisted for thousands of years, and layer upon layer of plant remains have become compressed as carbon-rich material called peat. Blocks of peat are cut, dried, and burned as fuel, especially in Ireland (**FIGURE 21.5**). Freshly harvested peat moss is also an important commercial product. The moss is dried and added to planting mixes to help soil retain moisture.

LIVERWORTS AND HORNWORTS

Liverworts may be the most ancient of the surviving plant lineages. The oldest known fossils of land plants are spores that resemble those of modern liverworts. In addition, genetic comparisons put liverworts near the base of the plant family tree.

Some liverwort gametophytes look leafy and others are flattened sheets. In the widespread liverwort genus *Marchantia*, eggs and sperm form on separate plants. The gametangia are elevated above the main gametophyte body on stalks (**FIGURE 21.6**). Members of this genus also reproduce asexually by producing small clumps of cells in cups on the gametophyte surface. Some *Marchantia* species can be pests in commercial greenhouses. Liverwort infestations are difficult to eradicate because the tiny spores can persist even after all plants are killed.

Hornworts have a flat, ribbonlike or rosette-shaped gametophyte and a pointy, hornlike sporophyte (**FIGURE 21.7**). The base of the sporophyte is embedded in the gametophyte, and spores form in an upright capsule at its tip. When spores mature, the tip of the capsule splits, releasing them.

Unlike the sporophyte of a moss or liverwort, that of a hornwort grows continually from its base. It also has chloroplasts and, in some cases, can survive even after the gametophyte dies. These traits, together with genetic similarities, suggest that hornworts are the closest living relatives of the vascular plants. As you will see, vascular plants have a sporophyte-dominated life cycle.

---

bryophyte Nonvascular plant; a moss, liverwort, or hornwort.
rhizoid Threadlike structure that holds a nonvascular plant in place.

TAKE-HOME MESSAGE 21.2

Mosses, liverworts, and hornworts are three lineages of low-growing plants that do not have lignin-reinforced vascular tissues. All have flagellated sperm that require a film of water to swim to eggs, and all disperse by releasing spores.

Nonvascular plants (bryophytes) are the only plants in which the gametophyte is largest and longest-lived. The sporophyte remains attached to the gametophyte even when mature.

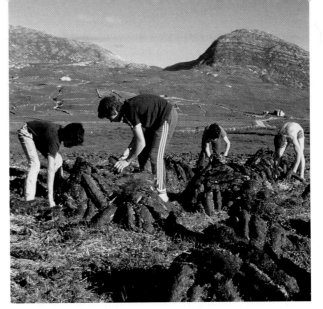

FIGURE 21.5 Cutting blocks of peat in Ireland for use as fuel. Peat is the compressed, carbon-rich remains of *Sphagnum* moss.

FIGURE 21.6 {Animated} Liverwort (*Marchantia*). Tiny sporophytes with yellow capsules form on umbrella-shaped, female gametangia.

FIGURE 21.7 Hornwort. Photosynthetic hornlike sporophytes grow from a flattened gametophyte body.

CREDITS: (5) © Fred Bavendam/ Peter Arnold, Inc.; (6) Dr. Annkatrin Rose, Appalachian State University; (7) age fotostock/ SuperStock.

Only vascular plants have lignin-strengthened vascular tissue. This innovation allowed evolution of larger, branching sporophytes with roots, stems, and leaves. Such sporophytes are the predominant generation in all vascular plants. Like nonvascular plants, **seedless vascular plants** have flagellated sperm that swim to eggs, and they disperse by releasing spores directly into the environment. The spores develop into tiny, short-lived gametophytes.

Two lineages of seedless vascular plants survived to the present. One (monilophytes) includes ferns and related groups, the other (lycophytes) includes club mosses and their relatives. These lineages diverged from a common ancestor before leaves and roots evolved, so each developed these features in a different way.

FERNS AND CLOSE RELATIVES

With 12,000 or so species, ferns are the most diverse and familiar seedless vascular plants. Most live in the tropics. A typical fern sporophyte has fronds (leaves) and roots that grow from a **rhizome**, a horizontal underground stem (**FIGURE 21.8 ❶**). Fiddleheads, the young, tightly coiled fronds of some ferns, are harvested from the wild as food.

Fern spores form in **sori** (singular, sorus), clusters of capsules (sporangia) that develop on the lower surface of fronds ❷. When these capsules pop open, spores disperse on the wind. After a spore germinates, it grows into a photosynthetic, heart-shaped gametophyte just a few centimeters wide ❸. Eggs and sperm form in chambers (gametangia) on the underside of the tiny gametophyte. Rain stimulates release of sperm, which swim through a film of water to reach and fertilize an egg ❹. The resulting zygote develops into a new sporophyte ❺, and its parental gametophyte dies.

Fern sporophytes vary in size and form. Some floating ferns have fronds only 1 millimeter long. Tree ferns can be 25 meters (80 feet) high (**FIGURE 21.9A**). Many tropical ferns are epiphytes, meaning they attach to and grow on a trunk or branch of another plant but do not withdraw any nutrients from it.

Whisk ferns and horsetails are close relatives of ferns. Most whisk ferns are in the genus *Psilotum*. *Their* sporophyte has leafless photosynthetic stems that grow from rhizomes (**FIGURE 21.9B**). Spores form in fused sporangia at the tips of short lateral branches. Florists use these whisk ferns to add visual interest to mixed bouquets.

The sporophyte of a horsetail (*Equisetum*) has hollow stems with tiny nonphotosynthetic leaves at the joints. Photosynthesis occurs in stems and leaflike branches

---

FIGURE 21.8 {Animated} Life cycle of a fern.

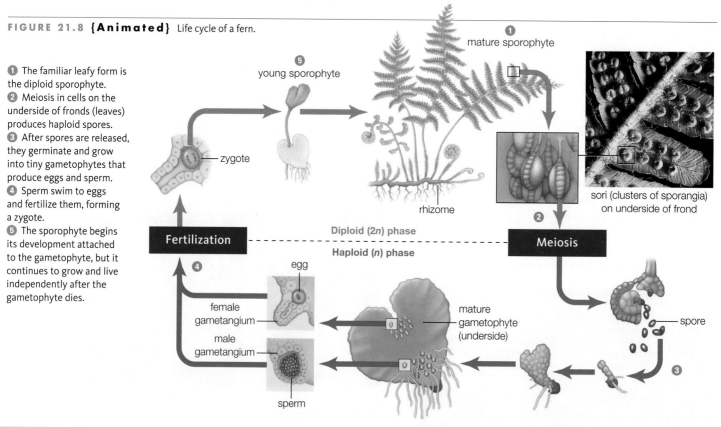

❶ The familiar leafy form is the diploid sporophyte.
❷ Meiosis in cells on the underside of fronds (leaves) produces haploid spores.
❸ After spores are released, they germinate and grow into tiny gametophytes that produce eggs and sperm.
❹ Sperm swim to eggs and fertilize them, forming a zygote.
❺ The sporophyte begins its development attached to the gametophyte, but it continues to grow and live independently after the gametophyte dies.

young sporophyte ❺

mature sporophyte ❶

zygote

sori (clusters of sporangia) on underside of frond

rhizome

Diploid (2n) phase

Haploid (n) phase

Fertilization

Meiosis ❷

egg ❹

female gametangium

male gametangium

sperm

mature gametophyte (underside)

spore

❸

CREDITS: (8) art, © Cengage Learning; photo, A. & E. Bomford/ Ardea, London.

A Tree ferns in Australia.

B Whisk fern (*Psilotum*)

C Horsetail (*Equisetum*)

D Club moss (*Lycopodium*)

FIGURE 21.9 Seedless vascular plant sporophytes. These plants disperse by releasing spores.

(**FIGURE 21.9C**). Deposits of silica in the stem support the plant and give stems a sandpaper-like texture that helps fend off herbivores. Before scouring powders and pads became widely available, people used stems of horsetails as pot scrubbers. Horsetail spores form on a **strobilus**, a soft cone-shaped structure composed of modified leaves.

LYCOPHYTES

Lycophytes include plants commonly known as quillworts, spikemosses, and club mosses. Club mosses of the genus *Lycopodium* are common in temperate forests (**FIGURE 21.9D**). Their sporophyte has a rhizome from which roots and upright stems with tiny leaves grow. When a

Lycopodium plant is several years old, it begins to make spore-producing strobili seasonally. *Lycopodium* is gathered from the wild for a variety of uses. The stems are used in wreaths and bouquets. Spores, which have a waxy, flammable coating, are sold as "flash powder" for special effects. When the spores are sprayed out as a fine mist and ignited, they produce a bright flame.

---

rhizome Stem that grows horizontally along or under the ground.
seedless vascular plant Plant that disperses by releasing spores and has xylem and phloem. For example, a club moss or fern.
sorus Cluster of spore-producing capsules on a fern leaf.
strobilus Of some nonflowering plants, a spore-forming, cone-shaped structure composed of modified leaves.

TAKE-HOME MESSAGE 21.3

Sporophytes with vascular tissue in their roots, stems, and leaves dominate the life cycle of seedless vascular plants.

Tiny, short-lived gametophytes produce flagellated sperm that swim to eggs through films of water.

Ferns, the most diverse seedless vascular plants, belong to the same lineage as whisk ferns and horsetails. Club mosses and related groups belong to another seedless vascular lineage.

CREDITS: (9A) © Klein Hubert/ Peter Arnold, Inc.; (9B) © Gerald D. Carr; (9C) © William Ferguson; (9D) © Martin LaBar, www.flickr.com/photos/martinlabar.

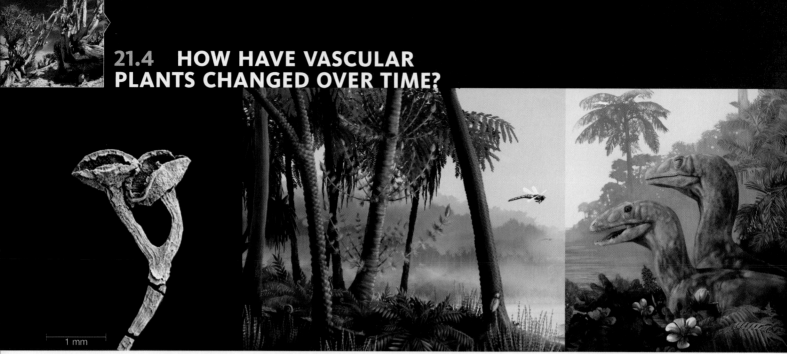

A Fossil of an early vascular plant (*Cooksonia*). Its stems always divided into two equal branches.

B Painting of a Carboniferous "coal forest." An understory of ferns is shaded by tree-sized relatives of modern horsetails and lycophytes.

C Early angiosperms such as magnolias (*foreground*) evolved while dinosaurs walked on Earth.

1 mm

FIGURE 21.10 Early vascular plants.

FROM TINY BRANCHERS TO COAL FORESTS

The oldest fossils of vascular plants are spores that date to about 450 million years ago, during the late Ordovician period. Early vascular plants such as *Cooksonia* stood only a few centimeters high and had a simple branching pattern, with no leaves or roots (**FIGURE 21.10A**). Spores formed at branch tips. By the early Devonian, taller species with a more complex branching pattern were common worldwide.

As the Devonian continued, a taller structure evolved in some seedless vascular plants. The oldest forest we know about existed about 385 million years ago in what is now upstate New York. Fossil stumps and fronds discovered at this site indicate that some plants of this forest stood about 8 meters (26 feet) high and resembled modern tree ferns in their structure.

During the Carboniferous period (359–299 million years ago), ancient relatives of horsetails and lycophytes evolved into massively stemmed giants (**FIGURE 21.10B**). Some stood 40 meters (more than 130 feet) high. After these forests first formed, climates changed, and the sea level repeatedly rose and fell. Over time, pressure and heat transformed the compacted organic remains of Carboniferous forests into **coal**. Often you will hear about annual production rates for coal or some other fossil fuel. In fact, we do not "produce" these materials. Coal is a nonrenewable source of energy, and one that we are on the way to depleting.

RISE OF THE SEED PLANTS

Seed plants evolved late in the Devonian period (about 365 million years ago) and gymnosperms lived beside seedless plants in Carboniferous forests. As Earth became cooler and drier during the Permian period (299–251 million years ago), gymnosperms replaced seedless plants in many habitats. Angiosperms, the flowering plants, first appear in the fossil record about 125 million years ago, during the Cretaceous period (**FIGURE 21.10C**).

Reproductive traits of seed-bearing plants put them at an advantage in dry habitats. Gametophytes of seedless vascular plants develop from spores that were released into the environment. By contrast, gametophytes of seed plants form protected inside reproductive parts on a sporophyte body (**FIGURE 21.11**). Pollen grains that give rise to male gametophytes develop from haploid spores that form inside **pollen sacs**. These spores are called **microspores**. Egg-producing gametophytes develop from haploid **megaspores** that form inside a protective chamber called an **ovule**.

A seed-bearing plant releases pollen grains, but holds onto its eggs. Wind or animals can deliver pollen from one seed plant to the ovule of another, a process called **pollination**. Because sperm of seed plants do not need to swim through a film of water to reach eggs, these plants can reproduce even during dry times.

After fertilization, an ovule develops into a seed, which contains an embryo sporophyte and food that nourishes it until it can make its own. By contrast, seedless plants release single-celled spores that do not have a store of food.

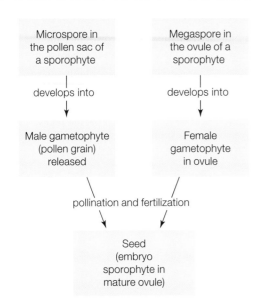

Microspore in the pollen sac of a sporophyte

|

develops into

↓

Male gametophyte (pollen grain) released

Megaspore in the ovule of a sporophyte

|

develops into

↓

Female gametophyte in ovule

pollination and fertilization

↓

Seed (embryo sporophyte in mature ovule)

FIGURE 21.11 How a seed forms.

Seed plants are also the only plants that produce true wood. As a woody plant grows, addition of lignin-stiffened xylem cells widens its parts. Wood may have first evolved as a means of improving water delivery through the plant, but it also provided structural advantages. Wood makes a plant sturdier and more resistant to mechanical stress, so it can grow taller and overshadow its competitors.

coal Fossil fuel formed over millions of years by compaction and heating of plant remains.
megaspore Haploid spore formed in ovules of seed plants; gives rise to an egg-producing gametophyte.
microspore Haploid spore formed in pollen sacs of seed plants; gives rise to a sperm-producing male gametophyte.
ovule Of seed plants, reproductive structure in which egg-bearing gametophyte develops; after fertilization, it matures into a seed.
pollen sac Of seed plants, reproductive structure in which pollen grains develop.
pollination Delivery of a pollen grain to the egg-bearing part of a seed plant.

TAKE-HOME MESSAGE 21.4

Seedless vascular plants arose before the seed-bearing lineages. They were widespread during the Carboniferous.

Seed plants produce pollen grains that wind or animals can carry to eggs. As a result, seed plants can reproduce under drier conditions than seedless plants.

The egg-bearing gametophyte of a seed plant forms in an ovule that becomes a seed after fertilization. Dispersing seeds rather than spores increases reproductive success.

PEOPLE MATTER

National Geographic
Explorer
JEFF BENCA

Like many children, Jeff Benca was fascinated by dinosaurs. As a teen he transferred his interest to another ancient group—the lycophytes. By the time he graduated from college, he had one of the world's largest lycophyte collections. Now a graduate student, he investigates what these early-diverging vascular plants can tell us about conditions in Earth's deep past.

Paleobotanists have long used fossil leaf shape of woody flowering plants as a tool for inferring ancient climatic conditions. For example, botanists know that woody angiosperms with more serrated leaf margins (like maples) are now prominent in temperate regions with cool, wet climates. By contrast woody angiosperms with smooth leaf margins (such as magnolias) now predominate in tropical regions. If ferns and lycophytes also show climate-influenced changes in leaf shape, their fossils could yield a wealth of information about Earth's distant past. The fossil record of angiosperms extends back 125 million years, but ferns and lycophytes have fossil records exceeding 360 million years.

To investigate how climate affects leaves of ferns and lycophytes, Benca grows members of these groups under a variety of conditions in climate-controlled growth chambers and compares their leaf shapes. He is also looking at how the shape of fern and lycophyte leaves varies with elevation (and climate) on a tropical mountain.

Aside from his research, Benca advocates conservation of lycophytes. Although this ancient lineage survived several mass extinctions, many species are now declining swiftly due to habitat loss. As a result, lycophytes are in need of increased research attention and protection.

Gymnosperms are vascular seed plants whose seeds are "naked," meaning that unlike the seeds of angiosperms they are not within a fruit. (*Gymnos* means naked and *sperma* is taken to mean seed.) However, many gymnosperms enclose their seeds in a fleshy or papery covering.

CONIFERS

Conifers, the most diverse and familiar gymnosperms, include 600 or so species of trees and shrubs that have needlelike or scalelike leaves, and produce woody seed cones. Conifers are typically more resistant to drought and cold than flowering plants, and they abound in cool forests of the Northern Hemisphere. Conifers include the tallest

trees in the Northern Hemisphere (redwoods), and the most abundant (pines). They also include the long-lived bristlecone pines shown in the chapter-opening photo.

Conifers are of great commercial importance. We use fir bark to mulch gardens, use oils from cedar in cleaning products, and eat seeds, or "pine nuts," of some pines. Pines also provide lumber for building homes, and some make a sticky resin that deters insects from tunneling into them. We use this resin to make turpentine, a paint solvent.

FIGURE 21.12 illustrates the life cycle of one conifer, the ponderosa pine. Seed cones and pollen cones develop on the same tree. Ovules form on cone scales of seed cones ❶. Inside the ovule, a megaspore forms by meiosis ❷ and

FIGURE 21.12 {**Animated**} Conifer (pine) life cycle.

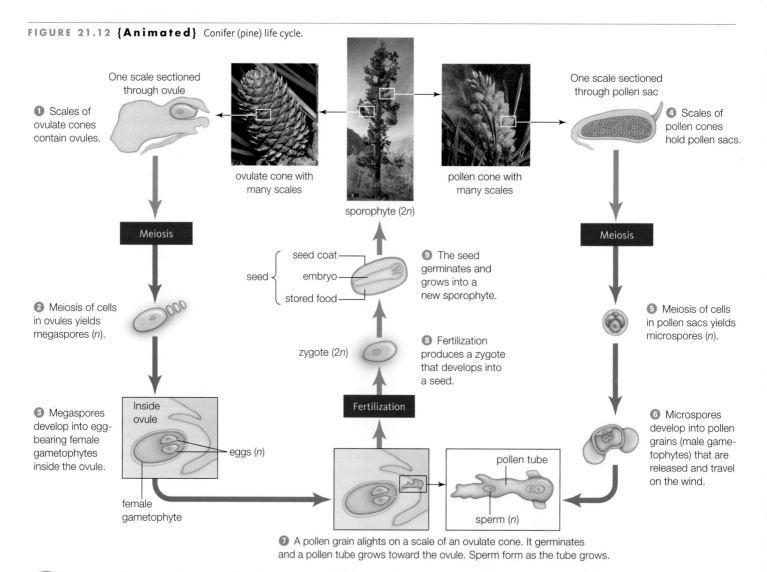

❶ Scales of ovulate cones contain ovules.

One scale sectioned through ovule

ovulate cone with many scales

sporophyte (2*n*)

One scale sectioned through pollen sac

❹ Scales of pollen cones hold pollen sacs.

pollen cone with many scales

Meiosis

Meiosis

❷ Meiosis of cells in ovules yields megaspores (*n*).

seed coat
seed { embryo
stored food

❾ The seed germinates and grows into a new sporophyte.

❺ Meiosis of cells in pollen sacs yields microspores (*n*).

zygote (2*n*)

❽ Fertilization produces a zygote that develops into a seed.

❸ Megaspores develop into egg-bearing female gametophytes inside the ovule.

Inside ovule

eggs (*n*)

female gametophyte

Fertilization

pollen tube

sperm (*n*)

❻ Microspores develop into pollen grains (male gametophytes) that are released and travel on the wind.

❼ A pollen grain alights on a scale of an ovulate cone. It germinates and a pollen tube grows toward the ovule. Sperm form as the tube grows.

 FIGURE IT OUT: Does the pollen tube grow through tissue of a male cone or a female cone?

Answer: A female cone. It grows after a pollen grain alights on a female cone.

CREDITS: (12) left, R. J. Erwin/Science Source; middle, Robert Potts, California Academy of Sciences; right, Robert & Linda Mitchell Photography; art, © Cengage Learning 2015.

develops into a female gametophyte ❸. Male cones hold pollen sacs ❹, where microspores form ❺ and develop into pollen grains ❺. The pollen grains are released and drift with the winds. Pollination occurs when one lands on the scale of a seed cone ❻. The pollen grain then germinates: Some cells develop into a pollen tube that grows through the ovule tissue and delivers sperm to the egg ❼. Pollen tube growth in gymnosperms is an astonishingly leisurely process. It typically takes about a year for the tube to grow through the ovule to the egg. When fertilization occurs, it produces a zygote ❽. Over about six months, the zygote develops into an embryo sporophyte that, along with tissues of the ovule, becomes a seed ❾. The seed is released, germinates, then grows and develops into a new sporophyte.

LESSER KNOWN LINEAGES

Cycads and ginkgos were most diverse about 200 million years ago. They are the only modern seed plants that have flagellated sperm. Sperm emerge from pollen grains, then swim in fluid produced by the plant's ovule.

The 130 species of modern cycads live mainly in the dry tropics and subtropics (**FIGURE 21.13A**). Cycads often resemble palms but the two groups are not close relatives. The "sago palms" commonly used in landscaping and as houseplants are actually cycads. Cycad seeds have a fleshy covering and were traditionally used as food and medicine in Guam and other regions. However, they contain toxins that increase the risk of neurodegenerative disease and cancers.

The only living ginkgo species is *Ginkgo biloba*, the maidenhair tree (**FIGURE 21.13B**). It is a deciduous native of China. Deciduous plants drop all their leaves at once seasonally. The ginkgo's pretty fan-shaped leaves and resistance to insects, disease, and air pollution make it a popular tree along city streets. Female trees produce fleshy plum-sized seeds with a strong unpleasant odor, so male trees are preferred for urban landscaping. Extracts of *G. biloba* have been touted as a possible memory aid and a treatment for Alzheimer's disease, but recent well-designed studies have found no such beneficial effect.

Gnetophytes include woody vines, tropical trees, and shrubs. Members of the genus *Ephedra* are evergreen desert shrubs with broomlike green stems and inconspicuous leaves (**FIGURE 21.13C**). Native Americans brewed tea using one species common in semiarid regions of the American West. Some Eurasian *Ephedra* species produce ephedrine, a stimulant similar to amphetamines. Another gnetophyte, *Welwitschia*, grows only in Africa's Namib

gymnosperm Seed plant whose seeds are not enclosed within a fruit; a conifer, cycad, ginkgo, or gnetophyte.

B Fan-shaped leaves and fleshy seeds of *Ginkgo biloba*.

A Cycad with fleshy seeds.

C Pollen cones of *Ephedra*, a gnetophye.

D *Welwitschia*, a gnetophyte, with seed cones and two long, wide leaves.

FIGURE 21.13 Gymnosperm diversity.

desert (**FIGURE 21.13D**). It has a taproot that grows deep into the soil, a short woody stem, and two long, straplike leaves. These leaves split lengthwise repeatedly, giving the plant a strange shaggy appearance. *Welwitschia* is very long-lived; some plants are more than a thousand years old.

TAKE-HOME MESSAGE 21.5

Gymnosperms are seed-bearing plants. Their eggs and seeds form on the surface of an ovule, not inside ovaries as occurs in flowering plants.

All gymnosperms produce pollen. In cycads and ginkgos, sperm emerge from pollen grains and swim through fluid released by the ovule. Other groups have nonmotile sperm.

FIGURE 21.14 Structure of a typical flower.

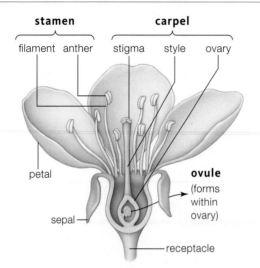

FLOWERS AND FRUITS

Angiosperms, the most diverse seed plant lineage, are the only plants that make flowers and fruits. A **flower** is a specialized reproductive shoot. Floral structure varies, but most flowers include the parts shown in **FIGURE 21.14**. Sepals, which usually have a green leaflike appearance, ring the base of a flower and enclose it until it opens. Inside the sepals are petals, which are often brightly colored. The petals surround the stamens. **Stamens** are organs that produce pollen. Typically a stamen consists of a tall stalk (the filament), topped by an anther that holds two pollen sacs. The innermost part of the flower is the **carpel**, the organ that captures pollen and produces eggs. The carpel consists of a stigma, style, and ovary. The sticky or hairy stigma, which is specialized for receiving pollen, sits atop a stalk called the style. At the base of the style is an **ovary**,

FIGURE 21.15 {**Animated**} Life cycle of a typical angiosperm.

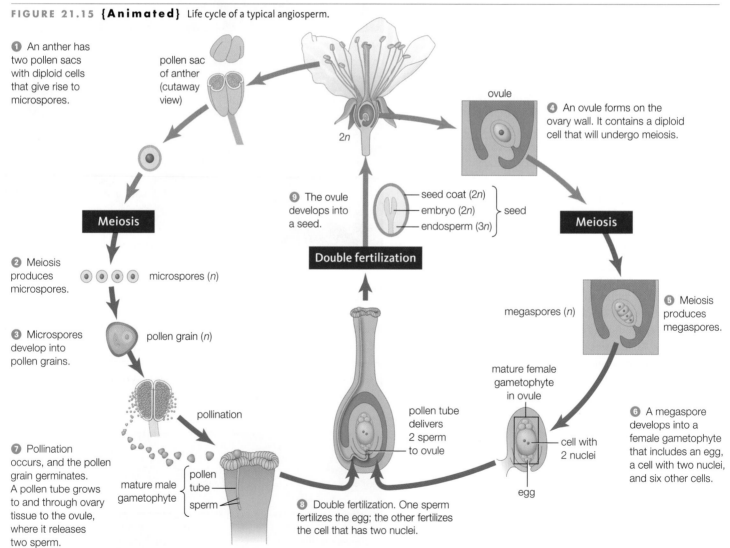

❶ An anther has two pollen sacs with diploid cells that give rise to microspores.

pollen sac of anther (cutaway view)

❷ Meiosis produces microspores.

microspores (n)

❸ Microspores develop into pollen grains.

pollen grain (n)

❼ Pollination occurs, and the pollen grain germinates. A pollen tube grows to and through ovary tissue to the ovule, where it releases two sperm.

pollination

mature male gametophyte

pollen tube

sperm

❽ Double fertilization. One sperm fertilizes the egg; the other fertilizes the cell that has two nuclei.

Double fertilization

pollen tube delivers 2 sperm to ovule

❾ The ovule develops into a seed.

seed coat (2n)
embryo (2n) } seed
endosperm (3n)

2n

ovule

❹ An ovule forms on the ovary wall. It contains a diploid cell that will undergo meiosis.

Meiosis

megaspores (n)

❺ Meiosis produces megaspores.

mature female gametophyte in ovule

❻ A megaspore develops into a female gametophyte that includes an egg, a cell with two nuclei, and six other cells.

cell with 2 nuclei

egg

a chamber that contains one or more ovules. The name angiosperm refers to the fact that seeds form within an ovary. (*Angio–* means enclosed chamber, and *sperma*, seed.) After fertilization, an ovule matures into a seed and the ovary becomes a **fruit**.

FIGURE 21.15 shows a typical flowering plant life cycle. Inside pollen sacs in the flower's anthers ❶, diploid cells produce microspores by meiosis ❷. The microspores develop into pollen grains (immature male gametophytes) ❸. At the same time, ovules form in an ovary at the base of a carpel ❹. Meiosis of cells in an ovule yields haploid megaspores ❺. The megaspores undergo mitosis to produce a female gametophyte that includes a haploid egg, a cell with two nuclei, and other cells ❻.

Pollination occurs when a pollen grain arrives on a receptive stigma ❼. The pollen grain germinates, and a pollen tube grows through the style to the ovary at the base of the carpel. Two nonflagellated sperm form inside the pollen tube as it grows.

Double fertilization occurs when a pollen tube delivers the two sperm into the ovule ❽. One sperm fertilizes the egg to create a zygote. The other sperm fuses with the cell that has two nuclei to form a triploid (3*n*) cell. After double fertilization, the ovule matures into a seed ❾. The zygote develops into an embryo sporophyte, and the triploid cell gives rise to the **endosperm**, a nutritious tissue that will serve as a source of food for the developing embryo.

MAJOR LINEAGES

Gene comparisons have identified the oldest angiosperm lineages among modern plants. Water lilies (FIGURE 21.16A) are among the basal angiosperms, meaning they belong to a lineage that branched off before the three major angiosperm lineages evolved. These major lineages are magnoliids, eudicots (true dicots), and monocots (FIGURE 21.16B–D). The 9,200 magnoliids include magnolias as well as avocados. The 80,000 **monocots** include palms, lilies,

A Water lily (basal angiosperm)   B Magnolia (magnoliid)

C Iris (monocot)   D Chickweed (eudicot)

FIGURE 21.16 Representatives of four angiosperm lineages. The vast majority of angiosperms are monocots or eudicots.

grasses, orchids, and irises. The 170,000 **eudicots** include most familiar broadleaf plants such as tomatoes, cabbages, poppies, and roses, as well as the cacti and all flowering shrubs and trees.

Monocots and eudicots derive their group names from the number of seed leaves, or **cotyledons**, in the embryo. Monocots have one cotyledon and eudicots have two. The two groups also differ in the arrangement of their vascular tissues, number of flower petals, and other traits. Some eudicots are woody, but no monocots produce true wood. We discuss differences between monocots and dicots in more detail in Section 25.1.

angiosperms Highly diverse seed plant lineage; only plants that make flowers and fruits.
carpel Floral reproductive organ that produces female gametophytes; typically consists of a stigma, style, and ovary.
cotyledon Seed leaf of a flowering plant embryo.
endosperm Nutritive tissue in the seeds of flowering plants.
eudicot Flowering plant in which the embryo has two cotyledons.
flower Specialized reproductive shoot of a flowering plant.
fruit Mature ovary of a flowering plant; encloses a seed or seeds.
monocot Flowering plant in which the embryo has one cotyledons.
ovary In flowering plants, the enlarged base of a carpel, inside which one or more ovules form and eggs are fertilized.
stamen Floral reproductive organ that produces male gametophytes; typically consists of an anther on the tip of a filament.

TAKE-HOME MESSAGE 21.6

Angiosperms are flowering plants. A flower is a special reproductive shoot that makes pollen in stamens and eggs in carpels.

Angiosperm seeds are enclosed within a fruit. The fruit forms after fertilization from tissue of the ovary, the chamber in which ovules formed.

Angiosperm seeds contain endosperm, a nutritive tissue.

Magnoliids, monocots, and eudicots are the main lineages of flowering plants.

It would be nearly impossible to overestimate the ecological importance of angiosperms. As the most abundant plants in the majority of land habitats, they provide food and shelter for a variety of animals. Their ecological significance is a reflection of their diversity, which stems from factors discussed below.

ACCELERATED LIFE CYCLE

Compared to gymnosperms, most angiosperms have a shorter life cycle. A dandelion or grass can grow from a seed, mature, and produce seeds of its own within a month or so. In contrast, gymnosperms such as pine trees take years to mature. Producing and dispersing seeds fast allows an angiosperm to expand its range faster than a gymnosperm.

PARTNERSHIPS WITH POLLINATORS

Flowers give angiosperms an edge by facilitating animal-assisted pollination. As seed plants evolved, some animals began feeding on their protein-rich pollen. The plants lost a bit of pollen, but benefited when the insects inadvertently transferred pollen from one plant to another of the same species. An animal that facilitates pollination by transferring pollen between plants is a **pollinator**. Most pollinators are insects (**FIGURE 21.17A**), but birds, bats, and other animals fulfill this role for some plants.

Over time, many flowering plants coevolved with their pollinators. (As Section 17.11 explained, coevolution refers to the joint evolution of two or more species as a result of their close ecological interactions.) Producing sugary nectar encourages more pollinator visits, which improves pollination rates and enhances seed production. Conspicuous petals and distinctive scents that attract pollinator attention also provide a selective advantage. So do mutations that alter floral shapes in ways that maximize the likelihood of pollen transfer onto a pollinator or from a pollinator to a receptive stigma.

ANIMAL-DISPERSED FRUITS

Many angiosperms also benefit by having animals disperse their seeds (**FIGURE 21.17B**). Some plants make seeds with hooks or spines that can stick to animal fur. Others make brightly colored, fleshy fruits that attract fruit-eating birds or mammals. Such plants benefit when the fruit eater later regurgitates their seeds or passes them unharmed in its feces. Some fruits have features that fend off animals that destroy seeds in the fruits they eat. For example, rodents tend to chew up seeds, so chile pepper fruits contain a compound (capsaicin) that tastes "hot" to rodents and other mammals. Birds do not chew seeds, cannot taste the compound, and so serve as the chile's main dispersers.

pollinator Animal that moves pollen, thus facilitating pollination.

> **TAKE-HOME MESSAGE 21.7**
> Accelerated life cycles and animal assistance in pollination and seed dispersal contribute to angiosperm success.

FIGURE 21.17 Animal assistants of flowering plants.

A Bees commonly serve as pollinators.

B Birds often eat fruits and disperse seeds.

UNIT 4
EVOLUTION AND BIODIVERSITY

Conservation

FIGURE 21.18 The Svalbard Global Seed Vault. To learn more about the vault and the seeds stored inside it, visit www.croptrust.org.

PLANT DIVERSITY IS DECLINING. We know of threats to about 12,000 wild plant species, and the actual number of threatened plants is no doubt much higher. As a result, many valuable sources of food, medicine, and other products could disappear before we ever learn their value.

A decline in the diversity of cultivated plants raises additional concerns. In the past, food crops were locale specific. People developed and planted plant varieties that did well in their region, and they saved seeds from their crops to plant the following year. Now, many traditional varieties of crop plants are disappearing as farmers worldwide turn to the same few large companies for seeds. Different varieties of plants are resistant to different diseases, so widespread planting of one variety increases the risk that a disease could decimate the global supply of a crop. The more varieties of a crop we plant, the more likely it is that some will resist a particular disease.

Sustaining the wild relatives of crop plants provides a form of insurance. Such plants provide a reservoir of genetic diversity that plant breeders

One way to ensure the survival of potentially useful plants is by storing their seeds in seed banks. Today, there are more than 1,500 seed banks around the world. The most ambitious, the Svalbard Global Seed Vault, was built in 2008 on a Norwegian island about 700 miles from the North Pole. This so-called doomsday vault serves as a backup for other seed banks (FIGURE 21.18). Here, deep inside a mountain, seeds are stored in a permanently chilled, earthquake-free zone 400 feet above sea level. The location was chosen to ensure that the seeds will remain high and dry even if global climate change causes the polar ice caps to melt. The vault also has an advanced security system and has been engineered to withstand any nearby explosions.

The Svalbard vault now holds the world's most diverse collection of seeds, with more than 750,000 samples and material from nearly every nation. The United States has stored seeds of its native crops such as chile peppers from New Mexico, as well as seeds that American scientists collected elsewhere in the world. Under the deep-freeze conditions in Svalbard, the seeds are expected to survive about

Summary

SECTION 21.1 **Plants** evolved from green algae. They are embryophytes; they form a multicelled embryo on the parental body. Key adaptations that allowed plants to move into dry habitats include a waterproof **cuticle** with **stomata**, and internal pipelines of vascular tissue (**xylem** and **phloem**) reinforced by **lignin**.

Plant life cycles involve an alternation of generations. Two types of two multicelled bodies form: a haploid **gametophyte** and a diploid **sporophyte**. The gametophyte predominates in the **nonvascular plants**, but in **vascular plants**, the sporophyte is larger and longer-lived. **Seeds** and **pollen grains** that can be dispersed without water are adaptations that contribute to the success of seed plants.

SECTION 21.2 **Bryophytes** are low-growing, nonvascular plants that disperse by releasing spores. They include three modern lineages: mosses, liverworts, and hornworts. All have a gametophye-dominated life cycle and produce flagellated sperm that swim through a film of water to eggs. Mosses are the most diverse bryophytes. **Rhizoids** attach them to soil or a surface. Remains of some mosses form peat, which is dried and burned as fuel.

SECTION 21.3 In **seedless vascular plants**, sporophytes have vascular tissues, and they are the larger, longer-lived phase of the life cycle. Typically the sporophyte's roots and shoots grow from a horizontal stem, or **rhizome**. Tiny free-living gametophytes make flagellated sperm that require water for fertilization. Ferns, the most diverse group of seedless vascular plants, produce spores in **sori**. Many ferns grow as epiphytes. Club mosses and horsetails produce spores in conelike **strobili**.

SECTION 21.4 Forests of giant seedless vascular plants thrived during the Carboniferous period. Later, heat and pressure transformed remains of these forests to **coal**. Seed plants rose to dominance during the Permian, as the climate became cooler and drier. Seed plant sporophytes have **pollen sacs**, where **microspores** form and develop into immature male gametophytes (pollen grains). They also have **ovules**, where **megaspores** form and develop into female gametophytes. **Pollination** unites the egg and sperm of a seed plant.

SECTION 21.5 **Gymnosperms** are seed plants that do not enclose their seeds within a fruit. Conifers have woody seed cones and include commercially important groups such as the pines. They are more resistant to drought and to cold than flowering plants. Cycads and ginkgos are gymnosperm lineages that have flagellated sperm and fleshy seeds. Gnetophytes include desert shrubs.

SECTION 21.6 **Angiosperms** are seed plants that make **flowers** and **fruits**. The **stamens** of a flower produce pollen inside pollen sacs. The **carpel** has a stigma specialized for receiving pollen, atop a stalk called the style. An **ovary** at the base of the carpel holds one or more ovules. After pollination, double fertilization occurs. One sperm delivered by the pollen tube fertilizes the egg and the other fertilizes a cell that has two nuclei. After fertilization, the flower's ovary becomes a fruit that contains one or more seeds. A flowering plant seed includes an embryo sporophyte and **endosperm**, a nutritious tissue. The two main angiosperm lineages, **eudicots** and **monocots**, differ in their number of **cotyledons** and other traits.

SECTION 21.7 Angiosperms are the most widely distributed and diverse plant group. Accelerated life cycles and partnerships with animal **pollinators** and seed dispersers contributed to their success.

SECTION 21.8 Sustaining many varieties of crop plants and their wild relatives ensures that plant breeders will have a reservoir of genetic diversity to tap into if widely planted varieties fail. Seed banks can help us maintain a wide variety of potentially valuable plant species.

Self-Quiz Answers in Appendix VII

1. The first plants were _____ .
   a. ferns   c. bryophytes
   b. flowering plants   d. conifers

2. Which of the following statements is false?
   a. Ferns produce seeds inside sori.
   b. Bryophytes do not have xylem or phloem.
   c. Gymnosperms and angiosperms produce seeds.
   d. Only angiosperms produce flowers.

3. In bryophytes, eggs are fertilized in a chamber on the _____ and a zygote develops into a _____ .
   a. sporophyte; gametophyte
   b. gametophyte; sporophyte
   c. sorus; cone

4. Horsetails and ferns are _____ plants.
   a. multicelled aquatic   c. seedless vascular
   b. nonvascular seed   d. seed-bearing vascular

5. Coal consists primarily of compressed remains of the _____ that dominated Carboniferous swamp forests.
   a. seedless vascular plants   c. flowering plants
   b. conifers   d. mosses

6. The _____ produce flagellated sperm.
   a. mosses   d. monocots
   b. ferns   e. a and b
   c. conifers   f. a through c

7. A seed is a _____ .
   a. female gametophyte   c. mature pollen grain
   b. mature ovule   d. modified microspore

8. True or false? Both spores and sperm of a seedless vascular plant are haploid.

Data Analysis Activities

Insect-Assisted Fertilization in Moss Plant ecologist Nils Cronberg suspected that crawling insects facilitate fertilization of mosses. To test his hypothesis, he carried out an experiment. He placed patches of male and female moss gametophytes in dishes, either next to one another or with water-absorbing plaster between them so sperm could not swim between plants. He then looked at how the presence or absence of insects affected the number of sporophytes formed. **FIGURE 21.19** shows his results.

1. Why is sporophyte formation a good way to determine if fertilization occurred?
2. How close did the male and female patches have to be for sporophytes to form in the absence of insects?
3. Does this study support the hypothesis that insects aid moss fertilization?
4. How might a crawling insect aid moss fertilization?

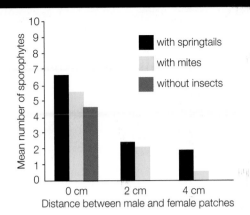

FIGURE 21.19 Sporophyte production in female moss patches with and without two types of crawling insects (springtails and mites). No sporophytes formed in the insect-free dishes when moss patches were 2 or 4 centimeters apart.

9. Only angiosperms produce _____ .
   a. pollen   c. fruits
   b. seeds   d. all of the above

10. The _____ do not have xylem or phloem.
    a. mosses   b. ferns   c. monocots   d. a and b

11. A waxy cuticle helps land plants _____ .
    a. conserve water   c. reproduce
    b. take up carbon dioxide   d. stand upright

12. Pollinators aid many _____ .
    a. conifers   c. angiosperms
    b. mosses   d. ferns

13. _____ produce seeds on woody cones.
    a. Cycads   c. Ginkgos
    b. Conifers   d. Hornworts

14. Match the terms appropriately.
    ___ bryophyte   a. seeds, but no fruit
    ___ seedless   b. flowers and fruits
         vascular plant   c. no xylem or phloem
    ___ gymnosperm   d. xylem and phloem,
    ___ angiosperm   but no ovule

15. Match the terms appropriately.
    ___ ovule   a. gamete-producing body
    ___ monocot   b. spore-producing body
    ___ gametophyte   c. becomes seed
    ___ sporophyte   d. horizontal stem
    ___ fruit   e. mature ovary
    ___ endosperm   f. nutritive tissue in seed
    ___ rhizome   g. where fern spores form
    ___ sorus   h. single haploid cell
    ___ microspore   i. one type of angiosperm

Critical Thinking

1. Early botanists admired ferns but found their life cycle perplexing. In the 1700s, they learned to propagate ferns by sowing what appeared to be tiny dustlike "seeds" that they collected from the undersides of fronds. Despite many attempts, the botanists could not locate the pollen source, which they assumed must stimulate these "seeds" to develop. Imagine you could write to these botanists. Compose a note that explains the fern life cycle and clears up their confusion.

2. In most plants the largest, longest-lived body is a diploid sporophyte. By one hypothesis, diploid dominance was favored because it allowed a greater level of genetic diversity. Suppose that a recessive mutation arises. It is mildly disadvantageous now, but it will be useful in some future environment. Explain why such a mutation would be more likely to persist in a fern than in a moss.

3. The photo at the *right* is a micrograph of a longitudinal section through the stem of a squash plant. The stem has been dyed with a substance that tints lignin red. Can you identify the red-ringed structures? Would you expect to find similar structures in the stem of a monocot such as a corn plant? Would you find them in the leafy green part of a moss?

CENGAGE brain.com To access course materials, please visit www.cengagebrain.com.

A spore-producing fruiting body of a stinkhorn fungus on a forest floor.

22

FUNGI

Links to Earlier Concepts

Before starting, review Figure 20.1 to get a sense of where fungi fit in the eukaryotic family tree. In this chapter you will learn about fungal interactions with cyanobacteria (19.5) and green algae (20.7). You will also draw on your knowledge of the organic molecules chitin (3.2) and lignin (21.1), and your understanding of the processes of nutrient cycling (1.2) and fermentation (7.6).

KEY CONCEPTS

ABSORPTIVE FEEDERS
Fungi include single-celled yeasts and multicelled molds and mushrooms. They secrete digestive enzymes onto organic matter, then absorb released nutrients.

SPORE PRODUCTION
Fungi produce spores sexually and asexually. The major fungal groups are defined by how they produce spores by meiosis.

FRUITING BODIES
Some sac fungi and most club fungi produce spores on multicelled fruiting bodies during sexual reproduction. Mushrooms are fungal fruiting bodies.

FUNGAL ECOLOGY
Most fungi act as decomposers. Some form mutually beneficial partnerships with photosynthetic cells, or with plant roots. Still others are parasites of plants or animals.

HUMAN USES OF FUNGI
We eat fungi, enlist them to produce foods and drinks, use them in genetic studies and biotechnology, and extract medicinal or psychoactive compounds from them.

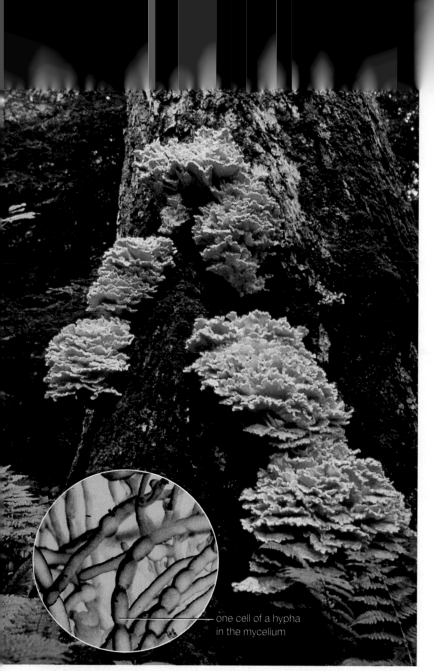

FIGURE 22.1 A multicelled club fungus growing on a tree. The inset micrograph shows the filaments (hyphae) that make up the body of fungi such as this one.

— one cell of a hypha in the mycelium

ABSORPTIVE FEEDERS

A **fungus** (plural, fungi) is a eukaryote that secretes digestive enzymes onto its food, then absorbs the resulting breakdown products. Most fungi are decomposers that feed on organic wastes and remains. A lesser number live on or in other living organisms, and some of these are parasites.

Fungal digestive enzymes can break down many sturdy structural proteins that animal digestive enzymes cannot. For example, fungi can digest the cellulose and lignin in plant cell walls, as well as keratin, the main protein in animal skin, claws, hair, and fur. The capacity to digest these tough structural materials makes fungi important both as decomposers and as parasites.

FILAMENTOUS STRUCTURE

Some fungi live as single cells, and these are informally called **yeasts**. Multicelled fungi live as a mesh of threadlike filaments collectively called a **mycelium** (plural, mycelia). Each filament in the mycelium is a **hypha** (plural, hyphae). A hypha consists of walled cells attached end to end (**FIGURE 22.1**). It grows by adding cells to it tips.

Fungal cell walls contain chitin, a polysaccharide also found in the body covering of crabs and insects. Depending on the fungal group, there may or may not be cross-walls between cells of a hypha. When cross-walls do exist, they are porous, so materials can flow between adjacent cells. Thus nutrients or water taken up in one part of a mycelium are shared with cells in other parts of the fungal body.

SPORE PRODUCERS

Fungi disperse by releasing microscopic spores. A fungal spore is typically one or more haploid (*n*) cells enclosed within a thick coat. When the spore germinates (becomes active), it grows into a new haploid mycelium.

Fungi produce spores both asexually and sexually (**FIGURE 22.2**). During asexual reproduction, multicelled fungi form spores by mitosis at the tips of specialized hyphae ❶. Sexual reproduction begins when two hyphae meet and the cytoplasm of cells at their tips fuses to

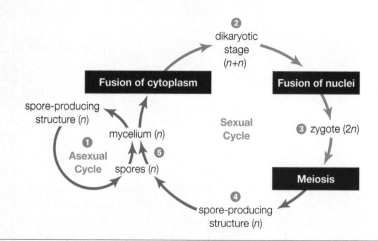

FIGURE 22.2 Generalized life cycle of a fungus.
❶ Asexual reproduction occurs when a haploid mycelium produces spores by mitosis at the tips of specialized hyphae.
❷ Sexual reproduction begins when haploid hyphae of two individuals meet and cells at their tips fuse. This cytoplasmic fusion produces a dikaryotic cell (a cell with two nuclei).
❸ Fusion of nuclei in a dikaryotic cell creates a diploid zygote.
❹ The zygote undergoes meiosis and produces a haploid spore-bearing structure.
❺ Haploid spores form by mitosis and germinate to form a new haploid mycelium.

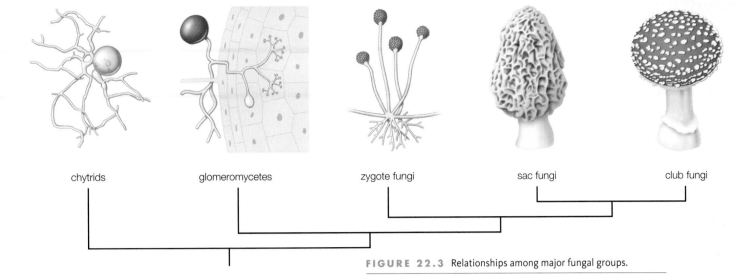

chytrids   glomeromycetes   zygote fungi   sac fungi   club fungi

FIGURE 22.3 Relationships among major fungal groups.

produce a dikaryotic cell ❷. **Dikaryotic** means having two genetically distinct types of nuclei (*n+n*). The fungal zygote forms when the two nuclei inside a dikaryotic cell fuse ❸. This diploid zygote undergoes meiosis and gives rise to a structure that produces haploid spores by mitosis ❹. Those spores germinate, releasing cells that divide by mitosis to form a new haploid mycelium ❺.

FIVE MAJOR SUBGROUPS

More than 70,000 fungal species have been named, and there may be a million yet to be discovered. Most fungi belong to one of five groups (**FIGURE 22.3**). **Chytrids** include the oldest fungal lineages, and are the only living fungi that make flagellated spores. Most are aquatic decomposers, but some live in the gut of herbivores, such as cattle and sheep, where they help their host digest cellulose. Others are parasites of plants or animals. **Glomeromycetes**

are soil fungi with hyphae that grow into plant roots and branch inside the cell walls of plant root cells. Most **zygote fungi** (zygomycetes) are molds that live in damp places. **Molds** grow as a mass of hyphae and reproduce asexually as long as food is plentiful. During sexual reproduction, zygote fungi produce a thick-walled structure called a zygospore.

Unlike the lineages mentioned thus far, sac fungi and club fungi have cross-walls between cells of their hyphae. Cross walls reinforce hyphae, so sac fungi and club fungi include larger-bodied species than other fungal groups.

Sac fungi (ascomycetes) reproduce sexually by producing spores in sac-shaped structures. They are the most diverse fungal group. Sac fungi include yeasts, molds, parasites of plants and animals, species that partner with photosynthetic cells to form lichens, and species such as morels that form large fruiting bodies. A fungal fruiting body is a spore-producing sexual organ made of intertwined hyphae.

Club fungi (basidiomycetes) reproduce sexually by producing spores in club-shaped structures. Most familiar mushrooms are fruiting bodies of club fungi. This group also includes some parasites.

chytrid Fungus with flagellated spores.
club fungi Fungi that produce spores in club-shaped structures during sexual reproduction.
dikaryotic Having two genetically distinct nuclei.
fungus Unicellular or multicellular eukaryotic heterotroph that digests food outside the body, then absorbs the resulting breakdown products. Has chitin-containing cell walls.
glomeromycete Fungus that partners with plant roots; fungal hyphae grow inside the cell walls of root cells.
hypha Component of a fungal mycelium; a filament made up of cells arranged end to end.
mold Fungus that grows as a mass of asexually reproducing hyphae.
mycelium Mass of threadlike filaments (hyphae) that make up the body of a multicelled fungus.
sac fungi Fungi that form spores in a sac-shaped structure during sexual reproduction.
yeast Fungus that lives as single cell.
zygote fungi Fungi that live in damp places and form a thick-walled zygospore during sexual reproduction.

> **TAKE-HOME MESSAGE 22.1**
>
> Fungi secrete digestive enzymes onto organic matter and absorb the released nutrients. They live as single cells or, more often, as a multicelled mycelium. Most are decomposers, but some live in or on other organisms.
>
> Fungi disperse by releasing spores that form by either mitosis or meiosis. Only the oldest lineage, the chytrids, produces flagellated spores.
>
> Glomeromycete fungi are soil fungi whose hyphae branch inside cell walls of root cells. Zygote fungi are typically molds.
>
> Sac fungi and club fungi have hyphae with cross-walls. Some members of both groups form large fruiting bodies.

The black bread mold (*Rhizopus stolinifera*) has a life cycle typical of zygote fungi (**FIGURE 22.4**). As long as food is plentiful, it grows as a haploid mycelium and produces spores by mitosis ❶. When the food supply dwindles, lack of food and proximity of a compatible sexual partner cause development of special side branches (gametangia) ❷. Zygote fungi do not have walls between their cells, so many haploid nuclei from within a hypha can flow into each gametangium. When the two gametangia come into contact, their walls break down, and their cytoplasm fuses. The result is an immature zygospore containing multiple nuclei from each parent ❸. As the zygospore matures, the haploid nuclei within it pair up and fuse, forming diploid nuclei. A mature zygospore contains multiple diploid nuclei and has a thick, protective wall ❹. It is the only diploid stage in the zygote fungus life cycle. When the zygospore germinates, a hypha emerges and cells at its tip undergo meiosis to produce haploid spores ❺.

Sac fungi include yeasts, molds, and species with large fruiting bodies. Yeasts usually reproduce asexually by budding (*left*), a process by which a descendant cell with a nucleus and a small amount of cytoplasm pinches off from a parental cell. When sac fungi that grow as molds reproduce asexually, they produce spores by mitosis at the tips of specialized hyphae (**FIGURE 22.5A**). When they or any other sac fungi reproduce sexually, spores form in a sac-shaped structure called an ascus. In some sac fungi, such as the cup fungi, the ascus forms on a large fruiting body called an ascocarp (**FIGURE 22.5B**).

A Asexual reproduction by the mold *Penicillium* (*left*) produces spores atop specialized hyphae (*right*).

haploid spore in ascus

B Cup fungi reproduce sexually by producing an ascocarp (*left*). Spores (*right*) form by meiosis of cells on the cup's concave surface.

FIGURE 22.5 Sac fungus reproduction.

FIGURE 22.4 {Animated} Life cycle of black bread mold, a zygote fungus.

❶ As long as food is plentiful, a haploid mycelium grows in size and produces spores by mitosis on specialized hyphae.
❷ When nutrients are limited and hyphae of two compatible individuals come into close proximity, they produce branches (gametangia) that grow toward one another. As these branches grow, haploid nuclei stream into them and accumulate at their tips.
❸ Cytoplasmic fusion of the gametangia produces a zygospore that contains many haploid nuclei from each parent.
❹ Nuclei within the zygospore pair up and fuse to produce a mature zygospore with many diploid nuclei.
❺ The zygospore germinates, and an aerial hypha emerges. Meiosis of cells within this hypha gives rise to haploid spores which are released from its tip.

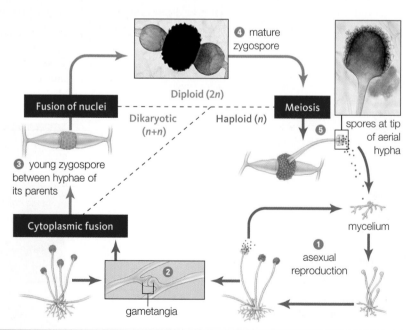

❹ mature zygospore

Fusion of nuclei

Diploid (2*n*)

Dikaryotic (*n+n*)

Haploid (*n*)

Meiosis

spores at tip of aerial hypha

❸ young zygospore between hyphae of its parents

❺

Cytoplasmic fusion

mycelium

❶ asexual reproduction

❷

gametangia

CREDITS: (4) art, © Cengage Learning; photos, © Ed Reschke; (5A) left, © Photo by Scott Bauer/USDA; right, © Dennis Kunkel Microscopy, Inc.; (5B) left, © Michael Wood/mykob.com.; right, © North Carolina State University, Dept. of Plant Pathology; (in text) © Dr. Dennis Kunkel/Visuals Unlimited.

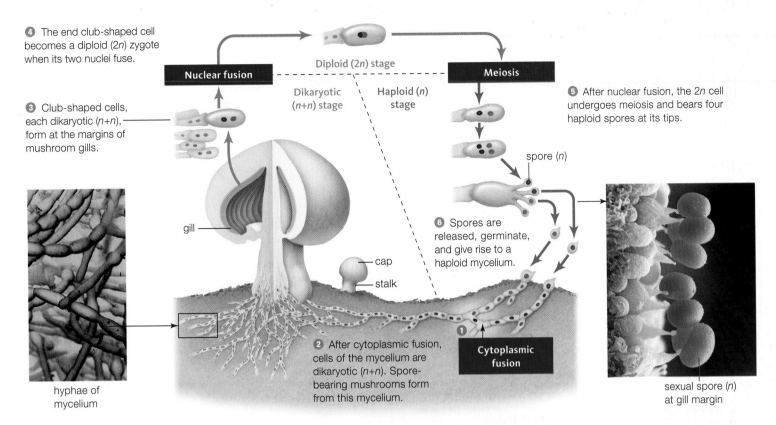

④ The end club-shaped cell becomes a diploid (2n) zygote when its two nuclei fuse.

Nuclear fusion

Diploid (2n) stage

Meiosis

Dikaryotic (n+n) stage

Haploid (n) stage

③ Club-shaped cells, each dikaryotic (n+n), form at the margins of mushroom gills.

⑤ After nuclear fusion, the 2n cell undergoes meiosis and bears four haploid spores at its tips.

spore (n)

gill

⑥ Spores are released, germinate, and give rise to a haploid mycelium.

cap

stalk

② After cytoplasmic fusion, cells of the mycelium are dikaryotic (n+n). Spore-bearing mushrooms form from this mycelium.

Cytoplasmic fusion

①

hyphae of mycelium

sexual spore (n) at gill margin

FIGURE 22.6 {Animated} Life cycle of a club fungus, the button mushroom *Agaricus bisporus*. The red and blue dots represent genetically distinct nuclei.

FIGURE IT OUT: What process produces a dikaryotic cell from two haploid cells?

Answer: Cytoplasmic fusion

When club fungi reproduce sexually, they form spores by meiosis in club-shaped cells called basidia. These cells form on a fruiting body (a basidiocarp) composed of dikaryotic hyphae. A button mushroom is a basidiocarp (**FIGURE 22.6**). Haploid hyphae of a such fungi grow in the soil and feed by decomposing organic material. Unlike the haploid hyphae of molds, those of the fungi that form fruiting bodies do not produce spores asexually.

When hyphae of two mushroom-forming club fungi meet, they fuse and form a dikaryotic mycelium ①. This mycelium continues to grow through the soil unseen and can reach great size. Mycelia of some mushroom-forming fungi extend for miles. Embryonic mushrooms form on the mycelium. When it rains, hyphae soak up water, and these tiny mushrooms expand and break through the soil surface ②. Producing fruiting bodies after a rain ensures that spores will disperse when conditions favor their survival.

The underside of a mushroom's cap has thin tissue sheets (gills) fringed with club-shaped, dikaryotic cells ③. Fusion of the nuclei in a dikaryotic cell forms a diploid zygote ④.

The zygote undergoes meiosis, forming four haploid spores ⑤. After dispersal, these spores germinate and the life cycle begins again ⑥.

Fruiting bodies of club fungi come in a dazzling variety of shapes, colors, and sizes. Some look like a coral or a rubbery seaweed. Roughly spherical puffballs can be more than a meter around. Stinkhorns, such as the one in the chapter opening photo, have a phallic shape and smell like rotting meat or feces. Flies and beetles attracted by this odor alight on the tip of the fruiting body, where they unknowingly pick up spores.

TAKE-HOME MESSAGE 22.2

Zygote fungi produce spores asexually until food runs out. Then they make a diploid zygospore that undergoes meiosis.

Sac fungi have diverse body forms and reproductive mechanisms. Some form fruiting bodies called ascocarps; others are yeast and molds that usually reproduce asexually.

Most club fungi produce fruiting bodies called basidiocarps and do not reproduce asexually.

CREDITS: (6) left, © Micrograph, Garry T. Cole, University of Texas, Austin/BPS; right, © Eye of Science/Science Source; art, © Cengage Learning.

NATURE'S RECYCLERS

Fungi provide an important ecological service by breaking down complex compounds in organic wastes and remains. When a fungus secretes digestive enzymes onto these materials, some soluble nutrients escape into nearby soil or water. Plants and other producers can then take up these substances to meet their own needs. Bacteria also serve as decomposers, but they tend to grow mainly on surfaces. By contrast, fungal hyphae can extend deep into a dead log or other bulky food source.

BENEFICIAL PARTNERS

Many fungi take part in a mutualism, an interspecific interaction that benefits both participants. For example, a **mycorrhiza** (plural, mycorrhizae) is a partnership between a soil fungus and the root of a vascular plant (**FIGURE 22.7**). An estimated 80 percent of the vascular plants form a mycorrhiza with a glomeromycete fungus. Hyphae of these fungi enter root cells and branch in the space between the cell wall and the plasma membrane. Some sac fungi and

FIGURE 22.9 Remains of a "zombie fly" infected by the zygote fungus *Entomophthora muscae*. An infected fly ceases normal activities, climbs to the top of stem, and clings there with outstretched wings until it dies. After it does, spore-bearing hyphae erupt through its abdominal wall and shed spores that can cause new infections.

FIGURE 22.7 Mycorrhiza; a fungus and a root of a hemlock tree.

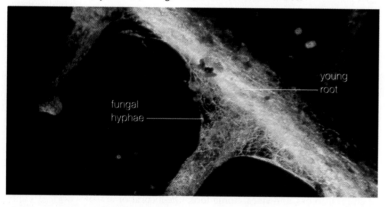

young root

fungal hyphae

FIGURE 22.8 {Animated} Lichens. A fungus partnered with green algal cells or cyanobacteria.

photosynthetic cell

fungal hyphae

A Structure of a leafy lichen.

B Lichen growing on a rock.

club fungi form mycorrhizae in which hyphae surround a root and grow between its cells. Most forest mushrooms are fruiting bodies of mycorrhizal sac fungi or club fungi.

Hyphae of all mycorrhizal fungi functionally increase the absorptive surface area of their plant partner. Hyphae are thinner than even the smallest roots and can grow between soil particles. The fungus shares water and nutrients taken up by its hyphae with root cells. In return, the plant supplies the fungus with sugars.

A **lichen** is a composite organism that consists of a sac fungus and either cyanobacteria or green algae (**FIGURE 22.8A**). The fungus makes up the bulk of a lichen's mass, with its hyphae surrounding the photosynthetic cells. These cells provide the fungus with sugars and, if the cells are cyanobacteria, with fixed nitrogen. Lichens play an important ecological role by colonizing places too hostile for most organisms, such as exposed rocks (**FIGURE 22.8B**). They break down the rock and produce soil by releasing acids and by holding water that freezes and thaws. When soil forms, plants can move in and take root. Long ago, lichens may have preceded plants onto land.

CREDITS: (7) © Gary Braasch; (8A) © Cengage Learning; (8B) © Mark E. Gibson/ Visuals Unlimited; (9) Tamara Kavalou/National Geographic Creative.

Fungal partners also enhance the nutrition of some animals. Chytrid fungi that live in the stomachs of grazing hoofed mammals such as cattle, deer, and moose aid their hosts by breaking down otherwise indigestible cellulose. Similarly, fungal partners of some ants and termites serve as an external digestive system. Leaf-cutter ants gather bits of leaf to sustain the fungus that lives in their colony. The ants cannot digest leaves, but they do eat the fungus.

PARASITES AND PATHOGENS

Many sac fungi and club fungi are plant parasites. Powdery mildews (sac fungi) and rusts and smuts (club fungi) are parasites that grow only in living plants. Their hyphae grow into cells of stems and leaves, where they suck up photosynthetically produced sugars. The resulting loss of nutrients stunts the plant, prevents it from producing seeds, and may eventually kill it. However, the plant usually does not die before the fungus has produced spores on the surface of its infected parts.

Other pathogenic fungi produce toxins that kill plant tissues, then feed on the resulting remains. The club fungus *Armallaria* causes root rot by infecting trees and woody shrubs in forests worldwide. Once an infected tree dies, the fungus decomposes the stumps and logs left behind. In one Oregon forest, the mycelium of a single honey mushroom (*A. ostoyae*) extends across nearly 4 square miles (10 km^2). It has been growing for an estimated 2,400 years.

Many more fungi infect plants than animals. Among animals, those that do not maintain a high body temperature are most vulnerable to fungal infections. Hundreds of fungal species infect insects, and some turn their hosts into seeming zombies, the better to disperse their spores (**FIGURE 22.9**).

Most human fungal infections involve body surfaces. Infected areas become raised, red, and itchy. For example, several species of fungus infect skin between the toes and on the sole of the foot, causing "athlete's foot." Fungal vaginitis (a vaginal yeast infection) occurs when a yeast (*Candida*) that normally lives in the vagina in low numbers undergoes a population explosion. Fungi also cause skin infections misleadingly known as "ringworm." No worm is involved. Rather, a ring-shaped lesion forms as fungal hyphae grow outward from the initial infection site. Life-threatening fungal infections are rare and usually occur only in people whose immune response is weak as a result of other factors.

---

lichen Composite organism consisting of a fungus and green algae or cyanobacteria.
mycorrhiza Mutually beneficial partnership between a fungus and a plant root.

CREDIT: (in text) Stephen Alvarez/National Geographic Creative.

PEOPLE MATTER

National Geographic Grantee DR. DeeAnn Reeder

DeeAnn Reeder is an expert on bats, with a particular interest in species that hibernate. As a National Geographic Society Grantee, she has explored bat diversity in the new country of South Sudan. She is also part of a team investigating white nose syndrome, a bat disease first described in New York in 2006. By early 2013, it had been discovered in 21 states and four Canadian provinces, and it had killed millions of North America's bats.

Bats with white nose syndrome fly when they should be hibernating, lose weight, and have fuzzy white filaments of the fungus *Geomyces destructans* on their wings, ears, and muzzle. Most fungal infections do not kill mammals, and fungi often infect animals weakened by other pathogens. Thus, Reeder and other biologists initially assumed the fungus was a symptom of a disease, rather than its cause. However, when they experimentally infected healthy bats with *G. destructans*, they found the fungus alone is sufficient to cause the disease. Reeder and others are now working to understand why the fungus has such deadly effects, which types of bat colonies are most susceptible to infection, and what can be done to halt the spread of the fungus.

TAKE-HOME MESSAGE 22.3

The decomposition of organic wastes and remains by fungal decomposers releases nutrients that other organisms can use.

Fungi that partner with plant roots or live in the animal gut enhance the nutrition of their hosts. Fungi also partner with cyanobacteria or green algae to form a lichen.

Parasitic fungi that infect plants either steal sugars from living cells or kill cells and digest their remains.

Fungi cause disease in plants more often than in animals. Animals with a high body temperature are least susceptible to fungal diseases.

Human fungal infections usually involve body surfaces and are rarely life-threatening.

Many fungal fruiting bodies serve as human food. Button mushrooms, shiitake mushrooms, and oyster mushrooms decompose organic matter, so these species are easily cultivated. By contrast, edible mycorrhizal fungi such as chanterelles, porcini mushrooms, morels, and truffles need a living plant partner, so they are typically gathered from the wild. Picking wild mushrooms is best done with the aid of someone experienced in identifying species. Each year thousands of people become ill after eating poisonous mushrooms they mistook for edible ones.

Truffle-producing fungi, which are highly prized by gourmets, have evolved an interesting dispersal strategy. Truffles form underground near their host trees and, when mature, produce an odor similar to that of an amorous male wild pig. Female wild pigs detect the scent and root through the soil in search of their seemingly subterranean suitor. When they unearth the truffles, they eat them, then disperse fungal spores in their feces. Human truffle hunters usually rely on trained dogs to sniff out the fungi.

FIGURE 22.10 Fungi as food. Sac fungi help us produce breads, wine, and blue cheeses.

Fermentation by fungi helps us make a variety of products. Fermentation by one mold (*Aspergillus*) helps make soy sauce. Another mold (*Penicillium*) produces the tangy blue veins in cheeses such as Roquefort (**FIGURE 22.10**). A packet of baker's yeast holds spores of the sac fungus *Saccharomyces cerevisiae*. When these spores germinate in bread dough, they ferment sugar and produce carbon dioxide that causes the dough to rise. Other strains of *S. cerevisiae* are used to make wine and beer, and also to produce ethanol biofuel.

Geneticists and biotechologists also make use of yeasts. Like *E. coli* bacteria, yeasts grow readily in laboratories and they have the added advantage of being eukaryotes like us. Checkpoint genes that regulate the eukaryotic cell cycle (Section 11.1) were first discovered in the yeast *S. cerevisiae*. This discovery was the first step toward our current understanding of how mutations of these genes cause human cancers. Genetically engineered *S. cerevisiae* and other yeasts are now used to produce proteins that serve as vaccines or other medicines.

Some naturally occurring fungal compounds have medicinal or psychoactive properties. The initial source of the antibiotic penicillin was a soil fungus (*Penicillium chrysogenum*). Another soil fungus gave us cyclosporin, an immune suppressant used to prevent rejection of transplanted organs. Ergotamine, a compound used to relieve migraines, was first isolated from ergot (*Claviceps purpurea*), a club fungus that infects rye plants. Ergotamine is also used in synthesis of the hallucinogen LSD. Another hallucinogen, psilocybin, is the active ingredient in so-called "magic mushrooms."

In Asia, dried remains of a fungus-infected caterpillar have been prized as a medicine for thousands of years. The fungus (*Ophiocordyceps sinensis*) infects a soil-dwelling moth larva. After the insect dies, a fungal fruiting body about the size of a blade of grass emerges above ground. When gathered from the wild and dried, the fungal fruiting bodies and attached insect remains are more expensive than gold. A compound (cordycepin) first extracted from this fungus boosts production of testosterone (the male sex hormone) in mice and shows promise as an anticancer drug.

TAKE-HOME MESSAGE 22.4

We eat fungal fruiting bodies and use yeasts to produce foods and beverages. Yeasts are also used in genetic studies, in production of recombinant proteins, and to synthesize ethanol as a biofuel.

Some fungi make compounds that are prized for their medicinal or psychoactive properties.

Conservation

FIGURE 22.11 Frogs killed by the chytrid fungus Bd at a high-elevation lake in California's Sierra Nevada Mountains.

THE DISPERSAL OF FUNGAL PATHOGENS BY GLOBAL TRADE AND TRAVEL CAN HAVE DEVASTATING EFFECTS ON ECOSYSTEMS.

In the early twentieth century, a plant-infecting sac fungus native to China was introduced to North America in imported plants. The fungus caused a chestnut blight that eliminated all mature American chestnut trees. Some American chestnuts persist as root systems, but the blight always kills them before they mature and reproduce.

Today, human-facilitated spread of a fungal pathogen is among the foremost causes of an amphibian extinction crisis. The fungus, *Batrachochytrium dendrobatidis*, is a chytrid known as Bd. It is native to Africa, where it infects African clawed frogs without sickening them.

International trade in African clawed frogs began in 1934, when scientists discovered the frogs could be used in pregnancy tests. If a female frog is injected with blood from a pregnant woman, hormones in her blood cause the frog to lay eggs. Until the 1950s, this frog-based test was the main method of determining pregnancy, so millions of African clawed frogs were exported for this purpose. The Bd chytrid traveled with them. It became established in new regions when people released infected frogs or dumped water with Bd spores into the environment. Bd now occurs on all continents except Antarctica, and trade in amphibians continues to introduce it into previously uninfected habitats.

The effect of Bd varies among amphibian species. Many frogs outside of Africa have little or no resistance to Bd, so their death rate from infection is extremely high (FIGURE 22.11). The fungus grows on an amphibian's skin, causing the skin to thicken. Thickened skin prevents the frog from absorbing water properly, so it eventually dies of dehydration.

Summary

SECTION 22.1 **Fungi** are heterotrophs that secrete digestive enzymes onto organic matter and absorb released nutrients. Their cell walls include chitin and they disperse by releasing spores. In a multicelled species, spores germinate and give rise to filaments called **hyphae**. The filaments typically grow as an extensive mesh called a **mycelium**. Depending on the group, the cells of a hypha may be haploid (n) or **dikaryotic** ($n+n$). Water and nutrients move freely between cells of a hypha.

The oldest fungal lineage, the **chytrids**, are a mostly aquatic group and the only fungi with flagellated spores. **Zygote fungi** include many familiar **molds** that grow on fruits, breads, and other foods. **Glomeromycetes** live in soil and extend their hyphae into plant roots. **Sac fungi** are the most diverse fungal group. They include single-celled **yeasts**, molds, and species that produce multicelled fruiting bodies. Most familiar mushrooms are fruiting bodies of **club fungi**. Multicelled sac fungi and club fungi can form large fruiting bodies because their hyphae, unlike those of other fungi, have porous cross walls between the cells. These walls reinforce the structure of a hypha.

SECTION 22.2 Mechanisms of spore formation differ among fungal groups. Zygote fungi such as bread molds usually reproduce asexually by producing spores atop specialized hyphae until food runs out. Then hyphae fuse to produce a diploid zygospore that undergoes meiosis and releases haploid spores.

Sac fungal yeasts reproduce asexually by budding. During sexual reproduction, a sac fungus produces spores in a sac-shaped structure (an ascus). In some sac fungi, including the cup fungi, the asci form on a fruiting body called an ascocarp.

Club fungi produce spores in club-shaped structures (basidia) on fruiting bodies called basidiocarps. Typically, a dikaryotic mycelium grows by mitosis. When conditions favor reproduction, a basidiocarp, also made of dikaryotic hyphae, develops. A mushroom is an example. Fusion of nuclei in dikaryotic club-shaped cells at the edges of gills produces diploid cells. Meiosis in these cells produces haploid spores.

SECTION 22.3 Fungi have many important roles in ecosystems. Most are decomposers. By breaking down organic wastes and remains, they make nutrients that were tied up in these materials available to producers.

A **lichen** is a composite organism composed of a fungus and photosynthetic cells of a green alga or cyanobacterium. The fungus, which makes up the bulk of the lichen body, obtains a supply of nutrients from its photosynthetic partner. Lichens are important pioneers in new habitats because they facilitate the breakdown of rock to form soil.

A **mycorrhiza** is an interaction between a fungus and a plant root. Fungal hyphae penetrate roots and supplement their absorptive surface area. The fungus shares absorbed mineral ions with the plant and obtains some photosynthetic sugars in return.

Fungi that parasitize plants either insert their hyphae into plant cells to steal sugars, or kill plant cells and suck up the released nutrients. Fungi parasitize animals less frequently than they do plants. Animals that have a low body temperature are most often infected. Some fungi infect insects and alter their behavior.

Fungi that infect humans tend to affect body surfaces, as when they cause athlete's foot or a vaginal yeast infection. Typically, fungi cause life-threatening infections only in people whose immune response is impaired.

SECTION 22.4 Many fungal fruiting bodies are edible, although some produce dangerous toxins. Fungi that carry out fermentation reactions help us produce food products, alcoholic beverages, and ethanol for use as a biofuel. Study of yeasts can provide insights into eukaryotic genetics. Recombinant yeasts produce vaccines and other desired proteins. Some compounds extracted from fungi are useful as medicines or psychoactive drugs.

SECTION 22.5 Human activities have introduced some fungal pathogens to new environments where they have negative effects on the health of other organisms. One sac fungus introduced to North America wiped out American chestnuts. Today, a chytrid fungus native to Africa threatens amphibian species worldwide.

Self-Quiz   Answers in Appendix VII

1. All fungi _____ .
   a. are multicelled
   b. form flagellated spores
   c. are heterotrophs
   d. all of the above

2. Most fungi obtain nutrients from _____ .
   a. wastes and remains
   b. living plants
   c. living animals
   d. photosynthesis

3. A fungus that usually lives as a mass of hyphae and reproduces asexually is called a _____ .
   a. lichen
   b. mold
   c. yeast
   d. mushroom

4. A _____ steals sugars from a living plant cell.
   a. rust or smut
   b. mushroom
   c. lichen
   d. mold

5. In many _____ , an extensive dikaryotic mycelium is the most conspicuous phase of the life cycle.
   a. chytrids
   b. zygote fungi
   c. sac fungi
   d. club fungi

6. A _____ produces spores by meiosis in an ascus.
   a. chytrid
   b. zygote fungus
   c. sac fungus
   d. club fungus

Data Analysis Activities

Fighting a Forest Fungus The club fungus *Armillaria ostoyae* infects living trees and acts as a parasite, withdrawing nutrients from them. After the tree dies, the fungus continues to feed on its remains. Fungal hyphae grow out from the roots of infected trees as well as the roots of dead stumps. If these hyphae contact roots of a healthy tree, they can invade and cause a new infection.

Canadian forest pathologists hypothesized that removing fungus-infected stumps after logging could help prevent tree deaths. To test this hypothesis, they carried out an experiment. In one region of a forest they removed stumps after logging. In another, they left stumps behind as a control. For more than 20 years, they recorded tree deaths and whether *A. ostoyae* caused them. **FIGURE 22.12** shows the results.

1. Which tree species was most often killed by *A. ostoyae* in control forests? Which was least affected by the fungus?
2. For the most affected species, what percentage of deaths did *A. ostoyae* cause in control and in experimental regions?
3. Looking at the overall results, do the data support the hypothesis? Does stump removal reduce tree mortality from *A. ostoyae*?

FIGURE 22.12 Results of a long-term study of how logging practices affect tree deaths caused by the fungus *A. ostoyae*. In the experimental forest, whole trees—including stumps—were removed (brown bars). The control half of the forest was logged conventionally, with the stumps left behind (blue bars).

7. A mushroom is _____ .
   a. the digestive organ of a club fungus
   b. the only part of the fungal body made of hyphae
   c. a reproductive structure that releases sexual spores
   d. the only diploid phase in the club fungus life cycle

8. Spores released from a mushroom's gills are _____ .
   a. dikaryotic
   b. diploid
   c. flagellated
   d. produced by meiosis

9. _____ by yeast helps us produce bread, soy sauce, and ethanol as a biofuel.
   a. Photosynthesis
   b. Fermentation
   c. Decomposition
   d. Budding

10. A _____ helps to break down rocks and form soil.
    a. chytrid
    b. glomeromycete
    c. mycorrhiza
    d. lichen

11. _____ are mycorrhizal fungi with hyphae that grow into a root cell and branch inside it.
    a. Glomeromycetes
    b. Chytrids
    c. Zygote fungi
    d. Club fungi

12. A truffle is an example of a _____ .
    a. spore
    b. lichen
    c. mycorrhizal fungus
    d. plant pathogen

13. Frogs worldwide are now threatened by a pathogenic _____ native to Africa.
    a. glomeromycete
    b. chytrid
    c. zygote fungus
    d. club fungus

14. Human fungal infections _____ .
    a. usually involve the skin
    b. typically produce hallucinations
    c. are often life-threatening
    d. all of the above

15. Match the terms appropriately.
    ___ hypha
    ___ chitin
    ___ chytrid
    ___ zygote fungus
    ___ club fungus
    ___ lichen
    ___ mycorrhiza

    a. produces flagellated spores
    b. component of fungal cell walls
    c. partnership between a fungus and photosynthetic cells
    d. filament of a mycelium
    e. fungus–root partnership
    f. bread mold is an example
    g. many form mushrooms

Critical Thinking

1. Developing antifungal drugs is more difficult than developing antibacterial drugs because compounds that harm fungi more frequently cause side effects in humans than compounds that harm bacteria. Explain why this is the case, given the evolutionary relationships among bacteria, fungi, and humans.

2. Bakers who want to be sure their yeast is alive "proof" it. They test the yeast's viability by putting a bit of it in warm water with some sugar. A few minutes later, they look for a sign the yeast has been active. What do they look for?

3. Molds usually reproduce sexually when food is running low. Why might sexual reproduction be more advantageous at this time than when food remains plentiful?

CENGAGE To access course materials, please visit
brain.com www.cengagebrain.com.

CREDIT: (12) After graph from www.pfc.forestry.ca.

Sea stars, sea anemones, and pink encrusting sponges in a Pacific Northwest tide pool.

23

ANIMALS I: MAJOR INVERTEBRATE GROUPS

Links to Earlier Concepts

This chapter draws on your knowledge of animal tissues and organs (Section 1.1) and of homeotic genes (10.2), fossils (16.3, 16.4), analogous structures (16.7), speciation (17.8), and biomarkers (18.3). You will see another use of chitin (3.2) and more effects of osmosis (5.6). You will learn how animals interact with dinoflagellates (20.4), protists that cause malaria (20.5), and flowering plants (21.7).

KEY CONCEPTS

INTRODUCING THE ANIMALS
Animals digest food in their body, and most move about. They evolved from a colonial protist. The overwhelming majority of modern animals are invertebrates.

SPONGES AND CNIDARIANS
Sponges filter food from water and have an asymmetrical body. Cnidarians are predators with a radially symmetrical body that has two tissue layers.

BILATERAL INVERTEBRATES
Most animals are bilaterally symmetrical and have organ systems. In flatworms, organs are hemmed in by tissue. In other bilateral animals, the organs reside in a body cavity.

THE MOST SUCCESSFUL ANIMALS
Arthropods are the most diverse animals. Crustaceans abound in seas, and insects on land. Insects play essential roles in ecosystems and have important economic and health effects.

RELATIVES OF CHORDATES
Echinoderms are on the same branch of the animal family tree as animals with backbones. Adults have a spiny skin and a radially symmetrical body.

Photograph by George Grall, National Geographic Creative.

Animals are multicelled heterotrophs whose unwalled body cells are typically diploid. Most animals ingest food (take it in) and digest it inside their body. Nearly all are motile (able to move from place to place) during all or part of their life.

This chapter describes major groups of **invertebrates**, animals that do not have a backbone. The next chapter focuses on vertebrates (animals with a backbone) and their closest invertebrate relatives. Keep in mind that although invertebrates have a simpler structure than vertebrates, they are not evolutionarily inferior. Some invertebrate lineages have been around for more than 500 million years, and about 95 percent of all animals are invertebrates.

FIGURE 23.1 shows an evolutionary tree for the major animal groups covered in this book, and we will use it as a guide to discuss evolutionary trends. All animals are multicellular ❶ and constitute the clade Metazoa. The earliest animals were probably aggregations of cells, and this level of organization persists in sponges. However, most other modern animals have cells organized as tissues ❷.

Tissue organization begins in animal embryos. Embryos of jellies and other cnidarians have two tissue layers: an outer **ectoderm** and an inner **endoderm**. In other modern animals, embryonic cells typically rearrange themselves to form a middle tissue layer called **mesoderm** (**FIGURE 23.2**). Evolution of a three-layer embryo allowed an important increase in structural complexity. Most internal organs in animals develop from embryonic mesoderm.

FIGURE 23.2 How a three-layer animal embryo forms. Most animals have this type of embryo.

Animals with the simplest structural organization are asymmetrical; you cannot divide their body into halves that are mirror images. Jellies, sea anemones, and other cnidarians have **radial symmetry**: Their body parts are repeated around a central axis, like spokes of a wheel ❸. Radial animals usually attach to an underwater surface or drift along. A radial body plan allows them to capture food that can arrive from any direction. Animals with a three-layer body plan typically have **bilateral symmetry**: The body's left and right halves are mirror images ❹. Such lineages typically undergo **cephalization**, an evolutionary process whereby many nerve cells and sensory structures become concentrated at the front of the body. These structures help the animal find food or avoid threats as it moves head-first through its environment.

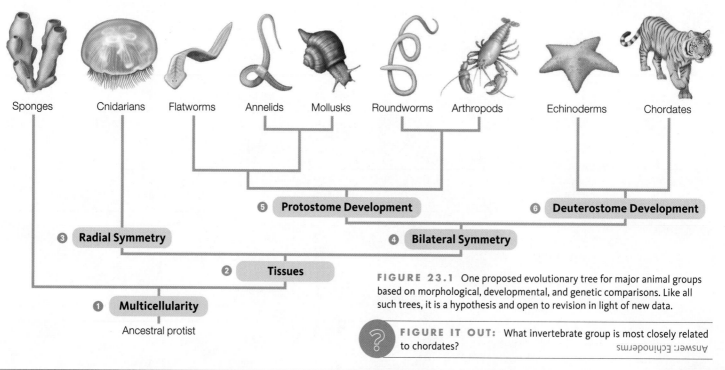

Sponges Cnidarians Flatworms Annelids Mollusks Roundworms Arthropods Echinoderms Chordates

❺ **Protostome Development**   ❻ **Deuterostome Development**

❸ **Radial Symmetry**   ❹ **Bilateral Symmetry**

❷ **Tissues**

❶ **Multicellularity**

Ancestral protist

FIGURE 23.1 One proposed evolutionary tree for major animal groups based on morphological, developmental, and genetic comparisons. Like all such trees, it is a hypothesis and open to revision in light of new data.

FIGURE IT OUT: What invertebrate group is most closely related to chordates?

Answer: Echinoderms

Developmental differences define the two clades of bilaterally symmetrical animals. Among **protostomes**, the first opening that appears on the embryo becomes the mouth ❺. *Proto–* means first and *stoma* means opening. In **deuterostomes**, the mouth develops from the second embryonic opening ❻.

Some animals digest food in a saclike cavity with a single opening. Most animals have a tubular gut, with a mouth at one end and an anus at the other. Parts of the tube are typically specialized for taking in food, digesting food, absorbing nutrients, or compacting the wastes. A tubular gut can carry out all of these tasks simultaneously, whereas a saclike cavity cannot.

A mass of tissues and organs surrounds the flatworm gut (FIGURE 23.3A). However, most bilateral animals have a fluid-filled body cavity around their gut. In a few animals such as roundworms this body cavity is only partially lined, in which case it is called a **pseudocoelom** (FIGURE 23.3B). More typically, bilateral animals have a **coelom**, a body cavity lined with a tissue derived from mesoderm (FIGURE 23.3C). In such animals, sheets of tissue called mesentery suspend the gut in the center of a fluid-filled cavity. Coelomic fluid cushions the gut and keeps it from being distorted by body movements. The fluid also helps distribute material through the body, and in some animals it plays a role in locomotion.

Most bilaterally symmetrical animals have some degree of **segmentation**, a division of a body into similar units repeated one after the other along the main axis. Evolution of segmentation allowed other innovations in body form to evolve. When many segments carry out the same function, some segments can become modified over evolutionary time, while others retain their original function.

FIGURE 23.3 {**Animated**} Animal body cavities. Most animals, and all vertebrates, have a coelomate body plan, as in C.

A Flatworms have no body cavity except their gut.

epidermis (from ectoderm)
tissues, organs (from mesoderm)
gut tissue (from endoderm)
gut cavity

B Roundworms have a fluid-filled pseudocoelm.

pseudocoelom
epidermis (from ectoderm)
tissues, organs (from mesoderm)
gut tissue (from endoderm)
gut cavity

C Annelids have a fluid-filled coelom with sheets of tissue (mesentery) that hold the gut in place.

coelom
epidermis (from ectoderm)
mesentery
tissues, organs (from mesoderm)
gut tissue (from endoderm)
gut cavity

animal Multicelled heterotroph with unwalled cells. Most ingest food and are motile during at least part of the life cycle.
bilateral symmetry Having paired structures so the right and left halves are mirror images.
cephalization Evolutionary trend toward having a concentration of nerve and sensory cells at the head end.
coelom Body cavity lined with tissue derived from mesoderm.
deuterostomes Lineage of bilateral animals in which the second opening on the embryo surface develops into a mouth.
ectoderm Outermost tissue layer of an animal embryo.
endoderm Innermost tissue layer of an animal embryo.
invertebrate Animal that does not have a backbone.
mesoderm Middle tissue layer of a three-layered animal embryo.
protostomes Lineage of bilateral animals in which the first opening on the embryo surface develops into a mouth.
pseudocoelom Unlined body cavity around the gut.
radial symmetry Having parts arranged around a central axis, like the spokes of a wheel.
segmentation Having a body composed of similar units that repeat along its length.

TAKE-HOME MESSAGE 23.1

Early animals had no body symmetry or tissues.

The next evolutionary step was a radially symmetrical body that develops from an embryo with two tissue layers.

Most modern animals have a bilaterally symmetrical body that develops from an embryo with three tissue layers.

Most bilaterally symmetrical animals have a coelom.

COLONIAL ORIGINS

According to the **colonial theory of animal origins**, the first animals evolved from a colonial protist. At first, all cells in the colony were similar. Each could reproduce and carry out all other essential tasks. Later, mutations produced cells that specialized in some tasks and did not carry out others. Perhaps these cells captured food more efficiently but did not make gametes, whereas others made gametes but did not catch food. The division of labor among interdependent cells made them more efficient, allowing the colonies with mutations to obtain more food and produce more offspring. Over time, additional types of specialized cell types evolved.

What was the protist ancestral to animals like? Choanoflagellates, the modern protists most closely related to animals, provide some clues. As Section 20.9 explains, choanoflagellates are flagellated cells that live either as single cells or as a colony of genetically identical cells. In their structure, choanoflagellate cells closely resemble some cells in the bodies of modern sponges.

EARLY EVOLUTION

FIGURE 23.4 The only named placozoan, *Trichoplax adhaerans*. It is about 2 millimeters wide and two micrometers thick. This one is colored red by the red algae it fed on.

Early animals may have been similar to **placozoans**, a little-known group of tiny marine organisms that have the simplest body and smallest genome of all modern animals. A placozoan has an asymmetrical body with four types of cells (**FIGURE 23.4**). Ciliated cells on its surface allow it to glide along the seafloor, where it ingests bacteria and algae. Genetic comparisons among living species suggest that placozoans may be the oldest surviving animal lineage.

Sponges are another ancient group. In Oman, sedimentary rocks laid down 635 million years ago contain traces of complex steroids that today are made only by marine sponges. Similarly aged rocks from Australia contain what appear to be fossils of sponge bodies.

A collection of 570-million-year-old fossils from Australia provide evidence of an early animal diversification. The fossil species, collectively known as Ediacarans, include a variety of soft-bodied organisms that may have been early marine invertebrates. Many Ediacarans are unlike any modern animals, whereas others appear to be related to some modern invertebrates (**FIGURE 23.5**). In general,

FIGURE 23.5 An Ediacaran fossil. *Spriggina* was about 3 centimeters (1 inch) long. By one hypothesis, it was a soft-bodied ancestor of arthropods, a group that includes modern crabs and insects.

the connections between Ediacarans and modern animals remain unclear. One biologist has even suggested some Ediacaran fossils are the remains of land-dwelling microbes, lichens, or fungi.

AN EXPLOSION OF DIVERSITY

Animals underwent a dramatic adaptive radiation during the Cambrian period (542–488 million years ago). By the end of this interval, all major animal lineages were present in the seas. What caused this Cambrian explosion in diversity? Rising oxygen levels and changes in global climate may have played a role. Also, supercontinents were breaking up. As landmasses moved, they could have isolated different populations, creating new opportunities for allopatric speciation (Section 17.9). Biological interactions also encouraged speciation. Once the first predators arose, mutations that produced defenses such as protective hard parts would have been favored. Mutations in homeotic genes (Section 10.2) may have sped things along. Some mutations in these genes could have resulted in changes in body form that proved adaptive as new predators arose or the habitat changed.

---

colonial theory of animal origins Hypothesis that the first animals evolved from a colonial protist.
placozoans Group of tiny marine animals having a simple asymmetrical body and a small genome; considered an ancient lineage.

TAKE-HOME MESSAGE 23.2

The ancestor of all animals was probably a colonial protist. It may have resembled choanoflagellates, the modern protist group most closely related to animals.

Animals probably originated more than 600 million years ago. Placozoans and sponges are ancient animal lineages that survived to the present day.

Environmental and biological factors encouraged a great adaptive radiation during the Cambrian period.

Sponges (phylum Porifera) are aquatic animals with a porous body that does not have tissues. The vast majority live in tropical seas, and nearly all are sessile, meaning they live fixed in place. Sponge bodies vary in size and shape. Some fit on a fingertip, whereas others stand meters tall. Asymmetrical vaselike or columnar forms are most common, but some sponges grow as a thin crust.

Flat, nonflagellated cells cover a sponge's outer surface, flagellated collar cells line the inner surface, and a jellylike extracellular matrix lies in between (**FIGURE 23.6**). In many sponges, cells in this matrix secrete fibrous proteins, glassy silica spikes, or both. These materials structurally support the body, and help fend off predators. Some protein-rich sponges are harvested from the sea, dried, cleaned, and bleached. Their rubbery protein remains (*left*) are then sold as bathing and cleaning supplies.

The typical sponge is a **suspension feeder** that eats material it filters from the surrounding water. Action of flagella on collar cells draws food-laden water through pores in a sponge's body wall. The collar cells filter food from the water and engulf it by phagocytosis. Digestion is intracellular. Amoeba-like cells in the matrix receive the breakdown products of digestion from collar cells and distribute them to other cells in the sponge body.

Most sponges are **hermaphrodites**, meaning each individual can produce both eggs and sperm. Typically, the sponge releases its sperm into the water (**FIGURE 23.7**) but holds onto its eggs. Fertilization produces a zygote that develops into a ciliated larva. A **larva** (plural, larvae) is a young, sexually immature stage in an animal life cycle. Sponge larvae swim briefly, then settle and become adults. Many sponges also reproduce asexually when small buds or fragments break away and grow into new sponges.

Some freshwater species can survive dry conditions by producing gemmules, tiny clumps of resting cells encased in a hardened coat. Gemmules are often dispersed by the wind. Those that land in a hospitable habitat become active and grow into new sponges.

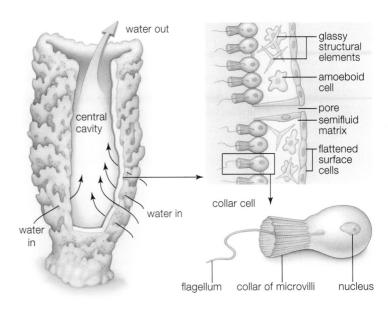

FIGURE 23.6 {Animated} Body plan of a simple sponge.

Labels: water out; glassy structural elements; amoeboid cell; central cavity; pore; semifluid matrix; flattened surface cells; water in; collar cell; flagellum; collar of microvilli; nucleus; water in

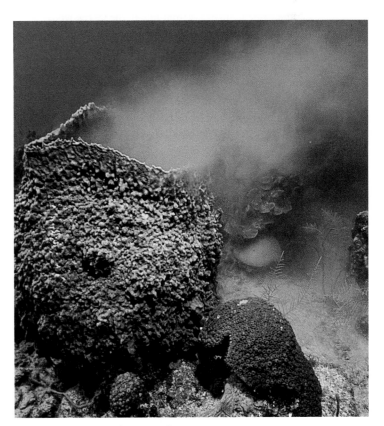

FIGURE 23.7 Barrel sponge releasing sperm.

hermaphrodite Animal that makes both eggs and sperm.
larva Sexually immature stage in some animal life cycles.
sponge Aquatic invertebrate that has no tissues or organs and filters food from the water.
suspension feeder Animal that filters food from water around it.

TAKE-HOME MESSAGE 23.3

Sponges are typically suspension feeders with a porous, asymmetrical body. Fibers and glassy spikes in the body wall support the body and help deter predators.

Sponges are hermaphrodites. Their ciliated larvae swim about briefly before settling and developing into adults.

CREDITS: (in text) © ultimathule/Shutterstock; (6) From Starr/Taggart/Evers/Starr, Biology, 13E. © 2013 Cengage Learning; (7) Marty Snyderman/Planet Earth Pictures.

Cnidarians (phylum Cnidaria) are radially symmetrical, mostly marine animals, such as sea anemones and jellies (also called jellyfish). They have a two-layered body, with an outer layer derived from ectoderm, and an inner layer from endoderm. Jellylike secreted material lies between the layers.

There are two basic cnidarian body plans, and both have a tentacle-ringed mouth (**FIGURE 23.8**). Medusae (singular, medusa) are dome-shaped, with a mouth on the dome's lower surface. Most swim or drift about. Polyps have an upward-facing mouth atop a cylindrical body that is typically attached to a surface.

Cnidarian life cycles vary. Most jellies have a life cycle in which polyps that reproduce asexually by budding alternate with gamete-producing medusae. Sea anemones, corals, and the hydras (a freshwater group) exist only as polyps that can both bud and produce gametes. In all cnidarians, the zygote produced by sexual reproduction develops into a bilaterally symmetrical ciliated larvae called a planula.

The name Cnidaria is from *cnidos*, the Greek word for the stinging nettle plant, and refers to the animals' mechanism of feeding. Cnidarians are predators. Their tentacles have **cnidocytes**, specialized stinging cells that help them capture prey. A cnidocyte contains a nematocyst, an organelle that functions like a jack-in-the-box (**FIGURE 23.9**). When prey brushes a nematocyst's trigger, a barbed thread pops out and delivers a dose of venom. People that

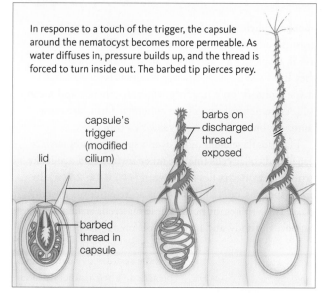

In response to a touch of the trigger, the capsule around the nematocyst becomes more permeable. As water diffuses in, pressure builds up, and the thread is forced to turn inside out. The barbed tip pierces prey.

capsule's trigger (modified cilium)

lid

barbed thread in capsule

barbs on discharged thread exposed

FIGURE 23.9 {Animated} Nematocyst action.

brush against a jellyfish can trigger this same response and end up with a painful sting. Some box jellies that live near Australia produce a venom so powerful that their sting occasionally kills people.

Tentacles move captured food to the mouth, which opens to a **gastrovascular cavity**. This saclike region functions in digestion and gas exchange. Unlike sponges, cnidarians digest their food extracellularly. Enzymes secreted into the gastrovascular cavity break down prey. Released nutrients are then absorbed and are distributed through the body by diffusion. Digestive waste exits through the mouth.

Cnidarians are brainless, but interconnecting nerve cells extend through their tissues as a **nerve net**. Body parts move when these nerve cells signal contractile cells to shorten. Contraction alters the shape of the animal by redistributing fluid trapped within the gastrovascular cavity. By analogy, think of what happens when you squeeze a water-filled balloon. A fluid-filled cavity that contractile cells exert force against is a **hydrostatic skeleton**. Many soft-bodied invertebrates have this type of skeleton.

FIGURE 23.8 {Animated} Cnidarian body plans and representative examples.

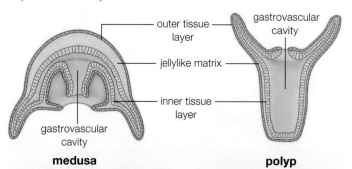

outer tissue layer

jellylike matrix

inner tissue layer

gastrovascular cavity

gastrovascular cavity

medusa

polyp

Moon jelly

Sea anemone

cnidarian Radially symmetrical invertebrate with two tissue layers; uses tentacles with stinging cells to capture food.
cnidocyte Stinging cell unique to cnidarians.
gastrovascular cavity A saclike gut that also functions in gas exchange.
hydrostatic skeleton Of soft-bodied invertebrates, a fluid-filled chamber that contractile cells exert force on.
nerve net Decentralized mesh of nerve cells that allows movement in cnidarians.

CREDITS: (8) top, © Cengage Learning; bottom left, © Boris Pamikov/Shutterstock; bottom right, © Brandon D. Cole/Corbis; (9) From Starr/Evers/Starr, Biology Today and Tomorrow with Physiology, 4E. © 2013 Cengage Learning.

FIGURE 23.10 A coral reef. The corals are colonies of polyps. Dinoflagellates in their tissues give them their color.

Most cnidarians are solitary, but colonial groups exist. Siphonophores such as the Portuguese man-of-war (*Physalia*) look like a single animal, but are colonies of many polyps and medusae. Coral reefs are built by colonies of polyps enclosed in a skeleton of secreted calcium carbonate. In a mutually beneficial relationship, photosynthetic dinoflagellates live inside each polyp's tissues (**FIGURE 23.10**). The protists receive shelter and carbon dioxide from the coral, and give it sugars and oxygen in return. If a reef-building coral loses its protist partners, an event called "coral bleaching," it may die.

TAKE-HOME MESSAGE 23.4

Cnidarians are radially symmetrical, mostly marine predators with two tissue layers. There are two body plans: medusa and polyp. In both, tentacles with stinging cells surround a mouth that opens onto a gastrovascular cavity. A nerve net interacts with the hydrostatic skeleton to allow movement.

Cnidarians include sea anemones, jellies, and corals. Reef-building corals secrete calcium carbonate that forms reefs.

PEOPLE MATTER

National Geographic
Explorer
DR. DAVID GRUBER

Biofluorescence is the process by which organisms absorb light of one wavelength and emit light of another. The stunning photograph *below*, taken by Dr. David Gruber, shows a coral polyp illuminated by blue light. The coral has proteins that absorb violet wavelengths, then emit green, orange, and red wavelengths.

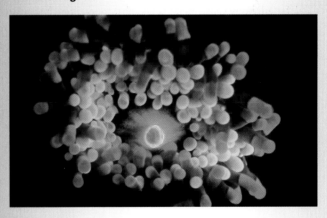

Nearly all known biofluorescent animals are cnidarians, so Gruber searches the world's reefs for species that glow. He and his research team have discovered over 30 new fluorescent proteins from corals, including the brightest one found to date. Recently, he has also been finding biofluorescence in several species of sharks, rays, and bony fishes. Fluorescent proteins are useful in science and medicine. They allow researchers to visualize specific cells and structures using fluorescence microscopy (Section 4.2). Among other applications, this technique can be used in early detection of cancers and to study how signals travel through the brain. We do not know how having biofluorescent proteins benefits cnidarians, but they are linked to coral health. Gruber also suspects that other reef-dwelling organisms recognize the fluorescence as a signal.

With this section, we begin our survey of protostomes, one of the two lineages of bilaterally symmetrical animals. All of these animals develop from a three-layered embryo.

Flatworms (phylum Platyhelminthes) are the simplest protostomes. They have a flattened body with an array of organ systems, but no body cavity other than a gastrovascular cavity. Like cnidarians, they rely entirely on diffusion to move nutrients and gases through their body. Some flatworms are free-living and others are parasites. Nearly all are hermaphrodites.

FREE-LIVING FLATWORMS

Most free-living flatworms live in tropical seas, and many of these are brilliantly colored (**FIGURE 23.11**). A lesser number live in fresh water, and a few live in damp places on land. Free-living flatworms typically glide along, propelled by the action of cilia that cover the body surface. Some marine species can also swim with an undulating motion.

Planarians are free-living flatworms common in ponds. They have a highly branched gastrovascular cavity (**FIGURE 23.12A**), and nutrients diffuse from the fine branches to all body cells. There is no anus; food enters and wastes leave through the mouth. The mouth is not on the planarian's head, but rather at the tip of a muscular tube (called the pharynx) that extends from the animal's lower surface.

A planarian's head has chemical receptors and eyespots that detect light. These sensory structures send messages to a simple brain that consists of paired groupings of nerve cell bodies (ganglia). A pair of nerve cords extend from the brain and run the length of the body (**FIGURE 23.12B**).

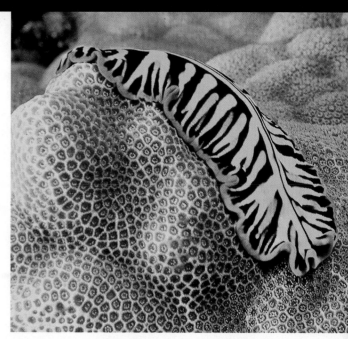

FIGURE 23.11 A marine flatworm. Brightly colored flatworms like this one are common inhabitants of coral reef ecosystems.

A planarian's body fluid has a higher solute concentration than the fresh water around it, so water tends to move into the body by osmosis. A system of tubes regulates internal water and solute levels by driving excess fluids out through a pore at the body surface (**FIGURE 23.12C**).

A planarian has female and male sex organs (**FIGURE 23.12D**), but cannot fertilize its own eggs. Freshwater planarians typically swap sperm. By contrast, some marine flatworms battle over who will assume the male role. In

FIGURE 23.12 {Animated} Organ systems of a planarian, a free-living, freshwater flatworm about a centimeter long.

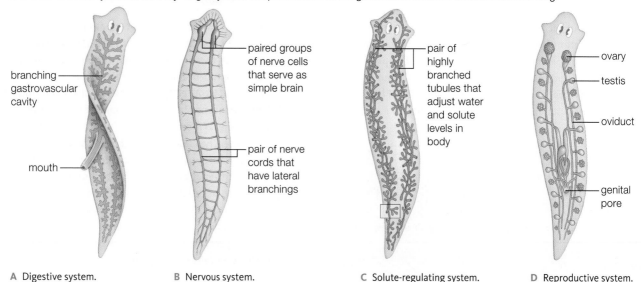

branching gastrovascular cavity

mouth

paired groups of nerve cells that serve as simple brain

pair of nerve cords that have lateral branchings

pair of highly branched tubules that adjust water and solute levels in body

ovary

testis

oviduct

genital pore

A Digestive system.　　B Nervous system.　　C Solute-regulating system.　　D Reproductive system.

① A person eats undercooked beef that contains a cyst (resting stage) of a tapeworm.

⑤ The larval tapeworm forms a cyst in cattle muscle tissue.

beef with larval tapeworm

proglottid   scolex

② In the human intestine, the cyst develops into an adult tapeworm that uses its barbed scolex to attach to the intestinal wall. The worm grows by adding new body units called proglottids. Over time, it can become many meters long.

③ Each proglottid makes eggs and sperm, which combine. Proglottids with fertilized eggs leave the body in feces.

proglottid with fertilized eggs

④ Cattle eat grass contaminated with proglottids or early larvae.

larva

FIGURE 23.13 {Animated} Life cycle of a beef tapeworm.

a behavior described as "penis fencing," each flatworm attempts to stab its penis into a partner's body and squirt in some sperm, while fending off its partner's attempts to do the same.

Planarians also reproduce asexually and some have an amazing capacity for regeneration. During asexual reproduction, the body splits in two near the middle, then each piece regrows the missing parts. This capacity for regrowth is also put to use when a planarian is injured, as by a predator. A planarian can regenerate itself even when more than 99 percent of its body is gone.

PARASITIC FLATWORMS

Flukes and tapeworms are parasitic flatworms whose life cycle often involves multiple hosts. Typically, larvae reproduce asexually in one or more intermediate hosts before developing into adults. Adults reproduce sexually in a final or definitive host. For example, aquatic snails are the intermediate host for blood fluke larvae (*Schistosoma*), but the adults can only reproduce sexually inside a mammal, such as a human. Humans become infected when they swim or stand in water where infected snails live. The infectious

larval form of the fluke crosses human skin and migrates into internal organs, where it develops into a sexually reproducing adult. The resulting disease, schistosomiasis, affects about 200 million people, with most cases in Southeast Asia and northern Africa.

Tapeworms are parasites that live and reproduce in the vertebrate gut. The head has a scolex, a structure with hooks or suckers that allow the worm to attach to the gut wall. Behind the head are body units called proglottids. Unlike planarians and flukes, tapeworms do not have a gastrovascular cavity. Instead, the worm absorbs nutrients from the food in the host's gut. **FIGURE 23.13** shows the life cycle of a beef tapeworm.

TAKE-HOME MESSAGE 23.5

Flatworms are bilateral animals with a simple nervous system, and a system for regulating water and solutes in internal body fluids. They develop from a three-layer embryo and do not have a coelom. Most groups have a gastrovascular cavity.

Free-living flatworms include many tropical marine species and the freshwater planarians.

Flukes and tapeworms are parasitic flatworms. Some are human pathogens.

flatworm Bilaterally symmetrical invertebrate with organs but no body cavity; for example, a planarian or tapeworm.

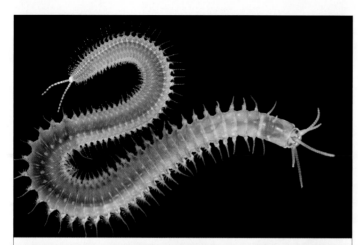

A The bristleworm uses its many appendages to burrow into sediment on marine mudflats. It is an active predator with hard jaws.

B The feather duster worm secretes and lives inside a hard tube. Feathery extensions on the head capture food from the water. Cilia move captured food to the mouth.

FIGURE 23.14 Polychaete worms.

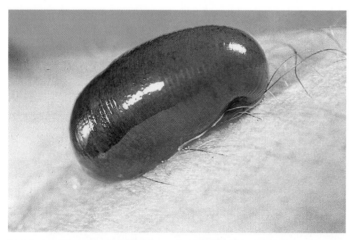

FIGURE 23.15 A leech feeding on human blood.

Annelids (phylum Annelida) are bilateral worms with a coelom and conspicuous segmentation, inside and out. They have a tubular gut and a closed circulatory system. In a **closed circulatory system**, blood flows through a continuous system of vessels. All exchanges between blood and the tissues take place across a vessel wall.

Two annelid subgroups, the polychaetes and oligochaetes, are named for the chitin-reinforced bristles called chaetae on their segments. Polychaetes have many bristles and oligochaetes have few. (*Poly*– means many; *oligo*– means few.) A third subgroup, the leeches, lacks bristles entirely.

MARINE POLYCHAETES

Polychaetes are mostly marine. Those commonly known as bristleworms or sandworms are active predators that use their chitin-hardened jaws to capture other soft-bodied invertebrates (**FIGURE 23.14A**). Each body segment has a pair of bristle-tipped paddlelike appendages that the worm uses to burrow in sediments and pursue prey.

Fan worms and feather duster worms live in a tube that they make from sand grains and mucus. The worm's head end protrudes from the tube and has elaborate tentacles to capture any food that drifts by (**FIGURE 23.14B**). Some other tube-dwelling polychaete worms live near deep-sea hydrothermal vents (Section 18.1). These worms can be up to 2.4 meters (7 feet) long. They do not have tentacles. In fact, as adults they do not even have a mouth. Rather than ingesting food, they rely entirely on the activity of chemoautotrophic bacteria that live inside them to provide nutrients. The bacteria take up dissolved materials from the water and use them to assemble organic compounds that the worm breaks down for energy.

LEECHES

A leech lacks bristles and has a sucker at either end of its body. Most leeches live in fresh water, but some are marine and others live in damp places on land. A typical leech is a scavenger or preys on small invertebrates. An infamous minority attach to a vertebrate, pierce its skin, and suck blood (**FIGURE 23.15**). Saliva of bloodsucking leeches contains a protein that prevents blood from clotting while the leech feeds. For this reason, doctors who reattach a severed finger or ear sometimes apply leeches to the reattached body part. Action of the leeches prevents clots from forming inside the newly reconnected blood vessels.

EARTHWORMS

Oligochaetes include marine and freshwater species, but the land-dwelling earthworms are most familiar. In the United States, most earthworms seen in backyards, bait

CREDITS: (14A) Darlyne A. Murawski, National Geographic Creative; (4B) © Jon Kenfield/ Bruce Coleman Ltd.; (15) J. A. L. Cooke/Oxford Scientific Films.

anus

clitellum head

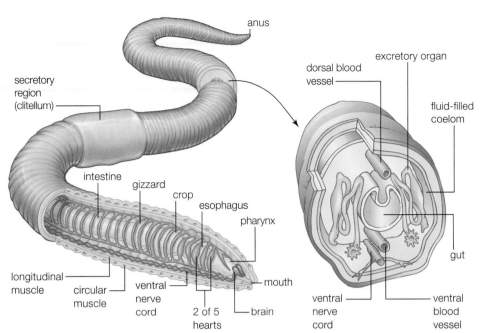

anus

secretory region (clitellum)

dorsal blood vessel

excretory organ

fluid-filled coelom

intestine gizzard

crop

esophagus

pharynx

longitudinal muscle

circular muscle

ventral nerve cord

2 of 5 hearts

brain

mouth

ventral nerve cord

gut

ventral blood vessel

FIGURE 23.16 {Animated} Body plan of an earthworm. Each segment contains a coelomic chamber full of organs. A gut, ventral nerve cord, and dorsal and ventral blood vessels run through all coelomic chambers.

FIGURE IT OUT: Why do people sometimes describe the body of a coelomate animal such as an earthworm as "a tube inside a tube"?

Answer: One tube, the gut, is inside another tube. The body wall. The fluid-filled coelom lies between the tubes.

shops, and compost heaps are introduced species native to Europe. However, some undisturbed habitats do retain native earthworms, including a species in Oregon that can reach more than a meter in length.

A cuticle of secreted proteins coats an earthworm's body (**FIGURE 23.16**). Visible grooves at the body surface correspond to internal partitions. Gas exchange occurs across the body surface, and the closed circulatory system helps distribute oxygen. Hearts in the anterior of the worm provide the pumping power to move the blood.

A fluid-filled coelom runs the length of the body and is divided into chambers, one per segment. A tubular gut extends through all coelomic chambers. Earthworms are scavengers that eat their way through the soil and digest organic debris. The worms improve soil by loosening its particles and by excreting tiny bits of organic matter that decomposers can easily break down. Excreted earthworm "castings" are sold as a natural fertilizer.

Most body segments have a pair of excretory organs that regulate the solute composition and volume of coelomic fluid. The organs collect coelomic fluid, adjust its composition, and expel waste through a pore in the body wall.

annelid Segmented worm with a coelom, complete digestive system, and closed circulatory system.
closed circulatory system Circulatory system in which blood flows through a continuous network of vessels; all materials are exchanged across the walls of those vessels.

A simple brain connects to a pair of nerve cords that run the length of the body. The brain coordinates locomotion and receives information from sensory cells, such as light-detecting cells in the worm's body wall.

The earthworm has two sets of muscles. Longitudinal muscles parallel the body's long axis, and circular muscles ring the body. The worm's coelomic fluid is a hydrostatic skeleton. Action of the muscles puts pressure on the fluid trapped inside body segments, causing them to change shape. When a segment's longitudinal muscles contract, the segment gets shorter and fatter. When circular muscles contract, a segment gets longer and thinner. Coordinated waves of contraction that run along the body propel the worm through soil.

Earthworms are hermaphrodites, but they cannot fertilize themselves. During mating, a secretory organ (the clitellum) produces mucus that glues two worms together while they swap sperm. Later, the same organ secretes a silky case that protects the fertilized eggs.

TAKE-HOME MESSAGE 23.6

Annelids are bilateral, coelomate, segmented worms. They include aquatic worms, earthworms, and leeches.

A closed circulatory system distributes materials through the annelid body.

CREDITS: (16) left, Courtesy of © Christine Evers; right, After Solomon, 8th edition, p. 624, figure 29-4.

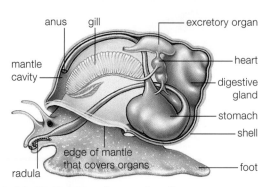

FIGURE 23.17 Body plan of an aquatic snail.

Labels: anus, gill, excretory organ, mantle cavity, heart, digestive gland, stomach, shell, edge of mantle that covers organs, foot, radula

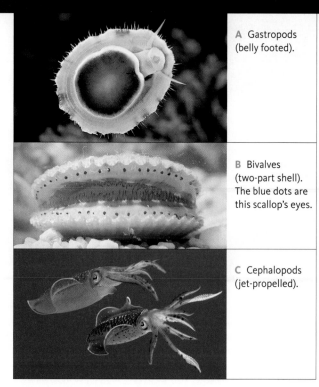

A Gastropods (belly footed).

B Bivalves (two-part shell). The blue dots are this scallop's eyes.

C Cephalopods (jet-propelled).

FIGURE 23.18 Representatives of the main mollusk groups.

Mollusks (phylum Mollusca) are bilaterally symmetrical invertebrates with a reduced coelom. Most dwell in the sea, but some live in fresh water or on land. All have a mantle, which is a skirtlike extension of the upper body wall that covers a mantle cavity (**FIGURE 23.17**). In shelled mollusks, the shell consists of a calcium-rich, bonelike material secreted by the mantle. Aquatic mollusks typically have one or more respiratory organs called gills inside their fluid-filled mantle cavity. All mollusks have a tubular gut. In most mollusks, the mouth contains a radula, a tonguelike organ hardened with chitin.

Aquatic mollusks typically have separate sexes and produce a ciliated swimming larva called a trochophore. Marine polychaetes have the same sort of larva, and this similarity is taken as evidence that annelids and mollusks shared a common trochophore-producing ancestor.

With more than 100,000 living species, mollusks are second only to arthropods in level of diversity. There are three main groups: gastropods, bivalves, and cephalopods (**FIGURE 23.18**).

GASTROPODS

Gastropods are the most diverse mollusk lineage. Their name means "belly foot," and most species glide about on the broad muscular foot that makes up most of the lower body mass (**FIGURE 23.18A**). A gastropod shell, when present, is one-piece and often coiled.

Gastropods have a distinct head that usually has eyes and sensory tentacles. In many aquatic species, a part of the mantle forms an inhalant siphon, a tube that the animal uses to draw water into its mantle cavity. The circulatory system of gastropods and bivalves is open. In an **open circulatory system**, vessels do not form a continuous loop. Instead, fluid (called hemolymph) leaves vessels and seeps around tissues before returning to the heart. Cells exchange substances with hemolymph while it is outside of vessels.

Gastropods include the only terrestrial mollusks. In snails and slugs that live on land, a lung replaces the gill.

Mucus secreted by glands on the foot protects the animal as it moves across dry, abrasive surfaces. Most mollusks have separate sexes, but land snails and slugs tend to be hermaphrodites. Unlike other mollusks, which produce a swimming larva, embryos of these groups develop directly into adults.

Nudibranchs, commonly called sea slugs, are marine gastropods with a greatly reduced shell. Nudibranch means "naked gills." Many nudibranchs defend themselves from predation using defensive weapons taken from their prey. Some eat sponges and store sponge toxins, secreting them when disturbed. Others eat cnidarians and store cnidocytes in outpouchings on their body (**FIGURE 23.19**).

BIVALVES

Bivalves include many mollusks that end up on dinner plates, including mussels, oysters, clams, and scallops (**FIGURE 23.18B**). All have a hinged, two-part shell. A bivalve has no obvious head, but many have simple

bivalve Mollusk with a hinged two-part shell.
cephalopod Predatory mollusk with a closed circulatory system; moves by jet propulsion.
gastropod Mollusk in which the lower body is a broad "foot."
mollusk Invertebrate with a reduced coelom and a mantle.
open circulatory system System in which hemolymph leaves vessels and seeps through tissues before returning to the heart.

CREDITS: (17) From Starr/Evers/Starr, Biology Today and Tomorrow with Physiology, 4E. © 2013 Cengage Learning; (18B) © Frank Park/ ANT Photo Library; (18C) Geoge Grall, National Geographic Creative.

The colorful projections on the backs of these nudibranchs function as gills. They also contain undischarged cnidocytes from cnidarians the nudibrachs ate. Discharge of these stored stinging cells in response to mechanical stimulation may help the nudibranchs fend off predators.

FIGURE 23.19 Spanish shawl nudibranchs.

eyes around the edge of the mantle. Most bivalves feed by drawing water into their mantle cavity and trapping food in mucus on the gills. Waving cilia on the gills direct particle-laden mucus to the mouth.

CEPHALOPODS

Cephalopods include squids (**FIGURE 23.18C**), nautiluses, octopuses (**FIGURE 23.20**), and cuttlefish. All are predators and most have beaklike, biting mouthparts in addition to a radula. Cephalopods move by jet propulsion. They draw water into their mantle cavity, then force it out through a funnel-shaped siphon. The foot has been modified into arms and/or tentacles that extend from the head. Cephalopod means "head-footed." Cephalopods include the fastest invertebrates (squids), the biggest (giant squid), and the smartest (octopuses). Of all invertebrates, octopuses have the largest brain relative to body size.

Five hundred million years ago, large cephalopods with a long, conelike shell were the top predators in the seas. Today, nautiluses have a coiled external shell, but all other cephalopods have a highly reduced shell or none. Shell loss may have been driven by competition with jawed fishes, which evolved 400 million years ago. Cephalopods with the smallest shell could be fastest and most agile. A speedier lifestyle required other changes as well. Of all mollusks, only cephalopods have a closed circulatory system. Competition with fishes also favored improved eyesight. Like vertebrates,

cephalopods have eyes with a lens that focuses light. As mollusks and vertebrates are not closely related, this type of eye is thought to have evolved independently in these groups. This is an example of convergent evolution.

FIGURE 23.20 Octopus.

TAKE-HOME MESSAGE 23.7

Mollusks are bilateral, soft-bodied, coelomate animals, the only ones with a mantle over the body mass.

Mollusks include snails and slugs that glide about on a huge foot, bivalves with a hinged two-part shell, and the jet-propelled cephalopods.

Roundworms, or nematodes (phylum Nematoda) are cylindrical worms with a pseudocoelom (**FIGURE 23.21**). They have a tubular digestive system, excretory organs, and a nervous system, but no circulatory or respiratory organs. Like arthropods such as insects, they have a cuticle that they periodically **molt** (shed and replace) as they grow. Most roundworms feed on organic debris in soil or water and are less than a millimeter long. Parasitic species tend to be larger: Some roundworms that infect whales can be meters long.

The soil roundworm *Caenorhabditis elegans* is frequently used in scientific studies. It is useful as a model for developmental processes because it has the same tissue types as more complex organisms, but it is transparent, has fewer

mouth   pseudocoelom   eggs in uterus   intestine   anus

FIGURE 23.21 {Animated} Body plan of a free-living roundworm (*Caenorhabditis elegans*).

than 1,000 body cells, and reproduces fast. In addition, its genome is about 1/30 the size of the human genome.

Several kinds of parasitic roundworms infect humans. Mosquito-transmitted roundworms cause a disfiguring tropical disease called lymphatic filariasis. The worms travel in the body's lymph vessels and destroy the vessels' valves so lymph pools in the lower limbs (**FIGURE 23.22A**). Elephantiasis, the common name for this disease, refers to fluid-filled, "elephant-like" legs. The swelling is permanent because lymph vessels remain damaged even after the worms have been eliminated.

The intestinal parasite *Ascaris lumbricoides* (**FIGURE 23.22B**) currently infects more than 1 billion people. Most of those affected live in developing tropical nations, but occasional infections occur in rural parts of the American Southeast. Typically an infected person has no symptoms, but a heavy infection can block the intestine.

Pinworms (*Enterobius vermicularis*) commonly infect children in the United States. The small worms, about the size of a staple, live in the rectum. At night, females crawl out and lay eggs on the skin around the anus. Their movement produces an itching sensation. Scratching to relieve the itch puts eggs onto fingertips and under fingernails. If swallowed, the eggs start a new infection.

Parasitic roundworms also infect our livestock, pets, and crop plants. A roundworm that lives in pigs can also infect humans who eat undercooked pork, causing trichinosis. Dogs are susceptible to heartworms transmitted by mosquitoes. Cats usually become infected by eating an infected rodent that serves as an intermediate host. Many crop plants are susceptible to nematode parasites. In some cases, the worms suck on plant roots and in others they actually enter the plant (**FIGURE 23.22C**). Either way, the infection stunts the plant's growth and lowers crop yields.

FIGURE 23.22 Parasitic roundworms.

A The grossly enlarged leg of the man on the left is a sign of lymphatic filariasis.

B Intestinal parasite, *Ascaris*, passed by a child.

C Plant-infecting roundworm entering a root.

molting Periodic shedding of an outer body layer or part.
roundworm Cylindrical worm with a pseudocoelom.

TAKE-HOME MESSAGE 23.8

Roundworms are bilateral worms with a cuticle that they molt as they grow. Organ systems almost fill their false coelom. Some are agricultural pests or human parasites.

CREDITS: (21) © Cengage Learning; (22A) Courtesy of © Emily Howard Staub and The Carter Center; (22B) CDC/Henry Bishop; (22C) William Wergin and Richard Sayre. Colorized by Stephen Ausmus.

Arthropods (phylum Arthropoda) are bilaterally symmetrical invertebrates with a tubular gut, an open circulatory system, and a reduced coelom. Modern representatives include spiders, lobsters, barnacles, centipedes, and insects. Trilobites, a now-extinct arthropod lineage, were the most abundant and diverse animal group in Cambrian seas (**FIGURE 23.23**). They disappeared about 425 million years ago, and we do not know why. Despite this loss, arthropods remain the most diverse animal phylum. In this section, we consider traits that contribute to their success.

A tough cuticle stiffened by chitin protects and supports the arthropod body. The cuticle is an **exoskeleton**, an external skeleton to which muscles attach. The cuticle does not inhibit movement because it is thin at the joints where two body parts connect. In fact, *arthropod* means jointed leg. The cuticle consists of secreted materials and does not grow, so, like roundworms, arthropods must periodically molt their cuticle and replace it with a larger one.

When some arthropods moved onto land, their exoskeleton supported their body against the force of gravity and helped them conserve water. Thus, arthropods thrive even in dry environments. The largest land invertebrate, the coconut crab, is an arthropod. It can weigh as much as 4 kilograms (about 9 pounds).

Aquatic arthropods have gills, but life on land required a different respiratory apparatus. The evolution of lungs or gas-delivering tracheal tubes allowed arthropods to breathe air as they moved onto land.

Arthropods have a segmented body plan. In most groups, some segments have fused to form distinct body regions. In crustaceans such as lobsters, segments of the head and thorax (midbody) form a unit called the cephalothorax (**FIGURE 23.24**). Modified segments and appendages give arthropods the ability to exploit resources in new ways. For example, in American lobsters, the appendages on one segment have evolved into large, muscular claws that can crush food. In flying insects, one or two body segments have wings that evolved from extensions of the body wall.

Well-developed sensory structures allow arthropods to monitor their environment. All arthropod lineages have one

FIGURE 23.23 Fossil trilobite. Over 20,000 species of this now-extinct group have been identified from fossils.

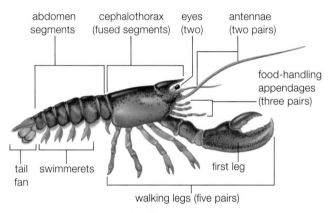

FIGURE 23.24 Body plan of an American lobster.

or more pairs of eyes. Some groups have **compound eyes**, which consist of many image-forming units that are highly sensitive to motion. Most arthropods also have paired **antennae** (singular, antenna), sensory structures that can detect chemicals in water or air.

Metamorphosis, a dramatic change in form between the larval and adult stages, occurs in most lineages. For instance, wingless caterpillars that chew leaves metamorphose into winged butterflies that fly, sip nectar, mate, and then deposit eggs. Evolution of metamorphosis allowed arthropods to, in essence, have two different bodies, each adapted to utilize a different set of resources and complete a different task. Having different bodies also keeps adults and juveniles from competing for the same resources.

antenna Of some arthropods, sensory structure on the head that detects touch and odors.
arthropod Invertebrate with jointed legs and a hard exoskeleton that is periodically molted.
compound eye Of some arthropods, a motion-sensitive eye made up of many image-forming units.
exoskeleton Hard external parts that muscles attach to and move.
metamorphosis Dramatic remodeling of body form during the transition from larva to adult.

TAKE-HOME MESSAGE 23.9

Arthropods are the most diverse animal phylum. A hardened, jointed exoskeleton, modified body segments, and specialized appendages, respiratory structures, and sensory structures contribute to their evolutionary success.

In many groups, larvae and adults have dramatically different body forms.

FIGURE 23.25 Horseshoe crabs.

A Spider (tarantula), a predator.

B Scorpion, a predator.

C Tick, a parasite.

D Dust mite, a scavenger (micrograph).

FIGURE 23.26 Arachnids. All have eight walking legs and no antennae.

CHELICERATES

A pair of feeding appendages (chelicerae) in front of the mouth distinguishes the **chelicerates**. Their head also has one or more pairs of eyes, but no antennae. The body is usually divided into a cephalothorax and an abdomen.

Horseshoe crabs are an ancient chelicerate lineage of marine bottom-feeders. A horseshoe-shaped shield covers their cephalothorax, and their last abdominal segment has evolved into a long spine that serves as a rudder (FIGURE 23.25). Each spring, eggs laid along Atlantic coasts by horseshoe crabs feed millions of migratory shorebirds.

Arachnids have four pairs of walking legs attached to their cephalothorax. They include spiders, scorpions, ticks, and mites, nearly all of which live on land (FIGURE 23.26). Spiders and scorpions are venomous predators. Spiders dispense venom through their chelicerae, which have been modified into fangs. Some catch prey in a web made of silk ejected by glands on their abdomen. Others such as tarantulas actively hunt and capture prey. Scorpions are active hunters too. They capture prey with pincers and dispense venom through a stinger on their abdomen.

Ticks are parasites that suck blood from vertebrates. Some can transmit human pathogens, such as the bacteria that cause Lyme disease (Section 19.5).

Mites include predators, scavengers, and parasites. Most are less than a millimeter long. Dust mites are scavengers that can cause discomfort to people who are allergic to their feces. Other mites that burrow into skin cause scabies in humans and mange in dogs.

MYRIAPODS

Myriapods have a head with one pair of antennae attached to an elongated body with many similar segments. Myriapod means "many footed," and centipedes and millipedes do have a lot of feet. Centipedes have a low-slung, flattened body with one pair of legs per segment, for a total of 30 to 50 legs (FIGURE 23.27A). These fast-moving predators use fangs to inject paralyzing venom. Most centipedes prey on insects, but some big tropical species eat small vertebrates. Millipedes are slower-moving animals that feed on decaying vegetation. Their cylindrical body has a cuticle hardened by calcium carbonate. There are two pairs of legs per segment, for a total of a few hundred (FIGURE 23.27B).

CRUSTACEANS

Most marine arthropods are **crustaceans**. Their great diversity and abundance are reflected in their nickname, "insects of the seas." Crustaceans have two pairs of antennae and a distinct cephalothorax and abdomen. In many, the exoskeleton is hardened by calcium.

CREDITS: (25) © Satin/Shutterstock; (26A) © Eric Isselée/Shutterstock.com; (26B) George Grall, National Geographic Creative; (26C) CDC/Dr. Christopher Paddock; (26D) Andrew Syred/Science Source.

A Centipede, a speedy predator.

B Millipede, a scavenger of decaying plant material.

FIGURE 23.27 **{Animated}** Myriapods.

A Antarctic krill.

B Copepod.

C Barnacle.

FIGURE 23.28 Examples of crustaceans. See also **FIGURE 23.24**.

You are probably familiar with some decapod crustaceans. This group of bottom-feeding scavengers includes the lobsters, crayfish, crabs, and shrimps. Decapod means ten-legged; members of this group typically have five pairs of walking legs on their cephalothorax.

Krill and copepods are small swimmers that eat plankton. They in turn serve as an important food source for larger animals. Krill, which have a shrimplike body a few centimeters long, swim in upper ocean waters (**FIGURE 23.28A**). They are so plentiful and nutritious that a 100-ton blue whale can subsist almost entirely on the krill it filters from seawater. Copepods live in oceans and lakes. Most are only millimeters long (**FIGURE 23.28B**).

Larval barnacles swim, but adults secrete a thick calcified shell and live fixed in place. They filter food from the water with feathery legs (**FIGURE 23.28C**). Adults cannot move about, so you would think that mating might be tricky. But barnacles tend to settle in groups, and most are hermaphrodites. An individual extends a penis, often several times its body length, out to neighbors.

A few crustaceans, including some crabs and the animals commonly called pill bugs (*right*), have adapted to life on land.

INSECTS

Insects are the most diverse arthropods. Until recently, they were thought to be close relatives of myriapods because of structural similarities. Then, gene comparisons made scientists rethink the connections. The currently favored hypothesis holds that insects descended from freshwater crustaceans. We consider insect diversity and ecology in detail in the next section.

arachnids Land-dwelling arthropods with no antennae and four pairs of walking legs; spiders, scorpions, mites, and ticks.
chelicerates Arthropod group with specialized feeding structures (chelicerae) and no antennae; arachnids and horseshoe crabs.
crustaceans Mostly marine arthropods with a calcium-hardened cuticle and two pairs of antennae; for example lobsters, crabs, krill, and barnacles.
myriapods Long-bodied terrestrial arthropods with one pair of antennae and many similar segments; centipedes and millipedes.

TAKE-HOME MESSAGE 23.10

Horseshoe crabs are an ancient lineage of marine bottom-feeders. They are most closely related to arachnids (spiders, scorpions, ticks, and mites), which live on land. Arachnids have four pairs of walking legs on their cephalothorax.

Centipedes and millipedes live on land. Members of this group have elongated bodies with many similar segments.

Crustaceans are mostly marine arthropods with two pairs of antennae and an exoskeleton hardened with calcium. They include bottom-feeding crabs and lobsters, tiny swimmers such as copepods and krill, filter-feeding barnacles, and the terrestrial pill bugs.

CREDITS: (27) © Eric Isselée/Shutterstock; (in text) © Chris Howey/Shutterstock.com; (28A) © David Tipling/Photographer's Choice/Getty Images; (28B) Herve Chaumeton/Agence Nature; (28C) Courtesy of Dave & Debra Wrobel.

With more than a million named species, **insects** are the most diverse class of animals. They are also breathtakingly abundant. By some estimates, ants alone make up about 10 percent of the total weight of all living land animals. Insects live on every continent, including Antarctica. Here we consider the traits that contribute to insect diversity and the ways that they interact with us and with other organisms.

CHARACTERISTICS OF INSECTS

Insects have a three-part body plan, with a distinct head, thorax, and abdomen (**FIGURE 23.29**). The head has one pair of antennae and two compound eyes. Three pairs of legs attach to the thorax. In winged insects, the thorax also has one or two pairs of wings. Like other arthropods, insects have a tubular gut and an open circulatory system. The insect respiratory system consists of tracheal tubes that carry air from openings on the insect's surface deep into the body where gas exchange occurs. The insect abdomen contains digestive organs, sex organs, and water-conserving excretory organs (Malpighian tubules) that serve the same function as vertebrate kidneys.

The earliest insects were wingless, ground-dwelling scavengers that did not undergo metamorphosis. A few modern insects such as bristletails and silverfish retain this type of body form and development. When they hatch from an egg, they look like a tiny adult, and they simply grow bigger with each molt.

Most modern insects have wings and undergo metamorphosis. Insects are the only winged invertebrates, and evolving an ability to fly gave them dispersal abilities unrivaled among other land invertebrates. Evolution of metamorphosis allowed insects to utilize multiple sets of resources. With incomplete metamorphosis, an egg hatches into a nymph that gradually takes on the adult form over the course of several molts. Cockroaches, grasshoppers, and

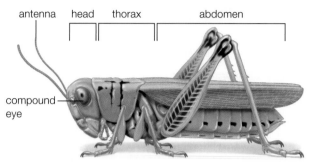

FIGURE 23.29 Body plan of an insect, a grasshopper.

dragonflies undergo incomplete metamorphosis. A dragonfly lives as an aquatic nymph for one to three years before emerging from the water and undergoing a final molt to the winged adult form.

With complete metamorphosis, a larva grows and molts without altering its form, then undergoes pupation. A pupa is a nonfeeding body in which larval tissues are remodeled into the adult form (**FIGURE 23.30**). Members of the four most diverse insect orders have wings and undergo complete metamorphosis. There are about 150,000 species of flies (Diptera), and at least as many beetles (Coleoptera). The order Hymenoptera includes 130,000 species of wasps, ants, and bees. Moths and butterflies are Lepidoptera, a group of about 120,000 species. As a comparison, consider that there are about 4,500 species of mammals.

INSECT ECOLOGY

Insects play essential roles in just about every land ecosystem. The vast majority of flowering plants are pollinated by members of the four diverse insect orders discussed above. Other insect orders contain few or no pollinators. Close interactions between pollinator and flowering plant lineages likely contributed to an increased rate of speciation that increased the diversity of both.

Insects serve as food for a variety of wildlife. Most songbirds nourish their nestlings on an insect diet. Those that migrate often travel long distances in order to nest and raise their young in areas where insect abundance is seasonally high. Aquatic larvae of insects such as dragonflies and mayflies serve as food for trout and other freshwater fish. Most amphibians and reptiles feed mainly on insects. Even humans eat insects. In many cultures, they are considered a tasty source of protein.

Insects dispose of wastes and remains. Flies and beetles quickly discover an animal corpse or a pile of feces (**FIGURE 23.31**). They lay their eggs in or on this organic material, which serves as food for their larvae. By their

FIGURE 23.30 Complete metamorphosis in a butterfly.

Larva
(leaf-eating,
wingless caterpillar)

Pupa
(remodeling
stage)

Adult
(winged
nectar feeder)

CREDITS: (29) From RUSSELL/WOLFE/HERTZ/STARR. Biology, 1E. Cengage Learning Inc. Reproduced by permission. www.cengage.com/permissions; (30) left and middle, © Jacob Hamblin/Shutterstock.com; right, © Laurie Barr/Shutterstock.com.

Dung beetles feed on feces. The beetles sniff out their stinky food, then form it into balls that they roll away and bury. The adult beetles may later eat the dung themselves, or the female may lay her eggs in it, in which case it feeds her larvae.

FIGURE 23.31 Dung beetles. Nature's clean-up crew.

actions, these insects keep wastes and remains from piling up, and help distribute nutrients through ecosystems.

HEALTH AND ECONOMIC EFFECTS

Plant-eating insects are our main competitors for plant products. Each year, they devour as much as one-third of all crops grown in the United States. Pine beetles and other insects bore into living trees and reduce lumber harvests. Other wood-boring beetles damage wooden buildings, as do some termites and ants.

Parasitic insects can pose a threat to human health and well-being. Mosquitoes cause more than 1 million deaths per year by transmitting malaria, West Nile fever, and other deadly diseases. Fleas transmit bubonic plague, and body lice spread typhus. Bedbugs (*left*) do not cause disease, but infestations are stressful and eliminating them can be costly. On the other hand, some insects help us keep pest species in check. For example, larvae of ladybird

beetles devour aphids that would otherwise suck juices from valuable crops.

Economically valuable products produced by insects include honey, silk, and shellac. Honey is floral nectar concentrated and stored by honeybees. Larval silk moths produce silk as they spin a cocoon in which to pupate. Asian bark-feeding bugs excrete shellac. We use it to give a shiny coating to wood products and to candies such as jelly beans.

insects Most diverse arthropod group; members have six legs, two antennae, and, in some groups, wings.

TAKE-HOME MESSAGE 23.11

Insects include the only winged invertebrates.

Most insects undergo metamorphosis, which allows them to exploit resources in two different ways over the course of their life.

Insects pollinate plants, serve as food for wildlife and humans, dispose of wastes and remains, and produce products such as silk. Some harm us by eating crops and spreading diseases.

In Section 23.1 we introduced the two major lineages of animals, protostomes and deuterostomes. Here we begin our survey of deuterostome lineages. Echinoderms are the most diverse invertebrate deuterostomes. We discuss other invertebrate deuterostomes and the vertebrates (also deuterostomes) in the next chapter.

Echinoderms (phylum Echinodermata) have interlocking spines and plates of calcium carbonate in their body wall. Their phylum name means "spiny-skinned." All begin life as bilateral free-swimming larvae, then develop into radially symmetrical adults with five parts (or multiples of five) arrayed around a central axis. The fact that the larva is bilateral suggests that echinoderms had a bilateral ancestor.

Sea stars (also called starfish) are the most familiar echinoderms (**FIGURE 23.32**). They do not have a brain, but do have a decentralized nervous system. Eyespots at the tips of the arms detect light and movement. A typical sea star is an active predator that moves about on tiny, fluid-filled tube feet. Tube feet are part of a **water–vascular system** unique to echinoderms. Fluid-filled canals extend into each arm, and side canals deliver coelomic fluid into muscular ampullae that function like the bulb on a medicine dropper. When an ampulla contracts, it forces fluid into a tube foot. The increase in internal fluid pressure extends the foot.

A sea star eats bivalve mollusks by forcing its stomach out through its mouth and into the bivalve's shell. Acid and enzymes secreted by the stomach kill the mollusk and begin to digest it. The partially digested food is then taken into the stomach, where digestion is completed with the aid of digestive glands that extend into the arms. Arms also hold reproductive organs. Each sea star is either male or female.

Gas exchange occurs by diffusion across the tube feet and tiny skin projections at the body surface. There are no specialized excretory organs.

In addition to sea stars, echinoderms include brittle stars, sea urchins, and sea cucumbers. Brittle stars are the most diverse and abundant echinoderms (**FIGURE 23.33A**). These scavengers generally live in deep water. They have a central disk and flexible arms that move in a snakelike way. Sea urchins have a stiff, rounded cover of calcium carbonate plates through which movable spines protrude (**FIGURE 23.33B**). Most graze on algae. Sea cucumbers are, as their name implies, cucumber-shaped, and have microscopic plates embedded in a soft body (**FIGURE 23.33C**). Most feed like earthworms, by burrowing through sediments and ingesting them. If attacked, a sea cucumber expels organs through its anus to distract the predator. If this defense succeeds and the sea cucumber escapes, its missing parts grow back. Sea stars also have great powers of regeneration; an animal can grow from one arm and a bit of central disk.

FIGURE 23.32 Sea star body plan.

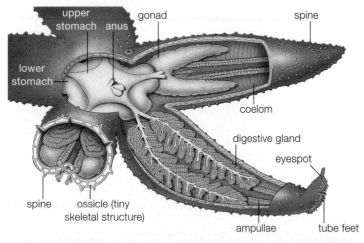

upper stomach
gonad
anus
spine
lower stomach
coelom
digestive gland
eyespot
spine
ossicle (tiny skeletal structure)
ampullae
tube feet

A Brittle star.

B Sea urchin.

C Sea cucumber.

FIGURE 23.33 Echinoderm diversity.

echinoderms Invertebrates with a water–vascular system and hardened plates and spines embedded in the skin or body.
water–vascular system Of echinoderms, a system of fluid-filled tubes and tube feet that function in locomotion.

TAKE-HOME MESSAGE 23.12

Echinoderms are spiny-skinned invertebrates that are radial as adults. They have a decentralized nervous system and a unique water–vascular system that functions in locomotion.

CREDITS: (32) © Cengage Learning; (33A) Stubblefield Photography/Shutterstock.com; (33B) © Derek Holzapfel/photos.com; (33C) Andrew David, NOAA/NMFS/SEFSC Panama City, Lance Horn, UNCW/ NURC-Phantom II ROV operator.

Conservation

FIGURE 23.34 A cone snail eating a fish that it has injected with venom.

THERE ARE ABOUT A THOUSAND SPECIES OF CONE SNAILS. Each species of these predatory snails produces a venom that contains around a hundred different peptides. Cone snail peptides typically act on a prey animal's nervous system. The snail catches prey such as a small fish by harpooning it with a modified radula, injecting it with venom, then engulfing it (**FIGURE 23.34**). The venom sedates the fish and dulls its pain, so it does not struggle and possibly damage the snail's harpoon.

The human nervous system uses the same chemical signals a fish nervous system does, so compounds used by a snail to sedate or anesthetize fish can be useful as human medicines. For example, an injectable painkiller sold under the brand name Prialt is a synthetic version of a cone snail peptide. It is far more powerful than morphine, yet not addictive. Another synthetic snail peptide is being tested as a treatment for epilepsy. Researchers have only begun to explore the potential of cone snail venom. Given the large number of cone snails and complexity of their venoms, there is plenty to do.

Nonvenomous invertebrates can also be a source of new medicines. Many invertebrates produce chemicals that have antibacterial, antiprotozoal, or antifungal activity. To develop new drugs with these properties, researchers extract compounds from invertebrates, then test the ability of the compounds to kill pathogens cultured in the laboratory. Researchers also test the effect of each compound on cultured human cells. An ideal candidate drug is one that kills pathogens, but does no harm to human cells. For example, some compounds made by marine sponges kill disease-causing protists (such as trypanosomes and apicomplexans), but have little effect on human cells growing in culture.

A new appreciation of the potential medicinal value of compounds produced by marine invertebrates has many researchers worried about the declining state of our oceans. Pollution, destructive harvesting methods, overharvesting, and climate change are likely to drive many potentially valuable species to extinction before we have time to discover the beneficial compounds they make.

Summary

SECTION 23.1 **Animals** are multicelled heterotrophs that digest food inside their body. Most have an embryo with three layers: **ectoderm**, **endoderm**, and **mesoderm**. Most animals are **invertebrates**. Early invertebrates had no body symmetry. Cnidarians have **radial symmetry**, but most animals have **bilateral symmetry** and underwent **cephalization**. Bilateral animals typically have a body cavity, either a **pseudocoelom** or a **coelom**. Many have **segmentation**, with repeating body units. There are two lineages of bilateral animals, **protostomes** and **deuterostomes**. **TABLE 23.1** summarizes the traits of major animal lineages discussed in this chapter.

SECTION 23.2 The **colonial theory of animal origins** states that animals evolved from a colonial protist. Early animals may have resembled modern **placozoans**, the simplest living animals. Sponges are the animals for which we have the earliest fossil evidence. They evolved more than 600 million years ago. A great adaptive radiation during the Cambrian gave rise to most modern animal lineages.

SECTION 23.3 **Sponges** have a porous body with no tissues or organs. These **suspension feeders** filter food from water. Each is a **hermaphrodite**, producing both eggs and sperm. The ciliated **larva** is the only motile stage.

SECTION 23.4 **Cnidarians** such as jellies, corals, and sea anemones are carnivores with two tissue layers. Only cnidarians have **cnidocytes**, which they use to capture prey. A **gastrovascular cavity** functions in both respiration and digestion. Cnidarians have a **hydrostatic skeleton**. A **nerve net** gives commands to contractile cells that redistribute fluid and change the body's shape.

SECTION 23.5 **Flatworms**, the simplest animals with organ systems, include marine species and the freshwater planarians, as well as parasitic tapeworms and flukes. Some tapeworms and flukes infect humans.

SECTION 23.6 **Annelids** are segmented worms. Their **closed circulatory system** and digestive, solute-regulating, and nervous systems extend through coelomic chambers. Annelids move when muscles exert force on coelomic fluid, altering the shape of segments in a coordinated manner. Oligochaetes include aquatic species and the familiar earthworms. Polychaetes are predatory marine worms. Leeches are scavengers, predators, or bloodsucking parasites.

SECTION 23.7 **Mollusks** have a reduced coelom and a sheetlike mantle that drapes back over itself. They include **gastropods** (such as snails), **bivalves** (such as scallops), and **cephalopods** (such as squids and octopuses). Except in the cephalopods, which are adapted to a speedy, predatory lifestyle, blood flows through an **open circulatory system**.

SECTION 23.8 **Roundworms** (nematodes) have an unsegmented, cylindrical body covered by a cuticle that is **molted** as the animal grows. Most are decomposers in soil, but some are parasites of plants or animals, including humans. One free-living soil roundworm is commonly used in studies of development.

SECTIONS 23.9–23.11 There are more than 1 million **arthropod** species. Their diversity is attributed to structural traits such as a hardened **exoskeleton**, jointed appendages, specialized segments, and sensory structures such as **antennae** and **compound eyes**. Dramatic body changes during **metamorphosis** allow some arthropods to exploit multiple resources during their lifetime.

Chelicerates include marine horseshoe crabs and the mostly terrestrial **arachnids** (spiders, scorpions, ticks, and mites). **Crustaceans** are the most abundant arthropods in the seas. They include bottom-feeding crabs, free-swimming krill and copepods, and the sessile shelled barnacles. Centipedes and millipedes are **myriapods**.

Insects include the only winged invertebrates. Some serve as decomposers and pollinators; others harm crops and transmit diseases.

SECTION 23.12 **Echinoderms** such as sea stars, brittle stars, sea urchins, and sea cucumbers belong to the deuterostome lineage. Spines and other hard parts embedded in their skin support the body. There is no central nervous system. A **water–vascular system** with tube feet functions in locomotion. Adults are radial, but larvae are bilateral, implying a bilateral ancestry.

SECTION 23.13 Invertebrate species are a largely untapped source of medicines. Compounds that predatory snails use to subdue their fish prey can sometimes be used as drugs because all vertebrates have similar nervous systems.

TABLE 23.1

Comparative Summary of Animal Body Plans

Group	Adult Symmetry	Embryonic Layers	Digestive Cavity	Circulatory System
Sponges	None	None	None	None
Cnidarians	Radial	2	Gastrovascular cavity	None
Protostomes				
Flatworms	Bilateral	3	Gastrovascular cavity	None
Annelids	Bilateral	3	Tubular gut	Closed
Mollusks	Bilateral	3	Tubular gut	Most open; cephalopods closed
Roundworms	Bilateral	3	Tubular gut	None
Arthropods	Bilateral	3	Tubular gut	Open
Deuterostomes				
Echinoderms	Radial	3	Tubular gut	Open
Vertebrates	Bilateral	3	Tubular gut	Closed

CREDIT: (Table 23.1) © Cengage Learning.

Data Analysis Activities

Use of Horseshoe Crab Blood   Horseshoe crab blood clots immediately upon exposure to bacterial endotoxins (Section 19.6), so it can be used to test injectable drugs for the presence of dangerous bacteria. To keep horseshoe crab populations stable, blood is extracted from captured animals, which are then returned to the wild. Concerns about the survival of animals after bleeding led researchers to do an experiment. They compared survival of animals captured and maintained in a tank with that of animals captured, bled, and kept in a similar tank. **FIGURE 23.35** shows the results.

1. In which trial did the most control crabs die? In which did the most bled crabs die?
2. Looking at the overall results, how did the mortality of the two groups differ?
3. Based on these results, would you conclude that bleeding harms horseshoe crabs more than capture alone does?

	Control Animals		Bled Animals	
Trial	Number of crabs	Number that died	Number of crabs	Number that died
1	10	0	10	0
2	10	0	10	3
3	30	0	30	0
4	30	0	30	0
5	30	1	30	6
6	30	0	30	0
7	30	0	30	2
8	30	0	30	5
Total	200	1	200	16

FIGURE 23.35 Mortality of young male horseshoe crabs kept in tanks during the two weeks after their capture. Blood was taken from half the animals on the day of their capture. Control animals were handled, but not bled. This procedure was repeated eight times with different sets of horseshoe crabs.

Self-Quiz   Answers in Appendix VII

1. True or false? Animal cells have chitin walls.

2. A coelom is a _____ .
   a. type of bristle   c. sensory organ
   b. resting stage   d. lined body cavity

3. Cnidarians alone have _____ .
   a. cnidocytes   c. a hydrostatic skeleton
   b. a mantle   d. a radula

4. Flukes are most closely related to _____ .
   a. tapeworms   c. arthropods
   b. roundworms   d. echinoderms

5. Which group has six legs and two antennae?
   a. crustaceans   c. spiders
   b. insects   d. horseshoe crabs

6. The _____ are mollusks with a hinged shell.
   a. bivalves   c. gastropods
   b. barnacles   d. cephalopods

7. _____ have the smallest genome of all living animals.
   a. Sponges   c. Jellies
   b. Placozoans   d. Flatworms

8. Which of these groups includes the most species?
   a. protostomes   c. arthropods
   b. roundworms   d. mollusks

9. The _____ include the only winged invertebrates.
   a. cnidarians   c. arthropods
   b. echinoderms   d. mollusks

10. The _____ move about on tube feet.
    a. cnidarians   c. annelids
    b. echinoderms   d. flatworms

11. Annelids and cephalopods have a(n) _____ circulatory system.
    a. open   b. closed

12. A pupa forms during the life cycle of some _____ .
    a. crustaceans   c. annelids
    b. echinoderms   d. insects

13. Match the organisms with their descriptions.
    ___ echinoderms   a. complete gut, pseudocoelom
    ___ mollusks   b. tube feet, spiny skin
    ___ sponges   c. simplest organ systems
    ___ cnidarians   d. body with lots of pores
    ___ flatworms   e. jointed exoskeleton
    ___ roundworms   f. mantle over body mass
    ___ annelids   g. segmented worms
    ___ arthropods   h. tentacles with stinging cells

Critical Thinking

1. Most hermaphrodites cannot fertilize their own eggs, but tapeworms can. Explain the advantages and disadvantages of such self-fertilization.

2. Acidity makes it harder for invertebrates to build structures containing calcium carbonate. List the types of animals that an increase in ocean acidity could harm.

3. Why are pesticides designed to kill insects more likely to harm lobsters and crabs than fish?

CENGAGE brain .com   To access course materials, please visit www.cengagebrain.com.

CREDIT: (35) left, Data: Walls, E., Berkson, J., *Fish. Bull.* 101:457–459 (2003); right, Jane Burton/ Bruce Coleman, Ltd.

CHAPTER 23   **397**
ANIMALS I:
MAJOR INVERTEBRATE GROUPS

Excavation of fossil dinosaur bones
in northern Wyoming. Much of our
information about vertebrate evolution
comes from studies of such fossil skeletons.

24

ANIMALS II: THE CHORDATES

Links to Earlier Concepts

As we continue our survey of animals, you may wish to review the discussion of vertebrates and the animal evolutionary tree (Sections 23.1, 23.2). The geologic time scale (16.6) will help put events discussed here in perspective. You will see more examples of fossils (16.3) and of homologous structures (16.7). You will draw on your understanding of speciation, adaptive radiation, extinction (17.10–17.13), and cladistics (17.12).

KEY CONCEPTS

CHARACTERISTICS OF CHORDATES
Four traits characterize chordate embryos: a supporting rod (notochord), a dorsal nerve cord, a pharynx with gill slits, and a tail that extends past the anus.

THE FISHES
Fishes were the first vertebrates. Most modern fishes have jaws. They include cartilaginous fishes such as sharks, and two lineages of bony fishes.

FROM WATER TO LAND
Tetrapods, animals that walk on four legs, evolved from a lineage of bony fishes. Amphibians, the first tetrapods, live on land, but their eggs must develop in water.

THE AMNIOTES
Amniotes are adapted to life on land. Reptiles (including birds) and mammals are the two modern amniote lineages. Dinosaurs are an extinct lineage of reptiles.

EARLY PRIMATES TO HUMANS
Primates have grasping hands with nails rather than claws. Our closest extinct relatives are primates that walked upright. Fossils and genetics provide information about our history.

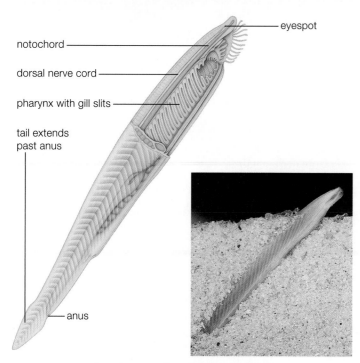

FIGURE 24.1 {Animated} Body plan and photo of a lancelet. Both adults and larvae have all four defining chordate traits.

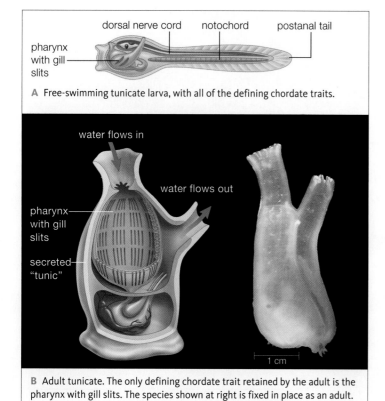

A Free-swimming tunicate larva, with all of the defining chordate traits.

B Adult tunicate. The only defining chordate trait retained by the adult is the pharynx with gill slits. The species shown at right is fixed in place as an adult.

FIGURE 24.2 {Animated} Tunicates.

CHORDATE CHARACTERISTICS

The previous chapter ended with a discussion of echinoderms, one of the deuterostome lineages. The other major deuterostome lineage is the **chordates** (phylum Chordata). These bilaterally symmetrical, coelomate animals typically have a complete digestive system and a closed circulatory system. Four traits of chordate embryos define the lineage:

1. A **notochord**, a rod of stiff but flexible connective tissue, extends the length of the body and supports it.
2. A dorsal, hollow nerve cord parallels the notochord.
3. Narrow gill slits open across the wall of the pharynx (the throat region).
4. A muscular tail extends beyond the anus.

Depending on the subgroup, some, none, or all of these embryonic traits persist in the adult.

Most chordate species are **vertebrates** (subphylum Vertebrata), animals that have a backbone. However, the chordates also include two lineages of marine invertebrates.

INVERTEBRATE CHORDATES

Lancelets (Cephalochordata) are invertebrates with an elongated body that retains all characteristic chordate features into adulthood (**FIGURE 24.1**). A lancelet is about 5 centimeters (2 inches) long. Its dorsal nerve cord connects to a simple brain. An eyespot at the end of the nerve cord detects light, but there are no paired sensory organs like those of fishes. Lancelets are suspension feeders. They usually bury themselves so only their head sticks out, then draw water in through their mouth. Food particles are filtered out as the water exits through the gill slits. Cilia on the gills move food particles to the gut. Lancelets are either male or female.

Tunicates (Urochordata) larvae have all the characteristic chordate features (**FIGURE 24.2A**). They swim about briefly, then undergo metamorphosis. The tail breaks down and other parts become rearranged. Adults retain only the pharynx with gill slits (**FIGURE 24.2B**). They secrete a carbohydrate-rich covering, or "tunic," that gives the group its common name. An adult feeds by drawing water in through an oral opening, capturing food on its gill slits, then expelling water through a second opening. Most tunicates are sessile, but those called salps drift or swim in the sea. Tunicates are hermaphrodites; an individual releases both eggs and sperm.

OVERVIEW OF CHORDATE EVOLUTION

Until recently, lancelets were considered the closest invertebrate relatives of vertebrates. An adult lancelet looks more like a fish than an adult tunicate does, but such apparent similarities can be deceiving. Studies of developmental processes and gene sequences have revealed that tunicates are closer to the vertebrates, as illustrated in **FIGURE 24.3**.

CREDITS: (1 left, 2A) From Starr/Taggart/Evers/Starr, Biology, 13E. © 2013 Cengage Learning; right, Runk & Schoenberger/Grant Heilman, Inc.; (2B left) From RUSSELL/WOLFE/HERTZ/STARR. Biology, 1E. © Cengage Learning Inc. Reproduced by permission. www.cengage.com/permissions; (2B right) © California Academy of Sciences.

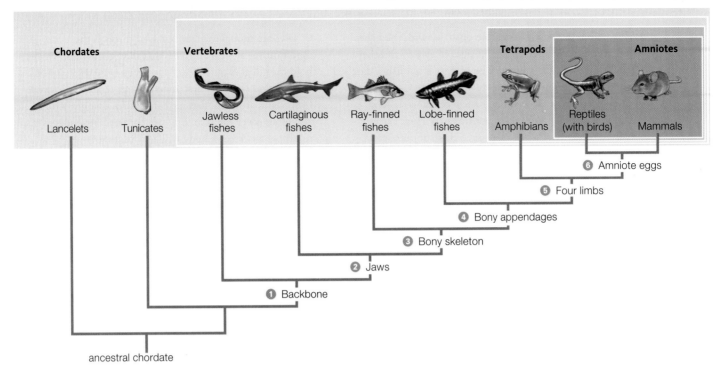

FIGURE 24.3 {Animated} Evolutionary tree diagram for the vertebrates with key traits for each clade. Boxes denote some of the clades that nest within the chordate clade and will be discussed again within the chapter.

Most chordates are vertebrates ❶. Their backbone and other skeletal elements are components of the vertebrate **endoskeleton**, or internal skeleton. The vertebrate endoskeleton consists of living cells and grows with an animal, so it does not have to be molted.

The first vertebrates were jawless fishes that sucked up or scraped up food. Later, hinged skeletal elements called jaws evolved ❷. Fishes with jaws were able to exploit new strategies for feeding. The vast majority of fishes and other modern vertebrates have jaws.

Jawless fishes had a skeleton of cartilage, and one group of jawed fishes (cartilaginous fishes) retains this trait. In other jawed animals, bone replaces cartilage as the major component of the skeleton ❸. Sturdy fins supported by bones evolved in one group of bony fishes (lobe-finned fishes) ❹. A branch from this lineage gave rise to the **tetrapods**—vertebrates that have four limbs or are descendants of a four-limbed ancestor ❺.

Early tetrapods spent some time on land, but laid their eggs in water. Eggs that enclosed an embryo within a series of waterproof membranes evolved later, in **amniotes** ❻. These specialized eggs and other adaptations to a dry habitat allowed amniotes to disperse widely on land. Modern amniotes include the animals traditionally known as reptiles (lizards, snakes, and turtles), as well as birds and mammals.

amniote Vertebrate whose egg has waterproof membranes that allow it to develop away from water; a reptile, bird, or mammal.
chordate Animal with an embryo that has a notochord, dorsal nerve cord, pharyngeal gill slits, and a tail that extends beyond the anus. For example, a lancelet or a vertebrate.
endoskeleton Internal skeleton made up of hardened components such as bones.
lancelet Invertebrate chordate that has a fishlike shape and retains the defining chordate traits into adulthood.
notochord Stiff rod of connective tissue that runs the length of the body in chordate larvae or embryos.
tetrapod Vertebrate with four legs, or a descendant thereof.
tunicate Invertebrate chordate that loses most of its defining chordate traits during the transition to adulthood.
vertebrate Animal with a backbone.

TAKE-HOME MESSAGE 24.1

All chordate embryos have a notochord, a dorsal hollow nerve cord, a pharynx with gill slits in its wall, and a tail that extends past the anus.

Most chordates are vertebrates, which have an internal skeleton that includes a backbone. The first vertebrates were jawless fishes.

A group of jawed fishes with a bony skeleton gave rise to four-legged animals (tetrapods) that colonized the land.

Amniotes, a tetrapod subgroup, have specialized eggs that allow them to develop away from water.

CREDIT: (3) © Cengage Learning.

We begin our survey of vertebrate diversity with the fishes. These were the first vertebrate lineages to evolve, and they remain the most fully aquatic. The earliest fossil fishes date to about 530 million years ago, during the late Cambrian period. They had a tapered body a few centimeters long, and a head with a pair of eyes, but no jaws. Their skeleton consisted of cartilage, the same tissue that supports your ears and nose.

| gill slits | gill support | jaw, derived from gill supports |
| A Jawless fish | | B Jawed fish |

FIGURE 24.4 {Animated} Proposed mechanism for the evolution of jaws. Modification of gill supports of a jawless fish **A** produced a hinged, two-part jaw in early jawed fishes **B**.

A Hagfish. It feeds on worms and scavenges on the seafloor.

B Parasitic lamprey. It attaches to another fish with its oral disk and scrapes off bits of flesh.

FIGURE 24.5 Modern jawless fishes.

Jaws are thought to have evolved through the modification of skeletal elements called gill arches, which hold the gill slits of jawless fishes open (**FIGURE 24.4**). Jawed fishes were the first animals with scales and paired fins. Scales are hard, flattened structures that grow from and often cover the skin. Fins are flattened appendages used to propel and steer a body while swimming.

JAWLESS FISHES

Hagfishes and lampreys are modern **jawless fishes**. Relationships among lampreys, hagfishes, and jawed fishes have long inspired debate. The most recent research indicates that hagfishes and lampreys are monophyletic; both belong to a lineage that branched off before jawed fishes evolved. Lampreys and hagfishes have a cartilage skeleton and a cylindrical body about a meter long. They do not have fins and, like a lancelet, they move with a wiggling motion. Although they have no jaws, they do have hard mouthparts made of keratin, the main protein in hair.

Hagfishes (**FIGURE 24.5A**) feed on soft-bodied invertebrates and dead or dying fish. When threatened, they secrete a slimy mucus. Although the slime deters most predators, humans still harvest hagfish. Most products sold as "eelskin" are really hagfish skin.

Many lampreys parasitize other fish. A parasitic lamprey (**FIGURE 24.5B**) attaches to a host fish, then uses its hard mouthparts to scrape off bits of flesh. In the early 1900s, parasitic Atlantic lampreys that entered the Great Lakes via newly built canals decimated populations of native fish such as trout. Fishery managers now lower lamprey numbers with dams, nets, and poisons.

CARTILAGINOUS FISHES

The mostly marine **cartilaginous fishes** (Chondrichthyes) are jawed fishes with a skeleton of cartilage. Multiple gill slits are uncovered and visible at the body surface, as they are in jawless fishes. On the lower surface of the body, a single multipurpose opening called the **cloaca** serves as the exit for digestive and urinary waste. The cloaca also functions in reproduction.

Most cartilaginous fishes are sharks, rays, or skates. Streamlined predatory sharks chase down and tear apart prey (**FIGURE 24.6A**). Other sharks are bottom-feeders that suck up invertebrates and act as scavengers. Still others strain plankton from the seawater. Rays have a flattened body with large pectoral fins and a long, thin tail. Manta rays glide through seawater and filter out plankton (**FIGURE 24.6B**). Stingrays are bottom-feeders. A sharp spearlike point at the tip of their tail defends them against predators. In some stingrays, the tail can deliver a dose of venom. Skates are bottom-feeders that resemble rays but have a shorter, thicker tail.

BONY FISHES

There are two modern lineages of bony fishes: ray-finned fishes and lobe-finned fishes. In both groups, bone replaces cartilage in some or most of the skeleton, and gill slits are typically hidden beneath a gill cover.

Ray-finned fishes have thin, weblike fins with flexible supports derived from skin. **FIGURE 24.7A** shows the internal anatomy of a typical ray-finned fish. Like all fishes, it has a closed circulatory system with one heart, and a urinary system with paired kidneys that filter blood, adjust its composition, and eliminate wastes. In most ray-finned fishes, urinary waste, digestive waste, and gametes exit the body through three separate openings. Ray-finned fishes typically have a gas-filled swim bladder. By adjusting the volume of gas in its swim bladder, a fish can change its buoyancy so that it remains suspended at the desired depth. With more than 21,000 freshwater and marine species, ray-finned fishes are the most diverse vertebrate group.

Lobe-finned fishes include coelacanths (Section 17.11) and lungfishes (**FIGURE 24.7B**). Their pelvic and pectoral fins are fleshy, with supporting bones inside them. Lungfishes have gills and one or two lungs. Their lungs are air-filled sacs with an associated network of tiny blood vessels. A lungfish gulps air into its lungs, then oxygen diffuses from its lungs into the blood. As the next section explains, bony fins and simple lungs proved advantageous when descendants of lobe-finned fishes ventured onto land.

---

cartilaginous fish Jawed fish with a skeleton of cartilage; a shark, ray, or skate.
cloaca Body opening that serves as the exit for digestive waste and urine; also functions in reproduction.
jawless fish Fish with a skeleton of cartilage, no fins or jaws; a lamprey or hagfish.
lobe-finned fish Jawed fish with fleshy fins that contain bones; a coelacanth or lungfish.
ray-finned fish Jawed fish with fins supported by thin rays derived from skin; member of most diverse lineage of fishes.

TAKE-HOME MESSAGE 24.2

Fishes are the most diverse vertebrates. Like other vertebrates, they have a closed circulatory system with one heart, and a urinary system with paired kidneys.

Lampreys and hagfishes are jawless fishes. Most fishes have jaws that evolved from gill supports.

Cartilaginous fishes such as sharks have a skeleton of cartilage. Bony fishes include the highly diverse ray-finned fishes and the lobe-finned fishes, which are the closest relatives of tetrapods.

A Galápagos shark, a fast-swimming predator.

B Manta ray, a slow-moving plankton feeder.

FIGURE 24.6 {Animated} Two cartilaginous fishes. Note the gill slits visible at the body surface of both fishes.

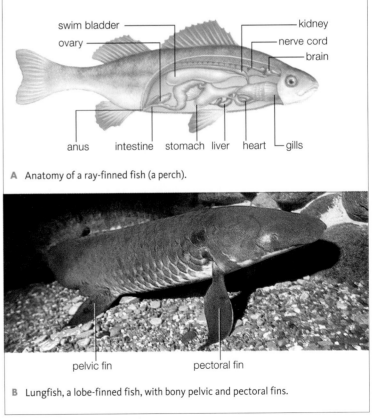

swim bladder — kidney
ovary — nerve cord
— brain
anus   intestine   stomach   liver   heart   gills

A Anatomy of a ray-finned fish (a perch).

pelvic fin   pectoral fin

B Lungfish, a lobe-finned fish, with bony pelvic and pectoral fins.

FIGURE 24.7 {Animated} Bony fishes. Both the ray-finned and lobe-finned lineages have covered gills and a skeleton that consists mainly of bone.

CREDITS: (6A) Jonathan Bird/Oceanic Research Group, Inc.; (6B) © Gido Braase/Deep Blue Productions; (7A) © Cengage Learning; (7B) © Wernher Krutein/photovault.com.

THE FIRST TETRAPODS

Amphibians are scaleless, land-dwelling vertebrates that typically breed in water. All are carnivores. Amphibians were the first tetrapods. Recently discovered fossil footprints from Poland show that amphibians were walking on land by about 395 million years ago, in the Devonian. The animal that left the footprints was about 2.5 meters (8 feet) long.

A variety of fossils demonstrate how fishes adapted to swimming evolved into four-legged walkers (**FIGURE 24.8**). Bones of a lobe-finned fish's pectoral fins and pelvic fins are homologous with those of an amphibian's front and hind limbs. During the transition to land, these bones became larger and better able to bear weight. Ribs enlarged and a distinct neck emerged, allowing the head to move independently of the rest of the body.

The transition to land was not simply a matter of skeletal changes. Lungs, which had previously served an accessory purpose, became larger and more complex. Division of the previously two-chambered heart into three chambers allowed blood to flow in two circuits, one to the body and one to those increasingly important lungs. Changes to the inner ear improved detection of airborne sounds. Eyes became protected from drying out by eyelids.

What drove the move onto land? An ability to spend time out of water would have been favored in seasonally dry places. In addition, it would have allowed individuals to escape aquatic predators and to access a new source of food—insects—which also evolved during the Devonian.

FIGURE 24.9 Salamander, with equal-sized forelimbs and hindlimbs.

MODERN AMPHIBIANS

Salamanders and newts have a body form similar to early tetrapods. Their tail is long, and their forelimbs are about the same size as their back limbs (**FIGURE 24.9**). When a salamander walks, the movements of its limbs and bending of its trunk resemble movements made by a fish swimming through water. Early tetrapods probably used this motion to walk in the water before one lineage ventured onto land.

Larval salamanders look like small versions of adults, except for the presence of gills. In a few species (axolotls), gills are retained into adulthood. More typically, gills disappear as the animal matures and lungs develop.

Frogs and toads belong to the most diverse amphibian lineage, with more than 5,000 species. The long, muscular

---

FIGURE 24.8 Fossil species from the late Devonian illustrate how a fish body became adapted for life on land.

❶ Fish (*Eusthenopteron*) with bony fins.

❷ Fish (*Tiktaalik*) with sturdier weight-bearing pectoral fins, wristlike bones, and enlarged ribs.

❸ Early amphibian (*Icthyostegna*) with well-developed ribs, and thick limbs with distinct digits.

CREDITS: (8) left, From Starr/Evers/Starr, Biology Today and Tomorrow with Physiology, 4E. © 2013 Cengage Learning; #1 & 3, © P. E. Ahlberg; #2, Illustration by © Kalliopi Monoyios; (9) Photo by James Bettaso, U.S. Fish and Wildlife Service.

A Long, muscular hindlimbs allow an adult frog to leap. Frogs spend much of their time in water.

B Toads have a thicker skin and can live away from water.

C Aquatic larvae (tadpoles) have gills, a long tail, and no limbs.

FIGURE 24.10 Frogs and toads. Both frogs and toads have longer hindlimbs than forelimbs and are capable of hopping or jumping.

hindlimbs of an adult frog allow it to swim, hop, and make spectacular leaps (**FIGURE 24.10A**). The much smaller forelimbs help absorb the impact of landings. Toads can hop, but they usually walk, and they have somewhat shorter hind legs than frogs (**FIGURE 24.10B**). Toads are also better adapted to dry conditions. Both frogs and toads undergo metamorphosis, during which the gilled, tailed larva (**FIGURE 24.10C**) transforms itself into an adult with lungs and no tail.

DECLINING DIVERSITY

Amphibian populations throughout the world are declining or disappearing. Researchers correlate many declines with shrinking or deteriorating habitats. For example, nearly all amphibians need to deposit their eggs and sperm in water,

and their larvae must develop in water. Thus, they prefer to breed in low-lying ground where rain collects and forms pools of standing water. Humans inadvertently destroy these appropriate breeding spots by leveling the ground.

Other factors that contribute to amphibian declines include introduction of new species in amphibian habitats, long-term shifts in climate, increases in ultraviolet radiation, water pollution, and the spread of pathogens and parasites such as the chytrid fungus discussed in Section 22.1.

amphibian Tetrapod with scaleless skin; it typically develops in water, then lives on land as a carnivore with lungs. For example, a frog or salamander.

TAKE-HOME MESSAGE 24.3

The tetrapod lineage branched off from the lobe-finned fishes. Amphibians are the oldest tetrapod lineage.

Lungs and a three-chambered heart adapt amphibians to life on land, but they typically lay their eggs in water.

Frogs and toads undergo metamorphosis from a gilled, tailed, limbless larva to an adult with four limbs and no tail.

Yutyrannus huali, whose name means "beautiful feathered tyrant," lived about 125 million years ago in what is now China. *Y. huali* did not fly, so its feathers probably served as insulation.

FIGURE 24.11 Artist's depiction of the largest feathered dinosaur yet discovered. A human figure is shown for scale.

Amniotes branched off from an amphibian ancestor about 300 million years ago, during the Carboniferous. A variety of traits adapt them to life in dry places. They have lungs, rather than gills, throughout their life. Their skin is rich in keratin, a protein that makes it waterproof. A pair of well-developed kidneys help conserve water, and fertilization usually takes place inside the female's body. Amniotes produce eggs in which an embryo develops bathed in fluid, so amniotes can develop on dry land. A series of membranes within the egg function in gas exchange, nutrition, and waste removal.

An early branching of the amniote lineage separated ancestors of mammals from the common ancestor of all modern **reptiles**. You probably do not think of birds as reptiles, but the reptile clade includes turtles, lizards, snakes, crocodilians, and birds:

Dinosaurs are extinct members of the reptile clade. Biologists define them by skeletal features, such as the shape of their pelvis and hips. Like other reptiles, dinosaurs produced amniote eggs. One dinosaur group, the theropods, includes many feathered species (**FIGURE 24.11**). Most

likely, the feathers benefited the dinosaurs by providing insulation. Like modern birds and mammals, these feathered dinosaurs may have been **endotherms**, animals that maintain their body temperature by adjusting their production of metabolic heat. Endotherm means "heated from within." Most nonbird reptiles are **ectotherms**, animals whose internal temperature varies with that of their environment.

Birds branched off from a theropod dinosaur lineage during the Jurassic, and are the only surviving descendants of dinosaurs. All dinosaurs became extinct by the end of the Cretaceous, probably as a result of an asteroid impact (Section 16.9).

---

dinosaur Group of reptiles that include the ancestors of birds; became extinct at the end of the Cretaceous.
ectotherm Animals whose body temperature varies with that of its environment.
endotherm Animal that maintains its temperature by adjusting its production of metabolic heat; for example, a bird or mammal.
reptile Amniote subgroup that includes lizards, snakes, turtles, crocodilians, and birds.

TAKE-HOME MESSAGE 24.4

Amniotes are animals that produce eggs in which the young can develop away from water. They have waterproof skin and highly efficient kidneys. Fertilization is typically internal.

An early divergence separated the ancestors of mammals from the ancestors of reptiles—a group in which biologists include turtles, lizards, snakes, crocodilians, and birds.

Birds evolved from a group of feathered dinosaurs.

CREDITS: (in text) © Cengage Learning; (11) Xing Lida, National Geographic Creative.

All modern reptiles have scales and a cloaca. With the exception of birds, which we consider next, all are ectotherms. They are often seen basking in the sun to warm their bodies.

Lizards and snakes constitute the most diverse group of modern reptiles. Their body is covered with overlapping scales. Most lizards and snakes lay eggs (FIGURE 24.12A), but females of some species brood eggs in their body and give birth to well-developed young. The live-bearers do not provide any nourishment to the offspring inside their body, as some mammals do.

The smallest lizard can fit on a dime (*left*). The largest, the Komodo dragon, grows up to 3 meters (10 feet) long. Most lizards are predators, although iguanas are herbivores.

The first snakes evolved during the Cretaceous, from short-legged, long-bodied lizards. Some modern snakes have bony remnants of hindlimbs, but most lack limb bones entirely. All are predators. Many have flexible jaws that help them swallow prey whole. All snakes have teeth, but not all have fangs. Rattlesnakes and other fanged types bite and subdue prey with venom they produce in modified salivary (saliva-producing) glands. Each year in the United States there are about 7,000 reported snake bites, five of them fatal. The bites are a defense response.

Turtles have a bony, keratin-covered shell attached to their skeleton. They lack teeth, but a thick layer of keratin covers their jaws, forming a horny beak (FIGURE 24.12B). Most turtles that live in the sea feed on invertebrates such as sponges or jellies; others feed mainly on sea grass. Freshwater turtles prey on fish and invertebrates. Land-dwelling turtles, which are commonly called tortoises, feed on plants.

Crocodilians—crocodiles, alligators, and caimans—are stealthy predators with a long snout and many sharp peglike teeth (FIGURE 24.12C). They spend much of their time in water and a long, powerful tail propels them when they swim. Crocodilians are the closest living relatives of birds. Like most birds, crocodilians are highly vocal and engage in complex parental behavior. During courtship males and females grunt and bellow. After a female mates, she digs a nest, lays eggs, then buries and guards them. The young call when they are ready to hatch, and their mother helps them dig their way out.

Lizards, snakes, and turtles have a three-chambered heart, but the crocodilians have a heart with four chambers. A four-chambered heart improves efficiency of oxygen delivery by preventing oxygen-poor blood from ever mixing with oxygen-rich blood.

A Hognose snakes emerging from leathery amniote eggs.

B A turtle in a defensive posture. Note the horny beak.

C Spectacled caiman, a crocodilian. All crocodilians are predators that spend much of their time in water.

FIGURE 24.12 {Animated} Examples of nonbird reptiles.

TAKE-HOME MESSAGE 24.5

All modern nonbird reptiles are ectotherms that have a scale-covered body.

Lizards and snakes have an elongated body with overlapping scales. Most lizards and all snakes are predators.

Turtles have a bony shell and a horny beak.

Crocodiles and alligators are the closest living relatives of birds. Like birds, they have a four-chambered heart and care for their eggs and hatchlings.

CREDITS: (in text) © S. Blair Hedges, Pennsylvania State University; (12A) © Z. Leszczynski/Animals Animals; (12B) Joel Sartore/National Geographic Creative; (12C) © Kevin Schafer/ Tom Stack & Associates.

24.6 WHAT ARE BIRDS?

FIGURE 24.13 An owl in flight. Muscles that connect the wing to the breastbone power flight.

Birds are the only living animals with feathers. Bird feathers have roles in flight, insulation, and courtship displays. They also shed water and thus help keep the skin beneath dry.

Most modern birds have a body well adapted to flight (**FIGURE 24.13**). Like humans, birds stand upright. In birds, the forelimbs have evolved into wings. Each wing is covered with long feathers that extend outward and increase its surface area. The feathers give the wing a shape that helps lift the bird. Flight muscles connect an enlarged sternum (breastbone) with a protruding keel to bones of the upper limb. When flight muscles contract, the resulting powerful downstroke lifts the bird.

Most birds are surprisingly lightweight, which helps them become and remain airborne. Air cavities inside a bird's bones keep its body weight low, as does the lack of a bladder (an organ that stores urinary waste in many other vertebrates). Rather than having heavy, bony teeth, birds have a beak made of keratin, which is lighter in weight.

Birds use a lot of energy in flight and to maintain their body temperature. Like mammals, birds are endotherms.

A unique system of air sacs keeps air flowing continually through a bird's lungs, ensuring an adequate oxygen supply to flight muscles. A four-chambered heart pumps blood quickly from the lungs to wing muscles and back. A bird also has a large heart for its size and a rapid heartbeat.

Flying requires good eyesight and a great deal of coordination. Compared to a lizard of a similar body weight, a bird has much larger eyes and a bigger brain. A bird's eyes are largely immobile. Thus, to alter its view, it must turn its highly flexible neck.

As in other reptiles, fertilization is internal. However, most male birds do not have a penis. To inseminate a female, a male must press his cloaca against hers, a maneuver poetically described as a cloacal kiss. After fertilization occurs in the female's body, she lays an egg with the characteristic amniote membranes (**FIGURE 24.14**). Nutrients from the yolk and water from the albumin in the egg sustain the developing embryo. Like crocodiles, birds encase their eggs in a hard calcium carbonate shell.

More than half of all bird species belong to a subgroup called perching birds. Sparrows, finches, jays, and other birds seen at backyard feeders are in this group. The next most diverse group, the hummingbirds, includes the most agile fliers and the only birds capable of flying backward. At the other extreme, penguins and the ratite birds such as ostriches can no longer become airborne. Penguins "fly" through water by flapping their wings in the same manner that other birds do when they fly through air.

FIGURE 24.14 **{Animated}** Bird's egg. The amnion, chorion, and allantois are membranes characteristic of amniote eggs.

yolk sac embryo amnion chorion allantois

hardened shell   albumin ("egg white")

bird Feathered reptile with a body adapted for flight.

TAKE-HOME MESSAGE 24.6

Birds are endothermic amniotes with feathers. Lightweight bones and highly efficient respiratory and circulatory systems adapt a bird to flight.

FURRY OR HAIRY MILK MAKERS

Mammals are furry or hairy animals in which females nourish their offspring with milk secreted from mammary glands. The group name is derived from the Latin *mamma*, meaning breast. Like birds, mammals have a four-chambered heart and are endotherms. Fur or hair helps them retain body heat.

In other vertebrates, an individual's teeth may vary in size, but they are all the same shape. Only mammals have teeth of four different shapes (**FIGURE 24.15**). This assortment of teeth allows mammals to process a wider variety of foods than other vertebrates.

FIGURE 24.15 {Animated}
Four types of mammalian teeth.

MODERN SUBGROUPS

Monotremes, the oldest mammalian lineage, lay eggs with a leathery shell. Only three monotreme species survive, the duck-billed platypus (**FIGURE 24.16A**) and two kinds of spiny anteater (echidna). Monotreme eggs hatch while young are still tiny, hairless, and blind. The young then cling to the mother or are held in a skin fold on her belly. A monotreme has mammary glands but no nipples. Young lap up milk that oozes from openings on their mother's skin.

Marsupials are pouched mammals. Young marsupials develop briefly in their mother's body, nourished by egg yolk and by nutrients that diffuse from the mother's tissues. They are born at an early developmental stage, and crawl to a permanent pouch on the surface of their mother's belly. A nipple in the pouch supplies milk that sustains continued development. Most of the 240 modern marsupials live in Australia and on nearby islands. Kangaroos and koalas are the best known. Opossums (**FIGURE 24.16B**) are the only marsupials native to North America.

In **placental mammals** (eutherians), maternal and embryonic tissues combine as an organ called the placenta. A placenta allows maternal and embryonic bloodstreams to transfer materials without mixing. Placental embryos grow faster than those of other mammals, and the offspring are born more fully developed. After birth, young suck milk

mammal Animal with hair or fur; females secrete milk from mammary glands.
marsupial Mammal in which young are born at an early stage and complete development in a pouch on the mother's surface.
monotreme Egg-laying mammal.
placental mammal Mammal in which maternal and embryonic bloodstreams exchange materials by means of a placenta.

A Platypuses are monotremes.

B Opossums are marsupials.

C Hamsters are placental mammals.

FIGURE 24.16 {Animated} Mammalian mothers and their young. All female mammals produce milk to feed offspring.

from nipples on their mother's surface (**FIGURE 24.16C**). Monotremes and marsupials have a cloaca, but placental mammals have separate openings that service the urinary, reproductive, and excretory systems.

Placental mammals tend to outcompete other mammals and are now dominant on all continents except Australia. Of the approximately 4,000 species, nearly half are rodents such as rats and mice. The next most diverse group is bats, with 1,000 species. Humans are primates, the lineage we discuss in the next section.

TAKE-HOME MESSAGE 24.7

Mammals are endothermic amniotes that have hair or fur. Young are nourished by milk secreted from the female's mammary glands.

Egg-laying monotremes, pouched marsupials, and placental mammals are subgroups. Placental mammals are now the dominant lineage in most regions.

PRIMATE CHARACTERISTICS

Primates are an order of placental mammals that includes humans, apes, monkeys, and their close relatives. Primates first evolved in tropical forests, and many of the group's characteristic traits arose as adaptations to life among the branches. Primate shoulders have an extensive range of motion (**FIGURE 24.17**). Unlike most mammals, a primate can extend its arms out to its sides, reach above its head, and rotate its forearm at the elbow. With the

FIGURE 24.17 Adapted to climbing. An orangutan (an Asian ape) demonstrates her wide range of shoulder motion and her ability to grasp with her hands and feet.

exception of humans, all living primates have both hands and feet capable of grasping. Mammals often have claws or hooves, but tips of primate fingers and toes typically have touch-sensitive pads protected by flat nails.

Most mammals have eyes set toward the side of their head, but primate eyes tend to face forward. As a result, both eyes view the same area, each from a slightly different vantage point. The brain integrates the signals it receives from the two eyes to produce a three-dimensional image. A primate's excellent depth perception adapts it to a life spent leaping or swinging from limb to limb.

Primates have a large brain for their body size. Compared to other mammals, primates devote more brain area to vision and information processing, and less to smell.

Primates have a varied diet, and their teeth reflect this lack of specialization. They have teeth for tearing flesh, as well as for grinding material.

Most primates spend their life in a social group that includes adults of both sexes. Female primates usually give birth to only one or two young at a time and provide care for an extended period after birth.

MODERN SUBGROUPS

FIGURE 24.18 shows relationships among living primates. The oldest surviving primate lineage includes the lemurs, agile climbers that live in the forests of Madagascar, an island off the coast of Africa. Lemurs are active during the day and eat mainly fruits, leaves, and flowers. They have poor color vision. Like most other mammals, lemurs have a prominent wet nose and a vertically split upper lip that attaches tightly to the underlying gum (**FIGURE 24.19A**).

FIGURE 24.18 Evolutionary tree for some modern primates.

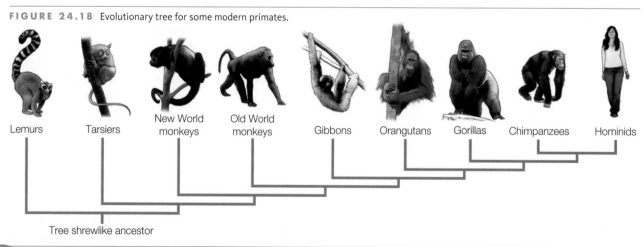

Lemurs | Tarsiers | New World monkeys | Old World monkeys | Gibbons | Orangutans | Gorillas | Chimpanzees | Hominids

Tree shrewlike ancestor

FIGURE IT OUT: Which modern primates are human ancestors?

Answer: None of them. All species ancestral to humans are extinct. We share a common ancestor with chimpanzees and bonobos.

A Lemur with a wet nose, cleft upper lip.

C Squirrel monkey (New World monkey) with flat face, prehensile tail.

E Gorilla, the largest ape.

B Tarsier with a dry nose, uncleft upper lip.

D Baboon (Old World monkey) with long nose, short tail.

F Chimpanzee, one of our two closest living relatives.

FIGURE 24.19 Primate diversity.

Tarsiers are small, nocturnal insect eaters that live in South Asia (**FIGURE 24.19B**). Like monkeys, apes, and humans, they are dry-nosed primates, with nostrils set in dry skin. Their upper lip is not cleft and has a reduced attachment to the gum. Evolution of a movable upper lip allowed a wider range of facial expressions and vocalizations.

Anthropoid primates—monkeys, apes, and humans—are typically active during the day and have good color vision (*anthropoid* means humanlike). New World monkeys (**FIGURE 24.19C**) climb through forests of Central and South America. They have a flat face and a nose with widely separated nostrils. A long tail helps them maintain balance. In many species, the tail is prehensile, meaning it can grasp things. Old World monkeys live in Africa, the Middle East, and Asia. They tend to be larger than New World monkeys and have a longer nose with closely set nostrils. Some are tree-climbing forest dwellers. Others, such as baboons (**FIGURE 24.19D**), spend most of their time on the ground in grasslands or deserts. Not all Old World monkeys have a tail, but in those that do it is short and never prehensile.

Most modern, tailless, nonhuman primates belong to the group commonly known as **apes**. About 24 species of small apes called gibbons inhabit Southeast Asian forests. They are sometimes referred to as "lesser apes," in comparison with the larger apes, or "great apes." The forest-dwelling orangutan of Sumatra and Borneo is the only surviving Asian great ape. All African great apes (gorillas, chimpanzees, and bonobos) live in social groups, and spend most of their time on the ground. Gorillas (**FIGURE 24.19E**), the largest living primates, live in forests and feed mainly on leaves. Chimpanzees (**FIGURE 24.19F**) and the bonobos, or pygmy chimpanzees, are our closest living relatives. The chimpanzee/bonobo lineage and the lineage leading to humans parted ways between 6 and 8 million years ago. Chimpanzees and bonobos eat fruit, but also catch insects and cooperatively hunt small mammals, including monkeys. The two species differ in their behavior, with chimpanzees engaging in more intraspecific aggression and bonobos spending more time in nonreproductive sex acts.

TAKE-HOME MESSAGE 24.8

Primates include lemurs, tarsiers, monkeys, apes, and humans.

Primate traits such as a flexible shoulder joint and grasping hands with nails are adaptations to climbing. Compared to other mammals, primates have a larger brain with a greater area devoted to vision and less to smell.

Humans are most closely related to apes, and the chimpanzees and bonobos are our closest living relatives.

anthropoid primate Humanlike primate; monkey, ape, or human.
ape Common name for a tailless nonhuman primate; a gibbon, orangutan, gorilla, chimpanzee, or bonobo.
primate Mammal having grasping hands with nails and a body adapted to climbing; for example, a lemur, monkey, ape, or human.

24.9 HOW DO HUMANS AND APES DIFFER?

Humans share an ancestor with great apes, but differ from them in many aspects. Compared to a chimpanzee, a human has a flatter face, a smaller jaw with reduced canine teeth, and a larger brain (**FIGURE 24.20**). Our bodies are similarly sized, but our brains are three times bigger.

We also walk differently. When gorillas and chimpanzees walk, they lean forward and support their weight on their knuckles. By contrast, humans walk upright. Habitual upright walking, or **bipedalism**, is the defining trait of hominins. **Hominins** include modern humans and all extinct species more closely related to us than to any other primate.

Evolution of bipedalism involved many skeletal changes (**FIGURE 24.21**). A knuckle-walking ape has a backbone with a C-shape, whereas the human backbone has an S-shaped curve that keeps our head centered over our feet. Apes have flat feet capable of grasping, but human feet have a pronounced arch and a non-opposable big toe. An ape's spinal cord enters near the rear of skull, whereas the spinal cord of a human enters at the skull's base.

FIGURE 24.20 Comparison of chimpanzee and human skulls.

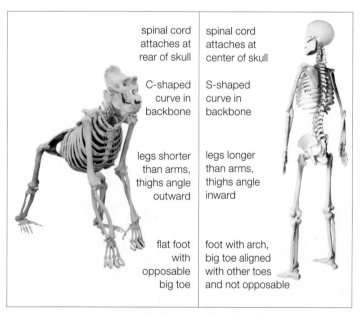

spinal cord attaches at rear of skull	spinal cord attaches at center of skull
C-shaped curve in backbone	S-shaped curve in backbone
legs shorter than arms, thighs angle outward	legs longer than arms, thighs angle inward
flat foot with opposable big toe	foot with arch, big toe aligned with other toes and not opposable

FIGURE 24.21 {**Animated**} Some skeletal differences between a knuckle-walking gorilla (*left*) and a bipedal human (*right*).

What favored the transition from a four-legged gait to bipedalism? A change in climate may have been a factor. Hominins evolved in Africa at a time when lush rain forests were giving way to woodlands interspersed with grassy plains. In this altered habitat, an ability to move efficiently across open ground would have been favored, and human walkers use less energy to move than chimpanzees do. Bipedalism also keeps a body cooler. A bipedal animal gains less heat from the ground than a four-legged walker and also intercepts less warming sunlight. In addition, an upright stance makes it easier to scan the horizon for predators, and it frees hands to gather and carry food or other resources.

Human hands also differ from those of apes. A human thumb is longer, stronger, and more maneuverable than that of a chimpanzee. Many monkeys and apes grasp objects in a power grip, but only humans routinely use a precision grip, pinching together the tips of the thumb and forefinger for fine manipulation of objects:

power grip   precision grip

Humans are the only living primates without a thick coat of body hair. We have about the same number of body hairs as other primates, but ours are shorter and finer, giving our skin a more naked appearance. Most likely the decrease in hominin hairiness was driven by a need to stay cool. Sweat evaporates more quickly from bare skin than from under thick hair, and an improved cooling ability would have reduced the risk of overheating while walking or running across hot, sunny grasslands.

The many differences between humans and apes did not arise all at once. Rather, as hominins evolved, different traits changed at different rates. Hominins walked upright for millions of years before their brain size began to increase.

bipedalism Habitual upright walking.
hominin Human or an extinct primate species more closely related to humans than to any other primates.

> **TAKE-HOME MESSAGE 24.9**
>
> Compared to apes, humans have a larger brain, more flexible hands, and less insulating body hair.
>
> Unlike apes, humans are bipedal, and have a skeleton that adapts them to this upright posture.
>
> Differences between apes and humans arose over millions of years as evolutionary forces altered our hominin ancestors.

CREDITS: (20) © Kenneth Garrett/ National Geographic Creative; (21) left, Bone Clones, www.boneclones.com; right, Gary Head; (in text) From Starr/Taggart, Biology: The Unity and Diversity of Life, 7E. © 1995 Cengage Learning.

Fossil skull fragments from *Sahelanthropus tchadensis* may be the oldest evidence of hominins. This species, which lived about 7 million years ago in west-central Africa, is known only from fossil skulls. The skulls opened to the spinal cord at their base, rather than at the rear, suggesting that this species walked upright. *S. tchadensis* had a hominid-like flat face, prominent brow, small canines, and a chimpanzee-sized brain. Another proposed early hominin, *Orrorin tugenensis*, lived about 6 million years ago in East Africa. Two sturdy fossilized femurs (thighbones) suggest that it stood upright; bipedal species have thicker femurs than four-legged walkers. In other traits, this species was apelike.

Ardipithecus ramidus was clearly a hominin. It lived in East Africa between 5.8 and 5.2 million years ago and left a wealth of fossil remains, including a largely complete skeleton of a female informally known as Ardi (**FIGURE 24.22A**). Features of the *A. ramidus* pelvis suggest that this species walked upright when on the ground. However, elongated arms, curved fingers, and an outwardly splayed big toe indicate it also spent time climbing along branches.

The best known early hominins, **australopiths**, belong to the genus *Australopithecus*, which lived in Africa from about 4 million to 1.2 million years ago. Australopith fossils reveal a trend toward smaller teeth and improvements in the ability to walk upright, but little increase in brain size.

Some *Australopithecus* species are considered likely human ancestors. One of these, *A. afarensis*, left behind

FIGURE 24.23 Reconstruction of *Australopithecus sediba*, a possible human ancestor that lived in South Africa 2 million years ago.

fossils of more than 300 individuals, among them a nearly complete female skeleton known as Lucy (**FIGURE 24.22B**). Two *A. afarensis* individuals walking across a layer of newly deposited volcanic ash may also have left the trail of 3.6-million-year-old footprints discovered in Tanzania. *A. afarensis* males stood about 1.5 to 1.8 meters (5 to 5.5 feet) tall, and females 1 meter (3 feet) tall. They had a pelvis and legs suited to upright walking, although their gait may not have been as fluid as that of modern humans. They also retained the long arms and curved fingers of a climber.

Australopithecus sediba, a species recently discovered in South Africa, is the most humanlike australopith discovered thus far (**FIGURE 24.23**). *A. sediba* lived about 2 million years ago. Its hands were remarkably humanlike and were probably capable of a precision grip. In addition, its brain, although chimpanzee-sized and largely apelike, has a humanlike frontal region.

australopith Extinct African hominins in the genus *Australopithecus*; some are considered likely human ancestors.

| A Ardi, an *Ardipithecus ramidus* (4.4 million years ago). | B Lucy, an *Australopithicus afarensis* (3.5 million years ago). |

FIGURE 24.22 Fossil skeletons of two early female hominins.

TAKE-HOME MESSAGE 24.10

Some African fossil species from as far back as 7 million years ago have features that suggest they were bipedal.

Ardipithecus ramidus, an East African hominin known from many fossils, walked upright on the ground, but retained many traits related to climbing.

Australopiths, a group of African hominins, show a trend toward improved upright walking, smaller teeth, and greater hand dexterity. Like other early hominins, they retained a chimpanzee-sized brain.

CREDITS: (22A) © Tim D. White 2009, fossilpix.org; (22B) © Dr. Donald Johanson, Institute of Human Origins; (23) Courtesy of © John Gurche.

24.11 WHAT SPECIES ARE IN THE GENUS *HOMO*?

A *Homo erectus.* Fossil of Turkana boy, who lived 1.6 million years ago in what is now Kenya.

B *Homo neanderthalensis.* Reconstruction of an adult male based on multiple fossils, each denoted by a different color.

C *Homo sapiens.* (Modern human.) Skeletal model of a typical adult male.

FIGURE 24.24 Some members of the genus *Homo*.

Modern humans, *Homo sapiens*, are the only surviving member of the genus *Homo*. Fossil species are typically assigned to this genus on the basis of their relatively large brain, although other factors such as tool use can play a role. Researchers disagree over how many extinct *Homo* species there were, with some lumping many fossils into a few species and others splitting the same fossils among a greater number of groups. From a scientific standpoint, both approaches are equally valid. Both lumpers and splitters formulate hypotheses about how a particular fossil relates to other known fossils. They then seek evidence (in the form of additional fossil discoveries) that will confirm or refute their hypothesis.

EARLY *HOMO* SPECIES

The most ancient named species in our genus, **Homo habilis**, lived in East Africa between 2.3 million and 1.4 million years ago. *Homo habilis* means "handy man" and is a reference to stone tools found in the same area as the fossil. *H. habilis* had a somewhat larger brain and smaller teeth than australopiths, but its size and limb proportions were quite apelike. Some researchers assign a few of the largest-brained fossils to a different species, *Homo rudolfensis*.

A dramatically different species of hominin appears in the fossil record beginning about 1.8 million years ago. Called **Homo erectus**, which means "upright man," it was taller than *H. habilis*, with body proportions more like those of modern humans. It also had smaller teeth and a larger brain. The most complete *H. erectus* fossil known is a skeleton of a juvenile male from Kenya, commonly referred to as Turkana boy (**FIGURE 24.24A**). Although this individual apparently died at about age nine, his brain was already twice the size of a chimpanzee's. *H. erectus* used a variety of stone tools to cut up animal carcasses, scrape meat from bones, and extract marrow. Most likely the meat came from scavenging, rather than hunting. Bits of burnt plant material and bone left behind by a million-year-old campfire inside a South African cave suggest that *H. erectus* may have also been the first species to cook.

By 1.75 million years ago, a population of *Homo* had become established in what is now the Republic of Georgia. They are informally known as the Dmanisi hominins for the place where they were discovered. Most researchers think the Dmanisi hominins are descended from *H. erectus* and place them in this species. Although the Dmanisi hominins have the smallest brains of any known *H. erectus* population, they were sophisticated tool makers.

H. erectus populations became established in Indonesia by 1.6 million years ago, and China by 1.15 million years ago. *H. erectus* is also considered a likely ancestor of Neanderthals and modern humans.

NEANDERTHALS

In the mid-1800s, scientists discovered 40,000-year-old humanlike fossils in Germany's Neander Valley and named them **Homo neanderthalensis**. Since then, many fossils with similar features have been unearthed, including a few largely complete skeletons. Scientists now consider Neanderthals our closest extinct relatives.

Neanderthals lived in Africa, the Middle East, Europe, and in central Asia as far east as Siberia. The last known population lived in seaside caves in Gibraltar until perhaps as recently as 28,000 years ago. Compared to modern humans, Neanderthals had a shorter, stockier build, with thicker bones and bulkier muscles (**FIGURE 24.24B**). A stocky body minimizes the surface area available for heat loss, and modern Arctic peoples have a similar body shape. Neanderthals had a braincase that was longer and lower than that of modern humans, but their brain was as big as ours or bigger. Their face had pronounced brow ridges and a large nose with widely spaced nostrils. Unlike modern humans, they typically lacked a protruding chin, an area of thickened bone in the middle of the lower jawbone. Fossils

CREDITS: (24A) Science VU/NMK/Visuals Unlimited, Inc.; (24B,C) Courtesy of © Blaine Maley, Washington University, St. Louis.

of Neanderthal individuals who survived despite disabilities such as the loss of a limb testify to a compassionate social structure. Some simple burials suggest possible symbolic thought. The anatomy of the voice box suggests Neanderthals were able to speak.

FLORES HOMININS

In 2003, scientists discovered 18,000-year-old hominin fossils on the Indonesian island of Flores. The fossilized individuals stood about a meter tall, and had a heavy brow. Their brain was australopith-sized, but shaped more like that of *H. erectus*. The media nicknamed the diminutive individuals "hobbits," a reference to small-bodied beings in the fiction of J.R.R. Tolkien. The scientists who discovered the fossils labeled them a new species, *Homo floresiensis*. Other scientists think that the fossils are modern humans with a genetic or nutritional disorder. Additional study of the existing fossils and of any new fossils discovered will determine which hypothesis is correct.

HOMO SAPIENS

Section 24.9 described the traits that characterize our species (*Homo sapiens*). To date, the oldest *H. sapiens* fossils discovered are two partial male skulls from Ethiopia, in East Africa. Known as Omo I and Omo II, they date to 195,000 years ago. The skulls were found in the same region where investigators also unearthed *H. sapiens* remains (two adult males and a child) from about 160,000 years. By 115,000 years ago, *H. sapiens* had extended their range into South Africa. The more recent global dispersal of this species is the topic of our next section.

Homo erectus Extinct hominin that arose about 1.8 million years ago in East Africa; migrated out of Africa.

Homo habilis Extinct hominin; earliest named *Homo* species; known only from Africa, where it arose 2.3 million years ago.

Homo neanderthalensis Extinct hominin; closest known relative of *H. sapiens*; lived in Africa, Europe, Asia.

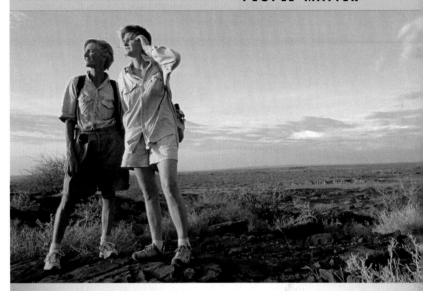

PEOPLE MATTER

National Geographic Explorers-in-Residence
**DR. LOUISE LEAKEY AND
DR. MEAVE LEAKEY**

Paleontologist Louise Leakey is a third-generation fossil-finder. Her grandfather, Louis Leakey, discovered and named *Homo habilis*, and her father, Richard Leakey, excavated the *Homo erectus* fossil known as "Turkana boy." She remembers the latter discovery well. She says, "At age 12, the discovery of the *Homo erectus* from the west side of Turkana was a very exciting time... We were able to engage and help and excavate it. There was a real sense of excitement about that excavation."

Louise now carries out her own research in the Turkana Basin, searching for fossils in collaboration with her mother, Meave. Both women are National Geographic Explorers. Among their accomplishments, they have recently shown that *Homo habilis* survived until at least 1.4 million years ago, and that it coexisted with *Homo erectus* for about half a million years. This long overlap between the two species argues against a widely held hypothesis that *H. habilis* was the ancestor of *H. erectus*. Louise and Meave Leakey have also discovered a 3.5-million-year-old skull that may belong to a previously unknown genus, and could be a human ancestor. They have tentatively named their find *Kenyanthropus platyops*, and continue to look for additional fossils that will confirm its identity as a new species.

CREDIT: (in text) Kenneth Garrett/National Geographic Creative.

24.12 WHAT DO OUR GENES REVEAL ABOUT HUMAN ORIGIN AND DISPERSAL?

We are all African. Regardless of where your recent ancestors lived, look far enough back and you'll discover your African roots. Both fossil finds and genetic studies indicate that our species originated in Africa. The oldest *Homo sapiens* fossils come from Ethiopia, and modern Africans are more genetically diverse than people of any other region. The large number of differences among African populations indicates that these populations have existed and have been accumulating random mutations for a very long time. Furthermore, most genetic variation seen in non-African populations is a subset of the variation found inside Africa. This is evidence that founder effects (Section 17.7) occurred when subsets of the African population left to colonize the rest of the world.

The ancestors of modern non-African populations began their journey out of Africa sometime between 80,000 and 60,000 years ago. Early in this journey, they encountered and successfully bred with Neanderthals. As a result, modern non-African peoples have a bit of Neanderthal DNA in their genome, whereas Africans do not. Modern humans would later live alongside Neanderthals in Europe and Asia, but to date there is no genetic evidence that matings in these regions contributed to our gene pool.

Our species expanded its range over tens of thousands of years as small groups ventured away from their homelands. As they did, unique mutations arose in different lineages and were passed along to descendants. Today, the distribution of these mutations among different ethnic groups provides evidence of the routes taken by the ancient travelers. By mapping the frequency of maternal and paternal genetic markers in modern peoples, geneticists have created a picture of when and where ancient humans moved around the world (**FIGURE 24.25**).

The first people to colonize Eurasia probably crossed from the Horn of Africa onto the Arabian peninsula. From there, they moved along the coastline to India, and reached Southeast Asia and Australia by 50,000 years ago. Shortly after this, another group traveled through the Middle East and into South Central Asia. Offshoots from this lineage colonized North Asia and Europe. Then, about 15,000 years ago, some people ventured across a land bridge that temporarily connected Siberia to North America. Over the next thousand years, their descendants spread to the tip of South America.

TAKE-HOME MESSAGE 24.12

Modern humans originated in Africa, and expanded their range worldwide over tens of thousands of years.

As humans left Africa, they interbred with Neanderthals, so modern non-African humans have some Neanderthal DNA.

Genetic differences among modern ethnic groups can be used to reconstruct the routes of early human migrations.

FIGURE 24.25 Human migration routes, as determined by genetic analysis. To learn more about how geneticists use genes to trace journeys and determine our ancestry, visit National Geographic's Genographic Project site at *https://genographic.nationalgeographic.com*.

CREDIT: (25) photo, NASA; data, National Geographic.

Education

ACHING BACKS ARE AMONG THE PRICES WE PAY FOR WALKING UPRIGHT. In most vertebrates, the backbone is oriented horizontally, so it does not have weight pressing down on it. Our upright stance forced our lower back to support the weight of our upper body and put us at a heightened risk for lower back pain and injuries.

Walking upright also puts tremendous pressure on our knees. When you walk, you place all of your body weight on first one leg then the other. By contrast, four-legged walkers typically distribute their weight across at least two limbs. In addition, we fully extend our legs, whereas apes maintain a bent-legged stance. Fully extending your leg while walking decreases the effort expended by your thigh muscles, but also increases the risk you will injure your knee.

The combination of a relatively large brain and a pelvis adapted to an upright stance also makes for a tight fit during labor (FIGURE 24.26). Giving birth is typically more difficult for humans than it is for other primates.

chimpanzee   human

FIGURE 24.26 Passage of the chimpanzee or human skull through the birth canal during labor. Both are shown from below.

Summary

SECTION 24.1 Four features define **chordate** embryos: a **notochord**, a dorsal hollow nerve cord, a pharynx with gill slits, and a tail extending past the anus. Some or all of these features persist in adults. Chordates include two groups of marine invertebrates, the **tunicates** and **lancelets**, but most are **vertebrates**, which have an **endoskeleton** that includes a backbone. The first vertebrates were jawless fishes. **Tetrapods** are vertebrates with four limbs. **Amniotes** are tetrapods that produce eggs that allow embryos to develop away from water.

SECTION 24.2 Fishes are fully aquatic vertebrates. The earliest fishes had no jaws, fins, or scales. Modern **jawless fishes**, the hagfishes and lampreys, also lack these traits. Jaws evolved by a modification of structures that support gill slits. **Cartilaginous fishes** such as sharks and rays have a skeleton of cartilage and a **cloaca** that functions in excretion and reproduction. There are two lineages of bony fishes. **Ray-finned fishes**, the most diverse vertebrate group, have fins reinforced with thin rays derived from skin, whereas bones support the fins of **lobe-finned fishes**.

SECTION 24.3 **Amphibians**, the first lineage of tetrapods, evolved from a lobe-finned fish ancestor. A variety of modifications including a three-chamber heart adapt amphibians to life on land. Modern amphibians such as frogs, toads, and salamanders are carnivores. Most spend some time on land, but return to the water to reproduce. Many amphibian species face the threat of extinction.

SECTION 24.4 A variety of traits adapt amniotes to life away from water. Their skin and kidneys help minimize water loss. Fertilization usually takes place inside the female's body. Amniote eggs encase a developing embryo in fluid, so they can develop away from water. **Reptiles** (which include birds and **dinosaurs**) belong to one amniote lineage; mammals to another. Birds descended

CREDITS: (in text) © Artens/Shutterstock.com; (26) Richard Schlecht/National Geographic Creative.

from dinosaurs. Some dinosaurs may have been **endotherms**, like modern birds and mammals. Nonbird reptiles are **ectotherms** that rely on environmental sources of heat.

SECTION 24.5 Lizards and snakes belong to the most diverse reptile lineage. All are carnivores with flattened scales. Turtles have a bony, keratin-covered shell and a horny beak rather than teeth. Crocodilians are aquatic carnivores and the closest relatives of birds. Like birds, they have a four-chamber heart and assist young.

SECTION 24.6 **Birds** are reptiles with feathers. Most have a body adapted to flight, with lightweight bones, a four-chamber heart, a beak rather than teeth, and a highly efficient respiratory system.

SECTION 24.7 **Mammals** nourish young with milk secreted by mammary glands, have fur or hair, and have more than one kind of tooth. Three lineages are egg-laying mammals (**monotremes**), pouched mammals (**marsupials**), and **placental mammals**, the most diverse group. Placental mammals develop faster than other mammals and are born at a later stage of development. They have become the primary mammal group in most regions. Rodents and bats are the most diverse groups of placental mammals.

SECTIONS 24.8, 24.9 **Primates** are a mammalian order adapted to climbing. They have flexible shoulder joints, grasping hands tipped by nails, and good depth perception. They rely on vision more than smell. Lemurs and their relatives are wet-nosed primates with a fixed upper lip. Most primates belong to the dry-nosed subgroup and have a movable upper lip. Old World monkeys, New World monkeys, **apes**, and humans share a common ancestor and are grouped as **anthropoids**. Apes and humans do not have a tail. The lineage leading to humans and the chimpanzee/bonobo lineage diverged from a common ancestor an estimated 6 to 8 million years ago.

Humans and our closest extinct ancestors are **hominins**, a group defined by **bipedalism**. We also have larger brains, a coat of finer hair, and more flexible hands than other primates. These traits evolved at different times.

SECTION 24.10 The earliest fossils that may be hominins date to 7 million years ago (**FIGURE 24.27**). *Ardipithecus ramidus* lived about 5 million years ago and walked upright on the ground, but also climbed among tree branches. **Australopiths** are a genus of chimpanzee-sized hominins that likely include some human ancestors. They walked upright, but had small brains.

SECTIONS 24.11, 24.12 The human genus (*Homo*) arose by 2 million years ago. The oldest named species, *H. habilis*, resembled australopiths, but had a slightly larger brain and may have made tools. They lived in Africa. *H. erectus* had a much larger brain and a body form like that of modern humans. *H. erectus* made tools and may have used fire. Some members of this species left Africa and became established in Europe and Asia. *H. erectus* is thought to be the ancestor of both Neanderthals (*Homo neanderthalensis*) and modern humans (*H. sapiens*). Neanderthals, our closest extinct relatives, had a big brain and a stocky body. They lived in Africa, Europe, and Asia, then disappeared about 28,000 years ago. Fossils on an Indonesian island may be another species, *H. floresiensis*.

Fossil evidence and genetic comparisons indicate that our species, *H. sapiens*, arose by about 195,000 years ago in East Africa. As humans moved out of Africa, they met and interbred with Neanderthals, so modern non-African populations contain some Neanderthal DNA. Geneticists can determine the paths taken by early humans by looking at differences in the frequency of genetic markers among modern ethnic groups.

SECTION 24.13 Modifications of the skeleton that adapt our body to bipedalism put us at risk for knee and back problems. Coupled with our large skull size, they make childbirth more difficult.

FIGURE 24.27 Estimated dates for the origin and extinction of some hominins discussed in this chapter. Relationships among them remain a matter of debate. However, *H. erectus* is considered a likely ancestor of *H. neanderthalensis* and *H. sapiens*.

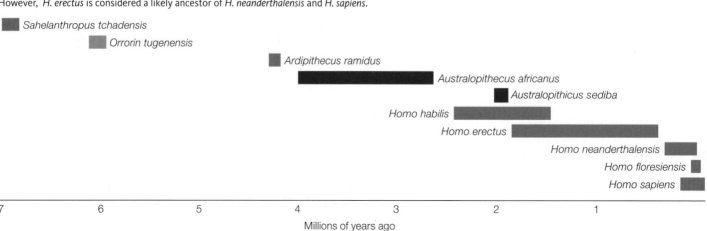

Sahelanthropus tchadensis
Orrorin tugenensis
Ardipithecus ramidus
Australopithecus africanus
Australopithicus sediba
Homo habilis
Homo erectus
Homo neanderthalensis
Homo floresiensis
Homo sapiens

| 7 | 6 | 5 | 4 | 3 | 2 | 1 |

Millions of years ago

Data Analysis Activities

Neanderthal Hair Color The *MC1R* gene regulates pigmentation in humans (Sections 14.1 and 15.1 revisited), so loss-of-function mutations in this gene affect hair and skin color. A person with two mutated alleles for this gene makes more of a reddish pigment than a brownish one, resulting in red hair and pale skin. DNA extracted from two Neanderthal fossils has an *MC1R* mutation that has not yet been found in humans. To see how this mutation affects activity of the *MC1R* gene, Carles Lalueza-Fox and her team introduced the mutant allele into cultured monkey cells (**FIGURE 24.28**).

1. How did *MC1R* activity in monkey cells with the mutant allele differ from that in cells with the normal allele?

2. What does this imply about the mutation's effect on Neanderthal hair color?

3. What purpose do the cells with the jellyfish gene for green fluorescent protein serve in this experiment?

FIGURE 24.28 *MC1R* activity in monkey cells transgenic for an unmutated *MC1R* gene, the Neanderthal *MC1R* allele, or the gene for green fluorescent protein (GFP). GFP is not related to *MC1R*.

Self-Quiz Answers in Appendix VII

1. All chordates have (a) _____ as embryos.
   a. backbone b. jaws c. notochord d. both b and c

2. The _____ are invertebrate chordates.
   a. echinoderms   c. lancelets
   b. hagfishes   d. lampreys

3. Vertebrate jaws evolved from _____ .
   a. gill supports b. ribs c. scales d. teeth

4. Sharks and rays are _____ .
   a. ray-finned fishes   c. jawless fishes
   b. cartilaginous fishes d. lobe-finned fishes

5. A divergence from _____ gave rise to tetrapods.
   a. ray-finned fishes   c. cartilaginous fishes
   b. lizards   d. lobe-finned fishes

6. Reptiles, including birds, belong to one major lineage of amniotes, and _____ belong to another.
   a. sharks   c. mammals
   b. frogs and toads   d. salamanders

7. Reptiles are adapted to life on land by _____ .
   a. tough skin   d. amniote eggs
   b. internal fertilization e. both a and c
   c. good kidneys   f. all of the above

8. The closest modern relatives of birds are _____ .
   a. crocodilians b. mammals c. turtles d. lizards

9. The defining trait of hominins is _____ .
   a. tool use b. bipedalism c. a large brain d. endothermy

10. Among living animals, only birds have _____ .
    a. a cloaca   c. feathers
    b. a four-chamber heart d. amniote eggs

11. *Homo erectus* _____ .
    a. was the earliest member of the genus *Homo*
    b. was one of the australopiths
    c. evolved in Africa and dispersed to many regions
    d. disappeared as the result of an asteroid impact

12. Match the organisms with the appropriate description.
    ___ tunicates   a. pouched mammals
    ___ fishes   b. invertebrate chordates
    ___ amphibians   c. feathered amniotes
    ___ primates   d. egg-laying mammals
    ___ birds   e. extinct hominins
    ___ monotremes   f. have grasping hands with nails
    ___ marsupials   g. first land tetrapods
    ___ placental   h. most diverse mammal
        mammals   lineage
    ___ australopiths   i. oldest vertebrate lineage

Critical Thinking

1. Researchers recently compared mitochondrial DNA from a fossil finger found in Siberia to mitochondrial DNA (mitoDNA) from modern humans. The sequence of the finger DNA differed from modern human DNA at an average of 385 sites. Neanderthal mitoDNA differs from modern human mitoDNA at an average of 202 sites, and chimpanzee mitoDNA differs from human mitoDNA at an average of 1,462 sites. Using this information, draw a tree that shows the relationship between chimpanzees, humans, Neanderthals, and the owner of this finger.

CREDIT: (28) From Starr/Taggart/Evers/Starr, Biology, 13E. © 2013 Cengage Learning.

Trichomes are outgrowths of leaf epidermal cells. Glandular types such as the ones on the surface of this marijuana leaf secrete substances that deter plant-eating animals. Marijuana trichomes secrete a chemical (tetrahydrocannabinol, or THC) that has a psychoactive effect in humans.

25

Links to Earlier Concepts

This chapter builds on the discussion of plant structure and life cycles in Section 21.1. It examines the anatomy of flowering plants (21.6) in terms of life's organization (1.1), and revisits carbohydrates (3.2), plant cell specializations (4.8, 4.10, 6.5), and differentiation (10.1).

PLANT TISSUES ⟩ KEY CONCEPTS

TYPES OF PLANT TISSUES

Most flowering plants have shoots and roots. All plant parts consist of the same tissues, but the arrangement of the tissues differs between monocots and eudicots.

STEM STRUCTURE

Stems support the plant body. A specialized structure allows some stems to have additional functions such as reproduction, water storage, and nutrient storage.

LEAF STRUCTURE

Leaves are plant parts that specialize in intercepting sunlight and exchanging gases for photosynthesis. Eudicot leaves in particular vary in shape.

ROOT STRUCTURE

Roots provide a large surface area for absorbing water and nutrients from soil, and often they anchor the plant. Each has a central column of vascular tissue.

PLANT GROWTH

Young plant parts grow by lengthening at their tips; older plant parts grow by thickening. Tree rings can be used to study past environmental conditions.

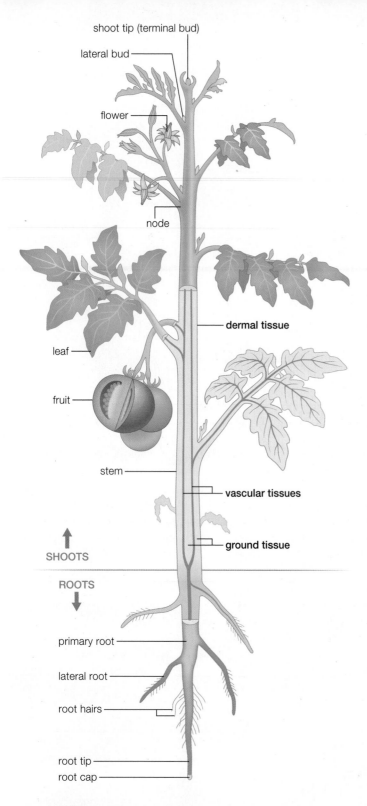

shoot tip (terminal bud)

lateral bud

flower

node

dermal tissue

leaf

fruit

stem

vascular tissues

ground tissue

SHOOTS ↑

ROOTS ↓

primary root

lateral root

root hairs

root tip

root cap

With more than 260,000 species (and counting), flowering plants dominate the plant kingdom. Magnoliids, eudicots (true dicots), and monocots (Section 21.6) are the major angiosperm groups. In this chapter, we focus mainly on the structure of eudicots and monocots. Eudicots include flowering shrubs and trees, vines, and many nonwoody plants such as tomatoes and dandelions. Lilies, orchids, grasses, and palms are examples of monocots.

Like cells of most other multicelled organisms, those in plants are organized as tissues, organs, and organ systems (Section 1.1). A vascular plant's body consists of two organ systems: shoots and roots (**FIGURE 25.1**). Most shoots are above the ground and most roots are below it, but as you will see, there are many exceptions.

A shoot system includes stems, leaves, and reproductive organs such as flowers. Stems provide a structural framework for the plant's growth. Leaves are specialized to intercept sunlight for photosynthetic production of sugars. Roots are specialized to absorb water and dissolved minerals, and they often serve to anchor the plant in soil. They are as essential as a plant's shoots, and often at least as extensive.

Stems, leaves, flowers, roots—all plant parts are composed of ground, vascular, and dermal tissues. **Ground tissues** constitute the bulk of the plant, and include the tissues specialized for photosynthesis and for storage. **Vascular tissues** form pipelines that thread through ground tissue and distribute water and nutrients to all parts of the plant body. **Dermal tissues** cover and protect the plant's exposed surfaces. All three types of plant tissues arise during lengthening of young roots and shoots. In some plants, older stems and roots thicken over seasons.

Monocots and eudicots have the same types of cells and tissues composing their parts, but the two lineages differ in many aspects of their organization and hence in their structure (**FIGURE 25.2**). The names of the groups refer to one such difference, the number of seed leaves, or cotyledons, in their embryos. The plant embryo in a monocot seed has a single cotyledon; the embryo in a eudicot seed has two. (Chapter 27 returns to embryonic development in plants.) As you will see, the tissue organization of shoots and roots also differs among eudicots and monocots.

FIGURE 25.1 {Animated} Body plan of a tomato plant. Vascular tissues (purple) conduct water and solutes. They thread through ground tissues that make up most of the plant body. Dermal tissue covers its surfaces.

dermal tissues Tissues that cover and protect the plant body.
ground tissues Tissues that make up the bulk of the plant body.
vascular tissues Tissues that distribute water and nutrients through a plant body.

FIGURE 25.2 {**Animated**} Some of the structural differences between eudicots and monocots.

Eudicots	Monocots

In seeds, two cotyledons (seed leaves of embryo) | In seeds, one cotyledon (seed leaf of embryo)

Flower parts in fours or fives (or multiples of four or five) | Flower parts in threes (or multiples of three)

Leaf veins usually forming a netlike array | Leaf veins usually running parallel with one another

Pollen grains with three pores or furrows | Pollen grains with one pore or furrow

Vascular bundles organized in a ring in ground tissue of stem | Vascular bundles throughout ground tissue of stem

National Geographic Explorer
DR. MARK OLSON

The ghosts of lost plants haunt Mark Olson. "When you know a plant from just one collection, all you know about it is that it exists . . . and where it was found, but we can't say much about it," Olson said. "We don't know if it's very rare and very restricted or if people have just been overlooking it."

All across the globe, plants that have been found, filed away, and forgotten are his passion. These plants are what drive the plant biologist to explore some of the most remote and dangerous spots on the planet. "The search for and rediscovery of these species include some of the highlights of my fieldwork—and some of the most heartbreaking—when it becomes clear that a species has probably become extinct," he said. Olson conducts field research from a powered paraglider, a flying machine that he describes as "like a moped in the air."

Olson knew early on that he wanted to be a biologist. During a post–high school turtle-tagging expedition to Costa Rica, Olson discovered a love for fieldwork. Less appealing was one collection method for zoological work. "We put tags on the sea turtles," Olson recalled, "[and the tags] crunched through their flippers. They gasp and wince and bleed all over the place. Obviously it hurts them." Plant collecting—a branch snipped here, a leaf pressed there—seemed less harmful to him, with lower impacts on sensitive populations. Besides, he said, "I thought plants were more interesting."

TAKE-HOME MESSAGE 25.1

Vascular plants typically have aboveground shoots and belowground roots. Both consist of ground, vascular, and dermal tissue systems.

Ground tissues make up most of a plant. Vascular tissues that thread through ground tissue distribute water and nutrients. Dermal tissues cover and protect plant surfaces.

Eudicots and monocots have the same types of tissues, but differ somewhat in their pattern of tissue organization.

CREDITS: (2) Eudicots from top, © Catalin Petolea/Shutterstock; © gresei/Shutterstock; Courtesy of Dr. Thomas L Rost; © Frans Holthuysen, Making the invisible visible, Electron Microscopist, Phillips Research; Monocots from top, © Dr. Morley Read/Shutterstock; © Imageman/Shutterstock; Gary Head; Courtesy of Janet Wilmhurst, Landcare Research, New Zealand; art, © Cengage Learning 2015; (in text) © Jim Webb/National Geographic Creative.

TABLE 25.1

Overview of Flowering Plant Tissues

Tissue Type	Main Components	Main Functions
Simple Tissues		
Parenchyma	Parenchyma cells	Photosynthesis, storage, secretion, tissue repair
Collenchyma	Collenchyma cells	Pliable structural support
Sclerenchyma	Fibers or sclereids	Structural support
Complex Tissues		
Vascular		
Xylem	Tracheids; vessel elements; parenchyma cells; sclerenchyma cells	Water-conducting tubes; structural support
Phloem	Sieve elements, parenchyma cells; sclerenchyma cells	Sugar-conducting tubes and their supporting cells
Dermal		
Epidermis	Epidermal cells, their secretions and outgrowths	Secretion of cuticle; protection; control of gas exchange and water loss
Periderm	Cork cambium; cork cells; parenchyma	Forms protective cover on older stems, roots

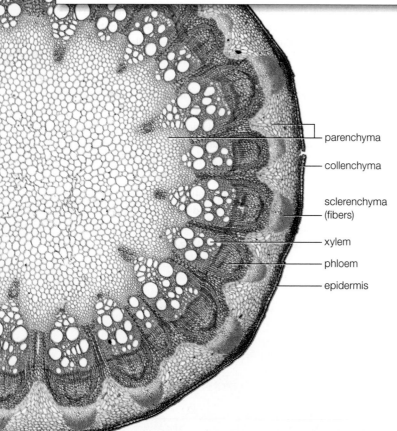

parenchyma

collenchyma

sclerenchyma (fibers)

xylem

phloem

epidermis

FIGURE 25.3 Locations of some tissues in the stem of *Clematis*, a eudicot.

In plants, simple tissues consist primarily of one type of cell; complex tissues have two or more cell types (**TABLE 25.1**). Some of these tissues are visible in **FIGURE 25.3**.

SIMPLE TISSUES

 Parenchyma is a simple tissue that makes up most of the soft internal parts of a plant. The shape of parenchyma cells varies with their function, but all have a thin, flexible cell wall (*left*). These cells are alive in mature tissue and can continue to divide, so they play an important role in wound repair. Parenchyma has other specialized roles that vary by the tissue's location. In leaves and soft stems, for example, chloroplast-containing parenchyma (*left*) is photosynthetic; parenchyma cells in stems and roots store starch, proteins, water, and oils in their central vacuoles. Other functions of parenchyma include structural support, nectar secretion, and gas exchange in leaves and stems.

 Collenchyma (*left*) is a simple tissue that supports rapidly growing plant parts such as young stems and leaf stalks. Collenchyma cells stay alive in mature tissue. A complex polysaccharide called pectin imparts flexibility to these cells' primary wall, which is thickened unevenly where three or more of the cells abut one another.

 Variably shaped cells of **sclerenchyma** die when they mature, but their thick, lignin-containing cell walls remain. This sturdy simple tissue helps plant parts resist stretching and compression. Fibers (*left*) are long, tapered sclerenchyma cells; they occur in bundles that support and protect vascular tissues in stems and leaves. The bundles flex and twist, but resist stretching. We use fibers of some plants in cloth, rope, paper, and other commercial products. Sclereids (*left*) are sclerenchyma cells that strengthen hard seed coats such as peach pits, and they make pear flesh gritty.

COMPLEX TISSUES

 The first dermal tissue to form on a plant is **epidermis**, which, in most species, consists of one layer of cells on the plant's outer surface (*left*). Epidermal cells secrete waxy substances on their outward-facing cell walls. The deposits form a waterproof cuticle that helps the

CREDITS: (3) Dr. Keith Wheeler/Science Source; (in text) from top, © Ross E. Koning, http://plantphys.info; © ISM/Phototake; © Ross E. Koning, http://plantphys.info; © Ross E. Koning, http://plantphys.info; © Kingsley R. kStern; © Donal L. Rubbelke/Lakeland Community College.

plant conserve water and repel pathogens. The epidermis of leaves and young stems includes specialized cells and, often, hairs and other epidermal cell outgrowths. Special paired epidermal cells form stomata. Plants control the diffusion of water vapor and gases across epidermis by opening and closing these tiny gaps (Section 6.5). In older stems and roots, a complex dermal tissue called periderm (*above*) replaces epidermis.

Ground tissue includes the tissues specialized for photosynthesis and for storage (the inset at *left* shows starch-packed organelles in the ground tissue of a potato). Ground tissue consists mostly of parenchyma, but can also include other simple tissues. Parenchyma cells that contain chloroplasts compose **mesophyll**, which is photosynthetic ground tissue.

Pipelines of complex vascular tissues (*left*) distribute water and nutrients through all parts of the plant body. The two types of vascular tissue, xylem and phloem, are typically bundled with sclerenchyma fibers in young plant parts. Both vascular tissues are composed of elongated conducting tubes.

Xylem, which conducts water and mineral ions, consists of vessel elements (**FIGURE 25.4A**) and tracheids (**FIGURE 25.4B**). Both types of cells are dead in mature tissue, but their stiff, waterproof walls remain. These interconnected walls form tubes that conduct water and also lend structural support to the plant. Water can move laterally between the tubes as well as upward through them (Section 26.4 returns to water flow through xylem).

Phloem, which conducts sugars and other organic solutes, consists of cells called sieve elements and their associated companion cells. Both types of cells are alive in mature tissue. Sieve elements connect end to end at sieve plates

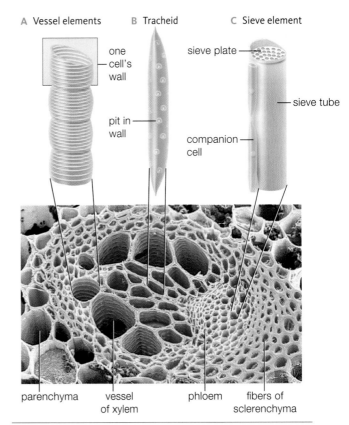

A Vessel elements   B Tracheid   C Sieve element

one cell's wall

pit in wall

sieve plate

sieve tube

companion cell

parenchyma   vessel of xylem   phloem   fibers of sclerenchyma

FIGURE 25.4 {Animated} Vascular tissues. Parenchyma cells and fibers of sclerenchyma are also visible in the micrograph.

FIGURE IT OUT: What are the green structures in some of the parenchyma cells?   Answer: Chloroplasts

(*left*), forming sieve tubes that conduct sugars to all parts of the plant (**FIGURE 25.4C**). Companion cells are a type of parenchyma. A companion cell provides each sieve element with metabolic support, and also transfers sugars into it (Section 26.6 returns to the details of sugar transport through phloem).

collenchyma Simple plant tissue composed of living cells with unevenly thickened walls; provides flexible support.
epidermis Dermal tissue; outermost layer of a young plant.
mesophyll Photosynthetic parenchyma.
parenchyma Simple tissue composed of living cells with different functions depending on location; main component of ground tissue.
phloem Complex vascular tissue of plants; its living sieve elements compose sieve tubes that distribute sugars.
sclerenchyma Simple plant tissue composed of cells that die when they are mature; their lignin-reinforced cell walls remain and structurally support plant parts. Includes fibers, sclereids.
xylem Complex vascular tissue of plants; its dead tracheids and vessel elements distribute water and mineral ions.

TAKE-HOME MESSAGE 25.2

Dermal tissues cover and protect plant surfaces. Epidermis, which includes epidermal cells, their secretions, and outgrowths, covers young plant surfaces.

Ground tissues make up most of a plant. Cells of parenchyma have diverse roles, including photosynthesis. Collenchyma and sclerenchyma support and strengthen plant parts.

Vascular tissues distribute water and solutes through ground tissue. In xylem, water and ions flow through tubes of dead tracheids and vessel elements. In phloem, sieve tubes that consist of living cells distribute sugars.

CREDITS: (in text) left column from the top, Science Photo Library/SuperStock; © age footstock/SuperStock; Garry DeLong/Science Source; right column, © M.I. Walker/Wellcome Images; (4) top, From Starr, Biology Today and Tomorrow, 1E. © 2005 Cengage Learning; bottom, Andrew Syred/Science Source.

Stems form the basic structure of a flowering plant, providing support and keeping leaves positioned for photosynthesis. They can grow above or below the soil, and many species have stems specialized for storage or asexual reproduction. Stems typically have **nodes**, which are regions that can bud and give rise to new shoots or roots.

Inside stems, xylem and phloem are organized as long, multistranded **vascular bundles**. The main function of vascular bundles is to conduct water, ions, and nutrients between different parts of the plant. Some components of the bundles—fibers and the lignin-reinforced walls of tracheids—also play an important role in supporting upright stems of land plants.

Vascular bundles extend through the ground tissue of all stems and leaves, but the arrangement of the bundles inside these plant parts differs between monocots and eudicots. The vascular bundles of monocot stems are typically distributed throughout the ground tissue (**FIGURE 25.5A**). By contrast, all of the vascular bundles inside a typical eudicot stem are arranged in a characteristic ring (**FIGURE 25.5B**). The ring divides the stem's ground tissue into distinct regions of pith (inside the ring) and cortex (outside the ring).

VARIATIONS

Many plants have modified stem structures that function in storage and reproduction. Some examples are listed below.

Stolons Stolons are stems that branch from the main stem of the plant and grow horizontally along the ground or just under its surface. Stolons may look like roots, but they have nodes (roots do not have nodes). Roots and leafy shoots

---

FIGURE 25.5 Comparing the structure of a young shoot from **A** a monocot and **B** a eudicot. Cells appear different colors in the sections because they have been stained with different dyes that bind to certain carbohydrates and lignin.

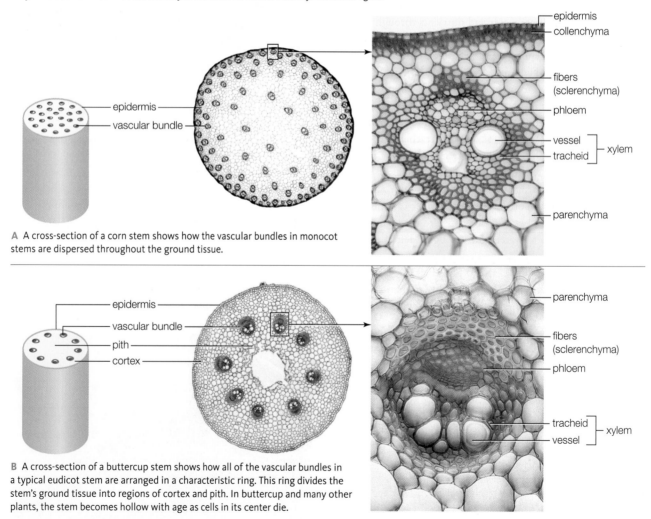

A A cross-section of a corn stem shows how the vascular bundles in monocot stems are dispersed throughout the ground tissue.

B A cross-section of a buttercup stem shows how all of the vascular bundles in a typical eudicot stem are arranged in a characteristic ring. This ring divides the stem's ground tissue into regions of cortex and pith. In buttercup and many other plants, the stem becomes hollow with age as cells in its center die.

that sprout from the nodes develop into new plants. Stolons are commonly called runners because in many plants they "run" along the surface of the soil (**FIGURE 25.6A**).

Bulbs A bulb is a short section of underground stem encased by overlapping layers of thickened, modified leaves called scales (**FIGURE 25.6B**). The scales develop from the base of the bulb, as do roots. Bulb scales contain starch and other substances that a plant holds in reserve for times when conditions in the environment are unfavorable for growth. When favorable conditions return, the plant then uses these stored substances to sustain rapid growth. The dry, paperlike outer scale of many bulbs serves as a protective covering.

Corms A corm is a squat, thickened underground stem that stores nutrients (**FIGURE 25.6C**). Like a bulb, a corm can grow roots from its base. Unlike a bulb, a corm has nodes.

Tubers Tubers are thickened portions of underground stolons; they are the plant's primary storage tissue. Tubers are like corms in that they have nodes from which new shoots and roots sprout, but no roots or shoots grow from their base (**FIGURE 25.6D**).

Rhizomes Some grasses have rhizomes, which are fleshy stems that typically grow under the soil and parallel to its surface. A rhizome is the main stem of the plant, and it also serves as the plant's primary storage tissue. Shoots that sprout from nodes grow aboveground for photosynthesis and flowering (**FIGURE 25.6E**).

Cladodes Many types of cacti and other succulents have cladodes, which are flattened, photosynthetic stems that store water. New plants form at the nodes. The cladodes of some plants appear leaflike, but most are unmistakably fleshy (**FIGURE 25.6F**).

---

node A region of stem where new shoots form.
vascular bundle In a stem or leaf, multistranded bundle formed by xylem, phloem, and sclerenchyma fibers.

A New plants sprout from runners (stolons) of a strawberry plant.

B Scales surround the stem at the center of an onion, which is a bulb.

C New shoots can arise from nodes on corms of crocus plants.

D Potatoes are tubers that grow on stolons. The "eyes" are the nodes of the tubers.

E The main stems of turmeric plants are underground rhizomes.

F Prickly pear and many other succulent plants have fleshy (sometimes spiky) cladodes.

FIGURE 25.6 Some examples of specialized stem structure.

CREDITS: (6A) © Anthony Tripodi, www.thecompostbin.com; (6B) Chase Studio/Science Source; (6C) © iStockphoto.com/mjutabor; (6D) © Ian Young, www.srgc.org.uk; (6E) © Dinodia Photo Library/Botanica/ Getty Images; (6F) © Chris Hellier/Corbis.

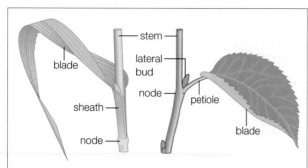

A Typical leaves of monocots (*left*) and eudicots (*right*).

B Examples of common leaf forms in eudicots. *Top row*: simple leaves; *bottom row*, compound leaves.

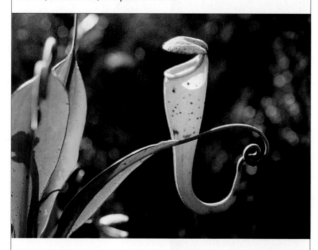

C Example of specialized leaf form. Carnivorous plants of the genus *Nepenthes* grow in nitrogen-poor soil. They secrete acids and protein-digesting enzymes into fluid in a cup-shaped modi-fied leaf. The enzymes release nitrogen from small prey, such as insects, frogs, and rats, that are attracted to odors from the fluid and then drown in it.

FIGURE 25.7 **Leaf structure.**

Most leaves are thin, with a high surface-to-volume ratio. They are the main organs of photosynthesis in most flowering plant species. Leaves also function in gas exchange, and they are the major site of evaporative water loss.

Monocot leaves tend to be long and narrow; the base of the leaf wraps around the stem, forming a sheath around it (**FIGURE 25.7A**). In eudicots, a short stalk called a petiole attaches the leaf to a stem. Eudicot leaves vary widely in their structure. Simple leaves are undivided, although many are lobed; compound leaves have blades divided into leaflets (**FIGURE 25.7B**). Some eudicot leaves are highly specialized (**FIGURE 25.7C**).

INTERNAL STRUCTURE

FIGURE 25.8 illustrates the internal structure of a typical eudicot leaf. The bulk of the leaf consists of mesophyll, which is photosynthetic parenchyma with air spaces between cells. Eudicot leaves are typically oriented perpendicular to the sun and have two layers of mesophyll. The uppermost layer is palisade mesophyll ❶. Cells in this layer have more chloroplasts than cells of the spongy mesophyll layer below. Cells of spongy mesophyll are more rounded than those of palisade mesophyll, and have larger air spaces between them ❷.

Leaves have **veins**, which are vascular bundles strengthened with sclerenchyma fibers. Inside each vein, strands of xylem transport water and dissolved mineral ions to photosynthetic cells, while strands of phloem transport products of photosynthesis (sugars) away from them ❸. In most eudicot leaves, large veins branch into a network of minor veins.

The outermost tissue of a leaf is a sheet of epidermis one cell thick ❹. This surface tissue may be smooth, sticky, or slimy. Outgrowths of epidermal cells can form hairs, scales, spikes, hooks, and other structures (some are shown in the chapter opening photo). Epidermal cells secrete a translucent, waxy cuticle that slows water loss. A leaf's upper surface, which receives the most direct sunlight, may secrete a thicker cuticle than the lower surface, which tends to be shaded. The lower surface usually has more stomata ❺. Guard cells on either side of each stoma may contain chloroplasts, but these are the only photosynthetic cells in leaf epidermis. As you will see in Section 26.5, changes in the shape of guard cells close stomata to prevent water loss, or open stomata to allow gases to cross the epidermis. Carbon dioxide needed for photosynthesis enters a leaf through stomata, then diffuses through air spaces to

vein A vascular bundle in a leaf or other plant part.

FIGURE 25.8 {Animated} Anatomy of a eudicot leaf.

The bulk of the leaf is mesophyll, a type of photosynthetic parenchyma. Eudicot leaves often have two distinct layers of this tissue: palisade mesophyll with elongated cells ❶, and spongy mesophyll with rounded cells ❷.

❸ Inside leaf veins, vascular bundles of xylem (blue) and phloem (pink) transport materials to and from photosynthetic cells.

❹ The leaf surface is epidermis with a secreted layer of cuticle.

❺ Gas exchanges between air inside and outside of the leaf occur at stomata.

❹ epidermis
❶ palisade mesophyll
❷ spongy mesophyll
xylem
❸ vascular tissue
phloem
❹ epidermis
❺ stomata

mesophyll cells. Oxygen released by photosynthesis diffuses in the opposite direction.

Monocot and eudicot leaves have a somewhat different internal structure. Blades of grass and other monocot leaves that grow vertically can intercept light from all directions. Such leaves typically have a single layer of mesophyll (FIGURE 25.9). Unlike a eudicot's branching veins, monocot veins are similar in length and run parallel with the leaf's long axis (as shown in FIGURE 25.1).

TAKE-HOME MESSAGE 25.4

Leaves are structurally adapted to intercept sunlight and exchange gases for photosynthesis.

Leaf components include veins (bundles of vascular tissue), mesophyll (photosynthetic cells), and cuticle-secreting epidermis.

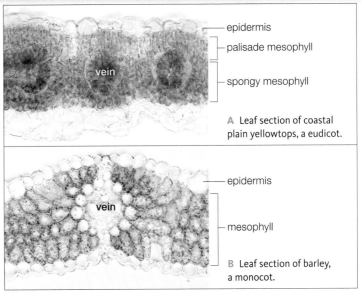

epidermis
palisade mesophyll
spongy mesophyll
vein

A Leaf section of coastal plain yellowtops, a eudicot.

epidermis
vein
mesophyll

B Leaf section of barley, a monocot.

FIGURE 25.9 Leaf cross-sections from a eudicot **A** and monocot **B**.

CREDITS: (8) © Cengage Learning 2011; (9) Masahiro Yamada, Michio Kawasaki, Tatsuo Sugiyama, Hiroshi Miyake, Mitsutaka Taniguchi; "Differential Positioning of C4 Mesophyll and Bundle Sheath Chloroplasts: Aggregative Movement of C4 Mesophyll Chloroplasts in Response to Environmental Stresses": Plant and Cell Physiology; (2009) 50(10: 1736–1749).

A Fibrous root systems have similar-sized adventitious roots that branch from nodes on the stem. The photo shows the fibrous root system of corn.

B Taproot systems consist of a large main root together with lateral roots that branch from it. The photo shows the taproot system of salsify.

FIGURE 25.10 {Animated} Root systems.

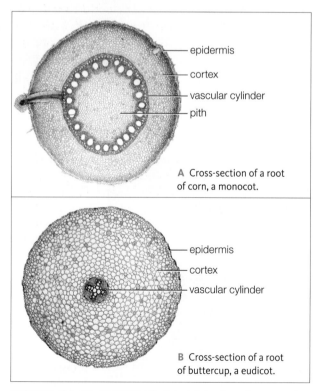

A Cross-section of a root of corn, a monocot.

- epidermis
- cortex
- vascular cylinder
- pith

B Cross-section of a root of buttercup, a eudicot.

- epidermis
- cortex
- vascular cylinder

FIGURE 25.11 Comparing the internal structure of young roots from monocots and eudicots.

Roots take up water and mineral ions, and transport these substances to other parts of the plant. The root system of a typical plant is at least as extensive as its shoot system. A large surface area and other specializations adapt roots for absorbing water and mineral ions from the soil (Chapter 26 returns to this topic).

As you will see in Chapter 27, the first structure to emerge from a seed is a root. In typical monocots, this primary root is quickly replaced with a mat of adventitious roots that sprout from nodes on the stem. All of the roots in the resulting **fibrous root system** are about equal in diameter—there is no dominant, central root (**FIGURE 25.10A**). In typical eudicots, the primary root that emerges from a seed thickens as it grows longer. It also develops many lateral roots, which, unlike adventitious roots, develop from other roots. A eudicot primary root together with its smaller lateral root branchings constitutes a **taproot system** (**FIGURE 25.10B**).

A column of vascular tissue called the **vascular cylinder** runs lengthwise through the center of each root. In a typical monocot root, the vascular cylinder divides ground tissue into regions of cortex and pith (**FIGURE 25.11A**). By contrast, there is no pith in the middle of the vascular cylinder of a typical eudicot root (**FIGURE 25.11B**). In these plants, xylem and phloem make up the bulk of the vascular cylinder (**FIGURE 25.12**).

root hair

1 mm

A root's dermal tissue is the plant's absorptive interface with soil. Epidermal cells on young roots often send out very thin extensions called **root hairs** (*left*). These structures are tiny, but many of them form. Collectively, they increase the root's surface area available for taking up soil water along with dissolved oxygen and mineral ions. Water and dissolved substances enter a root by crossing epidermal cells and seeping into parenchyma of the root's cortex. The water moves from cell to cell of the cortex until it reaches the vascular cylinder. The outer boundary of the vascular cylinder is a layer of cells called **endodermis** (Section 26.2 explains how endodermal cells help control uptake of solutes from soil water). Just inside the endodermis is **pericycle**, a layer of specialized parenchyma one or two cells thick. These cells retain the capacity to divide and differentiate, so they can give rise to several different types of structures. Lateral roots form from divisions of these cells (a new lateral root branching from pericycle is visible in the micrograph in **FIGURE 25.11A**).

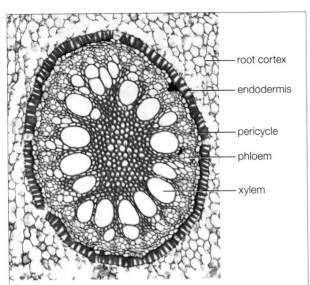

A Vascular cylinder in a root of iris, a monocot.

root cortex
endodermis
pericycle
phloem
xylem

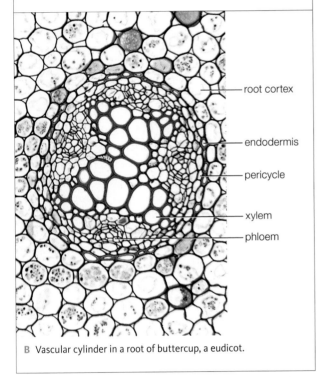

root cortex
endodermis
pericycle
xylem
phloem

B Vascular cylinder in a root of buttercup, a eudicot.

FIGURE 25.12 Comparing the arrangement of tissues inside monocot and eudicot vascular cylinders.

endodermis Outer layer of the vascular cylinder in a plant root; sheet of cells just outside the pericycle.
fibrous root system Root system composed of an extensive mass of similar-sized adventitious roots; typical of monocots.
pericycle Layer of cells just inside root endodermis.
root hairs Hairlike, absorptive extensions of a young cell of root epidermis.
taproot system In eudicots, an enlarged primary root together with all of the lateral roots that branch from it.
vascular cylinder A root's central column of vascular tissue.

CREDITS: (12A) Dr. Keith Wheeler/Science Source; (12B) © Dr. John D. Cunningham/Visuals Unlimited; (in text) © Jon Keeley.

PEOPLE MATTER

National Geographic Grantee
DR. JON KEELEY

Land plants typically get carbon for photosynthesis from carbon dioxide. CO_2 gas enters their tissues through open stomata on aboveground parts, mainly leaves. National Geographic grantee Jon Keeley discovered that one land plant gets its carbon a different way. This quillwort, *Isoetes andicola*, lives where few other species survive: above 4,000 meters (13,000 feet) in the Peruvian Andes, where the air is hot every day and the ground freezes every night. The ground, when not frozen, is oversaturated with oxygen-poor water that inhibits normal decay of organic matter.

The structure of *I. andicola* is unusual even for a seedless vascular plant (Section 21.3). Its tiny leaves have an extremely thick cuticle and only the tips are photosynthetic—adaptations that probably help protect the leaves from the intense light in the

plant's high-altitude habitat. The leaves have no stomata: Gas exchange occurs almost entirely through huge roots (*left*) that make up the bulk of the plant body. Photosynthetically produced oxygen emitted by the roots keeps the surrounding soil from being entirely anaerobic. The added oxygen helps the abundant organic matter in the soil to be broken down to carbon dioxide. The plant's roots take up the CO_2 from soil during the day, and fix carbon in a CAM pathway overnight (Section 6.5).

TAKE-HOME MESSAGE 25.5

Taproot systems consist of an enlarged primary root and lateral roots that branch from it. Fibrous root systems consist of adventitious roots that replace the primary root.

A vascular cylinder running lengthwise through each root contains long strands of xylem and phloem.

Roots absorb water and dissolved minerals from soil for distribution to the rest of the plant.

All plant tissues arise from the activity of **meristems**, which are regions of undifferentiated cells that can divide rapidly. When meristem cells divide, some of their descendants differentiate, giving rise to vascular, ground, and epidermal tissues as they enlarge and mature.

PRIMARY GROWTH

Plant parts lengthen by activity at **apical meristems** in the tips of shoots and roots. This lengthening is called **primary growth**. During a plant's primary growth, its stems and roots lengthen and it produces soft organs such as leaves.

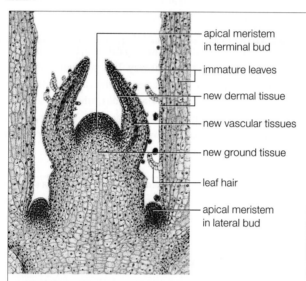

apical meristem in terminal bud

immature leaves

new dermal tissue

new vascular tissues

new ground tissue

leaf hair

apical meristem in lateral bud

A Primary growth in a shoot tip of *Coleus*, a eudicot.

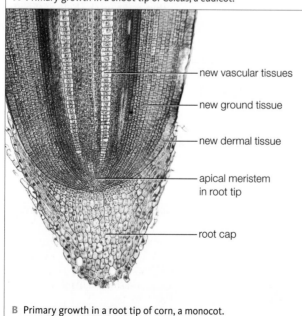

new vascular tissues

new ground tissue

new dermal tissue

apical meristem in root tip

root cap

B Primary growth in a root tip of corn, a monocot.

FIGURE 25.13 Zones of primary growth in a root and shoot.

In a shoot, primary growth occurs at the terminal bud, which is the shoot's tip (**FIGURE 25.13A**). A mass of apical meristem lies just below the surface of the bud. Cells at the center of the mass are completely undifferentiated, and they divide continually during the growing season. The divisions push some of the cells toward the edge of the mass. Cells that are displaced away from the center of the meristem begin to differentiate. The shoot grows longer mainly because differentiating cells under the mass of meristem elongate as they take on their specialized functions. The apical meristem remains at the tip of the lengthening shoot, continually renewing itself and also producing cells that divide and differentiate below it.

As a stem lengthens during primary growth, lateral buds form at the nodes. Depending on hormonal signals, divisions of apical meristem cells in the tip of a lateral bud can give rise to either a branch, a leaf, or a flower.

As in stems, primary growth in roots originates at apical meristems. Cells in the apical meristem of a root tip divide repeatedly, and some differentiate to form specialized tissues (**FIGURE 25.13B**). A root cap forms and protects the soft, young root as it grows through soil. Cells of the root cap are shed continually as the root lengthens.

SECONDARY GROWTH

Many eudicot and gymosperm species undergo **secondary growth**, during which their stems and roots thicken and become woody. The thickening originates at **lateral meristems**, which are cylindrical layers of meristem that run lengthwise through stems and roots. In roots, lateral meristems arise from pericycle; in shoots, they arise from bits of meristem between xylem and phloem in vascular bundles.

apical meristem Meristem in the tip of a shoot or root; gives rise to primary growth (lengthening).
bark In woody plants, all living and dead tissue that lies outside of the vascular cambium.
cork Tissue that waterproofs, insulates, and protects the surfaces of woody stems and roots.
cork cambium Lateral meristem that gives rise to periderm.
lateral meristem Vascular cambium or cork cambium; cylindrical sheet of meristem that runs lengthwise through shoots and roots; gives rise to secondary growth (thickening).
meristem Zone of undifferentiated plant cells; all plant growth arises from divisions of meristem cells.
periderm Plant dermal tissue that replaces epidermis during secondary growth of woody stems and roots.
primary growth Lengthening of young shoots and roots; originates at apical meristems.
secondary growth Thickening of older stems and roots; originates at lateral meristems.
vascular cambium Lateral meristem that produces secondary xylem and phloem.
wood Accumulated secondary xylem.

A lateral meristem called **vascular cambium** produces secondary vascular tissue: secondary phloem on its outer surface, and secondary xylem on its inner surface (**FIGURE 25.14**). **Wood** is secondary xylem that accumulates inside the cylinder of vascular cambium.

As a woody plant matures, its inner core of xylem thickens and displaces the vascular cambium toward the outside of the stem or root. Displaced cells of the vascular cambium divide in a widening circle, so this meristem tissue keeps its cylindrical form. Another lateral meristem, **cork cambium**, forms outside the cylinder of vascular cambium. Cork cambium produces **cork**, a protective tissue that consists of densely packed dead cells with thick, waxy walls. **Periderm** is a dermal tissue that comprises cork, cork cambium, and every other tissue between these two. What we call **bark** is an informal term for periderm and all other living and dead tissues that lie outside the ring of vascular cambium (**FIGURE 25.15**).

TAKE-HOME MESSAGE 25.6

Primary growth (lengthening) occurs at apical meristems in shoot and root tips.

Secondary growth, which thickens older roots and shoots, occurs at lateral meristems (vascular cambium and cork cambium) in many eudicots and gymnosperms.

Bark consists of all living and dead tissue that lie outside the vascular cambium.

FIGURE 25.14 {**Animated**} Secondary growth in a eudicot stem.

primary phloem
vascular cambium
primary xylem

cork cambium
secondary phloem
vascular cambium
secondary xylem

A In spring, primary growth resumes at terminal and lateral buds. Secondary growth occurs at vascular cambium and, in older shoots and roots, at cork cambium.

pith
endodermis
primary xylem
wood — secondary xylem
vascular cambium
phloem
bark — cork cambium
periderm — parenchyma
collenchyma
cork

FIGURE 25.15 Components of an older, woody eudicot stem.

division
differentiation
division
differentiation
division
differentiation
division
differentiation

X_1 X_1
P_1 P_1
X_2 X_2
P_2 P_2
X_1 X_1
X_2 X_2
X_3 X_3
P_1 P_1
P_2 P_2
P_3 P_3
P_1 P_1

Cells that differentiate on the pith (inner) side of the vascular cambium become part of xylem (X_1, X_2, X_3).

Cells that differentiate on the cortex (outer) side of the vascular cambium become part of phloem (P_1, P_2, P_3).

B Divisions of meristem cells in the vascular cambium expand the inner core of xylem, displacing the vascular cambium (orange) toward the surface of the stem or root.

CREDITS: (14) photo, © SeDmi/Shutterstock.com; art, From Starr/Taggart/Evers/Starr, Biology, 13E. © 2013 Cengage Learning; (15) Science Photo Library/SuperStock.

A Sap oozes from xylem in this freshly cut pine log. Sapwood is secondary xylem that is still functional. As a tree ages, the oldest xylem at the center of its trunk may no longer be able to transport fluid because it has clogged. This older xylem is called heartwood.

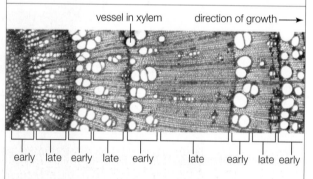

vessel in xylem   direction of growth ⟶

early   late   early   late   early   late   early   late early

B Early and late wood in an ash tree. The early wood formed during warm, wet springs. The late wood formed during warm, dry summers. Each band of early and late wood is one growth ring, or "tree ring."

1587–1589   1606–1612

C The relative thicknesses of a tree's rings can be used to estimate average annual rainfall long before records of climate were kept. This is a section of a bald cypress tree that was living near English colonists when they first settled in North America. Narrower annual rings mark years of severe drought.

FIGURE 25.16 Woody stems. Rings visible in the heartwood and sapwood are regions of early and late wood. In most temperate zone trees, one ring forms each year.

Wood's structure and function change with age. Over time, the secondary xylem at the center of an older woody stem can become so clogged by tannins, gums, and oils that it no longer transports fluid. Sapwood, the region of still-functional secondary xylem, lies between heartwood and vascular cambium. During spring in temperate zones, sugar-rich fluid (sap) travels through sapwood, from tree roots to buds (FIGURE 25.16A). Sap collected from maple trees as it starts to flow in spring is boiled to make maple syrup.

In trees that are dormant in winter, vascular cambium gives rise to large-diameter, thin-walled xylem cells (early wood) during spring. Late wood, with small-diameter, thick-walled xylem cells, forms during summer. Thus, a cross-section reveals rings that consist of alternating bands of early and late wood (FIGURE 25.16B). In tropical regions where weather does not vary seasonally, trees grow at the same rate all year and do not have rings.

Tree rings can be used to estimate average annual rainfall; to date archaeological ruins; to gather evidence of wildfires, floods, landslides, and glacier movements; and to study the ecology and effects of parasitic insect populations. How? Some species add wood over centuries, one ring per year. Count an old tree's rings, and you have an idea of its age. If you know the year in which the tree was cut, you can determine when a particular ring formed by counting rings backward from the outer edge. Thickness and other features of the rings offer clues about environmental conditions that prevailed during the years they formed.

Consider the case of early English settlers of the United States. In 1587, the first set of colonists arrived at what is now Roanoke Island, North Carolina, but all 150 of them were missing by 1589. A second set of settlers arrived at Jamestown, Virginia, in 1607. These colonists survived, but just barely; we know that more than 40 percent of them died in the summer of 1610 alone. Tree rings from nearby bald cypress trees revealed that the Roanoke settlers arrived for the worst drought in 800 years, and nearly a decade of severe drought struck Jamestown (FIGURE 25.16C). The corn crop of the Jamestown colony failed; a similar crop failure probably occurred at Roanoke. Jamestown is at the head of an estuary (a place where a river meets the ocean). During the drought, the river's water level must have dropped, so the settlers' drinking water would have mixed with ocean water and become salty. Piecing together these bits of evidence gives us an idea of what life must have been like for the settlers.

TAKE-HOME MESSAGE 25.7

The relative thickness and composition of a tree's annual rings hold clues to environmental conditions during its lifetime.

Exploration

FIGURE 25.17 Measuring a giant sequoia in California's Sequoia National Park.

A 2,000-YEAR-OLD GIANT SEQUOIA IS JUST CRANKING OUT WOOD. National Geographic Explorer Stephen Sillett discovered that sequoias and other long-lived trees increase wood production during old age. That may be because a tree's leaf area increases as its crown expands over a long life span. "What we're finding," says Sillett, "is that the rate of wood production in some species doesn't slow down until a tree gets to the end of its lifetime." Sillett and his team recently studied a 3,200-year-old giant sequoia tree in California's Sequoia National Park (**FIGURE 25.17**). By climbing and measuring this tree, they calculated that it holds more than 54,000 cubic feet (1,500 cubic meters) of wood and bark. That is a lot of wood and bark—and a lot of carbon-containing compounds. In an actively growing plant, photosynthetically produced sugars are continually remodeled into other carbon-containing compounds that end up in plant tissues. Carbon incorporated into sturdy plant

tissues such as wood can stay out of the atmosphere for thousands of years.

Sillett's findings are very relevant for carbon offsets, which are financial instruments designed to reduce global emissions of carbon dioxide and other carbon-based greenhouse gases. Companies and individuals buy carbon offsets to "offset" activities that release these greenhouse gases. The funds are then used to support projects aimed at reducing emissions of the gases, or activities that remove the gases from the atmosphere.

Some carbon offsets support activities such as increasing plant density in existing forests, and replanting deforested areas. Such activities typically cost less than other methods of removing carbon from the atmosphere, in part because they take advantage of the ability of plants to do this naturally. Forests worldwide absorb about 3 billion tons of CO_2 from the atmosphere every year, about one-third of the amount released by human activities.

Summary

SECTION 25.1 Most flowering plants have belowground roots and aboveground shoots, including stems, leaves, and flowers. Roots and shoots consist of ground, vascular, and dermal tissue systems. **Ground tissue** makes up the bulk of a plant, and **dermal tissues** protect its surfaces. **Vascular tissues** conduct water and nutrients to all parts of the plant. Monocots and eudicots have the same tissues organized in different ways.

SECTION 25.2 **Parenchyma, collenchyma,** and **sclerenchyma** are simple tissues; each consists of only one type of cell. **Mesophyll** is photosynthetic parenchyma. Living cells in collenchyma have sturdy, flexible walls that support fast-growing plant parts. Cells in sclerenchyma die at maturity, but their lignin-reinforced walls remain and support the plant. Stomata open across **epidermis,** a dermal tissue that covers soft plant parts. In vascular tissue, water and dissolved minerals flow through vessels of **xylem,** and sugars travel through vessels of **phloem.**

SECTION 25.3 **Vascular bundles** extending through stems conduct water and nutrients between different parts of the plant, and also help structurally support the plant body. In most eudicot stems, vascular bundles form a ring that divides the ground tissue into cortex and pith. In monocot stems, the vascular bundles are distributed throughout the ground tissue. New shoots and roots form at **nodes** on stems. Many stems are specialized for storage or for reproduction.

SECTION 25.4 Leaves, which are specialized for photosynthesis, contain mesophyll and vascular bundles (**veins**) between their upper and lower epidermis. Eudicots typically have two layers of mesophyll; monocots do not. Water vapor and gases cross cuticle-covered epidermis at stomata.

SECTION 25.5 Roots absorb water and mineral ions for the entire plant. Inside each is a **vascular cylinder** enclosed by **endodermis. Root hairs** increase the surface area of roots. Many monocots have a **fibrous root system** that consists of similar-sized adventitious roots. Most eudicots have a **taproot system**—an enlarged primary root with its lateral root branchings. Lateral roots arise from divisions of **pericycle** cells inside the root vascular cylinder.

SECTION 25.6 All plant tissues originate at **meristems,** which are regions of undifferentiated cells that retain their ability to divide. **Primary growth** (lengthening) arises at **apical meristems** in the tips of shoots and roots. **Secondary growth** (thickening) arises at **lateral meristems** (**vascular cambium** and **cork cambium**) in older stems and roots. Vascular cambium produces secondary xylem (**wood**) and secondary phloem. Cork cambium gives rise to **periderm,** which includes **cork. Bark** is all tissue that lies outside of the vascular cambium of a woody plant.

SECTION 25.7 In many trees, one ring forms each season. Tree rings hold information about environmental conditions that prevailed while the rings were forming. For example, the relative thicknesses of the rings reflect the relative availability of water.

SECTION 25.8 By the process of photosynthesis, plants naturally remove carbon from the atmosphere and incorporate it into their tissues. Carbon that is locked in molecules of wood and other durable plant tissues can stay out of the atmosphere for centuries.

Self-Quiz   Answers in Appendix VII

1. In plants, fibers are a type of _____ cell.
   a. parenchyma   c. collenchyma
   b. sclerenchyma   d. mesophyll

2. Ground tissue consists mainly of _____ .
   a. waxes and cutin   c. parenchyma cells
   b. lignified cell walls   d. cork but not bark

3. Which of the following cell types stay alive when they mature? Choose all that apply.
   a. companion cells   c. tracheids
   b. sieve elements   d. vessel elements

4. All of the vascular bundles inside a typical _____ are arranged in a ring.
   a. monocot stem   c. monocot root
   b. eudicot stem   d. eudicot root

5. True or false? Lateral roots form at nodes on roots.

6. Epidermis and periderm are _____ tissues.
   a. ground   b. vascular   c. dermal

7. A vascular bundle in a leaf is called _____ .
   a. xylem   b. mesophyll   c. a vein

8. Typically, vascular tissue is organized as _____ in stems and as _____ in roots.
   a. multiple vascular bundles; one vascular cylinder
   b. one vascular bundle; multiple vascular cylinders
   c. one vascular cylinder; multiple vascular bundles
   d. multiple vascular cylinders; one vascular bundle

9. An onion is a _____ (choose all that apply).
   a. root   c. bulb
   b. stem   d. corm

10. In a(n) _____ , the primary root is typically the largest.
    a. lateral meristem   c. fibrous root system
    b. adventitious root system   d. taproot system

11. The main function of root hairs is to _____ .
    a. conduct water from cortex to aboveground shoots
    b. increase the root's surface area for absorption
    c. anchor the plant in soil

Data Analysis Activities

Tree Rings and Droughts El Malpais National Monument, in west central New Mexico, has pockets of vegetation that have been surrounded by lava fields for about 3,000 years, so they have escaped wildfires, grazing animals, agricultural activity, and logging. Henri Grissino-Mayer generated a 2,129-year annual precipitation record using tree ring data from living and dead trees in this park (**FIGURE 25.18**).

1. The Mayan civilization began to suffer a massive loss of population around 770 A.D. Do these tree ring data reflect a drought condition at this time? If so, was that condition more or less severe than the dust bowl drought?

2. One of the worst population catastrophes ever recorded occurred in Mesoamerica between 1519 and 1600 A.D., when around 22 million people native to the region died. Which period between 137 B.C. and 1992 had the most severe drought? How long did that drought last?

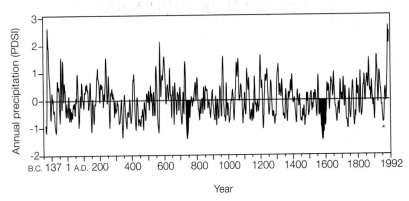

FIGURE 25.18 A 2,129-year annual precipitation record compiled from tree rings in El Malpais National Monument, New Mexico. Data was averaged over 10-year intervals; graph correlates with other indicators of rainfall collected in all parts of North America. PDSI: Palmer Drought Severity Index: 0, normal rainfall; increasing numbers mean increasing excess of rainfall; decreasing numbers mean increasing severity of drought.

* A severe drought contributed to a series of catastrophic dust storms that turned the midwestern United States into a "dust bowl" between 1933 and 1939.

12. Roots and shoots lengthen through activity at _____ .
    a. apical meristems   c. vascular cambium
    b. lateral meristems   d. cork cambium

13. The activity of lateral meristems _____ older roots and stems.
    a. lengthens   b. thickens   c. both a and b

14. Tree rings occur because _____ .
    a. there are droughts during the time the rings form
    b. environmental conditions influence xylem cell size
    c. heartwood alternates with sapwood
    d. periderm replaces epidermis

15. Match the plant parts with the best description.
    ____ vascular cambium   a. ground tissue
    ____ mesophyll   b. type of stem
    ____ wood   c. a lateral meristem
    ____ cortex   d. photosynthetic parenchyma
    ____ potato   e. secondary xylem
    ____ parallel veins   f. formed by epidermal cells
    ____ stomata   g. characteristic of monocot leaves

Critical Thinking

1. Oscar and Lucinda meet in a tropical rain forest and fall in love, and he carves their initials into the bark of a tree. They never do get together, though. Ten years later, still heartbroken, Oscar searches for the tree. Given what you know about primary and secondary growth, will he find the carved initials higher relative to ground level? If he goes berserk and chops down the tree, what kinds of growth rings will he see?

2. Is the plant with the yellow flower *above* a eudicot or a monocot? What about the plant with the purple flower?

3. Was the section shown at *right* taken from a stem or a root? Monocot or eudicot? How do you know?

4. Aboveground plant surfaces are covered with a waxy cuticle. Why do roots lack this protective coating?

5. Why do eudicot trees tend to be wider at the base than at the top?

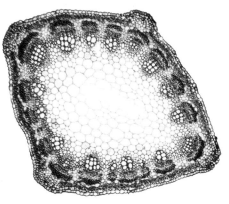

CENGAGE brain .com To access course materials, please visit www.cengagebrain.com.

CREDITS: (18) Data by Henri D. Grissino-Mayer; (in text) CT2, © Edward S. Ross; CT3, © Mike Clayton/University of Wisconsin Department of Botany.

Water flows through pitted walls of xylem tubes, visible in this lengthwise section through a sunflower stem. Ladderlike lines are rings of lignin. The spacing of the rings differs because older tubes stretch as living cells in adjacent tissue enlarge lengthwise.

26

PLANT NUTRITION AND TRANSPORT

Links to Earlier Concepts

Before beginning this chapter, be sure you understand plant anatomy (Sections 25.1–25.5) and adaptations to life on land (4.10, 21.1). Water movement through a plant depends on hydrogen bonding and cohesion (2.4). We revisit nutrients (1.2), ions (2.2), carbohydrates (3.2), osmosis (5.6), membrane transport (5.7), photosynthesis (6.3–6.5), aerobic respiration (7.1, 7.2), nitrogen fixation (19.5), and mycorrhizae (22.3).

KEY CONCEPTS

PLANT NUTRIENTS AND SOIL

Many plant structures are adaptations to limited availability of water and essential minerals. The amount of water and nutrients available for plant uptake depends on soil composition.

NUTRIENT UPTAKE BY ROOTS

Structural and functional specializations allow the roots of vascular plants to selectively take up nutrients from soil water. Mutualisms with microorganisms can enhance nutrient uptake.

WATER FLOWS THROUGH XYLEM

Xylem tubes consist of the interconnected walls of dead cells. Evaporation from leaves and stems drives the upward movement of water through these tubes inside a plant.

CONTROL OF WATER LOSS

A plant's cuticle minimizes water loss. The opening and closing of stomata balance water conservation with gas exchange.

SUGARS FLOW THROUGH PHLOEM

Phloem distributes sugars through tubes that consist of stacks of living cells. Sugars are loaded into phloem in regions that produce them, and unloaded in regions that use them.

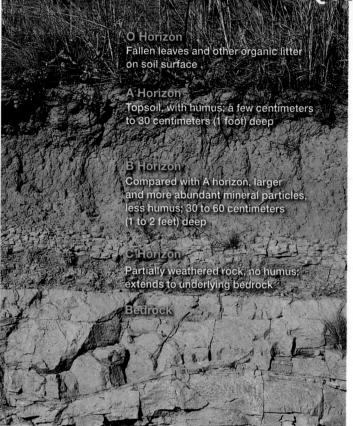

O Horizon
Fallen leaves and other organic litter
on soil surface

A Horizon
Topsoil, with humus; a few centimeters
to 30 centimeters (1 foot) deep

B Horizon
Compared with A horizon, larger
and more abundant mineral particles,
less humus; 30 to 60 centimeters
(1 to 2 feet) deep

C Horizon
Partially weathered rock, no humus;
extends to underlying bedrock

Bedrock

FIGURE 26.1 An example of soil horizons.

A plant needs sixteen elements to survive and grow. Nine of these are macronutrients, which are required in amounts above 0.5 percent of the plant's dry weight. Carbon, oxygen, and hydrogen are macronutrients, as are nitrogen, phosphorus, and sulfur (components of proteins and nucleic acids), potassium and calcium (which affect processes such as cell signaling), and magnesium (a component of chlorophyll). Chlorine, iron, boron, manganese, zinc, copper, and molybdenum are micronutrients, meaning they make up traces of the plant's dry weight. Among other roles, these elements serve as enzyme cofactors (Section 5.5).

PROPERTIES OF SOIL

Carbon, oxygen, and hydrogen atoms are abundantly available in carbon dioxide and water. Plants get the other elements they need when their roots take up minerals dissolved in soil water. Soils vary in their nutrient content and other properties, so some are better for plant growth than others. Soil consists mainly of mineral particles—sand, silt, and clay—that form by the weathering of rocks. Sand grains are about one millimeter in diameter. Silt particles are hundreds or thousands of times smaller than sand

grains, and clay particles are even smaller. Clay particles enhance the nutritive value of soils because they have a negative charge that attracts positively charged mineral ions in soil water. Thus, clay-rich soil retains dissolved nutrients that might otherwise trickle past roots too quickly to be absorbed. Sand and silt are also necessary for plant growth because they intervene between tiny particles of clay. Soils with too much clay pack so tightly that they exclude air— and the oxygen in it. Cells in a plant's roots, like cells in aboveground parts, require oxygen for aerobic respiration.

Soils with the best oxygen and water penetration are **loams**, which have roughly equal proportions of sand, silt, and clay. Most plants do best in loams that contain between 10 and 20 percent **humus**, which is decomposing organic material—fallen leaves, feces, and so on. Humus affects plant growth because it releases nutrients, and its negatively charged organic acids can trap positively charged mineral ions in soil water. Humus also swells and shrinks as it absorbs and releases water, and these changes in size aerate soil by opening spaces for air to penetrate. Humus tends to accumulate in waterlogged soils because water excludes air, and organic matter breaks down much more slowly in the absence of oxygen. Soils in swamps, bogs, and other perpetually wet areas often contain more than 90 percent humus. Very few types of plants can grow in these soils.

HOW SOILS CHANGE

Soils develop over thousands of years. They exist in different stages of development in different regions. Most form in layers, or horizons, that are distinct in color and other properties (**FIGURE 26.1**). Identifying the layers helps us compare soils in different places. For instance, the A horizon, which is **topsoil**, contains the greatest amount of organic matter, so the roots of most plants grow most densely in this layer. Grasslands typically have a deep layer of topsoil; tropical forests do not.

Minerals, salts, and other molecules dissolve in water as it filters through soil. **Leaching** is the process by which water removes soil nutrients and carries them away. Leaching is fastest in sandy soils, which do not bind nutrients as well as clay soils. **Soil erosion** is a loss of soil under the force of wind and water. Poor farming practices can also lead to erosion (**FIGURE 26.2**). Each year, about

humus Decaying organic matter in soil.
leaching Process by which water moving through soil removes nutrients from it.
loam Soil with roughly equal amounts of sand, silt, and clay.
soil erosion Loss of soil under the force of wind and water.
topsoil Uppermost soil layer; contains the most organic matter and nutrients for plant growth.

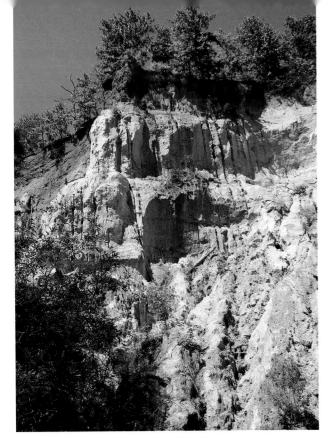

FIGURE 26.2 Runaway erosion in Providence Canyon, Georgia. European settlers who arrived in 1800 plowed the land straight up and down the hills. The furrows made excellent conduits for rainwater, which proceeded to carve out deep crevices that made even better rainwater conduits. The area became useless for farming by 1850. It now consists of about 445 hectares (1,100 acres) of deep canyons that continue to expand at the rate of about 2 meters (6 feet) per year.

25 billion metric tons of topsoil erode from croplands in the midwestern United States. The topsoil enters the Mississippi River, which then dumps it into the Gulf of Mexico. Nutrient loss because of such erosion affects not only plants that grow in the region, but also humans and other organisms that depend on the plants for survival.

TAKE-HOME MESSAGE 26.1

Plants require sixteen elements. All are available in water, air, and soil.

Soil consists mainly of mineral particles: sand, silt, and clay. Clay retains positively charged mineral ions in soil water.

Humus aerates soil, and like clay it retains positively charged mineral ions in soil water.

Most plants grow best in loams (soils with equal proportions of sand, silt, and clay) that contain 10 to 20 percent humus.

Leaching and erosion remove nutrients from soil.

PEOPLE MATTER

National Geographic Explorer
DR. JERRY GLOVER

What if a new grain of wheat holds the key to saving biodiversity, polluted ecosystems, and starving people? Agroecologist Jerry Glover is working on it, and he claims the future starts with the past. "Before agriculture, natural plant communities ruled the earth and kept ecosystems in perfect balance. How? Those plants were perennials, alive year-round and incredibly efficient at regulating processes like nutrient cycling and water management that protect ecosystem health. Their roots stretch deep below ground, controlling erosion and improving soil quality." Then everything changed. Humans harnessed vast swaths of the planet, replacing natural grasses with billions of acres of annual crops—plants that take much more than they give to crucial natural systems. Agriculture is now the number one man-made threat to global biodiversity and ecosystem function.

"It's time to put natural plant communities back in charge of the landscape," says Glover. "Annual crops must be planted from seed every year, literally starting over from scratch. That requires tremendous amounts of time, effort, and expense because annual crop species are very inefficient. They allow half of the nitrogen fertilizer farmers spread over fields to escape below the root zone or run off the soil surface. Growing annual crops requires extra fertilizer, heavy machinery, and disturbance of the land; and every year it's required again." Glover is part of a research team developing perennial crops—mainly grains—that could revolutionize agriculture and solve problems far beyond farm fields. Grains are cultivated on almost 70 percent of the world's agricultural land.

Why does this world beneath our feet matter so much? Many nutrients essential to human health come from the soil. Plants are the delivery system. "When we lose the health of our soil through erosion or degradation," says Glover, "crucial nutrients are no longer carried up to plants and passed on to humans. Studying this helps us see how perennial crops of the future could be farmed with less effort, more nutritional value, and at the high yields we'll need to feed a planet of seven to nine billion hungry people."

Water moves from soil, through a root's epidermis and cortex, to the vascular cylinder (FIGURE 26.3). Osmosis drives this movement, because fluid in the plant typically contains more solutes than soil water (Section 5.6). After water and mineral ions enter the vascular cylinder, xylem distributes them to the rest of the plant.

Most of the soil water that enters a root moves through cell walls ❶. Cell walls are permeable to water and ions, and in plants they are shared between adjacent cells (Section 4.10). The walls of tightly packed root cells form a pathway between epidermis and vascular cylinder. Thus, soil water can diffuse from epidermis, through the cortex, to the vascular cylinder without ever entering a cell.

Although soil water can reach the vascular cylinder by diffusing through cell walls, it cannot enter the cylinder the same way. Why not? A vascular cylinder is separated from root cortex by its endodermis, a tissue that consists of a single layer of tightly packed endodermal cells (Section 25.5). These cells secrete a waxy substance into their walls wherever they abut. The substance forms a **Casparian strip**, which is a waterproof band between the plasma membranes

of endodermal cells (FIGURE 26.4). A Casparian strip prevents water from diffusing through endodermal cell walls ❷. Thus, soil water can enter a vascular cylinder only by passing through the cytoplasm of an endodermal cell. Water enters the cytoplasm of an endodermal cell (or of any other cell in the root) by diffusing across its plasma membrane. Once inside a root cell's cytoplasm, the water diffuses from cell to cell through plasmodesmata (Section 4.10) until it enters xylem inside the vascular cylinder.

Water can diffuse across a lipid bilayer, but ions cannot (Section 5.7). Minerals dissolved in soil water enter a cell's cytoplasm only through transport proteins in its plasma membrane. Thus, transport proteins in root cell membranes control the types and amounts of ions that move from soil water into the body of the plant. This mechanism protects the plant from some toxic substances that may be in soil water. In addition, most minerals important for plant nutrition are more concentrated in the root than in soil, so they will not spontaneously diffuse into the root. These mineral ions must be actively transported into root cells. The transport occurs mainly

---

FIGURE 26.3 {**Animated**} Uptake of soil water by a root. In most flowering plants, plasma membrane transport proteins control the plant's absorption of mineral ions from soil water.

❶ Most soil water moves from epidermis to vascular cylinder by diffusing through root cell walls.

root hair

soil water

plasmodesma

dissolved minerals

water flow

vascular cylinder

pericycle

primary phloem

primary xylem

endodermis

Casparian strip

❷ The Casparian strip prevents soil water from diffusing through endodermal cell walls. To enter the vascular cylinder, water and dissolved mineral ions must enter cytoplasm by passing through the plasma membrane of a root cell.

cortex

epidermis

❸ Mineral ions actively transported into root hairs diffuse through plasmodesmata to the vascular cylinder.

Most flowering plants take part in mycorrhizae and other mutualisms that provide nutritional benefit. As Section 22.3 explained, a mycorrhiza is a mutually beneficial interaction between a root and a fungus that grows on or in it. Filaments of the fungus (hyphae) form a velvety cloak around roots or penetrate their cells. Collectively, the hyphae have a large surface area, so they absorb mineral ions from a larger volume of soil than roots alone. The fungus absorbs some sugars and nitrogen-rich compounds from root cells. In return, the root cells get some scarce minerals that the fungus is better able to absorb.

Certain plant species can form mutualisms with nitrogen-fixing *Rhizobium* bacteria (Section 19.5). The roots of these plants release certain compounds into the soil that are recognized by compatible bacteria. The bacteria respond by releasing signaling molecules that, in turn, trigger the roots to grow around and encapsulate the bacteria inside swellings called **root nodules** (FIGURE 26.5). The association is beneficial to both parties. The plants require a lot of nitrogen, but cannot use nitrogen gas ($N \equiv N$, or N_2) that is abundant in air. The bacteria in root nodules fix this gas to ammonia (NH_3), which is a form of nitrogen that the plant can use. In return for this nutrient, the plant provides an oxygen-free environment for the anaerobic bacteria, and shares its photosynthetically produced sugars with them.

root nodules Of some plant roots, swellings that contain nitrogen-fixing bacteria.

Casparian strip

vascular tissue

cortex

water and nutrients

FIGURE 26.4 {Animated} The Casparian strip. The micrograph shows a vascular cylinder in the root of an iris plant.

Parenchyma cells that make up endodermis are specialized to secrete a waxy substance into their walls wherever they touch. The secretions, which form a Casparian strip, prevent water from diffusing through endodermal cell walls to enter the vascular cylinder.

at the membrane of root hairs ❸. Once in cell cytoplasm, mineral ions diffuse from cell to cell through plasmodesmata until they enter xylem inside the vascular cylinder.

Casparian strip Waxy, waterproof band between the plasma membranes of root endodermal cells; seals abutting cell walls.

TAKE-HOME MESSAGE 26.2

Water moves from soil, through root endodermis and cortex, into the vascular cylinder. Transport proteins in root cell plasma membranes control the uptake of nutrients.

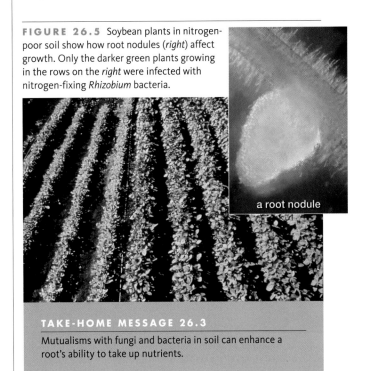

FIGURE 26.5 Soybean plants in nitrogen-poor soil show how root nodules (*right*) affect growth. Only the darker green plants growing in the rows on the *right* were infected with nitrogen-fixing *Rhizobium* bacteria.

a root nodule

TAKE-HOME MESSAGE 26.3

Mutualisms with fungi and bacteria in soil can enhance a root's ability to take up nutrients.

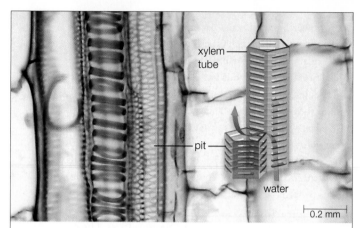

A Cells in xylem meet side to side at rows of holes (pits) in their walls. The pits match up, so water can flow through them into an adjacent cell. The micrograph shows a lengthwise section through a corn stem. Rings of lignin that was deposited in the walls of older vessel elements are visible.

B Most xylem vessels in angiosperms consist of stacked vessel elements, which connect end to end at perforated plates. Water flows vertically between cells through these plates. Water also flows laterally among tubes, through interconnected pits in the side walls of vessel elements.

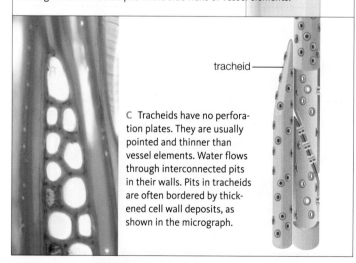

C Tracheids have no perforation plates. They are usually pointed and thinner than vessel elements. Water flows through interconnected pits in their walls. Pits in tracheids are often bordered by thickened cell wall deposits, as shown in the micrograph.

FIGURE 26.6 **Pipelines of xylem.** Water moves through holes in the secondary walls of dead vessel elements and tracheids that form these tubes.

Water that enters a root travels to the rest of the plant inside tubes of xylem. Remember from Section 25.2 that these tubes consist of the stacked, interconnected walls of dead cells: vessel elements and tracheids. Lignin deposited in rings or spirals into the walls of these cells imparts strength to the tubes, which in turn impart strength to the stem or other organ they service.

As xylem tissue is forming, its still-living cells deposit secondary wall material on the inner surface of their primary wall (Section 4.10). The secondary wall forms around plasmodesmata—but not over them—so the cytoplasm of adjacent cells stays connected. Just before the cells die, they digest away most of their primary wall. Small holes (pits) remain in the secondary walls where plasmodesmata had once connected the living cells. Thus, in mature xylem tubes, water flows laterally through the pits, between adjacent cells (**FIGURE 26.6A**).

The main water-conducting tubes in angiosperms consist of stacked **vessel elements**. As these cells die, large holes form in their end walls (where they meet end to end). The resulting perforation plates may help break up air bubbles that form in the tubes (**FIGURE 26.6B**).

Tracheids, like vessel elements, die in stacks to form water-conducting tubes in xylem. Unlike vessel elements, tracheids have no perforation plates; their ends are typically pointed and closed (**FIGURE 26.6C**). Being very narrow, tracheids are more resistant to vertical compression than vessel elements, so in addition to conducting water these cells can have a substantial role in structural support.

Pits in the sides of vessels and tracheids are often bordered by accumulated secondary wall material that contains pectins. Pectins shrink when dry, and swell when wet. When mineral-rich water flows through a bordered pit, the border swells and eventually plugs the hole. Thus, water tends to flow toward the thirstiest regions of the plant, where bordered pits are dry and open.

COHESION–TENSION THEORY

How does water in xylem move all the way from roots to leaves that may be more than 100 meters (330 feet) above the soil? Tracheids and vessel elements that compose xylem tubes

cohesion–tension theory Explanation of how transpiration creates a tension that pulls a cohesive column of water upward through xylem, from roots to shoots.
tracheids Tapered cells of xylem that die when mature; their interconnected, pitted walls remain and form water-conducting tubes.
transpiration Evaporation of water from aboveground plant parts.
vessel elements Of xylem, cells that form in stacks and die when mature; their pitted walls remain to form water-conducting tubes. Each tube consists of a stack of vessel elements that meet end to end at perforation plates.

are dead, so these cells cannot be expending any energy to pump water upward against gravity. The movement of water in vascular plants is driven by two features of water: evaporation and cohesion (Section 2.4). By the **cohesion–tension theory**, water in xylem is pulled upward by air's drying power, which creates a continuous negative pressure called tension. The tension extends from leaves at the tips of shoots to roots that may be hundreds of feet below.

Most of the water that a plant takes up is lost by evaporation, typically from stomata on the plant's leaves and stems (**FIGURE 26.7 ❶**). The evaporation of water from aboveground plant parts is called **transpiration**. Transpiration's effect on water inside a plant is a bit like what happens when you suck a drink through a straw. Transpiration puts negative pressure (pulls) on continuous columns of water in xylem. A column of water resists breaking into droplets as it moves through a narrow conduit such as a straw or a xylem tube. Why? Water molecules are connected by hydrogen bonds, so a pull on one tugs all of them. Thus, the negative pressure created by transpiration (tension) pulls on the entire column of water that fills a xylem tube ❷. Because of water's cohesion, the tension extends from leaves that may be hundreds of feet in the air, down through stems, into young roots where water is being absorbed from soil ❸.

The movement of water through vascular plants is driven mainly by transpiration, but evaporation is only one of many processes in plants that involve the loss of water molecules. Metabolic pathways that use water also contribute to the negative pressure that results in water movement. For example, water molecules delivered by xylem are used as electron donors in the light reactions of photosynthesis. These reactions split the water molecules into oxygen and hydrogen ions (Section 6.4).

water molecule

TAKE-HOME MESSAGE 26.4

Water moves inside continuous tubes of xylem that thread from roots to shoots. The tubes consist of interconnected, pitted secondary walls of dead cells—tracheids and vessel elements.

Transpiration, the evaporation of water from aboveground plant parts, puts columns of water in xylem into a continuous state of tension from shoots to roots.

Tension pulls water upward through the plant. The collective strength of many hydrogen bonds (cohesion) keeps the water from breaking into droplets as it rises through xylem tubes.

CREDIT: (7) From Starr/Taggart/Evers/Starr, Biology, 13E. © 2013 Cengage Learning.

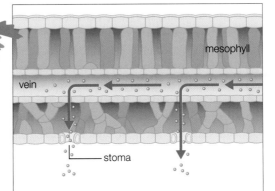

mesophyll

vein

stoma

❶ Water evaporates from leaves and other aboveground plant parts, a process called transpiration.

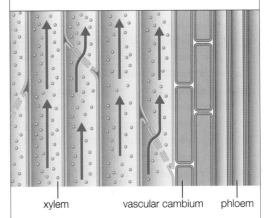

xylem   vascular cambium   phloem

❷ The evaporation exerts tension (pulls) on the narrow columns of water that fill xylem tubes. The tension occurs because liquid water has cohesion. Hydrogen bonds among water molecules collectively impart cohesion to liquid water.

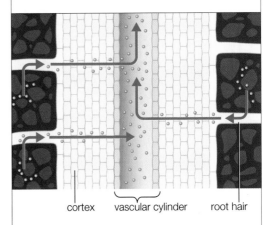

cortex   vascular cylinder   root hair

❸ The tension inside xylem tubes extends from leaves to roots, where water molecules are being taken up from the soil.

FIGURE 26.7 {Animated} Cohesion–tension theory of water transport in vascular plants.

guard cells

closed stoma

open stoma

In land plants, at least 90 percent of the water taken up by roots is lost by evaporation. Only about 2 percent is used in metabolism, but that amount must be maintained or cellular processes will shut down. A waterproof cuticle (Section 4.10) helps a land plant conserve the water it already holds in its tissues. The cuticle also restricts gas exchanges with air. Gas exchange is important because the plant needs to take in carbon dioxide for photosynthesis, and oxygen for aerobic respiration. Stomata (Section 21.1) help land plants balance gas exchange with water conservation. A stoma is an opening between a pair of **guard cells**, which are specialized cells of epidermis (**FIGURE 26.8**). When guard cells swell with water, they bend slightly so a gap (the stoma) forms between them (*left*). Open stomata allow gases and water vapor to cross the epidermis. When guard cells lose water, they collapse against one another, so the stoma between them closes.

Stomata open or close based on environmental cues that trigger changes in osmotic pressure (Section 5.6). For example, when the sun comes up in the morning, the light causes guard cells to begin pumping potassium ions into their cytoplasm. Water follows the ions by osmosis, plumping the guard cells so the gap between them opens. Carbon dioxide from the air diffuses through the open stomata into the plant's tissues, and photosynthesis begins.

guard cell One of a pair of cells that define a stoma across the epidermis of a leaf or stem.

cuticle

epidermis

stoma

guard cells

FIGURE 26.8 Water-conserving structures on a pincushion leaf. In this species, guard cells are recessed beneath a ledge of cuticle. The ledge creates a small cup that traps moist air above the stoma.

TAKE-HOME MESSAGE 26.5

A plant's cuticle restricts water loss from its surfaces, but it also restricts gas exchange necessary for metabolism.

Opened stomata allow gas exchange across epidermis; closed stomata limit water loss.

phloem

FIGURE 26.9 **Sieve plates.** The scanning electron micrograph on the *left* shows sieve plates on the ends of two side-by-side sieve elements. The light micrograph on the *right* shows sieve plates (arrows) in two columns of phloem. Red stripes are lignin rings in xylem.

Conducting tubes of phloem are called **sieve tubes** (Section 25.2). Each sieve tube consists of living cells—a stack of **sieve elements**. Unlike the cells that make up xylem tubes, sieve elements have no pits in their walls; fluid flows through their ends only. During differentiation of phloem, plasmodesmata connecting the sieve elements in a stack enlarge greatly, sometimes up to 100-fold. The resulting pitted end walls, which are called sieve plates after their appearance, separate stacked sieve elements in mature tissue (**FIGURE 26.9**).

As a sieve element matures, it loses most of its organelles, including the nucleus, Golgi bodies, and almost all of its ribosomes. How can it stay alive? Each sieve element has an associated **companion cell** that arises by division of the same parent cell. The companion cell retains its nucleus and other components. Many plasmodesmata connect the cytoplasm of the two cells, so the companion cell can provide all metabolic functions necessary to sustain its paired sieve element—for decades, in some cases.

PRESSURE FLOW THEORY

A plant produces sugar molecules during photosynthesis. Some of these molecules are used by the cells that make them. The remainder move into sieve tubes, where they are conducted to other parts of the plant. The movement of sugars and other organic molecules through phloem is called **translocation**. Inside sieve tubes, fluid rich in sugars—mainly sucrose—flows from a **source** (a region of plant tissue where sugars are being produced or released from storage) to a **sink** (a region where sugars are being broken down for energy, remodeled into other compounds, or stored for later use). Photosynthetic tissues are typical source regions; tissues of developing shoots and fruits are typical sink regions.

Why does sugar-rich fluid flow from source to sink? A pressure gradient between the two regions drives the movement (**FIGURE 26.10**). Consider how photosynthesizing mesophyll cells in a leaf produce far more sugar than they use for their own metabolism. Their activity sets up the leaf as a source region. Excess sugar molecules diffuse from photosynthesizing mesophyll cells into adjacent companion cells through plasmodesmata. Depending on the species and the source region, sugar molecules may also be pumped into a companion cell through active transport proteins in its membrane (Section 5.7). Either way, the sugar molecules then diffuse from the companion cells to their associated sieve elements through other plasmodesmata ❶. This sugar loading increases the solute concentration of cytoplasm in a sieve element so that it becomes hypertonic (Section 5.6) with respect to the surrounding cells. Water follows the sugar by osmosis, moving into the sieve element from the surrounding cells ❷. The rigid cell walls of a mature sieve element cannot expand very much, so the influx of water raises the osmotic pressure (turgor) inside the cell. This pressure can be very high—up to five times higher than that of an automobile tire. The high fluid pressure pushes the sugar-rich cytoplasm from one sieve element to the next, toward a sink region where the osmotic pressure is lower ❸. Pressure inside a sieve tube decreases at a sink because sugars leave the tube in this region. Sugar molecules move into companion cells (either through plasmodesmata or by active transport), and then diffuse into sink cells through plasmodesmata. Water follows, again by osmosis ❹, so turgor inside sieve elements decreases in these regions. The explanation of how osmotic pressure pushes sugar-rich fluid inside a sieve tube from source to sink is called the **pressure flow theory**.

companion cell In phloem, specialized parenchyma cell that provides metabolic support to its partnered sieve element.
pressure flow theory Explanation of how a difference in turgor between sieve elements in source and sink regions pushes sugar-rich fluid through a sieve tube.
sieve elements Living cells that compose sugar-conducting sieve tubes of phloem. Each sieve tube consists of a stack of sieve elements that meet end to end at sieve plates.
sieve tube Sugar-conducting tube of phloem; consists of stacked sieve elements.
sink Region of plant tissue where sugars are being used or stored.
source Region of a plant tissue where sugars are being produced or released from storage.
translocation Movement of organic compounds through phloem.

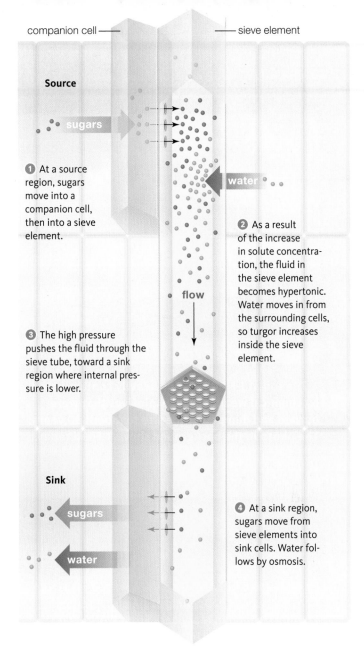

FIGURE 26.10 Translocation of organic compounds in phloem from source to sink. Water molecules are represented by blue balls; sugar molecules, by red balls. Each sieve tube is a stack of living sieve elements that meet end to end at perforation plates. Each sieve element has an associated companion cell that provides it with metabolic support.

TAKE-HOME MESSAGE 26.6

A sieve tube consists of stacked sieve elements separated by porous end walls (sieve plates). Each sieve element is connected by plasmodesmata to a companion cell.

At source regions, sugars move into companion cells, then into sieve tubes. Sugars exit sieve tubes at sink regions.

A pressure gradient pushes sugar-rich fluid inside a sieve tube from a source to a sink.

Application: LEAFY CLEANUP

A The soil at J-Field became heavily contaminated by chemical weapons and explosives that were burned and dumped at the site for about 30 years. The photo in the background shows J-Field today.

Sustainability

FIGURE 26.11 Examples of phytoremediation. A Poplar trees are helping to remove toxic waste left behind in the soil during the Army's 60-year use of J-Field to test and dispose of weapons. B Plants cleanse contaminated stormwater at Ford Motor Company's Rouge Center.

HOW DO WE CLEAN UP CONTAMINATED SOIL?

Consider what's happening at J-Field, Aberdeen Proving Ground in Maryland. From World War I until the 1970s, the United States Army tested and disposed of weapons at this site (FIGURE 26.11A). Chemicals, chemical weapons, and explosives were burned in open pits, together with plastics, solvents, and other wastes. Lead, arsenic, mercury, and other metals heavily contaminated the soil and groundwater. So did highly toxic organic compounds, including TCE (trichloroethylene). TCE damages the nervous system, lungs, and liver, and exposure to large amounts of it can be fatal.

To clean up the soil and protect nearby Chesapeake Bay, the Army and the Environmental Protection Agency turned to phytoremediation: the use of plants to take up and concentrate or degrade environmental contaminants. In the case of organic toxins such as TCE, the best phytoremediation strategies use plants with biochemical pathways that break down the compounds to less toxic molecules. So, in 1996, the Army planted poplar trees that cleanse groundwater by taking up TCE and other organic pollutants in it. The trees' roots take up water from the soil. Along with the water come nutrients and chemical contaminants, including TCE. Although TCE is toxic to animals, it does not harm the trees. The poplars break down some TCE, but they release most of the toxin into the atmosphere. Airborne TCE is the lesser of two evils: It breaks down much more quickly in air than it does in groundwater. Analyses at J-Field since the poplars were planted show that the phytoremediation

CREDITS: (11A) background, © Billy Wrobel, 2004; inset, © OPSEC Control Number #4 077-A-4.

B **A 10-acre green roof over a truck manufacturing plant is the heart of a phytoremediation system that cleanses contaminated storm water as it moves across Ford Motor Company's Rouge Center. The photo in the background shows the Rouge Center in 1927.**

strategy is working. By 2001, the trees had removed 60 pounds of TCE from the soil and groundwater. In addition, they had helped foster communities of microorganisms that were also breaking down toxins. Researchers estimate that the trees will have removed the majority of contaminants from J-Field by 2030.

At Ford Motor Company's Rouge Center in Dearborn, Michigan, decades of steelmaking left soil contaminated with highly carcinogenic compounds known as polycyclic aromatic hydrocarbons, or PAHs. With funding from the automaker, researchers developed a phytoremediation system based on native plants, which also boosted a sitewide initiative to restore the facility's native wildlife habitat (FIGURE 26.11B). The site's plantings are attracting insects, birds, and other wildlife while aggressively accelerating the natural degradation process of

toxins. "If left undisturbed, it would take decades or centuries for these contaminants to naturally decompose," said researcher Clayton Rugh. "What our research is indicating is that we can achieve at least 50 percent degradation in three to five years—and that's at the very least. Some [species] seem to be approaching 70 percent in just three growing seasons."

With metal pollutants, the best phytoremediation strategies use plants that take up toxins and store them in aboveground tissues. The toxin-laden plant parts can then be harvested for safe disposal. This strategy is being tested in Ukraine, where in 1986 an accident at the Chernobyl nuclear power plant released huge amounts of radioactive material that still heavily contaminates the region. Transgenic sunflowers planted on rafts in heavily contaminated ponds quickly take up radioactive cesium (a metal) from the water.

Summary

SECTION 26.1 Plant growth requires steady sources of elemental nutrients. Oxygen, carbon, and hydrogen atoms are abundant in air and water; nitrogen, phosphorus, sulfur, and other elements are available in soil.

The availability of water and mineral ions in a particular soil depends on its proportions of sand, silt, and clay, and also on its **humus** content. **Loams** have roughly equal proportions of sand, silt, and clay. **Leaching** and **soil erosion** deplete nutrients from soil, particularly **topsoils.**

SECTION 26.2 Transport proteins in root cell plasma membranes control the plant's uptake of substances in soil water. Endodermal cells that form the vascular cylinder's outer layer deposit a waterproof band called a **Casparian strip** into their abutting walls. The strip keeps soil water from diffusing around these cells into root xylem. Substances such as ions in soil water must pass through membrane transport proteins of an endodermal cell (or other root cell). Once in cytoplasm, the ions diffuse from cell to cell and into xylem through plasmodesmata.

SECTION 26.3 Many plants form mutualisms with microorganisms. Fungi associate with young roots in mycorrhizae, which enhance a plant's ability to absorb mineral ions from soil. Nitrogen fixation by bacteria in **root nodules** gives a plant extra nitrogen. In both cases, the microorganisms receive some sugars made by the plant.

SECTION 26.4 Water and dissolved mineral ions flow through xylem from roots to shoot tips. Xylem tubes consist of stacks of dead cells: **tracheids** and **vessel elements.** Water moves through the perforated and lignin-reinforced secondary walls of these cells.

The **cohesion–tension theory** explains how water moves through xylem: **Transpiration** (evaporation from aboveground plant parts, mainly at stomata) pulls water upward inside xylem tubes from roots to leaves. The cohesion of water molecules keeps the columns of fluid continuous inside the narrow xylem tubes.

SECTION 26.5 A cuticle helps a plant conserve water; stomata help it balance water conservation with gas exchange required for photosynthesis and aerobic respiration. A stoma is a gap between two **guard cells.** Environmental signals trigger guard cells to pump ions into or out of their cytoplasm; water follows the ions by osmosis. Water moving into guard cells plumps them, so the stoma opens. Water diffusing out of the cells causes them to collapse against each other, so the stoma closes.

SECTION 26.6 Sugars move through a plant by **translocation** in phloem's sieve tubes, which consist of stacked **sieve elements** separated by perforated sieve plates. By the **pressure flow theory**, the movement of sugar-rich fluid through a **sieve tube** is driven by a pressure gradient between **source** and **sink**. **Companion cells** load sugars into sieve elements at sources.

SECTION 26.7 The ability of plants to take up substances from soil water is the basis for phytoremediation, the use of plants to remove pollutants from a contaminated area.

Self-Quiz Answers in Appendix VII

1. Carbon, hydrogen, and oxygen are _____ for plants.
   a. macronutrients   d. required elements
   b. micronutrients   e. both a and b
   c. trace elements   f. both a and d

2. Decomposing matter in soil is called _____ .
   a. clay   c. silt
   b. humus   d. sand

3. A vascular cylinder consists of _____ .
   a. exodermis   d. xylem and phloem
   b. endodermis   e. b and d
   c. root cortex   f. all of the above

4. A _____ strip between abutting endodermal cell walls forces water and solutes to move through these cells rather than around them.
   a. cutin   b. Casparian   c. cohesion   d. cellulose

5. The nutrition of some plants is enhanced by a mutually beneficial association between a root and a fungus. The association is known as a _____ .
   a. root nodule   c. root hair
   b. mycorrhiza   d. hypha

6. Water evaporation from plant parts is called _____ .
   a. translocation   c. transpiration
   b. cohesion   d. tension

7. Water transport from roots to leaves occurs by _____ .
   a. a pressure gradient inside sieve tubes
   b. different solutes at source and sink regions
   c. the pumping force of xylem vessels
   d. transpiration, tension, and cohesion of water

8. Tracheids are part of _____ .
   a. cortex   c. phloem
   b. mesophyll   d. xylem

9. Sieve tubes are part of _____ .
   a. cortex   c. phloem
   b. mesophyll   d. xylem

10. A waterproof cuticle _____ .
    a. minimizes water loss through plant surfaces
    b. inhibits gas exchange between the plant and the air
    c. both a and b

11. When guard cells swell, _____ .
    a. transpiration ceases   c. stomata open
    b. sugars enter phloem   d. root cells die

Data Analysis Activities

TCE Uptake by Transgenic Plants Plants used for phyto-remediation take up organic pollutants, then transport the chemicals to plant tissues, where they are stored or broken down. Researchers are now designing transgenic plants with enhanced ability to take up or break down toxins. In 2007, Sharon Doty and her colleagues published the results of their efforts to design plants for phytoremediation of soil and air containing organic solvents. The researchers used *Agrobacterium tumefaciens* (Section 15.5) to deliver a mammalian gene into poplar plants. The gene encodes cytochrome P450, an enzyme involved in the breakdown of a range of organic molecules, including solvents such as TCE. **FIGURE 26.12** shows data from one test on the resulting transgenic plants.

1. How many transgenic plants did the researchers test?
2. In which group did the researchers see the slowest rate of TCE uptake? The fastest?
3. On day 6, what was the difference between the TCE content of air around planted transgenic plants and that around vector control plants?
4. Assuming no other experiments were done, what two explanations are there for the results of this experiment? What other control might the researchers have used?

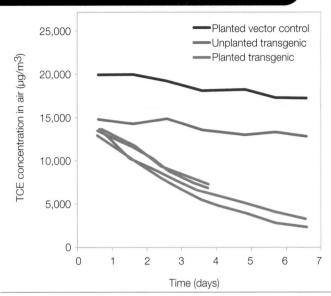

FIGURE 26.12 TCE uptake from air by transgenic poplar plants. Individual potted plants were kept in separate sealed containers with an initial 15,000 micrograms of TCE (trichloroethylene) per cubic meter of air. Samples of the air in the containers were taken daily and measured for TCE content. Controls included a tree transgenic for a Ti plasmid with no cytochrome P450 in it (vector control), and a bare-root transgenic tree (one that was not planted in soil).

12. Stomata open in response to light when _____ .
    a. ions flow into guard cell cytoplasm
    b. ions flow out of guard cell cytoplasm
    c. water evaporates out of guard cells

13. In phloem, organic compounds flow through _____ .
    a. collenchyma cells   c. vessels
    b. sieve elements   d. tracheids

14. Sugar transport from leaves to roots occurs by _____ .
    a. a pressure gradient inside sieve tubes
    b. different solutes at source and sink regions
    c. the pumping force of xylem vessels
    d. transpiration, tension, and cohesion of water

15. Match the concepts of plant nutrition and transport.
    ____ stomata   a. end of a vessel element
    ____ nutrient   b. takes up soil water and nutrients
    ____ sink   c. balance water loss with gas
    ____ root system   exchange
    ____ hydrogen   d. cohesion in xylem tubes
       bonds   e. sugars unloaded from sieve tubes
    ____ xylem   f. distributes sugars through the
    ____ phloem   plant body
    ____ perforation   g. required element
       plate   h. distributes water through the
                             plant body

Critical Thinking

1. What are the three structures shown in the micrographs in **FIGURE 26.13**? From which tissue(s) do the structures originate?

2. Which biological molecules incorporate nitrogen atoms? Nitrogen deficiency stunts plant growth; leaves yellow and then die. How do you think nitrogen deficiency causes these symptoms?

3. You just returned home from a three-day vacation. Your severely wilted plants tell you they were not watered before you left. Being aware of the cohesion–tension theory of water transport, explain what happened to them.

4. When you dig up a plant to move it from one spot to another, the plant is more likely to survive if some of the soil around the roots is transferred along with the plant. Formulate a hypothesis that explains this observation.

5. If a plant's stomata are made to stay open at all times, or closed at all times, it will die. Why?

FIGURE 26.13 Name the mystery structures.

CREDITS: (12) From Starr/Taggart/Evers/Starr, Biology, 13E. © 2013 Cengage Learning; (13A–B) H. A. Core, W. A. Cote, and A. C. Day, Wood Structure and Identification, 2nd Ed., Syracuse University Press, 1979; (13C) Alison W. Roberts, University of Rhode Island.

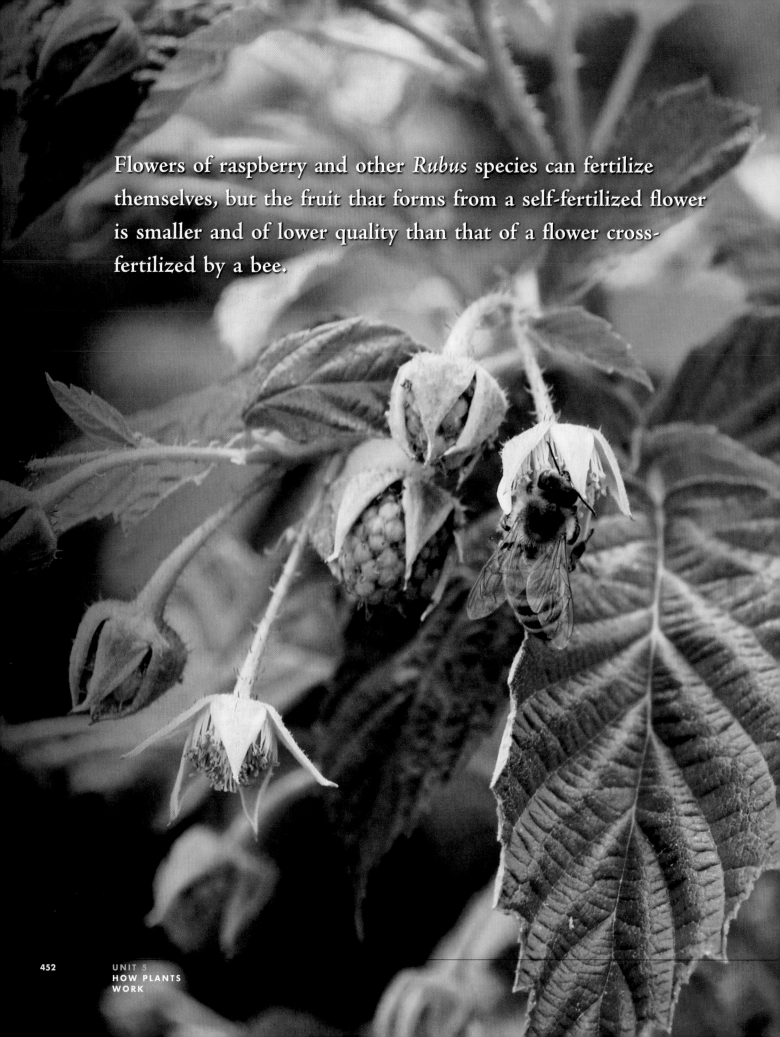

Flowers of raspberry and other *Rubus* species can fertilize themselves, but the fruit that forms from a self-fertilized flower is smaller and of lower quality than that of a flower cross-fertilized by a bee.

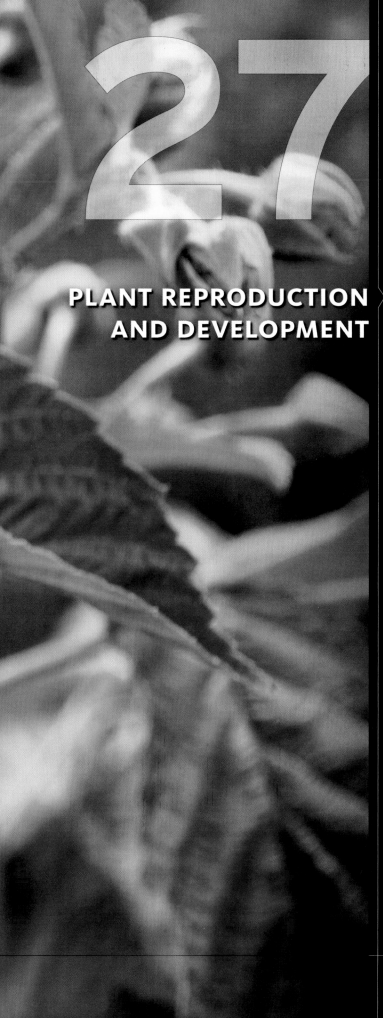

27

PLANT REPRODUCTION AND DEVELOPMENT

Photograph by © Alan McConnaughey. www.flickr.com/photos/engripiman.

Links to Earlier Concepts

A review of plant structures and their functions (Sections 4.8, 4.10, 6.4, 6.5, 25.1–25.6, 26.3, 26.5), life cycles (12.2, 21.1, 21.6, 21.7), and evolution (21.4) will be helpful. This chapter revisits carbohydrate hydrolysis (3.1, 3.2), animal hormones (3.3), membrane transport proteins (5.7), pigments (6.1), clones (8.6), gene expression (9.1) and control (10.1–10.3), reproductive modes (12.1), meiosis (12.3), Mendel's pea plants (13.3), polyploidy (14.5, 17.10), and coevolution (17.11).

KEY CONCEPTS

THE FUNCTION OF FLOWERS
Flowers are shoots specialized for reproduction. Modified leaves form their parts. Flowers of many plants are specialized to attract and reward coevolved animal pollinators.

GAMETES AND FERTILIZATION
Male and female gametophytes develop inside the reproductive parts of flowers. Pollination is followed by double fertilization. As in animals, signals are key to sex.

SEEDS AND FRUIT
After fertilization, ovules mature into seeds. As seeds develop, tissues of the ovary and often other parts of the flower mature into fruits, which function in seed dispersal.

GROWTH AND DEVELOPMENT
Plant growth includes germination, root and shoot development, flowering, fruit formation, and dormancy. Plant hormones bring about and coordinate these activities.

RESPONSES TO THE ENVIRONMENT
Plants respond to environmental cues by altering patterns of growth. Cyclic patterns are responses to recurring environmental patterns. Living and nonliving stressors trigger defensive responses.

Flowers are the reproductive structures of angiosperms (Section 21.6). The form and composition of flowers vary dramatically among species, but all develop at the tips of special reproductive shoots (**FIGURE 27.1**). A flower's parts are modified leaves that develop from a thickened region of stem called a receptacle ❶. A typical flower has four spirals or rings (whorls) of modified leaves. As the flower forms, expression of floral identity genes (Section 10.3) determines the fate of each whorl. Typically, the outermost whorl is a calyx, which is a ring of leaflike sepals ❷. Sepals of most flowers are photosynthetic and inconspicuous; they serve to protect the flower's more delicate parts. Just inside the calyx is the corolla (from the Latin *corona*, or crown), a whorl of petals ❸. Petals are usually the largest and most brightly colored parts of a flower. Inside the corolla is a whorl of **stamens**, the reproductive organs that produce the plant's male gametophytes. In most flowers, stamens consist of a thin filament with an **anther** at the tip ❹. A typical anther contains four pouches called pollen sacs. **Pollen grains**, which are immature male gametophytes, form inside pollen sacs. The flower's innermost whorl consists of modified leaves folded and fused into one or more carpels. A **carpel**

FIGURE 27.2 UV-reflecting patterns in flower petals. The image on the *left* shows a primrose flower as we see it. The image on the *right* shows the same flower photographed with a special filter that allows us to see reflected UV light, here represented by the color red. The bull's-eye pattern guides bees, which can see UV light, directly to the flower's reproductive parts.

is the reproductive organ that produces the plant's female gametophytes ❺. A carpel—or a compound structure that consists of multiple fused carpels—is commonly called a pistil. The upper region of a carpel is a sticky or hairy **stigma** that is specialized to receive pollen grains. Typically, the stigma sits on top of a slender stalk called a style. The lower, swollen region of a carpel is the **ovary**, which contains one or more ovules. An **ovule** is a bulge of tissue in which a female gametophyte forms.

POLLINATION

Sexual reproduction in flowering plants involves **pollination**, the arrival of pollen on a receptive stigma. Pollen is typically transferred to a stigma by a **pollination vector**: an animal, wind, or other environmental agent. Animal pollination vectors are called **pollinators**.

Flower traits such as petal color that are not directly related to reproduction are evolutionary adaptations that attract coevolved pollinators (Section 21.7). An animal that is attracted to a particular flower often picks up pollen on a visit, then inadvertently transfers it to another flower

FIGURE 27.1 {Animated} Anatomy of a typical flower. Male gametophytes are produced by stamens; female gametophytes, by carpels.

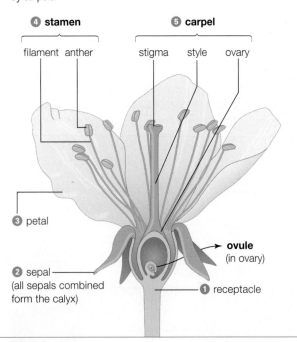

❹ stamen — filament, anther
❺ carpel — stigma, style, ovary
❸ petal
❷ sepal (all sepals combined form the calyx)
ovule (in ovary)
❶ receptacle

anther Part of the stamen that produces pollen.
carpel Floral reproductive organ that consists of an ovary, stigma, and often a style.
flower Specialized reproductive structure of a flowering plant.
nectar Sweet fluid exuded by some flowers; attracts animal pollinators.
ovary In flowering plants, the enlarged base of a carpel, inside which one or more ovules form.
ovule Of a seed-bearing plant, a structure inside an ovary in which a female gametophyte forms.
pollen grain Immature male gametophyte of a seed plant.
pollination The arrival of pollen on a receptive stigma.
pollination vector Environmental agent that moves pollen grains from one plant to another.
pollinator An animal pollination vector.
stamen Floral reproductive organ that consists of an anther and, often, a filament.
stigma Upper part of a carpel; adapted to receive pollen.

on a later visit. The more specific the attraction, the more efficient the transfer of pollen among plants of the same species. Thus, flower traits tend to reflect the abilities and preferences of their pollinator allies. For example, bees have a keen sense of smell and they can see UV light, so bee-pollinated flowers tend to be fragrant, with a bull's-eye pattern of UV-reflecting pigments in their petals (**FIGURE 27.2**). Bee-pollinated flowers also attract and communicate dynamically with individual bees via electric fields. Birds, which rely more on their excellent sense of vision than their relatively poor sense of smell, are attracted to bright red, unscented flowers (**FIGURE 27.3A**). Night-flying bats have a good sense of smell but poor vision, so bat-pollinated flowers tend to be large and light-colored, with a strong nighttime fragrance (**FIGURE 27.3B**). Not all flowers smell sweet; odors like dung or rotting flesh beckon beetles and flies.

Rewards offered by a flower reinforce a pollinator's memory of a visit, and encourage the animal to seek out other flowers of the same species. Many flowers exude a sweet fluid called **nectar** that is prized by many pollinators. Nectar is the only food for most adult butterflies, and it is the food of choice for hummingbirds. Honeybees convert nectar to honey, which helps feed the bees and their larvae through the winter. Bees also collect protein-rich pollen to feed themselves and their larvae. Many beetles also feed primarily on pollen. Pollen is the only reward for a pollinator of roses, poppies, and other flowers that do not produce nectar. Some flowers offer unusual rewards such as caffeine (which enhances the pollinator's memory of the plant's location) or sex (**FIGURE 27.3C**).

Some flower specializations prevent pollination by all but one type of pollinator. For example, nectar or pollen at the bottom of a long floral tube may be accessible only to an insect with a matching feeding device. In some plants, stamens adapted to brush against a pollinator's body or lob pollen onto it will function only when triggered by that pollinator. Such relationships are to both species' mutual advantage: A flower that captivates the attention of an animal has a pollinator that spends its time seeking (and pollinating) only those flowers. Pollinators also benefit when they receive an exclusive supply of the flower's reward.

Grasses and other plants pollinated by wind do not benefit by attracting animals, so they do not waste resources making scented, brilliantly colored, or nectar-laden flowers. Wind-pollinated flowers are typically small, pale, and odorless. Wind disperses pollen randomly throughout the environment, so these flowers typically make and release pollen grains by the billions, insurance in numbers that some of their pollen will reach a receptive stigma.

A **Birds**. Pollen accumulates on the feathers of a greater double-collared sunbird as it sips nectar from a bottlebrush flower.

B **Mammals**. A lesser long-tongued fruit bat sips nectar from (and pollinates) flowers of wild banana.

C **Insects**. Female burnet moths perch on purple blossoms—preferably pincushion flowers—when they are ready to mate. The visual combination attracts male moths; the activity of the moths pollinates the flowers.

FIGURE 27.3 Examples of animals pollinating flowers.

TAKE-HOME MESSAGE 27.1

Flowers are the reproductive structures of angiosperms. The different parts of a flower (sepals, petals, stamens, and carpels) are modified leaves.

The parts of flowers that produce male gametophytes are stamens, which typically consist of a filament with an anther at the tip. Pollen forms inside the anthers.

The parts of flowers that produce female gametophytes are carpels, which typically consist of stigma, style, and ovary. The gametophyte forms in an ovule inside the ovary.

Flower traits reflect a dependence on pollination vectors.

FIGURE 27.4 {Animated} Overview of the life cycle of a typical flowering plant (compare **FIGURE 27.5**). The photo shows flowers on a cherry tree.

The life cycle of flowering plants (**FIGURE 27.4**) is dominated by the sporophyte, a diploid spore-producing plant body that grows by mitotic cell divisions of a fertilized egg. Spores that form by meiosis inside a sporophyte's flowers develop into haploid gametophytes, which produce gametes (Section 12.2). The production of female gametes begins when a mass of tissue—the ovule—starts growing on the inner wall of an ovary (**FIGURE 27.5 ❶**). One cell in the middle of the mass undergoes meiosis and cytoplasmic division, forming four haploid **megaspores ❷**. Three of the four megaspores typically disintegrate. The remaining megaspore undergoes three rounds of mitosis without cytoplasmic division, thus producing a single cell that has eight haploid nuclei ❸. The cytoplasm of this cell divides unevenly, forming a seven-celled embryo sac that constitutes the female gametophyte ❹. The gametophyte

is enclosed and protected by layers of cells, or integuments, that developed from the outer layers of the ovule. One of the cells in the gametophyte, the endosperm mother cell, has two nuclei ($n + n$). Another cell is the egg.

The production of male gametes begins as masses of diploid, spore-producing cells form by mitosis inside anthers. Walls typically develop around the masses, so four pollen sacs form ❺. Each cell inside the pollen sacs undergoes meiosis and cytoplasmic division to form four haploid **microspores ❻**. Mitosis and differentiation of a microspore produce a pollen grain ❼. A pollen grain consists of two cells, one inside the cytoplasm of the other, enclosed by a durable coat. The coat will protect the cells inside on their journey to meet an egg. After the pollen grains form, they enter **dormancy**, a period of suspended metabolism, before being released from the anther when the pollen sacs split open ❽.

A pollen grain that lands on a receptive stigma **germinates**, which means it resumes metabolic activity after a period of dormancy. When a pollen grain germinates, its outer cell develops into a tubular outgrowth called a pollen tube ❾. Its inner cell undergoes mitosis to produce two sperm cells (the male gametes) within the pollen tube. A pollen tube together with its contents of male gametes constitutes the mature male gametophyte. The pollen tube grows from its tip down through the tissues of the style and ovary toward the ovule, carrying with it the two sperm cells. Chemical signals secreted by the female gametophyte guide the pollen tube's growth to the embryo sac within the ovule. Many pollen tubes may grow down into a carpel, but usually only one penetrates the female gametophyte.

When a pollen tube penetrates the female gametophyte, it releases the two sperm cells ❿. Flowering plants undergo **double fertilization**, in which one of the sperm cells delivered by the pollen tube fuses with (fertilizes) the egg and forms a diploid zygote; the other sperm cell fuses with the endosperm mother cell, forming a triploid ($3n$) cell. This cell gives rise to triploid **endosperm**, a nutritious tissue that forms only in seeds of flowering plants. When the seed sprouts, endosperm will sustain rapid growth of the seedling until its new leaves begin photosynthesis.

dormancy Period of temporarily suspended metabolism.
double fertilization Mode of fertilization in flowering plants in which one sperm cell fuses with the egg, and a second sperm cell fuses with the endosperm mother cell.
endosperm Nutritive tissue in the seeds of flowering plants.
germinate To resume metabolic activity after dormancy.
megaspore Of seed plants, haploid spore that forms in an ovule and gives rise to an egg-producing gametophyte.
microspore Of seed plants, haploid spore that gives rise to a pollen grain.

TAKE-HOME MESSAGE 27.2

A pollen grain that germinates on a stigma develops into the male gametophyte, which consists of a pollen tube and two sperm cells. The pollen tube grows into the carpel, enters an ovule, and releases the sperm cells.

Double fertilization occurs when one of the sperm cells delivered by the pollen tube fuses with the egg, and the other fuses with the endosperm mother cell.

CREDITS: (4) photo, © Martin Ruegner/Photographer's Choice RF/Getty Images; art, © Cengage Learning 2015.

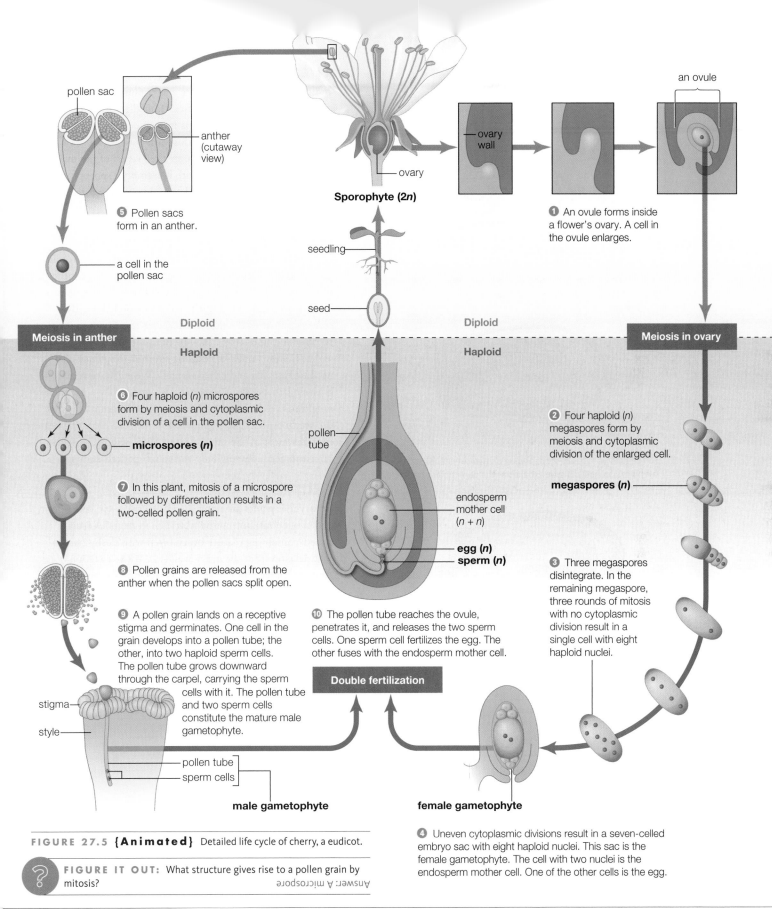

Sporophyte (2n)

pollen sac

anther (cutaway view)

5 Pollen sacs form in an anther.

a cell in the pollen sac

Diploid

Meiosis in anther

Haploid

6 Four haploid (n) microspores form by meiosis and cytoplasmic division of a cell in the pollen sac.

microspores (n)

7 In this plant, mitosis of a microspore followed by differentiation results in a two-celled pollen grain.

8 Pollen grains are released from the anther when the pollen sacs split open.

9 A pollen grain lands on a receptive stigma and germinates. One cell in the grain develops into a pollen tube; the other, into two haploid sperm cells. The pollen tube grows downward through the carpel, carrying the sperm cells with it. The pollen tube and two sperm cells constitute the mature male gametophyte.

stigma

style

pollen tube

sperm cells

male gametophyte

seedling

seed

pollen tube

endosperm mother cell (n + n)

egg (n)
sperm (n)

10 The pollen tube reaches the ovule, penetrates it, and releases the two sperm cells. One sperm cell fertilizes the egg. The other fuses with the endosperm mother cell.

Double fertilization

ovary

an ovule

ovary wall

1 An ovule forms inside a flower's ovary. A cell in the ovule enlarges.

Diploid

Meiosis in ovary

Haploid

2 Four haploid (n) megaspores form by meiosis and cytoplasmic division of the enlarged cell.

megaspores (n)

3 Three megaspores disintegrate. In the remaining megaspore, three rounds of mitosis with no cytoplasmic division result in a single cell with eight haploid nuclei.

female gametophyte

4 Uneven cytoplasmic divisions result in a seven-celled embryo sac with eight haploid nuclei. This sac is the female gametophyte. The cell with two nuclei is the endosperm mother cell. One of the other cells is the egg.

FIGURE 27.5 {Animated} Detailed life cycle of cherry, a eudicot.

FIGURE IT OUT: What structure gives rise to a pollen grain by mitosis?

Answer: A microspore

CREDIT: (5) © Cengage Learning.

CHAPTER 27 **457**
PLANT REPRODUCTION AND DEVELOPMENT

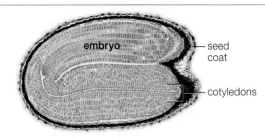

A After fertilization, a *Capsella* flower's ovary develops into a fruit, and an embryo forms inside each of the ovary's ovules.

B The embryo is heart-shaped when its two cotyledons start forming. Endosperm tissue expands as the parent plant transfers nutrients into it.

C In eudicots like *Capsella*, nutrients are transferred from endosperm into two cotyledons as the embryo matures. The developing embryo becomes shaped like a torpedo when the enlarging cotyledons bend.

D A tough seed coat forms around the mature embryo and its two enlarged cotyledons.

FIGURE 27.6 {Animated} Embryonic development of shepherd's purse (*Capsella*), a eudicot.

THE EMBRYO SPOROPHYTE FORMS

In flowering plants, the zygote and triploid ($3n$) cell produced by double fertilization immediately begin mitotic divisions. The zygote develops into an embryo, and the triploid cell develops into endosperm (**FIGURE 27.6**). As the embryo matures, the outer cell layers of the ovule develop into a tough seed coat. The embryo sporophyte, its reserves of food, and the seed coat are now a mature ovule, a self-contained package called a **seed**.

As an embryo is developing, the parent plant transfers nutrients to the ovule. These nutrients accumulate in endosperm mainly as starch with some lipids and proteins. Typical eudicot embryos transfer nutrients in endosperm to their two cotyledons, so most of the nutrients in a mature eudicot seed are stored in the enlarged cotyledons. By contrast, most of the nutrient reserves in a mature monocot seed remain in endosperm. The nutrients in endosperm and cotyledons nourish seedling sporophytes. They also nourish humans and other animals. We cultivate cereals—grasses such as rice, wheat, rye, oats, and barley—for their nutritious seeds. The embryo (the germ) contains most of the seed's protein and vitamins, and the seed coat (the bran) contains most of the minerals and fiber. Milling removes bran and germ, leaving only the starch-packed endosperm.

FRUITS

Embryonic plants are nourished by nutrients in endosperm and cotyledons, but not by nutrients in fruits. A **fruit** is a seed-containing mature ovary, often with fleshy tissues that develop from the ovary wall (**FIGURE 27.7A**). Apples, oranges, and grapes are familiar fruits, but so are many "vegetables" such as shell beans, tomatoes, eggplant, and squash. True fruits such as cherries consist only of the ovary wall and its contents. Other floral parts, such as

FIGURE 27.7 Parts of a fruit develop from parts of a flower.

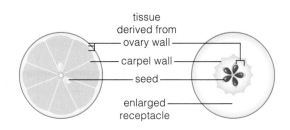

A The tissues of an orange develop from the ovary wall.

B The flesh of an apple is an enlarged receptacle.

FIGURE IT OUT: How many carpels were there in the flower that gave rise to this orange? Answer: Eight

CREDITS: (6A,C,D) Michael Clayton, University of Wisconsin; (6B) © David T. Webb; (6A, 7) © Cengage Learning.

petals, sepals, stamens, or receptacle, expand along with the ovary in accessory fruits. Most of the flesh of an apple is an enlarged receptacle (FIGURE 27.7B).

Simple fruits, such as pea pods, acorns, and shepherd's purse, are derived from one ovary. By contrast, aggregate fruits are derived from separate ovaries of one flower that mature as a cluster. A blackberry (*right*) is an aggregate of dozens of small, individual fleshy fruits. A strawberry is also an aggregate fruit; the flower's carpels turn inside out as the fruits form, and the receptacle expands and becomes red, juicy flesh. The hard "seeds" on the surface (*left*) are individual dry fruits.

The function of a fruit is to protect and disperse seeds. Just as flower structure is adapted to certain pollination vectors, so are fruits adapted to certain dispersal vectors: environmental agents such as water or wind, or mobile organisms such as birds. Adaptations to a specific dispersal mechanism are reflected in a fruit's form. Fruits dispersed by the wind tend to be lightweight with breeze-catching specializations (FIGURE 27.8A). Tufted fruits such as those of thistle, cattail, dandelion, and milkweed may be blown as far as 10 kilometers (6 miles) from the parent plant. Fruits dispersed by water can float, and they have water-repellent outer layers (FIGURE 27.8B). The fruits of many plants have specializations that facilitate dispersal by animals (FIGURE 27.8C). Some have hooks or spines that stick to the feathers, feet, fur, or clothing of more mobile species. Colorful, fleshy, or fragrant fruits attract birds and mammals that disperse seeds. The animal may eat the fruit and discard the seeds, or eat the seeds along with the fruit. Abrasion of the seed coat by teeth or by digestive enzymes in an animal's gut can help the seed germinate after it departs in feces.

fruit Mature ovary of a flowering plant, often with accessory parts; encloses a seed or seeds.
seed Embryo sporophyte of a seed plant packaged with nutritive tissue inside a protective coat.

TAKE-HOME MESSAGE 27.3

After double fertilization, the zygote develops into an embryo, and the endosperm becomes enriched with nutrients. A seed is a mature ovule that consists of an embryo sporophyte, its food reserves, and a seed coat.

A fruit is a mature ovary, with or without accessory tissues that develop from other parts of the flower.

A fruit protects and disperses seeds. Fruit specializations are adaptations to particular dispersal vectors.

A **Wind-dispersed fruits**. *Left*, dry outgrowths of the ovary wall of a maple fruit form "wings" that catch the wind and spin the seeds away from the parent tree. *Right*, wind that lifts the hairy modified sepals of a dandelion fruit may carry the attached seed miles away from the parent plant.

B **Water-dispersed fruits**. *Left*, fruits of sedges native to American marshlands have seeds encased in a bladderlike envelope that floats. *Right*, buoyant fruits of the coconut palm have tough, waterproof husks. They can float for thousands of miles in seawater.

C **Animal-dispersed fruits**. *Left*, curved spines attach cockle-bur fruits to the fur of animals (and clothing of humans) that brush past it. *Right*, the red, fleshy fruits of hawthorn plants are an important food source for cedar waxwings, which disperse the fruits' seeds in their feces.

FIGURE 27.8 Examples of adaptations that aid fruit dispersal.

An embryonic plant complete with shoot and root apical meristems forms as part of a seed (**FIGURE 27.9**). The embryonic shoot (the plumule) is separated from the embryonic root (radicle) by a section of stem called hypocotyl. As the seed matures, the embryo may dry out and enter a period of dormancy. A dormant embryo can rest in its protective seed coat for many years before it resumes metabolic activity and germinates.

BREAKING DORMANCY

Seed dormancy is a climate-specific adaptation that allows germination to occur when conditions in the environment are most likely to support the growth of a seedling. For example, seeds of many annual plants native to cold winter regions are dispersed in autumn. If the seeds germinated immediately, the tender seedlings would not survive the coming winter. Instead, the seeds remain dormant until spring, when milder temperatures and longer day length favor the growth of seedling sporophytes. By contrast, the weather in regions near the equator does not vary by season. Seeds of most plants native to such regions do not enter dormancy; they can germinate as soon as they become mature.

Other than the presence of water, the triggers for germination differ by species. Some seed coats are so dense that they must be abraded or broken (by being chewed, for example) before water can even enter the seed. Seeds of many cool-climate plants require exposure to freezing temperatures; those of some lettuce species, to bright light. In seeds of some species native to regions that have periodic wildfires, germination is inhibited by light and enhanced by smoke;

FIGURE 27.9 Anatomy of a seed.
Left, corn, a monocot; *right,* pea, a eudicot.
As dormancy ends, cell divisions resume mainly at apical meristems of the plumule (the embryonic shoot) and radicle (the embryonic root). Plumule and radicle are separated by hypocotyl, a section of embryonic stem. In monocot grasses such as corn, the plumule is protected by a sheathlike coleoptile.

A As a corn grain (seed) germinates, its radicle and coleoptile emerge from the seed coat. The radicle develops into the primary root. The coleoptile grows upward and opens a channel through the soil to the surface, where it stops growing.

B The plumule develops into a primary shoot that emerges from the coleoptile and begins photosynthesis.

FIGURE 27.10 {Animated} Early growth of corn, a typical monocot.

CREDITS: (9A) left, © Mike Clayton/University of Wisconsin; (9B) right, © Jubal Harshaw/Shutterstock.com; (10A,B,C art) From Starr/Taggart/Evers/Starr, Biology, 13E. © 2013 Cengage Learning; (10A photo) © Barry L. Runk/Grant Heilman, Inc.; (10B,C photos) Nigel Cattlin/Visuals Unlimited.

① The seed coat splits and the embryonic root tip emerges.
② The embryonic stem emerges from the seed and bends in the shape of a hook.
③ As the stem lengthens, it drags the two cotyledons upward toward the surface of the soil.
④ Exposure to light makes the stem straighten.
⑤ Primary leaves emerge from between the cotyledons and begin photosynthesis.
⑥ Cotyledons typically undergo a period of photosynthesis, then wither and fall off the stem.

FIGURE 27.11 {Animated} Early growth of the common bean, a typical eudicot.

in others, germination does not occur unless the seeds have been previously burned. Such requirements are evolutionary adaptations to life in a particular environment. All maximize a seedling's chance of survival.

The process of germination begins with water seeping into a seed. Water causes the seed's internal tissues to swell, forcing the seed coat to rupture. After the seed's coat breaks, oxygen diffuses into the tissues. The water also provokes a series of events that activate hydrolysis enzymes, which begin to break down stored starches into sugar subunits (more about this process in Section 27.8). Cells in the embryo's meristems (Section 25.6) use the sugars and the oxygen to run aerobic respiration. Energy released from the sugar breakdown fuels rapid divisions of the meristem cells, and the embryonic plant begins to grow. Germination ends when the first part of the embryo—the embryonic root, or radicle—breaks out of the seed coat.

AFTER GERMINATION

The pattern of early growth that occurs after germination varies. For example, in corn and other monocots, a rigid sheath called a **coleoptile** protects the primary (first) shoot as it grows straight upward through soil (**FIGURE 27.10**). The embryo's single cotyledon, which typically stays beneath the soil, functions mainly to transfer endosperm breakdown products to the embryo. In eudicot seedlings, the primary

shoot is not protected by a coleoptile (**FIGURE 27.11**). In a typical eudicot pattern of development, the radicle emerges from the seed ①, followed by the hypocotyl. The hypocotyl bends into a hook shape as it lengthens ②. The bent hypocotyl pulls the cotyledons upward through the soil until it reaches the surface ③. There, exposure to light causes the hypocotyl to straighten ④. Primary leaves emerge from between the cotyledons and begin photosynthesis ⑤. The cotyledons typically undergo a period of photosynthesis before shriveling ⑥. Eventually, the cotyledons fall off the lengthening stem, and the young plant's new leaves produce all of its food.

Germination is the first step in plant development. As a sporophyte grows and matures, its tissues and organs develop in characteristic patterns. Leaves form in predictable shapes and sizes, stems and roots lengthen and thicken, flowering occurs at a certain time of year, and so on. As you will see in the next few sections, these patterns are outcomes of gene expression and environmental influences. Gene expression in plants is regulated by hormones and other signaling molecules, just as it is in animals.

coleoptile Rigid sheath that protects a growing embryonic shoot of monocots.

Most flowering plants can reproduce asexually by **vegetative reproduction**, in which new roots and shoots grow from extensions or pieces of a parent plant. Each new plant is a clone, a genetic replica of its parent. For example, new roots and shoots can sprout from nodes on modified stems (**FIGURE 27.12**). Entire forests of quaking aspen trees are actually stands of clones that grew from root suckers, which are shoots that sprout from shallow, cordlike lateral roots. Suckers appear after aboveground parts of the aspens are damaged or removed. One stand of quaking aspens in Utah consists of about 47,000 shoots and stretches for 107 acres. Such clones are as close as any organism gets to being immortal. One of the oldest known plants is a clone: the one and only population of King's holly, which consists of several hundred stems along a river gully in Tasmania. Radiometric dating of the plant's fossilized leaf litter shows that the clone is at least 43,600 years old—predating the last ice age!

AGRICULTURAL APPLICATIONS

For thousands of years, we humans have been taking advantage of the natural capacity of many plants to reproduce asexually. For example, almost all houseplants, woody ornamentals, and orchard trees are clones that have been grown from stem fragments (cuttings) of a parent plant. Propagating some plants from cuttings may be as simple as jamming a broken stem into the soil. This method uses the plant's ability to form new roots and shoots from nodes on a stem. Other plants must be grafted. Grafting means inducing a cutting to fuse with the tissues of another plant. Often, the stem of a desired plant is spliced onto the roots of another.

Propagating a plant from cuttings ensures that offspring will have the same desirable traits as the parent. Consider familiar orchard apples, which are descendants of a wild species native to central Asia. Domesticated apple varieties are grafted because species in this genus do not breed true for fruit traits—color, flavor, size, sweetness, and texture (**FIGURE 27.13**). Most apple trees grown from seed produce unpalatable fruit. In the early 1800s, John Chapman (known as Johnny Appleseed) grew millions of apple trees from seed in the midwestern United States. He sold the trees to homesteading settlers, who made hard cider from the otherwise inedible apples. About one of every hundred trees produced sweet, tasty fruit; its lucky owner would graft the tree and patent it. An estimated 16,000 varieties of edible apples were discovered during this era. Few of them remain; only 15 varieties now account for 90 percent of the apples sold in U.S. grocery stores. All are clones of Chapman's original trees, and all are still grafted.

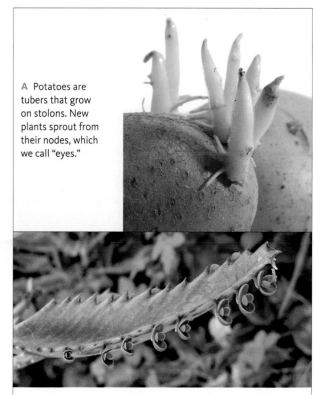

A Potatoes are tubers that grow on stolons. New plants sprout from their nodes, which we call "eyes."

B New plants form at nodes on leaflike modified stems (cladodes) of many succulents such as this devil's backbone plant.

FIGURE 27.12 Examples of asexual reproduction in plants.

Grafting is also used to increase the hardiness of a desirable plant. In 1862, the plant louse *Phylloxera* was accidentally introduced into France via imported American grapevines. European grapevines had little resistance to this tiny insect, which attacks and kills the root systems of the vines. By 1900, *Phylloxera* had destroyed two-thirds of the vineyards in Europe, thus devastating the wine-making industry for decades. Today, French vintners routinely graft their prized grapevines onto the roots of *Phylloxera*-resistant American vines.

With **tissue culture propagation**, individual cells (typically from meristem) can be coaxed to divide and form embryos in a laboratory. This technique yields millions of genetically identical offspring from a single parent plant. It is frequently used in research aimed at improving food crops, and also to propagate rare or hybrid ornamental plants such as orchids.

In some flowering plant species, fruits may form even in the absence of fertilization. Fruits that develop from unfertilized flowers may have underdeveloped seeds or none at all. Plants with mutations that cause ovules or embryos to abort during development bear seedless fruit; such plants are necessarily sterile and must be propagated

FIGURE 27.13 Apple trees do not breed true for fruit traits. These fruits of 21 wild trees vary in flavor, sweetness, and texture.

by grafting. Seedless grapes and navel oranges are like this. All commercially produced bananas are seedless because the plants that bear them are triploid (3*n*). During meiosis, the three chromosomes cannot be divided equally between the two spindle poles, so gametes do not form and neither do seeds. Grafting bananas and other monocots is notoriously difficult (if not impossible), so seedless banana plants are propagated by cutting off and replanting shoots that sprout from their corms (Section 25.3).

Polyploid plants are common in nature (Sections 14.5 and 17.10), but it may take a long time for one to arise spontaneously. Plant breeders often use a microtubule poison called colchicine to artificially increase the frequency of polyploidy. Tetraploid (4*n*) plants produced by colchicine treatment are then crossed with diploid (2*n*) individuals. The resulting offspring are triploid and sterile: They make seedless fruit on their own or after pollination (but not fertilization) by a diploid plant. Seedless watermelons are produced this way.

tissue culture propagation Laboratory method in which individual plant cells (typically from meristem) are induced to form embryos.
vegetative reproduction Growth of new roots and shoots from extensions or fragments of a parent plant; form of asexual reproduction in plants.

27.6 WHAT REGULATES GROWTH AND DEVELOPMENT IN PLANTS?

In typical animals, most development occurs before adulthood. By contrast, most development in typical plants occurs in the adult body. Plants, unlike animals, cannot move about to avoid unfavorable conditions. Instead, each plant adapts to its environment. It does so by adjusting development in response to cues such as temperature, gravity, night length, the availability of water and nutrients, and even the presence of pathogens or herbivores.

Plant cells coordinate developmental activities by communicating with one another via **plant hormones**, extracellular signaling molecules that exert their effects at very low concentrations. All plant cells have the ability to make and release hormones, but each hormone is produced only in certain regions of the plant body at any given time. The release may occur in a region of the body that is far from cells in a targeted tissue, such as when cells in an actively growing root release cytokinins that keep shoot tips actively growing too. Some plant hormones have localized effects, such as when ethylene released from a cell in a ripening fruit affects the releasing cell as well as other cells in the same tissue.

Most molecules that act as hormones in plants do not act as hormones in animals, and vice versa. For example, plants make phytoestrogens that are structurally similar to animal estrogens (Section 3.3). The two types of compounds have similar effects in mammals, but in plants, phytoestrogens defend against fungal attack. The difference arises from the way the receptors for these compounds work in cells that bear them. In plants, as in animals, a cell detects a hormone via the receptor proteins it bears. Binding of a plant hormone to its receptor initiates a response in a plant cell that typically involves a change in gene expression. This response varies depending on cell type, receptor, and the concentration of the hormone. In addition, one plant hormone can enhance or oppose another's effects on the same cell. Some hormones dampen or enhance the expression of others, and most influence their own expression. This complex interplay gives rise to localized patterns of gene expression that can vary in cyclic patterns and even from one cell layer to the next.

plant hormone Extracellular signaling molecule of plants that exerts its effect at very low concentration.

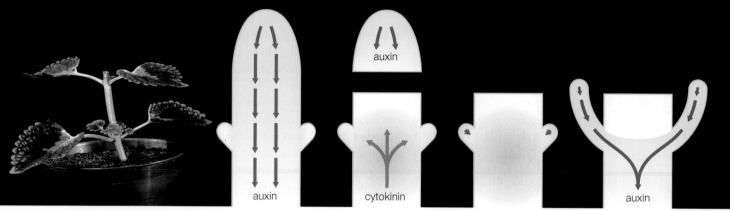

A A shoot can continue to grow despite losing its tip. The loss of a shoot's tip ends its main supply of auxin—a signal that breaks dormancy in lateral buds.

B Auxin flowing through a shoot keeps the level of cytokinin low in the stem.

C Removing the tip ends auxin flow in the stem. As the auxin level declines, the cytokinin level rises.

D The cytokinin stimulates cell division in apical meristem of lateral buds. The cells begin to produce auxin.

E Auxin transport away from the buds down through the stem causes the buds to lengthen.

FIGURE 27.14 Interaction of auxin and cytokinin in the release of apical dominance.

The plant hormone **auxin** plays a central role in all aspects of plant development, embryonic and ongoing. It causes young plant cells to elongate, so it promotes lengthening in soft plant parts. Auxin also influences the levels and effects of other plant hormones involved in growth.

Auxin is present in almost all plant tissues, but is unevenly distributed through them. It is made mainly in shoot apical meristems and in young leaves, and transported elsewhere. Auxin produced in shoot tips is loaded into phloem and travels to roots, where it is unloaded into root cells. A different mechanism dominates its movement over shorter distances. Once auxin enters a cell, it can exit only through active transport proteins called efflux carriers. Efflux carriers are not always distributed evenly around a cell's plasma membrane, and their placement can change over time. When efflux carriers in adjacent cells "point" in the same direction, they direct the flow of auxin through a tissue. In an actively lengthening shoot, for example, efflux carriers are positioned on the side of the cell closest to the base of the stem. Thus, auxin flows down through cells of the stem, where it encourages the cells to lengthen. Such directional transport, which is unique among plant hormones, establishes auxin concentration gradients that have a central role in coordinating the actions of other hormones.

A **cytokinin** is a plant hormone that affects meristem cell division and differentiation, stimulates development of lateral buds, and inhibits development of lateral roots. Some cytokinin is synthesized locally in stems, but most is produced in roots and transported to shoots in xylem. Auxin and cytokinin often influence the same cells, and in different contexts can enhance or oppose one another's effects. For example, in root apical meristem, auxin supports division of undifferentiated meristem cells, and cytokinin signals the cells to differentiate. In this context, the two hormones work in opposition to maintain the balance of differentiating and undifferentiated cells. By contrast, in shoot apical meristem, both hormones support cell division and prevent differentiation.

When a shoot is lengthening at the tip, its lateral buds are typically dormant, an effect called **apical dominance**. Auxin maintains apical dominance by regulating production and transport of cytokinin in a stem, and by promoting expression of an enzyme that breaks it down. If a shoot's tip breaks off, its source of auxin disappears, so the cytokinin level rises in the stem (**FIGURE 27.14A,B**). The cytokinin moves into lateral buds and stimulates cell divisions of apical meristem inside them (**FIGURE 27.14C**). These newly active meristem cells produce auxin, which is transported away from the bud tips and down the stem (**FIGURE 27.14D**). The movement causes the lateral buds to lengthen and form new shoots (**FIGURE 27.14E**).

---

apical dominance Effect in which a lengthening shoot tip inhibits the growth of lateral buds.
auxin Plant hormone that causes lengthening; also has a central role in growth by coordinating the effects of other hormones.
cytokinin Plant hormone that promotes cell division in shoot apical meristem and cell differentiation in root apical meristem. Often interacts antagonistically with auxin.

TAKE-HOME MESSAGE 27.7

Auxin promotes lengthening; it also affects the levels and effects of other plant hormones (such as cytokinin) involved in growth and development.

CREDITS: (14A) Jerome Wexler/Visuals Unlimited; (14B–E) From Starr/Evers/Starr, Biology Today and Tomorrow with Physiology, 4E. © 2013 Cengage Learning.

In 1926, researcher E. Kurosawa was studying what Japanese call *bakanae*, the "foolish seedling" effect. The stems of rice seedlings infected with a fungus, *Gibberella fujikuroi*, grew twice the length of uninfected seedlings. The abnormally elongated stems were weak and spindly, and eventually they toppled. Kurosawa discovered that he could induce the lengthening experimentally by applying extracts of the fungus to seedlings. Many years later, other researchers purified the substance from fungal extracts that brought about stem lengthening in plants (**FIGURE 27.15**). They named it gibberellin, after the fungus.

A **gibberellin**, as we now know, is a plant hormone that promotes growth in all flowering plants, among other functions. It causes a stem to lengthen between the nodes by inducing cell division and elongation. Along with auxin, gibberellin stimulates expansion along the long axis of a plant organ. Thus, it increases the length of the organ, and of the plant itself. The short stature of Mendel's dwarf pea plants (Section 13.3) is the result of a mutation that reduces the rate of gibberellin synthesis. A defective gibberellin receptor can result in a dwarf phenotype too. Gibberellin is also involved in slowing the aging of leaves and fruits, breaking dormancy in seeds, germination of seeds, and, in some plants, flowering. Seeds also make gibberellin. Seedless grapes tend to be smaller than seeded varieties because their undeveloped seeds do not produce normal amounts of gibberellin. Farmers often spray their seedless grape plants with synthetic gibberellin, which increases the size of the resulting fruit.

Gibberellin works by inhibiting inhibitors, thus removing the brakes on some cellular processes. During germination of a barley seed, for example, absorbed water causes cells of the embryo to release gibberellin (**FIGURE 27.16**).

FIGURE 27.15 Stem-lengthening effect of gibberellin. The three tall cabbage plants were treated with gibberellin. The two short plants in front of the ladder were not treated.

A Absorbed water causes cells of a barley embryo to release gibberellin, which diffuses through the seed into the aleurone layer of the endosperm.

B Gibberellin causes cells of the aleurone layer to produce amylase. This enzyme diffuses into the starch-packed endosperm.

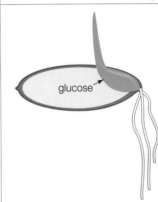

C The amylase breaks down starch into glucose. The glucose diffuses into the embryo and is used for aerobic respiration. Energy released by the reactions of aerobic respiration fuels meristem cell divisions in the embryo.

FIGURE 27.16 Gibberellin's role in germination, as illustrated in a seed of barley (a monocot).

The hormone diffuses into the aleurone, a protein-rich layer of cells surrounding endosperm. The presence of gibberellin causes these cells to destroy a transcriptional repressor (Section 10.1). The result is transcription of the gene for amylase—the enzyme that breaks the bonds between starch's glucose monomers (Section 3.2). The cells start producing amylase and releasing it into the endosperm's starchy interior, where it breaks down stored starch molecules. The embryo then begins to use the released glucose for aerobic respiration, which fuels rapid cell divisions of meristem cells in the radicle and plumule.

gibberellin Plant hormone that induces stem elongation; also helps seeds break dormancy.

TAKE-HOME MESSAGE 27.8
Gibberellin causes lengthening in plants by stimulating cell division and elongation along the long axis of stems and other organs. Among other effects, it also helps mobilize nutrients in a seed during germination.

CREDITS: (15) © Sylvan H. Wittwer/Visuals Unlimited; (16) From Starr/Evers/Starr, Biology Today and Tomorrow with Physiology, 4E. © 2013 Cengage Learning.

27.9 WHAT ARE SOME EFFECTS OF ABSCISIC ACID AND ETHYLENE?

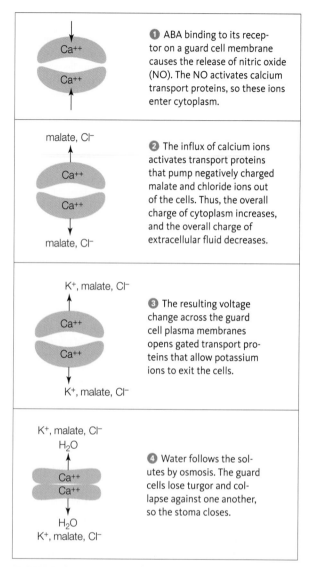

❶ ABA binding to its receptor on a guard cell membrane causes the release of nitric oxide (NO). The NO activates calcium transport proteins, so these ions enter cytoplasm.

❷ The influx of calcium ions activates transport proteins that pump negatively charged malate and chloride ions out of the cells. Thus, the overall charge of cytoplasm increases, and the overall charge of extracellular fluid decreases.

❸ The resulting voltage change across the guard cell plasma membranes opens gated transport proteins that allow potassium ions to exit the cells.

❹ Water follows the solutes by osmosis. The guard cells lose turgor and collapse against one another, so the stoma closes.

FIGURE 27.17 **ABA mediates stomata closure.** An osmotic pressure decrease triggered by abscisic acid causes stomata to close.

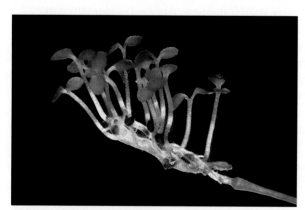

FIGURE 27.18 **ABA prevents seed germination.** Part of the ABA signaling pathway in this thale cress plant has been knocked out. Its seeds germinated before they had a chance to disperse.

ABSCISIC ACID

Abscisic acid (**ABA**) is a plant hormone that was named because its discoverers thought it mainly mediated **abscission**, the process by which a plant sheds leaves or other parts (we return to this topic in Section 27.11). However, ABA was later discovered to have a much greater role in plant stress responses than in abscission. Temperature extremes, lack of water, and other environmental stresses trigger an increase in ABA synthesis, release, and transport, so that the level of this hormone rises in the plant's tissues. In turn, the ABA increase induces expression of genes that help the plant survive the adverse conditions (Section 27.12 returns to stress responses in plants).

ABA is part of the mechanism that closes stomata to prevent water loss by transpiration (Section 26.5). When soil water becomes scarce, root cells release ABA. The hormone travels through the plant's vascular system to leaves and stems, where it binds to receptors on guard cell plasma membranes. ABA binding causes a plant cell to release a gas called nitric oxide (NO). The nitrogen atom in an NO molecule has an unpaired electron, so it is a free radical with potent effects inside cells. Plants use it as a hormone. In guard cells, NO activates membrane transport proteins that allow calcium ions to enter the cytoplasm (**FIGURE 27.17 ❶**). Cells use calcium ions for signaling purposes, so the concentration of these ions in cytoplasm is tightly regulated. In the presence of ABA, an increase in cytoplasmic calcium ion concentration triggers transport proteins to pump negatively charged malate (an organic acid) and chloride (Cl^-) out of the cell **❷**. As a result, the overall charge of guard cell cytoplasm increases relative to that of the extracellular environment. A difference in charge is called voltage; when the voltage across guard cell plasma membranes changes, gated transport proteins in the membranes open. The opened gates allow potassium ions (K^+) to follow the charge gradient and exit the cells **❸**. Water follows the solutes by osmosis, and the stomata close as the guard cells lose turgor and collapse against one another **❹**.

In addition to mediating stress responses, ABA also plays a role in embryo maturation and fruit ripening, and like cytokinin it suppresses lateral root formation. ABA that accumulates in a seed as it forms, matures, and dries out prevents the seed from germinating too early. It exerts this effect mainly by inhibiting expression of genes involved in cell wall loosening and expansion—both critical processes for growth of an embryonic plant. ABA also inhibits gibberellin synthesis. Thus, a seed cannot germinate until its ABA level declines (**FIGURE 27.18**).

CREDITS: (17) From Starr/Taggart/Evers/Starr, Biology, 13E. © 2013 Cengage Learning; (18) Taishi Umezawa, Kazuo Nakashima, Takuya Miyakawa, Takashi Kuromori, Masaru Tanokura, Kazuo Shinozaki, and Kazuko Yamaguchi-Shinozaki. Molecular Basis of the Core Regulatory Network in ABA Responses: Sensing, Signaling and Transport. Plant Cell Physiol (2010) 51(11): 1821–1839 first published online October 26, 2010. doi:10.1093/pcp/pcq156, by permission of Oxford University Press.

FIGURE 27.19 **Ethylene production during strawberry formation and ripening.** Oscillations are normal daily cycles (see Section 27.11).

ETHYLENE

The plant hormone **ethylene** is part of regulatory pathways that govern a wide range of metabolic and developmental processes in plants, including germination, growth, abscission, ripening, and stress responses. Ethylene is a gas that is soluble in water, and it freely crosses lipid bilayers. Cells in all parts of a plant can produce this hormone.

Two enzymes are involved in ethylene synthesis, and each occurs in multiple versions encoded by slightly different genes. Expression of some of these genes is inhibited by ethylene (a negative feedback loop); expression of the others is enhanced by ethylene (a positive feedback loop). Negative feedback loops produce a basal level of ethylene that helps fine-tune ongoing metabolic and developmental processes such as growth and cell expansion. For example, in roots, ethylene produced in a negative feedback loop enhances the transcription of genes for producing auxin and its efflux carriers (remember, auxin inhibits lengthening in roots). Positive feedback loops produce large amounts of ethylene required for intermittent processes such as germination, defense responses, abscission, and fruit formation and ripening (**FIGURE 27.19**). Consider how a strawberry fruit ripens. ABA that accumulates in the fruit as it forms and enlarges triggers production of ethylene in a positive feedback loop. The resulting ethylene burst enhances transcription of genes whose products have several effects associated with ripening. Chloroplasts are converted to chromoplasts (Section 4.8) as their (green) chlorophylls break down and carotenoids such as (red) lycopene and (orange and yellow) beta-carotenes accumulate inside the organelles. Firm cell walls and middle lamellae break down. Starch and organic acids are converted to sugars, and aromatic molecules are produced. The resulting color change, softening, and increased palatability attract animals that can disperse the strawberry's seeds.

Because ethylene is a gas, it can diffuse from one fruit to initiate ripening in another. Humans use this property to artificially ripen several types of fruit. Hard, unripe fruit can be transported long distances with less damage than soft, ripe fruit. Upon arrival at its final destination, the fruit is exposed to synthetic ethylene, which jump-starts the positive feedback ripening loop.

One of the ripening genes whose expression is induced by ethylene encodes an enzyme that breaks down pectin in plant cell walls. In 1994, the FDA approved "Flavr Savr" tomatoes, which had been genetically engineered to underproduce this enzyme. The tomatoes could be ripened artificially with ethylene, but the delayed softening doubled their shelf life. Flavr Savr tomatoes were available in stores for only a few years before their production was stopped.

abscisic acid (ABA) Plant hormone involved in stomata function and stress responses; inhibits germination.
abscission Process by which plant parts are shed.
ethylene Gaseous plant hormone that participates in germination, abscission, ripening, and stress responses.

TAKE-HOME MESSAGE 27.9

Abscisic acid inhibits germination and growth. It also triggers stomata closure and fruit ripening.

Ethylene participates in ongoing metabolic and developmental processes, and in intermittent processes such as fruit ripening.

A Regardless of how a corn seed is oriented in soil, the seedling's primary root always grows down, and its primary shoot always grows up.

B These seedlings were rotated 90° counterclockwise after they germinated. The plant adjusts to the change by redistributing auxin, and the direction of growth shifts as a result.

C In the presence of auxin transport inhibitors, seedlings do not adjust their direction of growth after a 90° counterclockwise rotation. Mutations in genes that encode auxin efflux carriers have the same effect.

FIGURE 27.20 Gravitropism.

statoliths

A This micrograph shows heavy, starch-packed statoliths settled on the bottom of gravity-sensing cells in a corn root cap.

B This micrograph was taken ten minutes after the root in A was rotated 90°. The statoliths are already settling to the new "bottom" of the cells.

FIGURE 27.21 Gravity and statoliths.

FIGURE IT OUT: In which direction was this root rotated?

Answer: Counterclockwise

Plants respond to environmental stimuli by adjusting their growth. In this way, each plant optimizes its opportunities for photosynthesis, absorption of water and nutrients, reproduction, and other factors that affect its fitness.

ENVIRONMENTAL TRIGGERS

An adjustment of growth in response to environmental stimuli is called a **tropism**. Tropisms are typically mediated by hormones, as the following examples illustrate.

Gravity Even if a seedling is turned upside down just after germination, its primary root and shoot will curve so the root grows downward and the shoot grows upward (**FIGURE 27.20**). This and any other growth response to gravity is called **gravitropism**. A root or shoot "bends" because of differences in auxin concentration that arise after directional auxin transport. In shoots, auxin enhances cell elongation, so auxin that accumulates on one side of a shoot causes the shoot to bend away from that side. Auxin has the opposite effect in roots: Auxin that accumulates on one side of a growing root causes the root to bend toward that side.

Gravity-sensing mechanisms of many organisms are based on organelles called statoliths. Plant statoliths are amyloplasts (Section 4.8) stuffed with dense grains of starch. They occur in root cap cells, and also in specialized cells at the edge of vascular tissues in the stem. Starch grains are heavier than cytoplasm, so statoliths tend to sink to the lowest region of the cell, wherever that may be (**FIGURE 27.21**). A shift in statolith position causes auxin efflux carriers to be redistributed to the down-facing side of the root or stem. Chloroplasts function as gravity-sensing organelles in shoots, because they specifically accumulate starch.

Light Light streaming in from one direction causes a stem to curve toward its source. This response, **phototropism**, orients certain parts of the plant in the direction that maximizes the amount of light intercepted by its photosynthetic cells. Phototropism in shoots occurs in response to blue light absorbed by nonphotosynthetic pigments called phototropins. In a shoot tip or coleoptile, light-energized phototropins repress transcription of a gene whose product causes auxin efflux carriers to be distributed evenly around the cell membrane. Thus, a

---

gravitropism Plant growth in a direction influenced by gravity.
phototropism Plant growth in a direction influenced by light.
thigmotropism Plant growth in a direction influenced by contact.
tropism In plants, directional growth response to an environmental stimulus.

CREDITS: (20A) Michael Clayton, University of Wisconsin; (20B,C) © Muday, G.K. and P. Haworth (1994), "Tomato root growth, gravitropism, and lateral development: Correlations with auxin transport." Plant Physiology and Biochemistry 32, 193–203, with permission from Elsevier Science; (21) Micrographs courtesy of Randy Moore from "How Roots Respond to Gravity," M. L. Evans, R. Moore, and K. Hasenstein, Scientific American, December 1986.

FIGURE 27.22 **Phototropism.** Auxin-mediated differences in cell elongation between two sides of a coleoptile-protected primary shoot induce bending toward light. Red dots signify auxin molecules.

cell exposed to a directional light source ends up with efflux carriers positioned mainly on its shady side. The polarization directs auxin flow toward the shaded side of

the structure, causing cells on that side to elongate more than cells on the illuminated side (FIGURE 27.22). The difference causes the entire structure to bend toward the light as it lengthens (*left*).

On the interior of a cell, a different mechanism causes chloroplasts to move in a tropic response to light. Chloroplasts are dragged from one position to another on actin filament tracks of the cytoskeleton. In high-intensity light, leaf chloroplasts move toward internal tissues where they are more shielded (FIGURE 27.23). This adaptation minimizes damage from excess electrons accumulating in electron transfer chains of the light reactions (Section 6.4). In low-intensity light, chloroplasts move in the opposite direction—toward leaf surfaces—thus maximizing their exposure to the light for photosynthesis. Blue light drives the movement in both cases.

Leaves or flowers of some plants change position in response to the changing angle of the sun throughout the day, a phototropic response called heliotropism (from Greek *helios*, sun). The mechanism that drives heliotropism is not understood, but it may be similar to phototropism because it has been observed to coincide with differential elongation of cells in stems, and it also occurs in response to blue light.

Contact A plant's contact with an object may cause a change in the direction of its growth, a response called **thigmotropism** (*thigma* means touch in Greek). We see thigmotropism when a vine's shoot touches a wire, for example (*left*). The mechanism that gives rise to the response is not well understood, but an immediate increase in cytoplasmic concentration of calcium

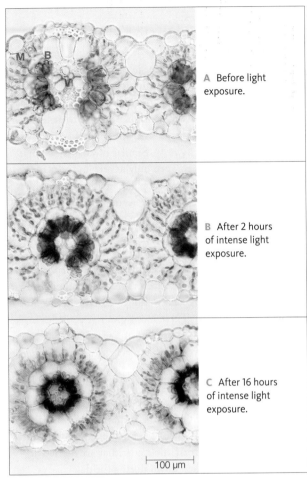

A Before light exposure.

B After 2 hours of intense light exposure.

C After 16 hours of intense light exposure.

⊢ 100 μm ⊣

FIGURE 27.23 Movement of chloroplasts in response to intense light, as seen in leaf sections of millet, a C4 plant. The chloroplasts respond by moving away from the external surfaces of the leaf, toward internal tissues that are more shielded from the light. Mesophyll (M), bundle sheath cells (B), and vascular bundles (V).

that accompanies contact is likely to play a role. Plants (and animals) have plasma membrane transport proteins that flood cytoplasm with calcium ions upon mechanical disturbance of the membrane. Several gene products that can sense calcium ions are involved, as well as nitric oxide and a hormone called jasmonic acid. These molecules trigger unequal growth rates of cells on opposite sides of the shoot, which coils in response. A similar mechanism causes roots to grow away from contact, so they "feel" their way around rocks and other impassable objects in the soil.

TAKE-HOME MESSAGE 27.10

Via hormones, plants adjust the direction and rate of growth in response to environmental stimuli such as gravity, light, contact, and mechanical stress.

CREDITS: (22A, B) © Cengage Learning; (23) Eri Maai, Shouu Shimada, Masahiro Yamada, Tatsuo Sugiyama, Hiroshi Miyake, Mitsutaka Taniguchi; The avoidance and aggregative movements of mesophyll chloroplasts in C4 monocots in response to blue light and abscisic acid; *Journal of Experimental Botany*, doi:10.1093/jxb/err008, by permission of Oxford University Press; (in text) top, © Cathlyn Melloan/Stone/Getty Images; bottom, © Gary Head.

27.11 HOW DO PLANTS SENSE AND RESPOND TO RECURRING ENVIRONMENTAL CHANGE?

DAILY CHANGE

A **circadian rhythm** is a cycle of biological activity that repeats every twenty-four hours or so (circadian means "about a day"). For example, a bean plant holds its leaves horizontally during the day but folds them close to its stem at night. Bean plants exposed to constant light or constant darkness for a few days will continue to move their leaves in and out of the "sleep" position at the time of sunrise and sunset (**FIGURE 27.24**). Similar mechanisms cause flowers of some plants to open only at certain times of day. For example, the flowers of plants pollinated mainly by night-flying bats open, secrete nectar, and release fragrance only at night. Periodically closing flowers protects the delicate reproductive parts when the likelihood of pollination is typically lowest.

Circadian rhythms are driven by interconnected feedback loops involving transcription factors that regulate their own expression (typically, by methylation and demethylation of histones, Section 10.1). These loops give rise to cycles in the levels of more than 30 percent of a plant cell's mRNAs (**FIGURE 27.25**). Cyclic shifts in gene expression underlie cyclic shifts in metabolism, for example between daytime starch-building reactions and nighttime starch-consuming reactions. Components of photosystems, ATP synthases, and other proteins used in photosynthesis are among the many gene products produced during the day and broken down at night. By contrast, molecules that are needed at night are typically broken down during the day.

At least six types of pigments provide light input into these internal circadian "clocks," but the best known are those called phytochromes and cryptochromes. **Phytochromes** absorb red light; light with a wavelength of 660 nanometers (red) causes their structure to change from an inactive to an active form. Light with a wavelength of 730 nanometers (far-red, which predominates in shade) changes the molecule back to its inactive form. Cryptochromes absorb blue and UV light.

SEASONAL CHANGE

Except at the equator, the length of daylight varies with the season. Days are longer in summer than in winter, and

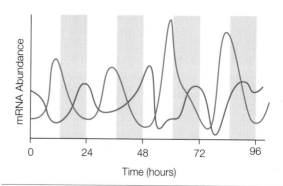

FIGURE 27.25 Circadian cycles of gene expression for some genes involved in temperature stress responses.

Plants were kept in constant light; gray bars show nighttime hours. Molecules that help the plants tolerate cold nights and hot days are produced just before they are actually needed. The blue line shows the averaged expression of 46 cold tolerance genes; the red line, averaged expression of 30 warm tolerance genes.

 FIGURE IT OUT: At what time of day is expression of cold tolerance genes lowest? Answer: Early morning

the difference increases with latitude. Plants respond to these seasonal changes in light availability with seasonally appropriate behaviors such as entering or breaking dormancy. **Photoperiodism** refers to an organism's response to changes in the length of day relative to night.

Flowering is a photoperiodic response in many species. Such species are termed long-day or short-day plants depending on which season they flower. These terms are somewhat misleading, as the main trigger for flowering is the length of night, not the length of day (**FIGURE 27.26**). Irises, oats, clover, and other long-day plants flower only when the hours of darkness fall below a critical value, typically in summer. Chrysanthemums, strawberries, and other short-day plants flower only when the hours of darkness are greater than some critical value. Flowering is not photoperiodic in sunflowers, tomatoes, roses, and other day-neutral plants.

Length of night is not the only cue for flowering. Some plants flower in spring only if they have been exposed to

---

FIGURE 27.24 {Animated} A circadian rhythm: leaf movements by a young bean plant. Physiologist Frank Salisbury kept this plant in darkness for twenty-four hours. Despite the lack of light cues, the leaves kept on folding and unfolding at sunrise (6 A.M.) and sunset (6 P.M.).

1 A.M.

6 A.M.

Noon

3 P.M.

10 P.M.

Midnight

CREDITS: (24) © Frank B. Salisbury. (25) From Starr/Evers/Starr, Biology Today and Tomorrow with Physiology, 4E. © 2013 Cengage Learning.

a prolonged period of cold during the preceding winter, a process called **vernalization**. Researchers suspect that plant cells perceive temperature via their plasma membrane, which varies in lipid composition and calcium ion permeability depending on temperature. Regardless of the mechanism of detection, a "cold" signal influences gene expression in these plant species.

Yearly cycles of abscission and dormancy are photoperiodic responses. Plants that periodically drop their leaves before a period of dormancy are typically native to regions that are too dry or too cold for optimal growth during part of the year. For example, deciduous trees of the northeastern United States begin to lose their leaves in autumn, around September. The trees remain dormant during the months of harsh winter weather that would otherwise damage leaves and buds. Growth resumes in spring (April), when milder conditions return. On the opposite side of the world, many tree species native to tropical monsoon forests of south Asia lose their leaves during the summer dry season, which is between November and May. Although the region receives a lot of rain annually, almost none of it falls during this period of the year. Dormancy offers the trees a way to survive the extended droughtlike conditions. New growth reappears at the beginning of June, just in time to be supported by the ample water of monsoon rains.

Abscission of fruits and leaves is mediated by ethylene. Let's use a horse chestnut tree native to southeastern Europe as an example. In this species, most root and shoot growth occurs between spring and early summer, from April to July. By midsummer, the tree is producing fruits and seeds. In August, the growing season is coming to a close, and nutrients are being routed to stems and roots for storage during the forthcoming period of dormancy. The ripe fruits (**FIGURE 27.27A**) and seeds release ethylene that diffuses into nearby twigs, petioles, and fruit stalks. The ethylene is a signal for cells in these zones to produce enzymes that digest their own walls. The cells bulge as their walls soften, and separate from one another as the extracellular matrix that cements them together dissolves. Tissue in the abscission zone weakens, and the structure above it drops. A scar often remains where the structure had been attached (**FIGURE 27.27B**).

circadian rhythm A biological activity that is repeated about every 24 hours.
photoperiodism Biological response to seasonal changes in the relative lengths of day and night.
phytochrome A light-sensitive pigment that helps set plant circadian rhythms based on length of night.
vernalization Stimulation of flowering in spring by prolonged exposure to low temperature in winter.

A A flash of red light at 660 nm interrupting a long night causes plants to respond as if the night were short. Long-day plants flower; short-day plants do not.

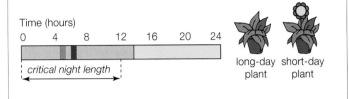

B A flash of far-red light at 730 nm cancels the effect of a red light flash. Short-day plants flower; long-day plants do not.

FIGURE 27.26 {Animated} Experiments showing that long- or short-day plants flower in response to night length. Each horizontal bar represents 24 hours. Blue indicates night length; yellow, day length.

 FIGURE IT OUT: Which type of pigment detected the light flashes in these experiments?

Answer: A phytochrome

A Ripening chestnuts emit ethylene that stimulates abscission of the fruits and nearby leaves.

B Horse chestnut trees take their name from abscission zones that leave horseshoe-shaped scars in this species.

FIGURE 27.27 Abscission as part of the normal life cycle of deciduous trees such as chestnuts.

TAKE-HOME MESSAGE 27.11

Plants respond to recurring cues from the environment with recurring cycles of activity. Pigments provide input into circadian cycles.

The main environmental cue for flowering is the length of night relative to the length of day, which varies seasonally in most places. Low winter temperatures stimulate spring flowering in some plant species.

The timing of seasonal abscission and dormancy is an evolutionary adaptation to recurring periods of environmental conditions that do not favor growth.

CREDITS: (26) From Starr/Evers/Starr, Biology Today and Tomorrow with Physiology, 4E. © 2013 Cengage Learning; (27A) © Randy Hjelsand/iStockphoto.com; (27B) © Adrian Chalkley.

A plant cannot run away from stressful situations: It either adapts to the adverse conditions or dies. Plant stressors are biotic (imposed by pathogens and herbivores) or abiotic (caused by nonliving environmental conditions). Plants have defenses against both types of stressors. For example,

A Saliva of a tobacco budworm chewing on a leaf of a tobacco plant triggers the plant to emit a combination of 11 volatile secondary metabolites.

B Red-tailed wasps are attracted to the unique chemical signature emitted by the plant. They follow the trail of aromatic chemicals back to the source.

C A wasp that finds a budworm attacks it and deposits an egg inside of it. When the egg hatches, a larva emerges and begins to eat the budworm, which eventually dies.

FIGURE 27.28 Interspecific plant defenses. Plant cells release a particular combination of volatile secondary metabolites in response to being chewed by a particular insect species. The chemical signature attracts wasps that parasitize the insect.

FIGURE 27.29 Evidence of a hypersensitive response in a leaf. Brown spots are dead tissue where germinating fungi penetrated the leaf's epidermis, triggering a release of hydrogen peroxide and nitric oxide that resulted in plant cell suicide.

wounding of a leaf, such as occurs when an insect chews on it, triggers the production of ABA, hydrogen peroxide, ethylene, and jasmonic acid. Jasmonic acid in turn increases transcription of genes whose products include a number of volatile chemicals that the plant releases into the air. These compounds are called secondary metabolites because they are not required for the immediate survival of the organism that makes them. Volatile secondary metabolites released in response to herbivory are detected by wasps that parasitize insects (**FIGURE 27.28**). These chemicals are also detected by neighboring plants, which respond by increasing their own production of ethylene and jasmonic acid.

Abiotic stressors such as temperature extremes or lack of water trigger ABA synthesis. You learned in Section 27.9 that ABA is part of a response that causes a plant's stomata to close when water is scarce, thus preventing water loss by transpiration. Stomata close after transport proteins move calcium ions into guard cells, and a nitric oxide burst produced in response to ABA activates these proteins. ABA and nitric oxide also participate in biotic stress responses. Consider that receptors on plant cells recognize molecules specific to microbial pathogens, including flagellin, a protein component of bacterial flagella. Flagellin binding to one of these receptors triggers a burst of ethylene synthesis. When ethylene is not present, ethylene receptors block transcription of a set of genes involved in defense. When ethylene is present, it binds to its receptors and locks them in an inactive form that marks them for destruction. Thus, ethylene synthesis lifts the brakes on production of molecules used in defense. The cell starts producing more receptors that detect bacterial flagella—a positive feedback loop that sensitizes the plant to the presence of more bacteria. Any additional bacteria that bind to the accumulated flagellin receptors trigger an ABA-mediated nitric oxide burst that immediately closes stomata. Closing stomata defends the plant against bacterial invasion because bacteria cannot penetrate plant epidermis: They can enter plant tissues only through wounds or open stomata.

Mutualistic bacteria and fungi avoid triggering a plant's defense responses by exchanging chemical signals with it. For example, you learned in Section 26.3 that *Rhizobium* bacteria in soil are attracted to compounds released from root cells. Those compounds are flavonoids, a type of secondary metabolite. *Rhizobium* bacteria respond to flavonoids by secreting a substance that is recognized by the plant as a signal to form a nodule.

A pathogen that penetrates a plant's epidermis triggers a large surge of hydrogen peroxide and nitric oxide that causes cells in the infected region to commit suicide. This "hypersensitive" response can prevent a pathogen from spreading to other parts of the plant, because it often kills the pathogen along with the infected tissue (FIGURE 27.29). However, a hypersensitive response is ineffective against pathogens that gain nutrients by killing cells outright. Some sac fungi, for example, use toxins to kill their plant hosts, then absorb nutrients released from their decomposing tissues. A different, long-term defense response, **systemic acquired resistance**, increases resistance of the whole plant body to attack by a wide range of fungi and other pathogens, as well as tolerance to abiotic stresses. Systemic acquired resistance begins when an infected tissue releases an as yet unknown signal that travels to other parts of the plant, where it triggers cells to produce salicylic acid, a molecule similar to aspirin. This hormone increases transcription of hundreds of genes whose products confer general hardiness to the plant. Among the molecules that may be produced are lignin (which increases the strength of plant cell walls), compounds that break down structural components of fungal cell walls, antioxidants, and flavonoids. Consider epicatechin, a flavonoid produced by cacao trees (the source of chocolate). Epicatechin prevents hardening of "pegs" that develop on germinating spores of many fungi. Fungi use these tough pegs to punch through plant epidermal tissue.

Like many other secondary metabolites of plants, epicatechin has medicinal effects in humans. For example, it protects against oxidative tissue damage that typically occurs after a stroke or a heart attack. Consuming foods such as dark chocolate (which is rich in epicatechin) on a daily basis has been shown to reduce the heart muscle damage that a heart attack causes by 52 percent; and reduce the brain damage that a stroke causes by 32 percent. As an added benefit, epicatechin enhances memory and kills cancer cells. Epicatechin probably works its magic in humans because it activates an enzyme that produces nitric oxide in blood vessel walls. Nitric oxide relaxes muscles in the vessel walls, causing the vessels to widen. In mammals, nitric oxide is part of hormonal systems that regulate blood vessel width, and it is necessary for proper function of endothelial cells that make up the vessels.

---

systemic acquired resistance In plants, inducible whole-body resistance to a wide range of pathogens and abiotic stressors.

TAKE-HOME MESSAGE 27.12

Detection of plant pathogens can trigger stomatal closure or cell death.

Systemic acquired resistance triggered by pathogen attacks increases a plant's ability to withstand biotic and abiotic stresses.

National Geographic Explorer
DR. GRACE GOBBO

When Grace Gobbo walks through a Tanzanian rain forest, she doesn't see only trees, flowers, and vines. She sees cures. For centuries, medicinal plants used by traditional healers have been at the heart of effective health care in this lush African nation. With expensive imported pharmaceuticals unaffordable for most of the population, traditional cures often provide the only relief for illness. But today, both the lush landscape and indigenous medical knowledge are disappearing. Gobbo hopes her efforts to preserve natural remedies and native habitat will help reverse the trend.

Growing up in a Christian family with a doctor for a father, Gobbo dismissed traditional healing as witchcraft. Then coursework in botany exposed her to evidence she couldn't ignore. "We studied cases where a particular plant successfully treated coughs," she recalls. "Laboratory results proved it stopped bacterial infection." Intrigued, Gobbo began interviewing traditional healers in her own area who described their success using plants to treat a wide range of ailments, including skin and chest infections, stomach ulcers, diabetes, heart disease, mental illness, and even cancer. To date, she has recorded information shared by more than 80 healers, entering notes and photographs about plants and their uses into a computer database. "Before now, these facts existed only as an oral tradition," she explains. "Nothing was written down. The knowledge is literally dying out with the elders since today's young generation considers natural remedies old-fashioned." Gobbo wants to capture and preserve the irreplaceable facts before they are lost, and convince young people to appreciate their value. "In this part of the world, modern medicine is not enough; most people can't afford it. Traditional healing has so much potential. Local communities are comfortable with this approach; it just needs to be more accessible. But the longer we wait, the more knowledge disappears. We need to act now, and act fast."

Sustainability

FIGURE 27.30 Honeybees learn and remember the locations of flowers, but pesticides may be making them lose their way.

A SINGLE HONEYBEE VISITS HUNDREDS, SOMETIMES THOUSANDS, OF FLOWERS A DAY IN SEARCH OF NECTAR AND POLLEN. Then it must find its way back to the hive, navigating distances up to eight kilometers (five miles) to communicate the location of the flowers to other bees. Bees depend on "scent memory" to find flowers teeming with nectar and pollen. Their ability to rapidly learn, remember, and communicate with each other has made them highly efficient pollinators, responsible for the existence of nearly a third of the food we eat. They have a similar impact on the food supplies of wildlife.

Long-term exposure to low levels of pesticides might impair a bee's ability to carry out its pollen mission. Many researchers suspect that synthetic pesticides called neonicotinoids are an important factor in colony collapse disorder (CCD), a rapid die-off seen in millions of honeybees throughout the world since 2006. Neonicotinoids are now the most widely used insecticides in the United States, and they are still being used in other countries—about 2.5 million acres of croplands in total. The chemicals are systemic, which means they are taken up by all tissues of a plant treated with them, including the nectar and pollen that honeybees collect from flowers as they forage (FIGURE 27.30).

Neonicotinoids mimic the neurotoxic (nerve-killing) effect of nicotine, a natural insecticide made by plants such as tobacco, and they impair a bee's learning and memory. "Honeybees learn to associate floral colors and scents with the quality of food rewards," says Geraldine Wright, a neuroscientist at Newcastle University in England. Neonicotinoids affect the neurons involved in these behaviors, so bees exposed to these pesticides are likely to have difficulty communicating with other members of the colony. Another pesticide, coumaphos, is commonly used to treat hives infested with parasitic Varroa mites. These mites are often found in beehives affected by CCD. Wright's research shows that coumaphos makes honeybees even more vulnerable to the effects of neonicotinoids.

Neonicotinoids also increase bees' vulnerability to fungal infection even in amounts too tiny to detect in the insects themselves. Even dewdrops that form on neonicotinoid-treated plants apparently contain enough of the insecticide to affect bees.

Summary

SECTION 27.1 **Flowers** consist of modified leaves at the ends of specialized branches of angiosperms. Sepals surround petals, which in turn surround **stamens** and **carpels**. A stamen consists of an **anther** on a thin filament. Anthers produce **pollen grains**. A carpel consists of a **stigma**, often a style, and an **ovary** inside which one or more **ovules** develop. The female gametophyte forms inside an ovule.

Pollination is the arrival of pollen on a receptive stigma. A flower's shape, pattern, color, and fragrance typically reflect an evolutionary relationship with a particular **pollination vector**, often a coevolved animal. Coevolved **pollinators** receive **nectar**, pollen, or another reward for visiting a flower.

SECTION 27.2 Meiosis of diploid cells inside pollen sacs of anthers produces haploid **microspores**. Each microspore develops into a pollen grain that is released from a pollen sac after a period of **dormancy**.

Meiosis and cytoplasmic division of a cell in an ovule produces four **megaspores**, one of which gives rise to the female gametophyte. One of the seven cells of the gametophyte is the egg; another is the endosperm mother cell. A pollen grain **germinates** on a stigma and forms a pollen tube that contains two sperm cells. The tube grows through carpel tissues to the egg. In **double fertilization**, one of the sperm cells in the pollen tube fertilizes the egg, forming a zygote; the other fuses with the endosperm mother cell and gives rise to triploid **endosperm**.

SECTION 27.3 After double fertilization, the ovary wall and sometimes other tissues mature into a **fruit** that encloses the seeds. A **seed** is a mature ovule: an embryo sporophyte and endosperm enclosed within a seed coat. Nutrients in endosperm or cotyledons make seeds a nutritious food source. Fruit traits are adaptations to dispersal by specific vectors.

SECTION 27.4 Seeds often undergo a period of dormancy that does not end until species-specific environmental cues trigger germination. The radicle emerges from the seed coat at the end of germination. Some monocot plumules are sheathed by a protective **coleoptile**; eudicot hypocotyls form a hook that pulls cotyledons up through soil.

SECTION 27.5 Many types of flowering plants can produce clonal offspring by **vegetative reproduction**. Some are propagated commercially by grafting; the common laboratory technique of **tissue culture propagation** is used to propagate some valuable ornamentals.

SECTIONS 27.6–27.9 Plants continue to develop through their lifetime. **Plant hormones** promote or arrest development in regions of a plant by stimulating or inhibiting cell division, differentiation, or enlargement. Some have roles in occasional responses such as pathogen defense. Hormones work together or in opposition, and many have different effects in different regions of the plant.

Summary continued

Auxin promotes lengthening and also coordinates the action of other hormones involved in growth. A unique transport system that is responsive to internal and external conditions distributes auxin directionally. The polar distribution of auxin directs development of plant organs, such as when auxin gradients maintain **apical dominance** in a growing shoot tip. **Cytokinin** acts together with auxin, often antagonistically, to balance growth with development in shoot and root tips. **Gibberellin** lengthens stems between nodes, and it is required for seed germination. **Abscisic acid** (**ABA**) plays a part in **abscission**, but a greater role in seed germination and stress responses (including stomata closure in response to dry conditions). **Ethylene** is produced in negative and positive feedback loops. Negative feedback loops are part of regulating ongoing metabolism and development; positive loops provoke special processes such as abscission, ripening, and defense responses.

SECTION 27.10 A **tropism** is an adjustment in the direction of plant growth in response to environmental cues such as gravity (**gravitropism**), light (**phototropism**), or contact (**thigmotropism**).

SECTION 27.11 **Circadian rhythms** are driven by gene expression feedback loops that have input from nonphotosynthetic pigments such as **phytochromes**. **Photoperiodism** is a response to change in the length of day relative to night. Seasonal cycles of abscission and dormancy are adaptations to seasonal changes in environmental conditions. Some plants require prolonged exposure to cold before they can flower (**vernalization**).

SECTION 27.12 A nitric oxide burst is part of a hypersensitive defense response that closes stomata or kills the cell in response to pathogen detection. Pathogens trigger **systemic acquired resistance**. Some plant secondary metabolites function in defense. A few of these compounds, including a number of flavonoids, are beneficial to human health.

SECTION 27.13 Colony collapse disorder (CCD) is killing honeybees. Declining bee populations negatively affect plant populations as well as other animal species that depend on the plants, including humans. Widely used neonicotinoid pesticides probably contribute to CCD.

Self-Quiz Answers in Appendix VII

1. The arrival of pollen grains on a receptive stigma is called _____ .

2. An animal pollinator may receive _____ when it visits a flower of a coevolved plant (choose all that apply).
   a. pollen   c. pesticides
   b. nectar   d. fruit

3. A _____ contains one or more ovaries in which eggs develop, fertilization occurs, and seeds mature.
   a. pollen sac   c. receptacle
   b. carpel   d. sepal

4. In flowers, the structures that produce male gametophytes are called _____ ; those that produce female gametophytes are called _____ .
   a. pollen grains; flowers   c. anthers; stigma
   b. stamens; carpels   d. megaspores; microspores

5. Seeds are mature _____ ; fruits are mature _____ .
   a. ovaries; ovules   c. ovules; ovaries
   b. ovules; stamens   d. stamens; ovaries

6. Cotyledons develop as part of _____ .
   a. carpels   c. embryo sporophytes
   b. accessory fruits   d. flowers

7. In some species, exposure to _____ is a trigger for seed germination.
   a. light   c. smoke
   b. cold   d. all can be triggers

8. The three main parts of a typical mature eudicot seed are the _____ .
   a. pollen grain, egg, and seed coat
   b. embryo, endosperm, and seed coat
   c. megaspores, microspores, and ovule
   d. embryo, cotyledons, and seed coat

9. A new plant forms from a stem that broke off of the parent plant. This is an example of _____ .
   a. nodal cloning   c. asexual reproduction
   b. exocytosis   d. tissue culture propagation

10. Banana plants produce seedless fruit because they are _____ .
   a. triploid   c. propagated by grafting
   b. monocots   d. treated with colchicine

11. Plant hormones _____ .
   a. often have multiple, overlapping effects
   b. are active in developing plant embryos
   c. are active in adult plants
   d. may have different effects in different tissues
   e. all of the above

12. In some plants, flowering is a _____ response.
   a. phototropic   c. photoperiodic
   b. gravitropic   d. thigmotropic

13. Match the response with its main trigger.
   ___ phototropism   a. contact with an object
   ___ gravitropism   b. blue light
   ___ thigmotropism   c. a long period of cold
   ___ photoperiodism   d. gravity
   ___ vernalization   e. sun position
   ___ heliotropism   f. night length

14. Which of the following statements is false?

    a. Auxin and gibberellin promote stem elongation.

    b. Cytokinin promotes cell division in shoot tips.

    c. Abscisic acid promotes water loss and dormancy.

    d. Ethylene promotes fruit ripening and abscission.

15. Match the observation with the main hormone.

___ ethylene	a. Your cabbage plants bolt (they form elongated flowering stalks).
___ cytokinin	
___ auxin	b. The potted plant in your room is leaning toward the window.
___ gibberellin	
___ abscisic acid	c. The last of your apples is getting really mushy.
	d. The seeds of your roommate's marijuana plant do not germinate no matter what he does to them.
	e. Lateral buds are sprouting.

Critical Thinking

1. The oat coleoptiles on the *left* have been modified: either cut or placed in a light-blocking tube. Which ones will still bend toward a directional light source?

2. Is the seedling shown on the *right* a monocot or eudicot? How can you tell?

3. Belgian scientists discovered that certain mutations in thale cress cause excess auxin production. Predict the mutations' impact on the plant's phenotype.

4. Humans have no stomata to close, and plants have no blood vessels, but nitric oxide operates as a hormone on both structures. In fact, NADPH oxidase, the plasma membrane enzyme that produces nitric oxide in plants, also occurs in human white blood cells, where it produces a nitric oxide burst in response to detection of bacterial flagellin inside the body. This response is mediated by abscisic acid, just as it is in plants—and all animals. How can it be that humans and plants have the same molecules mediating the same response to the same bacterial protein?

CREDITS: (31A) © Steven D. Johnson. (31B–C, in text CT1) From Starr/Evers/Starr, Biology Today and Tomorrow with Physiology, 4E. © 2013 Cengage Learning; (in text CT2) © Jubel Harshaw/Shutterstock.

Data Analysis Activities

Who's the Pollinator? *Massonia depressa* is a low-growing succulent plant native to the desert of South Africa. The dull-colored flowers of this monocot develop at ground level, have tiny petals, emit a yeasty aroma, and produce a thick, jellylike nectar. These features led researchers to suspect that desert rodents such as gerbils pollinate this plant. To test their hypothesis, the researchers trapped rodents in areas where *M. depressa* grows and checked them for pollen. They also put some plants in wire cages that excluded mammals, but not insects, to see whether fruits and seeds would form in the absence of rodents. Results are shown in **FIGURE 27.31**.

1. How many of the 13 captured rodents showed some evidence of pollen from *M. depressa*?

2. Would this evidence alone be sufficient to conclude that rodents are the main pollinators of this plant?

3. How did the average number of seeds produced by caged plants compare with that of control plants?

4. Do these data support the hypothesis that rodents are required for pollination of *M. depressa*? Why or why not?

A The dull, petal-less, ground-level flowers of *Massonia depressa* are accessible to rodents, who push their heads through the stamens to reach the nectar at the bottom of floral cups. Note the pollen on the gerbil's snout.

Type of rodent	Number caught	# with pollen on snout	# with pollen in feces
Namaqua rock rat	4	3	2
Cape spiny mouse	3	2	2
Hairy-footed gerbil	4	2	4
Cape short-eared gerbil	1	0	1
African pygmy mouse	1	0	0

B Evidence of visits to *M. depressa* by rodents.

	Mammals allowed access to plants	Mammals excluded from plants
Percent of plants that set fruit	30.4	4.3
Average number of fruits per plant	1.39	0.47
Average number of seeds per plant	20.0	1.95

C Fruit and seed production of *M. depressa* with and without visits by mammals. Mammals were excluded from plants by wire cages with openings large enough for insects to pass through. 23 plants were tested in each group.

FIGURE 27.31 Testing pollination of *M. depressa* by rodents.

mputee Amanda Kitts tests a bionic arm
eveloped at Johns Hopkins. Like an arm
made of skin, muscle, and bone, it responds
o signals from her nervous system.

28

ANIMAL TISSUES AND ORGAN SYSTEMS

Links to Earlier Concepts

The chapters in this unit focus on the structure and function of animal bodies. This chapter applies what you learned about levels of organization (Section 1.1) to animal bodies, and it expands on the nature of multicelled body plans (23.1). You may wish to review cell junctions (4.10), the surface-to-volume ratio (4.1), diffusion and transport proteins (5.6, 5.7), aerobic respiration (7.1), and energy conversion pathways (7.7).

KEY CONCEPTS

ORGANIZATION OF ANIMAL BODIES

In most animals, cells are organized as tissues, organs, and organ systems. Animal structure is shaped by natural selection, and constrained by physical and developmental factors.

ANIMAL TISSUES

Epithelial tissues cover the body's surfaces and line its cavities. Connective tissues provide support. Muscle tissues bring about movement. Nervous tissue receives, integrates, and communicates information.

ANIMAL ORGAN SYSTEMS

Vertebrate body cavities hold many of the body's organs. Organs work cooperatively to carry out the tasks essential to survival and reproduction.

THE SKIN

Skin is an organ composed of multiple types of tissue that collectively protect a body, allow detection of external stimuli, and help to conserve water and control temperature.

INTEGRATING ACTIVITIES

Negative feedback mechanisms play an important role in homeostasis. Sensory receptors inform the brain of changes in the internal environment, and the brain tells organs and tissues to respond.

| A **Cell**
(muscle cells) | B **Tissue**
(cardiac muscle) | C **Organ** (heart) | D **Organ system**
(circulatory system) | E **Body** |

FIGURE 28.1 Levels of organization in a vertebrate (human) body.

LEVELS OF ORGANIZATION

In all animals, development produces a body with multiple types of cells (**FIGURE 28.1A**). In most animals, these cells are organized as tissues (**FIGURE 28.1B**). Four types of tissue occur in all vertebrate bodies:

1. Epithelial tissue covers body surfaces and lines the internal cavities such as the gut.
2. Connective tissue holds body parts together and provides structural support.
3. Muscle tissue moves the body or its parts.
4. Nervous tissue detects stimuli and relays information.

Each tissue contains unique cell types not present in other tissues. For example, contractile cells occur in muscle tissue, but not in nervous tissue or epithelial tissue.

Typically, animal tissues are organized into organs. An organ consists of two or more tissues arranged in a way that allows the organ to carry out specific tasks. Consider the human heart, an organ that includes all four tissue types (**FIGURE 28.1C**). The wall of the heart is made up mostly of cardiac muscle tissue. A sheath of connective tissue encloses the heart, and epithelial tissue lines the heart's internal chambers. Nervous tissue delivers signals to and from the heart. Coordinated action of these tissues together allows the heart to pump blood, imparting the pressure that moves blood through the body.

In organ systems, two or more organs and other components interact physically, chemically, or both in a common task. For example, in the vertebrate circulatory system, the pressure generated by a beating heart (an organ) moves blood (a tissue) through blood vessels (organs), thereby transporting gases and solutes to and from all body cells (**FIGURE 28.1D**). Multiple organ systems interact to sustain the body as a whole.

AN INTERNAL ENVIRONMENT

By weight, an animal body consists mainly of water with dissolved salts, proteins, and other solutes. The bulk of this body fluid is inside cells. The rest is **extracellular fluid**, the internal environment in which body cells live. In vertebrates, extracellular fluid consists mainly of **interstitial fluid**, which is the fluid in spaces between cells, and plasma, which is the fluid portion of the blood.

In order for body cells to stay alive, conditions in the internal environment—including temperature and solute concentrations—must remain within a narrow range. Keeping conditions of the internal environment within this range is an important aspect of homeostasis (Section 1.2).

---

extracellular fluid Of a multicelled organism, body fluid outside of cells; serves as the body's internal environment.
interstitial fluid Fluid in spaces between body cells.

TAKE-HOME MESSAGE 28.1

In most animals, cells are organized as tissues. Each tissue consists of cells of a specific type that cooperate in carrying out a particular task. Tissues are organized into organs, which in turn are components of organ systems.

Extracellular fluid is the external environment of body cells. Maintaining the solute concentration and temperature of this fluid is an important part of homeostasis.

CREDITS: (1A, D) © Cengage Learning 2014; (1B) © Ed Reschke; (1C) From Starr/Evers/Starr, Biology Today and Tomorrow with Physiology, 4E. © 2013 Cengage Learning; (1E) Image © Yuri Arcurs, Used under license from Shutterstock.com.

An animal's structural traits (its anatomy) evolve in concert with its functional traits (its physiology). Both types of traits are genetically determined and vary among individuals. In each generation, those traits that best help individuals survive and reproduce in their environment are preferentially passed on. Over many generations, these adaptive traits become altered in ways that reflect their function in a specific environment.

Physical laws constrain the evolution of body structure. For example, dissolved substances travel through extracellular fluid by diffusion (Section 5.6). However, diffusion alone could not sustain a large or thick body because gases, nutrients, and wastes would not move quickly enough through the body to keep up with cellular metabolism. Thus, an animal with a massive body must have a mechanism for distributing material through the body. In vertebrates, a circulatory system serves this purpose. This system includes a network of extensively branched blood vessels that extends through the body (**FIGURE 28.2A**). Every living cell is close enough to a blood vessel to exchange substances with it by diffusion.

As another example, vertebrates faced new physical challenges when they left their aquatic habitat behind and moved onto land (Section 24.3). Gases enter or leave an animal's body by diffusing across a moist respiratory surface. In an aquatic organism, the surrounding water both delivers oxygen and moistens the respiratory surface. By contrast, a land animal must extract oxygen from air, which can dry a respiratory surface. The evolution of lungs allowed vertebrates to maintain a moist respiratory surface inside their body. Cells inside a lung secrete a fluid that keeps this surface damp (**FIGURE 28.2B**).

Evolution by natural selection involves incremental modifications of existing tissues or organs. Consider the evolution of lungs, which first arose as an outpouching from the gut of a bony fish. These fishes had gills, but evolution of a simple lung improved their ability to survive even in poorly oxygenated water. The fish swallowed air to fill its lung, then oxygen diffused from the lung into its blood. Fishes with lungs were the ancestors of tetrapods, and after vertebrates moved onto land, lungs became larger and additional internal partitions that increased the surface area available for gas exchange evolved.

Although the details of lung structure changed, the anatomical connection to the gut did not. As a legacy of the lungs' origin in an ancient fish, the human throat connects to both the digestive tract and respiratory tract. As a result of this dual connection, food sometimes goes where air should, causing a person to choke. It would be safer if food and air entered the body through separate passageways. However,

A Branching vessels of a vertebrate circulatory system distribute substances to cells throughout a large body.	B Lungs with a moist internal surface provide a site where gases can dissolve and move into and out of the body.

FIGURE 28.2 Examples of anatomical solutions to physiological challenges in the human body.

FIGURE 28.3 Bat, with forelimbs modified to function as wings. No vertebrate has both forelimbs and wings.

because evolution modifies existing structures, it often does not produce the most optimal body plan possible.

An existing body framework imposes architectural constraints. For example, the ancestors of all modern land vertebrates had a body plan with four limbs. When wings evolved in birds and bats, they did so by modification of existing forelimbs, not by new limbs sprouting (**FIGURE 28.3**). Although it might be advantageous to have both wings and arms, no living or fossil vertebrate with such a body plan has ever been discovered.

TAKE-HOME MESSAGE 28.2

Anatomical traits are shaped by physical constraints such as the requirement that a large body cannot evolve without evolution of a circulatory system to distribute material through it.

New anatomical traits typically arise by modification of existing structures. This process constrains animal body plans and can produces structures with less than optimal function.

CREDITS: (2A) Biophoto Associates/ Photo Researchers, Inc.; (2B) © PhotoDisc/ Getty Images, with art by Lisa Starr; (3) © Kirsanov/ Shutterstock.com.

GENERAL CHARACTERISTICS

Most of what you see when you look in a mirror—your skin, hair, and nails—consists of epithelial tissue or structures derived from it. Epithelium even covers the outer surface of your eyeballs. On the inside, epithelium lines your body's many tubes and cavities, including blood vessels, airways, and the passages that make up the digestive, urinary, and reproductive tracts.

Epithelial tissue, or epithelium (plural, epithelia), is a sheetlike tissue consisting of tightly packed cells with little extracellular material between them. One surface of an epithelium faces the environment or some body fluid. The opposite surface is glued to an underlying tissue by **basement membrane**, a layer of proteins secreted by the epithelium. Blood vessels do not run through epithelium, so nutrients reach cells by diffusing from adjacent tissue.

Tight junctions (Section 4.10) occur only in epithelial tissue. These junctions join the plasma membranes of adjacent cells so securely that fluids cannot seep between cells. An epithelium with tight junctions can keep fluid contained within a particular body compartment. For example, tight junctions connect the epithelial cells that line your gut. This epithelium serves as a barrier that prevents highly acidic stomach fluid from leaking out and damaging underlying tissue.

Epithelial tissues that undergo a lot of mechanical stress such as those of the skin have many adhering junctions. These junctions function like buttons that hold a shirt closed. They connect the plasma membranes of cells at distinct points but do not form a tight seal.

Animals constantly renew their epithelial cells. For example, you shed and replace about 0.7 kilogram (1.5 pounds) of skin each year. Replacing those cells requires many cell divisions, and so provides many opportunities for cancer-causing DNA replication errors to occur. Thus, epithelium is the animal tissue most likely to become cancerous. An epithelial cell cancer is called a carcinoma.

TYPES OF EPITHELIAL TISSUE

Different types of epithelia differ in their number of cell layers and the shapes of cells within those layers. A simple epithelium is one cell thick, whereas stratified epithelium has multiple cell layers. **FIGURE 28.4** shows the three types of simple epithelium. Cells in squamous epithelium are flattened or scalelike. (*Squama* is the Latin word for scale.) Cells of cuboidal epithelium are short cylinders that look like cubes when viewed in cross-section. Cells in columnar epithelium are taller than they are wide.

Simple squamous epithelium, the thinnest type of epithelium, functions in the exchange of materials. Gases and some nutrients diffuse across it easily. This type of epithelium lines blood vessels and the inner surface of the lungs. In contrast, thicker stratified squamous epithelium has a protective function. This type of tissue makes up the outer layer of human skin.

Cells of cuboidal and columnar epithelium function in absorption and secretion. Cells in some cuboidal and columnar epithelial tissues have fingerlike projections called **microvilli** at their free surface. Microvilli increase the surface area across which substances can be absorbed. Microvilli of the simple columnar epithelium in your small intestine help you absorb nutrients released by digestion of food.

In other tissues, such as those of the upper airways and oviducts, the free epithelial surface has cilia (Section 4.9). Coordinated waving of cilia in airways moves mucus that has trapped tiny inhaled particles away from lungs. Cilia in oviducts propel an egg toward the uterus (womb).

Some epithelial cells specialize in secretion of substances that function outside the cell. In most animals, such secretory cells cluster in glands. A gland is a multicelled

---

Simple squamous epithelium
- Lines blood vessels, the heart, and air sacs of lungs
- Allows substances to cross by diffusion

Simple cuboidal epithelium
- Lines kidney tubules, ducts of some glands, reproductive tract
- Functions in absorption and secretion, movement of materials

Simple columnar epithelium
- Lines some airways, parts of the gut
- Functions in absorption and secretion, protection

mucus-secreting gland cell

FIGURE 28.4 Types of simple epithelium.

National Geographic Explorer
DR. BRENDA LARISON

Most animals have pigment-producing epithelial cells in their skin. In zebras, these cells give rise to a distinctive pattern of black and white stripes. National Geographic Young Explorer Brenda Larison investigates how this striping pattern arises, and also how the stripes could be adaptive.

There are many hypotheses about the adaptive value of zebra stripes, including camouflage, predator confusion, improved thermoregulation, and avoidance of insect bites that can transmit disease. To figure out which (if any) of these hypotheses are correct, Larison looks for correlations between striping patterns and environmental variables. Larison has found that zebras from northern populations tend to be more striped than those farther south. She is testing the hypothesis that striping increases with the density of disease-carrying flies.

FIGURE 28.5 Striping mutation in a zebra colt.

To determine which genes govern striping, Larison collects and compares DNA samples from zebra populations with different patterns. Sequencing DNA allows her to correlate genetic variation with stripe variation. Mutations that disrupt striping (FIGURE 28.5) also provide valuable information.

To learn more about Larison's research, visit her website: www.how-the-zebra-got-its-stripes.com.

structure that releases substances onto the skin or into a body cavity or fluid. **Exocrine glands** have ducts or tubes that deliver their secretions onto an internal or external surface. Exocrine secretions include mucus, saliva, tears, digestive enzymes, earwax, and breast milk. In animals such as poison dart frogs, exocrine ducts secrete venom that protects the animal from predators. **Endocrine glands** have no ducts. They release signaling molecules called hormones into interstitial fluid. Most commonly, hormones enter the bloodstream, which distributes them throughout the body.

Claws, nails, hooves, fur, hair, beaks, and feathers form when specialized epithelial cells produce large amounts of keratin, a fibrous protein (Section 3.4). The visible part of a hoof, hair, or feather consists of the remains of such cells. Other specialized epithelial cells produce pigments that impart color to these keratin-rich body parts, as well as to the skin. We consider these cells in Section 28.8.

basement membrane Secreted layer that attaches an epithelium to an underlying tissue.
endocrine gland Ductless gland; secretes hormones.
epithelial tissue Sheetlike animal tissue that covers outer body surfaces and lines internal tubes and cavities.
exocrine gland Gland that secretes milk, sweat, saliva, or some other substance through a duct.
microvilli Thin projections from the plasma membrane of some epithelial cells; increase the surface area of the cell.

TAKE-HOME MESSAGE 28.3

Epithelia are sheetlike tissues that line the body's surface and its cavities, ducts, and tubes. They function in protection, absorption, and secretion.

Some epithelia have cilia or microvilli at their surface.

Epithelial tissues undergo continual turnover.

Gland cells are secretory epithelial cells.

Specialized epithelial cells that produce large amounts of keratin are the source of hair, nails, hooves, and feathers.

A Loose connective tissue
- Underlies most epithelia
- Provides elastic support, stores fluid

B Dense, irregular connective tissue
- Deep in skin and wall of gut, in kidney capsule
- Binds parts together, provides support, protection

C Dense, regular connective tissue
- Tendons and ligaments
- Stretchable attachment between parts

D Cartilage
- Internal framework of ears, nose, airways; covers ends of bones
- Supports soft tissues, cushions, reduces friction at joints

E Adipose tissue
- Under skin and around the heart and kidneys
- Stores energy-rich lipids, cushions body parts, serves as insulation

F Bone tissue
- Bulk of most vertebrate skeletons
- Protects soft tissues, functions in movement, stores minerals, produces blood cells

G Blood
- Connective tissue with fluid matrix (plasma) and cellular components
- Transports substances, acts in body defenses, and helps maintain temperature

FIGURE 28.6 {Animated} Vertebrate connective tissues.

GENERAL CHARACTERISTICS

Connective tissues consist of cells scattered within an extracellular matrix of their own secretions. There are two categories of unspecialized connective tissues—loose and dense. Cartilage, bone tissue, adipose tissue, and blood are specialized connective tissues.

Most connective tissue contains fibroblasts. These cells secrete an extracellular matrix containing polysaccharides and the proteins collagen and elastin. Both are fibrous proteins that aggregate as elongated strands. Collagen is the most abundant protein in an animal body. Elastin is springier than collagen, and it abounds in tissues that must stretch out, then spring back into shape.

Synthesizing collagen requires vitamin C, and a deficiency in this vitamin causes the nutritional disorder known as scurvy. Early in this disorder, connective tissue surrounding tiny blood vessels breaks down, so gums bleed and small bruiselike spots appear on the skin. If scurvy continues untreated, the bones will weaken. Collagen is the main component of scar tissue, so a person with scurvy cannot heal cuts and scrapes. Eventually, this disorder can be fatal.

TYPES OF CONNECTIVE TISSUE

Loose connective tissue is the most common connective tissue in a vertebrate body. It consists mainly of fibroblasts, collagen fibers, and elastin fibers widely scattered in a gel-like matrix (**FIGURE 28.6A**). Loose connective tissue underlies most epithelia, and it surrounds nerves and blood vessels. It also holds abdominal organs in place.

In **dense, irregular connective tissue**, fibroblasts are interspersed among a tight mesh of randomly arranged collagen fibers (**FIGURE 28.6B**). The random arrangement of collagen fibers allows the tissue to withstand stretching in any direction. Dense, irregular connective tissue makes up deep skin layers, underlies the lining of the gut, and forms a protective capsule around the kidneys and the testes.

Dense, regular connective tissue consists of fibroblasts in orderly rows between parallel, tightly packed bundles of collagen fibers (**FIGURE 28.6C**). This parallel organization maximizes the strength of a tissue that is typically pulled in a single direction, parallel to the fibers. Dense, regular connective tissue is the main tissue in tendons and ligaments. Tendons connect skeletal muscle to bones. Ligaments attach one bone to another.

Cartilage has a matrix of collagen fibers and rubbery, compression-resistant glycoproteins. Living cartilage cells secrete the matrix that surrounds them (**FIGURE 28.6D**). Some fish such as lampreys and sharks have a cartilage skeleton. In humans, as in all bony fishes and tetrapods, cartilage forms a model for the developing skeleton, then bone

Like other marine mammals, walruses have a layer of blubber beneath their skin. Fat is less dense than water, so being encased in blubber helps a walrus float. Blubber is also springy. Unlike most adipose tissue, it includes many collagen and elastin fibers that cause it to spring back when compressed. This springiness reduces the energy the walrus expends while swimming. A coat of blubber also helps a walrus retain body heat. Even when the outside temperature dips far below freezing, a walrus's core body temperature remains about the same as yours.

FIGURE 28.7 Blubber-encased walrus resting on an ice floe. Blubber is a special type of adipose tissue.

replaces most of it. After birth, cartilage still supports the outer ears, nose, and throat. It covers the ends of bones and acts as a shock absorber between segments of the backbone. Blood vessels do not extend through cartilage, as they do in other connective tissues.

Adipose tissue consists mainly of cells that make and store triglycerides (Section 3.3). These cells have little matrix between them, and a fat-filled vacuole fills their interior (**FIGURE 28.6E**). Tiny blood vessels that run between the cells carry fatty acids to or from the tissue. Adipose tissue is the body's main energy reservoir, and it cushions and protects body parts. It also serves as

insulation. A special type of adipose tissue celled blubber helps marine mammals retain heat (**FIGURE 28.7**).

Bone tissue is a connective tissue in which bone cells secrete and are surrounded by a collagen-rich matrix hardened by calcium and phosphorus (**FIGURE 28.6F**). Bone tissue is the main tissue of bones.

Blood (**FIGURE 28.6G**) is considered a connective tissue because its cellular components (red blood cells, white blood cells, and platelets) descend from stem cells in bone. Red blood cells transport oxygen. White blood cells defend the body against pathogens. Platelets function in clot formation. Cellular components of blood drift along in the plasma, a fluid extracellular matrix consisting of water with dissolved proteins, nutrients, gases, and other substances.

---

adipose tissue Connective tissue specializing in fat storage.
blood Fluid connective tissue consisting of plasma and cellular components (red cells, white cells, platelets) that form in bones.
bone tissue Connective tissue that consists of cells surrounded by a mineral-hardened matrix of their own secretions.
cartilage Connective tissue that consists of cells surrounded by a rubbery matrix of their own secretions.
connective tissue Animal tissue with an extensive extracellular matrix; provides structural and functional support.
dense, irregular connective tissue Connective tissue that consists of randomly arranged fibers and scattered fibroblasts.
dense, regular connective tissue Connective tissue that consists of fibroblasts arrayed between parallel arrangements of fibers.
loose connective tissue Connective tissue that consists of fibroblasts and fibers scattered in a gel-like matrix.

TAKE-HOME MESSAGE 28.4

Connective tissues support, protect, organize, and insulate other tissues. They consist of living cells within an extracellular matrix.

Soft connective tissues consist of extracellular matrix with fibroblasts and fibers in characteristic proportions and arrangements.

Cartilage, bone, adipose tissue, and blood are specialized connective tissues. Cartilage and bone are both structural materials. Adipose tissue is a reservoir of energy. Blood, a fluid connective tissue, transports materials.

In **muscle tissue**, cells contract (shorten) in response to stimulation, then they relax and passively lengthen. Coordinated contractions of layers or rings of muscles move the body or propel material through it. Muscle tissue occurs in most animals, but we focus here on the arrangements of muscle found in vertebrates.

SKELETAL MUSCLE

Skeletal muscle tissue, the functional partner of bone (or cartilage), helps move and maintain the positions of the body and its parts. Skeletal muscle tissue has parallel arrays of long, cylindrical muscle fibers (**FIGURE 28.8A**). These fibers are multinucleated cells that form when groups of cells fuse together during embryonic development. The interior of each fiber is taken up by many long threadlike structures (myofibrils) that consist of row after row of contractile units. Because these rows are aligned the same way in the many myofibrils, skeletal muscle has a striated, or striped, appearance under the microscope.

Skeletal muscle tissue makes up 40 percent or so of the weight of an average human. Reflexes activate it, but we can also make it contract when we want to. Thus skeletal muscles are commonly called "voluntary" muscles.

CARDIAC MUSCLE

Cardiac muscle tissue is found only in the heart wall (**FIGURE 28.8B**). Like skeletal muscle tissue, it appears striated. Unlike skeletal muscle, it has branching cells, each with a single nucleus. Cardiac muscle cells abut at their ends, where adhering junctions prevent them from being ripped apart during forceful contractions. Signals to contract pass swiftly from cell to cell at gap junctions along their length. The signals make all cells in cardiac muscle tissue contract as a unit.

SMOOTH MUSCLE

We find layers of **smooth muscle tissue** in the wall of some blood vessels and soft internal organs, such as the stomach, uterus, and bladder. This tissue's unbranched cells contain a nucleus at their center and are tapered at both ends (**FIGURE 28.8C**). Contractile units are not arranged in an orderly repeating fashion, so smooth muscle tissue does not appear striated. Smooth muscle contracts more slowly than skeletal muscle, but its contractions can be sustained longer. These contractions propel material through the gut, alter the diameter of blood vessels, and adjust how much light enters the pupil of the eye.

Smooth muscle and cardiac muscle are said to be "involuntary" muscle, because most people cannot make these types of muscle contract at will.

A Skeletal muscle

- Long, cylindrical cells with multiple nuclei and conspicuous striping (striations)

- Interacts with bone to bring about movement, maintain posture

- Reflex activated, but also under voluntary control

B Cardiac muscle

- Striated cells attached end to end, each with a single nucleus

- Found only in the heart wall

- Contraction is not under voluntary control

C Smooth muscle

- Cells with a single nucleus, tapered ends, and no striations

- In walls of some blood vessels, the digestive tract, the reproductive tract, bladder, and other hollow organs

- Contraction is not under voluntary control

FIGURE 28.8 {Animated} Muscle tissues.

---

cardiac muscle tissue Muscle of the heart wall.
muscle tissue Tissue that consists mainly of contractile cells.
skeletal muscle tissue Muscle that interacts with skeletal elements to move body parts; under voluntary control.
smooth muscle tissue Muscle that lines blood vessels and forms the wall of hollow organs.

TAKE-HOME MESSAGE 28.5

Muscle tissue consists of cells that contract when stimulated.

Skeletal muscle interacts with skeletal elements. Cardiac muscle is found only in the heart wall. Blood vessels and many soft internal organs have smooth muscle in their walls.

CREDITS: (8A,B) Ed Reschke; (8C) Biophoto Associates/Photo Researchers, Inc.; (8A–C) art, From Starr/Evers/Starr, Biology Today and Tomorrow with Physiology, 3E. © 2010 Cengage Learning.

FIGURE 28.9 Examples of nervous system actions. Detecting a fly and controlling the tongue that catches it are nervous system functions.

Nervous tissue allows an animal to collect information about its internal and external environment, to integrate that information, and to control glands and muscles (**FIGURE 28.9**). It is the main tissue of the vertebrate brain and spinal cord, and of the nerves that extend through the body.

Nervous tissue consists of specialized signaling cells called **neurons**, and the cells that support them (**FIGURE 28.10**). A neuron has a central cell body that contains a nucleus and other organelles. Cytoplasmic extensions that project from the cell body receive and send electrochemical signals. When a neuron receives sufficient stimulation, an electrical signal travels along its plasma membrane to the ends of one of its cytoplasmic extensions. Here, the arrival of an electrical signal causes the neuron to release chemical signaling molecules. These molecules diffuse across a small gap to an adjacent neuron, muscle fiber, or gland cell, and alter that cell's behavior.

Your nervous system has more than 100 billion neurons. There are three types. Sensory neurons are excited by specific stimuli, such as light or pressure. Interneurons receive and integrate sensory information. They store information and coordinate responses to stimuli. In vertebrates, interneurons occur mainly in the brain and spinal cord. Motor neurons relay commands from the brain and spinal cord to glands and muscle cells.

Neuroglial cells, also called neuroglia, keep neurons positioned where they should be, and provide them with metabolic support. Neuroglia constitute a significant portion of nervous tissue. For example, they make up more than half of your brain volume. Neuroglial cells also wrap around the signal-sending cytoplasmic extensions of most motor neurons. They act as insulation and speed the rate at which electrical signals travel along the neurons.

---

nervous tissue Animal tissue composed of neurons and supporting cells; detects stimuli and controls responses to them.
neuron One of the cells that make up communication lines of nervous systems; transmits electrical signals along its plasma membrane and sends chemical messages to other cells.

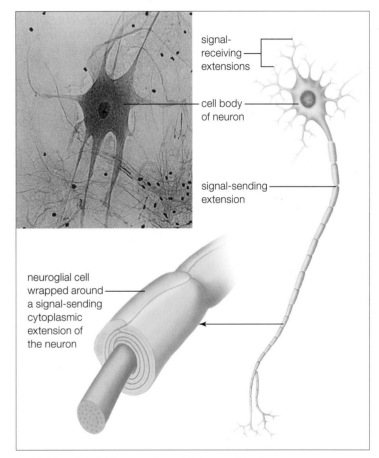

FIGURE 28.10 Neuron and associated neuroglial cell.

 FIGURE IT OUT: What region of the neuron contains most of its organelles?
Answer: The cell body

TAKE-HOME MESSAGE 28.6

Nervous tissue, which consists of neurons and neuroglial cells, is the main component of the brain, spinal cord, and nerves.

Different kinds of neurons detect specific stimuli, integrate information, and issue or relay commands to other tissues.

CREDITS: (9) © Kim Taylor/ Bruce Coleman, Ltd; (10 top) © Triarch/ Visuals Unlimited; (10 bottom) © Cengage Learning.

① Integumentary System

Protects body from injury, dehydration, pathogens; moderates temperature; excretes some wastes; detects external stimuli.

② Nervous System

Detects external and internal stimuli; coordinates responses to stimuli; integrates organ system activities.

③ Endocrine System

Secretes hormones that control activity of other organ systems. (Male testes added.)

④ Muscular System

Moves the body and its parts; maintains posture; produces heat to maintain body temperature.

⑤ Skeletal System

Supports and protects body parts; site of muscle attachment; produces red blood cells; stores minerals.

⑥ Circulatory System

Distributes materials and heat throughout the body; helps maintain pH.

FIGURE 28.11 {Animated} Human organ systems and their functions.

ORGANS AND ORGAN SYSTEMS

As previously noted, tissues interact structurally and functionally in organs. Organs in turn interact in organ systems. **FIGURE 28.11** shows the organ systems of a human body, but keep in mind that all vertebrates have the same array of systems.

The integumentary system includes skin and structures derived from it such as hair and nails ①. We discuss skin's functions in detail in the next section.

The nervous system is the body's main control center ②. The brain, spinal cord, and nerves are part of this system, as are sensory organs such as the eyes. The endocrine system consists of hormone-secreting endocrine glands and cells ③. The endocrine system works closely with the nervous system and, like that system, controls other organ systems.

The muscular system consists of individual muscles that move the body and its parts ④. This system also plays an important role in regulating body temperature by generating heat. The skeletal system is the body's framework ⑤. It protects internal organs and serves as a point of attachment for skeletal muscles. It also stores minerals and produces blood cells. Bones are organs of the skeletal system.

The circulatory system consists of the heart and blood vessels ⑥. It cooperates with the respiratory, digestive,

and urinary systems in delivering oxygen and nutrients to cells throughout the body, and clearing away their wastes (**FIGURE 28.12**). It also helps regulate body temperature by conveying heat from the body's warm core to the skin where heat can be lost to the environment. The lymphatic system consists of vessels that move fluid (lymph) from tissues to the blood, and organs (lymph nodes, tonsils, and

FIGURE 28.12 Organ system interactions that keep the body supplied with essential substances and eliminate unwanted wastes.

❼ Lymphatic System

Collects and returns tissue fluid to the blood; defends the body against infection, cancers.

❽ Respiratory System

Takes in the oxygen for aerobic respiration; expels carbon dioxide released by this pathway.

❾ Digestive System

Takes in food and water; breaks food down and absorbs needed nutrients, then eliminates food residues.

❿ Urinary System

Maintains volume and composition of blood; excretes excess fluid and wastes.

⓫ Reproductive System

Female: Produces eggs; nourishes and protects developing offspring. Male: Produces and transfers sperm to a female.

---

the spleen) that help protect the body against pathogens ❼.

The respiratory system includes the lungs and the airways that lead to them ❽. Its main function is to deliver oxygen from the air to the blood, and to expel carbon dioxide from blood into the air. Oxygen is needed for aerobic respiration.

The digestive system takes in food, breaks it down, delivers nutrients to the blood, and eliminates undigested wastes ❾. It includes organs of the gut (esophagus, stomach, intestine), as well as glandular organs such as the liver and pancreas, which supply substances that function in digestion.

The urinary system consists of kidneys (organs that filter blood and create urine), the bladder, and ducts that deliver urine to the body surface for excretion ❿. It removes wastes from blood, and adjusts blood volume and solute composition.

The reproductive system of both sexes includes gamete-making organs (ovaries or testes) and the ducts through which gametes travel ⓫. In females, it also includes a uterus, the organ in which offspring develop.

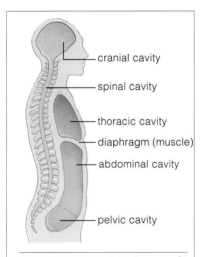

cranial cavity

spinal cavity

thoracic cavity

diaphragm (muscle)

abdominal cavity

pelvic cavity

FIGURE 28.13 {Animated}
Body cavities that hold human organs.

Some organs are components of more than one organ system. For example, the pancreas is an endocrine gland and a digestive organ.

FIGURE 28.13 shows the body cavities that hold organs. A cranial cavity in the head holds the brain, and a spinal cavity in the back holds the spinal cord. Like other vertebrates, humans are bilateral and have a lined body cavity, or coelom (Section 23.1). A sheet of smooth muscle called the diaphragm divides the human coelom into two cavities. The upper (thoracic) cavity holds the heart and lungs. Digestive organs, including the stomach, intestines, and liver, are located in the lower cavity's abdominal region. The pelvic region of the lower cavity holds the bladder and reproductive organs.

TAKE-HOME MESSAGE 28.7

Organs consist of multiple tissues and are themselves components of organ systems. Interactions among organ systems sustain the body.

Skin, a vertebrate's largest organ, serves as a barrier between an animal and its external environment. We discuss skin's role in excluding pathogens in detail in Section 34.2. Sensory receptors in skin keep the brain informed of external conditions, and skin functions in temperature control. Skin is also the site of vitamin D production. In all land vertebrates, skin helps prevent excessive water loss.

COMPONENTS OF HUMAN SKIN

Skin consists of two layers, a thin upper epidermis and the dermis beneath it (**FIGURE 28.14**).

Epidermis is a stratified squamous epithelium with an abundance of adhering junctions and no extracellular matrix. Human epidermis consists mainly of keratinocytes, cells that make the waterproof protein keratin.

Mitotic cell divisions in deep epidermal layers continually produce new keratinocytes that displace older cells upward toward the skin's surface. As cells move upward, they move farther and farther away from underlying connective tissues where blood vessels deliver nutrients and gases. Eventually the cells, deprived of these essential substances, die and become flattened. Dead cells at the skin surface form an abrasion-resistant layer that helps prevent water loss.

The deepest epidermal layer also contains melanocytes, cells that make pigments called melanins that end up in

FIGURE 28.15 Vitiligo. In television reporter Lee Thomas, this noncontagious disorder has caused death of melanocytes on his hands, arms, and face.

keratinocytes. Variations in human skin color arise from differences in the distribution and activity of melanocytes, and in the type of melanin they produce. One melanin is brown to black. Another is red to yellow. The effect of melanocytes can be seen with vitiligo, a skin disorder in which destruction of these cells results in light patches of skin (**FIGURE 28.15**).

FIGURE 28.14 {Animated} Skin structure. Skin components, such as glands, differ from one body region to the next.

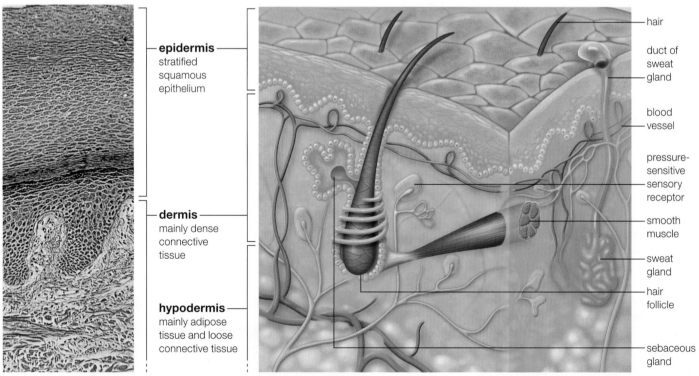

epidermis
stratified
squamous
epithelium

dermis
mainly dense
connective
tissue

hypodermis
mainly adipose
tissue and loose
connective tissue

hair

duct of
sweat
gland

blood
vessel

pressure-
sensitive
sensory
receptor

smooth
muscle

sweat
gland

hair
follicle

sebaceous
gland

CREDITS: (14) left, © John D. Cunningham/ Visuals Unlimited; right, From Starr/Evers/Starr, Biology Today and Tomorrow with Physiology, 4E. © 2013 Cengage Learning; (15) © Michael Shore Photography.

Dermis consists primarily of dense connective tissue with stretch-resistant elastin fibers and supportive collagen fibers. Blood vessels, lymph vessels, and sensory receptors weave through the dermis. Dermis is thicker than epidermis, and more resistant to tearing. Leather is animal dermis that has been treated with chemicals.

The dermis connects to the hypodermis, a layer of connective and adipose tissue. The thickness of hypodermis varies among body regions. The hypodermis beneath the skin of our eyelids is thin, with few adipose cells. By contrast, the hypodermis of our buttocks contains many adipose cells.

Sweat glands, hair follicles, and oil glands consist of epidermal cells that migrated into the dermis during early development. Sweat glands help cool the body by secreting sweat, which is mostly water. Hair follicles produce hairs. Living cells reside at the base of the follicle. These cells divide every 24 to 72 hours, making them among the fastest-dividing cells in the body. As they divide, they push the cells above them upwards. The portion of the hair that extends beyond the skin surface is keratin-rich remains of dead cells. Each hair has a smooth muscle attached to it that reflexively contracts in response to cold or fright, thus making the hair stand upright. Secretions from a sebaceous gland (an oil gland) next to each hair follicle keep the hair and the skin surrounding it soft and smooth.

SUN AND THE SKIN

Melanin produced by skin functions as a sunscreen, absorbing ultraviolet (UV) radiation that could otherwise damage underlying skin layers. When a patch of skin is exposed to sunlight, melanocytes in that region make more of the brownish-black melanin, resulting in a "tan."

A bit of UV exposure is a good thing; it stimulates skin to produce a molecule that the body converts to vitamin D. We need vitamin D to absorb calcium ions from food. However, UV exposure also causes the breakdown of folate, one of the B vitamins. Among other problems, a folate deficiency during pregnancy damages an offspring's developing nervous system.

Variations in skin color among human populations probably evolved as adaptations to differences in sunlight exposure. Humans arose in equatorial Africa, where the sun's rays are intense and daylength does not decline dramatically in the winter. In this environment, melanin-rich skin that protected folate still made plenty of vitamin D. Later, some humans moved to more northerly regions, where sunlight is less intense, winter days are short, and more time is spent indoors or bundled in clothing. Under these circumstances, skin with fewer melanocytes is advantageous. During cold, dark winters, having lighter skin makes it easier to get enough sunlight to maintain an adequate level of vitamin D.

Dark skin provides more UV protection than light skin, but in anyone, prolonged or repeated UV exposure damages collagen and causes elastin fibers to clump. Chronically tanned skin becomes less resilient and begins to look leathery. UV harms DNA, and the damage increases the risk of skin cancer. Melanoma, the most dangerous skin cancer, arises when melanocytes divide uncontrollably.

As people age, their epidermal cells divide less frequently. Glandular secretions that kept the skin soft and supple dwindle. Thickness and elasticity of the dermis decline as collagen and elastin fibers become sparse. Permanent wrinkles appear in places where facial expressions once produced temporary creases.

Excessive tanning accelerates this aging process, as does smoking. Smoking lessens the flow of blood to the skin, depriving it of oxygen and nutrients. Damaging effects of sun are localized to sun-exposed regions, but smoking harms skin throughout the body.

CULTURED SKIN PRODUCTS

Skin is the only organ that is already grown artificially for widespread medical uses. Most commercially available cultured skin products are made using infant foreskins removed during routine circumcisions. The foreskin (a tissue that covers the tip of the penis) provides a rich source of keratinocytes and fibroblasts. These cells are grown in culture with other biological materials to produce thin sheets of cells that can be used to cover wounds, burns, or sores. Unlike natural skin, cultured skin does not include melanocytes, sweat glands, oil glands, and other differentiated structures.

---

dermis Deep layer of skin that consists of connective tissue with nerves and blood vessels running through it.
epidermis Outermost tissue layer; in animals, the epithelial layer of skin.

> **TAKE-HOME MESSAGE 28.8**
>
> Skin consists of an epidermis of epithelial tissue, and a dermis of dense connective tissue with blood vessels and nerves running through it. Hypodermis underlies the skin.
>
> Signals from sensory receptors in the skin inform the brain about the external environment. Skin also serves as a barrier against pathogens, aids in production of vitamin D, and functions in temperature regulation.

28.9 HOW DO ORGAN SYSTEMS INTERACT IN HOMEOSTASIS?

Homeostasis, again, is the process of maintaining the body's internal environment within a tolerable range. In vertebrates, homeostasis involves interactions among sensory receptors, the brain, and muscles and glands. A **sensory receptor** is a cell or cell component that responds to a specific stimulus such as temperature or light. Sensory receptors involved in homeostasis function like internal watchmen; they monitor the body for changes. Information from sensory receptors throughout the body flows to an integrator. In vertebrates, the brain usually serves as the integrator. It evaluates the incoming information, then signals effectors—muscles and glands—to take any necessary actions to keep the body functioning properly.

Homeostasis typically involves a **negative feedback mechanism**, in which a change brings about a response that reverses the change. An air conditioner with a thermostat provides a familiar nonbiological example of a negative feedback mechanism. A person sets the air conditioner to a desired temperature. When the temperature rises above this preset point, a sensor in the air conditioner detects the change and turns the unit on. When the temperature declines to the desired level, the thermostat detects the change and turns off the air conditioner.

A similar mechanism operates when you exercise on a hot day. Muscle activity generates heat, and your body's internal temperature rises (**FIGURE 28.16**). Sensory receptors in the skin detect the increase and signal your brain. In response, the brain sends signals that increase the flow of blood from the body's hot interior to the skin. This shift maximizes the amount of heat given off to the

surrounding air. At the same time, sweat glands in the skin increase their output. Evaporation of sweat helps cool the body surface. You breathe faster and deeper, speeding the transfer of heat from the blood in your lungs to the air. Hormonal changes make you feel more sluggish. As your activity level slows and your rate of heat loss increases, your temperature falls.

Receptors in the skin also notify your brain when the external environment becomes chilly. The brain then sends out signals that decrease blood flow to your skin, thus reducing the amount of heat sent to the body surface, where it would be lost to the surrounding air. At the same time, reflex contractions of smooth muscle in the skin pull on hair so that it stands up, causing "goose bumps." Erect hair insulates the body better than hair that lies flat. With prolonged cold, the brain commands skeletal muscles to contract ten to twenty times a second. This shivering response dramatically increases heat production by muscles.

negative feedback mechanism A change causes a response that reverses the change; important mechanism of homeostasis.
sensory receptor Cell or cell component that responds to a specific stimulus, such as temperature or light.

> **TAKE-HOME MESSAGE 28.9**
> Sensory receptors detect changes and notify the brain, which in turn sends signals to organs throughout the body.
> Homeostasis often involves negative feedback mechanisms.

FIGURE 28.16 {Animated} Negative feedback mechanism that maintains human body temperature under hot conditions.

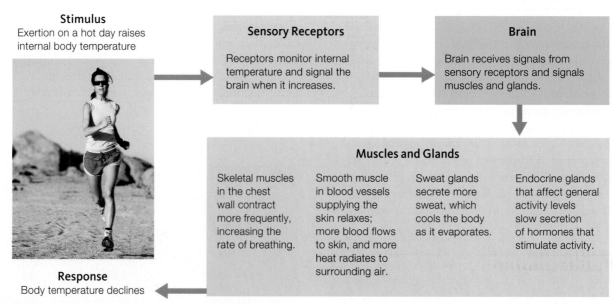

CREDITS: (16) photo, © Photoroller/ Shutterstock; art, From Starr/Evers/Starr, Biology Today and Tomorrow with Physiology, 4E. © 2013 Cengage Learning.

28.10 Application: GROWING REPLACEMENT TISSUES

Education

FIGURE 28.17 Regeneration of a sea star. Stem cells in the remaining bit of central disk give rise to replacement parts.

ANIMALS COMMONLY REPLACE TISSUES LOST TO INJURY. Invertebrates have the greatest capacity for regeneration. For example, some sea stars can regrow an entire body from a single arm and a bit of the central disk (FIGURE 28.17). No vertebrate can grow a body from a limb, but some salamanders can regrow a limb, and many salamanders and lizards can replace a lost tail. Mammals do not replace limbs or tails, although like other animals they can replace skin and blood cells.

Stem cells are the key to producing new or replacement tissues. A **stem cell** is a cell that can divide and produce more stem cells, or differentiate into one of the specialized cells that characterize specific body parts. In short, all cells in an animal body "stem" from stem cells.

Human embryonic stem cells form soon after fertilization, when mitotic divisions produce a cluster of cells collectively smaller than the head of a pin. Each cell in the cluster is "pluripotent," meaning it can develop into any of the cell types in a human body. Stem cells become more specialized as development continues. For example, stem cells in adult bone can become blood cells, but not muscle cells or nerve cells.

Skin cells, blood cells, and other cell types that your body replaces on an ongoing basis arise continually from adult stem cells. This is why you can replace skin or blood lost to injury. However, unlike a sea star or salamander, human adults have few stem cells capable of becoming muscle or nerve tissue. Thus, these tissues are not replaced if they are damaged or lost. When the human spinal cord is cut, the result is a permanent paralysis. New nervous tissue does not form to replace the damage. Similarly, a heart attack weakens the heart by killing irreplaceable cardiac muscle cells.

Manipulating embryonic stem cells is one way to produce replacement muscle or nerve cells for people who need them. Clinical studies involving such replacement cells began recently. In 2011, researchers modified embryonic stem cells and used them to treat two patients blinded by eye diseases. A year later, the implanted cells had survived and produced moderate improvements in vision. Ongoing clinical trials will test this treatment in a larger group of patients and determine whether early stem cell treatment can prevent vision loss.

Embryonic stem cells must be derived from human embryos that have been donated or produced for this purpose. However, altering cells such as fibroblasts through biotechnology may allow us to grow replacement tissues using cells derived from adults. Adult cells that have been treated so they behave like embryonic stem cells are called induced pluripotent stem cells (IPSCs).

The first IPSCs were produced in 2006. If IPSCs are shown to be equivalent to embryonic cells, they could open the way to personalized tissue replacements. For example, a person who lost cardiac muscle to a heart attack could have his or her skin cells induced to become IPSCs. Those IPSCs could then be made to differentiate into cardiac muscle cells. Such cells would be less likely to be rejected than cells derived from another individual.

stem cell Cell that can divide to produce more stem cells or differentiate into a specialized cell type.

CREDIT: Francois Michonneau/FLMNH.

Summary

SECTIONS 28.1, 28.2 Most animals have four types of tissues organized as organs and organ systems. **Extracellular fluid** serves as the body's internal environment. In humans, it consists mainly of interstitial fluid and plasma. Animal structure is influenced by physical constraints and evolutionary history.

SECTION 28.3 **Epithelial tissue** has one free surface. Cells at the other surface secrete a **basement membrane**. Some epithelial cells have cilia or **microvilli** at their free surface. Gland cells are specialized epithelial cells. **Endocrine glands** are ductless and secrete hormones into blood. **Exocrine glands** secrete substances such as milk or digestive enzymes through ducts.

SECTION 28.4 **Connective tissues** "connect" tissues to one another, both functionally and structurally. Different types bind, organize, support, strengthen, protect, and insulate other tissues. All contain cells scattered within an extracellular matrix of their own secretions.

Loose connective tissue; dense, regular connective tissue; and **dense, irregular connective tissue** have the same components but differ in their structural details. They are soft connective tissues. **Cartilage**, **bone tissue**, **adipose tissue**, and **blood** are specialized connective tissues.

SECTION 28.5 **Muscle tissues** contract (shorten) when stimulated. They help move the body and its component parts. The three types are **skeletal muscle**, **cardiac muscle**, and **smooth muscle tissue**. Skeletal muscle and cardiac muscle tissues appear striated. Only skeletal muscle is under voluntary control.

SECTION 28.6 **Neurons** in **nervous tissue** make up communication lines through the body. Different kinds detect, integrate, and assess information about internal and external conditions, and deliver commands to muscles and glands that carry out responses. Nervous tissue also contains neuroglial cells, or neuroglia. These cells protect and support the neurons.

SECTION 28.7 An organ system consists of two or more organs that interact chemically, physically, or both in tasks that help keep individual cells as well as the whole body functioning. All vertebrates have the same set of organ systems. Many internal organs reside inside body cavities. The human thoracic, abdominal, and pelvic cavities are regions of our coelom. Organ systems interact to provide cells with the materials that they need, and to rid the body of wastes.

SECTION 28.8 Vertebrate skin is a large organ. It functions in protection and temperature control, monitors external conditions, and aids in production of vitamin D. Skin consists of an outer **epidermis** and a deeper **dermis**. Keratin makes skin waterproof and melanin give it its color. Hypodermis underlies skin.

SECTION 28.9 Homeostasis requires **sensory receptors** that detect changes, an integrating center (the brain), and effectors (muscles and glands) that bring about responses. Homeostasis often involves a **negative feedback mechanism**: A change causes the body to respond in a way that reverses the change.

SECTION 28.10 A **stem cell** can divide to form more stem cells or differentiate to form specialized cells. Embryonic stem cells can produce any cell type in the body. Cells of adults are less versatile, but it may be possible to induce them to behave like embryonic stem cells.

Self-Quiz   Answers in Appendix VII

1. _____ tissues are sheetlike with one free surface.
   a. Epithelial   c. Nervous
   b. Connective   d. Muscle

2. _____ form a waterproof seal between cells.
   a. Tight junctions   c. Gap junctions
   b. Adhering junctions   d. all of the above

3. Glands are derived from _____ tissue.
   a. epithelial   c. muscle
   b. connective   d. nervous

4. Most _____ have many collagen and elastin fibers.
   a. epithelial tissues   c. muscle tissues
   b. connective tissues   d. nervous tissues

5. _____ is mostly plasma.
   a. Adipose tissue   c. Cartilage
   b. Blood   d. Bone

6. Your body converts excess carbohydrates and proteins to fats. _____ specializes in storing the fats.
   a. Epithelial tissue   c. Adipose tissue
   b. Dense connective tissue   d. both b and c

7. Cells of _____ can shorten (contract).
   a. epithelial tissue   c. muscle tissue
   b. connective tissue   d. nervous tissue

8. _____ muscle tissue has a striated appearance and is under voluntary control.
   a. Skeletal   c. Cardiac
   b. Smooth   d. a and c

9. _____ detects and integrates information about changes and controls responses to those changes.
   a. Epithelial tissue   c. Muscle tissue
   b. Connective tissue   d. Nervous tissue

10. Skin darkens when exposed to sunlight because _____ produce more pigment.
    a. melanocytes   c. neuroglial cells
    b. keratinocytes   d. neurons

Growing Skin to Heal Wounds Diabetes is a disorder in which the blood sugar level is not properly controlled. Among other complications, diabetes reduces blood flow to the lower legs and feet. As a result, about 3 million diabetes patients have ulcers (open wounds that do not heal) on their feet.

Fibroblasts and keratinocytes can be grown to produce a cultured skin product (*left*) that is placed over wounds to help them heal. **FIGURE 28.18** shows the results of a clinical experiment that tested the effect of the cultured skin product versus standard treatment for diabetic foot wounds.

A sheet of Apligraf, a cultured skin product.

Patients were randomly assigned either to the experimental treatment group or to the control group. Their progress was monitored for 12 weeks.

1. What percentage of wounds had healed at 8 weeks with standard treatment? When treated with cultured skin?

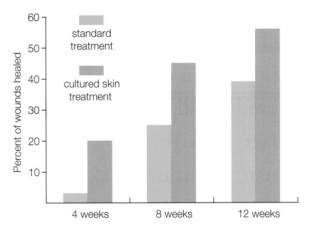

FIGURE 28.18 Results of a study comparing standard treatment for diabetic foot ulcers to use of a cultured cell product. Bars show the percentage of foot ulcers that had completely healed.

2. What percentage of wounds had healed at 12 weeks with standard treatment? When treated with cultured skin?
3. How early was the healing difference between the control and treatment groups apparent?

11. The heart and lungs are in the _____ cavity.
    a. thoracic   c. cranial
    b. pelvic   d. abdominal

12. With negative feedback, a change induces a response that _____ that change.
    a. increases   b. reverses

13. Sunlight encourages _____ production by skin.
    a. vitamin D   c. collagen
    b. folate   d. both a and b

14. Hair and nails are keratin-rich structures formed by _____ tissue.
    a. muscle   c. epithelial
    b. nervous   d. connective

15. Match the terms with the most suitable description.
    ____ exocrine gland   a. strong, pliable; like rubber
    ____ endocrine gland   b. secretion through duct
    ____ cartilage   c. deep skin layer
    ____ dermis   d. contracts, not striated
    ____ smooth muscle   e. assist and support neurons
    ____ bone   f. gives color to skin
    ____ melanin   g. lines lungs
    ____ blood   h. cells in a hardened matrix
    ____ neuroglia   i. fluid connective tissue
    ____ simple, squamous   j. ductless secretion
         epithelium

Critical Thinking

1. Many people oppose the use of animals for testing the safety of cosmetics. They argue that alternative test methods are available, such as use of lab-grown human tissues. Given what you learned in this chapter, speculate on the advantages and disadvantages of tests that use lab-grown tissues as opposed to living animals.

2. In winter, dark-skinned immigrants to Sweden are more likely to have a vitamin D deficiency than light-skinned people native to this region. Why?

3. Each level of biological organization has emergent properties that arise from interactions at a lower level. For example, cells have a capacity for inheritance that the molecules making up the cell do not. Can you think of an emergent property of a tissue? Of an organ that contains that tissue?

4. The micrograph to the *right* shows cells from the lining of an airway leading to the lungs. The gold cells are ciliated and the darker brown ones secrete mucus. What type of tissue is this? How can you tell?

CREDITS: (in text, left) Courtesy of © Organogensis, Inc., www.organogensis.com; (18) © Cengage Learning; (in text, right) CNRI/Photo Researchers, Inc.

A volunteer wired for a study of brain activity. The electrodes will detect traces of electrical signals produced by neurons inside his skull.

UNIT 6
HOW ANIMALS
WORK

29

NEURAL CONTROL

Links to Earlier Concepts

In this chapter, you will draw on your knowledge of potential energy (Section 5.1), diffusion and concentration gradients (5.6), passive and active transport (5.7), and exocytosis (5.8). You will revisit the body plans of a few invertebrates (23.4, 23.5, 23.11) and the typical chordate traits (24.1). You will increase your knowledge of nervous tissue (28.6) and be reminded of alcohol's negative effects (5.9).

KEY CONCEPTS

NERVOUS SYSTEMS
Most animals have a nervous system. Cnidarians have a nerve net. Bilaterally symmetrical animals have a system with a central control organ in the head.

ACTION POTENTIALS
Action potentials transmit signals within a neuron. During an action potential, ion flow briefly reverses the charge across a neuron's plasma membrane.

SYNAPSES
Chemical signals convey information between a neuron and another cell. Psychoactive drugs interfere with this intercellular communication.

VERTEBRATE NERVOUS SYSTEM
The vertebrate central nervous system consists of a brain and spinal cord. The peripheral system consists of many nerves that connect the brain and spinal cord to the rest of the body.

HIGHER BRAIN FUNCTIONS
The cerebral cortex is the most recently evolved part of the brain. In humans, it governs conscious behavior and interacts with the limbic system in forming and retrieving memories.

Photograph by Maggie Steber, National Geographic Creative.

497

For an animal body to function as an integrated whole, its cells must communicate with their neighbors, and often with cells some distance away. This intercellular communication typically involves three steps. First, a signaling molecule released by one cell reversibly binds to a receptor on or in another cell. Second, the signal is transduced, meaning it is converted into a form that has an effect inside the signal-receiving cell. Third, the signal-receiving cell responds to the signal.

Two organ systems—the nervous system and the endocrine system—facilitate long-distance communication among cells of an animal body. The endocrine system coordinates cell activities by way of molecules called hormones that travel in the blood. We discuss this system in detail in Chapter 31. Here, we focus on the nervous system.

A Sea anemones have a nerve net but no central organizing center.

B Planarian flatworms have a pair of nerve cords and paired ganglia that serve as a brain.

ganglia   nerve cords

brain

C Insects have paired ventral nerve cords with a ganglion in each segment. The cords connect to a simple brain.

nerve cords with ganglia

FIGURE 29.1 {Animated} Examples of invertebrate nervous systems.

As Section 28.6 explained, neurons make up the communication lines of nervous systems. **Neurons** transmit electrical signals along their plasma membrane and also send chemical messages to other cells. In most animals, **neuroglial cells** support the neurons.

NERVE NET

Animals with radial symmetry have a mesh of inter-connected neurons called a **nerve net**. Information flows in all directions among cells of the nerve net, and there is no centralized, controlling organ that functions like a brain. Such a system is adaptive when food or threats can arrive from any direction. Sea anemones and other cnidarians (Section 23.1) are the simplest animals with a nerve net. By causing cells in the body wall to contract, a cnidarian nerve net can alter the size of the mouth, change the body's shape, or shift the position of the tentacles.

Echinoderms (Section 23.12) are also radial, and they too have a nerve net. However, the echinoderm system is a bit more complex because it includes nerves. A **nerve** is a bundle of neuron fibers (cytoplasmic extensions) wrapped in connective tissue. In sea stars, a ring of nerves surrounds the mouth and a nerve extends from this ring into each arm.

GETTING A HEAD

Most animals have bilateral symmetry, with paired organs arranged on either side of the main body axis (Section 23.1). The evolution of bilateral body plans was accompanied by **cephalization**: Neurons that detect and process information became concentrated at the body's anterior end, or "head."

Planarian flatworms are bilateral animals with a simple nervous system. A pair of ganglia in the head serves as an integrating center (**FIGURE 29.1B**). Each **ganglion** (plural, ganglia) consists of a cluster of neuron cell bodies. (The cell body is the part of the neuron that holds the cell's nucleus and other organelles.) The planarian's ganglia receive signals from eyespots and chemical-detecting cells on the head. They also connect to a pair of nerve cords that run along the animal's ventral (lower) surface. A **nerve cord** consists of nerve fibers (cytoplasmic extensions) of many neurons, and it runs the length of the body. Nerves branch from the nerve cord and cross the body.

Annelids and arthropods have paired nerve cords that run along the ventral surface and connect to a simple brain (**FIGURE 29.1C**). A **brain** is a central control organ of a nervous system. It receives and integrates sensory information, regulates internal processes, and sends out signals that bring about movements.

The complexity of mollusk nervous systems varies dramatically among groups. Clams and other bivalves are

CREDITS: (1A) From Starr/Taggart, Biology: The Unity and Diversity of Life, 8E. © 1998 Cengage Learning; (1B) © Cengage Learning; (1C) From RUSSELL/WOLFE/HERTZ/STARR, Biology, 1E. © 2008 Cengage Learning Inc. Reproduced with permission. www.cengage.com/permissions.

brainless, having instead widely separated ganglia that serve as local control centers. On the other hand, cephalopods such as octopuses have the largest and most complex nervous system of any invertebrate group. An octopus has a proportionately larger brain than many fish or reptiles.

THE VERTEBRATE NERVOUS SYSTEM

A dorsal nerve cord (a nerve cord that runs along the back) is one of the defining features of chordate embryos (Section 24.1). In vertebrates, the dorsal nerve cord evolved into a brain and spinal cord, which together constitute the animal's **central nervous system** (FIGURE 29.2). Nerves that extend from the central nervous system through the rest of the body constitute the **peripheral nervous system**.

The human peripheral nervous system consists of 12 cranial nerves that connect to the brain and 31 spinal nerves that connect to the spinal cord (FIGURE 29.3). Most cranial nerves, and all spinal nerves, carry signals both to and from the central nervous system. Consider the sciatic nerve, which runs from the sacral region of the spinal cord, through the buttock, and down the leg. When someone touches your thigh, the sciatic nerve carries signals from receptors in the skin to the spinal cord. When you move your leg, the nerve carries commands for the movement from the spinal cord to skeletal muscles in the leg.

---

brain Central control organ of a nervous system; receives and integrates sensory information, regulates internal conditions, and sends out signals that result in movements.
central nervous system Of vertebrates, the brain and spinal cord.
cephalization Evolutionary trend whereby nerve cells and sensory structures become concentrated in the head of a bilateral animal.
ganglion Cluster of nerve cell bodies.
nerve Neuron fibers bundled inside a sheath of connective tissue.
nerve cord Bundle of nerve fibers running the length of a body.
nerve net Of cnidarians, a mesh of interacting neurons with no central control organ.
neuroglial cell Cell that supports neurons.
neuron One of the cells that make up communication lines of nervous systems; transmits electrical signals along its plasma membrane and sends chemical messages to other cells.
peripheral nervous system Of vertebrates, nerves that carry signals between the central nervous system and the rest of the body.

TAKE-HOME MESSAGE 29.1

Cnidarians and echinoderms have a nerve net, a meshlike array of neurons with no central control organ.

Bilateral animals typically are cephalized, with ganglia or a brain in the head. Bilateral invertebrates usually have a pair of ventral nerve cords. In contrast, the chordates have one dorsal nerve cord.

The vertebrate nervous system includes a well-developed brain, a spinal cord, and peripheral nerves.

CENTRAL NERVOUS SYSTEM
Brain, Spinal Cord

PERIPHERAL NERVOUS SYSTEM
Cranial and Spinal Nerves

Autonomic Nerves	Somatic Nerves
Nerves that carry signals to smooth muscle, cardiac muscle, and glands	Nerves that carry signals to and from skeletal muscle, tendons, and the skin
Sympathetic Division / Parasympathetic Division	
Two sets of nerves that often signal the same effectors; have opposing effects	

FIGURE 29.2 {Animated} Functional divisions of vertebrate nervous systems. The spinal cord and brain constitute the central nervous system. The peripheral nervous system includes spinal nerves, cranial nerves, and their branches, which extend throughout the body. Peripheral nerves carry signals to and from the central nervous system.

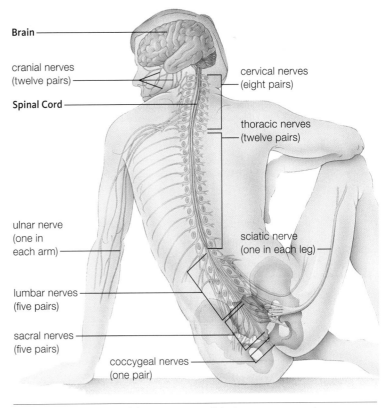

Brain
cranial nerves (twelve pairs)
Spinal Cord
ulnar nerve (one in each arm)
lumbar nerves (five pairs)
sacral nerves (five pairs)
coccygeal nerves (one pair)
cervical nerves (eight pairs)
thoracic nerves (twelve pairs)
sciatic nerve (one in each leg)

FIGURE 29.3 Some of the major nerves of the human nervous system.

CREDITS: (2) © Cengage Learning; (3) From Starr/Taggart/Evers/Starr, Biology, 13E. © 2013 Cengage Learning.

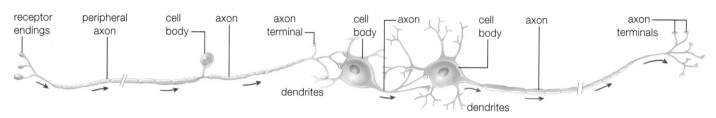

A Sensory neurons have a long axon with receptor endings at one end and axon terminals at the other.

B Interneurons have many dendrites and a short axon.

C Motor neurons have many dendrites and a long axon.

FIGURE 29.4 Typical structure of the three types of neurons. Arrows indicate the direction of information flow among them.

In vertebrate nervous systems, information typically flows from sensory neurons, to interneurons, to motor neurons (**FIGURE 29.4**). **Sensory neurons** are neurons that detect a stimulus such as light or touch. When activated by this stimulus, they usually signal an interneuron. **Interneurons** both receive signals from and send signals to other neurons. An interneuron may signal another interneuron or a motor neuron. **Motor neurons** control muscles and glands.

FIGURE 29.5 {Animated} The functional zones of a motor neuron.

❶ Dendrites and the cell body are the neuron's input zone. They receive chemical signals from another neuron and convert them to electrical signals.

❷ Electrical signals spread to a trigger zone at the start of an axon.

❸ If the electrical signals are sufficiently strong, they are conducted along the axon to its terminal endings.

❹ Axon terminals are a signal output zone. They release chemical signals that influence another cell. In the case of a motor neuron, signals affect a muscle cell or gland cell.

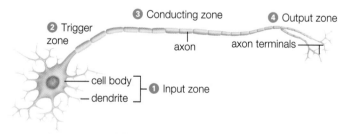

axon Of a neuron, a cytoplasmic extension that transmits electrical signals along its length and secretes chemical signals at its endings.
dendrite Of a motor neuron or interneuron, a cytoplasmic extension that receives chemical signals sent by other neurons and converts them to electrical signals.
interneuron Neuron that both receives signals from and sends signals to other neurons. Located mainly in the brain and spinal cord.
motor neuron Neuron that controls a muscle or gland.
sensory neuron Neuron that is activated when its receptor endings detect a specific stimulus, such as light or pressure.

All neurons have a cell body, a region that holds the nucleus and other organelles. Cytoplasmic extensions that project from the cell body send out and receive chemical signals. All neurons have one **axon**, a special cytoplasmic extension that transmits electrical signals along its length and releases chemical signals at its terminals. Some neurons also have **dendrites**, cytoplasmic extensions that receive chemical signals from other neurons.

Sensory neurons do not receive signals from other cells, so the axon is their only cytoplasmic extension. One end of this axon has receptor endings that detect a specific stimulus; the other has signal-sending axon terminals (**FIGURE 29.4A**).

Interneurons and motor neurons both receive and send signals, so they have dendrites as well as an axon. Most vertebrate interneurons are located entirely in the brain or spinal cord. They have a short axon (**FIGURE 29.4B**). Motor neurons have a cell body in the brain or spinal cord, and an axon that extends out to the muscle or gland they command (**FIGURE 29.4C**). Axons of some motor neurons extend from your spinal cord to your toes.

FIGURE 29.5 shows the functional zones of a motor neuron. The dendrites and cell body are an input zone, where the neuron receives chemical signals and converts them to electrical signals ❶. The part of the axon nearest the cell body is a trigger zone ❷. Arrival of an electrical signal here triggers signals that flow along the conducting zone of the axon ❸ to the axon terminals. Axon terminals are the output zone: They release signaling molecules that influence other cells ❹.

TAKE-HOME MESSAGE 29.2

All neurons have a cell body with organelles and an axon that sends chemical signals to other cells.

Interneurons and motor neurons have signal-receiving dendrites. A sensory neuron has no dendrites. One end of its axon has receptor endings that detect a specific stimulus.

CREDITS: (4) From Starr/Taggart/Evers/Starr, Biology, 13E. © 2013 Cengage Learning; (5) © Cengage Learning.

RESTING POTENTIAL

Animals cells have an electric gradient across their plasma membrane; cytoplasmic fluid near this membrane has more negatively charged ions and proteins than extracellular fluid does. As in a battery, the separation of charge constitutes potential energy that we measure as voltage. The voltage across a cell's membrane is called **membrane potential**. Researchers measure membrane potential across a neuron's axon by inserting one electrode into the axon and another into the fluid just outside of it:

The membrane potential of a neuron that is not being excited is the **resting potential**. This potential is usually about −70 millivolts. (A millivolt [mV] is one-thousandth of a volt.) The negative sign indicates that the inside of the neuron is more negative than the outside.

Resting potential arises from the distribution of charged proteins and small ions. The cytoplasm of a neuron at rest has more negatively charged proteins than the extracellular fluid. Being large and charged, these proteins cannot diffuse across the lipid bilayer of the cell membrane. Positively charged potassium ions (K^+) and positively charged sodium ions (Na^+) also influence resting potential. These ions can move in and out of the neuron with the assistance of transport proteins.

Transport proteins called sodium–potassium pumps (Section 5.7) move two potassium ions into the cell for every three sodium ions they move out (**FIGURE 29.6A**). Because these pumps move more positively charged ions out of the cell than into it, they increase the charge gradient across the membrane. The pumps also contribute to concentration gradients for sodium and potassium ions across the membrane.

Sodium ions cannot cross a resting neuron's membrane, but potassium ions can. Some potassium ions leave the cell through passive transport proteins in the membrane (**FIGURE 29.6B**). Movement of potassium outward increases the charge difference across the membrane.

A Sodium–potassium pumps actively transport 3 sodium ions (Na^+) out of a neuron for every 2 potassium ions (K^+) they pump in.

B Passive transporters allow K^+ ions to leak across the plasma membrane, down their concentration gradient.

C Voltage-sensitive channels for K^+ or Na^+ ions are shut (*left*) when a neuron is at rest. They open (*right*) during an action potential.

FIGURE 29.6 Transport proteins in a neuron's membrane.

In summary, the cytoplasm of a resting neuron has more negatively charged proteins than interstitial fluid. It also has fewer sodium ions (Na^+) and more potassium ions (K^+). We illustrate the difference below, with the white minus sign representing negatively charged proteins:

interstitial fluid	150 Na$^+$	5 K$^+$	
plasma membrane			
cytoplasm	15 Na$^+$	150 K$^+$	65 −

ACTION POTENTIAL

Neurons and muscle cells are said to be "excitable" because they can undergo an **action potential**—an abrupt reversal in the electric gradient across the plasma membrane. The charge reversal occurs when sodium and potassium ions follow their concentration gradients through voltage-gated ion channels, which are passive transport proteins that open only during an action potential (**FIGURE 29.6C**). Neurons have voltage-gated channels in the membrane of their trigger zone and conducting zone. We continue our discussion of action potentials in the next section.

---

action potential Abrupt reversal of the charge difference across a neuron membrane.
membrane potential Voltage difference across a cell membrane; arises from differences in charge on opposite sides of the membrane.
resting potential Membrane potential of a neuron at rest.

TAKE-HOME MESSAGE 29.3

The cytoplasm of a resting neuron is more negatively charged than extracellular fluid. The impermeability of the membrane to negatively charged proteins and the activity of transport proteins contribute to this resting potential.

A resting neuron also has concentration gradients for sodium and potassium across its membrane, with more sodium outside and more potassium inside.

A neuron can undergo an action potential, in which voltage-gated channels open and the membrane potential reverses abruptly.

29.4 WHAT HAPPENS DURING AN ACTION POTENTIAL?

1 Neuron's trigger zone at resting potential, with voltage-gated channels closed. White pluses and minuses indicate that the cytoplasm's charge is negative relative to that of interstitial fluid.

2 Membrane potential reaches threshold, causing gated sodium (Na⁺) channels to open. Na⁺ flows through the channels from interstitial fluid into the cytoplasm. This inward flow of positively charged ions reverses the charge across the neuron membrane.

3 High membrane potential causes gated Na⁺ to close, and gated potassium (K⁺) channels to open. K⁺ flows out and membrane potential becomes negative. At the same time, diffusion of Na⁺ ions in the neuron triggers opening of Na⁺ gates in an adjacent region.

4 The decline in voltage at the site of the original action potential causes gated potassium channels to shut. After an action potential occurs, gated sodium channels briefly become unable to open. As a result, an action potential moves in one direction only, toward the axon terminals.

FIGURE 29.7 {**Animated**} Membrane events during an action potential. The drawings illustrate one region of an axon membrane.

An action potential begins in a neuron's trigger zone, the part of the axon adjacent to the cell body (**FIGURE 29.7**). When a neuron is at rest, this region's gated channels for sodium and potassium are closed, and there are more negatively charged ions inside the axon than outside it **1**.

A stimulus such as a signal from another neuron shifts the membrane potential in the trigger zone. If the stimulus is large enough, the membrane potential reaches **threshold potential**, the potential at which gated sodium channels in the trigger zone open and an action potential begins.

A POSITIVE FEEDBACK MECHANISM

When gated sodium channels open in a trigger zone, they allow sodium ions (Na^+) to follow their concentration gradient and diffuse from interstitial fluid into the neuron's cytoplasm **2**. As these positively charged ions flow in, they make the cytoplasm more positively charged. This increase in charge causes gated sodium channels in nearby regions of membrane to open, which in turn allows more sodium ions to flow into the cytoplasm, and so on. This is an example of a **positive feedback mechanism**, in which an activity intensifies because of its own occurrence. Positive feedback ensures that an action potential is an all-or-nothing event: Once the membrane potential in the trigger zone reaches threshold level, an action potential always occurs.

A MAXIMUM VALUE

All action potentials are the same size. When an action potential is triggered, the axon's membrane potential quickly shoots up to about +30 mV (**FIGURE 29.8**). A positive

FIGURE 29.8 An action potential. This graph shows how the membrane potential reverses and then restores itself. Numbers on the graph correlate with the numbered graphics in **FIGURE 29.7**.

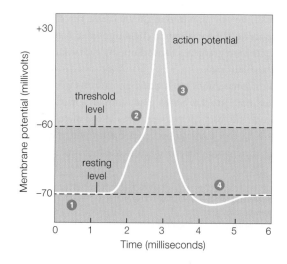

CREDITS: (7) From Starr/Taggart/Evers/Starr, Biology, 13E. © 2013 Cengage Learning; (8) © Cengage Learning.

axon

myelin sheath
around axon

node (unsheathed region
of the axon)

FIGURE 29.9 Myelinated axon. Neuroglial cells produce the sheath that wraps around and insulates the axon.

membrane potential indicates that cytoplasm has more positively charged ions than interstitial fluid on the other side of the membrane. Membrane potential cannot exceed +30 mV, because when it reaches this level, gated sodium channels close, and gated potassium channels open ❸. As positively charged potassium ions (K⁺) diffuse out of the cell through the now-open channels, the axon's cytoplasm once again becomes more negatively charged than interstitial fluid. This decline in membrane potential causes gates on gated potassium channels to shut.

In summary, during an action potential, membrane potential rises from the resting potential to a peak value, then declines once again to resting potential. The whole process takes only a few milliseconds.

CONDUCTION ALONG AN AXON

An action potential is self-propagating and does not weaken with distance. It travels along an axon, affecting each patch of membrane only briefly. When voltage-gated sodium channels open, some of the sodium ions that rush inward diffuse into adjacent regions of cytoplasm. The arrival of positive ions raises the membrane potential in these regions to threshold level, setting in motion an action potential in adjacent patches of membrane ❹. Sodium channels open in one region of membrane after another, and the action potential moves along the axon from trigger zone to terminals. The action potential moves only in one direction because it cannot move backward. After a voltage-gated sodium channel closes, it cannot open for a brief period.

myelin Fatty material produced by neuroglial cells; insulates axons and thus speeds conduction of action potentials.
positive feedback mechanism A response intensifies the conditions that caused its occurrence.
threshold potential Neuron membrane potential at which gated sodium channels open, causing an action potential to occur.

However, gated sodium channels in regions farther along the axon's membrane can and do swing open as these regions reach threshold.

Most vertebrate axons have associated neuroglial cells that increase the rate of conduction along the axon. The neuroglia make **myelin**, a fatty material that wraps around the axon (**FIGURE 29.9**). Ions cannot cross myelin, so a myelinated axon undergoes action potentials only at nodes, where there is no myelin. The membrane at each node contains many gated sodium channels. By jumping from node to node in a myelinated axon, an action potential can move as fast as 120 meters per second. By contrast, in unmyelinated axons, the maximum speed of conduction is about 10 meters per second.

Multiple sclerosis (MS) is a nervous system disorder that arises when white blood cells mistakenly attack and destroy myelin sheaths in the brain and spinal cord. As myelin becomes replaced by scar tissue, the speed at which action potentials travel declines. As a result, people with multiple sclerosis experience muscle weakness, fatigue, impaired coordination, numbness, and vision problems.

TAKE-HOME MESSAGE 29.4

An action potential begins in a neuron's trigger zone. When threshold potential is reached, gated sodium channels open and the charge difference across the membrane reverses. Self-propagating voltage reversals that do not weaken with distance occur at consecutive patches of membrane as the action potential travels toward axon terminals.

At each patch of membrane, an action potential ends when potassium ions flow out of the neuron, and the voltage difference across the membrane is restored. Action potentials move only toward axon terminals, because gated sodium channels cannot reopen immediately after an action potential.

Myelin-producing neuroglial cells that associate with most vertebrate neurons speed conduction of action potentials.

CREDIT: (9) From Starr/Evers/Starr, Biology Today and Tomorrow with Physiology, 4E. © 2013 Cengage Learning.

TRANSMISSION, RECEPTION, TRANSDUCTION

Action potentials cannot pass directly from a neuron to another cell. Instead, signaling molecules relay signals between neurons or between a neuron and a muscle or gland. The region where an axon terminal sends chemical

❶ Action potentials flow along the axon of a motor neuron to neuromuscular junctions, where an axon terminal forms a synapse with a muscle fiber.

axon of a motor neuron

neuromuscular junction

❷ The axon terminal stores chemical signaling molecules (green) called neurotransmitter inside vesicles.

axon terminal of motor neuron

plasma membrane of muscle fiber

vesicle

❸ The arrival of an action potential causes exocytosis of these vesicles, and neurotransmitter enters the synaptic cleft.

synaptic cleft

❹ The plasma membrane of the muscle fiber has receptors for neurotransmitter. These receptors are also passive transport proteins.

binding site for neurotransmitter (no neurotransmitter bound)

channel closed

❺ Binding of neurotransmitter causes a shape change that allows ions to flow into the postsynaptic cell.

neurotransmitter

ion flows through now-open channel

FIGURE 29.10 {Animated} Communication at a synapse. This example depicts what occurs at a neuromuscular junction, a synapse between an axon terminal of a motor neuron and the muscle fiber that the neuron controls.

signals to a neuron, a muscle fiber, or a gland cell is a **synapse**. The signal-sending neuron at a synapse is called a presynaptic cell. A fluid-filled synaptic cleft about 20 nanometers wide separates its axon terminal from the input zone of a postsynaptic cell (the cell that receives the signal). For comparison, a hair is 100,000 nanometers wide.

FIGURE 29.10 illustrates how signals are transmitted at a **neuromuscular junction**, a synapse between a motor neuron and a skeletal muscle fiber. Action potentials travel along the neuron's axon to the axon terminals ❶. The terminals have vesicles filled with **neurotransmitter**, a type of signaling molecule that relays messages between cells at a synapse ❷. Neurotransmitter is made in the cell body, then moved to axon terminals where it is stored until an action potential arrives. Arrival of an action potential at an axon terminal triggers exocytosis; neurotransmitter-filled vesicles move to the plasma membrane and fuse with it, releasing the neurotransmitter into the synaptic cleft ❸.

The plasma membrane of a postsynaptic cell has receptor proteins that reversibly bind neurotransmitter ❹. Motor neurons release the neurotransmitter acetylcholine (ACh), and skeletal muscle has receptors for this molecule. Binding of ACh to one of these receptors causes a change in the receptor's shape. The receptor is also a passive transport protein, and when it changes shape, sodium ions can travel through it, from interstitial fluid into the muscle cell ❺.

Like a neuron, a muscle fiber can undergo an action potential. The influx of sodium caused by the binding of ACh drives the muscle fiber's membrane toward threshold potential. Once this threshold is reached, action potentials stimulate muscle contraction. We detail this process in Section 32.7.

After neurotransmitter molecules do their work, they must be removed from synaptic clefts to make way for new signals. Reuptake of neurotransmitter by presynaptic cells is part of this process. In addition, enzymes in the membrane of postsynaptic cells break down neurotransmitter. At a neuromuscular junction, the muscle cell membrane contains an enzyme that breaks down ACh.

SIGNAL AND RECEPTOR VARIETY

The effect a neurotransmitter has on a postsynaptic cell depends on the type of neurotransmitter and the type of receptor it binds to. For example, binding of ACh to receptors on skeletal muscle encourages muscle contraction, whereas binding of ACh to receptors on cardiac muscle inhibits contraction. The two types of muscle respond differently to ACh because they have different ACh receptors. ACh also acts in the brain, where it affects alertness and plays a role in memory.

FIGURE 29.11 Synaptic density. This interneuron is stained with a yellow fluorescent dye that indicates the location of many synapses.

ACh is one of many vertebrate neurotransmitters. Norepinephrine and epinephrine (commonly known as adrenaline) are neurotransmitters that prepare the body to respond to stress or excitement. Dopamine influences reward-based learning and acts in fine motor control. Serotonin influences mood and memory. Glutamate is the main excitatory signal in the central nervous system. Endorphins are the body's natural pain relievers.

SYNAPTIC INTEGRATION

A postsynaptic cell typically receives messages from many neurons (FIGURE 29.11). An interneuron in the brain can be on the receiving end of hundreds to thousands of synapses. At each synapse, the incoming signal may be excitatory and push the membrane potential closer to threshold. Or the signal may be inhibitory and nudge the potential away from threshold. Through **synaptic integration**, a neuron sums all inhibitory and excitatory signals arriving at its input zone. When excitatory signals outweigh inhibitory ones, an action potential occurs.

neuromuscular junction Synapse between a neuron and a muscle.
neurotransmitter Chemical signal released by axon terminals.
synapse Region where a neuron's axon terminals transmit signaling molecules (neurotransmitter) to another cell.
synaptic integration The summation of excitatory and inhibitory signals by a postsynaptic cell.

TAKE-HOME MESSAGE 29.5

Action potentials travel to a neuron's axon terminals, where they cause release of neurotransmitter into the synaptic cleft.

A neurotransmitter is a type of signaling molecule that can have an excitatory or inhibitory effect on a postsynaptic cell.

The response of a postsynaptic cell is determined by the sum of all excitatory and inhibitory signals arriving at its input zone at the same time.

29.6 HOW DO DRUGS ACT AT SYNAPSES?

FIGURE 29.12 Commonly used psychoactive drugs. Alcohol, coffee, and nicotine. All alter the function of synapses in the brain.

Psychoactive drugs alter brain function by acting at synapses in the brain (FIGURE 29.12). They do so by a variety of mechanisms. Some drugs mimic a neurotransmitter's effect on a postsynaptic cell. For example, morphine and heroin bind to receptors for endorphins (natural pain relievers), and they elicit the same effects—pain relief and feelings of well-being. In other cases, binding of a drug prevents, rather than mimics, a neurotransmitter's actions. For example, caffeine binds to and inactivates receptors for adenosine, a neurotransmitter that causes drowsiness. Other drugs encourage or inhibit neurotransmitter release from a presynaptic cell. Alcohol makes us drowsy because it encourages adenosine release. Still other drugs interfere with reuptake of neurotransmitter from the synaptic cleft. For example, cocaine slows reuptake of several neurotransmitters, including dopamine.

Some prescription drugs can treat mental disorders by slowing reuptake of a neurotransmitter. Attention deficit hyperactivity disorder (ADHD), which impairs the ability to concentrate and to control impulses, is treated with drugs that slow dopamine reuptake. Depression is treated with drugs that inhibit reuptake of serotonin.

Drug addiction has many causes, but dopamine plays an important role in creating dependency. Behaviors such as eating, which enhances survival, or engaging in sex, which enhances reproduction, result in a surge of dopamine. This response helps individuals learn to repeat evolutionarily beneficial behaviors. When drugs cause dopamine release or prevent its reuptake, they hijack this ancient learning pathway. Drug users inadvertently teach themselves that the drug is essential to their well-being.

TAKE-HOME MESSAGE 29.6

Psychoactive drugs affect signal transmission in the brain by encouraging or inhibiting release of a neurotransmitter, blocking or mimicking its action, or affecting its reuptake.

CREDITS: (11) Courtesy of Riken Brain Science Institute; (12) Szasz-Fabian Jozsef/Shutterstock.com.

CHAPTER 29 505
NEURAL CONTROL

The vertebrate peripheral nervous system includes all nerves that originate outside or extend outside the brain or spinal cord. Each nerve has an outer layer of connective tissue surrounding bundles of axons (**FIGURE 29.13**). There are two major functional divisions of the peripheral system: the somatic nervous system and the autonomic nervous system.

SOMATIC NERVES

Nerves of the **somatic nervous system** carry signals for voluntary movement from the central nervous system to skeletal muscle. They also relay signals from sensory receptors that monitor external conditions to the central nervous system. Signals from sensory neurons of the somatic system result in conscious sensations. The somatic system allows you both to wiggle your toes and to feel someone tickling them.

Nerves of the somatic motor system relay signals to muscles via a one-neuron pathway. The cell body of a somatic motor neuron resides in the brain or spinal cord, and its axon extends out to the muscle it controls.

AUTONOMIC NERVES

Nerves of the **autonomic nervous system** relay signals from the central nervous system to smooth muscle, cardiac muscle, and glands. They also relay signals about internal conditions from sensory receptors in internal organs to the central nervous system. For example, signals that travel along autonomic nerves both adjust your heart rate and tell your brain when your blood pressure drops too low.

Nerves of the autonomic system relay signals to muscles and glands via a two-neuron pathway. The axon of the first neuron (the preganglionic neuron) extends from a cell body in the brain or spinal cord to a ganglion (a cluster of cell

FIGURE 29.13 **{Animated}** Structure of a peripheral nerve.

bodies) outside the central nervous system. In the ganglion, endings of this axon release ACh at synapses with what are called postganglionic neurons. Axons of these neurons extend out to and synapse on an organ or gland.

There are two types of motor neurons in the autonomic system: sympathetic and parasympathetic. They operate antagonistically, meaning signals of one type oppose signals from the other (**FIGURE 29.14**).

Under most circumstances, signals from **parasympathetic neurons** dominate. These neurons promote housekeeping tasks, such as digestion and urine formation, bringing about what is called a rest and digest response. Both presynaptic and postsynaptic parasympathetic neurons release ACh at synapses. A preganglionic parasympathetic neuron synapses with four or five postganglionic neurons, all of which signal the same organ, so parasympathetic stimulation tends to have localized effects.

Signals from **sympathetic neurons** increase in times of stress, excitement, and danger. When you are startled, frightened, or angry, signals from these neurons raise your heart rate and blood pressure, make you sweat more and breathe faster, and induce adrenal glands to secrete epinephrine (adrenaline). In what is called the fight–flight response, sympathetic signals put an individual in a state of arousal, ready to fight or make a fast getaway.

A preganglionic axon of a sympathetic neuron releases ACh at synapses with as many 20 postganglionic neurons. These postganglionic neurons secrete norepinephrine at synapses with a variety of organs, so sympathetic stimulation tends to have a widespread effect.

Most organs receive opposing signals from the sympathetic and parasympathetic systems (**FIGURE 29.15**). For instance, both sympathetic and parasympathetic neurons synapse with smooth muscle cells in the gut wall. Norepinephrine released by sympathetic neurons tells

FIGURE 29.14 Functional divisions of the peripheral nervous system.

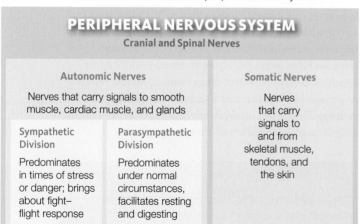

PERIPHERAL NERVOUS SYSTEM		
Cranial and Spinal Nerves		
Autonomic Nerves		Somatic Nerves
Nerves that carry signals to smooth muscle, cardiac muscle, and glands		Nerves that carry signals to and from skeletal muscle, tendons, and the skin
Sympathetic Division	Parasympathetic Division	
Predominates in times of stress or danger; brings about fight–flight response	Predominates under normal circumstances, facilitates resting and digesting	

Sympathetic Effects		Parasympathetic Effects
Widens pupils	**Eyes**	Narrows pupils
Thickens saliva	**Salivary glands**	Thins saliva
Increases heart rate	**Heart**	Decreases heart rate
Widens airways	**Airways**	Constricts airways
Slows secretions and movements	**Stomach**	Increases secretions and movements
Slows secretions to digestive tract	**Liver, pancreas**	Increases secretions to digestive tract
Increases secretion	**Adrenal gland**	Decreases secretion
Slows secretions and movements	**Small intestine, large intestine**	Increases secretions and movements
Inhibits urination	**Bladder**	Stimulates urination
Promotes ejaculation	**Genitals**	Promotes erection, lubrication

optic nerve
vagus nerve
(all ganglia in organs)
pelvic nerve

midbrain
medulla oblongata
cervical nerves (8 pairs)
thoracic nerves (12 pairs)
lumbar nerves (5 pairs)
sacral nerves (5 pairs)

(most ganglia near spinal cord)

FIGURE 29.15 {Animated} Autonomic nerves and their effects. Signals travel along a two-neuron pathway. Red areas in the brain or spinal cord indicate the location of preganglionic neuron cell bodies. Axons of these neurons synapse on a second neuron at a ganglion. Most sympathetic ganglia are close to the spinal cord. Parasympathetic ganglia are in or near the organs they affect.

FIGURE IT OUT: What effect does stimulation of the vagus nerve (a parasympathetic nerve) have on the heart?

Answer: It decreases heart rate.

the cells to slow their contractions, whereas ACh from parasympathetic neurons tells the same cells to speed up contractions. Synaptic integration determines the outcome of these conflicting commands.

Drugs that mimic norepinephrine or increase the amount of it at a synapse have an effect similar to natural activation of sympathetic neurons. For example, amphetamines and related drugs such as Ecstasy dilate the pupils (the dark area in the eye) and increase heart rate by triggering norepinephrine release and interfering with its reuptake.

Drugs that block norepinephrine's effect are used to treat a variety of disorders. For example, drugs called beta blockers lower heart rate and blood pressure by binding to and blocking norepinephrine receptors in blood vessel walls and the heart.

autonomic nervous system Division of the peripheral nervous system that relays signals to and from internal organs and glands.
parasympathetic neurons Neurons of the autonomic system that encourage digestion and other "housekeeping" tasks in the body.
somatic nervous system Division of the peripheral nervous system that controls skeletal muscles and relays sensory signals about movements and external conditions.
sympathetic neurons Neurons of the autonomic system that are activated during stress and danger.

TAKE-HOME MESSAGE 29.7

Nerves of the peripheral nervous system extend through the body and connect with the central nervous system.

The somatic portion of this system controls skeletal muscle, and conveys information about the external environment to the central nervous system.

The autonomic portion of this system controls smooth muscle, cardiac muscle, and glands. It conveys information about the internal environment to the central nervous system.

Most organs receive both sympathetic and parasympathetic stimulation from the autonomic system. Sympathetic signals prepare a body for "fight-or-flight," whereas parasympathetic signals encourage "resting and digesting."

The vertebrate central nervous system (CNS) includes the brain and spinal cord. Three connective tissue layers called **meninges** form a continuous covering that encloses these organs. **Cerebrospinal fluid** fills the space between meninges, a central canal in the spinal cord, and brain ventricles, which are open spaces within the brain (**FIGURE 29.16**). This clear fluid consists of water and small molecules filtered out of the blood.

A mechanism known as the **blood–brain barrier** controls the composition and concentration of cerebrospinal fluid. Cells that make up the walls of brain capillaries stick so tightly to one another that fluid cannot seep between them, as it does in most capillaries. Molecules and ions in blood can pass from blood into cerebrospinal fluid only by crossing the cells of a capillary. Nutrients—particularly glucose—can cross these cells and enter cerebrospinal fluid, but wastes and many harmful drugs and toxins cannot.

Two tissues called white matter and dark matter make up the bulk of the brain and spinal cord. **White matter** consists mainly of myelin-sheathed axons. In the central nervous system, a bundle of such axons is called a **tract**, rather than a nerve. **Gray matter** contains cell bodies, dendrites, and unmyelinated axon terminals. Thus, synapses of the central nervous system are located within the gray matter.

The **spinal cord** is the portion of the central nervous system that runs through the backbone and connects peripheral nerves to the brain. In humans, it is a cylinder about as thick as a thumb (**FIGURE 29.17**). The cord

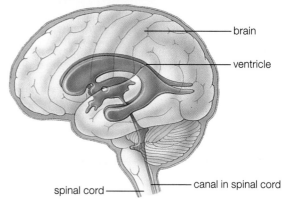

FIGURE 29.16 Location of cerebrospinal fluid (shown in blue) in and around the brain and spinal cord.

has an outer layer of white matter. Its interior contains gray matter and a central canal. In a cross-section of the spinal cord, the gray matter has a butterfly-like shape.

Places where axons of peripheral nerves enter or exit the spinal cord are called nerve roots. Dorsal roots (roots toward the rear of the backbone) contain axons of sensory neurons. Cell bodies of these neurons are in root ganglia just outside the spinal cord. Ventral roots (roots near the front of the backbone) contain axons of motor neurons. Cell bodies of these neurons are in the spinal cord's gray matter.

The spinal cord plays a role in many reflexes. A **reflex** is an automatic response to a stimulus, a movement or other action that does not require conscious thought. Basic reflexes, which do not require any learning, occur when the spinal cord or the brain stem automatically signals muscles to contract in response to a certain sensory signal.

Spinal reflexes do not involve the brain. The stretch reflex, which causes a muscle to contract after some force stretches it, is an example (**FIGURE 29.18**). Consider what happens when you hold a bowl as someone drops fruit into it ❶. The sudden addition of a piece of fruit increases the weight of the bowl, causing the biceps muscle in your upper arm to lengthen. Passive lengthening of the biceps excites a sensory receptor called a muscle spindle that wraps around a muscle. Excitation of the receptor endings triggers an action potential that flows along the axon of the sensory neuron toward the spinal cord ❷. In the spinal cord, the axon of the sensory neuron synapses on dendrites of one of the motor neurons that controls the biceps ❸. Binding of neurotransmitter released by the sensory neuron to receptors on the motor neuron causes the motor neuron to undergo an action potential ❹. An action potential causes the motor neuron to release ACh at the neuromuscular junction ❺. In response to this signal, the biceps contracts and steadies the arm against the additional weight ❻. The entire process occurs without your needing to think of it.

FIGURE 29.17 {**Animated**} Location and organization of the spinal cord.

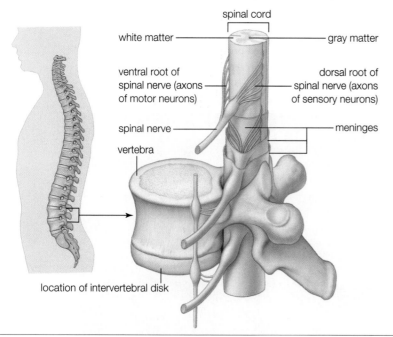

spinal cord

white matter

gray matter

ventral root of spinal nerve (axons of motor neurons)

dorsal root of spinal nerve (axons of sensory neurons)

spinal nerve

meninges

vertebra

location of intervertebral disk

Stimulus

1 Addition of fruit to a bowl stretches the biceps muscle of the arm holding the bowl.

2 Stretching out of the biceps stimulates muscle spindles, which are receptor endings of a sensory neuron. The stimulation triggers an action potential that travels along the sensory neuron's axon to the spinal cord.

white matter

gray matter

3 In the cord's gray matter, axon terminals of the sensory neuron synapse with a motor neuron, causing it to undergo an action potential.

4 The action potential travels along the axon of the motor neuron to the biceps muscle.

Response

6 Stimulation of the biceps muscle causes it to contract, so the bowl is held steady.

5 When the action potential arrives at the motor neuron's axon terminals, it triggers the neuron to release ACh. The ACh triggers the biceps muscle to contract.

axon terminals of motor neuron that synapse with a muscle fiber in biceps

muscle spindle (receptor endings of a sensory neuron)

FIGURE 29.18 {Animated} The stretch reflex. This is a spinal reflex; it does not involve the brain.

An injury to the spinal cord can cause loss of sensation and paralysis. Symptoms depend on where the cord is damaged. Tracts carrying signals to and from the upper body are higher in the cord than those that govern the lower body. An injury to the lumbar region of the back often paralyzes the legs. An injury to higher cord regions can paralyze all limbs, as well as muscles used in breathing. Unlike peripheral nerves, tracts of the spinal cord do not grow back. Spinal cord injuries cause permanent disability.

Doctors can temporarily halt transmission of signals through the spinal cord to provide pain relief to a specific region of the body. For example, the most common way of lessening pain during childbirth is through epidural anesthesia. During this procedure, a doctor puts painkiller in the space between the meninges and spinal cord. The drug is administered where it will partially numb the body from the waist down, without otherwise impairing perception or interfering with motor function.

blood–brain barrier Protective mechanism that prevents unwanted substances from entering cerebrospinal fluid.
cerebrospinal fluid Fluid that surrounds the brain and spinal cord and fills ventricles within the brain.
gray matter Central nervous system tissue that consists of neuron axon terminals, cell bodies, and dendrites, along with neuroglial cells.
meninges Membranes that enclose the brain and spinal cord.
reflex Automatic response that occurs without conscious thought or learning.
spinal cord Portion of the central nervous system that connects peripheral nerves with the brain.
tract Bundle of axons in the central nervous system.
white matter Central nervous system tissue consisting mainly of myelinated axons.

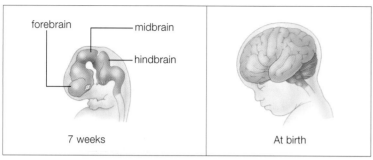

forebrain — midbrain — hindbrain

7 weeks | At birth

FIGURE 29.19 Development of the human brain.

hypothalamus   thalamus

cerebrum

corpus callosum

midbrain
brain stem — pons
medulla oblongata

cerebellum

Forebrain	
Cerebrum	Localizes, processes sensory inputs; initiates, controls skeletal muscle activity; governs memory, emotions, and, in humans, abstract thought
Thalamus	Relays sensory signals to and from cerebral cortex; has a role in memory
Hypothalamus	With pituitary gland, functions in homeostatic control. Adjusts volume, composition, temperature of internal environment; governs behaviors that ensure homeostasis (e.g., thirst, hunger)
Midbrain	Relays sensory input to forebrain, affects coordination
Hindbrain	
Pons	Bridges cerebrum and cerebellum; also connects spinal cord with midbrain. With the medulla oblongata, controls rate and depth of respiration
Cerebellum	Coordinates motor activity for moving limbs and maintaining posture, and for spatial orientation
Medulla oblongata	Relays signals between spinal cord and pons; functions in reflexes that affect heart rate, blood vessel diameter, and respiratory rate. Also involved in vomiting, coughing, other reflexive functions

FIGURE 29.20 {Animated} Major components of the human brain and their functions.

As a vertebrate embryo develops, its embryonic neural tube develops into a spinal cord and a brain. The brain becomes organized as three functional regions: the forebrain, midbrain, and hindbrain (**FIGURE 29.19**). The hindbrain connects to the spinal cord and functions in reflexes and coordination. It is the brain region that has changed least over evolutionary time. By contrast, there has been an evolutionary trend toward a decrease in the size of the midbrain and an increase in the size of the forebrain.

An adult human brain weighs about 1,400 grams, or 3 pounds. It contains about 100 billion interneurons, and neuroglia make up more than half of its volume. **FIGURE 29.20** shows the structure of a human brain. Other vertebrate brains have the same functional areas, although the relative size of the areas varies among species.

The hindbrain has three regions. The **medulla oblongata**, which connects to the spinal cord, influences heartbeat and breathing. It also controls reflexes such as swallowing, coughing, vomiting, and sneezing. Just above the medulla oblongata is the **pons**, which also affects breathing. Pons means "bridge," a reference to tracts that extend through the pons to the midbrain.

Closer to the rear of the skull is the plum-sized **cerebellum**, which controls posture, coordinates voluntary movements, and plays a role in learning new motor skills. The cerebellum is densely packed with neurons, having as many as all other brain regions combined. Among other ill effects of excessive alcohol intake, it disrupts coordination by impairing cerebellum function. Police officers evaluate the extent of this impairment by asking a person suspected of driving while drunk to walk a straight line. Over the long term, excessive alcohol consumption can kill cells in the cerebellum, causing it to shrink. This is why chronic alcoholics often walk with a shuffling gait. On the other hand, routinely practicing an athletic skill improves cerebellum function and motor coordination.

The pons, medulla, and midbrain are collectively referred to as the brain stem. In humans, the midbrain is the smallest of the three brain regions. It plays a role in reward-based learning and in voluntary movement. Death of dopamine-producing neurons in one part of the midbrain causes Parkinson's disease. Affected people first develop tremors (unintentional shaky movements). Later, all voluntary movement, including speech, may become difficult.

The forebrain contains the **cerebrum**, the largest part of the human brain. The cerebrum receives sensory signals, integrates information, and initiates voluntary actions. A fissure divides the cerebrum into right and left hemispheres connected by a thick band of tissue (the corpus callosum) that relays signals between them. Each hemisphere has an

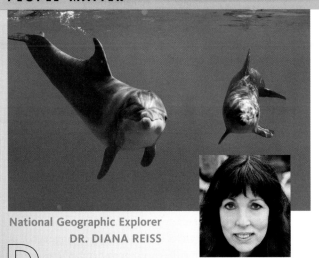

National Geographic Explorer
DR. DIANA REISS

Diana Reiss has worked with dolphins in aquariums to learn about the nature of the intelligence of these socially complex mammals. She says, "I became fascinated with dolphins because they have such large and complex brains and are highly gregarious, yet so little was known about the nature of their communication and type of intelligence. These remarkable mammals share with us many abilities we once thought were uniquely human or that we shared only with our closest relatives, the great apes." In fact, when brain size is adjusted for body size, dolphins are second only to humans in braininess.

To investigate dolphins' capacity for self-recognition, Reiss marked animals with a dark spot and provided them with a mirror. The dolphins oriented themselves in front of the mirror so that they could examine the mark on their reflection, indicating that they understood the mirror showed their reflection, rather than another dolphin. Most children do not recognize themselves in a mirror until they are 18 to 24 months old. The only other animals known to have this capacity for self-recognition are great apes and some elephants.

Dolphins and great apes share an ancestor that lived about 95 million years ago, but since that time they have traveled along two separate and very different evolutionary paths. Although their brains do not look much alike, the two groups show what Reiss calls cognitive convergence. Both live in social groups and have evolved impressive mental abilities. They recognize themselves, learn by imitation, and can be taught to use a simple symbol-based keyboard to communicate with humans. Reiss notes, "Much of dolphin learning is similar to what we see with young children."

Reiss's work with dolphins has made her a strong advocate for their conservation. She continues to speak out against the Japanese harvest of dolphins for use as human food and the capture of wild dolphins for aquariums and tourist attractions.

outer layer of gray matter called the cerebral cortex. Our large cerebral cortex is the part of the brain responsible for our unique capacities such as language and abstract thought. We discuss its functions in more detail in the next section.

The **thalamus** is a two-lobed structure that sorts sensory signals and sends them to the proper region of the cerebral cortex. It also influences sleep and wakefulness. Damage to the thalamus can cause a person to go into a permanent sleeplike state called a coma. In the rare genetic disorder fatal familial insomnia, thalamus deterioration causes an inability to sleep, followed by a coma, then death.

The **hypothalamus** ("under the thalamus") is the center for homeostatic control of the internal environment. It receives information about the state of the body and regulates thirst, appetite, sex drive, and body temperature. It also interacts with the adjacent pituitary gland as a central control center for the endocrine system. We discuss endocrine functions of the hypothalamus in Chapter 31.

cerebellum Hindbrain region that coordinates voluntary movements.
cerebrum Forebrain region that controls higher functions.
hypothalamus Forebrain control center for homeostasis-related and endocrine functions.
medulla oblongata Hindbrain region that influences breathing and controls reflexes such as coughing and vomiting.
pons Hindbrain region that influences breathing and serves as a bridge to the adjacent midbrain.
thalamus Forebrain region that relays signals to the cerebrum; affects sleep–wake cycles.

TAKE-HOME MESSAGE 29.9

The anterior end of an embryonic neural tube develops into a brain with three functional regions.

Structures in the hindbrain regulate breathing, play a role in reflexes such as sneezing, and coordinate movements.

The midbrain has a role in learning and voluntary movement.

The forebrain, our largest brain region, regulates homeostatic processes, integrates sensory information, initiates voluntary actions, and allows language and abstract thought.

The human **cerebral cortex**, the outermost portion of the cerebrum, is a 2-millimeter-thick layer of gray matter. Over the course of human evolution, this layer has become increasingly folded. Folds allowed humans to add additional gray matter while minimizing the increase in brain volume; a larger brain requires a larger skull, which can pose problems during childbirth. Prominent folds in the cortex are used as landmarks to define the lobes of each cerebral hemisphere (**FIGURE 29.21**).

The cortex of the frontal lobe allows us to make reasoned choices, concentrate on tasks, plan for the future, and behave appropriately in social situations. During the 1950s, more than 20,000 people had their frontal lobes damaged by frontal lobotomy, the surgical destruction of frontal lobe tissue. Lobotomy was used to treat mental illness, personality disorders, and even headaches. It made patients calmer, but blunted their emotions and impaired their ability to plan, concentrate, and behave appropriately.

The two cerebral hemispheres differ somewhat in their function. In the 90 or so percent of people that are right-handed, the left hemisphere plays the major role in movement and in language, whereas mathematical tasks, such as adding two numbers, typically activate areas of the right hemisphere. Broca's area, an area that translates thoughts into speech, is usually in the left frontal lobe.

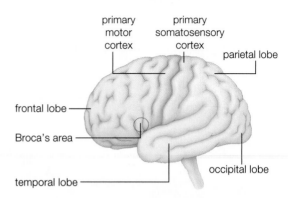

FIGURE 29.21 Lobes of the brain (indicated by pink, yellow, green, and blue) and some named functional regions.

Damage to Broca's area often prevents a person from speaking, but does not affect understanding of language. Note that, despite their differences, both hemispheres are flexible. If a stroke or injury damages one side of the brain, the other hemisphere can take on new tasks. People can even function with a single hemisphere.

Although most functions involve many brain regions, we can pinpoint regions of the cortex that have primary responsibility for certain tasks. The main region involved in voluntary movement is the **primary motor cortex** at the rear of each frontal lobe. Neurons of this region are laid out like a map of the body, with body parts capable of fine movements taking up the greatest area (**FIGURE 29.22**). The primary somatosensory cortex at the front of the parietal lobe receives sensory input from the skin and joints. A primary visual cortex at the rear of each occipital lobe receives signals from eyes. A primary auditory cortex in the temporal lobe acts in hearing.

Nearly all sensory and motor signals cross over on their way to and from the brain. Thus, commands to move parts on the body's left side originate in the right hemisphere, and visual signals from the left eye end up in the right hemisphere's occipital lobe.

FIGURE 29.22 The primary motor cortex. The graphic of the brain (below right) shows the location of the left hemisphere's primary motor cortex in pink. The graphic beside it shows a cross section of this region, the location of neurons that control various body regions, and the degree of control of those regions. Body parts that appear disproportionately large, such as hands, are the most finely controlled.

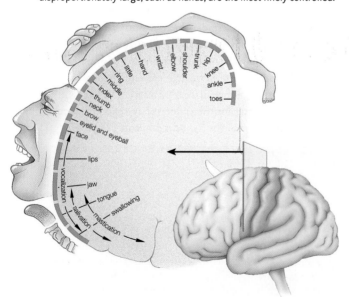

cerebral cortex Outer gray matter layer of the cerebrum; region responsible for most complex behavior.
primary motor cortex Region of frontal lobe that controls voluntary movement.

TAKE-HOME MESSAGE 29.10

The cerebrum's outer layer of gray matter (the cerebral cortex) is responsible for planning and abstract thought, initiating movements, and sensory perception.

The two cerebral hemispheres differ somewhat in their function. Each hemisphere receives information from, and sends commands to, the opposite side of the body.

CREDITS: (21) © Cengage Learning; (22) left, After Penfield and Rasmussen, *The Cerebral Cortex of Man*, © 1950 Macmillan Library Reference. Renewed 1978 by Theodore Rasmussen; right, © Cengage Learning 2015.

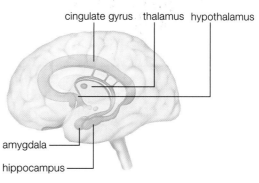

cingulate gyrus   thalamus   hypothalamus

amygdala

hippocampus

FIGURE 29.23 Components of the limbic system. These structures play a role in emotion and memory.

THE EMOTIONAL BRAIN

Emotions such as sadness, fear, and fury arise in part from the **limbic system**, a set of structurally and functionally related structures deep within the brain (**FIGURE 29.23**). Exactly how these structures give rise to different emotions is poorly understood, but we do know a bit about some of their functions. For example, the hypothalamus summons up the physiological changes that accompany emotions. Signals from the hypothalamus make our heart pound and our palms sweat when we are fearful. The cingulate gyrus helps us control our emotions. The adjacent, almond-shaped amygdala becomes active when we are fearful, as well as when we perceive fear in others. The amygdala is often overactive in people with panic disorders.

MAKING MEMORIES

At a cellular level, memory formation involves altering the number and placement of synaptic connections among existing neurons. The cerebral cortex receives information continually, but only a fraction of it is stored as a memory. Memory forms in stages. Short-term memory lasts seconds to hours. This type of memory holds a few bits of information: a set of numbers, words of a sentence, and so forth. In long-term memory, larger chunks of information can be stored more or less permanently.

Different types of memories are stored and brought to mind by different mechanisms. Repetition of motor tasks creates skill memories that can be highly persistent. Learn to ride a bicycle, dribble a basketball, or play the piano, and you are unlikely to lose that skill. Forming skill memories

involves neurons in the cerebellum, which controls motor activity. Declarative memory stores facts and impressions. It helps you remember how a lemon smells, that a quarter is worth more than a dime, and the address of your home.

The **hippocampus** (plural, hippocampi), a structure adjacent to the amygdala, plays an essential role in the formation of declarative memories. Interactions between the amygdala and the hippocampus give rise to learned fears. The role of the hippocampus in memory was first discovered in the 1950s after a man known as HM had both his hippocampi surgically removed to treat his seizures. In addition to alleviating HM's seizures, the surgery destroyed his ability to form new memories. Five minutes after meeting a person, HM was unable to remember that they had ever met. He still retained memories of pre-surgery events, indicating that the hippocampus is not the site for long-term memory storage. Additional evidence of the hippocampus's role in memory comes from people with Alzheimer's disease. The hippocampus is one of the first brain regions destroyed by this disorder. Like HM, people in early-stage Alzheimer's usually have impaired short-term memory, but retain their memories of long-ago events.

The hippocampus is one of the very few brain regions where new neurons continue to arise during adulthood. It it is not yet clear how the new neurons assist in memory formation. By one hypothesis, they help make room for new memories by disrupting connections among existing cells.

hippocampus Brain region essential to formation of declarative memories.
limbic system Group of structures deep in the brain that function in expression of emotion.

TAKE-HOME MESSAGE 29.11

The structures of the limbic system interact to produce the physiological and mental features of emotions.

Memory formation also involves structures deep within the brain, especially the hippocampus. Forming memories involves altering synaptic connections.

The activity of neurons in the cerebral cortex causes voltage fluctuations that are transmitted across the skull to the skin of the scalp. To detect these fluctuations, electrodes are attached to the scalp, as shown in this chapter's opening photo. An electroencephalograph (EEG) is a graph of this electrical activity over time. EEGs provide information about a person's level of wakefulness, so they are frequently used to monitor people during sleep studies. Each of the various stages of sleep is characterized by a specific EEG pattern. EEGs provide information about the level of

FIGURE 29.24 PET scan images from a normal brain and the brain from a person affected by Parkinson's disease. Red and yellow indicate areas of high glucose uptake by dopamine-secreting neurons. Parkinson's disease causes death of such neurons in a region of the midbrain.

FIGURE 29.25 Pain-related brain activity with or without virtual reality goggles as revealed by fMRI. The goggles allow patients to enter a virtual world, distracting them as they undergo a painful procedure. Note the reduced extent of high-activity areas (red, orange, and yellow) with the goggles.

activity across the entire cerebrum and can show what is happening over intervals as short as a millisecond. However, they do not offer much information about the exact location of the active cells.

Other methods allow scientists to look more closely at what is happening in specific brain regions. Positron-emission tomography (PET) tracks the uptake of radioactively labeled glucose to reveal areas of metabolic activity in the brain (FIGURE 29.24). Glucose is the main energy source for brain cells, and active cells take up more than resting cells.

PET scans have also been used to study the effects of cell phone radiation on the brain. One such recent experiment showed increased metabolic activity in the brain cells nearest an active phone. Whether the increased metabolism has a harmful effect on the brain remains an open question. For now, many health officials recommend using a headset or the speakerphone setting to keep the radiation-emitting part of the phone some distance away from the brain.

Functional magnetic resonance imaging (fMRI) reveals details of brain activity by detecting changes in blood flow. Active brain cells use more oxygen than resting cells, and increased blood flow provides the necessary oxygen. FIGURE 29.25 shows results of an fMRI study in which virtual reality goggles were used to reduce perception of pain.

To study the structure, genetics, and biochemistry of human brain cells, scientists need brain tissue. "Brain banks" are repositories of such tissue. The largest brain bank, the Harvard Brain Tissue Resource Center, has thousands of donated brains, most from people who had degenerative brain disorders (such as Parkinson's disease) or psychiatric illnesses (such as schizophrenia). This federally funded center supplies tissue samples to researchers who investigate the underlying causes of these conditions. For example, microscopic analysis of samples provided by the center allowed researchers to determine that the prefrontal cortex of schizophrenics is smaller than normal, not because schizophrenics have fewer brain cells in this region, but because their cells are unusually tightly packed, with fewer synapses among them.

TAKE-HOME MESSAGE 29.12

EEGs provide information about the electrical activity in a living brain.

PET scans and fMRI images reveal which parts of a living brain are most active.

Comparison of normal and abnormal brain tissue allows researchers to investigate brain disorders.

CREDITS: (24) © From Neuro Via Clinical Research Program, Minneapolis VA Medical Center; (25) Image by Todd Richards and Aric Bills, U.W., copyright Hunter Hoffman, U.W.

Education

THE BRAIN IS A SURPRISINGLY DELICATE ORGAN. It's only about as firm as Jell-O or warm butter. Head impacts or rapid stops can cause this soft, squishy organ to slam against the inside of the bony skull, causing a traumatic brain injury called a concussion. Symptoms of a concussion can include confusion, dizziness, blurred vision, headache, difficulty concentrating, altered sleep patterns, and, in some severe cases, loss of consciousness.

Usually, the brain resumes normal function within 7 to 10 days after a concussion. However, repeated head injuries can cause chronic traumatic encephalopathy (CTE), a neurodegenerative disorder that involves memory loss, depression and suicidal impulses, and eventually dementia. Affected brains resemble those of people affected by Alzheimer's disease. In both cases, the brain is smaller than normal, has enlarged ventricles, and accumulates deposits of a protein called tau.

Concussions are an occupational hazard for football players. Some pay a hefty price in terms of brain health. In 2011, Dave Duerson, a 50-year-old former player for the Chicago Bears football team, shot himself in the chest. He left behind a request that his brain be donated to a brain bank devoted to the study of sport-related brain injuries. Examination of his brain revealed the extensive degenerative brain damage characteristic of CTE.

Retired professional football players are three times more likely than the general population to die of neurogenerative diseases. They are also more likely to be diagnosed with clinical depression, with risk of this disorder rising as the number of concussions sustained increases.

Publicity about brain injuries and brain damage in professional football players has also led researchers to reconsider the danger concussions pose to amateur athletes. There is mounting evidence that even a single concussion can create permanent deficits. A recent study of college athletes found that those with a history of concussion tended to have slightly abnormal EEGs, a lower-than-normal ability to inhibit motor responses, and a somewhat altered gait.

Concerns about concussions have led to rule changes in a variety of professional and amateur sports organizations. The National Hockey League, for example, has tightened its rules on head shots, and some youth soccer leagues have banned heading the ball. Sports organizations are also stepping up efforts to educate coaches and athletes about the symptoms of concussion and the risks of returning to play too quickly after such injuries. The goal is to maintain the positive aspects of sports, while minimizing the risk that participants will sustain a brain-altering injury.

Summary

SECTION 29.1 Most animals have **neurons** and supporting **neuroglial cells.** Cnidarians and echinoderms have a **nerve net. Cephalization** occurred in bilateral animals. Bilateral invertebrates have a nervous system with a cluster of **ganglia** at the head end that functions as a **brain,** ventral **nerve cords** running the length of the body, and **nerves** extending out from the nerve cords. Vertebrates have a **central nervous system** (brain and spinal cord) and a **peripheral nervous system.**

SECTIONS 29.2, 29.3 **Dendrites** of a neuron receive signals; endings of **axons** transmit signals. A **sensory neuron** has receptor endings and an axon. **Interneurons** and **motor neurons** have an axon and many dendrites. The voltage difference across a neuron plasma membrane is a **membrane potential.** At **resting potential** the interior of the neuron is negative relative to the interstitial fluid. An **action potential** is a brief reversal of this charge difference.

SECTION 29.4 An action potential occurs only if a disturbance causes membrane potential to rise to **threshold potential.** The action potential begins when gated sodium channels open. **Positive feedback** causes even more sodium gates to open, so sodium ions rush into the axon. The influx makes the charge of the axon's cytoplasm more positive than that of extracellular fluid. As a result, gated potassium channels open and potassium ions rush out. Sodium–potassium pumps restore the resting membrane potential. Most vertebrate axons have a covering of **myelin** that speeds transmission of action potentials.

SECTIONS 29.5, 29.6 Neurons signal other neurons, muscle fibers, or gland cells at **synapses.** An action potential triggers the release of **neurotransmitter** from a presynaptic cell's axon terminals. Neurotransmitter molecules diffuse across the synaptic cleft and bind to receptors on the postsynaptic cell. For example, at a **neuromuscular junction,** a motor neuron releases acetylcholine that binds to receptors on a muscle fiber.

Different neurotransmitters have inhibitory or excitatory effects on a postsynaptic cell. The postsynaptic cell's response is determined by **synaptic integration** of messages arriving at the same time.

Psychoactive drugs mimic neurotransmitters, or disrupt their release or uptake. Drug addiction taps into reward-based learning pathways that involve dopamine release.

SECTION 29.7 Nerves are bundles of axons that carry signals through the body. The peripheral nervous system is functionally divided into the **somatic nervous system,** which controls skeletal muscles, and the **autonomic nervous system,** which controls internal organs and glands. **Sympathetic neurons** of the autonomic system increase their output in times of stress or danger. During less stressful times, signals from **parasympathetic neurons** encourage "resting and digesting."

SECTION 29.8 The brain and **spinal cord** consist of **white matter,** which contains myelinated axons in **tracts,** and **gray matter,** which contains cell bodies, dendrites, and axon terminals. Synapses occur in gray matter. The spinal cord and brain are enclosed by **meninges** and cushioned by **cerebrospinal fluid.** A mechanism known as the **blood–brain barrier** controls the composition of the cerebrospinal fluid. Spinal reflexes involve peripheral nerves and the spinal cord. A **reflex** is an automatic response to stimulation; it does not require conscious thought.

SECTIONS 29.9–29.12 The neural tube of a vertebrate embryo develops into the spinal cord and brain. The hindbrain connects to the spinal cord. It includes the **pons** and **medulla oblongata,** which regulate breathing and other vital tasks, and the **cerebellum,** which coordinates motor activity. The midbrain functions in movement and reward-based learning. The forebrain includes the **thalamus,** which affects wakefulness; the **hypothalamus,** a control center for homeostasis; and the **cerebrum.** The outer portion of the cerebrum, the **cerebral cortex,** governs complex functions. Its **primary motor cortex** controls voluntary movement. The cerebral cortex interacts with the **limbic system,** including the **hippocampus,** in emotions and memory.

EEGs record the electrical activity of neurons in the brain. PET scans and fMRI studies pinpoint areas of high neuron activity. Brain banks are repositories of donated tissue used for studies of brain anatomy and function.

SECTION 29.13 Sudden jolts or blows to the head can cause a concussion. Repeated brain trauma can cause a condition similar to Alzheimer's disease.

Self-Quiz   Answers in Appendix VII

1. _____ relay messages from the brain and spinal cord to muscles and glands.
   a. Motor neurons   c. Interneurons
   b. Sensory neurons   d. Neuroglia

2. When a neuron is at rest, _____ .
   a. it is at threshold potential
   b. gated sodium channels are open
   c. it holds less sodium than the interstitial fluid
   d. both a and c

3. Action potentials occur when _____ .
   a. potassium gates close
   b. a stimulus pushes membrane potential to threshold
   c. sodium–potassium pumps become active
   d. neurotransmitter is reabsorbed

4. Neurotransmitters are released by _____ .
   a. axon terminals   c. dendrites
   b. the cell body   d. the myelin sheath

Data Analysis Activities

Prenatal Effects of Ecstasy   Animal studies are often used to assess effects of prenatal exposure to illicit drugs. For example, Jack Lipton used rats to study the effect of prenatal exposure to MDMA, the active ingredient in the drug Ecstasy. He injected pregnant female rats with either MDMA or saline solution (the control) during the period of prenatal brain formation. Twenty-one days after the pups were born, Lipton tested their response to a new environment. He placed each young rat in a new cage and used a photobeam system to record how much each rat moved around before settling down. **FIGURE 29.26** shows his results.

1. Which rats moved most (caused the most photobeam breaks) during the first 5 minutes in a new cage: those prenatally exposed to MDMA or the controls?
2. How many photobeam breaks did MDMA-exposed rats make during their second 5 minutes in the new cage?
3. Which rats moved most in the last 5 minutes?
4. Does this study support the hypothesis that exposure to MDMA affects a developing rat's brain?

FIGURE 29.26 Effect of prenatal exposure to MDMA on activity levels of 21-day-old rats placed in a new cage. Movements were detected when the rat interrupted a photobeam. Rats were monitored at 5-minute intervals for a total of 20 minutes. Blue bars are average numbers of photobeam breaks by rats whose mothers received saline; red bars are photobeam breaks for rats whose mothers received MDMA.

5. Myelin that insulates axons is made by _____ .
   a. neuroglial cells   c. sensory neurons
   b. motor neurons   d. interneurons

6. Skeletal muscles are controlled by _____ .
   a. sympathetic nerves   c. somatic nerves
   b. parasympathetic nerves   d. both a and b

7. When something frightens you, _____ neurons increase their output.
   a. sympathetic   b. parasympathetic

8. Damage to the _____ disrupts short-term memory.
   a. hypothalamus   c. peripheral nerves
   b. hippocampus   d. spinal cord

9. EEGs detect _____ .
   a. sodium concentration   c. electrical activity
   b. changes in blood flow   d. glucose uptake

10. _____ have a pair of ventral nerve cords.
    a. sea stars   b. vertebrates   c. insects   d. sea anemones

11. Alcohol affects coordination by affecting the _____ .
    a. pons   c. spinal cord
    b. cerebellum   d. hypothalamus

12. Myelinated axons make up the brain's _____ .
    a. white matter   c. gray matter
    b. ventricles   d. meninges

13. Match the terms with their descriptions.
    ___ thalamus   a. coordinates motor activity
    ___ dopamine   b. connects the hemispheres
    ___ limbic system   c. protects brain and spinal
    ___ corpus callosum   cord from some toxins
    ___ cerebral cortex   d. one type of neurotransmitter
    ___ cerebellum   e. support team for neurons
    ___ neuroglia   f. wrap brain and spinal cord
    ___ ganglion   g. roles in emotion, memory
    ___ blood–brain   h. most complex integration
        barrier   i. cluster of neuron cell bodies
    ___ meninges   j. regulates sleep–wake cycle

Critical Thinking

1. In human newborns, especially premature ones, the blood–brain barrier is not yet fully developed. Why does this make it especially important to prevent them from taking in toxins?

2. Injections of botulinum toxin (Botox) into facial muscles (a type of skeletal muscle) can prevent movements that cause facial skin to wrinkle. Botox acts by preventing the release of a neurotransmitter. Which one?

3. Some survivors of disastrous events develop post-traumatic stress disorder (PTSD). Brain-imaging studies of people with PTSD showed that their hippocampi were shrunken and their amygdala unusually active. Given the functions of these regions, what sort of symptoms would you expect in people with PTSD?

Wolves investigating a scent. Animals differ in their sensory abilities, and a wolf's sense of smell is a hundred or more times keener than a human's.

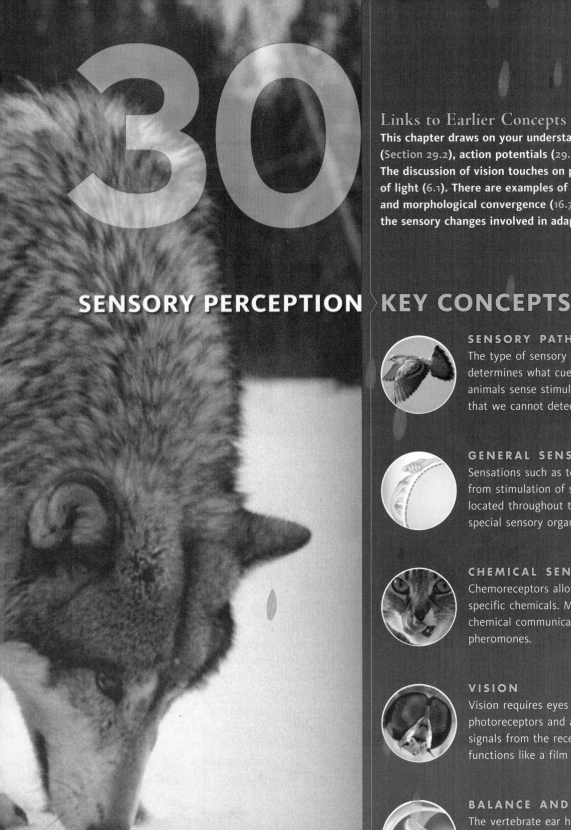

30

SENSORY PERCEPTION

Links to Earlier Concepts

This chapter draws on your understanding of sensory neurons (Section 29.2), action potentials (29.4), and reflexes (29.8). The discussion of vision touches on pigments and properties of light (6.1). There are examples of X-linked inheritance (14.3) and morphological convergence (16.7). You will also reconsider the sensory changes involved in adapting to life on land (24.3).

KEY CONCEPTS

SENSORY PATHWAYS

The type of sensory receptors an animal has determines what cues it can respond to. Some animals sense stimuli such as magnetic fields that we cannot detect.

GENERAL SENSES

Sensations such as touch, pain, or cold arise from stimulation of sensory receptors that are located throughout the body, rather than in special sensory organs.

CHEMICAL SENSES

Chemoreceptors allow animals to taste and smell specific chemicals. Many animals also detect chemical communication compounds called pheromones.

VISION

Vision requires eyes with a dense array of photoreceptors and a brain that integrates signals from the receptors. A vertebrate eye functions like a film camera.

BALANCE AND HEARING

The vertebrate ear has a role in both hearing and the sense of balance. Mechanoreceptors in the inner ear play a role in both senses.

THE ROLE OF SENSORY RECEPTORS

Sensory neurons monitor conditions and detect changes in the internal and external environment. Recall that sensory neurons have stimulus-detecting receptor endings at one end of their axon (Section 29.2). Excitation of these sensory receptors triggers an action potential in the neuron.

Several types of sensory receptors are common across animal groups. **Thermoreceptors** respond to heat or to cold. **Mechanoreceptors** detect touch, position relative to gravity, and movement. **Pain receptors** (nociceptors) detect injury. **Chemoreceptors** detect concentrations of specific chemical substances. **Photoreceptors** incorporate light-sensitive pigments that respond to light energy.

Animals monitor the external environment in different ways depending on the kinds and numbers of sensory receptors they have. Some animals have sensory receptors that we lack. For example, some animals have sensory receptors that allow them to detect magnetic fields (**FIGURE 30.1**). Others simply have more sensitive receptors than we do. Honeybees can detect ultraviolet and infrared radiation, whereas we detect only visible light.

ASSESSING SENSORY INPUT

Sensory information arrives at the brain in the form of action potentials, which are all the same size (Section 29.4). The brain uses three variables to determine the location and intensity of a stimulus. The first variable is the nerve that delivers the action potentials. For example, action potentials arriving via the optic nerve are interpreted as arising from visual stimuli. That is why you "see stars" if you press on your eye in a dark room. The second variable is the frequency of action potentials. A higher frequency denotes a stronger stimulus. Press lightly on skin and a mechanoreceptor responds with a few action potentials per second. Press harder and the receptor increases its firing rate. Finally, the number of sensory receptors firing gives the brain information about stimulus intensity. A gentle tap on the arm activates fewer receptors than a slap.

Stimulus duration can affect a sensory neuron's firing rate. In **sensory adaptation**, sensory neurons cease firing in

FIGURE 30.1 Animal magnetism. Pigeons and sea turtles are among the animals that detect variations in Earth's magnetic field and use this information to navigate.

spite of continued stimulation. Walk into a house where an apple pie is baking and you notice the sweet scent of baking apples immediately. Then, within a few minutes, the scent seems to lessen. The odor does not change in intensity, but chemoreceptors in your nose undergo sensory adaptation.

SENSATION VERSUS PERCEPTION

Sensation is the detection of sensory signals. Sensations of touch, pain, and cold arise from action of sensory neurons distributed throughout the body. Other sensations arise from special sensory organs such as eyes or ears.

Perception arises when the brain assigns meaning to sensations. Consider what happens when you watch a plane fly away. As the distance between you and the plane increases, the image of the plane on your eye becomes smaller and smaller. You perceive this change in sensation as indicative of increasing distance, rather than a shrinking plane.

chemoreceptor Sensory receptor that responds to a chemical.
mechanoreceptor Sensory receptor that responds to pressure, position, or acceleration.
pain receptor Sensory receptor that responds to tissue damage.
perception The meaning a brain derives from a sensation.
photoreceptor Sensory receptor that responds to light.
sensation Detection of a stimulus.
sensory adaptation Slowing or cessation of a sensory receptor's response to an ongoing stimulus.
thermoreceptor Temperature-sensitive sensory receptor.

TAKE-HOME MESSAGE 30.1

Sensation arises when one of the many types of sensory receptors detects specific stimuli. Nerves carry signals to brain regions that assess a stimulus according to which nerve delivered the signal, the frequency of action potentials, and the number of neurons that have been excited by the stimulus.

Perceptions arise when the brain interprets sensations.

General senses involve action of receptors throughout the body. By contrast, special senses arise from receptors located in specific sensory organs, such as eyes or ears. Smell, taste, vision, hearing, and the sense of equilibrium (balance) are special senses, which we consider in later sections of this chapter. Here we focus on the general senses.

SOMATIC AND VISCERAL SENSATION

Our general senses are responsible for two types of sensation, somatic and visceral. **Somatic sensations** arise from sensory neuron receptor endings in skin or skeletal muscle, or near joints. Sensations of heat and cold arise from thermoreceptors in skin, and sensations of touch and pressure from skin's mechanoreptors. Somatic pain arises from pain receptors in skin, muscles, or joints. The sense of where your body parts are (proprioception) arises from mechanoreceptors at joints or in muscles. Muscle spindles, sensory receptors that sense muscle stretching (Section 29.8), play a part in proprioception.

Signals involved in somatic sensation travel through the spinal cord and then onward to the somatosensory cortex, a part of the cerebral cortex. As in the motor cortex (Section 29.10), neurons in the somatosensory cortex are arrayed like a map of the body (**FIGURE 30.2**). As a result of this organization, somatic sensations are easily localized to a specific region of the body; it is easy for you to say exactly where someone is touching you.

Visceral sensations arise from sensory receptors in the walls of internal organs. For example, the feeling that your bladder or stomach is full arises from the activity of mechanoreceptors in the walls of those organs. Visceral pain occurs as a response to a smooth muscle spasm, inadequate blood flow to an organ, overstretching of a hollow organ such as the stomach, and other abnormal conditions. Signals from neurons involved in visceral sensations do not map onto the cortex in a region-specific fashion as somatic signals do. Thus, visceral sensations are not as easily localized as somatic ones. It is not easy to say exactly where you have a stomachache.

PAIN AND PAIN RELIEF

Pain is perception of a tissue injury. It serves a protective function by causing an animal to withdraw from the cause of injury and behave in a way that promotes healing.

---

endorphin One type of natural painkiller molecule.
pain Perception of tissue injury.
somatic sensations Sensations such as touch and pain that arise when sensory neurons in skin, muscle, or joints are activated.
visceral sensations Sensations that arise when sensory neurons associated with organs inside body cavities are activated.

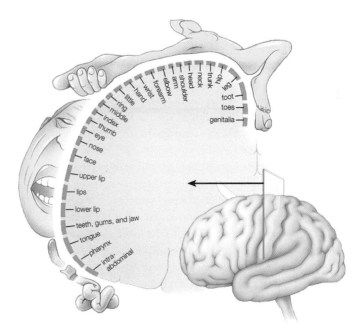

FIGURE 30.2 Primary somatosensory cortex. In each hemisphere, this strip of cerebral cortex receives somatic sensory signals. The graphic depicts a slice through the left somatosensory cortex and shows regions that receive sensory signals from different body parts. Body parts that appear disproportionately large in this diagram (such as fingertips and face) have the most sensory receptors.

Pain arises when injured body cells release local signaling molecules such as histamine and prostaglandins. These substances activate nearby pain receptors, causing action potentials to travel along axons of sensory neurons to the spinal cord. Here, the axons synapse with spinal interneurons that relay signals about pain to the brain. Natural painkillers called **endorphins** act by discouraging spinal interneurons from sending signals about pain to the brain. By contrast, a natural chemical called substance P enhances pain perception by making spinal interneurons more likely to send signals on. Pain-relieving drugs interfere with transmission of pain signals. For example, aspirin reduces pain by slowing production of prostaglandins. Synthetic opiates such as morphine mimic endorphins.

TAKE-HOME MESSAGE 30.2

Somatic sensations start with stimulation of sensory receptors in skin, skeletal muscle, and joints. Signals are relayed to the spinal cord, then to the somatosensory cortex.

Visceral sensations begin with stimulation of sensory receptors in the walls of internal organs. Signals are relayed to the spinal cord, and then to many areas in the brain.

Pain is the sensation associated with tissue damage. Endorphins and synthetic pain relievers interfere with signals that inform the brain about pain.

SENSE OF SMELL

A sense of smell allows animals to detect food, mates, or predators, and helps them identify landmarks. An animal's **olfactory receptors** respond to chemicals in the air or water that surrounds it. Binding of specific molecules to these chemoreceptors triggers action potentials that give rise to odor perception.

Most invertebrates sense the world around them primarily through smell. Bilateral invertebrates usually have a concentration of olfactory receptors at their head end. In insects and crustaceans, paired antennae function as the primary olfactory organs. In snails and slugs, a pair of sensory tentacles serve this purpose.

Vertebrates have olfactory receptors in the lining of their nasal cavity. Humans have hundreds of types of receptors, each with endings that bind and respond to a different type of odorant molecule (FIGURE 30.3 ❶). Axons of chemoreceptive sensory neurons extend through the base of the skull and into the brain's olfactory bulb ❷, where they synapse on interneurons ❸. When excited, the interneurons send signals to other brain regions such as the limbic system and the cerebral cortex ❹.

An average person can discriminate between and remember about 10,000 different odors. When you recognize an odor, such as the scent of a rose, you are responding to a distinctive mix of odorant molecules. These

molecules excite a unique subset of your nose's sensory neurons, thus triggering a unique pattern of excitation in the cerebral cortex. Through experience, your brain has come to associate this pattern of excitatory signals with its source.

FIGURE 30.4 {Animated} Taste receptors in the human tongue. Taste buds are clusters of receptor cells and supporting cells inside epithelial papillae. One type, a circular papilla, is shown in section here.

taste bud

hairlike ending of taste receptor

sensory nerve

section through circular papilla

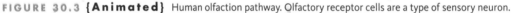

FIGURE 30.3 {Animated} Human olfaction pathway. Olfactory receptor cells are a type of sensory neuron.

olfactory bulb of brain

interneuron

bone of skull

nasal epithelium with supporting cells (tan) and olfactory receptor cells (red, blue, green)

ending of receptor cells in mucosa of nasal cavity

❹ Axons of the interneurons relay the signal onward to the limbic system, cerebral cortex, and other parts of the brain.

❸ In the olfactory bulb, axons of receptor cells synapse with interneurons. Each interneuron receives signals from many receptor cells, all sensitive to the same odorant.

❷ Binding of an odorant triggers an action potential that travels along the axon of the receptor cell. The axon extends through the skull into the brain's olfactory lobe.

❶ Inhaled odorant molecules bind to receptor endings of cells in the nasal lining. Each type of olfactory receptor cell (red, green, or blue here) binds one type of odorant.

CREDITS: (3, 4A, 4C–D) © Cengage Learning; (4B) From Starr/Taggart, Biology: The Unity and Diversity of Life, 8E. © 1998, Cengage Learning.

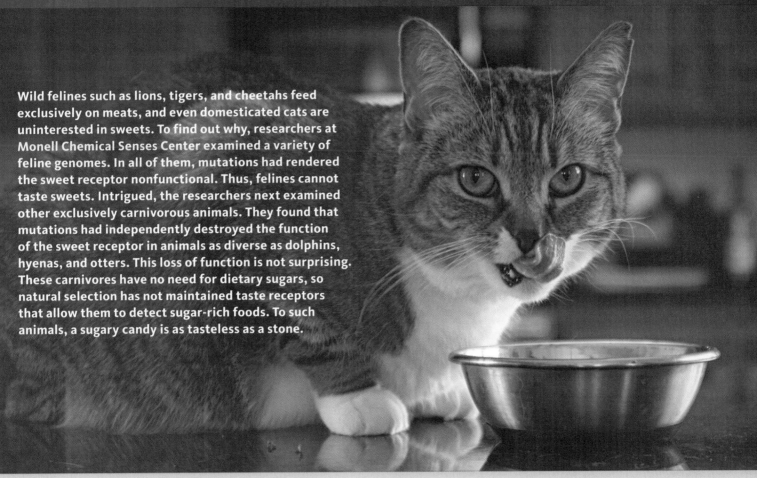

Wild felines such as lions, tigers, and cheetahs feed exclusively on meats, and even domesticated cats are uninterested in sweets. To find out why, researchers at Monell Chemical Senses Center examined a variety of feline genomes. In all of them, mutations had rendered the sweet receptor nonfunctional. Thus, felines cannot taste sweets. Intrigued, the researchers next examined other exclusively carnivorous animals. They found that mutations had independently destroyed the function of the sweet receptor in animals as diverse as dolphins, hyenas, and otters. This loss of function is not surprising. These carnivores have no need for dietary sugars, so natural selection has not maintained taste receptors that allow them to detect sugar-rich foods. To such animals, a sugary candy is as tasteless as a stone.

FIGURE 30.5 Carnivore taste perception.

In addition to environmental odors, many animals produce and detect **pheromones**, chemical communication signals that are secreted by one individual and alter the behavior of another member of its species. For example, a female silk moth releases a sex pheromone that a male silk moth can detect from as far as a kilometer away. The male has receptors for the pheromone on his antennae. In land vertebrates, pheromone receptors are typically clustered in a **vomeronasal organ** at the base of the nasal cavity. Humans have a reduced version of this organ. Whether we make and respond to pheromones remains a matter of debate.

SENSE OF TASTE

Taste receptors are chemoreceptors that help animals avoid poisons and detect appropriate food items. An octopus tastes potential food with receptors in suckers on its tentacles; a fly tastes with receptors in its antennae and feet. Humans taste with taste buds, which are mainly embedded in the upper surface of the tongue (**FIGURE 30.4**). These sensory organs are located in specialized epithelial structures, called papillae, that look like raised bumps on the tongue's upper surface.

Perceived taste arises from a combination of signals produced by different types of taste receptors. Humans have receptors that respond to *sweetness* (elicited by glucose and the other simple sugars), *sourness* (acids), *saltiness* (sodium chloride or other salts), *bitterness* (plant toxins, including alkaloids), *umami* (elicited by amino acids such as glutamate, which is found in cheese and aged meat), and— as recently discovered—*fattiness* (fatty acids).

All mammals generally have the same types of taste receptors, although some carnivores have lost the ability to taste sweet (**FIGURE 30.5**).

---

olfactory receptor Chemoreceptor involved in the sense of smell.
pheromone Chemical that serves as a communication signal among members of an animal species.
taste receptor Chemoreceptor involved in the sense of taste.
vomeronasal organ Pheromone-detecting organ of vertebrates.

DIVERSITY OF VISUAL SYSTEMS

Some invertebrates, such as earthworms, have photoreceptors dispersed across the body surface or clustered in parts of it. They use light as a cue to orient their body or adjust their biological clock, but they do not have a sense of vision. Vision is detection of light in a way that provides a mental image of objects in the environment. It requires eyes and a brain with a capacity to interpret visual stimuli. Eyes are sensory organs with photoreceptors. Absorption of light by pigment molecules in a photoreceptor triggers action potentials that are sent to the brain.

Formation of an image requires an eye with a **lens**, a transparent structure that bends light rays so they converge on photoreceptors. Insects have **compound eyes** with many lens-containing units (**FIGURE 30.6A**). The insect brain constructs images based on the light intensities detected by the different units. Compound eyes do not provide the clearest vision, but they are great at detecting movement.

Cephalopod mollusks such as squids and octopuses have the most complex eyes of any invertebrate (**FIGURE 30.6B**). Their **camera eyes** have an adjustable opening that allows light to enter a dark chamber. Each eye has a single lens that focuses incoming light onto a **retina**, a tissue densely packed with photoreceptors. The retina of a camera eye is analogous to the light-sensitive film used in a traditional film camera. Compared to compound eyes, camera eyes provide a more defined and detailed image.

Vertebrates also have camera eyes. Because vertebrates are not closely related to cephalopod mollusks, camera eyes are presumed to have evolved independently in the two lineages. This is an example of morphological convergence (Section 16.7).

Many vertebrates have eyes on either side of their head, an arrangement that maximizes their visual field (the portion of their environment that they can see). Primates, including humans, have eyes at the front of their head. Having eyes that face forward enables depth perception, because the same visual field can be surveyed simultaneously from two slightly different positions. The brain compares the overlapping information it receives to determine the distance between objects in the visual field.

ANATOMY OF THE HUMAN EYE

A human eyeball sits in a protective, cuplike, bony cavity called the orbit. Skeletal muscles that run from the rear of the eye to bones of the orbit move the eyeball. Eyelids, eyelashes, and tears protect the eye tissues. Periodic blinking spreads a film of tears over the eyeball's exposed surface. A protective mucous membrane, called the conjunctiva, lines the inner surface of eyelids and folds back to cover

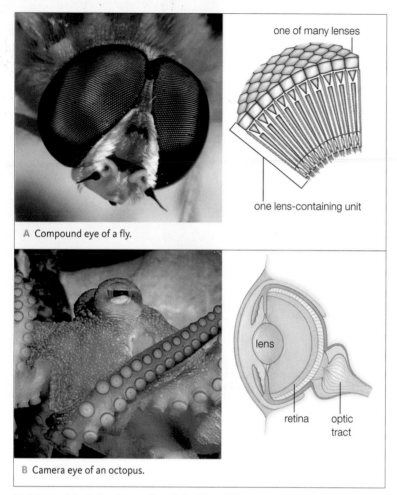

A Compound eye of a fly.

one of many lenses

one lens-containing unit

B Camera eye of an octopus.

lens

retina   optic tract

FIGURE 30.6 Two types of invertebrate eye.

sclera

choroid

iris

lens

pupil

cornea

aqueous humor

ciliary muscle

vitreous body

retina

fovea

optic disk (blind spot)

part of optic nerve

FIGURE 30.7 {Animated} Structure of the human eye.

CREDITS: (6A) left, Ablestock.com/photos.com; right, From Starr/Taggart/Evers/Starr, Biology, 13E. © 2013 Cengage Learning; (6B) left, G. Ziesler/ZEFA, right, After M. Gardiner, The Biology of Vertebrates, McGraw-Hill, 1972; (7) © Cengage Learning.

the back and sides of the eye's outer surface. Conjunctivitis, commonly called pinkeye, is an inflammation of this membrane. It is caused by a viral or bacterial infection.

The eyeball is spherical with a three-layered structure (**FIGURE 30.7**). A **cornea** made of transparent crystallin protein covers the front of the eyeball. A dense, white, fibrous sclera covers the rest of the eye's outer surface.

The eye's middle layer includes the choroid, which is darkened by the brownish pigment melanin. This dark layer prevents light reflection within the eyeball. Attached to the choroid and suspended behind the cornea is a muscular, doughnut-shaped **iris**. Light enters the eye's interior through the **pupil**, an opening at the center of the iris. Smooth muscles of the iris adjust the pupil's diameter. The pupil shrinks in bright light and widens in low light, thus regulating the amount of light that enters the eye.

A ciliary body—a tissue that consists of muscle, fibers, and secretory cells—attaches to the choroid and holds the lens in place behind the pupil. The stretchable, transparent lens is shaped like a bulging disk about 1 centimeter (1/2 inch) across.

The eye has two internal chambers. The ciliary body produces aqueous humor, the fluid in the anterior chamber. A jellylike fluid called vitreous humor fills the chamber behind the lens. The innermost layer of the eye, the retina, lines the rear of this chamber.

The cornea and lens both bend incoming light so that rays converge on the retina. The image formed on the retina is upside down and the mirror image of the real world:

The brain makes the necessary adjustments so you perceive the environment in the correct orientation.

camera eye Eye with an adjustable opening and a single lens that focuses light on a retina.
compound eye Eye that has many units, each with its own lens.
cornea Clear, protective covering at the front of a vertebrate eye; helps focus light on the retina.
iris Circular muscle that adjusts the shape of the pupil to regulate how much light enters the eye.
lens Disk-shaped structure that bends light rays so they fall on an eye's photoreceptors.
pupil Adjustable opening that allows light into a camera eye.
retina Photoreceptor-containing layer of tissue in an eye.
visual accommodation Process of making adjustments to lens shape so light from an object falls on the retina.

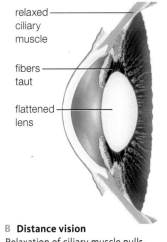

A **Near vision**	B **Distance vision**
Contraction of ciliary muscle allows fibers to slacken and the lens becomes fatter and rounder.	Relaxation of ciliary muscle pulls fibers taut, stretching the lens so it becomes thinner and flatter.

FIGURE 30.8 Human visual accommodation.

FIGURE IT OUT: The thicker a lens, the more it bends light. Does the lens bend light more in distance vision or close vision?

Answer: Light rays are bent more with close vision.

FOCUSING MECHANISMS

When you see an object, you are perceiving light rays reflected from that object. Light rays reflected from near and distant objects hit the eye at different angles. By the process of **visual accommodation**, the ciliary muscle in an eye adjusts the shape of the lens, causing all rays to become focused in such a way that they form an image on the retina.

Curvature of the lens determines the extent to which light rays will bend. A flat lens will focus light from a distant object onto the retina. However, the lens must be rounder to focus light from close objects. When you read, the ciliary muscle contracts, and fibers that connect this muscle to the lens slacken. Decreased tension on the lens allows it to round up enough to focus light from the page onto your retina (**FIGURE 30.8A**). Gaze into the distance and the ciliary muscle around the lens relaxes, allowing the lens to flatten (**FIGURE 30.8B**).

TAKE-HOME MESSAGE 30.4

Vision requires eyes with a dense array of photoreceptors and a brain that integrates signals from them.

A lens bends light so it falls on photoreceptors. A compound eye consists of many units, each with its own lens. A camera eye with a single lens evolved independently in cephalopods and vertebrates.

Your eye adjusts the shape of the lens depending on whether you are focusing on a near object or a distant one.

As explained in the previous section, the cornea and lens bend light rays so they converge on the retina. The human retina contains two types of light-detecting cells. Each has stacks of membranous disks that contain pigment (**FIGURE 30.9A**). Visual pigments (called opsins) are derived from vitamin A, which is why a deficiency in this vitamin can impair vision. **Rod cells**, the most abundant photoreceptor cells, detect dim light and respond to changes in light intensity. They provide coarse vision and detect motion. In a human eye, rods are concentrated at the edges of the retina. All rods have the same pigment (rhodopsin), which absorbs light in the green-blue part of the spectrum.

Cone cells provide acute daytime vision and allow us to detect colors. There are three types of cone cell, each with a slightly different version of the cone pigment (photopsin). One cone pigment absorbs mainly red light, another absorbs mainly blue, and a third absorbs green. Normal human color vision requires all three kinds of cones. The **fovea**, a pit in the central region of the retina, has the greatest density of cones. With normal vision, most light rays fall on the fovea.

The retina has a multilayered organization (**FIGURE 30.9B**). It forms during development as an outgrowth from the brain, and so is considered an extension of the brain. Like other brain tissue, the retina includes interneurons. When a pigment in a rod cell or cone cell absorbs light, action potentials flow from that cell to three types of interneurons (horizontal cells, bipolar cells, and amacrine cells) in the layers above. These interneurons integrate signals from the photoreceptors, and send signals to other interneurons called ganglion cells. Bundled axons of ganglion cells constitute the optic nerve.

The region of the retina through which the optic nerve exits lacks photoreceptors. It cannot respond to light and thus causes a "blind spot" in our vision (**FIGURE 30.9B**). We all have a blind spot in each eye, but we usually do not notice it because the information missed by one eye is provided to the brain by the other.

Signals from the right visual field of each eye travel along an optic nerve to the brain's left hemisphere. Signals from the left visual field travel to the right hemisphere. Each optic nerve ends in a brain region (the lateral geniculate nucleus) that integrates incoming signals. From here, the signals are conveyed to the visual cortex, where the final integration process produces visual sensations.

---

cone cell Photoreceptor that provides sharp vision and allows detection of color.
fovea Retinal region where cone cells are most concentrated.
rod cell Photoreceptor that is active in dim light; provides coarse perception of image and detects motion.

A The two types of photoreceptor cells in the retina.

cone cell
rod cell
stacked, pigmented membranous disks

horizontal cell
bipolar cell
amacrine cell
ganglion cell
cone cell
rod cell
incoming rays of light

B Multilayered structure of the retina.

blood vessel
start of optic nerve (blind spot)
fovea (region with most cones)

C Magnified view of the retina as seen through the pupil.

FIGURE 30.9 {Animated} Structure of the retina. The two types of photoreceptors, rods and cones, lie at the very rear of the retina, beneath layers of signal-processing neurons.

TAKE-HOME MESSAGE 30.5

When stimulated by light, rod cells and cone cells send signals to interneurons in the retina. These neurons integrate signals, then send action potentials along the optic nerve to the brain. Final integration of signals occurs in the visual cortex.

CREDITS: (9A,B) Based on www.occipita.cfa.cmu.edu; (9C) Courtesy of Dr. Bryan Jones, University of Utah School of Medicine.

Sometimes one or more types of cones are missing or impaired. The result is color blindness. With red–green color blindness, an X-linked recessive trait (Section 14.3), it is difficult to distinguish between red and green. Like other X-linked traits, red–green color blindness shows up most often in males. In people of European descent, about 8 percent of males and 0.5 percent of females are affected. The trait is about half as common in Africans and Asians.

A variety of problems can prevent light rays from converging on the retina as they should. With astigmatism, vision is blurred at all distances by an unevenly curved cornea. With nearsightedness, distant objects are out of focus. This can occur if the distance from the cornea to the retina is longer than normal (**FIGURE 30.10A**), or when ciliary muscles contract too much. With farsightedness, close objects are out of focus, either because the distance from the cornea to the retina is unusually short (**FIGURE 30.10B**) or ciliary muscles are too weak. Either way, light rays from nearby objects get focused behind the retina.

Glasses, contact lenses, or surgery can correct most focusing problems. Glasses and contact lenses bend light before it reaches the eye. Laser surgery (LASIK) reshapes the cornea. Typically, LASIK can eliminate the need for glasses during most activities, although some older adults still need reading glasses. However, chronic eye irritation is a common complication.

As people age, changes in the structure of proteins in their lens often affect vision. The lens becomes less flexible, so most people over age forty have somewhat impaired near vision. Other changes to lens proteins can cloud the lens, a condition called a cataract. Smoking, steroid use, and some diseases such as diabetes promote cataract formation, as does excessive exposure to ultraviolet radiation. Typically, both eyes are affected. At first, a cataract scatters light and blurs vision (**FIGURE 30.11A**). Eventually, the lens may become fully opaque, causing blindness. Worldwide, about 16 million people remain blinded by age-related cataracts. Cataract surgery, a common procedure in developed countries, can restore normal vision by replacing a clouded lens with a clear plastic implant.

In the United States, the leading cause of blindness among older adults is age-related macular degeneration (AMD). The macula, the part of the retina around and including the fovea, is essential to clear vision. Destruction of photoreceptors in the macula clouds the center of the visual field more than the periphery (**FIGURE 30.11B**). Damage caused by AMD usually cannot be reversed, but drug injections and laser therapy can slow its progression. A treatment involving cells derived from embryonic stem cells is also being tested.

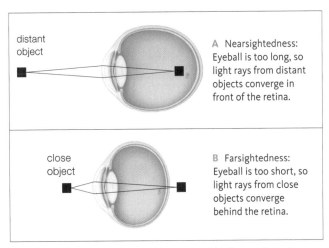

A Nearsightedness: Eyeball is too long, so light rays from distant objects converge in front of the retina.

B Farsightedness: Eyeball is too short, so light rays from close objects converge behind the retina.

FIGURE 30.10 Focusing problems caused by abnormal eye shape.

A With cataracts.

B With macular degeneration.

FIGURE 30.11 Simulations of vision with two common age-related disorders.

Glaucoma results when too much aqueous humor builds up inside the eyeball. The increased fluid pressure damages blood vessels and ganglion cells. It can also interfere with peripheral vision and visual processing. Although we often associate chronic glaucoma with old age, the conditions that give rise to the disorder start to develop long before symptoms arise. Screening for glaucoma allows doctors to detect the increased fluid pressure before the damage becomes severe. They can then manage the disorder with medication, surgery, or both.

TAKE-HOME MESSAGE 30.6

Defective cone cells result in color blindness.

A misshapen eyeball can cause nearsightedness or farsightedness. A lens that has become inflexible with age also causes farsightedness.

Other age-related vision disorders include cataracts (clouding of the lens), macular degeneration (loss of photoreceptors), and glaucoma (excessive aqueous humor).

PROPERTIES OF SOUND

Hearing is the detection of sound, a form of mechanical energy. Sounds arise when a vibrating object causes pressure variations in air, water, or some other medium. When you clap your hands or shout, you create pressure waves that move through the air. The amplitude (height) of those waves determines how loud a sound is (FIGURE 30.12A). We measure loudness in decibels. The human ear can detect a 1-decibel difference between sounds. Normal conversation is about 60 decibels, a food blender operating at high speed produces a sound of about 90 decibels, and a chain saw makes a 100-decibel noise.

A sound's frequency, the number of wave cycles per second, or hertz (Hz), determines its pitch. The more waves per second, the higher the pitch (FIGURE 30.12B). Humans can hear sounds in the range of 20 to 20,000 Hz.

VERTEBRATE EARS

Water readily transfers vibrations to body tissues, so fishes do not need elaborate ears to detect sound waves. Air is less efficient at transferring sound waves to body tissues, so vertebrates that moved onto land faced a sensory challenge.

Features that maximize the efficiency of sound transfer are most highly developed in mammalian ears (FIGURE 30.13). Unlike amphibians and reptiles, most mammals have an **outer ear** that collects sound waves and funnels them inward ❶. A skin-covered flap of cartilage called the pinna projects from the side of the head. Sound waves collected by the pinna enter the auditory canal, which is the air-filled passage that leads to the middle ear.

The **middle ear**, which consists of the eardrum and middle ear bones, amplifies sound waves and transmits them to the inner ear. An eardrum, or tympanic membrane, first evolved in amphibians, and in these animals it is visible as a round area on each side of the head. In mammals, sound waves that travel through the auditory canal make the eardrum vibrate. Behind the eardrum, an air-filled cavity holds three small bones commonly referred to as the hammer, anvil, and stirrup ❷. These bones transmit the force of sound waves from the eardrum to the inner ear.

The **inner ear**, which consists of the vestibular apparatus and the cochlea, functions in hearing and balance. We discuss the sense of balance in the next section. Here we focus on the sound-detecting function of the **cochlea**, a pea-sized, fluid-filled structure that resembles a coiled snail shell (the Greek *koklias* means snail). Membranes divide the interior of the cochlea into three fluid-filled ducts ❸. When sound waves make the three tiny bones of the middle ear vibrate, the stirrup pushes against the oval window. This elastic membrane is the boundary between the middle and inner ear. Each time the oval window bows inward, the movement creates a pressure wave in the fluid inside the cochlea. Waves that travel through the cochlear fluid cause the walls of the cochlea's three ducts to vibrate.

FIGURE 30.12 Properties of sound waves.

Soft
Loud

A Same frequency, different amplitude.

Low note
High note

B Same amplitude, different frequency.

FIGURE 30.13 {**Animated**} Structure and function of the human ear.

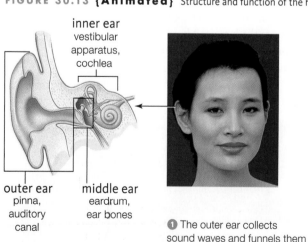

inner ear
vestibular apparatus, cochlea

outer ear
pinna, auditory canal

middle ear
eardrum, ear bones

❶ The outer ear collects sound waves and funnels them to the middle ear.

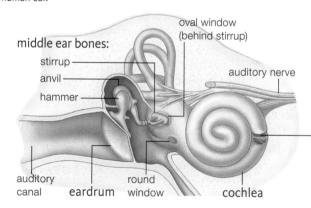

middle ear bones:
stirrup
anvil
hammer

oval window (behind stirrup)

auditory nerve

auditory canal
eardrum
round window
cochlea

❷ The middle ear amplifies sound. Arrival of sound waves via the auditory canal causes the eardrum to vibrate. Middle ear bones transmit these vibrations to the inner ear's fluid-filled cochlea.

A structure called the organ of Corti sits on the membrane at the base of the middle duct (the basilar membrane). The organ of Corti contains mechanoreceptors that are called hair cells because they have tufts of hairlike nonmotile cilia that protrude into an overlying membrane ❹. When pressure waves cause this membrane to move, the mechanical energy deforms the hair cell plasma membrane just enough to let ions slip across it and stimulate an action potential. An auditory nerve carries action potentials from each cochlea to the brain.

The louder the sound, the more hair cells become excited, and the more action potentials flow to the brain. Perceived pitch depends on which part of the cochlea membrane vibrates most. High-pitched sounds vibrate one area and low-pitched sounds vibrate another. More vibrations make more hair cells in that region fire.

cochlea Coiled, fluid-filled structure in the inner ear that holds the mechanoreceptors involved in hearing.
inner ear Fluid-filled vestibular apparatus and cochlea.
middle ear Eardrum and the tiny bones that transfer sound to the inner ear.
outer ear External ear (pinna) and the air-filled auditory canal.

TAKE-HOME MESSAGE 30.7

The mammalian outer ear collects sound waves and directs them to the middle ear.

In the middle ear, vibrations of the eardrum are amplified via movement of small bones. These bones set fluid in the cochlea of the inner ear in motion.

Movement of fluid in cochlea ducts results in excitation of hair cells. An auditory nerve carries action potentials from each ear to the brain.

PEOPLE MATTER

National Geographic Grantee
DR. FERNANDO MONTEALEGRE-Z
studies insect hearing.

Many animals hear sounds outside our range of hearing. Elephants, giraffes, and whales communicate through infrasound, which is pitched too low for us to hear. Bats, rodents, and many insects communicate by way of ultrasound, which is too high for us to hear.

Fernando Montealegre-Z (University of Lincoln, UK) studies ultrasound production and hearing in katydids, which are grasshopper-like insects. Katydids make sounds with their wings, and detect them with ears on their forelegs. Montealegre-Z found that one South American katydid has ears that function remarkably like ours. Each of its forelegs has two eardrums that, like our eardrums, vibrate in response to sound waves. A lever functions like bones of our middle ear to transmit vibrations from the eardrums to a fluid-filled organ analogous to a human cochlea.

Another katydid that Montealegre-Z discovered and is currently studying makes the highest-pitched sound of any known animal. It produces and hears sounds at frequencies as high as 150,000 hertz.

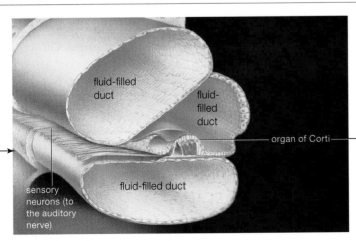

fluid-filled duct

fluid-filled duct

organ of Corti

fluid-filled duct

sensory neurons (to the auditory nerve)

❸ Movement of a bone against the oval window creates pressure waves inside the fluid-filled ducts of the cochlea (shown here in cross-section).

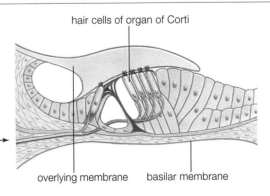

hair cells of organ of Corti

overlying membrane   basilar membrane

❹ Movement of the basilar membrane beneath the organ of Corti bends the organ's hair cells against an overlying membrane. This bending causes action potentials that travel along the auditory nerve to the brain.

CREDITS: (13-4) © Cengage Learning; (in text) Courtesy of Fernando Montealegre-Z.

A Vestibular apparatus inside a human ear.

B Components of one of the organs inside a semicircular canal.

FIGURE 30.14 {Animated} Organs of equilibrium.

Organs of equilibrium monitor the body's position and motions, providing what we commonly refer to as our sense of balance. In vertebrates, the fluid-filled **vestibular apparatus** in the inner ear contains the organs of equilibrium. The organs are located in the vestibular apparatus's three semicircular canals and in two sacs called the saccule and utricle (**FIGURE 30.14A**). Organs of equilibrium contain mechanoreceptive hair cells similar to those that function in hearing. Changes in fluid pressure inside the canals and sacs make the cilia of these cells bend, triggering action potentials.

The three **semicircular canals** of the vestibular apparatus function in *dynamic* equilibrium, the special sense related to angular movement and rotation of the head. Among other things, you can use this sense to keep your eyes locked on an object when you turn your head or nod.

The three semicircular canals are oriented at right angles to one another, so moving the head in any direction—front/back, up/down, or left/right—moves the fluid inside at least one of them. An organ of equilibrium rests on the bulging base of each canal. Cilia of its hair cells are embedded in a jellylike mass (**FIGURE 30.14B**). Movement of fluid inside the canal pushes this mass, and the resulting pressure initiates action potentials in hair cells. The brain receives signals from semicircular canals on both sides of the head and integrates this information.

Organs in the saccule and utricle function in *static* equilibrium. They help the brain monitor the head's position in space when you move in a straight line. They also help keep the head upright and maintain posture. In the saccule and utricle, a jellylike mass weighted with calcite crystals lies just above hair cells. Tilt your head, or start or stop moving, and gravity causes this mass to shift. As it shifts, hair cells bend and alter their rate of action potentials.

The brain also takes into account information from the eyes, and from receptors in skin, muscles, and joints. Integration of the information allows perception of the body's position and motion in space.

A stroke, an inner ear infection, or loose particles in the semicircular canals cause vertigo, which is a sensation that the world is moving or spinning around. Vertigo can also arise from conflicting sensory inputs, as when you stand at a great height and look down. The vestibular apparatus reports that you are standing motionless, but your eyes tell your brain that your body is floating in space.

Mismatched signals also cause motion sickness. On a curvy road, passengers in a car experience changes in acceleration and direction that scream "motion" to their vestibular apparatus. At the same time, their eyes, which are viewing the interior of the car, tell their brain that the body is at rest. Driving minimizes motion sickness because the driver focuses on sights outside the car, making visual signals consistent with vestibular signals.

organs of equilibrium Sensory organs that respond to body position and motion; function in sense of balance.
semicircular canals Organs of equilibrium that respond to rotation and angular movement of the head; part of the vestibular apparatus.
vestibular apparatus System of fluid-filled sacs and canals in the inner ear; contains organs of equilibrium.

TAKE-HOME MESSAGE 30.8

Organs of equilibrium in the inner ear inform the brain about the body's position and forces of gravity, velocity, and acceleration.

Application: COCHLEAR IMPLANTS

Education

FIGURE 30.15 Aiden Kenny with cochlear implants. The implants, visible in the x-ray at right, bypass the parts of his ears that do not work and carry electronic signals to his auditory nerves.

TAMMY KENNY REMEMBERS WHEN SHE FIRST LEARNED THAT HER BABY WAS DEAF. "I would just hold him in my arms and cry," she says, "knowing he couldn't hear me. How would he ever get to know me? One time, my husband banged pots together, hoping for a response." Aiden never heard the noise.

He hears banging pots now. In February 2009, when Aiden was 10 months old, surgeons at Johns Hopkins Hospital snaked thin lines with 22 electrodes into each cochlea (FIGURE 30.15). A microphone outside each ear picks up sounds and sends them to a speech processor that converts the sounds into electrical signals. The electrodes in the cochlea pick up these signals and generate action potentials in the appropriate cochlear regions. These action potentials then travel along the auditory nerves to the brain.

"The day they turned on the implant, a month after surgery, we noticed he responded to sound," Tammy Kenny says. "He turned at the sound of my voice. That was amazing." Within months of the surgery, a child who had grown increasingly quiet spoke the words his hearing parents longed for: Mama and Dada. Because Aiden got the implants

at a very young age, he has a good chance of developing clear speech.

Cochlear implants first became available about 30 years ago. Today, more than 220,000 people around the world benefit from these devices.

Deaf individuals who receive a cochlear implant as adults typically do not regain as much of their hearing as people who receive the implants as young children. This is because when a child is born deaf, the brain reorganizes itself. Brain regions that would usually function in hearing do not simply sit idle, but rather are recruited to function in vision. Thus, deaf people often have more acute vision than those with normal hearing. Once this reorganization occurs early in life, it is largely irreversible. The brain of a deaf adult who receives a cochlear implant cannot re-reorganize itself to begin processing auditory information.

Sound perception with an implant is not the same as normal hearing. People who lose their hearing after they know a language learn to associate signals from the implant with what they know of language. People who never heard spoken language before receiving their implant typically require training to learn speech and language.

Summary

SECTION 30.1 The sensory world in which an animal lives depends on the type of sensory receptors it has. Types of receptors include **chemoreceptors**, **thermoreceptors**, **pain receptors**, **mechanoreceptors**, and **photoreceptors**. Some animals have sensory abilities that we do not, such as an ability to detect magnetic fields.

The brain evaluates action potentials from sensory receptors based on which of the nerves delivers them, their frequency, and the number of axons firing. Continued stimulation of a receptor can lead to **sensory adaptation**. **Sensation** is detection of a stimulus, whereas **perception** involves assigning meaning to a sensation.

SECTION 30.2 The general senses arise from receptors throughout the body. **Somatic sensations** arise from receptors in the skin and in skeletal muscles. Signals from these receptors flow to the somatosensory cortex, where interneurons are organized like maps of individual parts of the body surface. **Visceral sensations** originate from receptors in the walls of soft organs and tend to be diffuse. **Pain** is the perception of tissue damage. **Endorphins** lessen signals about pain.

SECTION 30.3 The senses of taste and smell involve chemoreceptors. In humans, **taste receptors** are concentrated in taste buds of the tongue and mouth. **Olfactory receptors** line the nasal passages. Many vertebrates have a **vomeronasal organ** that responds to **pheromones**, which are chemical signals that convey social information among animal members of the same species.

SECTIONS 30.4–30.6 An eye is a sensory organ that contains a dense array of photoreceptors. Insects have a **compound eye**, with many individual units. Each unit has a **lens**, a structure that bends light rays so they fall on photoreceptors. Like squids and octopuses, humans have **camera eyes**, with an adjustable opening that lets in light, and a single lens that focuses the light on a **retina**. A transparent **cornea** covers the front of the human eye and helps bend light rays. Light enters the eye through the **pupil**, the adjustable opening at the center of the **iris**. **Visual accommodation** is the alteration of lens shape to focus on objects at different distances.

Rod cells and **cone cells** are the eyes' photoreceptors. Cone cells provide color vision and detailed images. They are most abundant in the **fovea**.

Common vision disorders result from defective or degenerating photoreceptors, misshapen eyes, a clouded lens, or excess aqueous humor.

SECTIONS 30.7–30.8 Sound is a form of mechanical energy—pressure waves that vary in amplitude and frequency. Humans have a pair of ears with three functional regions. The **outer ear** collects sound waves. The eardrum and tiny bones of the **middle ear** amplify sound waves and transmit them to the **inner ear**. The inner ear includes the vestibular apparatus and the **cochlea**: a coiled, fluid-filled structure with three ducts. Pressure waves traveling through the fluid inside the cochlea bend hair cells embedded in one of the cochlear membranes. Sounds get sorted out according to their frequency. Mechanical energy of pressure waves is converted to action potentials that are relayed along auditory nerves to the brain.

The **vestibular apparatus**, a system of fluid-filled sacs and canals in the inner ear, houses **organs of equilibrium** that detect forces related to the body's position and motion. The **semicircular canals** of the vestibular apparatus respond to rotational and angular movements of the head.

SECTION 30.9 Cochlear implants allow deaf people to perceive sound. They convert sounds to electrical signals that cause action potentials.

Self-Quiz

1. The pain of a stomachache is an example of a _____ .
   a. somatic sensation   c. sensory adaptation
   b. visceral sensation   d. spinal reflex

2. _____ is a decrease in the response to an ongoing stimulus.
   a. Perception   c. Sensory adaptation
   b. Visual accommodation   d. Somatic sensation

3. Which is a somatic sensation?
   a. taste   c. touch   e. a through c
   b. smell   d. hearing   f. all of the above

4. Chemoreceptors play a role in the sense of _____ .
   a. taste   c. touch   e. both a and b
   b. smell   d. hearing   f. all of the above

5. In the _____ , neurons are arranged like maps that correspond to different parts of the body surface.
   a. visual cortex   c. organ of Corti
   b. retina   d. somatosensory cortex

6. Mechanoreceptors in the _____ send signals to the brain about the body's position and motion.
   a. eye   b. ear   c. tongue   d. nose

7. The middle ear functions in _____ .
   a. detecting shifts in body position
   b. amplifying and transmitting sound waves
   c. sorting sound waves out by frequency

8. Substance P _____ .
   a. increases pain-related signals
   b. is a natural painkiller
   c. is the active ingredient in aspirin

9. The organ of Corti contains receptors that signal in response to _____ .
   a. heat   b. sound   c. light   d. pheromones

Occupational Noise and Hearing Loss Frequent exposure to noise of a particular pitch can cause death of hair cells in the part of the cochlea's coil that responds to that pitch.

FIGURE 30.16 Effects of age and occupational noise exposure. The graph shows the threshold hearing capacities (in decibels) for sounds of different frequencies (given in hertz, or cycles per second) in a 25-year-old carpenter (●), a 50-year-old carpenter (●), and a 50-year-old who did not have any on-the-job noise exposure (●).

Many workers are at risk for such frequency-specific hearing loss because they work with or around noisy power tools. Taking precautions such as using ear plugs to reduce sound exposure is important. Noise-induced hearing loss can be prevented, but once it occurs it is irreversible. Dead hair cells are not replaced.

FIGURE 30.16 shows the threshold decibel levels at which sounds of different frequencies can be detected by an average 25-year-old carpenter, a 50-year-old carpenter, and a 50-year-old who has not been exposed to on-the-job noise. Sound frequencies are given in hertz (cycles per second). The more cycles per second, the higher the pitch.

1. Which sound frequency was most easily detected by all three people?
2. How loud did a 1,000-hertz sound have to be for the 50-year-old carpenter to detect it?
3. Which of the three people had the best hearing in the range of 4,000 to 6,000 hertz? Which had the worst?
4. Based on these data, would you conclude that the hearing decline in the 50-year-old carpenter was caused by age or by job-related noise exposure?

10. Color vision begins with stimulation of _____ .
    a. hair cells   b. rod cells   c. cone cells   d. neuroglia

11. Visual accommodation involves adjustment to the shape of the _____ .
    a. conjunctiva   b. retina   c. orbit   d. lens

12. When you view a close object, your lens gets _____ .
    a. flatter   b. rounder   c. darker   d. cloudier

13. _____ in the vestibular apparatus function in balance.
    a. Hair cells   b. Rod cells   c. Cone cells   d. Neuroglia

14. _____ are chemical signals released by one individual that affect the behavior of another individual.
    a. Hormones   c. Pheromones
    b. Neurotransmitters   d. Endorphins

15. Match each structure with its description.
    ___ rod cell   a. protects eyeball
    ___ cochlea   b. detect head movements
    ___ lens   c. detects pheromones
    ___ sclera   d. detects dim light
    ___ cone cell   e. contains chemoreceptors
    ___ taste bud   f. focuses rays of light
    ___ semicircular   g. sorts out sound waves
        canals   h. detects color
    ___ pinna   i. collects sound waves
    ___ vomeronasal organ

Critical Thinking

1. If you injure your leg, pain prevents you from putting too much weight on the affected leg. Shielding the injury gives it time to heal. An injured insect shows no such shielding response when its leg is injured. Some have cited the lack of such a response as evidence that insects do not feel pain. On the other hand, insects do produce substances similar to one of our natural painkillers. Is the presence of these compounds in insects sufficient evidence to conclude that they do feel pain?

2. In humans, photoreceptors are most concentrated at the very back of the eyeball. In birds of prey, including owls and hawks, the greatest density of photoreceptors is in a region closer to the eyeball's roof. When these birds are on the ground, they cannot see objects even slightly above them unless they turn their head almost upside down as shown at the *left*. What is the adaptive advantage of this type of retina structure?

An arctic hare sheds the white winter coat that hid it against snow to reveal a dark summer coat. The hormone melatonin governs such seasonal changes.

31

ENDOCRINE CONTROL

Links to Earlier Concepts

This chapter discusses steroids (Section 3.3) and proteins (3.4) that act as hormones. It draws on your knowledge of lipid bilayers (5.6), sex determination (10.3), sympathetic nerve function (29.7), and brain anatomy (29.9). There are many examples of negative feedback mechanisms (28.9). Although we focus mainly on the vertebrate endocrine system, we also consider hormonal control of arthropod molting (23.9).

KEY CONCEPTS

HORMONE ACTION

A hormone travels in the blood and binds to receptors on or inside target cells. Binding of the hormone to the receptor triggers a response in the target cell.

VERTEBRATE ENDOCRINE GLANDS

All vertebrate endocrine systems include most of the same hormone-producing glands. The endocrine system interacts closely with the nervous system.

A CENTRAL CONTROL POINT

The hypothalamus and pituitary gland deep in the vertebrate forebrain are connected structurally and functionally. Together, they coordinate activities of many other glands.

RESPONSES TO CHANGE

Some glands alter their secretion of hormones in response to internal changes such as a shift in blood glucose level, or to external factors such as changes in day length.

INVERTEBRATE HORMONES

Some invertebrate hormones are homologous to vertebrate hormones, whereas others are unique to a specific invertebrate lineage.

Animal hormones are intercellular communication molecules that are secreted by endocrine cells, distributed by the blood, and typically act some distance from their source. Hormone-secreting cells lie adjacent to tiny blood vessels (capillaries), and hormones enter the bloodstream by moving through tiny openings in the walls of these vessels.

Cells throughout the body are exposed to a hormone, but only cells with appropriate receptors respond to it. Cells with those receptors are the hormone's target cells. A hormone receptor is a protein that transduces the hormonal signal into a form that can alter the activity of a target cell.

CATEGORIES OF HORMONES

There are two major categories of hormones, those derived from amino acids and those derived from cholesterol. **Amino acid–derived hormones** include amine hormones (modified amino acids), peptide hormones (short chains of amino acids), and protein hormones (longer chains of amino acids). These hormones are typically polar, so they dissolve easily in blood, which is mostly water. Like other polar molecules, protein and peptide hormones cannot diffuse across a lipid bilayer. These hormones always bind to receptors at the plasma membrane of a target cell.

FIGURE 31.1 Mechanisms of hormone action.

FIGURE IT OUT: Why does protein hormone action require a second messenger?

Answer: Protein hormones do not enter target cells.

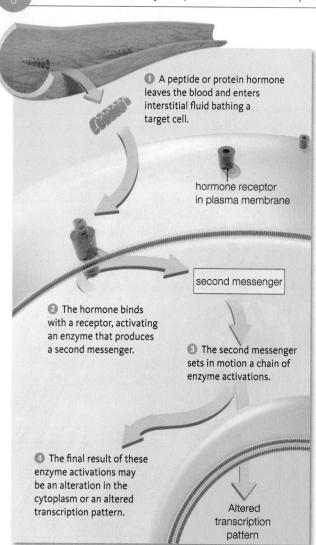

❶ A peptide or protein hormone leaves the blood and enters interstitial fluid bathing a target cell.

hormone receptor in plasma membrane

second messenger

❷ The hormone binds with a receptor, activating an enzyme that produces a second messenger.

❸ The second messenger sets in motion a chain of enzyme activations.

❹ The final result of these enzyme activations may be an alteration in the cytoplasm or an altered transcription pattern.

Altered transcription pattern

A Protein and peptide hormones act by way of a second messenger.

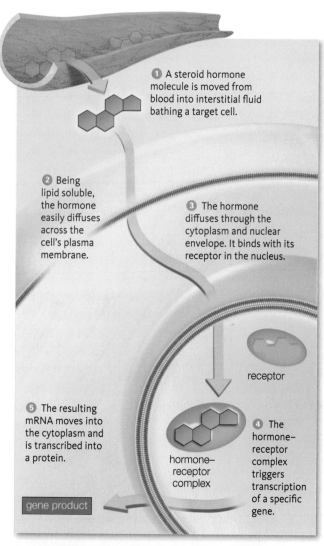

❶ A steroid hormone molecule is moved from blood into interstitial fluid bathing a target cell.

❷ Being lipid soluble, the hormone easily diffuses across the cell's plasma membrane.

❸ The hormone diffuses through the cytoplasm and nuclear envelope. It binds with its receptor in the nucleus.

receptor

❺ The resulting mRNA moves into the cytoplasm and is transcribed into a protein.

hormone–receptor complex

❹ The hormone–receptor complex triggers transcription of a specific gene.

gene product

B Steroid hormones can enter and act inside a target cell.

When a hormone binds to a receptor in the plasma membrane, a second messenger transmits the signal into the cell (FIGURE 31.1A). A second messenger is a molecule that forms inside a cell in response to an external signal, and it triggers a change in cellular activities. Formation of the second messenger sets in motion a chain of events that bring about the target cell's response.

In many cases, the cascade of reactions that result from second messenger formation culminates in activation of an enzyme already present in the cytoplasm. Consider glucagon, a protein hormone that is secreted by your pancreas and targets cells in your liver. As you may recall, the liver contains the body's main store of glycogen (Section 7.7). Binding of glucagon to its receptor in the plasma membrane of a liver cell sets in motion a chain of reactions that results in activation of an enzyme that breaks down glycogen. Breakdown of glycogen releases glucose. As you will learn in Section 31.8, glucagon helps regulate the concentration of glucose in your blood.

Sometimes the target of one hormone is another endocrine cell and second messenger formation affects hormone secretion by the target cell. We call a hormone that encourages hormone secretion by its target cell, a releasing hormone. For example, the pituitary gland in your brain produces a releasing hormone that targets the thyroid gland in your neck. Binding of the releasing hormone to thyroid cells sets in motion events that result in an influx of calcium ions into cells of the thyroid. This calcium influx causes exocytosis of vesicles filled with thyroid hormone. Other hormones, called inhibiting hormones, discourage their target cells from secreting a hormone.

The effects of second messenger formation sometimes extend into the nucleus, bringing about changes in gene expression. However, protein and peptide hormones cannot enter the nucleus and directly affect genes.

Steroid hormones, which are synthesized from cholesterol, do have direct effects on gene expression. Steroid hormones are nonpolar, so they dissolve in lipids, but not in water. To travel through the bloodstream, a steroid hormone must be attached to a water-soluble plasma protein. A steroid hormone typically diffuses into a target cell and binds to receptors, forming a hormone–receptor complex. The receptor protein may be in the cytoplasm or in the nucleus. In either case, the hormone–receptor complex functions in the nucleus, where it binds to a promoter in the target cell's DNA. Recall that a promoter is a region where RNA polymerase binds (Section 9.2). Binding of the hormone–receptor complex to a promoter increases or decreases the rate of transcription of a nearby gene or set of genes. Therefore, the hormone–receptor complex is a transcription factor (Section 10.1). FIGURE 31.1B illustrates this mechanism of steroid hormone action.

Once secreted into the blood, hormones remain active for a limited period. Some are taken up and broken down in the kidney or the liver. Others are taken into the cell they affect and broken down there. The amount of time it takes to clear a hormone from the blood varies. Hormones derived from amino acids are typically cleared from the blood more quickly than steroid hormones.

HORMONE RECEPTOR FUNCTION

Many hormones target more than one type of cell, and they elicit a different response in each cell type. For example, ADH (antidiuretic hormone) affects urine formation when it binds to receptors on vertebrate kidney cells. It also triggers contraction when it binds to receptors on smooth muscle cells in blood vessel walls. The differing responses to a single hormone are an outcome of variations in the structure of ADH receptors. In each kind of cell, a different kind of receptor summons up a different response.

Mutations that alter receptor proteins can interfere with hormone function. For example, people affected by total androgen insensitivity syndrome are genetically male (XY) and make the male sex hormone testosterone, but lack functional receptors for it. In such individuals, embryonic testes form, but do not descend into the scrotum. Genitals appear female, so affected individuals are typically identified as girls at birth. Often their condition is not discovered until puberty. Being genetically male, they do not have ovaries, so they never develop breasts, or menstruate.

---

amino acid–derived hormone An amine (modified amino acid), peptide, or protein that functions as a hormone.
animal hormone Intercellular signaling molecule that is secreted by an endocrine gland or cell and travels in the blood.
second messenger Molecule that forms inside a cell when a hormone binds to a receptor in the plasma membrane; sets in motion reactions that alter activity inside the cell.
steroid hormone Lipid-soluble hormone derived from cholesterol.

TAKE-HOME MESSAGE 31.1

Hormones are intercellular communication molecules derived from amino acids or cholesterol.

Blood distributes hormones throughout the body, but a hormone only affects those cells that have receptors for it.

Protein and peptide hormones must bind to receptors at the cell surface, whereas steroid hormones can bind inside cells.

Variations in receptors allow different types of cells to respond differently to the same hormone.

Endocrine glands are aggregations of epithelial cells that produce and secrete hormones into the blood. In addition to the major glands, cells of many internal organs such as the small intestine and heart contain some hormone-secreting endocrine cells. All endocrine glands and cells are collectively referred to as an animal's endocrine system. FIGURE 31.2 and TABLE 31.1 provide an overview of the main glands of the human endocrine system and the hormones they produce. Other vertebrates generally have the same glands and produce the same hormones.

Portions of the endocrine system and nervous system are so closely linked that scientists sometimes refer to the two systems collectively as the neuroendocrine system. Both endocrine glands and neurons receive signals from the hypothalamus, a command center in the forebrain (Section 29.9). Most organs respond to both hormones and signals from the nervous system.

Hormones influence brain development, both before and after birth. They also affect nervous processes such as sleep–wake cycles, emotion, mood, and memory. Conversely, the nervous system regulates hormone secretion. For example, stimulation of the sympathetic nervous system (such as by a stressful situation) increases the secretion of some hormones and decreases the secretion of others.

endocrine gland Aggregation of epithelial cells that secrete a hormone or hormones into the blood.

TAKE-HOME MESSAGE 31.2

The vertebrate endocrine system includes major glands, as well as endocrine cells in other organs.

The endocrine system is closely aligned with the nervous system and shares some components with it.

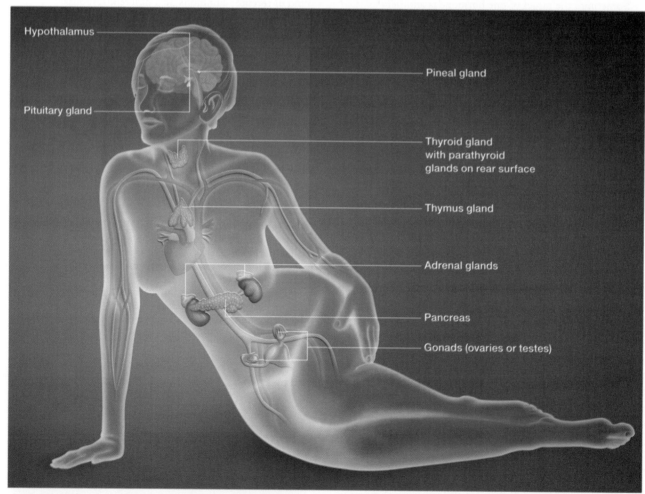

FIGURE 31.2 {Animated} Major glands of the human endocrine system. Other vertebrates typically have the same glands.

CREDIT: (2) From Starr/Evers/Starr, Biology Today and Tomorrow with Physiology, 4E. © 2013 Cengage Learning.

TABLE 31.1

Examples of Human Endocrine Glands, Their Hormones, and Hormone Actions

Gland	Hormone(s)	Main Target(s)	Primary Actions
Hypothalamus	Releasing and inhibiting hormones	Anterior pituitary	Encourage or discourage release of other hormones
Posterior pituitary gland	Antidiuretic hormone (ADH; vasopressin)	Kidneys	Induces water conservation as required to control extracellular fluid volume and solute concentrations
	Oxytocin	Mammary glands	Induces milk movement into secretory ducts
		Uterus	Induces uterine contractions during childbirth
Anterior pituitary gland	Adrenocorticotropic hormone (ACTH)	Adrenal cortex	Stimulates release of cortisol
	Thyroid-stimulating hormone (TSH)	Thyroid gland	Stimulates release of thyroid hormone
	Follicle-stimulating hormone (FSH)	Ovaries, testes	In females, stimulates estrogen secretion, egg maturation; in males, helps stimulate sperm formation
	Luteinizing hormone (LH)	Ovaries, testes	In females, stimulates progesterone secretion, ovulation, corpus luteum formation; in males, stimulates testosterone secretion, sperm release
	Prolactin	Mammary glands	Stimulates and sustains milk production
	Growth hormone (GH)	Most cells	Promotes growth in young; induces protein synthesis, cell division in adults
Pineal gland	Melatonin	Brain	Influences daily biorhythms, seasonal changes
Thyroid gland	Thyroid hormone	Most cells	Regulates metabolism; roles in growth, development
	Calcitonin	Bone	Lowers calcium level in blood
Parathyroids	Parathyroid hormone	Bone, kidney	Elevates calcium level in blood
Adrenal glands	Cortisol	Most cells	Promote breakdown of glycogen, fats, and proteins as energy sources; thus help raise blood level of glucose
	Aldosterone	Kidney	Promote sodium reabsorption (sodium conservation); help control the body's salt–water balance
	Epinephrine (adrenaline) and norepinephrine	Most cells	Promotes fight–flight response
Pancreas	Insulin	Liver, muscle, adipose tissue	Promotes cell uptake of glucose; thus lowers glucose level in blood
	Glucagon	Liver	Promotes glycogen breakdown; raises blood glucose
Gonads			
Testes (in males)	Androgens (including testosterone)	Sex organs	Required in sperm formation, development of genitals, maintenance of sexual traits, growth, and development
Ovaries (in females)	Estrogens	Uterus, breasts	Required for egg maturation and release; preparation of uterine lining for pregnancy and its maintenance in pregnancy; genital development
	Progesterone	Uterus	Prepares, maintains uterine lining for pregnancy; stimulates development of breast tissues
Thymus gland	Thymulin, thymosins	T lymphocytes	Encourages maturation of T lymphocytes (T cells)

The **hypothalamus** functions as the main center for control of the internal environment. It lies deep inside the forebrain and connects, structurally and functionally, with the **pituitary gland**. In humans, the pea-sized pituitary has two lobes (**FIGURE 31.3**). The pituitary's posterior lobe releases hormones synthesized by neurosecretory cells in the hypothalamus. A **neurosecretory cell** is a specialized type of neuron that responds to an action potential by releasing a hormone into the blood. The anterior lobe of the pituitary synthesizes its own hormones but releases them in response to hormones produced in the hypothalamus.

POSTERIOR PITUITARY FUNCTION

FIGURE 31.4A illustrates how the hypothalamus and the posterior lobe of the pituitary gland interact to produce and secrete a hormone. Cell bodies of neurosecretory cells in the hypothalamus synthesize peptide hormones that are transported along the cells' axons to axon terminals in the posterior pituitary. An action potential triggers the terminals of these axons to release the hormone into the blood.

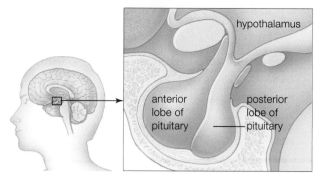

FIGURE 31.3 The two lobes of the pituitary gland.

The posterior pituitary releases two hormones, antidiuretic hormone (ADH) and oxytocin. Antidiuretic hormone targets kidney cells and reduces urine output. We discuss its action in more detail in Section 37.3. Oxytocin targets cells of smooth muscle in the uterus (womb) and mammary glands. It causes uterine contractions during childbirth and moves milk into milk ducts when a woman nurses a child, events we will discuss in Section 38.15.

FIGURE 31.4 {Animated} Pituitary function.

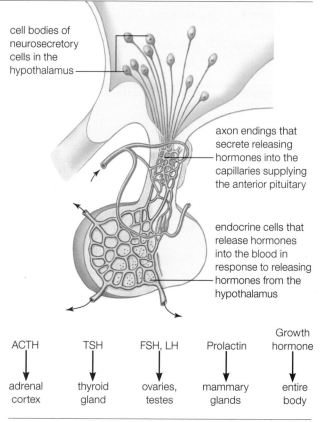

A Posterior pituitary function. Axon endings in the posterior pituitary secrete two hormones made by cell bodies in the hypothalamus.

B Anterior pituitary function. Endocrine cells in the anterior pituitary produce six hormones and secrete them in response to hypothalamic releasing hormones.

CREDITS: (3) From Starr/Taggart/Evers/Starr, Biology 12E. © 2009 Cengage Learning; (4) © Cengage Learning.

ANTERIOR PITUITARY FUNCTION

The anterior pituitary makes peptide hormones and secretes them in response to hormones from the hypothalamus (FIGURE 31.4B). Most hypothalamic hormones that act on the anterior pituitary are releasing hormones. However, the hypothalamus also produces inhibiting hormones.

Four hormones produced by the anterior pituitary act on other endocrine glands. Adrenocorticotropic hormone (ACTH) stimulates the release of cortisol by adrenal glands. Thyroid-stimulating hormone (TSH) causes the thyroid gland to secrete thyroid hormone. Follicle-stimulating hormone (FSH) and luteinizing hormone (LH) affect sex hormone secretion and production of gametes by gonads (a male's testes or a female's ovaries).

The anterior pituitary also produces two additional hormones. Prolactin contributes to breast development at puberty and governs milk production after a woman gives birth. **Growth hormone (GH)** affects target cells throughout the body. It affects metabolism, causing a decrease in fat storage and an increase in synthesis of muscle proteins. It also encourages production of new bone and cartilage.

HORMONAL GROWTH DISORDERS

Normally, GH production surges during teenage years, causing a growth spurt, then declines with age. Over-secretion of growth hormone during childhood leads to pituitary gigantism. A person affected by this disorder has a normal body form, but is unusually tall. When excessive growth hormone secretion continues into or begins during adulthood, the result is acromegaly. With this disorder, continued deposition of new bone and cartilage enlarges and eventually deforms the hands, feet, and face. The skin thickens, and the lips and tongue increase in size. Internal organs are also affected; the heart may become enlarged. Untreated, acromegaly can cause serious health problems. The most common cause of gigantism and acromegaly is a pituitary tumor (FIGURE 31.5).

Too little growth hormone during childhood can cause pituitary dwarfism. Adults affected by this disorder are normally shaped, but small. Injections of recombinant human growth hormone (rhGH) increase the growth rate of children who have a naturally low level of this hormone.

FIGURE 31.5 Sultan Kosen, the tallest living man, with his medical team at the University of Virginia. Kosen had a pituitary tumor that caused excessive growth hormone secretion. Treatment successfully halted his growth at 8 foot, 3 inches (2.5 meters).

However, this treatment remains somewhat controversial. Many people object to the idea that short stature is a defect that should be "cured."

Recombinant growth hormone is also used by athletes who value its ability to encourage growth of muscle. Use of hormones to enhance athletic ability is prohibited in all sports, but the practice continues.

growth hormone Anterior pituitary hormone that regulates growth and metabolism.
hypothalamus Forebrain region that controls processes related to homeostasis and has endocrine functions.
neurosecretory cell Specialized neuron that secretes a hormone into the blood in response to an action potential.
pituitary gland Pea-sized endocrine gland in the forebrain; interacts closely with the adjacent hypothalamus.

TAKE-HOME MESSAGE 31.3

The hypothalamus contains neurosecretory cells. Some of these cells have axons that extend into the posterior pituitary and release hormones from this structure.

Endocrine cells in the anterior pituitary produce hormones of their own. These hormones are secreted in response to releasing hormones produced in the hypothalamus.

Some hormones released by the pituitary regulate secretion by other glands; others directly affect organs such as the kidney. Growth hormone has effects throughout the body.

Like the hypothalamus and pituitary, the pea-sized **pineal gland** lies deep inside the brain. This pinecone-shaped gland secretes the hormone **melatonin**, but only under low-light or dark conditions. Melatonin secretion slows when the retina detects light and action potentials flow along the optic nerve to the brain. Because the amount of light varies with time of day, and day length varies seasonally, melatonin secretion rises and falls in daily and seasonal cycles.

Melatonin helps regulate human sleep–wake cycles. Under natural lighting, melatonin secretion increases each day after darkness falls. The increase triggers drowsiness and a drop in body temperature. Exposure to bright light at night can cause insomnia by altering melatonin secretion patterns. Melatonin supplements are sometimes taken as a sleep aid or to help minimize jet lag. This condition arises when a person travels across multiple time zones and their internal clock does not match up with the new local time.

In many animals, changes in melatonin secretion patterns trigger seasonal adjustments in behavior or appearance. For example, changes in the amount of melatonin secreted determine when an arctic hare switches between its white winter coat and its darker summer coat, as shown in this chapter's opening photo. In some male songbirds, long winter nights lead to an increase in melatonin secretion. The rise in melatonin indirectly prevents singing and other courtship behaviors by slowing secretion of the male sex hormone testosterone. As long as the level of testosterone stays low, the bird will not sing. In the spring, there are fewer hours of darkness, so the melatonin level in the bird's blood declines, testosterone rises, and the bird begins to sing.

melatonin Pineal gland hormone that regulates sleep–wake cycles and seasonal changes.
pineal gland Endocrine gland in the brain that secretes melatonin under low-light or dark conditions.

TAKE-HOME MESSAGE 31.4

Under low-light conditions, the pineal gland produces melatonin, a hormone that affects sleep–wake cycles.

Seasonal changes in melatonin production regulate seasonal behavior and coloration changes in many animals.

METABOLIC AND DEVELOPMENTAL EFFECTS OF THYROID HORMONE

The **thyroid gland** is an endocrine gland at the base of the neck. It secretes two iodine-containing molecules (triiodothyronine and thyroxine) that we will refer to collectively as **thyroid hormone**. Thyroid hormone increases the metabolic activity of cells throughout the body.

The anterior pituitary gland and hypothalamus regulate thyroid hormone secretion by a negative feedback loop (**FIGURE 31.6**). A decline in the level of thyroid hormone causes the hypothalamus to secrete thyroid-releasing hormone (TRH) ❶. This releasing hormone causes the anterior pituitary to secrete thyroid-stimulating hormone (TSH) ❷. TSH in turn stimulates the secretion of thyroid hormone ❸. When the blood level of thyroid hormone rises, the hypothalamus stops secreting TRH, and the decline in this hormone causes a slowdown in secretion of TSH by the anterior pituitary ❹.

In humans, a diet deficient in iodine can cause thyroid hormone deficiency, or hypothyroidism. Hypothyroidism can also arise when the body's immune system mistakenly attacks the thyroid. In either case, ongoing stimulation of the thyroid can cause goiter (an enlarged thyroid). Because thyroid hormone increases the body's metabolic rate, a deficiency typically causes fatigue, increased sensitivity to cold temperature, and weight gain. By contrast, an excess of

FIGURE 31.6 Control of thyroid hormone (TH) secretion.

FIGURE IT OUT: What effect does a high level of TH have on TSH secretion?

Answer: It lowers TSH secretion.

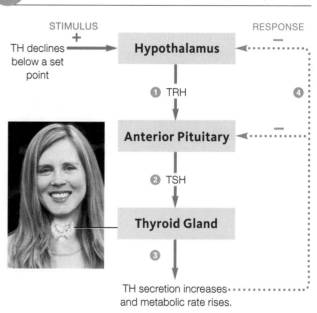

STIMULUS

+

TH declines below a set point → **Hypothalamus**

RESPONSE

−

❶ TRH

❹

Anterior Pituitary

−

❷ TSH

Thyroid Gland

❸

TH secretion increases and metabolic rate rises.

Thyroid hormone regulates amphibian metamorphosis, so scientists use tadpoles to test whether a chemical affects thyroid function. Commercially reared tadpoles are exposed to a chemical, then examined for developmental abnormalities as frogs. Such tests have shown that a variety of pollutants common in our drinking water interfere with normal thyroid function.

FIGURE 31.7 Spadefoot toad tadpoles undergoing metamorphosis.

thyroid hormone causes nervousness and irritability, chronic fever, and weight loss. In addition, hyperthyroidism induces tissues behind the eyeball to swell, causing eyes to bulge.

Thyroid hormone has developmental effects too. In humans, hypothyroidism during infancy or early childhood can result in cretinism, a syndrome of stunted growth and impaired mental capacity. In amphibians, thyroid hormone is essential for metamorphosis (**FIGURE 31.7**).

HORMONAL REGULATION OF BLOOD CALCIUM LEVEL

There are four **parathyroid glands**, each about the size of a grain of rice, on the thyroid's posterior surface. They produce **parathyroid hormone** (PTH), which regulates the concentration of calcium ions in the blood. When the

blood's calcium ion concentration declines, PTH secretion increases. PTH increases the blood calcium level by causing the release of calcium ions from bone, increasing calcium ion reabsorption by kidneys, and increasing synthesis of vitamin D, which helps the intestine absorb calcium from food.

A tumor or other disorder that increases parathyroid secretion can cause osteoporosis. In this disorder, bones lose calcium and become weak and easily broken.

Calcitonin, a hormone produced by the thyroid, opposes the effect of parathyroid hormone by encouraging bones to take up and incorporate calcium. In many animals, it plays an important role in calcium homeostasis. In humans, however, calcitonin secretion occurs mainly during childhood, and adult blood calcium is regulated primarily by the parathyroids. Calcitonin supplements are sometimes used as a treatment for osteoporosis.

calcitonin Thyroid hormone that encourages bones to take up and incorporate calcium.
parathyroid glands Four small endocrine glands on the rear of the thyroid that secrete parathyroid hormone.
parathyroid hormone Hormone that regulates the concentration of calcium ions in the blood.
thyroid gland Endocrine gland in the base of the neck that secretes thyroid hormone and calcitonin.
thyroid hormone Iodine-containing hormones that collectively increase metabolic rate and play a role in development.

TAKE-HOME MESSAGE 31.5

The thyroid gland produces iodine-containing hormones that increase the body's overall metabolic rate. These hormones also play a role in childhood development.

Regulation of blood calcium level depends primarily on parathyroid hormone.

CREDIT: (7) Bruce Farnsworth.

There are two **adrenal glands**, one above each kidney. (In Latin *ad–* means near, and *renal* refers to the kidney.) Each is about the size of a big grape and has two functional regions, an outer cortex and an inner medulla.

The **adrenal cortex** releases steroid hormones. One of these hormones, aldosterone, acts in kidneys and makes urine more concentrated. Section 37.3 explains this process in detail. The adrenal cortex also makes and secretes small amounts of the sex hormones, which we discuss in the next section. Here we will focus on **cortisol**, an adrenal cortex hormone that affects metabolism and immune responses.

A negative feedback mechanism controls cortisol secretion (**FIGURE 31.8**). A decrease in cortisol triggers secretion of CRH (corticotropin-releasing hormone) by the hypothalamus ❶. CRH then stimulates secretion of ACTH by the anterior pituitary ❷. ACTH causes release of cortisol ❸ from the adrenal cortex. The resulting rise in the level of cortisol lowers the secretion of CRH, and the resulting decline in ACTH level slows secretion of CRH ❹.

Cortisol helps maintain the concentration of glucose in blood by inducing liver cells to break down their store of glycogen, and also by suppressing the uptake of glucose by most cells. Cortisol also induces adipose cells to break down fats, and skeletal muscles to break down proteins. Molecules produced by the breakdown can serve as fuel for aerobic respiration (Section 7.7).

The **adrenal medulla** contains neurosecretory cells that respond to stimulation by releasing norepinephrine and epinephrine into the blood. The release has the same effect on a target organ as stimulation by a sympathetic nerve: It brings on a fight–flight response (Section 29.7).

HORMONES, STRESS, AND HEALTH

With injury, illness, or anxiety, the nervous system overrides the feedback loop governing cortisol and levels of this hormone rise. This stress response helps the body deal with an immediate threat by diverting resources from maintenance tasks to support a state of arousal. A stress response is adaptive for short periods of time, as when an animal is fleeing from a predator. However, long-term elevation of cortisol (as by chronic stress) is unhealthy because it interferes with immunity, memory, and sexual function. It also raises the risk of cardiovascular problems. Similar effects occur with Cushing's syndrome, in which a chronic high level of cortisol results from an adrenal gland tumor, pituitary tumor that causes excess secretion of ACTH, or ongoing use of the drug cortisone (cortisone is often prescribed to relieve chronic inflammation; the body converts it to cortisol).

An abnormally low level of cortisol, as occurs with Addison's disease, can cause health problems too. Symptoms include fatigue, depression, weight loss, and darkening of the skin. If the cortisol level falls too low, blood sugar and blood pressure can decline to life-threatening levels. Addison's disease can be treated with synthetic cortisone.

adrenal cortex Outer portion of adrenal gland; secretes aldosterone and cortisol.
adrenal gland Endocrine gland that is located atop the kidney.
adrenal medulla Inner portion of adrenal gland; secretes epinephrine and norepinephrine.
cortisol Adrenal cortex hormone that influences metabolism and immunity; secretions rise with stress.

STIMULUS + Blood level of cortisol declines. → **Hypothalamus** RESPONSE −

adrenal cortex
adrenal medulla

❶ CRH

❹

Anterior Pituitary

❷ ACTH

Rise of cortisol level in the blood inhibits the secretion of CRH and ACTH.

Adrenal Cortex

❸

Cortisol secretion increases and has the following effects:

Cellular uptake of glucose from blood slows in many tissues, especially muscles (but not in the brain).

Protein breakdown accelerates, especially in muscles. Some of the amino acids freed by this process get converted to glucose.

Fats in adipose tissue are degraded to fatty acids and enter blood as an alternative energy source, indirectly conserving glucose for the brain.

kidney

FIGURE 31.8 Control of cortisol secretion.

FIGURE IT OUT: What effect does cortisol have on proteins in muscle?
Answer: It increases breakdown of proteins.

CREDIT: (8) © Cengage Learning.

FIGURE 31.9 Secondary sexual characteristics. Testosterone secreted by testes stimulates growth of a male lion's mane (*left*). A lioness (*right*) produces little testosterone, and does not develop a mane.

Primary reproductive organs (gonads) produce gametes. They also produce **sex hormones**, which are steroid hormones essential to reproductive function. Sex hormones also influence **secondary sexual characteristics**—traits that differ between the sexes but do not function directly in reproduction (**FIGURE 31.9**).

Males and females produce the same sex hormones, but in very different proportions. Testes (male gonads) secrete mainly testosterone. **Testosterone** causes male genitals to form in embryos. During sexual maturation, it triggers sperm formation and development of secondary sexual characteristics. In humans, these traits include facial hair and an enlarged larynx (voice box) that lowers the voice.

Ovaries (female gonads) produce mainly estrogens and progesterone. **Estrogens**, the primary female sex hormones, are responsible for maturation and maintenance of sex organs and for female sexual secondary traits. In humans, these traits include enlarged breasts and fat deposition at the hips. **Progesterone** prepares the body for pregnancy and maintains the uterus if a pregnancy does occur.

---

estrogens Sex hormones that function in reproduction and cause development of female secondary sexual characteristics.
progesterone Sex hormone that prepares a female body for pregnancy and helps maintain a pregnancy.
secondary sexual characteristics Traits that differ between the sexes but do not play a direct role in reproduction.
sex hormone Steroid hormone produced by gonads; functions in reproduction and may affect secondary sexual characteristics.
testosterone Sex hormone responsible for development of male sex organs and secondary sexual characteristics.

Hormones secreted by the hypothalamus and anterior pituitary govern sex hormone secretion (**FIGURE 31.10**). A releasing hormone from the hypothalamus causes the anterior pituitary to secrete follicle-stimulating hormone (FSH) and luteinizing hormone (LH). FSH and LH then cause gonads to secrete sex hormones. Chapter 38 returns to the role of sex hormones in reproduction.

FIGURE 31.10 Control of sex hormone secretion.

The hypothalamus produces gonadotropin-releasing hormone (GnRH).

In response to GnRH, the anterior pituitary secretes follicle-stimulating hormone (FSH) and luteinizing hormone (LH).

In response to FSH and LH, gonads (testes or ovaries) secrete sex hormones.

TAKE-HOME MESSAGE 31.7

Sex hormones function in reproduction. They also give rise to secondary sexual characteristics.

Hormones secreted by the hypothalamus and pituitary govern sex hormone secretion.

The **pancreas**, which lies in the abdominal cavity, behind the stomach (**FIGURE 31.11**), has both exocrine and endocrine functions. Its exocrine cells secrete digestive enzymes into the small intestine. Its endocrine cells are grouped in clusters called pancreatic islets. Beta cells, the most abundant cells in the pancreatic islets, secrete **insulin**—a hormone that causes its target cells to take up and store glucose. After a meal, a rise in the concentration of glucose in the blood stimulates beta cells to release insulin. Insulin's main targets are liver, fat, and skeletal muscle cells. In muscle and adipose cells especially, insulin triggers glucose uptake. In all target cells, it encourages synthesis of fats and proteins and inhibits their breakdown. These cellular responses to insulin lower the level of glucose in the blood (**FIGURE 31.11 ❶–❺**).

Pancreatic islets also contain alpha cells. These endocrine cells secrete the peptide hormone **glucagon** when the concentration of glucose falls below a set point. The released glucagon binds to its receptors on liver cells, which respond by activating enzymes that break glycogen into glucose subunits. This response to glucagon raises the level of glucose in blood (**FIGURE 31.11 ❻–❿**). By working in opposition, glucagon and insulin secreted by the pancreas maintain that level within a range that keeps cells functioning properly.

Regulation of blood glucose is disrupted in diabetes mellitus, a common metabolic disorder. Its name, loosely translated as "passing honey-sweet water," is a reference to the sweet urine produced by diabetics. Their urine is sweet because liver, fat, and muscle cells do not take up and store glucose as they should. The resulting high blood sugar (hyperglycemia) disrupts normal metabolism. Harmful molecules accumulate, and these cause vision and hearing loss, skin infections, poor circulation, nerve damage, and other complications associated with diabetes.

There are two main types of diabetes mellitus. Type 1 develops after the body mounts an autoimmune response against its insulin-secreting beta cells. Certain white blood

FIGURE 31.11 {Animated} *Above,* the location of the pancreas. *Right,* how cells that secrete insulin and glucagon work antagonistically to adjust the level of glucose in the blood.

❶ After a meal, glucose enters blood faster than cells can take it up, so blood glucose increases.

❷ The increase stops pancreatic cells from secreting glucagon, and ❸ stimulates other pancreastic cells to secrete insulin.

❹ In response to insulin, adipose and muscle cells take up and store glucose; cells in the liver and muscle make more glycogen.

❺ As a result, the blood level of glucose declines to its normal level.

❻ Between meals, blood glucose declines as cells take it up and use it for metabolism.

❼ The decrease encourages glucagon secretion, and ❽ slows insulin secretion.

❾ In the liver, glucagon causes cells to break glycogen down into glucose, which enters the blood.

❿ As a result, blood glucose increases to the normal level.

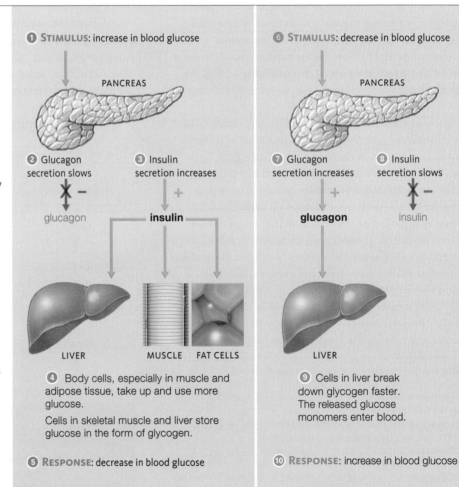

❶ **STIMULUS:** increase in blood glucose

PANCREAS

❷ Glucagon secretion slows

❸ Insulin secretion increases

glucagon

insulin

LIVER   MUSCLE   FAT CELLS

❹ Body cells, especially in muscle and adipose tissue, take up and use more glucose.
Cells in skeletal muscle and liver store glucose in the form of glycogen.

❺ **RESPONSE:** decrease in blood glucose

❻ **STIMULUS:** decrease in blood glucose

PANCREAS

❼ Glucagon secretion increases

❽ Insulin secretion slows

glucagon

insulin

LIVER

❾ Cells in liver break down glycogen faster. The released glucose monomers enter blood.

❿ **RESPONSE:** increase in blood glucose

FIGURE 31.12 Insulin pump. This device delivers insulin into a diabetic's body to maintain blood glucose within normal levels.

cells wrongly identify the cells as foreign (nonself) and destroy them. Environmental factors add to a genetic predisposition to the disorder. Symptoms usually appear in childhood and adolescence, which is why this metabolic disorder is known as juvenile-onset diabetes. All affected individuals require insulin injections (FIGURE 31.12).

With type 2 diabetes, insulin levels are normal or even high, but target cells do not respond to the hormone as they should, so blood sugar levels remain elevated. Symptoms typically start to develop in middle age, when insulin production declines. Genetics is a factor, but obesity increases the risk. Diet, exercise, and oral medications can control most cases of type 2 diabetes. Even so, if glucose levels are not lowered, pancreatic beta cells receive continual stimulation. Eventually they will falter, and so will insulin production. When that happens, a type 2 diabetic may require insulin injections.

Rates of type 2 diabetes are soaring worldwide. By one estimate, more than 150 million people are now affected. Western diets and sedentary lifestyles are contributing factors. The prevention of diabetes and its complications is acknowledged to be among the most pressing public health priorities around the world.

glucagon Pancreatic hormone that raises blood glucose level.
insulin Pancreatic hormone that lowers blood glucose level.
pancreas Organ that secretes digestive enzymes into the small intestine, and insulin and glucagon into the blood.

TAKE-HOME MESSAGE 31.8

Two pancreatic hormones with opposing effects (glucagon and insulin) regulate the concentration of sugar in the blood.

Diabetes is a metabolic disorder caused by either a lack of insulin or an impaired response to insulin.

Until recently, the hormones and receptors of the vertebrate endocrine system were thought to be a derived trait (unique to vertebrates). However, researchers have discovered that some components of this system also occur in invertebrates. Roundworms, annelids, mollusks, and a variety of other invertebrates make steroid hormones (and receptors for them) that are homologous to those made by vertebrates. The homology suggests that the signaling mechanisms using these steroids and receptors evolved long ago, in the common ancestor of all bilateral animals. Invertebrates do not have the same glands as vertebrates do, but they produce the homologous hormones in other glands. For example, octopuses produce estrogens, progesterone, and cortisol in a gland near their eye.

Hormone-signaling systems unique to invertebrates have also evolved. For example, hormones unique to arthropods control molting, the periodic shedding of the exoskeleton (FIGURE 31.13). In these animals, a molting gland produces and stores a steroid hormone called ecdysone. Ecdysone is distributed through the body at molting time.

FIGURE 31.13 Effect of ecdysone. A "soft-shelled" blue crab (bottom) with the old cuticle that ecdysone stimulated it to molt.

TAKE-HOME MESSAGE 31.9

Some invertebrate hormones and receptor proteins are homologous to those in vertebrates. The homology suggests a long history of hormonal signaling using these molecules.

Some invertebrate hormones, such as those involved in arthropod molting, have no vertebrate counterpart.

FIGURE 31.14 A potential source of endocrine disruption. Phthalates, common in scented products, can alter the levels of some hormones.

WE ARE AWASH IN MANMADE CHEMICALS.
We drink from plastic bottles, wear synthetic fabrics that we wash in synthetic soaps, slather ourselves with synthetic skin products, and dose our food with synthetic pesticides. Synthetic chemicals enter our bodies when we ingest them, inhale them, or absorb them across our skin.

We know from experience that some synthetic chemicals are harmful. For example, DDT (a pesticide) and PCBs (used to make electronic products, caulking, and solvents) are endocrine disrupters. These substances interfere with hormone synthesis, metabolism, or function. DDT was banned in 1972 and PCBs in 1979, but the chemicals persist in the environment because they are highly stable and were in widespread use for many years.

Phthalates (pronounced THAL-aytes) are potential endocrine disrupters that remain in widespread use. These chemicals are used to make plastics more flexible and to stabilize fragrances in scented products. Laboratory studies have demonstrated that phthalates inhibit testosterone synthesis in rats, and exposure of male rats to phthalates during prenatal development

interferes with development of their sex organs. Epidemiological studies suggest phthalates may have similar effects in humans. In adult men, a high concentration of phthalates is correlated with a low testosterone level and decreased sperm quality. Having a high phthalate level during pregnancy is correlated with an increased likelihood of giving birth to a son with an undescended testicle.

Phthalates also disrupt the function of other hormones. Phthalates are not approved for use in human foods, but in 2011 a Taiwanese company illegally added them to a variety of foods and drinks. Children who had ingested these items had a lowered level of TSH (the pituitary hormone that stimulates thyroid hormone production). The reduction in TSH was dose dependent; the more contaminated food and drink a child had taken in, the greater his or her reduction in TSH level. Results of this horrible unplanned experiment are consistent with epidemiological studies that implicate phthalates in disrupted thyroid function. Other studies have found a positive correlation between phthalate exposure and diabetes.

In light of the increasing evidence that exposure to phthalates has negative health effects, some

O
‖
OH
OH
‖
O

a phthalate

efforts have been made to reduce the use of these chemicals. Phthalates were widely used in pacifiers and teething toys until 2007, when a U.S. law went into effect limiting the phthalate content of products intended for kids under age twelve. Phthalates have also been largely eliminated from cling-wraps and other American-made products designed to come into contact with food.

However, opportunities for phthalate exposure remain. Vinyl, which releases phthalates into the air, is common in furniture, flooring, mattress covers, and shower curtains. Phthalates also remain in artificially scented products ranging from air fresheners to personal care products. Pediatrician Sheela Sathyanarayana found that the more scented products a mother used on her infant, the higher the level of phthalates in the child's urine. Sathyanarayana's study did not demonstrate any ill effects related to children's elevated phthalate level. Nevertheless, the American Academy of Pediatrics recommends that parents use only unscented products on infants and young children. Similarly, many obstetricians recommend that women who are pregnant, nursing, or planning on becoming pregnant use personal care products specifically labeled as phthalate-free.

PEOPLE MATTER

National Geographic Explorer
DR. TYRONE HAYES

Frogs have fascinated Dr. Tyrone Hayes since he began exploring the swamps of South Carolina as a child. Today he studies the effects of synthetic pesticides on amphibians. Hayes is best known for reporting that atrazine, a widely used synthetic herbicide, has endocrine-disrupting effects in amphibians. Hayes found that exposure to atrazine feminizes male tadpoles. It causes some genetically male frogs to develop ovaries in addition to testes, or in place of them.

Hayes's work has inspired other researchers to carry out their own investigations of atrazine's effects. As a result, we now have evidence that atrazine alters endocrine function in fish, rats, mice, and quail, as well as a variety of different species of frogs. In addition, studies of cultured human cells have shown that atrazine increases the rate at which these cells convert testosterone to estrogen. The resulting rise in estrogen and decrease in testosterone may explain the feminizing effects of this herbicide.

Hayes's willingness to educate the public about his research and that of others has greatly increased awareness of atrazine as a water pollutant. In 2013, Syngenta, the company that makes atrazine, began paying out a $105 million settlement to community water suppliers across the United States. The payments are meant to reimburse these communities for costs incurred when they had to filter atrazine out of their drinking water supply. Runoff of atrazine from agricultural fields in these communities had resulted in water with an atrazine level too high to be considered safe by regulatory agencies.

Summary

SECTION 31.1 **Animal hormones** travel through blood and carry signals between cells in distant parts of the body. **Steroid hormones** can diffuse across cell membranes, but **amino acid–derived hormones** bind to plasma membrane receptors and cause formation of a **second messenger**.

SECTION 31.2 The vertebrate endocrine system includes **endocrine glands** and endocrine-secreting cells in other organs. The endocrine system is closely tied to the nervous system, and the two share some components.

SECTION 31.3 The **hypothalamus** contains **neurosecretory cells** that secrete hormones into the blood in response to action potentials. It interacts with the **pituitary gland** as a major center of homeostatic control. The posterior pituitary releases two hormones made by cell bodies in the hypothalamus: antidiuretic hormone, which acts on kidney cells, and oxytocin, which targets smooth muscle in mammary glands and the uterus.

Releasing hormones and inhibiting hormones secreted by the hypothalamus control secretion of hormones made in the anterior lobe of the pituitary. Four anterior pituitary hormones target other endocrine glands (the adrenal cortex, thyroid gland, and gonads). Another anterior pituitary hormone encourages milk production. **Growth hormone** (GH) secreted by the anterior pituitary acts throughout the body. Pituitary gigantism and dwarfism result from mutations that influence GH function.

SECTION 31.4 Under low-light conditions, the **pineal gland** deep inside the brain produces **melatonin**. This hormone influences sleep–wake cycles and regulates seasonal changes in many animals.

SECTION 31.5 Secretion of iodine-containing **thyroid hormone** by the **thyroid gland** is governed by a negative feedback loop involving the anterior pituitary and hypothalamus. Thyroid hormone increases the body's overall metabolic rate, and plays a role in human development. In amphibians, it is necessary for metamorphosis.

Four **parathyroid** glands located at the rear of the thyroid gland produce **parathyroid hormone**, which increases the concentration of calcium ions in the blood. **Calcitonin** from the thyroid has the opposite effect.

SECTION 31.6 An **adrenal gland** sits atop each kidney. The **adrenal cortex** secretes aldosterone, which acts on the kidneys, and **cortisol**. Cortisol secretion is governed by a negative feedback loop to the anterior pituitary and hypothalamus. In times of stress, the nervous system overrides feedback controls that normally keep the cortisol level stable. Norepinephrine and epinephrine released by neurons of the **adrenal medulla** trigger a fight–flight response just as stimulation from the sympathetic nervous system does.

SECTION 31.7 Gonads (ovaries and testes) produce **sex hormones**: steroid hormones with roles in reproduction and in development of **secondary sexual traits**. Testes secrete mainly **testosterone**. Ovaries produce **estrogens** that govern female secondary sexual traits, and along with **progesterone** function in female reproduction.

In both sexes, follicle-stimulating hormone (FSH) and luteinizing hormone (LH) from the anterior pituitary govern sex hormone production. LH and FSH secretion are in turn controlled by gonadotropin-releasing hormone secreted by the hypothalamus.

SECTION 31.8 Insulin and glucagon secreted by islet cells of the **pancreas** are the main regulators of blood glucose level. **Insulin** stimulates glucose uptake by muscle, fat, and liver cells and thus lowers blood glucose. **Glucagon** causes liver cells to release glucose, which increases blood glucose. Diabetes is a disorder in which insulin is not produced or the body does not respond to it.

SECTION 31.9 Some invertebrate hormones and receptors are homologous to those in vertebrates. Invertebrates also have hormones with no vertebrate counterpart. For example, the steroid hormone ecdysone regulates molting in arthropods such as crabs.

SECTION 31.10 Endocrine disrupters are synthetic substances that interfere with the function of the endocrine system. Phthalates, which are chemicals used in plastics and scented products, are an example.

Self-Quiz   Answers in Appendix VII

1. The _____ hormones enter cells and function as transcription factors.
   a. steroid   b. protein   c. peptide   d. both b and c

2. Antidiuretic hormone is produced by cell bodies in the hypothalamus but released from the _____ .
   a. anterior pituitary   c. kidney
   b. posterior pituitary   d. pineal gland

3. Overproduction of _____ causes gigantism.
   a. growth hormone   c. insulin
   b. cortisol   d. melatonin

4. Steroid hormones are synthesized from _____ .
   a. amines   b. peptides   c. proteins   d. cholesterol

5. _____ lowers blood sugar level.
   a. Melatonin   b. Glucagon   c. Insulin   d. Calcitonin

6. When the hypothalamus detects a low concentration of thyroid hormone in the blood, it secretes a releasing hormone that acts on the _____ .
   a. anterior pituitary gland   c. thyroid gland
   b. parathyroid gland   d. pineal gland

7. In addition to hormones, the _____ secretes enzymes that function in digestion.
   a. hypothalamus   c. pineal gland
   b. pancreas   d. parathyroid gland

Data Analysis Activities

Sperm Counts Down on the Farm Contamination of water by agricultural chemicals affects the reproductive function of some animals. Are there effects on humans? Epidemiologist Shanna Swan and her colleagues studied sperm collected from men in four cities in the United States (**FIGURE 31.15**). The men were partners of women who had become pregnant and were visiting a prenatal clinic, so all were fertile. Of the four cities, Columbia, Missouri, is located in the county with the most farmlands. New York City in New York represents an area with no agriculture.

	Location of Clinic			
	Columbia, Missouri	Los Angeles, California	Minneapolis, Minnesota	New York, New York
Average age	30.7	29.8	32.2	36.1
Percent nonsmokers	79.5	70.5	85.8	81.6
Percent with history of STD	11.4	12.9	13.6	15.8
Sperm count (million/ml)	58.7	80.8	98.6	102.9
Percent motile sperm	48.2	54.5	52.1	56.4

FIGURE 31.15 Data from a study of sperm collected from men who were partners of pregnant women that visited prenatal health clinics in one of four cities. STD stands for sexually transmitted disease.

1. Where did researchers record the highest and lowest sperm counts?
2. In which cities did samples show the highest and lowest sperm motility (ability to move)?
3. Aging, smoking, and sexually transmitted diseases adversely affect sperm. Could differences in any of these variables explain the regional differences in sperm count?
4. Do these data support the hypothesis that living near farmlands can adversely affect male reproductive function?

---

8. Secretion of _____ stimulates breakdown of bone and activation of vitamin D.
   a. glucagon
   b. melatonin
   c. thyroid hormone
   d. parathyroid hormone

9. _____ is necessary for amphibian metamorphosis and normal development of the human nervous system.
   a. Testosterone
   b. Melatonin
   c. Thyroid hormone
   d. Cortisol

10. During stressful times, the adrenal glands increase their secretion of _____ .
    a. iodine
    b. aldosterone
    c. cortisol
    d. both b and c

11. The male sex hormone testosterone is secreted in response to a hormone secreted by the _____ .
    a. testes
    b. ovaries
    c. pituitary gland
    d. pancreas

12. Match each term with its most suitable description.
    ___ adrenal medulla
    ___ thyroid gland
    ___ parathyroid glands
    ___ pancreatic islets
    ___ pineal gland
    ___ hypothalamus
    a. secretion affected by light
    b. control(s) other glands
    c. regulate(s) blood calcium level
    d. release(s) epinephrine
    e. secrete(s) insulin, glucagon
    f. requires iodine to function

13. Both vertebrates and invertebrates produce _____ .
    a. ecdysone
    b. estrogen
    c. thyroid hormone
    d. glucagon

14. Match the hormone with its most suitable description.
    ___ melatonin
    ___ thyroid hormone
    ___ cortisol
    ___ estrogen
    ___ testosterone
    ___ glucagon
    ___ insulin
    a. encourages glucose uptake
    b. elevated in Cushing's syndrome
    c. increases metabolic rate
    d. affects seasonal behavior
    e. encourages breakdown of glycogen
    f. causes development of male secondary sexual traits
    g. causes development of female secondary sexual traits

Critical Thinking

1. As a result of global climate change, snow melt in the arctic is occuring increasingly earlier in the year. Why does this change increase the risk of predation for arctic hares?

2. A tumor in the pituitary gland can cause a woman to produce milk even when she is not pregnant. In which lobe of the pituitary would such a tumor be located, and what hormone would it affect?

3. A diabetic who injects too much insulin can lose consciousness. Explain why injecting excess insulin could impair brain function. An injection of glucagon can reverse this effect. Explain how.

A cheetah, the fastest animal on land. Long legs and a flexible backbone help it achieve remarkable speeds.

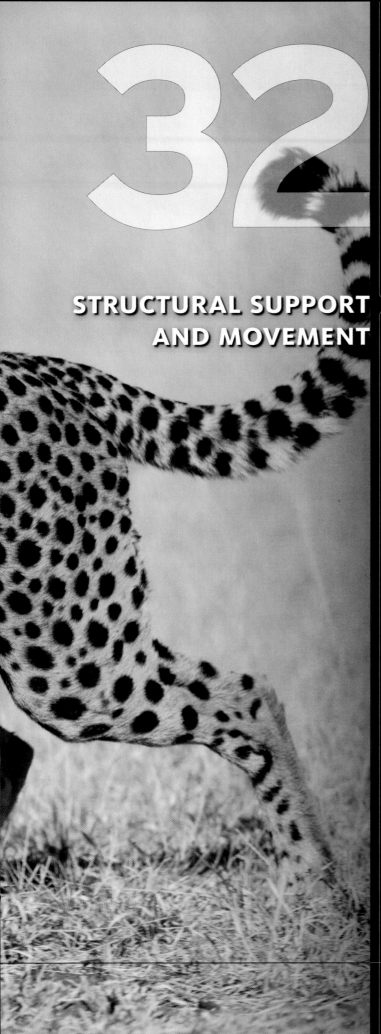

32

STRUCTURAL SUPPORT AND MOVEMENT

Links to Earlier Concepts

This chapter elaborates on some animal traits and evolutionary trends introduced in Chapters 23 and 24. You will build on your knowledge of connective tissue (28.4), muscle tissue (28.5), neuromuscular junctions (29.5), and hormonal effects on bone (31.5). There is an example of active transport (5.7), and the discussion of muscle contraction involves a detailed look at the role of actin and myosin (4.9).

KEY CONCEPTS

MEANS OF LOCOMOTION

All animals move during some part of their life cycle. Locomotion requires overcoming friction and gravity. Variations in body form adapt animals to different types of locomotion.

THREE TYPES OF SKELETONS

Muscles exert force against a skeleton. A skeleton may consist of a fluid in an enclosed space, hard external parts, or hard internal parts.

THE VERTEBRATE ENDOSKELETON

Vertebrate skeletons consist of cartilage and (usually) bone. Bones are living organs that protect and support body parts. Some also produce blood cells. Bones interact at joints.

SKELETAL MUSCLE ACTION

Most skeletal muscles move body parts by pulling on bone, but some pull on soft tissue. Muscles often operate in pairs, with the action of one opposing the action of its partner.

MECHANISM OF CONTRACTION

Long, multinucleated fibers filled with protein filaments run the length of a muscle. In response to nervous signals, ATP-fueled interactions among these filaments bring about contraction.

All animals move. During part or all of their life, they are capable of **locomotion**—self-propelled movement from place to place. As adults, even sessile animals (those that live fixed in place) usually move some body parts. Consider barnacles, which begin life as free-swimming larvae, then settle and secrete a protective shell. Although adults remain in one place, they still wave their feathery legs to capture food from the water around them. Other animals move about on a daily basis to find food and escape from predators.

Animals use diverse mechanisms of locomotion. They swim through water; fly through air; run, walk, or crawl along surfaces; or burrow through soil and sediments. Despite these differences, the same physical law governs all movement: For every action, there is an equal and opposite reaction. For an animal to move in one direction, it must exert a force in the opposite direction. Jet propulsion by squids provides a simple example of this effect (**FIGURE 32.1**). To move, a squid fills an internal cavity (the mantle cavity) with water, then shoots that water out through a small opening. As the water streams out in one direction, the squid moves in the opposite direction. By analogy, think of what happens if you inflate a balloon, then release it without tying it shut. As the rubber of the balloon contracts, force exerted by air rushing out makes the balloon shoot the opposite way.

FIGURE 32.1
Jet-propelled squid.

water shoots this way   squid moves this way

More typically, aquatic animals that swim do so by pushing at water through body movements and movements of flippers or fins. Animals also move along surfaces, both underwater and on land. When doing so, they propel themselves by pushing against those surfaces.

FIGURE 32.2 Tuna, a streamlined swimmer.

FIGURE 32.3 Dog walking. Elevating the body above the ground and having only some feet contact the ground at any given time minimizes the effects of friction.

The effects of friction and gravity increase the amount of energy an animal must expend to move. Water is denser than air, so moving through it produces more friction. Think of how much harder it is to walk through waist-deep water than to walk on land. Aquatic animals that benefit by swimming fast typically have a streamlined body that reduces the effects of friction (**FIGURE 32.2**). Aquatic animals are generally somewhat buoyant, so gravity is less of a constraint for them than it is for land animals.

Snails, snakes, and other animals that creep or slither along surfaces expend energy largely to overcome friction with that surface. Snails reduce friction by secreting a lubricating mucus from their large foot. A snake's smooth scales can have a similar effect. By adjusting the angle of the scales in different parts of its body, a snake can minimize friction everywhere except the region where it relies on the effect of friction in pushing against the ground.

Animals that walk or run minimize friction's effects by reducing the surface area in contact with the ground. Limbs partially or fully elevate their body and only some feet touch the ground at any given time (**FIGURE 32.3**).

The cheetah (shown in the chapter opening photo) is the fastest land animal. It can sprint as fast as 65 miles per hour (about 100 kilometers per hour), although it cannot sustain that speed for long. A variety of traits contribute to the cheetah's speed. Compared to other big cats, a cheetah has longer legs relative to its body size, a wider range of motion at its hips and shoulders, and a longer, more flexible backbone. Together, these features maximize the cheetah's stride length. The cheetah also has a unique sprinting stride; When its back legs land, its backbone becomes bent into a tight C shape. When the animal pushes off again, its spine recoils and helps to force the front of the body forward.

CREDITS: (1) © eye-blink/Shutterstock.com; (2) © Mauricio Handler/National Geographic Creative; (3) © Eric Isselee/ Shutterstock.com.

Elastic tissue plays a locomotive role in many animals. Consider kangaroos, which usually move by hopping. Each time a kangaroo lands, elastic material in its hind legs compresses. The compression is a form of stored energy that is released when the material expands during the next hop.

A capacity for flight evolved independently in insects, birds, mammals, and an extinct group of reptiles called pterosaurs. To fly, an animal must overcome gravity to become and stay airborne, and must also generate a force to propel itself forward. Wing shape is key to flight. A bird wing typically has the same shape as an airplane wing. In cross-section, its upper surface is convex (bulges outward), while the lower surface is flat or slightly concave (sunken). When such a wing cuts through the air, air flowing over the upper surface of the wing travels a greater distance than air flowing over the lower surface, and thus must move faster. The difference in air velocity across the two surfaces creates lift, an upward force, that opposes gravity (**FIGURE 32.4**).

Flying, jumping, swimming, and all other forms of locomotion involve interactions between muscles and a skeleton. These interactions, as well as the additional functions of the skeletal system, are the subject of the sections that follow.

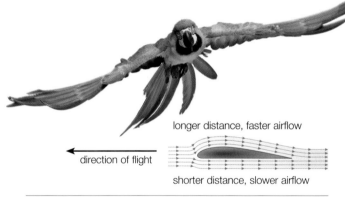

longer distance, faster airflow

← direction of flight

shorter distance, slower airflow

FIGURE 32.4 Parrot in flight. Air flows faster over the rounded upper surface of its wings than the flatter lower surface. This difference in air velocity creates an upward force called lift.

locomotion Self-propelled movement from place to place.

TAKE-HOME MESSAGE 32.1

All animals are capable of locomotion at some point in their life cycle.

To move, an animal must expend energy to overcome the effects of gravity and friction.

CREDITS: (4) top, © Eric Isselee/Shutterstock.com; bottom, © Cengage Learning 2015; (in text) inset, Mark Thiessen/National Geographic Creative; background, © projectdesignstudio/iStockphoto.com.

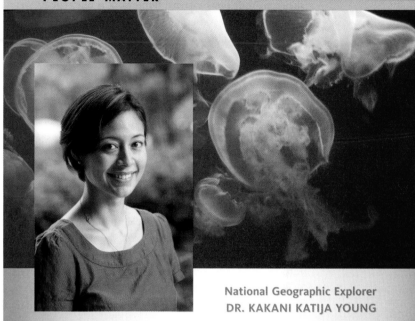

PEOPLE MATTER

National Geographic Explorer
DR. KAKANI KATIJA YOUNG

When aquatic animals move, they set the water around them in motion. Bioengineer Dr. Kakani Katija Young studies these movements and their effects on aquatic habitats. Along with her colleagues, she devised a system that uses lasers and a high-speed camera to visualize and analyze currents created by swimming animals. Young began her studies of aquatic locomotion with jellies because they have a simple symmetrical body. She discovered that as a jelly propels itself by rhythmic contractions of its bell, it creates doughnut-shaped rings of water that quickly dissipate into the surrounding ocean. The rings and the water the jellies transport with them as they move create a rotational flow that mixes fluid in the ocean.

The effect of individual jellies moving might seem insignificant, but Young explains that enormous numbers of jellies, small fish, krill, and copepods churn the seas on a daily basis. She thinks the collective movement of these creatures in our seas could be as important to ocean circulation and global climate as the winds and tides. Her research could provide important new reasons to protect endangered sea life because, while winds and tides operate constantly, animals can disapper. "The decline and collapse of fisheries may have already severely changed the amount of biogenic energy animals can contribute to mixing our oceans," she warns. "Our data could underscore the need for drastic conservation measures."

Muscles bring about movement by interacting with a skeleton. Your bony internal framework is one type of skeleton. In many other animals, muscles exert force against fluid-filled chambers or external hard parts.

INVERTEBRATE SKELETONS

A system of fluid-filled internal chambers makes up the **hydrostatic skeleton** of soft-bodied invertebrates such as sea anemones and worms. For example, an earthworm's coelom is divided into many fluid-filled chambers, one per segment (Section 23.6). Movement occurs when muscles exert force against these chambers (**FIGURE 32.5**). Two sets of muscles squeeze the chambers to alter the shape of body segments, much as squeezing a water-filled balloon changes the balloon's shape. Circular muscle rings each earthworm segment; when this muscle contracts, the segment gets longer and narrower. Longitudinal muscle runs the length of each segment; when this muscle contracts, the segment gets shorter and wider. Coordinated changes in the shape of the earthworm's many body segments move it through the soil.

FIGURE 32.5 Hydrostatic skeleton of an earthworm. A worm moves when muscles put pressure on coelomic fluid in individual body segments, causing the segments to change shape.

An **exoskeleton** is a cuticle, shell, or other hard external body part that receives the force of a muscle contraction. For example, muscles attached to the cuticle of a fly's thorax alter the shape of the thorax, causing the attached wings to flap up and down (**FIGURE 32.6**). The arthropod exoskeleton has the advantage of also protecting the soft body tissues inside it. However, external skeletons have some drawbacks. An exoskeleton consists of noncellular secreted material, so it cannot grow with the animal. As an arthropod grows, it must periodically molt its old skeleton and replace it with a larger one. Repeatedly producing new exoskeleton uses resources that could otherwise be put to use in growth or reproduction. In addition, after an arthropod molts, it remains highly vulnerable to predators until its new exoskeleton hardens.

An **endoskeleton** is an internal framework of hard parts. For example, the endoskeleton of echinoderms such as sea stars consists of hardened calcium-rich plates.

THE VERTEBRATE ENDOSKELETON

All vertebrates have an endoskeleton. In sharks and other cartilaginous fishes, it consists of cartilage, a rubbery connective tissue. Other vertebrate skeletons include some cartilage, but consist mostly of bone tissue (Section 28.4).

The term "vertebrate" refers to the **vertebral column**, or backbone, a feature common to all members of this group (**FIGURES 32.7** and **32.8**). The backbone supports the body, serves as an attachment point for muscles, and protects the spinal cord that runs through a canal inside it. Bony segments called **vertebrae** (singular, vertebra) make up the backbone. **Intervertebral disks** of cartilage between vertebrae act as shock absorbers.

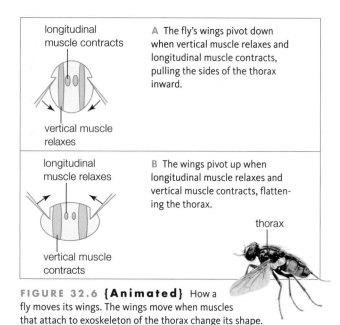

A The fly's wings pivot down when vertical muscle relaxes and longitudinal muscle contracts, pulling the sides of the thorax inward.

longitudinal muscle contracts

vertical muscle relaxes

B The wings pivot up when longitudinal muscle relaxes and vertical muscle contracts, flattening the thorax.

longitudinal muscle relaxes

vertical muscle contracts

thorax

FIGURE 32.6 {Animated} How a fly moves its wings. The wings move when muscles that attach to exoskeleton of the thorax change its shape.

FIGURE 32.7 Skeletal elements typical of early reptiles.

☐ axial skeleton

☐ appendicular skeleton

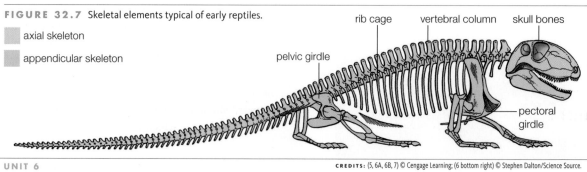

pelvic girdle

rib cage   vertebral column   skull bones

pectoral girdle

The vertebral column and bones of the head and rib cage constitute the **axial skeleton**, the bones that make up the main axis of the body. The **appendicular skeleton** consists of bones of the appendages (limbs or bony fins), and those that connect appendages to the axial skeleton (the pectoral girdle at the shoulders and the pelvic girdle at the hip).

You learned earlier how vertebrate skeletons have evolved over time. For example, jaws are derived from the gill supports of ancient jawless fishes (Section 24.2). As another example, bones in the limbs of land vertebrates are homologous to those inside the fins of lobe-finned fishes (Section 24.3).

For a closer look at vertebrate skeletal features, consider a human skeleton (**FIGURE 35.8**). The skull's flattened cranial bones fit together as a braincase. Facial bones include cheekbones and other bones around the eyes, the bone that forms the bridge of the nose, and the bones of the jaw.

Ribs and the breastbone, or sternum, form a protective cage around the heart and lungs. Both males and females have twelve pairs of ribs.

The vertebral column extends from the base of the skull to the pelvic girdle. Viewed from the side, our backbone has an S shape that keeps our head and torso centered over our feet when we stand upright.

The scapula (shoulder blade) and clavicle (collarbone) are bones of the human pectoral girdle. The thin clavicle transfers force from the arms to the axial skeleton. The upper arm has a single bone called the humerus. The forearm has two bones, the radius and ulna. Carpals are bones of the wrist, metacarpals are bones of the palm, and phalanges (singular, phalanx) are finger bones.

The pelvic girdle consists of two hip bones that connect to the sacrum to form a basin-shaped ring. The pelvic girdle protects organs inside the pelvic cavity and supports the weight of the upper body when you stand upright. Bones of the leg include the femur (thighbone), patella (kneecap), and the tibia and fibula (bones of the lower leg). The fibula serves as a point of muscle attachment, but does not bear weight. Tarsals are ankle bones, and metatarsals are bones of the sole of the foot. Like the bones of the fingers, those of the toes are called phalanges.

---

appendicular skeleton Of vertebrates, bones of the limbs or fins and the bones that connect them to the axial skeleton.
axial skeleton Bones of the main body axis; skull, backbone.
endoskeleton Internal skeleton consisting of hard parts.
exoskeleton Of some invertebrates, hard external parts that muscles attach to and move.
hydrostatic skeleton Of soft-bodied invertebrates, a fluid-filled chamber that muscles exert force against, redistributing the fluid.
intervertebral disk Cartilage disk between two vertebrae.
vertebrae Bones of the backbone, or vertebral column.
vertebral column Backbone.

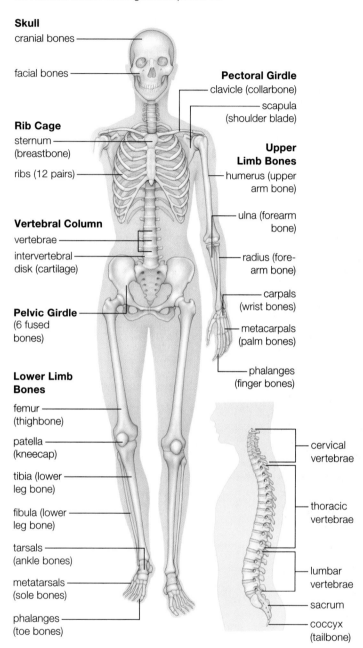

FIGURE 32.8 **{Animated}** Major bone (tan) and cartilage (light blue) elements of the human skeleton. Lower right, side view of the vertebral column showing its S-shaped curve.

Skull
cranial bones
facial bones

Rib Cage
sternum (breastbone)
ribs (12 pairs)

Vertebral Column
vertebrae
intervertebral disk (cartilage)

Pelvic Girdle (6 fused bones)

Lower Limb Bones
femur (thighbone)
patella (kneecap)
tibia (lower leg bone)
fibula (lower leg bone)
tarsals (ankle bones)
metatarsals (sole bones)
phalanges (toe bones)

Pectoral Girdle
clavicle (collarbone)
scapula (shoulder blade)

Upper Limb Bones
humerus (upper arm bone)
ulna (forearm bone)
radius (forearm bone)
carpals (wrist bones)
metacarpals (palm bones)
phalanges (finger bones)

cervical vertebrae
thoracic vertebrae
lumbar vertebrae
sacrum
coccyx (tailbone)

TAKE-HOME MESSAGE 32.2

In animals with a hydrostatic skeleton, muscle contractions alter the shape of fluid-filled chambers. In those with an exoskeleton, muscles pull on hard external parts. In those with an endoskeleton, muscles pull on hard internal parts.

The vertebrate endoskeleton consists of cartilage and bone.

BONE STRUCTURE AND FUNCTION

The 206 bones of an adult human's skeleton range in size from middle ear bones as small as a grain of rice to the massive thighbone, or femur, which weighs about a kilogram (2 pounds). The femur and other bones of the arms and legs are long. The ribs, the sternum, and most bones of the skull are flat. Still other bones, such as the carpals in the wrists, are short and roughly squarish in shape.

Each bone is wrapped in a dense connective tissue sheath that has nerves and blood vessels running through it. Bone tissue consists of bone cells in a secreted extracellular matrix (Section 4.10). The matrix is mostly collagen, a fibrous protein, hardened by calcium and phosphorus ions.

A long bone such as a femur includes two types of bone tissue, compact bone and spongy bone (**FIGURE 32.9**). **Compact bone** is the dense bone that makes up the shaft of long bones such as the femur. It consists of many concentric rings of mineralized bone tissue, with living bone cells in spaces between the rings. Nerves

TABLE 32.1
Functions of Bone
1. **Movement**. Bones interact with skeletal muscle to change or maintain positions of the body and its parts.
2. **Support**. Bones support and anchor muscles.
3. **Protection**. Many bones form hardened chambers or canals that enclose and protect soft internal organs.
4. **Mineral storage**. Bones are a reservoir of calcium and phosphorus ions. Deposits and withdrawals of these ions help maintain their consistent concentration in body fluids.
5. **Blood cell formation**. Only certain bones contain the tissue where blood cells form.

FIGURE 32.9 {Animated} Structure of a human femur.

and blood vessels run through a canal in the center of each ring. The knobby ends of long bones are filled with **spongy bone**. Spongy bone is strong yet lightweight; its matrix has many cavities.

Bone marrow is the soft tissue that fills the cavities inside a bone. The **red marrow** that fills spaces in spongy bone is the major site of blood cell formation. **Yellow marrow** fills the central cavity of an adult femur and most other mature long bones. It consists mainly of fat. In cases of extreme blood loss, yellow marrow can convert to red marrow. **TABLE 32.1** summarizes the functions of bone.

BONE FORMATION AND TURNOVER

A cartilage skeleton forms in all vertebrate embryos. In sharks and other cartilaginous fishes, the cartilage skeleton persists into adulthood. In other vertebrates, embryonic cartilage serves as a model for a bony skeleton. Before birth, mineralization of this model transforms most of it to bone.

Until a person is about twenty-four years old, bone cells secrete more matrix than they break down, so bone mass increases. Later in life, bone-producing cells become less active and bone mass gradually declines. However, bone remodeling occurs throughout life. The body must constantly repair the microscopic fractures that result from normal movements. In addition, bone is built and broken down in response to hormonal signals. Bones store most of the body's calcium. Parathyroid hormone, the main regulator of blood calcium, raises the concentration of calcium ions in the blood by encouraging the breakdown of calcium-rich bone matrix. Other hormones also affect bone turnover. The sex hormones estrogen and testosterone encourage deposition of bone. Cortisol, the stress hormone, slows it.

Osteoporosis is a disorder in which bone loss outpaces bone formation. As a result, the bones become weaker and more likely to break (**FIGURE 32.10**). Osteoporosis is most common in postmenopausal woman because they

A Normal spongy bone.   B Bone weakened by osteoporosis.

FIGURE 32.10 Effect of osteoporosis.

produce little of the sex hormones that encourage bone deposition. However, osteoporosis can also occur in men.

To reduce your risk of osteoporosis, ensure that your diet provides adequate levels of calcium and of vitamin D, which facilitates calcium absorption from the gut. Avoid smoking and excessive alcohol intake (both slow bone deposition). Get regular exercise to encourage bone renewal, and avoid excessive intake of cola soft drinks. Several studies have shown that women who drink more than two colas a day have lower-than-normal bone density.

JOINTS: WHERE BONES MEET

A **joint** is an area where bones come together. Connective tissue holds bones securely in place at fibrous joints such as those between cranial bones. Pads or disks of cartilage connect bones at cartilaginous joints, forming a flexible connection that allows a bit of movement. Cartilaginous joints connect vertebrae to one another and connect some ribs to the sternum. Joints of the hip, shoulder, wrist, elbow, and knee are synovial joints, the most common type of joint. In a synovial joint, the ends of bones are covered with cartilage and enclosed in a fluid-filled capsule. Cords of dense connective tissue called **ligaments** hold the bones of a synovial joint in place (**FIGURE 32.11**).

Different kinds of synovial joints allow different movements. Ball-and-socket joints at the shoulders and hips allow rotational motion. At other joints, including some in

the wrists and ankles, bones glide over one another. Joints at elbows and knees function like a hinged door, allowing the bones to move back and forth in one plane only.

Sprains, the most common joint injury, occur when ligaments become overstretched or torn. Athletes often tear cruciate ligaments in the knee joint and require surgery. "Cruciate" means cross, and these ligaments cross one another in the center of the knee joint and stabilize the knee. When these ligaments are torn, bones may shift so the knee gives out when a person tries to stand.

A dislocation occurs when the bones of a joint move out of place. It is usually highly painful and requires immediate treatment. Bones must be repositioned in their proper places and immobilized for a time to allow healing.

Arthritis is chronic inflammation of a joint. The most common type of arthritis, osteoarthritis, usually appears in old age, after cartilage wears down at a specific joint or joints. Rheumatoid arthritis is a disorder in which the immune system mistakenly attacks all of the body's synovial joints. It can occur at any age, and women are two to three times more likely than men to be affected.

FIGURE 32.11 {Animated} Anatomy of the knee, a hinge-type synovial joint. Ligaments hold bones in place. Wedges of cartilage called menisci (singular, meniscus) provide additional stability.

- femur
- patella
- cartilage
- cruciate ligaments
- menisci
- tibia
- fibula

compact bone Dense bone; makes up the shaft of long bones.
joint Region where bones meet.
ligament Strap of dense connective tissue that holds bones together at a joint.
red marrow Bone marrow that makes blood cells.
spongy bone Lightweight bone with many internal spaces; contains red marrow.
yellow marrow Bone marrow that is mostly fat; fills cavity in most long bones.

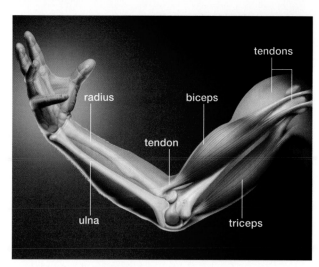

FIGURE 32.12 **{Animated}** Anatomy of the human upper arm. When the biceps contracts and the triceps relaxes, the forearm is pulled toward the upper arm. When the triceps contracts and the biceps relaxes, the arm straightens at the elbow.

 FIGURE IT OUT: What bone does the biceps pull on?

Answer: The radius

Vertebrate skeletal muscles are sometimes referred to as voluntary muscles because they function mainly in intentional movement. However, skeletal muscles also participate in reflex actions such as the stretch reflex (Section 29.8). In addition, skeletal muscle plays a role in thermoregulation; muscle activity releases heat.

A sheath of dense connective tissue encloses each vertebrate skeletal muscle and extends beyond it to form a cordlike or straplike **tendon**. Most often, tendons attach each end of a muscle to different bone. Typically one end of a muscle attaches to a bone or bones that remain fixed in place, and the other to a bone that is moved by the muscle's contraction. Consider, for example, the biceps muscle in the upper arm (**FIGURE 32.12**). At one end of this muscle, two tendons attach it to the scapula (shoulder blade). At the opposite end of the muscle, a tendon attaches it to the radius, a bone in the forearm. When the biceps contracts (shortens), the elbow bends and the forearm is pulled toward the shoulder. You can feel the biceps contract if you extend one arm out, palm up, then place your other hand over the muscle and slowly bend your arm at the elbow.

Although the biceps shortens only about a centimeter when it contracts, the forearm moves through a much greater distance. The elbow and many other joints function like a lever, a mechanism in which a rigid structure pivots about a fixed point (the bones are the rigid structures and the joints are the fixed points). Use of a lever allows a small force, such as that exerted by a contracting biceps, to overcome a larger one, such as the gravitational force acting on the forearm.

Keep in mind that muscles can pull but cannot push. To achieve the greatest range of motion, muscles work in opposition, with the action of one muscle reversing action of another. For example, the triceps in the upper arm opposes the biceps. When the biceps muscle contracts, the triceps relaxes and the forearm is pulled toward the shoulder. Contraction of the triceps coupled with relaxation of the biceps reverses this movement, straightening the arm.

Other muscles are involved in less conspicuous but equally important movements. For example, skeletal muscles associated with the rib cage function during breathing. We discuss the action of these muscles in detail in Section 35.5. For now, it is enough to know that their contractions help expand the chest cavity when you inhale.

Although most skeletal muscles pull on bones, some tug on other tissues. Some skeletal muscles pull facial skin to bring about changes in expression. Others attach to and move the eyeball, or open and close eyelids. Skeletal muscle also composes some sphincters. A **sphincter** is a ring of muscle in a tubular organ or at a body opening. The sphincter of skeletal muscle that encircles the urethra (the tube through which urine exits the body) allows voluntary control of urination. Another at the anus provides control over defecation.

Some animals have boneless muscular organs capable of making complex movements. The mammalian tongue is one such organ. Some tongue muscles have one end attached to the floor of the mouth and one free end. Others are located entirely within the tongue and have no bony attachment whatsoever. They help alter the shape of the tongue by exerting pressure on one another and on connective tissue within the tongue. An elephant's trunk (*right*) is another boneless muscular organ.

sphincter   Ring of muscle in a tubular organ or at a body opening.
tendon   Strap of dense connective tissue that connects a skeletal muscle to bone.

TAKE-HOME MESSAGE 32.4

Most skeletal muscles cause movement of a body part by pulling on a bone. Other skeletal muscles pull on and move skin or another soft body part.

Muscles often function in pairs, with the action of one muscle reversing action of the other.

CREDITS: (12) From Starr/Evers/Starr, Biology Today and Tomorrow with Physiology, 3E. © 2010 Cengage Learning; (in text) FWStudio/Shutterstock.com.

Properties of skeletal muscle arise from the composition and arrangement of its component fibers (**FIGURE 32.13**). As previously noted, a muscle is enclosed within a sheath of connective tissue ❶. This tissue extends beyond the muscle as a tendon. Additional connective tissue encloses bundles of muscle fibers that constitute the bulk of the muscle ❷. Each **skeletal muscle fiber** is a roughly cylindrical cell that runs parallel to the long axis of the muscle ❸. The muscle fiber forms before birth by the fusion of many embryonic cells, so it contains many nuclei, which are positioned at its outer edges. The fiber also contains large numbers of mitochondria, which supply the energy necessary for muscle contraction.

The bulk of the muscle fiber's interior is filled with thousands of threadlike **myofibrils** ❹. A myofibril consists of many identical contractile units, called **sarcomeres**, attached end to end. Each end of a sarcomere is delineated by a Z line, a mesh of cytoskeletal elements that attach the sarcomere to its neighbors. The Z stands for *zwischen*, the German word for "between," and refers to the fact that a sarcomere is the region between two Z lines.

A sarcomere contains parallel arrays of two types of protein filaments. Thick filaments at the sarcomere's center are flanked by thin filaments, which attach to the Z lines at the sarcomere's ends. Thick filaments consist of **myosin**, a motor protein (Section 4.9) that has a long tail and a clublike head with two binding sites. One of the sites can bind ATP and break it into ADP and phosphate, releasing energy in the process. The other binding site is for **actin**, a globular protein that is the main component of thin filaments. As you will learn in the next section, the head of a myosin molecule uses energy from ATP to bind to and move along an adjacent actin filament.

FIGURE 32.13 **{Animated}** Skeletal muscle components.

Skeletal muscle fibers, myofibrils, thin filaments, and thick filaments all run parallel with a muscle's long axis. As a result, all sarcomeres in all fibers of a skeletal muscle work together and pull in the same direction. Skeletal muscle and cardiac muscle appear striated because Z lines and other sarcomere components in all their fibers are aligned with one another. Smooth muscle fibers have sarcomeres too, but because these sarcomeres are not aligned, smooth muscle does not have a striped appearance.

actin Globular protein that plays a role in cell movements; the main component of thin filaments in myofibrils.
myofibril Within a muscle fiber, a threadlike contractile component made up of sarcomeres arranged end to end.
myosin ATP-dependent motor protein; comprises thick filaments in a sarcomere.
sarcomere Contractile unit of skeletal and cardiac muscle.
skeletal muscle fiber Multinucleated contractile cell that runs the length of a skeletal muscle.

TAKE-HOME MESSAGE 32.5

Sarcomeres are the basic units of contraction in skeletal muscle. Sarcomeres are lined up end to end in myofibrils that run parallel with muscle fibers. These fibers, in turn, run parallel with the whole muscle.

The parallel orientation of skeletal muscle components focuses a muscle's contractile force in a particular direction.

CREDITS: (13) bottom right photo, © Don Fawcett/Visuals Unlimited; top art, © Cengage Learning 2015; bottom left art, From Starr/Taggart/Evers/Starr, Biology, 13E. © 2013 Cengage Learning.

The **sliding-filament model** explains how interactions between thick and thin filaments bring about muscle contraction. Neither actin nor myosin filaments change length, and the myosin filaments do not change position. Instead, myosin heads bind to actin filaments and slide them toward the center of a sarcomere. As the actin filaments are pulled inward, the ends of the sarcomere are drawn closer together, and the sarcomere shortens:

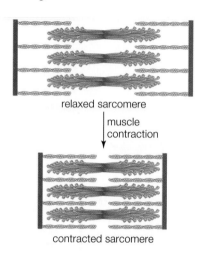

relaxed sarcomere

muscle contraction

contracted sarcomere

FIGURE 32.14 provides a step-by-step look at events during muscle contraction, starting with the sarcomere in a resting muscle fiber. In a relaxed sarcomere, sites where myosin could bind to actin are blocked. The myosin heads of thick filaments have bound ATP molecules and are in a low-energy conformation ❶. Removing a phosphate group (P_i) from a bound ATP energizes a myosin head in a manner analogous to stretching a spring ❷. The myosin head remains in a high-energy conformation, with bound ADP and phosphate, until a signal from the nervous system excites the muscle (a process we consider in the next section). When this signal arrives, myosin heads attach to actin. The attachment constitutes a cross-bridge between the thin and thick filaments ❸. Attachment releases a phosphate group from myosin and triggers a power stroke ❹. Like a stretched spring returning to its original shape, a myosin head snaps back toward the sarcomere center. As it does, it pulls the attached thin filament along with it.

During the power stroke, a myosin head releases bound ADP. Afterward, the head can bind to a new molecule of ATP and return to its low-energy conformation ❺. In the process, the myosin head releases its grip on actin, and the cross-bridge is lost. Loss of one cross-bridge does not allow a thin filament to slip backward because other cross-bridges hold it in place. During a contraction, many myosin heads repeatedly bind, move, and release an adjacent thin filament.

❶ In a relaxed sarcomere, myosin-binding sites on actin are blocked. The myosin heads have bound ATP, and are in their low-energy conformation.

❷ The myosin heads remove a phosphate group from the ATP. Absorbing energy released by breaking the phosphate bond boosts the myosin heads to a high-energy conformation. ADP and phosphate remain bound to each head.

❸ A signal from the nervous system opens up the myosin-binding sites on actin. Each myosin head attaches to actin and releases its bound phosphate group, thus forming a cross-bridge between thick and thin filaments.

❹ The release of the phosphate group triggers a power stroke, in which the myosin heads snap inward and release ADP. As the heads contract, they pull the attached thin filaments inward.

❺ Another ATP binds to each myosin head, causing it to release actin and return to its low-energy conformation.

FIGURE 32.14 {Animated} Sliding-filament model of muscle contraction.

sliding-filament model Explanation of how interactions among actin and myosin filaments shorten a sarcomere and bring about muscle contraction.

TAKE-HOME MESSAGE 32.6

During muscle contraction, sarcomeres shorten when myosin binds to actin and pulls thin filaments toward the center of the sarcomeres.

Contraction does not change the length of muscle filaments or the position of thick (myosin) filaments.

CREDITS: (in text) © Cengage Learning; (14) From Starr/Taggart/Evers/Starr, Biology, 13E. © 2013 Cengage Learning.

MOTOR CORTEX AND MOTOR NEURONS

Most commands for voluntary movement originate in the portion of the cerebral cortex known as the primary motor cortex (Section 29.10). Signals from this brain region travel to and excite a motor neuron in the spinal cord (**FIGURE 32.15 ❶**). As you know, the axon of a such a neuron extends to a skeletal muscle and synapses with it at a neuromuscular junction ❷. When an action potential arrives at this junction, it triggers the release of the neurotransmitter acetylcholine (ACh).

Muscle fibers have receptors for ACh in their plasma membrane. Binding of ACH by these receptors triggers an action potential that travels along the muscle fiber's membrane, then down membrane extensions called transverse tubules or T tubules ❸. T tubules convey action potentials to the **sarcoplasmic reticulum**, a specialized endoplasmic reticulum that wraps around myofibrils and stores calcium ions. When an action potential arrives, the sarcoplasmic reticulum releases these ions into the muscle fiber's cytoplasm. The influx of calcium clears myosin-binding sites on actin filaments. Actin and myosin then interact, and muscle contraction gets under way. When contraction ends, calcium pumps in the sarcoplasmic reticulum's membrane actively transport the ions back into the organelle. As the calcium ion concentration in cytoplasm drops, myosin-binding sites become blocked again and the muscle fiber rests.

MOTOR UNITS

A motor neuron has many terminal endings, and each synapses on a different fiber inside a muscle. A motor neuron and all of the muscle fibers it synapses with constitute one **motor unit**. Stimulate a motor neuron, and all the muscle fibers in its motor unit contract. The nervous system cannot make only some fibers in a motor unit contract.

The mechanical force generated by a contracting muscle—the **muscle tension**—depends on the number of muscle fibers contracting. Some tasks require more muscle tension than others, so the number of muscle fibers controlled by a single motor neuron varies. In motor units that bring about small, fine movements such as those that control muscles that move the eye, one motor neuron synapses with only 5 or so muscle fibers. By contrast, muscles that must frequently exert a large amount of force, have many fibers per motor unit. For example, the biceps of the arm has about 700 muscle fibers per motor unit. Having many fibers pulling the same way at once increases the force a motor unit can generate.

❶ A signal travels along the axon of a motor neuron, from the spinal cord to a skeletal muscle.

❷ The signal is transferred from the motor neuron to the muscle at neuromuscular junctions. Here, ACh released by the neuron's axon terminals diffuses into the muscle fiber and causes action potentials.

❸ Action potentials propagate along a muscle fiber's plasma membrane down to T tubules, then to the sarcoplasmic reticulum, which releases calcium ions. The ions promote interactions of myosin and actin that result in contraction.

FIGURE 32.15 {Animated} Nervous control of skeletal muscle contraction.

motor unit One motor neuron and the muscle fibers it controls.
muscle tension Force exerted by a contracting muscle.
sarcoplasmic reticulum Specialized endoplasmic reticulum in muscle cells; stores and releases calcium ions.

TAKE-HOME MESSAGE 32.7

Most commands for voluntary movement originate in the motor cortex. They reach a muscle by way of a motor neuron.

Arrival of an action potential at a neuromuscular junction excites a muscle fiber. T tubules convey the excitatory signal to the sarcoplasmic reticulum, which releases calcium ions. The rise in calcium ion concentration allows myosin to bind to actin so contraction can occur.

Each motor neuron synapses with multiple fibers in the same muscle.

32.8 HOW DO MUSCLES FUEL THEIR CONTRACTIONS?

ENERGY-RELEASING PATHWAYS

Muscles produce ATP by three main pathways (FIGURE 32.16). First, they tap into their store of creatine phosphate, a compound that can transfer a phosphate to ADP to form ATP ❶. Some athletes and people with muscle disorders take creatine supplements to increase the amount of creatine phosphate available to their muscle. Such supplementation can enhance the performance of tasks that require a quick burst of muscle activity.

Most of the ATP used by a muscle during prolonged, moderate activity is produced by aerobic respiration ❷. Glucose derived from glycogen stored in the muscle fuels this pathway for the first five to ten minutes of contractions. After that, glucose and fatty acids delivered by the blood are broken down. Fatty acids are the main fuel for activities that last more than half an hour (Section 7.7).

Lactate fermentation is the third source of ATP ❸. Some pyruvate is converted to lactate by fermentation even in resting muscle, but the rate of fermentation increases during exercise. This pathway produces ATP less efficiently than aerobic respiration, but unlike aerobic respiration, it operates even when the oxygen level in a muscle is low.

FIGURE 32.16 {Animated} How muscles make ATP.

TYPES OF MUSCLE FIBERS

The primary mechanism of ATP production varies among muscle fibers. Red fibers have an abundance of mitochondria and produce ATP mainly by aerobic respiration. They are colored bright red by **myoglobin**, a protein that, like hemoglobin, reversibly binds oxygen. When the oxygen level in blood is high, oxygen diffuses into muscle fibers and binds to myoglobin. During periods of muscle activity, the myoglobin releases bound oxygen, for use in aerobic respiration. By contrast, white fibers have no myoglobin and few mitochondria, and make ATP mainly by lactate fermentation.

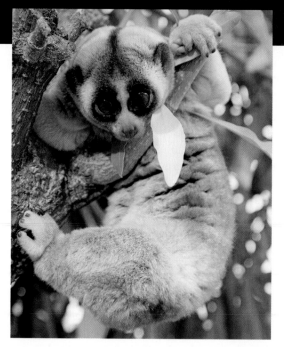

FIGURE 32.17 Loris, a slow-moving primate, whose limbs have a large proportion of slow red fibers. Creeping cautiously along branches helps a loris escape the attention of predators.

Muscle fibers can also be subdivided into fast fibers or slow fibers depending on the speed with which their myosin converts ATP to ADP. All white fibers are fast fibers. They contract rapidly but do not produce sustained contractions. The muscles that move your eye consist mainly of white fibers. Red fibers can be either fast or slow. Fast red fibers predominate in the human triceps muscle, which must often react quickly. Muscles that play a role in maintaining an upright posture, such as some muscles of the back, consist mainly of slow red fibers.

For any given muscle, the relative proportions of fiber types vary among species and reflect the pattern of muscle usage. Limb muscles of cheetahs, which are renowned for their sprinting ability, contain a large proportion of white fibers. By contrast, limb muscles of stealthy, slow-moving lorises (FIGURE 32.17) have mostly slow red fibers. Similarly, among human athletes, successful sprinters tend to have a higher-than-average percentage of fast, white fibers in their leg muscles whereas marathoners tend to have a high percentage of slow, red fibers.

myoglobin Muscle protein that reversibly binds oxygen.

TAKE-HOME MESSAGE 32.8

Muscle contraction requires ATP, which can be formed by transfer of a phosphate from creatine phosphate, aerobic respiration, or lactate fermentation.

Muscle fibers vary in their capacity for aerobic respiration and the rate at which their myosin converts ATP to ADP.

Education

FIGURE 32.18 Prolonged periods of sitting in front of a television or computer alter muscle metabolism and raise the risk of chronic disease.

YOUR BODY IS LIKE A MACHINE THAT IMPROVES WITH USE. Engaging in aerobic exercise—low intensity, but long duration—makes your skeletal muscles more resistant to fatigue. It increases a muscle's blood supply by spurring growth of new capillaries, increases the number of mitochondria and amount of myoglobin in existing red muscle fibers, and encourages conversion of white fibers to red ones. Engaging in resistance exercise, such as weight lifting, encourages synthesis of additional actin and myosin filaments. The resulting increase in muscle mass allows for stronger contractions.

On the other hand, prolonged sitting can be a hazard to your health (FIGURE 32.18). When you sit, your leg muscles decrease their production of lipoprotein lipase (LPL), an enzyme that facilitates uptake of fatty acids and triglycerides from the blood. Decreased LPL activity raises the amount of lipids in the blood—and the risk of cardiovascular disease and diabetes.

There is increasing evidence that the health risks associated with prolonged muscle inactivity persist even if a person also gets regular exercise. In other words, exercising for an hour each morning, although it improves your health in many respects, does not cancel out the negative metabolic effects of sitting in place for hours later in the day.

The best way to prevent the health problems associated with a low LPL concentration is to avoid sitting for long intervals. When you must sit to carry out a task, take periodic short breaks to stand or walk around. Any activity that requires your leg muscles to support your weight leads to increased production of LPL.

Summary

SECTION 32.1 All animals are capable of **locomotion** during part or all of their life cycle. Friction and gravity oppose efforts to move. In water, buoyancy reduces the effects of gravity, but friction is greater than on land. Streamlined bodies help swimming animals minimize drag in water. Many animals that creep along the ground have evolved smooth body parts or an ability to secrete mucus that reduces friction. Air is less dense than water, so most land animals that walk, run, hop, or fly expend energy mainly to overcome gravity. The wing shape of flying animals helps lift them off the ground.

SECTION 32.2 Animals move when their muscles pull on skeletal elements. Soft-bodied invertebrates have a **hydrostatic skeleton**, chambers full of fluid that muscle contractions redistribute. Arthropods have an **exoskeleton** of secreted hard parts at the body surface. An **endoskeleton** consists of hardened parts inside the body. Echinoderms and vertebrates have an endoskeleton.

All vertebrates have similar skeletal components. The vertebrate skull, vertebral column, and ribs constitute the **axial skeleton**. The **vertebral column** consists of **vertebrae** with **intervertebral disks** between them. Bony fins or limbs and the pectoral and pelvic girdles that attach them to the backbone constitute the **appendicular skeleton**.

SECTION 32.3 Bones consist of living cells in a secreted matrix of collagen hardened with calcium and phosphorus. In addition to having a role in movement, bones store minerals and protect organs. The shaft of a long bone such as a femur consists of **compact bone** that contains **yellow marrow**. Lightweight **spongy bone**, as in the ends of long bones, contains **red marrow** that makes blood cells. In a human embryo, bones develop from a cartilage model. Even in adults, bones are continually remodeled. A **joint** is an area of close contact between bones. At most joints, one or more **ligaments** of dense connective tissue hold bones in place.

SECTION 32.4 Skeletal muscles bring about voluntary movements of body parts, take part in reflexes, function in breathing, and generate heat that warms the body. A sheath of connective tissue surrounds each skeletal muscle and extends beyond it as a **tendon**. Most often, the tendon connects the muscle to a bone. A muscle can only exert force in one direction; it can pull but not push. Some skeletal muscles work in pairs to oppose one another's actions. The biceps and triceps of the arm are an example. Skeletal muscles also function as **sphincters**.

SECTIONS 32.5, 32.6 The internal organization of a skeletal muscle promotes a strong, directional contraction. A **skeletal muscle fiber** contains many **myofibrils**. Each myofibril consists of **sarcomeres**, basic units of muscle contraction, lined up end to end. A sarcomere contains parallel arrays of **actin** and **myosin** filaments. The **sliding-filament model** describes how ATP-driven sliding of actin filaments past myosin filaments shortens the sarcomere. Shortening of all sarcomeres in all myofibrils of all muscle fibers brings about muscle contraction.

SECTIONS 32.7, 32.8 Motor neurons control skeletal muscle. Each motor neuron and the skeletal muscle fibers it synapses on constitute a **motor unit**. Acetylcholine released at a neuromuscular junction triggers action potentials in muscle fibers. The action potential is propagated along the plasma membrane of the fiber, and along T tubules to the **sarcoplasmic reticulum**. Calcium ions released by this organelle allow actin and myosin heads to interact so muscle contraction can occur. **Muscle tension** is the force generated by muscle contraction.

Aerobic respiration, lactate fermentation, and phosphate transfers from creatine phosphate provide muscle fibers with the ATP needed for contraction. Red fibers have oxygen-storing **myoglobin** and many mitochondria. They make ATP mainly by aerobic respiration. White fibers have no myoglobin and they make ATP mainly by fermentation. Most muscles consist of a mix of red and white fibers.

SECTION 32.9 Exercise can increase muscle strength and make a muscle less easily fatigued. Prolonged muscle inactivity, as occurs when you sit for long periods, causes changes in muscle metabolism that increase the risk of health problems.

Self-Quiz Answers in Appendix VII

1. A hydrostatic skeleton consists of _____ .
   a. a fluid-filled chamber or chambers
   b. hardened plates at the surface of a body
   c. internal hard parts
   d. none of the above

2. Release of _____ from the sarcoplasmic reticulum opens binding sites and allows actin and myosin to interact.
   a. ACh   c. calcium
   b. potassium   d. oxygen

3. Bones move when _____ muscles contract.
   a. cardiac   c. smooth
   b. skeletal   d. all of the above

4. A ligament connects _____ .
   a. bones at a joint   c. a muscle to a tendon
   b. a muscle to a bone   d. a tendon to bone

5. Calcium release from bone is stimulated by _____ .
   a. parathyroid hormone   c. myoglobin
   b. estrogen   d. cortisol

6. Action of the _____ muscle is opposed by action of the triceps muscle.

7. Skeletal muscle can only _____ bones.
   a. pull on   b. push against

Data Analysis Activities

Building Stronger Bones Tiffany (*right*) was born with multiple fractures in her limbs. By age six, she had undergone surgery to correct more than 200 bone fractures. Her fragile bones are symptoms of osteogenesis imperfecta (OI), a genetic disorder caused by a mutation in a gene for collagen. As bone is laid down, collagen forms a scaffold for deposition of mineralized bone tissue. The scaffold forms improperly in children with OI. **FIGURE 32.19** shows the results of a test of a drug for OI. Bone growth and health of treated children, all less than two years old, were compared to that of a control group of similarly affected, same-aged children who did not receive the drug.

1. How many treated children had bone growth (an increase in vertebral area)? How many untreated children?
2. How did the rate of fractures in the two groups compare?
3. Do the results support the hypothesis that this drug increases bone growth and reduces fractures in children with OI?

Treated child	Vertebral area in cm^2 (Initial)	(Final)	Fractures per year	Control child	Vertebral area in cm^2 (Initial)	(Final)	Fractures per year
1	14.7	16.7	1	1	18.2	13.7	4
2	15.5	16.9	1	2	16.5	12.9	7
3	6.7	16.5	6	3	16.4	11.3	8
4	7.3	11.8	0	4	13.5	7.7	5
5	13.6	14.6	6	5	16.2	16.1	8
6	9.3	15.6	1	6	18.9	17.0	6
7	15.3	15.9	0	Mean	16.6	13.1	6.3
8	9.9	13.0	4				
9	10.5	13.4	4				
Mean	11.4	14.9	2.6				

FIGURE 32.19 Results of a clinical trial of a drug treatment for osteogenesis imperfecta (OI), also known as brittle bone disease. Nine children with OI received the drug. Six others were untreated controls. The surface area of specific vertebrae was measured before and after treatment. An increase in vertebral area during the 12-month period of the study was used as an indicator of bone growth. Researchers also recorded the number of fractures occurring during the 12-month trial.

8. _____ is a motor protein that has binding sites for ATP and actin.
   a. Myoglobin   b. Myosin   c. Lactate   d. Creatine

9. A sarcomere shortens when _____ .
   a. thick filaments shorten
   b. thin filaments shorten
   c. both thick and thin filaments shorten
   d. none of the above

10. ATP for muscle contraction can be formed by _____ .
    a. aerobic respiration
    b. lactate fermentation
    c. transfer of a phosphate from creatine phosphate
    d. all of the above

11. Red muscle fibers get their color from _____ .
    a. ATP   b. myosin   c. myoglobin   d. collagen

12. A motor unit is _____ .
    a. a muscle and the bone it moves
    b. two muscles that work in opposition
    c. the amount a muscle shortens during contraction
    d. a motor neuron and the muscle fibers it controls

13. Cheetahs and human sprinters tend to have a high proportion of _____ fibers in their leg muscles.
    a. white   b. fast red   c. slow red

14. The _____ helps reduce friction during locomotion.
    a. external skeleton of a fly
    b. elongated backbone of a cheetah
    c. streamlined body of a predatory fish
    d. hydrostatic skeleton of an earthworm

15. Match each item with its description.
    ___ tendon
    ___ Z line
    ___ myoglobin
    ___ joint
    ___ actin
    ___ red marrow
    ___ metacarpals
    ___ muscle fiber
    ___ sarcoplasmic reticulum

    a. stores and releases calcium
    b. all in the hands
    c. produces blood cells
    d. multinucleated contractile cell
    e. area of contact between bones
    f. at sarcomere ends
    g. reversibly binds oxygen
    h. connects muscle to bone
    i. main component of thin filaments in sarcomere

Critical Thinking

1. People with some muscle-weakening disorders such as muscular dystrophy sometimes benefit from creatine supplements. How might these supplements be beneficial?

2. After death, a person no longer makes ATP, so calcium stored in the sarcoplasmic reticulum diffuses down its concentration gradient into the muscle cytoplasm. The result is rigor mortis—an unbreakable state of muscle contraction that stiffens the body for a few days until muscles begin to decay. Explain why this contraction occurs.

3. Continued strenuous activity can cause lactate to accumulate in muscles. After the activity stops, the lactate is converted into pyruvate and used as an energy source. Explain how pyruvate can be used to produce ATP.

CENGAGE brain.com To access course materials, please visit www.cengagebrain.com

Hummingbirds have the fastest heart rate of any vertebrate. During flight, their heart beats up to 1,500 times per minute to keep flight muscles well supplied with oxygen.

33

Links to Earlier Concepts

This chapter expands on earlier introductions to animal circulatory systems (Sections 23.6, 23.7, 24.3, 24.5). It draws on your knowledge of hemoglobin (3.4, 9.5), cell junctions (4.10), and diffusion and osmosis (5.6). We consider the function of epithelium (28.3), cardiac muscle (28.5), and autonomic nerves (29.7), discuss the role of cholesterol (3.3) and see more examples of morphological convergence (16.7).

CIRCULATION

KEY CONCEPTS

CIRCULATORY SYSTEMS

A circulatory system includes blood vessels, and one or more hearts. In an open circulatory system vessels are open-ended. In a closed system, they form a closed loop with the heart.

THE HEART

The four-chambered human heart pumps blood through two circuits: one to the lungs and back and the other through the body and back. A natural pacemaker stimulates heart contraction.

BLOOD AND BLOOD VESSELS

Vertebrate blood consists of red blood cells, white blood cells, and platelets suspended in plasma. Blood flows through vessels that vary their structure and function.

CARDIOVASCULAR DISORDERS

Circulatory function declines when the heart's rhythm is disrupted or blood vessels become clogged. Heart disease arises when vessels that supply blood to heart muscle constrict.

LINKS TO THE LYMPHATIC SYSTEM

Fluid that leaves capillaries enters the lymph vascular system, which returns it to the blood. Lymphoid organs monitor lymph for infectious agents and other threats to health.

33.1 HOW DO ANIMALS MOVE MATERIALS TO AND FROM BODY CELLS?

All animals must keep their cells supplied with nutrients and oxygen, and all must rid themselves of cellular wastes. Some invertebrates, including cnidarians and flatworms, rely on diffusion alone to accomplish these tasks. In such animals, nutrients and gases reach cells by diffusing across a body surface and then diffusing through the interstitial fluid (the fluid between cells). Diffusion occurs too slowly to move materials quickly over a long distance, so animals that rely entirely on diffusion to distribute materials have a body plan in which all cells lie close to a body surface.

OPEN AND CLOSED CIRCULATORY SYSTEMS

A **circulatory system** is an organ system that speeds the distribution of materials within an animal's body. It typically includes one or more **hearts** (muscular pumps) that propel a circulatory fluid through vessels that extend throughout the body.

Arthropods and most mollusks have an **open circulatory system**, in which a heart or hearts pump circulatory fluid into open-ended vessels. The fluid, which is called **hemolymph**, leaves the vessels and mixes with the interstitial fluid, where it makes direct exchanges with cells before being drawn back into the heart through openings in the heart wall (**FIGURE 33.1A**).

By contrast, annelids, cephalopod mollusks, and all vertebrates have a **closed circulatory system**, in which vessels form a closed loop. Fluid pumped through a closed circulatory system is called **blood.** A heart or hearts pump

the blood through a continuous series of vessels (**FIGURE 33.1B**). A closed circulatory system distributes substances faster than an open one. Large blood vessels called **arteries** carry blood from a heart toward body tissues. Here, transfers between blood and cells take place by diffusion across the thin walls of **capillaries**, the smallest-diameter blood vessels. Large-diameter blood vessels called **veins** return blood to the heart.

EVOLUTION OF VERTEBRATE CIRCULATORY SYSTEMS

All vertebrates have a closed circulatory system with a single heart. However, the structure of the heart and the circuits through which blood flows vary among vertebrate groups. In most fishes, the heart has two chambers, and blood flows in a single circuit (**FIGURE 33.2A**). One chamber of the heart, an atrium (plural, atria), receives blood. From there, the blood enters a ventricle, a chamber that pumps blood out of the heart. Pressure exerted by contractions of the ventricle drives blood through a series of vessels, into capillaries inside each gill, through capillaries in body tissues and organs, and back to the heart. The pressure imparted to the blood by the ventricle's contraction is dissipated as blood travels through capillaries, so the blood is not under much pressure when it leaves the gill capillaries, and even less as it travels back to the heart.

Adapting to life on land involved coordinated modifications of respiratory and circulatory systems. Amphibians and most reptiles have a three-chambered

FIGURE 33.1 {Animated} Comparison of open and closed invertebrate circulatory systems.

A Open circulatory system. A grasshopper's long, tubular heart pumps circulatory fluid (hemolymph) through a large vessel and out into tissue spaces. Hemolymph mingles with interstitial fluid, exchanges materials with cells, then reenters the heart through openings in its wall.

pump → spaces or cavities in body tissues

aorta / heart

B Closed circulatory system. An earthworm's hearts pump blood through a continuous system of vessels that extend through the body. Exchanges between blood and the tissues take place across the wall of the smallest vessels.

pump — large-diameter blood vessels (rapid flow) — capillary bed (many small vessels that serve as a diffusion zone)

dorsal blood vessel — gut cavity — ventral blood vessels — two of five hearts

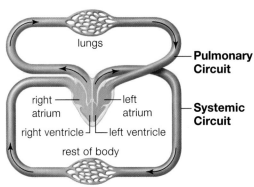

A The fish heart has one atrium and one ventricle. Force imparted by the ventricle's contraction propels blood through a single circuit.

B In amphibians and most reptiles, the heart has three chambers: two atria and one ventricle. Blood flows in two partially separated circuits. Oxygenated blood and oxygen-poor blood mix a bit in the ventricle.

C In birds and mammals, the heart has four chambers: two atria and two ventricles. Oxygenated blood and oxygen-poor blood do not mix.

FIGURE 33.2 {Animated} Vertebrate circulatory systems. In this and other diagrams, red represents vessels carrying oxygenated blood and blue represents vessels carrying oxygen-poor blood.

heart, with two atria emptying into one ventricle (**FIGURE 33.2B**). Blood flows faster through a circulatory system with a three-chambered heart, because it moves through two partially separated circuits. The force of one contraction propels blood through the **pulmonary circuit**, to the lungs and then back to the heart. (The Latin word *pulmo* means lung.) A second contraction sends the oxygenated blood through the **systemic circuit**. This circuit extends through capillaries in body tissues and returns to the heart.

The ventricle became fully separated into two chambers in birds and mammals. Their four-chambered heart has two atria and two ventricles (**FIGURE 33.2C**). With two fully separate circuits, only oxygen-rich blood flows to tissues. Such a system has the added advantage of allowing blood pressure to be regulated independently in each circuit.

Strong contraction of the heart's left ventricle moves blood quickly through the lengthy systemic circuit. The right ventricle contracts more gently, protecting the delicate lung capillaries that would be blown apart by higher pressure.

The four-chambered heart of mammals and birds is an example of morphological convergence (Section 16.7). The two groups do not share an ancestor with a four-chambered heart. Rather, this trait evolved independently in each group. Enhanced blood flow provided by a four-chambered heart supports the high metabolism of these endothermic (heated from within) animals (Section 24.4). Endotherms have higher energy needs than comparably sized ectotherms because much of the energy they release by aerobic respiration is lost to the environment as heat. Rapid blood flow delivers the large amount of oxygen required to keep heat-generating aerobic reactions going nonstop.

artery Large-diameter vessel that carries blood away from the heart.
blood Circulatory fluid of a closed circulatory system.
capillary Small-diameter blood vessel; exchanges with interstitial fluid occur across its wall.
circulatory system Organ system consisting of a heart or hearts and vessels that distribute circulatory fluid through a body.
closed circulatory system Circulatory system in which blood flows through a continuous system of vessels, and substances are exchanged across the walls of the smallest vessels.
heart Muscular organ that pumps blood through a body.
hemolymph Fluid that circulates in an open circulatory system.
open circulatory system Circulatory system in which hemolymph leaves vessels and flows among tissues before returning to the heart.
pulmonary circuit Circuit through which blood flows from the heart to the lungs and back.
systemic circuit Circuit through which blood flows from the heart to the body tissues and back.
vein Large-diameter vessel that returns blood to the heart.

TAKE-HOME MESSAGE 33.1

Most animals have a circulatory system. Some invertebrates have an open circulatory system, in which hemolymph flows out of vessels and seeps around tissues. Other invertebrates and all vertebrates have a closed circulatory system, in which blood is always within the heart or blood vessels.

Fishes have a one-circuit circulatory system. All other vertebrates have a short pulmonary circuit that carries blood to and from lungs, and a longer systemic circuit that moves blood to and from the body's other tissues.

A four-chambered heart evolved independently in birds and mammals. It allows strong contraction of one ventricle to speed blood through the systemic circuit, while a weaker contraction of the other ventricle protects lung tissue.

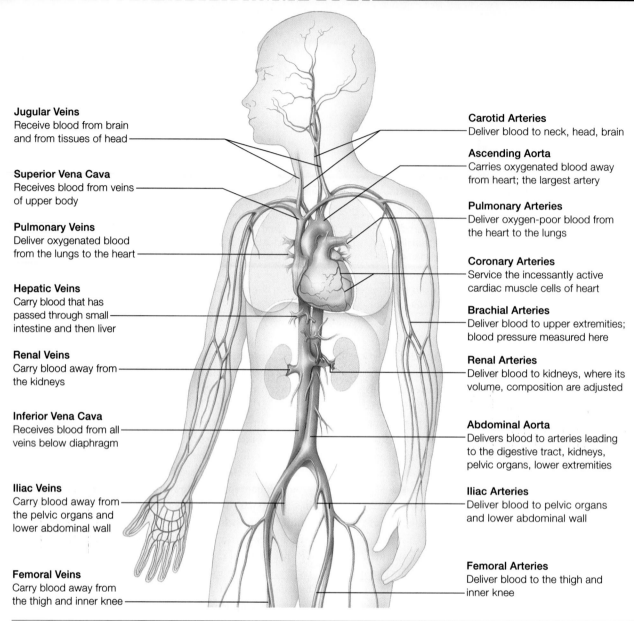

Jugular Veins
Receive blood from brain and from tissues of head

Superior Vena Cava
Receives blood from veins of upper body

Pulmonary Veins
Deliver oxygenated blood from the lungs to the heart

Hepatic Veins
Carry blood that has passed through small intestine and then liver

Renal Veins
Carry blood away from the kidneys

Inferior Vena Cava
Receives blood from all veins below diaphragm

Iliac Veins
Carry blood away from the pelvic organs and lower abdominal wall

Femoral Veins
Carry blood away from the thigh and inner knee

Carotid Arteries
Deliver blood to neck, head, brain

Ascending Aorta
Carries oxygenated blood away from heart; the largest artery

Pulmonary Arteries
Deliver oxygen-poor blood from the heart to the lungs

Coronary Arteries
Service the incessantly active cardiac muscle cells of heart

Brachial Arteries
Deliver blood to upper extremities; blood pressure measured here

Renal Arteries
Deliver blood to kidneys, where its volume, composition are adjusted

Abdominal Aorta
Delivers blood to arteries leading to the digestive tract, kidneys, pelvic organs, lower extremities

Iliac Arteries
Deliver blood to pelvic organs and lower abdominal wall

Femoral Arteries
Deliver blood to the thigh and inner knee

FIGURE 33.3 {**Animated**} Major blood vessels of the human cardiovascular system.

The term "cardiovascular" comes from the Greek *kardia* (for heart) and Latin *vasculum* (vessel). In the human cardiovascular system, the heart pumps blood through two circuits. Each includes a network of blood vessels that carry blood from the heart to a capillary bed and back to the heart. **FIGURE 33.3** shows the major arteries and veins of the cardiovascular system.

THE PULMONARY CIRCUIT

Pulmonary arteries and pulmonary veins are the main vessels of the pulmonary circuit (**FIGURE 33.4A**). The right ventricle pumps oxygen-poor blood into a pulmonary

trunk that divides into two pulmonary arteries ❶. One **pulmonary artery** delivers blood to each lung ❷. As blood flows through pulmonary capillaries, it picks up oxygen and gives up carbon dioxide. The oxygen-enriched blood then returns to the heart in **pulmonary veins** ❸, which empty into the left atrium.

THE SYSTEMIC CIRCUIT

Oxygenated blood travels from the heart, to body tissues, and back by way of the systemic circuit (**FIGURE 33.4B**). The heart's left ventricle pumps blood into the body's largest artery, the **aorta** ❹. Branches from the aorta convey blood to regions throughout the body. The initial portion of the aorta (the ascending aorta) carries blood toward the head. The carotid arteries, which service the brain, and coronary arteries, which service heart muscle, branch off from the ascending aorta. The aorta then turns and descends through the thorax, continuing into the abdomen. Branches from descending portions of the aorta service most internal organs and the lower limbs. For example, renal arteries deliver blood to the kidneys, and femoral arteries carry blood into each leg.

Blood traveling in the systemic circuit gives up oxygen and picks up carbon dioxide as it flows through capillaries in organs. The blood then returns to the heart by way of two large veins ❺. The **superior vena cava** returns blood from the head, neck, upper trunk, and arms. Smaller veins such as the carotid veins and coronary veins drain into the superior vena cava. The longer **inferior vena cava** returns blood from the lower trunk and legs. Renal veins and femoral veins are among the vessels that drain into the inferior vena cava.

In most cases, blood flows through only one capillary bed before returning to the heart. However, blood that passes through the capillaries in the small intestine enters a vein (the hepatic portal vein) that delivers it to a capillary bed in the liver ❻. Journeying through these two capillary beds allows blood to pick up glucose and other substances absorbed from the gut, and deliver them to the liver. The liver stores some of the absorbed glucose as glycogen (Section 3.2). It also breaks down some ingested toxins, including alcohol (Section 5.9).

---

aorta Large artery that receives oxygenated blood pumped out of the heart's left ventricle.
inferior vena cava Vein that delivers blood from the lower body to the heart.
pulmonary artery Vessel carrying blood from the heart to a lung.
pulmonary vein Vessel carrying blood from a lung to the heart.
superior vena cava Vein that delivers blood from the upper body to the heart.

TAKE-HOME MESSAGE 33.2

In the pulmonary circuit, pulmonary arteries carry oxygen-poor blood to lungs and pulmonary veins return oxygenated blood to the heart.

In the systemic circuit, oxygenated blood is pumped into the aorta. Blood travels to body tissues, then returns to the heart via the superior or inferior vena cava.

In most cases, blood travels through a single capillary bed, but blood that flows through intestinal capillaries flows through capillaries in the liver before returning to the heart.

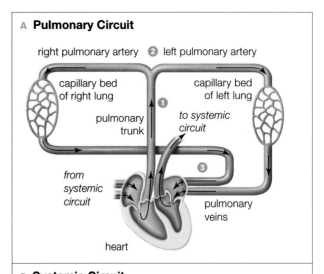

A Pulmonary Circuit

right pulmonary artery ❷ left pulmonary artery

capillary bed of right lung
capillary bed of left lung
❶
pulmonary trunk
to systemic circuit
❸
from systemic circuit
pulmonary veins
heart

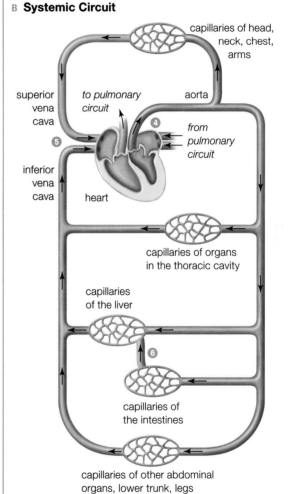

B Systemic Circuit

capillaries of head, neck, chest, arms
superior vena cava
to pulmonary circuit
aorta
❹
from pulmonary circuit
❺
inferior vena cava
heart
capillaries of organs in the thoracic cavity
capillaries of the liver
❻
capillaries of the intestines
capillaries of other abdominal organs, lower trunk, legs

FIGURE 33.4 {Animated} Circuits of the human cardiovascular system.

FIGURE IT OUT: Do all veins carry oxygen-poor blood?

Answer: No. Pulmonary veins carry oxygen-rich blood from lung capillaries to the heart.

A human heart lies in the thoracic cavity, beneath the breastbone and between the lungs (**FIGURE 33.5A**). It is enclosed within a sac (the pericardium) that consists of two layers of connective tissue. Fluid between the layers reduces the friction between them as the heart changes shape.

The heart wall consists mostly of cardiac muscle cells. Endothelium, a type of simple squamous epithelium (Section 28.3), lines the heart's chambers.

A septum divides the heart into right and left sides (**FIGURE 33.5B**). Each side has two chambers: an **atrium** that receives blood from veins, and a **ventricle** that pumps blood into arteries. A pressure-sensitive atrioventricular (AV) valve between the two chambers functions like a one-way door to control blood flow. High fluid pressure forces the valve open. When this pressure declines, the valve swings shut, preventing blood from moving backward. Other pressure-sensitive valves control blood flow into pulmonary arteries and the aorta.

Oxygen-poor blood delivered to the right atrium by the superior and inferior venae cavae flows through the right AV valve into the right ventricle. The right ventricle pumps this blood through the pulmonary valve into the pulmonary arteries, and through the pulmonary circuit.

Oxygenated blood returns to the left atrium via pulmonary veins. This blood flows through the left AV valve into the left ventricle. The left ventricle pumps the blood through the aortic valve into the aorta. From here, it flows to tissues of the body.

THE CARDIAC CYCLE

The series of events that occur from the onset of one heartbeat to the next are collectively called the **cardiac cycle** (**FIGURE 33.6**). During this cycle, the heart's chambers alternate through **diastole** (relaxation) and **systole** (contraction). First, the relaxed atria expand with blood ❶. Fluid pressure forces open the AV valves, so blood flows into the relaxed ventricles. Next, the atria contract ❷, expanding the ventricles by forcing more blood into them. Once filled, the ventricles contract. Contraction raises the fluid pressure inside the ventricles. The increased pressure forces open the aortic and pulmonary valves. Blood flows through these valves and out of the ventricles ❸. Now emptied, the ventricles relax while the atria fill again ❹.

During the cardiac cycle a "lub-dup" sound can be heard through the chest wall. Each "lub" is the sound of the heart's AV valves closing. Each "dup" is the sound of the aortic and

---

FIGURE 33.5 Location and structure of a human heart.

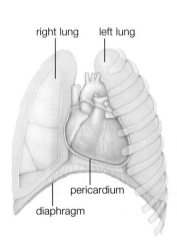

right lung   left lung

pericardium

diaphragm

A (*Above*) The heart is located between the lungs, and is protected by the ribs.

B (*Right*) Cutaway view of a human heart. Red arrows indicate the flow of oxygenated blood; blue arrows, oxygen-poor blood.

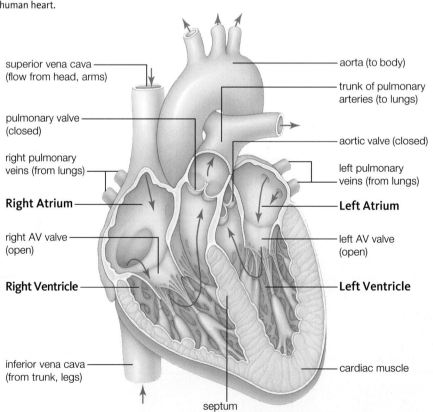

superior vena cava (flow from head, arms)

aorta (to body)

trunk of pulmonary arteries (to lungs)

pulmonary valve (closed)

aortic valve (closed)

right pulmonary veins (from lungs)

left pulmonary veins (from lungs)

Right Atrium

Left Atrium

right AV valve (open)

left AV valve (open)

Right Ventricle

Left Ventricle

inferior vena cava (from trunk, legs)

cardiac muscle

septum

pulmonary valves closing. If a valve does not close properly, some blood is forced backward through the defective valve, making a whooshing sound known as a heart murmur. Valve defects can be corrected with surgery, but most do not threaten health.

Blood circulation is driven by contracting ventricles; contraction of atria only helps fill ventricles. The structure of the cardiac chambers reflects their different functions. Atria need only generate enough force to squeeze blood into ventricles, so they have relatively thin walls. Ventricle walls are more thickly muscled because their contraction must generate enough pressure to propel blood through an entire cardiovascular circuit. The left ventricle, which pumps blood through the long systemic circuit, has thicker walls than the right ventricle, which pumps blood to the lungs and back.

SETTING THE PACE

Like skeletal muscle, cardiac muscle has orderly arrays of sarcomeres that contract by a sliding-filament mechanism (Section 32.6). Unlike skeletal muscle cells, cardiac muscle cells have gap junctions (Section 4.10) that connect the cytoplasm of adjacent cells. The connection allows action potentials to spread swiftly between cardiac muscle cells.

The **sinoatrial (SA) node**, a clump of specialized cells in the wall of the right atrium (**FIGURE 33.7**), is known as the cardiac pacemaker because it sets the heart rate. About seventy times a minute, the SA node generates an action potential that spreads across the atria, causing them to contract. Simultaneously, the action potential travels through specialized noncontractile muscle fibers to the **atrioventricular (AV) node**. This clump of cells is the only place where action potentials can cross to ventricles. The time it takes for an action potential to cross the AV node allows blood from atria to fill ventricles before they contract.

From the AV node, the action potential travels along noncontractile conducting fibers in the septum between the heart's left and right halves. The fibers extend to the heart's lowest point and up the ventricle walls. In response to the arrival of action potentials, ventricles contract from the bottom up, with a twisting motion.

---

atrioventricular (AV) node Clump of cells that conveys excitatory signals between the atria and ventricles.
atrium Heart chamber that receives blood from veins.
cardiac cycle Sequence of contraction and relaxation of heart chambers that occurs with each heartbeat.
diastole Relaxation phase of the cardiac cycle.
sinoatrial (SA) node Cardiac pacemaker; group of cells that spontaneously emits rhythmic action potentials that result in contraction of cardiac muscle.
systole Contractile phase of the cardiac cycle.
ventricle Heart chamber that pumps blood into arteries.

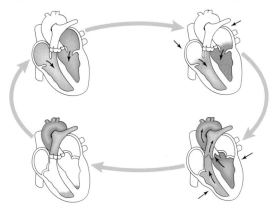

❶ Relaxed atria fill. Fluid pressure opens AV valves, so blood flows into the relaxed ventricles.

❷ The atria contract, squeezing more blood into the relaxed ventricles.

❹ Blood flows into arteries, decreasing pressure in ventricles. The pressure decline causes aortic and pulmonary valves to close.

❸ Ventricles start to contract. Rising pressure pushes AV valves shut. As the pressure continues to rise, aortic and pulmonary valves open.

FIGURE 33.6 {Animated} The cardiac cycle.

 FIGURE IT OUT: Which numbered graphic shows the onset of ventricular systole?   Answer: ❸

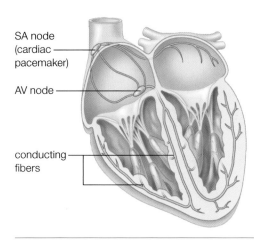

SA node (cardiac pacemaker)

AV node

conducting fibers

FIGURE 33.7 {Animated} Cardiac conduction system.

TAKE-HOME MESSAGE 33.3

The four-chambered heart is a muscular pump partitioned into two halves, each with an atrium and a ventricle.

Atria receive blood from veins and pump it into ventricles. Forceful contraction of ventricles propels blood into arteries and provides the driving force for blood circulation.

The SA node is the cardiac pacemaker. Its spontaneous, rhythmic action potentials make cardiac muscle fibers of the heart wall contract in a coordinated fashion.

Vertebrate blood is a fluid connective tissue with many functions. It carries essential oxygen and nutrients to cells, and carries their metabolic wastes to various organs for disposal. It facilitates internal communications by distributing hormones, and it also serves as a highway for cells and proteins that protect and repair tissues. In birds and mammals, blood helps maintain a stable internal temperature by distributing heat generated by muscle activity to the skin, where it can be lost to the surroundings.

The 5 liters of blood (a bit more than 10 pints) in an average-sized human adult account for about 6 to 8 percent of the individual's body weight. Blood is—as the saying goes—thicker than water. Dissolved substances and suspended cells contribute to its greater viscosity. FIGURE 33.8 shows the components of vertebrate blood.

PLASMA

The fluid portion of the blood, which is called **plasma**, constitutes about 50 to 60 percent of the blood volume. Plasma is mostly water with plasma proteins dissolved in it. More than half of the proteins in plasma are albumins, which are made only by the liver. The high albumin content of blood helps create a solute concentration gradient that draws water into capillaries. As you will see in Section 33.8, this osmosis plays an important role in exchanges between blood and tissues. Albumins and other plasma proteins also function in transport of steroid hormones, fat-soluble

vitamins, and other lipids. Still other plasma proteins have a role in blood clotting or immunity. Dissolved ions, gases, sugars, amino acids, and vitamins also travel through the bloodstream in plasma.

CELLULAR COMPONENTS

The cellular portion of blood consists of various blood cells and platelets. All arise from stem cells in bone marrow.

Red Blood Cells Erythrocytes, or **red blood cells**, transport oxygen from lungs to aerobically respiring cells, and facilitate movement of carbon dioxide to the lungs. In all mammals, red blood cells lose their nucleus and other organelles as they develop. Mature red blood cells are flexible disks with a depression at their center. Their flexibility allows them to slip easily through narrow blood vessels, and their flattened shape facilitates gas exchange.

A mature red blood cell contains a large amount of hemoglobin. You learned about this protein in Section 3.4. Most oxygen that enters the blood travels to tissues while bound to the heme group of hemoglobin. In addition to hemoglobin, a mature red blood cell contains sugars, RNAs, and other molecules that sustain it for about 120 days. Ongoing replacements keep a healthy person's red blood cell count at a fairly stable level.

Red blood cells are the most abundant type of blood cell. Healthy human adults have between 4 and 6 million of these cells per microliter of blood. (A microliter is one-millionth of a liter.) During reproductive years, women typically have a lower red blood cell count than men, because women lose blood during menstruation.

Anemia is a disorder in which the red blood cell count declines or hemoglobin is defective. As a result, oxygen delivery and metabolism falter. Anemia can arise as a result of a dietary iron deficiency (iron is needed to make hemoglobin), destruction of red blood cells by pathogens (as occurs in malaria), excessive blood loss (as from unusually heavy menstrual bleeding), and genetic disorders. Sickle-cell anemia arises from a mutation that causes hemoglobin to form large clumps at low oxygen levels. The clumps distort red blood cells so they get stuck in small blood vessels (Section 9.5).

White Blood Cells Leukocytes, or **white blood cells**, dispose of cellular debris and defend the body against pathogens. We discuss the role of white blood cells in detail in the next chapter, but here is a brief preview. Neutrophils, the most abundant white cells, are phagocytes that engulf bacteria and cellular debris. Eosinophils are specialized to attack larger parasites, such as worms. Basophils and mast

plasma

cells and platelets

red blood cell   white blood cell   platelet

FIGURE 33.8 {Animated} Components of vertebrate blood. The micrograph shows the cellular components.

Stimulus

A blood vessel is damaged.

Phase 1 response

The vessel constricts.

Phase 2 response

Platelets stick together, plugging the site.

Phase 3 response

Clot formation:

1. Enzyme cascade results in activation of the enzyme thrombin.
2. Thrombin converts fibrinogen, a plasma protein, to fibrin threads.
3. Fibrin forms a net that entangles cells and platelets, forming a clot.

FIGURE 33.9 {Animated} Hemostasis. The micrograph shows the final clotting phase—blood cells and platelets in a fibrin net.

cells secrete chemicals that have a role in inflammation. Monocytes are white cells that circulate in the blood for a few days, then move into the tissues, where they develop into phagocytic cells known as macrophages. Macrophages interact with lymphocytes to bring about immune responses. There are two types of lymphocytes, B cells and T cells. T cells mature in the thymus. Both protect the body against specific threats.

Leukemias are cancers that originate in stem cells of bone marrow. They cause overproduction of abnormal white blood cells that do not function properly. Lymphomas are cancers that arise from B or T lymphocytes in lymph glands. Division of these cancerous lymphocytes produces tumors in lymph nodes and other parts of the lymphatic system.

Platelets   A **platelet** is a membrane-wrapped fragment of cytoplasm that arises when a large cell (a megakaryocyte) breaks up. Once formed, a platelet will remain functional for up to nine days. Hundreds of thousands of platelets circulate in the blood, ready to take part in **hemostasis**. This process stops blood loss from an injured vessel and provides a framework to begin repairs.

Hemostasis begins when an injured vessel constricts (narrows), reducing blood loss (**FIGURE 33.9**). Platelets adhere to the injured site and release substances that attract more platelets. Plasma proteins convert blood to a gel and form a clot. During clot formation, fibrinogen, a soluble plasma protein, is converted to insoluble threads of fibrin. **Fibrin** forms a mesh that traps cells and platelets.

Clot formation involves a cascade of enzyme reactions. Fibrinogen is converted to fibrin by the enzyme thrombin, which circulates in blood as the inactive precursor prothrombin. Prothrombin is activated by an enzyme that is activated by another enzyme, and so on. If a mutation affects any one of the enzymes that act in the cascade of clotting reactions, blood may not clot properly. Such mutations cause the genetic disorder hemophilia. A vitamin K deficiency can also impair clotting, because this vitamin plays a role in the cascade of enzyme reactions.

fibrin Threadlike protein formed during blood clotting from the soluble plasma protein fibrinogen.
hemostasis Process by which blood clots in response to injury.
plasma Fluid portion of blood.
platelet Cell fragment that helps blood clot.
red blood cell Hemoglobin-filled blood cell that carries oxygen.
white blood cell Blood cell with a role in housekeeping and defense.

TAKE-HOME MESSAGE 33.4

Blood consists mainly of plasma, a protein-rich fluid that carries wastes, nutrients, and some gases.

Blood cells and platelets form in bone marrow and are transported in plasma. Red blood cells contain hemoglobin that carries oxygen from lungs to tissues. White cells help defend the body from pathogens. Platelets are cell fragments that, like some plasma proteins, have a role in clotting.

CREDIT: (9) Professor P. Motta/Department of Anatomy/University La Sapienca, Rome/Science Source.

RAPID TRANSPORT IN ARTERIES

Blood pumped out of ventricles enters arteries. These large-diameter vessels are ringed by smooth muscle and have an outer covering of highly elastic connective tissue (**FIGURE 33.10A**). Like all other blood vessels and the heart, they are lined by endothelium.

Elastic properties of an artery help keep blood flowing, even when the ventricles relax. With each ventricular contraction, the pressure exerted by blood forced into an artery makes the artery wall bulge outward. Then, as the ventricle relaxes, the artery wall springs back like a rubber band that has been stretched. As the artery wall recoils, it pushes blood in the artery a bit farther away from the heart.

The bulging of an artery with each ventricular contraction is the **pulse**. You can feel a person's pulse by placing your finger on a pulse point, a body region where an artery runs close to the body surface. For example, to feel the pulse in your radial artery, put your fingers on your inner wrist near the base of your thumb (**FIGURE 33.11**).

ADJUSTING FLOW AT ARTERIOLES

All blood pumped out of the right ventricle always flows through pulmonary arteries to your lungs. In the systemic circuit, about 20 percent of the blood always flows through the carotid arteries to the brain. The body

FIGURE 33.11 Checking the pulse in the radial artery, which delivers blood to the hand.

adjusts the distribution of blood across the rest of the systemic circulation according to its needs. It makes these adjustments primarily by altering the diameter of **arterioles**, blood vessels that branch from an artery and deliver blood to capillaries.

Each arteriole (**FIGURE 33.10B**) is ringed by smooth muscle that responds to commands from the central nervous system. For example, activation of the sympathetic nervous system triggers the fight–flight response (Section 29.7). This response includes **vasodilation** (widening) of arterioles in the limbs, so more blood flows to skeletal muscles. At the same time, **vasoconstriction** (narrowing) of arterioles that deliver blood to the gut decreases their share of the blood supply. Activation of the parasympathetic nervous system has the opposite effect.

Arterioles also adjust blood flow in response to metabolic activity in nearby tissue. During exercise, skeletal muscle uses up oxygen and releases carbon dioxide and lactic acid. Arterioles delivering blood to the muscle widen in response to these changes.

---

arteriole Blood vessel that conveys blood from an artery to capillaries.
pulse Brief expansion of artery walls that occurs when ventricles contract.
vasoconstriction Narrowing of a blood vessel when smooth muscle that rings it contracts.
vasodilation Widening of a blood vessel when smooth muscle that rings it relaxes.

---

from the heart

to the heart

valve

endothelium

smooth muscle

connective tissue

capillary network

B Arteriole

D Venule

endothelium

A Artery   C Capillary   E Vein

FIGURE 33.10 {Animated} Structural comparison of blood vessels. The innermost layer of all vessels and the heart is endothelium, a type of simple squamous epithelium.

TAKE-HOME MESSAGE 33.5

Arteries are thick-walled, large-diameter vessels. Stretching and recoil of arteries helps keep blood moving.

Smooth muscle in the wall of arterioles allows adjustments to blood flow in the systemic circuit.

CREDITS: (10) From Russell/Wolfe/Hertz/Starr, *Biology*, 1e. © 2008 Cengage Learning, Inc.; (11) caimacanul/Shutterstock.com.

Blood pressure is the pressure exerted by blood against the wall of the vessel that encloses it. Because the right ventricle contracts less forcefully than the left ventricle, blood entering the pulmonary circuit is under less pressure than blood entering the systemic circuit. In both circuits, blood pressure is highest in arteries, and declines as blood flows through the circuit, being lowest in veins (**FIGURE 33.12**).

Blood pressure is usually measured in the brachial artery of the upper arm (**FIGURE 33.13**). Two pressures are recorded. **Systolic pressure**, the highest pressure of a cardiac cycle, occurs as contracting ventricles force blood into the arteries. **Diastolic pressure**, the lowest blood pressure of a cardiac cycle, occurs when ventricles are relaxed. Blood pressure is measured in millimeters of mercury (mm Hg), a standard unit for measuring pressure. It is written as systolic value/diastolic value. Normal blood pressure is about 120/80 mm Hg, or "120 over 80."

Blood pressure depends on the total blood volume, how much blood the ventricles pump out (cardiac output), and the degree of arteriole dilation. When blood pressure rises or falls, sensory receptors in the aorta and in carotid arteries of the neck signal the medulla oblongata, a region of the hindbrain (Section 29.9). In a reflexive response, the medulla oblongata sends signals that result in appropriate changes in cardiac output and arteriole diameter. Vasodilation of arterioles lowers blood pressure; vasoconstriction raises it. This reflex response adjusts blood pressure over the short term. Over the longer term, kidneys adjust blood pressure by regulating the amount of fluid lost as urine and thus determining the total blood volume.

An inability to regulate blood pressure can result in hypertension, a disorder in which resting blood pressure remains above 140/90. The cause of hypertension is often unknown. Heredity is a factor, and African Americans have an elevated risk. Diet can play a role; in some people, high salt intake causes water retention that raises blood pressure. High blood pressure is dangerous because it makes the heart and kidneys work harder, thus increasing risk of heart disease or kidney failure.

---

blood pressure Pressure exerted by blood against a vessel wall.
diastolic pressure Blood pressure when ventricles are relaxed.
systolic pressure Blood pressure when ventricles are contracting.

TAKE-HOME MESSAGE 33.6

Blood pressure is the fluid pressure exerted against a vessel wall. It is recorded as systolic/diastolic pressure.

Adjustments to arteriole diameter, cardiac output, and blood volume regulate blood pressure.

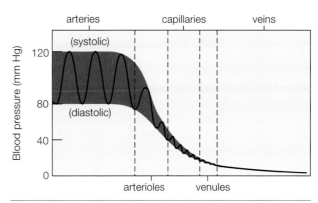

FIGURE 33.12 Plot of fluid pressure changes as a volume of blood flows through the systemic circuit. Systolic pressure occurs when ventricles contract; diastolic, when ventricles are relaxed.

FIGURE 33.13 **{Animated}** Measuring blood pressure. Typically, a hollow inflatable cuff attached to a pressure gauge is wrapped around the upper arm. The cuff is inflated with air, putting pressure on blood vessels of the arm. Eventually, this pressure becomes so high that it cuts off blood flow through the brachial artery, the main artery of the upper arm.

As air in the cuff is slowly released, blood begins to spurt through the artery when ventricles contract and blood pressure is highest. Spurts of blood flow can be heard through a stethoscope as soft tapping sounds. The blood pressure at this point is the systolic pressure. It is typically about 120 mm Hg. Millimeters of mercury (mm Hg) is a standardized unit of pressure.

More air is released from the cuff. Eventually the sounds stop because blood is flowing continuously, even when ventricles are the most relaxed. The pressure when the sounds stop is the diastolic pressure, the lowest pressure during a cardiac cycle—usually about 80 mm Hg.

Right, compact monitors are now available that automatically test and record systolic/diastolic blood pressure.

CREDITS: (12) © Cengage Learning; (13) top, Sheila Terry/Science Source; bottom, Courtesy of Oregon Scientific, Inc.

As blood flows through a circuit, it moves fastest through arteries, slower in arterioles, and slowest in capillaries. Flow velocity then picks up a bit as the blood returns to the heart. The slowdown in capillaries occurs because the body has tens of billions of capillaries. Their collective cross-sectional area is far greater than that of the arterioles that deliver blood to them, or the veins that carry blood away. By analogy, think about what happens if a narrow river (representing few larger vessels) delivers water to a wide lake (representing the many capillaries):

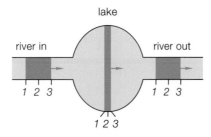

The flow rate is constant, with an identical volume moving from points 1 to 3 in each interval. However, flow velocity decreases in the lake. When the volume of water spreads out through a larger cross-sectional area it flows forward a shorter distance during the specified interval.

Slow flow through the small capillaries enhances the rate of exchanges between the blood and interstitial fluid. The more time blood spends in a capillary, the more time it has for those exchanges to take place.

Materials move between capillaries and body cells in several ways. The capillary wall consists of a single layer of endothelial cells. In most tissues, there are spaces between these cells, so the capillary wall is a bit leaky. This leakiness comes into play mainly at the arterial end of a capillary. Here, pressure exerted by the beating heart forces plasma fluid out through spaces between cells and into the surrounding interstitial fluid (**FIGURE 33.14** ❶). Plasma proteins, including albumin, are too big to exit through the spaces between cells, so they remain in the vessel.

Along the length of the capillary, oxygen released by red blood cells diffuses from blood into the interstitial fluid, while nutrients such as glucose are transported in the same direction by membrane proteins ❷. Carbon dioxide (CO_2) diffuses from interstitial fluid into the capillary, and other metabolic wastes are transported into it ❸. Near the venous end of the capillary bed, where blood pressure is lower, water moves by osmosis from the interstitial fluid into the protein-rich plasma ❹.

As a result of all the leaking and osmotic movement of fluid, there is a small net outward flow from a capillary bed into interstitial fluid. Fluid lost from the bloodstream by this process is returned by the lymphatic system. Some interstitial fluid enters lymph capillaries ❺, which drain into lymphatic ducts that return fluid to veins near the heart. We consider the lymph vascular system in more detail in Section 33.10.

TAKE-HOME MESSAGE 33.7

The rate of flow drops in capillaries, where substances are exchanged between blood and interstitial fluid.

Substances leave the blood in plasma that leaks between blood vessel cells, by diffusing out of vessels, or by transport through membrane proteins in the vessel wall. At the venous end of a capillary, water moves into blood by osmosis.

Lymph capillaries that associate with blood capillaries take up interstitial fluid and return it to the blood.

FIGURE 33.14 {**Animated**} Capillary exchange and connections with the lymphatic system.

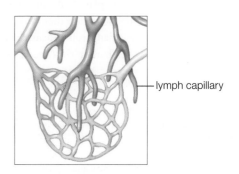

blood to venule

❹ Near the venule, water enters blood by osmosis.

❸ CO_2 diffuses and other wastes are transported into plasma.

❷ O_2 diffuses, and nutrients such as glucose are transported, out of blood and into interstitial fluid.

proteins remain in capillary

water

protein-free plasma

blood from arteriole

❶ At the arterial end of a capillary, high blood pressure forces some protein-free plasma out between cells of the capillary wall.

cells surrounded by interstitial fluid

lymph capillary

❺ Some fluid leaked by blood capillaries enters neighboring lymph capillaries. This fluid, now called lymph, returns to the bloodstream when large lymph vessels drain into veins at the base of the neck.

Blood from multiple capillaries flows into a **venule**, which is a thin-walled vessel that carries blood to veins. Veins carry blood through the final stretch of a circuit and return it to the heart.

By the time blood reaches veins, most of the pressure imparted by ventricular contractions has dissipated. Of all blood vessels, veins have the lowest blood pressure. The vein wall can stretch quite a bit under pressure, much more so than an arterial wall. As a result, veins act as reservoirs for great volumes of blood. When you are at rest, they hold about 60 percent of your total blood volume.

Several mechanisms help blood at low pressure move through veins and back toward the heart. First, veins have one-way valves that prevent backflow. These valves automatically shut when blood in the vein starts to reverse direction. For example, valves in the large veins of your leg prevent blood from moving downward in response to gravity when you stand. All vertebrates typically have the same types of arteries and veins, but the number and location of valves in those veins varies (**FIGURE 33.15**).

Smooth muscle in a vein's wall also facilitates blood flow. When this muscle contracts, the vein stiffens so it cannot hold as much blood. As a result, pressure on blood in the vein rises and the blood is forced toward the heart.

Skeletal muscles used in limb movements help move blood through veins too. When these muscles contract, they bulge and press on neighboring veins, squeezing the blood inside these veins toward the heart (**FIGURE 33.16**). Exercise-induced deep breathing also raises pressure inside veins. The lungs and thoracic cavity expand during inhalation, forcing adjacent organs against veins. As with skeletal muscles, the resulting increase in pressure forces blood in a vein forward through a valve.

Sometimes one or more valves in a vein become damaged, causing blood to accumulate in that vein. Damaged valves in the legs can cause varicose veins, which are bulging, twisted veins. Such veins can also arise because of an inherited weakness of the vein wall. Chronic high blood pressure or an occupation that requires prolonged standing can increase the risk that a person will have varicose veins.

When blood pools in a vein, it may clot. A clot that forms inside a blood vessel and remains in place is called a thrombus. A clot or part of a clot that breaks loose and travels through blood vessels to a new location is called an embolus. For example, a pulmonary embolus (an embolus in an artery in the lung) usually arises after a blood clot that formed in a vein in the thigh breaks off and travels through the heart into the lung.

---

venule Blood vessel that conveys blood from capillaries to a vein.

CREDITS: (15) Jiri Haureljuk/Shutterstock.com; (16) © Cengage Learning.

FIGURE 33.15 Moving blood against the force of gravity. When a giraffe lowers its head to drink, gravity pulls oxygen-poor blood in its veins toward the brain. Seven valves in each jugular vein prevent unwanted backflow through the neck. By contrast, humans, who seldom lower their head below their heart, have only one valve in their jugular vein. When a giraffe lifts its head, high blood pressure keeps oxygen-rich blood flowing uphill to the brain. Giraffes have the highest blood pressure of any vertebrate.

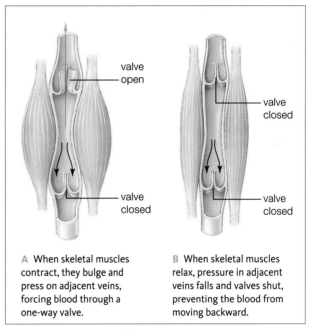

valve open

valve closed

valve closed

valve closed

A When skeletal muscles contract, they bulge and press on adjacent veins, forcing blood through a one-way valve.

B When skeletal muscles relax, pressure in adjacent veins falls and valves shut, preventing the blood from moving backward.

FIGURE 33.16 How skeletal muscle activity encourages blood flow through veins.

TAKE-HOME MESSAGE 33.8

Veins are the body's main blood reservoir. The amount of blood in the veins is adjusted depending on activity level.

Blood pressure is lowest in veins. Blood inside veins moves toward the heart with the help of one-way valves, contraction of skeletal muscle, and muscles of respiration.

The leading cause of death in the United States is cardiovascular disease, which kills about one million people every year. Tobacco smoking tops the list of risk factors, but family history, hypertension, high cholesterol, diabetes mellitus, and obesity also contribute to risk.

ARRHYTHMIAS

Electrocardiograms, or ECGs, record the electrical activity of a beating heart (FIGURE 33.17). They can also reveal arrhythmias, which are abnormal heart rhythms. Bradycardia, an abnormally slow heart rate, is an arrhythmia that can arise from a thyroid hormone deficiency or an SA node malfunction. If the slow flow threatens health, an artificial pacemaker can be implanted to restore a normal heart rate. Tachycardia is a faster-than-normal heart rate. Many people experience palpitations, which are occasional episodes of tachycardia. Palpitations can be brought on by stress, drugs such as caffeine, an overactive thyroid, or an SA node malfunction.

Atrial fibrillation is an arrhythmia in which the atria do not contract normally, but instead quiver. This malfunction slows blood flow, resulting in an increased risk of clot formation. People with atrial fibrillation are often given anticlotting medication to lower their risk of having a stroke—an interruption of blood flow that kills brain cells. Most strokes arise when a thrombus blocks a blood vessel in the brain.

Ventricular fibrillation is an even more dangerous arrhythmia. Ventricles quiver, and pumping falters or stops, causing loss of consciousness and—if a normal rhythm is not restored—death.

An ECG (above) is a graph showing electrical changes that can be detected by electrodes attached to the skin (*left*). The changes arise as a result of the activity of the SA node and transmission of action potentials through the heart.

FIGURE 33.17 {Animated} Electrocardiogram.

A device called a defibrillator can sometimes restore a normal heart rhythm in a person with atrial or ventricular fibrillation. A defibrillator has paddles that deliver an electrical shock to the chest to reset the SA node. Someone who has had ventricular fibrillation may be treated by implanting of a defibrillator that will automatically provide a shock should another episode occur.

ATHEROSCLEROSIS AND HEART DISEASE

In atherosclerosis, buildup of lipids in the arterial wall narrows the space inside the vessel. As you may know, cholesterol plays a role in this "hardening of the arteries." The human body requires cholesterol to make cell

A Normal artery.

FIGURE 33.18 Normal and clogged arteries.

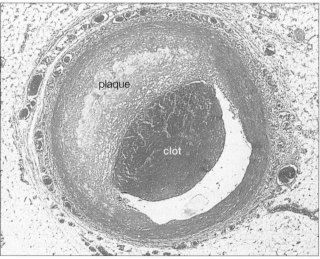

B Artery narrowed by an atherosclerotic plaque. A clot has adhered to the plaque, further narrowing the artery.

CREDITS: (17) left, © Alexander Raths/Shutterstock.com; right, From Starr/Taggart/Evers/Starr, Biology, 13E.
© 2013 Cengage Learning; (18A) © Ed Reschke; (18B) Biophoto Associates/Science Source.

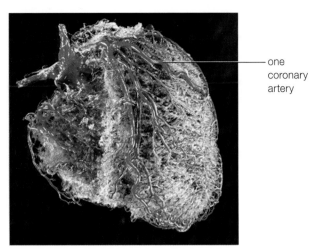

one coronary artery

FIGURE 33.19 Blood vessels that service the heart. To make this three-dimensional cast, resins were injected into vessels, then cardiac tissues were dissolved.

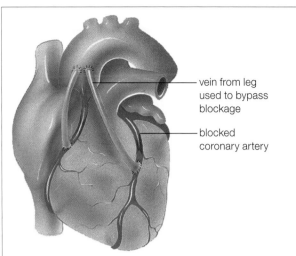

vein from leg used to bypass blockage

blocked coronary artery

A Coronary bypass surgery. Veins from another part of the body are used to divert blood past the blockages. This graphic shows a "double bypass," in which veins are placed to divert blood around two blocked coronary arteries.

plaque flattened by balloon angioplasty

stent (metal mesh) placed to keep artery open

B Balloon angioplasty and placement of a stent. A balloonlike device is inflated inside an artery to open it and flatten the plaque, then a tube of metal (the stent) is left in place to keep the artery open.

FIGURE 33.20 Two ways of treating blocked coronary arteries, the main cause of heart attacks.

membranes, myelin sheaths, bile salts, and steroid hormones (Section 3.3). The liver makes enough cholesterol to meet these needs, but more is absorbed from food in the gut. Genetics affects how different people's bodies deal with an excess of dietary cholesterol.

Most of the cholesterol dissolved in blood is bound to protein carriers (Section 3.4). The resulting complexes are known as low-density lipoproteins, or LDLs, and most cells can take them up. A lesser amount is bound up in high-density lipoproteins, or HDLs. Cells in the liver metabolize HDLs, using them in the formation of bile, which the liver secretes into the gut. Eventually, bile leaves the body in feces.

When the LDL level in blood rises, so does the risk of atherosclerosis. The first sign of trouble is a buildup of lipids in an artery's endothelial lining. The lipids attract white blood cells, which invade the vessel wall. Smooth muscle proliferates and a fibrous cap forms. Eventually, a mass called an atherosclerotic plaque bulges into the vessel's interior, narrowing its diameter and slowing blood flow (FIGURE 33.18). A hardened plaque can abrade an artery wall, thereby triggering clot formation.

With heart disease, atherosclerosis affects vessels that supply blood to heart muscle (FIGURE 33.19). A heart attack occurs when a coronary artery is completely blocked, most commonly by a clot. If the blockage is not removed quickly, cardiac muscle cells die, causing permanent damage to the heart. Clot-dissolving drugs can restore blood flow if they are given within an hour of the onset of an attack, so a suspected heart attack should receive prompt attention.

A blocked coronary artery can be treated with coronary bypass surgery, in which doctors open a person's chest and use a blood vessel from elsewhere in the body (usually a leg vein) to divert blood around the affected artery (FIGURE 33.20A). It can also be treated by angioplasty, a procedure in which the artery is mechanically widened. In balloon angioplasty, doctors inflate a small balloon in a blocked artery to flatten a plaque. Afterwards, a wire mesh tube called a stent may be inserted into the vessel to ensure that it stays open (FIGURE 33.20B).

TAKE-HOME MESSAGE 33.9

Arrhythmias are abnormal heart rhythms. The most dangerous, ventricular fibrillation, is treated with electric shocks to the heart.

Atherosclerosis narrows blood vessels, thus increasing the risk of heart attack and stroke.

33.10 WHAT ARE THE FUNCTIONS OF THE LYMPHATIC SYSTEM?

LYMPH VASCULAR SYSTEM

The **lymph vascular system** is a portion of the lymphatic system consisting of vessels that collect water and solutes from interstitial fluid, then deliver them to the circulatory system. The lymph vascular system includes lymph capillaries and vessels (**FIGURE 33.21**). Fluid that moves through these vessels is the **lymph**.

The lymph vascular system serves three functions. First, its vessels serve as drainage channels for fluid that leaked out of capillaries and must be returned to the circulatory system (Section 33.7). Second, it delivers fats absorbed by the small intestine to the blood. Third, it transports cellular debris, pathogens, and foreign cells to the lymph nodes.

Fluid enters lymph capillaries through clefts between cells in their walls. These capillaries merge into larger-diameter lymph vessels. Two mechanisms move lymph through these vessels. First, slow wavelike contractions of smooth muscle in the walls of large lymph vessels propel lymph forward. Second, as with veins, the bulging of adjacent skeletal muscles helps move fluid along. Like veins, lymph vessels have one-way valves that prevent backflow.

The largest lymph vessels converge on collecting ducts that empty into veins near the heart. Each day, these ducts deliver about 3 liters of fluid to the circulation.

LYMPHOID ORGANS AND TISSUES

Organs and tissues of the lymphatic system have roles in the body's responses to injury and attack. These components include the lymph nodes, spleen, thymus, and tonsils.

Lymph nodes are small masses of tissue with many lymphocytes inside them. Before entering blood, lymph trickles through at least one node. Lymphocytes that recognize a pathogen or toxin in lymph can divide rapidly to form cellular armies that eliminate the threat from the body.

The **spleen**, a fist-sized organ, is located in the upper left abdomen. In embryos, the spleen is a site of red blood cell formation. After birth, it functions in immunity and in quality control of the blood. Phagocytic white blood cells in the spleen engulf and digest any pathogens or worn-out red cells and platelets in the blood that passes through it.

The **thymus**, a hormone-producing organ located beneath the sternum (breastbone) is central to immunity. As white blood cells called T lymphocytes travel through the thymus, they become capable of recognizing pathogens.

The next chapter discusses the lymphatic system's role in immunity in more detail.

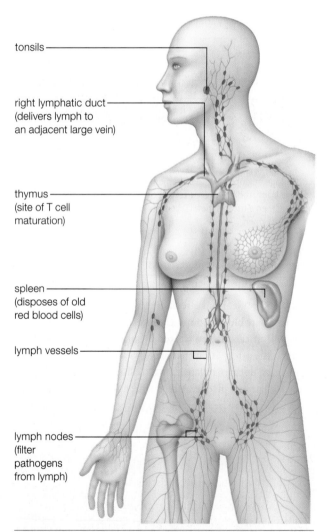

tonsils

right lymphatic duct
(delivers lymph to
an adjacent large vein)

thymus
(site of T cell
maturation)

spleen
(disposes of old
red blood cells)

lymph vessels

lymph nodes
(filter
pathogens
from lymph)

FIGURE 33.21 {Animated} Components of the human lymphatic system.

lymph Fluid in the lymph vascular system.
lymph node Small mass of lymphatic tissue through which lymph filters; contains many lymphocytes (B and T cells).
lymph vascular system System of vessels that takes up interstitial fluid and carries it (as lymph) to the blood.
spleen Large lymphoid organ that functions in immunity and filters pathogens, old red blood cells, and platelets from the blood.
thymus Hormone-producing organ in which T cells mature.

TAKE-HOME MESSAGE 33.10

The lymphatic system returns fluid to the circulatory system and helps defend the body against pathogens.

The lymph vascular portion of the system consists of many tubes that collect and deliver excess water and solutes from interstitial fluid to blood. It also delivers absorbed fats to the blood, and delivers disease agents to lymph nodes.

Lymph nodes filter the lymph and the spleen filters the blood to remove any possible pathogens.

Get Involved

FIGURE 33.22 Chest compressions keep blood moving to brain cells of a person whose heart has stopped.

IN CARDIAC ARREST, THE HEART STOPS, BLOOD FLOW HALTS, AND CELLS BEGIN TO DIE. Brain cells starved of oxygen are the first to be affected.

An inborn pacemaker defect causes most cardiac arrests in people under age 35. In older people, heart disease usually causes the stoppage.

Likelihood of surviving a cardiac arrest increases if a person receives chest compressions immediately after the event (FIGURE 33.22). Such compressions can keep oxygenated blood flowing to brain cells. With traditional cardiopulmonary resuscitation (CPR), a rescuer alternates between blowing into a person's mouth to inflate the lungs and compressing the chest to keep blood moving. A newer method, CCR (cardiocerebral resuscitation), relies on chest compressions alone. It is as good as or even better than CPR at saving people with sudden cardiac arrest. CCR has the added benefit of not requiring people to have mouth-to-mouth contact with a stranger.

Neither CPR nor CCR can restart a heart. Doing that requires a defibrillator. Fortunately, automated external defibrillators (AEDs) are increasingly available in public places. You may have noticed a sign indicating where one is stored (FIGURE 33.23). An AED provides simple voice commands that direct the user to attach its electrodes to a person in distress. The AED then determines whether the person has a heartbeat and, if required, shocks the heart. Having AEDs widely available helps to ensure that a person who suffers a cardiac arrest does not have to wait for arrival of an ambulance to receive a shock that might restart the heart.

FIGURE 33.23 Sign indicating location of an AED.

The presence of a bystander willing to carry out CPR or CCR or to use an AED often means the difference between life and death. Yet only about 15 percent of sudden cardiac arrest victims get such help before professional medical personnel arrive. Unfortunately, most people do not know how to administer chest compressions or use an AED. A half-day course given by the American Red Cross or another community health organization can teach you both skills. Learning these skills is something we can all do to help one another.

Summary

SECTION 33.1 A **circulatory system** distributes substances through an animal's body. Some invertebrates have an **open circulatory system**; their **hemolymph** leaves vessels and seeps around tissues. In other invertebrates and all vertebrates, a **closed circulatory system** confines **blood** inside a **heart** and blood vessels. **Arteries** carry blood away from the heart, **capillaries** exchange substances between blood and interstitial fluid, and **veins** return blood to the heart.

In fish, blood flows through a single circuit. Evolution of a two-circuit system accompanied the evolution of lungs. In this system, the **pulmonary circuit** moves blood to the lungs and back to the heart. The longer **systemic circuit** moves blood to other body tissues and back to the heart.

SECTION 33.2 Humans and other tetrapods have a closed, two-circuit circulatory system. In the pulmonary circuit, **pulmonary arteries** carry blood to lungs and **pulmonary veins** return it to the heart. In the systemic circuit, blood is pumped out of the heart into the **aorta**, and returns to the heart via the **inferior vena cava** and **superior vena cava**. In most cases, blood flows through only one capillary system. Blood in intestinal capillaries will later flow through liver capillaries. The liver stores nutrients and neutralizes some toxins.

SECTION 33.3 A human heart is partitioned into two halves, each with an **atrium** above a **ventricle**. Oxygen-poor blood from the body enters the right atrium and moves through a valve into the right ventricle, which pumps blood through a valve into the pulmonary circuit. Oxygen-rich blood enters the heart's left atrium and moves through a valve into the left ventricle, which pumps the blood through a valve into the systemic circuit.

During one **cardiac cycle**, all heart chambers undergo rhythmic relaxation (**diastole**) and contraction (**systole**). Contraction of ventricles provides the force that powers movement of blood through blood vessels. Contraction of atria only fills the ventricles.

The **sinoatrial (SA) node** in the right atrium serves as the cardiac pacemaker. Action potentials that originate in the SA spread across atria by way of gap junctions and trigger atrial contraction. The action potentials then spread to ventricles by way of the **atrioventricular (AV) node**. The delay between atrial and ventricular contraction allows ventricles to fill fully before they contract.

SECTION 33.4 Blood consists of **plasma**, blood cells, and platelets. Plasma is mostly water. It carries dissolved nutrients and gases. The most abundant plasma protein, albumin, is made by the liver. Albumin helps transport lipids and encourages water to move into capillaries by osmosis. **Red blood cells** contain hemoglobin that functions in oxygen transport. **White blood cells** have roles in tissue maintenance and repair, and in defenses against pathogens.

Platelets and **fibrin** act in **hemostasis** (clotting). Platelets and all blood cells arise from stem cells in bone.

SECTIONS 33.5, 33.6 **Blood pressure** results from force exerted by contracting ventricles. It declines as blood proceeds through a circuit. Blood pressure is recorded as **systolic pressure** (pressure when ventricles contract) over **diastolic pressure** (pressure when ventricles relax). Thick elastic walls of arteries help keep blood moving forward even as ventricles relax. A **pulse** is a brief expansion of an artery caused by ventricular contraction. **Arterioles** are the main site for regulation of blood flow through the systemic circuit. Arterioles widen or constrict in response to action potentials that originate in the nervous system, as well as to changes in local conditions. **Vasodilation** of arterioles supplies more blood to a region. **Vasoconstriction** decreases the blood supply.

SECTIONS 33.7, 33.8 Blood flow slows more in capillaries than other vessels because of their collectively larger cross-sectional area. Capillaries are the site of exchanges with cells. Blood pressure forces protein-free plasma out of a capillary at its arterial end, and water moves into the capillary by osmosis at its venous end. **Venules** carry blood from capillaries to veins. Valves and action of skeletal muscles help keep blood in veins moving.

SECTION 33.9 Abnormal heart rhythms can slow or halt blood flow. Flow is also impaired when atherosclerosis narrows the interior of a blood vessel. Narrowing of coronary arteries causes heart disease.

SECTION 33.10 The lymphatic system interacts with the circulatory system. The **lymph vascular system** takes up excess interstitial fluid, as well as fats absorbed from the small intestine, and delivers them to blood. It also delivers bloodborne pathogens to lymph nodes. **Lymph nodes** filter **lymph**, and white blood cells in the nodes attack any pathogens. The **spleen** filters the blood and removes old red blood cells. T lymphocytes (a kind of white blood cell) mature in the **thymus**.

SECTION 33.11 When the heart stops pumping, blood flow halts and cells begin to die. CPR can keep some oxygenated blood moving to cells, but it cannot restart a heart. Reestablishing the normal rhythm requires a shock from a defibrillator.

Self-Quiz Answers in Appendix VII

1. All vertebrates have _____ .
   a. a closed circulatory system
   b. a two-chambered heart
   c. lungs
   d. all of the above

2. In _____, blood flows through two separate circuits.
   a. birds   b. mammals   c. fish   d. both a and b

3. The _____ circuit carries blood to and from lungs.

Data Analysis Activities

The Stroke Belt Epidemiologists refer to a swath of states in the Southeast (Alabama, Arkansas, Georgia, Mississippi, North Carolina, South Carolina, and Tennessee) as the "stroke belt" because of the unusually high incidence of stroke deaths there. These states have a higher proportion of blacks and more rural residents who have limited access to medical services, compared with other states. **FIGURE 33.24** compares the rates of stroke deaths in stroke-belt states and in New York State.

1. How does the rate of stroke deaths among blacks living in the stroke belt compare with whites in the same region?
2. How does the rate of stroke deaths among blacks living in New York compare with whites in the same region?
3. Which group has the higher rate of stroke deaths, blacks living in New York, or whites living in the stroke belt?
4. Do these data support the hypothesis that the higher proportion of stroke deaths in the stroke belt is more likely to arise from differences in access to health care than from differences in ethnic composition?

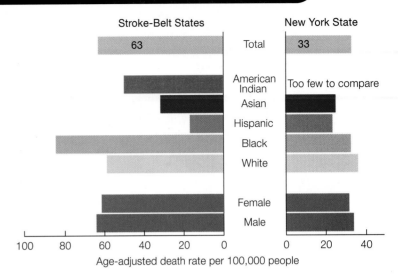

FIGURE 33.24 Comparison of the age-adjusted rate of deaths by stroke in the "stroke-belt" states of the southeastern United States and in New York State. Death risk in each region is broken down by ethnic group and by sex.

---

4. The most abundant protein in plasma is _____ .
   a. hemoglobin   c. albumin
   b. fibrin   d. collagen

5. Platelets function in _____ .
   a. oxygen transport   c. thermal regulation
   b. clotting of blood   d. both a and b

6. Most oxygen in blood is transported _____ .
   a. in red blood cells   c. in platelets
   b. in white blood cells d. dissolved in plasma

7. Blood flows directly from the left atrium to _____ .
   a. the aorta   c. the right atrium
   b. the left ventricle   d. the pulmonary arteries

8. Contraction of _____ drives the flow of blood through the aorta and pulmonary arteries.
   a. atria   b. veins   c. arterioles   d. ventricles

9. Blood pressure is highest in the _____ and lowest in the _____ .
   a. arteries; veins   c. veins; arteries
   b. arterioles; venules   d. capillaries; arterioles

10. At rest, the largest volume of blood is in _____ .
    a. arteries   b. veins   c. capillaries   d. arterioles

11. Which heart chamber has the thickest wall?
    a. right atrium   c. left atrium
    b. right ventricle d. left ventricle

12. A pulmonary _____ carries oxygen-poor blood.
    a. artery   b. vein

13. Lymph nodes filter _____ .
    a. blood   c. plasma
    b. lymph   d. all of the above

14. Which is more dangerous?
    a. atrial fibrillation   b. ventricular fibrillation

15. Match the terms with their descriptions.
    ___ capillary   a. filters out pathogens
    ___ lymph node   b. cardiac pacemaker
    ___ atrium   c. blood vessel with valves
    ___ ventricle   d. largest artery
    ___ SA node   e. receives blood from veins
    ___ vein   f. exchange site
    ___ aorta   g. receives blood from atrium

Critical Thinking

1. Long-distance flights can raise the risk of thrombus formation. Physicians suggest that air travelers drink plenty of fluids and periodically walk around the cabin. Explain how these precautions lower the risk of clot formation.

2. Explain why a blood clot that forms in the leg, then breaks free as an embolus, is more likely to become stuck in a lung than in the brain.

3. Beta blockers are drugs that interfere with stimulation of organs by nerves of the sympathetic system. Would these drugs be used to treat an excessively slow heart rate or an excessively high one?

SOURCE: (24) National Vital Statistics System—Mortality (NVSS-M), NCHS, CDC.

A human T cell (pink) scans the surface of a dendritic cell (blue) wrapped around it. If the T cell recognizes molecules on the dendritic cell that signal danger such as a bacterial invader, the T cell will initiate an immune response specifically targeting the threat.

34

IMMUNITY

Links to Earlier Concepts

This chapter revisits bacteria and viruses (Sections 4.4, 19.1, 19.2) as pathogens. Proteins (3.4), cell structure and function (4.10, 5.8), genetics (13.4), the internal environment (28.1), epithelia and skin (28.3, 28.8), the nervous system (29.4, 29.9), the circulatory and lymphatic systems (33.4, 33.7, 33.10), and diseases (15.6, 33.9) come up again in the context of immunity.

KEY CONCEPTS

IMMUNE DEFENSES
Vertebrates have three lines of immune defense: surface barriers, innate immunity, and adaptive immunity. White blood cells and signaling molecules function in immune responses.

SURFACE BARRIERS
Body surfaces come into constant contact with microbial pathogens. Physical, mechanical, and chemical barriers prevent most microbes from entering body tissues.

INNATE IMMUNITY
Innate immune responses involve a set of general, fast defenses—phagocytic white blood cells, complement, inflammation, and fever—that quickly rid the body of most invaders.

ADAPTIVE IMMUNITY
In an adaptive immune response, white blood cells interact to destroy specific pathogens or altered body cells. Antibodies and other antigen receptors are central to these responses.

IMMUNITY IN OUR LIVES
Vaccines are important in worldwide health programs. Allergies, immune deficiencies, and autoimmune disorders are the result of faulty immune mechanisms.

Photograph, Dr. Olivier Schwartz, Institut Pasteur/Science Source.

TABLE 34.1

Innate and Adaptive Immunity Compared

	Innate Immunity	Adaptive Immunity
Response time	Immediate	About a week
How antigen is detected	Fixed set of receptors for pathogen-associated molecular patterns (PAMPs)	Antigen receptors produced by gene recombinations
Specificity	About 1,000 PAMPs	Billions of antigens
Antigen memory	None	Long-term

FIGURE 34.1 One physical barrier to infection: Mucus and the mechanical action of cilia can keep pathogens from getting a foothold in the airways that lead to the lungs. Bacteria and other particles get stuck in mucus secreted by goblet cells (gold). Cilia (pink) on other cells sweep the mucus toward the throat for disposal.

INTEGRATED RESPONSES TO THREATS

You continually cross paths with a tremendous array of viruses, bacteria, fungi, parasitic worms, and other agents of disease, but you need not lose sleep over this. Humans coevolved with these pathogens, so you have defenses that protect your body from them. The evolution of **immunity**, an organism's capacity to resist and combat infection, began well before multicelled eukaryotes evolved from free-living cells. Mutations in the genes for membrane proteins introduced new molecular patterns that were unique in cells of a given type. As multicellularity evolved, so did mechanisms of identifying the patterns as self, or belonging to one's own body.

By about 1 billion years ago, nonself recognition had also evolved. Cells of all modern multicelled eukaryotes bear a set of receptors that collectively can recognize around 1,000 different nonself cues, which are called pathogen-associated molecular patterns (PAMPs). As their name suggests, PAMPs occur mainly on or in pathogens. They include proteins that make up bacterial flagella and pili (Section 4.4), some components of bacterial cell walls, double-stranded RNA unique to some viruses, and so on. A PAMP is an example of **antigen**, which is any molecule or particle recognized by the body as nonself. Binding of a cell's receptors to antigen triggers a set of immediate, general defense responses. In mammals, for example, the binding activates **complement**: a set of proteins that circulate in inactive form throughout the body in blood and tissue fluids. Activated complement proteins mark antigenic particles for uptake by phagocytic white blood cells (Section 5.8), and they can also destroy foreign cells.

Pattern receptors and the responses they trigger are part of **innate immunity**, a set of immediate, general defenses that help protect all multicelled organisms from infection. Vertebrate animals have an additional set of defenses carried out by interacting cells, tissues, and proteins. This **adaptive immunity** tailors immune defenses to a vast array of specific pathogens that an individual may encounter during its lifetime. **TABLE 34.1** compares the two types of immunity.

THREE LINES OF DEFENSE

The mechanisms of adaptive immunity evolved within the context of innate immunity. The two systems were once thought to operate independently of each other, but we now know they function together. We describe both systems together in terms of three lines of defense. The first line of defense includes the physical, chemical, and neutrophil monocyte basophil lymphocyte eosinophil

mechanical barriers that usually keep pathogens from entering the internal environment (**FIGURE 34.1**). Innate immunity, the second line of defense, begins after a tissue is damaged, or after antigen is detected inside the body. Its general response mechanisms quickly rid the body of many invaders. An innate immune response triggers adaptive immunity, the third line of defense. White blood cells divide to form huge populations that target a specific antigen and destroy anything bearing it. Some white blood cells that form during an adaptive response persist after the infection ends. If the same antigen returns, these memory cells mount a secondary response.

THE DEFENDERS

White blood cells participate in both innate and adaptive immune responses. Many kinds circulate through the body in blood and lymph; others populate the lymph nodes, spleen, and other tissues. A few are shown in **FIGURE 34.2**. All communicate with one another by secreting and responding to chemical signaling molecules. These molecules, which include proteins and polypeptides called **cytokines**, allow cells throughout the body to coordinate their activities during an immune response.

Different types of white blood cells are specialized for specific tasks. Those that are phagocytic engulf and digest pathogens, dead cells, or other particles. **Neutrophils**, which circulate in blood, are the most abundant phagocytic cell. Phagocytic **macrophages** that migrate through tissues and tissue fluids develop from monocytes that patrol the blood. **Dendritic cells**, which are also phagocyic, alert the adaptive immune system to the presence of antigen in solid tissue.

Many white blood cells have secretory vesicles called granules, which can contain cytokines, local signaling molecules, destructive enzymes, and toxins such as hydrogen peroxide. In response to a trigger such as antigen binding, these cells degranulate (they release the contents of their granules). Neutrophils have granules, as do **eosinophils** that target parasites too big for phagocytosis. **Basophils** and **mast cells** degranulate in response to injury or antigen. Mast cells, unlike most other white blood cells, stay anchored in tissues. These cells are often closely associated with nerves, and they

also degranulate in response to signaling molecules secreted by cells of the endocrine and nervous systems.

Lymphocytes are a special category of white blood cells that have a central role in adaptive immunity. There are several kinds of **T cells** (T lymphocytes), including cytotoxic T cells that can kill infected or cancerous body cells. **B cells** (B lymphocytes) make antibodies. A lymphocyte called an **NK cell** (natural killer cell) kills cancerous body cells undetectable by cytotoxic T cells. Collectively, lymphocytes have the capacity to target billions of specific antigens.

adaptive immunity In vertebrates, set of immune defenses that can be tailored to specific pathogens encountered by an organism during its lifetime.
antigen A molecule or particle that the immune system recognizes as nonself. Triggers an immune response.
B cell B lymphocyte. Lymphocyte that can make antibodies.
basophil Circulating white blood cell with granules.
complement A set of proteins that circulate in inactive form in blood, and when activated play a role in immune responses.
cytokines Signaling molecules secreted by white blood cells.
dendritic cell Phagocytic white blood cell that alerts the immune system to the presence of antigen in solid tissues.
eosinophil White blood cell that targets multicelled parasites.
immunity The body's ability to resist and fight infections.
innate immunity In all multicelled organisms, set of immediate, general defenses against infection.
macrophage Phagocytic white blood cell that patrols tissues and tissue fluids.
mast cell White blood cell with granules that is anchored in many tissues; factor in inflammation.
neutrophil Circulating phagocytic white blood cell.
NK cell Natural killer cell. Lymphocyte that can kill cancer cells undetectable by cytotoxic T cells.
T cell T lymphocyte. Lymphocyte central to adaptive immunity; some kinds target infected or cancerous body cells.

TAKE-HOME MESSAGE 34.1

Innate immunity of multicelled organisms comprises a system of immediate, general defenses that are triggered by a fixed number of antigens.

Vertebrate adaptive immunity is a system of defenses that can specifically target billions of different antigens.

White blood cells are central to both systems; signaling molecules such as cytokines integrate their activities.

FIGURE 34.3 The bacterial cause of acne, *Propionibacterium acnes*.

0.5 µm

A One of the bacterial species in plaque, *Streptococcus mutans*, is a major contributor to tooth decay and periodontitis.

B Micrograph of toothbrush bristles scrubbing plaque on the surface of a tooth.

FIGURE 34.4 Dental plaque.

NORMAL FLORA

Your skin is in constant contact with the external environment, so it picks up many microorganisms. It normally teems with about 200 different kinds of yeast, protozoa, and bacteria. If you showered today, there are probably thousands of microorganisms on every square inch of your external surfaces. If you did not, there may be billions. They tend to flourish in warm, moist areas, such as between the toes. Huge populations inhabit cavities and tubes that open on the body's surface, including the eyes, nose, mouth, and anal and genital openings.

Microorganisms that typically live on human surfaces, including the interior tubes and cavities of the digestive and respiratory tracts, are called **normal flora**. Our surfaces provide them with a stable environment and nutrients. In return, their populations deter more dangerous species from colonizing (and penetrating) body surfaces. Normal flora in the digestive tract help us digest food, and they also make essential nutrients such as vitamins K and B_{12}.

Normal flora are helpful only on body surfaces; many can cause or worsen many conditions when they invade tissues. Consider a major constituent of normal flora, *Propionibacterium acnes* (**FIGURE 34.3**). This bacterium feeds on sebum, a greasy mixture of fats, waxes, and glycerides that lubricates hair and skin. Glands in the skin secrete sebum into hair follicles. During puberty, higher levels of steroid hormones trigger an increase in sebum production. Excess sebum combines with dead, shed skin cells and blocks the openings of hair follicles. *P. acnes* can survive on the surface of the skin, but far prefers anaerobic habitats such as the interior of blocked hair follicles. There, they multiply to tremendous numbers. Secretions of the flourishing *P. acnes* populations leak into internal tissues of the follicles and initiate inflammation. The resulting pustules are called acne.

A few of the 400 or so species of normal flora in the mouth are part of **dental plaque**, a thick biofilm of various bacteria and occasional archaea, their extracellular products, and saliva glycoproteins. Plaque sticks tenaciously to teeth (**FIGURE 34.4**). Some of the bacteria in plaque are fermenters. The lactic acid they produce dissolves minerals that make up the tooth, resulting in holes called cavities.

In young, healthy people, tight junctions (Section 4.10) normally seal gum epithelium to teeth. The tight seal prevents oral microorganisms from entering gum tissue. As we age, the connective tissue beneath the epithelium thins, so the seal between gums and teeth weakens. Deep pockets form, and a nasty collection of anaerobic bacteria and archaea tends to accumulate in them. The microorganisms secrete destructive enzymes and acids that cause

CREDITS: (3) Kwangshin Kim/Science Source; (4) www.zahnarzt-stuttgart.com.

inflammation of the surrounding gum tissues, a condition called periodontitis. Periodontal wounds are an open door to the circulatory system and its arteries, and all species of oral bacteria associated with periodontitis are also found in atherosclerotic plaque. Atherosclerosis is now known to be a disease of inflammation. What role oral microorganisms play in atherosclerosis is not yet clear, but one thing is certain: They contribute to the inflammation that fuels coronary artery disease.

Other serious illnesses associated with normal flora include pneumonia; ulcers; colitis; whooping cough; meningitis; abscesses of the lung and brain; and cancers of the colon, stomach, and intestine. The bacterial agent of tetanus, *Clostridium tetani*, is considered a normal inhabitant of human intestines. The bacteria responsible for diphtheria, *Corynebacterium diphtheriae*, was normal skin flora before widespread use of the vaccine eradicated the disease. *Staphylococcus aureus*, a resident of human skin and linings of the mouth, nose, throat, and intestines, is also a leading cause of human bacterial disease. Antibiotic-resistant strains of *S. aureus* are now widespread. A particularly dangerous kind, MRSA (methicillin-resistant *S. aureus*), is resistant to a wide range of antibiotics. MRSA is now a permanent resident of hospitals worldwide (Section 17.14).

BARRIERS TO INFECTION

In contrast to body surfaces, the blood and tissue fluids of healthy people are typically sterile (free of microorganisms). Surface barriers (TABLE 34.2) usually prevent normal flora from entering the body's internal environment. The tough outer layer of skin (Section 28.8) is an example. Microorganisms flourish on skin's waterproof, oily surface, but they rarely penetrate its thick layer of dead cells (FIGURE 34.5). The thinner epithelial tissues that line the body's interior tubes and cavities also have surface barriers. Sticky mucus secreted by cells of these linings can trap microorganisms. The mucus contains **lysozyme**, an enzyme that kills bacteria. In the sinuses and respiratory tract, the coordinated beating of cilia sweeps trapped microorganisms away before they have a chance to breach the delicate walls of these structures.

Your mouth is a particularly inviting habitat for microorganisms because it offers plenty of nutrients, warmth, moisture, and surfaces for colonization. Accordingly, it harbors huge populations of normal flora that can resist lysozyme in saliva. Microorganisms that get swallowed are typically killed by gastric fluid, a potent brew of protein-digesting enzymes and acid in the stomach. Any that survive passage to the small intestine are usually killed by strong salts secreted into the fluid there. The hardy ones

TABLE 34.2

Examples of Surface Barriers

Mechanical	Mucus; broomlike action of cilia; flushing action of tears, saliva, urination, diarrhea
Chemical	Secretions (sebum, other waxy coatings); low pH of urine, gastric juices, urinary and vaginal tracts; lysozyme
Physical	Established populations of normal flora; epithelia that line tubes and cavities such as the gut and eye sockets; skin

skin surface

dead cells

living cells

5 μm

FIGURE 34.5 One surface barrier to infection: the epidermis of human skin. Its thick, waterproof layer of dead cells usually keeps normal skin flora from penetrating internal tissues.

that reach the large intestine must compete with about 500 resident species that are specialized to live there and have already established large populations. Any that displace normal flora are typically flushed out by diarrhea.

Lactic acid produced by *Lactobacillus* helps keep the vaginal pH outside the range of tolerance of most fungi and other bacteria. Urination's flushing action usually prevents pathogens from colonizing the urinary tract.

dental plaque On teeth, a thick biofilm composed of bacteria, their extracellular products, and saliva proteins.
lysozyme Antibacterial enzyme in body secretions such as saliva and mucus.
normal flora Microorganisms that typically live on human surfaces, including the interior tubes and cavities of the digestive and respiratory tracts.

TAKE-HOME MESSAGE 34.2

Surface barriers usually keep microorganisms that contact or inhabit body surfaces from invading the internal environment.

Skin's tough epidermis is one barrier to infection. Mucus, lysozyme, and the sweeping action of cilia can protect the linings of internal tubes and cavities.

Resident populations of normal flora deter more dangerous microorganisms from colonizing the body's internal and external surfaces.

CREDITS: (5) Veronika Burmeister/Visuals Unlimited, Inc.; (Table 34.2) © Cengage Learning.

What happens if a pathogen slips by surface defenses and enters the body's internal environment? A second line of defense—the fast-acting, general mechanisms of innate immunity—can keep an invading pathogen from establishing a population in body tissues or fluids.

COMPLEMENT

Inactive forms of about 30 different kinds of complement proteins circulate in the blood and interstitial fluid of vertebrate animals. Some of these proteins become activated when they encounter cytoplasmic or mitochondrial proteins leaking out of damaged body cells. Others are activated by antigen, or antibody bound to antigen (we return to antibodies in the next section). Activated complement proteins activate other complement proteins, which activate other complement proteins, and so on. These cascading

reactions quickly produce huge amounts of activated complement. The activated proteins diffuse into surrounding tissues to form a concentration gradient around an affected site. Some activated complement proteins bind to pathogens, forming a coating that encourages phagocytic white blood cells to engulf them. Others assemble into structures that can insert themselves into a lipid bilayer of a foreign cell or ailing body cell, opening large channels in the plasma membrane that cause the cell to burst (FIGURE 34.6A).

Healthy body cells continuously produce proteins that inactivate complement, a negative feedback mechanism that prevents a complement activation cascade from spreading too far into healthy tissue. Microorganisms do not make these proteins, so they are preferentially singled out for destruction.

PHAGOCYTOSIS

Dendritic cells, macrophages, and neutrophils bear receptors for activated complement, and these phagocytic cells can follow a complement gradient back to its origin. Dendritic cells are concentrated in the lining of respiratory airways and other tissues that contact the external environment. Phagocytosis by these cells plays a critical role in protecting the lungs from pathogens and other harmful particles. However, the main function of dendritic cells is to present antigen to T cells (more on how this works in Section 34.6).

Macrophages in interstitial fluid engulf essentially everything except undamaged body cells, but they are more than just scavengers. Upon engulfing antigen, a macrophage secretes cytokines that alert the adaptive immune system to the presence of the threat.

A neutrophil that engulfs a microorganism degranulates, and the released enzymes and toxins destroy all cells in the vicinity—even healthy body cells. Recently, researchers discovered that neutrophils literally explode in response to a certain combination of signaling molecules and complement, in the process ejecting their nuclear DNA and associated proteins along with the contents of their granules. The mixture solidifies into a net that traps pathogens in the vicinity of the released antimicrobial compounds (FIGURE 34.6B). Neutrophil nets are very effective at killing bacteria.

INFLAMMATION

Tissue damage or infection triggers **inflammation**, a fast, local response that simultaneously destroys affected tissues and jump-starts the healing process (FIGURE 34.7). Inflammation begins when a white blood cell degranulates. Degranulation can occur in response to a number of stimuli, including pattern receptor binding to antigen, for example on the surface of a bacterium ❶. Activated complement proteins also trigger degranulation when they bind to receptors on a

membrane attack complex   pore

A Complement. Activated complement can assemble into membrane attack complexes that insert themselves into a lipid bilayer (*left*). The resulting pores (*right*) cause the cell to burst.

B Neutrophil nets. Two *Klebsiella* bacteria (purple) are ensnared in material that has been ejected by a neutrophil in lung tissue.

FIGURE 34.6 {**Animated**} Two mechanisms of adaptive immunity, complement activation and neutrophil nets.

CREDITS: (6A) left, From Starr/Evers/Starr, Biology Today and Tomorrow with Physiology, 4E. © 2013 Cengage Learning; right, Robert R. Dourmashkin, courtesy of Clinical Research Centre, Harrow, England; (6B) ©2010, Papayannopoulos et al. Originally published in J. Cell Biol. 191:677–691.doi: 10.1083/jcb.201006052 (Image by Volker Brinkman and Abdul Hakkim).

white blood cell's plasma membrane. Among the substances released by a degranulating cell are local signaling molecules called prostaglandins and histamines ❷. The release of these substances has two effects. First, nearby arterioles widen. Blood flow to the area increases, speeding the arrival of more white blood cells. Second, spaces open between cells that make up nearby capillary walls. Phagocytic white blood cells easily exit the capillaries through the spaces ❸. By the time this occurs, any invading cells have become coated with activated complement ❹, which makes them easy targets for the phagocytic cells ❺.

Symptoms of inflammation include redness and warmth that result from increased blood flow to the affected area. The increased permeability of capillary walls allows plasma proteins to escape into interstitial fluid. The fluid becomes hypertonic with respect to blood, and water follows by osmosis. The tissue swells with excess fluid, putting pressure on nerves and thus causing pain.

Inflammation continues as long as its triggers do. Once these stimuli subside, for example after invading bacteria have been cleared from an infected tissue, macrophages produce compounds that suppress inflammation and promote tissue repair. If the stimulus persists, inflammation becomes chronic. Chronic inflammation does not benefit the body. Rather, it causes or contributes to many diseases, including asthma, Crohn's disease, rheumatoid arthritis, atherosclerosis, diabetes, and cancer.

FEVER

Infection sometimes causes **fever**, which is a temporary rise in body temperature above the normal 37°C (98.6°F). Some cytokines stimulate brain cells to make and release prostaglandins, which act on the hypothalamus (Section 29.9) to raise the body's internal temperature set point. As long as the temperature of the body is below the new set point, the hypothalamus sends out signals that cause blood vessels in the skin to constrict, which reduces heat loss from the skin. The signals also trigger reflexive movements called shivering, or "chills," that increase the metabolic heat output of muscles. Together, these responses raise the body's internal temperature.

Fever enhances immune defenses by increasing the rate of enzyme activity, thus speeding up metabolism, tissue repair, and the formation and activity of phagocytic cells. Higher temperature also slows the rate of division in some pathogens, and this gives white blood cells an advantage in the proliferation race against them (more about this in Sections 34.6 and 34.8).

A fever is a sign that the body is fighting something, so it should never be ignored. However, a fever of 40.6°C

FIGURE 34.7 {Animated} Example of inflammation as a response to bacterial infection.
❶ Pattern receptors on mast cells in the tissue recognize and bind to bacterial antigen.
❷ The mast cells release signaling molecules (blue dots) that cause arterioles to widen. The resulting increase in blood flow reddens and warms the tissue.
❸ The signaling molecules also increase capillary permeability, which allows phagocytic white blood cells to squeeze through the vessel walls into the tissue. Plasma proteins that leak out of the capillaries cause the tissue to swell with fluid.
❹ Bacterial antigens activate complement (purple dots). Activated complement binds to the bacteria.
❺ Phagocytic white blood cells in the tissue quickly recognize and engulf the complement-coated bacteria.

(105°F) or less does not necessarily require treatment in an otherwise healthy adult. Body temperature usually will not rise above that value, but if it does, immediate hospitalization is recommended because a fever of 42°C (107.6°F) can result in brain damage or death.

fever A temporary, internally induced rise in core body temperature above the normal set point.
inflammation A local response to tissue damage or infection; characterized by redness, warmth, swelling, and pain.

TAKE-HOME MESSAGE 34.3

Antigen or tissue damage activates complement. Activated complement recruits phagocytic white blood cells, coats pathogens in an affected area, and kills foreign or ailing cells.

Phagocytic white blood cells release cytokines after engulfing antigen-bearing particles such as complement-coated microorganisms. The cytokines trigger fever and alert the immune system to the presence of the threat.

Inflammation occurs when granular white blood cells release local signaling molecules that increase blood flow and attract phagocytic cells to a site of tissue damage or infection.

If innate immune mechanisms do not quickly rid the body of an invading pathogen, an infection may become established in internal tissues. By that time, long-lasting mechanisms of adaptive immunity have already begun to target the invaders specifically. These mechanisms are triggered by white blood cells that detect antigen via antigen receptors. Plasma membrane proteins that recognize PAMPs are one type of antigen receptor. Your T cells bear special antigen receptors called **T cell receptors**, or TCRs. Part of a TCR recognizes antigen as nonself. Another part recognizes certain proteins in the plasma membrane of body cells as self. These self-proteins are called **MHC markers** (*left*) after the major histocompatibility complex genes that encode them. MHC genes have thousands of alleles, so the cells of even closely related individuals rarely bear the same MHC markers.

an MHC marker

Antibodies are another type of antigen receptor. **Antibodies** are Y-shaped proteins made and secreted by B cells. Many antibodies circulate in blood, and they can enter interstitial fluid during inflammation, but they do not kill pathogens directly. Instead, they activate complement and facilitate phagocytosis. Antibody binding can prevent pathogens from attaching to body cells, and also neutralize some toxic molecules.

Each antibody molecule can bind to a specific antigen. The tips of the "Y" are two antigen-binding sites with a specific distribution of bumps, grooves, and charge. These sites are the receptor part of an antibody: They can bind only to antigen with a complementary distribution of bumps, grooves, and charge (**FIGURE 34.8**). Antigen-binding sites vary greatly among antibodies, so they are called hypervariable regions. Each antibody also has a constant region that determines its structural identity, or class: IgG, IgA, IgE, IgM, or IgD (Ig stands for immunoglobulin, another name for antibody). The different classes serve different functions (**TABLE 34.3**). Most of the antibodies circulating in blood and tissue fluids are IgG, which binds pathogens, neutralizes toxins, and activates complement. IgG is the only antibody that can cross the placenta to protect a fetus before its own immune system is active.

heavy chain variable region
binding site for antigen
light chain variable region
light chain constant region
heavy chain constant region

A An antibody molecule consists of four polypeptide chains joined in a Y-shaped configuration. The chains fold up to form two antigen-binding sites.

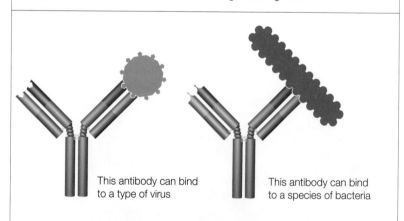

This antibody can bind to a type of virus

This antibody can bind to a species of bacteria

B The antigen-binding sites of each antibody are unique. They bind only to an antigen that has a complementary distribution of bumps, grooves, and charge.

FIGURE 34.8 Antibody structure.

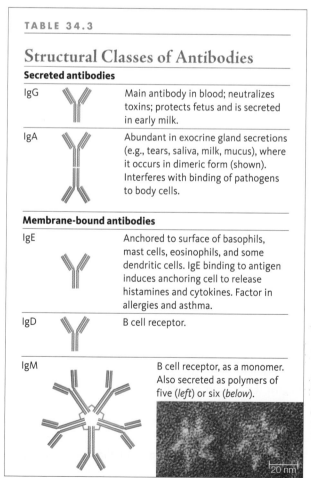

TABLE 34.3

Structural Classes of Antibodies

Secreted antibodies

IgG		Main antibody in blood; neutralizes toxins; protects fetus and is secreted in early milk.
IgA		Abundant in exocrine gland secretions (e.g., tears, saliva, milk, mucus), where it occurs in dimeric form (shown). Interferes with binding of pathogens to body cells.

Membrane-bound antibodies

IgE		Anchored to surface of basophils, mast cells, eosinophils, and some dendritic cells. IgE binding to antigen induces anchoring cell to release histamines and cytokines. Factor in allergies and asthma.
IgD		B cell receptor.
IgM		B cell receptor, as a monomer. Also secreted as polymers of five (*left*) or six (*below*).

20 nm

CREDITS: (in text, 8, Table 34.3 left) From Starr/Taggart/Evers/Starr, Biology, 13E. © 2013 Cengage Learning; (Table 34.3 right) © R. Dourmashkin/Wellcome Images.

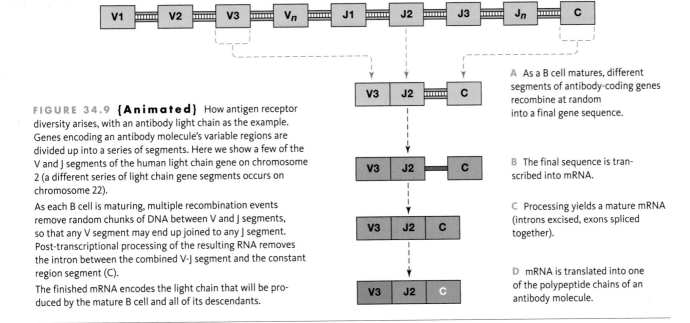

FIGURE 34.9 {Animated} How antigen receptor diversity arises, with an antibody light chain as the example. Genes encoding an antibody molecule's variable regions are divided up into a series of segments. Here we show a few of the V and J segments of the human light chain gene on chromosome 2 (a different series of light chain gene segments occurs on chromosome 22).

As each B cell is maturing, multiple recombination events remove random chunks of DNA between V and J segments, so that any V segment may end up joined to any J segment. Post-transcriptional processing of the resulting RNA removes the intron between the combined V-J segment and the constant region segment (C).

The finished mRNA encodes the light chain that will be produced by the mature B cell and all of its descendants.

A As a B cell matures, different segments of antibody-coding genes recombine at random into a final gene sequence.

B The final sequence is transcribed into mRNA.

C Processing yields a mature mRNA (introns excised, exons spliced together).

D mRNA is translated into one of the polypeptide chains of an antibody molecule.

IgA is the main antibody in mucus and other exocrine gland secretions (Section 28.3). IgA is secreted as a dimer (two antibodies bound together), which makes the molecule stable enough to patrol harsh environments such as the interior of the digestive tract. There, IgA encounters pathogens before they contact body cells. Bound to antigen, IgA interacts with mast cells, basophils, macrophages, and NK cells to initiate inflammation.

IgE made and secreted by B cells gets incorporated into the plasma membrane of mast cells, basophils, and some types of dendritic cells. Binding of antigen to membrane-bound IgE triggers the anchoring cell to release the contents of its granules.

B cell

B cell receptor

B cell receptors are IgM or IgD antibodies that are not secreted; they stay attached to the B cell's plasma membrane. IgM is also secreted as polymers of five or six antibodies. The polymers are very efficient at binding antigen and activating complement.

ANTIGEN RECEPTOR DIVERSITY

Humans can make billions of unique antigen receptors. This diversity arises because the genes that encode these receptors occur in several segments on different chromosomes, and there are several different versions of each segment (FIGURE 34.9). The segments become spliced together during B and T cell differentiation, but which version of each segment gets spliced into the antigen receptor gene of a particular cell is random. As a B cell or

T cell differentiates, it ends up with one of about 2.5 billion different combinations of gene segments.

Like all other blood cells, lymphocytes form in bone marrow. A new B cell is already making receptors before it even leaves the marrow. The base of each receptor is embedded in the lipid bilayer of the cell's plasma membrane, and the two arms of the "Y" project into the extracellular environment. A mature B cell bristles with more than 100,000 receptors. T cells also form in bone marrow, but they mature in the thymus gland, which is part of the endocrine system (Section 31.2). There, they encounter hormones that stimulate them to make receptors.

---

antibody Y-shaped antigen receptor protein made only by B cells.
B cell receptor Antigen receptor on the surface of a B cell; an antibody that has not been released from the B cell's plasma membrane.
MHC markers Self-proteins on the surface of human body cells.
T cell receptor (TCR) Antigen receptor on the surface of a T cell.

TAKE-HOME MESSAGE 34.4

Each B cell and T cell makes antigen receptors that can bind a specific antigen. Humans are capable of producing billions of unique antigen receptors.

Antibodies released into the circulatory system activate complement and facilitate phagocytosis. B cell receptors are antibodies that are not secreted; they remain attached to the B cell's plasma membrane.

T cell receptors can discriminate between self (MHC markers) and nonself (antigen).

TWO ARMS OF ADAPTIVE IMMUNITY

Like a boxer's one-two punch, adaptive immunity has two separate arms: two types of responses that work together to eliminate diverse threats. Why two arms? Not all threats present themselves in the same way. For example, bacteria, fungi, or toxins can circulate in blood or interstitial fluid. These threats are intercepted quickly by phagocytic cells that initiate an **antibody-mediated immune response**. In this response, B cells are triggered to make antibodies specific to antigen detected in extracellular fluid. However, an antibody-mediated immune response is not the most effective way of countering other threats. For example, viruses, bacteria, fungi, and protists that reproduce inside body cells may be vulnerable to an antibody-mediated response only when they slip out of one cell to infect another. Such intracellular pathogens are targeted primarily by the **cell-mediated immune response**, in which cytotoxic T cells and NK cells detect and destroy infected or cancerous body cells.

FIGURE 34.10 {Animated} Primary and secondary immune responses. A first exposure to an antigen causes a primary immune response in which effector cells fight the infection. Memory cells that also form initiate a faster, stronger secondary response if the antigen returns at a later time.

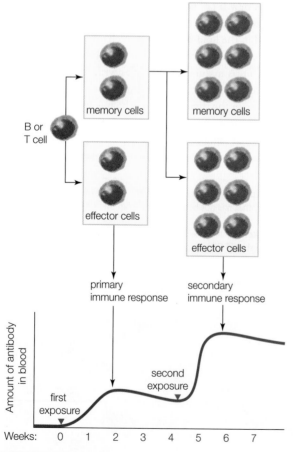

Effector cells form during both antibody-mediated and cell-mediated immune responses. **Effector cells** are lymphocytes that act at once in a primary immune response. Some **memory cells** also form, and these long-lived lymphocytes are reserved for possible future encounters with the same antigen. Memory cells can persist for decades after the initial infection ends. If the same antigen enters the body at a later time, these memory cells carry out a faster, stronger secondary response (**FIGURE 34.10**).

Lymphocytes interact with phagocytic cells to effect the four defining characteristics of adaptive immunity:

Self/Nonself Recognition, based on the ability of T cell receptors to recognize self (in the form of MHC markers), and that of all antigen receptors to recognize nonself (in the form of antigen).

Specificity, which means that adaptive immune responses are tailored to combat specific antigens.

Diversity, which refers to the diversity of antigen receptors on a body's collection of lymphocytes. There are potentially billions of different antigen receptors, so an individual has the potential to counter billions of different threats.

Memory, the capacity of the adaptive immune system to "remember" an antigen (via memory cells). It takes about a week for B and T cells to respond in force the first time they encounter an antigen. If the same antigen shows up again, the response is faster and stronger.

INTERCEPTING ANTIGEN

A new lymphocyte is "naive," which means that no antigen has bound to its receptors yet. B cell receptors can bind directly to antigen, but T cell receptors cannot. T cell receptors recognize and bind only to antigen that has been processed by an antigen-presenting cell. Macrophages, B cells, and dendritic cells do the processing and presenting (**FIGURE 34.11**). First, one of these cells engulfs a bacterium or any other antigen-bearing particle ❶. A vesicle that contains the antigen-bearing particle forms in the

antibody-mediated immune response Immune response in which antibodies are produced in response to an antigen.
cell-mediated immune response Immune response involving cytotoxic T cells and NK cells that destroy infected or cancerous body cells.
effector cell Antigen-sensitized B cell or T cell that forms in an immune response and acts immediately.
memory cell Long-lived, antigen-sensitized B cell or T cell that can act in a secondary immune response.

MHC molecule

lysosome

① ② ③ ④

FIGURE 34.11 Antigen processing: What happens when a B cell, macrophage, or dendritic cell engulfs an antigenic particle (here, a bacterium).

❶ An endocytic vesicle forms around a bacterium as it is engulfed by a phagocytic cell.

❷ The vesicle fuses with a lysosome, which contains enzymes and MHC molecules.

❸ Lysosomal enzymes digest the bacterium to molecular bits. The bits bind to MHC molecules.

❹ The vesicle fuses with the cell's plasma membrane by exocytosis. When it does, the antigen–MHC complex becomes displayed on the cell's surface.

cell's cytoplasm and fuses with a lysosome ❷. Remember from Section 4.6 that lysosomes are vesicles filled with powerful digestive enzymes. These enzymes now proceed to break down the ingested particle into molecular bits. Lysosomes also contain MHC markers that bind to some of the antigen-bearing bits ❸. The resulting antigen–MHC complexes become displayed at the cell's surface when the vesicles fuse with (and become part of) the plasma membrane ❹. The display of MHC markers paired with antigen fragments serves as a call to arms for T cells.

Antigen-bearing particles in blood end up in the spleen; those in solid tissues or interstitial fluid end up in lymph nodes. Phagocytic white blood cells migrate to these organs after engulfing antigen-bearing particles. Particles can also enter these organs directly, in which case they are engulfed by dendritic cells, macrophages, and B cells stationed inside. Either way, the antigen-bearing particles are processed by phagocytic cells, which become antigen-presenting cells.

Every day, billions of T cells filter through each lymph node and the spleen. As they do, they come into close contact with arrays of antigen-presenting cells that have taken up residence in these organs (**FIGURE 34.12**). As you will see shortly, T cells with receptors that recognize and bind to antigen presented by a phagocytic cell stimulate production of effector cells that carry out an immune response. During an infection, the lymph nodes swell because T cells accumulate inside them. When you are ill, you may notice your swollen lymph nodes as tender lumps under the jaw or elsewhere in your body. The tide of battle turns when the effector cells have destroyed most of the antigen-bearing agents. With less antigen present, fewer lymphocytes form.

FIGURE 34.12 Lymph is filtered through at least one node before it merges with the bloodstream. The fluorescence micrograph shows T cells (blue) that are passing through a lymph node and interacting with populations of resident B cells (green) and antigen-presenting dendritic cells (red).

TAKE-HOME MESSAGE 34.5

Lymphocytes interact with phagocytic white blood cells to bring about vertebrate adaptive immunity, which has four defining characteristics: self/nonself recognition, specificity, diversity, and memory.

The two arms of adaptive immunity work together. Antibody-mediated responses target antigen in blood or interstitial fluid; cell-mediated responses target altered body cells.

Effector and memory cells form during adaptive responses. Memory cells are set aside; if the antigen returns at a later time, these cells initiate a faster, stronger secondary response.

T cell receptors can recognize their specific antigen only in conjunction with MHC markers displayed on the surface of an antigen-presenting cell. The recognition process occurs in lymph nodes and the spleen.

CREDITS: (11) © Cengage Learning; (12 top) Image courtesy of Dr. Fabien Garcon, The Babraham Institute; (12 bottom) From Starr/Taggart/Evers/Starr, Biology, 13E. © 2013 Cengage Learning.

34.6 WHAT HAPPENS DURING AN ANTIBODY-MEDIATED IMMUNE RESPONSE?

In an antibody-mediated immune response, B cells are triggered to make antibodies specific to a particular antigenic particle detected in extracellular fluid. This type of response is often called the humoral response, because it pertains mainly to elements in the blood and other

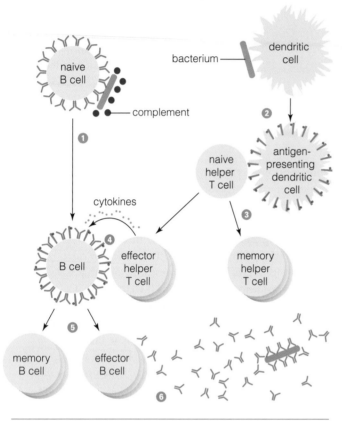

FIGURE 34.13 {**Animated**} Example of an antibody-mediated immune response.

❶ B cell receptors on a naive B cell bind to an antigen on the surface of a bacterium (red). The bacterium's complement coating (purple dots) triggers the B cell to engulf it. Bacterial fragments bound to MHC markers become displayed at the surface of the B cell.

❷ A dendritic cell engulfs the same kind of bacterium that the B cell encountered. Bacterial fragments bound to MHC markers become displayed at the surface of the dendritic cell.

❸ Antigen–MHC complexes displayed by the dendritic cell are recognized by TCRs on a naive helper T cell. The two cells interact, and then the T cell begins to divide repeatedly by mitosis. Its descendants differentiate into effector and memory cells.

❹ TCRs on one of the effector cells recognize and bind to the antigen–MHC complexes on the B cell. Binding causes the T cell to secrete cytokines (blue dots).

❺ The cytokines induce the B cell to undergo repeated mitotic divisions. Its many descendants differentiate into effector B cells and memory B cells.

❻ The effector B cells begin making and secreting huge numbers of antibodies, all of which recognize the same antigen as the original B cell receptor. The new antibodies circulate throughout the body and bind to any remaining bacteria.

body fluids (from Latin *umor*, body fluid). The secreted antibodies bind to the antigenic particle, thus facilitating its uptake by phagocytic white blood cells. Bound antibodies also can keep a pathogen from infecting other cells, neutralize a toxin, and help eliminate both from the body.

If we liken B cells to assassins, then each one has a genetic assignment to liquidate one particular target: an antigen-bearing extracellular pathogen or toxin. Antibodies are their molecular bullets, as the following example illustrates. Suppose that you accidentally nick your finger. Being opportunists, some *Staphylococcus aureus* cells on your skin immediately enter the cut, invading your internal environment. Complement in interstitial fluid quickly attaches to carbohydrates in the bacterial cell walls, and complement activation cascades begin.

Within an hour, complement-coated bacteria tumbling along in lymph vessels reach a lymph node. There, they filter past an army of naive B cells (**FIGURE 34.13**). One of the naive B cells residing in that lymph node makes antigen receptors that recognize a polysaccharide in *S. aureus* cell walls ❶. Via those receptors, the B cell binds to the polysaccharide on one of the bacteria. The complement coating stimulates the B cell to engulf the bacterium. The B cell is now activated.

Meanwhile, more *S. aureus* cells have been secreting metabolic products into interstitial fluid around your cut. The secretions are attracting phagocytic cells. A dendritic cell engulfs several bacteria, then migrates to the lymph node in your elbow. By the time it gets there, it has digested the bacteria and is displaying their fragments as antigens bound to MHC markers on its surface ❷.

In the lymph node, one of your T cells recognizes and binds to the *S. aureus* antigen on the dendritic cell ❸. This T cell is called a helper T cell because it helps other lymphocytes produce antibodies and kill pathogens. The helper T cell and the dendritic cell interact for about 24 hours and then disengage. The helper T cell returns to the circulatory system and begins to divide, and a huge population of identical helper T cells forms. These clones differentiate into effector and memory cells, each of which has receptors that recognize the same *S. aureus* antigen.

Let's go back to that B cell in the lymph node. By now, it has digested the engulfed bacterium, and it is displaying bits of *S. aureus* bound to MHC molecules on its plasma membrane. The new helper T cells recognize the antigen–MHC complexes displayed by the B cell. One of these helper T cells binds to the B cell. Like long-lost friends, the two cells stay together for a while and communicate ❹. One of the messages that is communicated consists of cytokines secreted by the helper T cell. The cytokines stimulate the

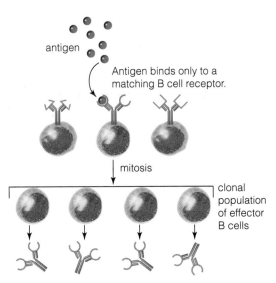

antigen

Antigen binds only to a
matching B cell receptor.

mitosis

clonal
population
of effector
B cells

Many effector B cells secrete many antibodies.

FIGURE 34.14 Clonal selection. Only lymphocytes with receptors that bind to antigen divide and differentiate. This example shows clonal selection of B cells.

B cell to undergo repeated mitotic divisions after the two cells disengage. A huge clonal population of descendant cells forms, and these B cells differentiate into effector and memory cells ❺. The effector B cells start releasing antibodies ❻. These antibodies are a secreted version of the original B cell's receptors, so they recognize the same *S. aureus* antigen. By the theory of clonal selection, the B cell was "selected" because its receptors bound to the antigen. B cells with receptors that did not bind the antigen did not divide to form huge clonal populations (FIGURE 34.14).

Tremendous numbers of antibodies now circulate throughout the body and attach themselves to any *S. aureus* cells. An antibody coating prevents the bacteria from attaching to body cells and brings them to the attention of phagocytic cells for quick disposal. Antibodies also glue the foreign cells together into clumps, a process called **agglutination**. The clumps are quickly removed from the circulatory system by the liver and spleen.

agglutination The clumping together of foreign cells bound by antibodies; the clumps attract phagocytic cells.

TAKE-HOME MESSAGE 34.6

During an antibody-mediated response, B cells produce antibodies that bind to an antigen in blood or interstitial fluid.

Antibody binding can prevent a pathogen from entering body cells, neutralize a toxin, and facilitate the elimination of both from the body.

34.7 HOW DOES ABO BLOOD TYPING WORK?

As you learned in Section 13.4, a carbohydrate on red blood cell membranes occurs in two forms. This carbohydrate is called H antigen. People with one form of the H antigen have type A blood; people with the other form have type B blood. People with both forms have type AB blood; those with neither are type O.

Early in life, each individual starts making antibodies that recognize molecules foreign to the body, including any nonself form of the H antigen:

ABO Type	H Antigen Form on Red Cells	Antibodies Present
A	A	anti-B
B	B	anti-A
AB	both A and B	none
O	neither A nor B	anti-A, anti-B

If a blood transfusion becomes necessary, it is especially important to know which H antigens your blood cells carry. A transfusion of incompatible red blood cells can cause a potentially fatal transfusion reaction in which the recipient's antibodies recognize and bind to antigens on the transfused cells. The binding activates complement, which punctures the membranes of the foreign cells, thus releasing a massive amount of hemoglobin that can very quickly cause the kidneys to fail.

Identifying red blood cell surface antigens helps prevent pairing of incompatible transfusion donors and recipients, and also alerts physicians to blood incompatibility problems that may arise during pregnancy. A typical blood typing test involves mixing drops of a patient's blood with antibodies to the different forms of red blood cell antigens. Agglutination occurs when the cells bear antigens recognized by the antibodies (FIGURE 34.15).

FIGURE 34.15 **ABO blood typing test.** In such tests, samples of a patient's blood are mixed with antibodies to H antigens. Agglutination (clumping) shows the presence of antigen.

Type A   Type B   Type AB   Type O

anti-B

anti-A

 FIGURE IT OUT: A person with which blood type can receive a blood transfusion of the other types?   Answer: Type AB

TAKE-HOME MESSAGE 34.7

An agglutination test reveals which version of an antigen (the H antigen) occurs on a person's red blood cells.

A cell-mediated immune response involves the production of cytotoxic T cells and other lymphocytes that recognize specific intracellular pathogens. This type of immune response does not involve antibodies: Antibody-mediated immune responses target pathogens that circulate in blood and interstitial fluid, but they are not as effective against pathogens inside cells.

Ailing body cells typically display certain antigens that are not found on healthy cells. For example, cancer cells display altered body proteins, and body cells infected with intracellular pathogens display polypeptides of the infecting agent. Both types of cell are detected and killed in a cell-mediated response.

THE ROLE OF CYTOTOXIC T CELLS

A cell-mediated immune response often starts in interstitial fluid during inflammation, when a dendritic cell recognizes, engulfs, and digests a sick body cell or the remains of one (FIGURE 34.16). The dendritic cell begins to display antigen that was part of the sick cell ❶ as it migrates to the spleen or a lymph node. There, the dendritic cell presents its antigen–MHC complexes to huge populations of naive helper T cells ❷ and naive cytotoxic T cells ❸. (The chapter opener photo shows an antigen-presenting dendritic cell being inspected by a naive T cell.) Some of the naive T cells have receptors that recognize and bind to the complexes on the dendritic cell. The binding activates these T cells.

Activated helper T cells begin to divide, and their many descendants differentiate into effector and memory cells ❹. The new effector cells recognize and bind to the antigen–MHC complexes displayed by the macrophages. Interacting with a helper T cell causes a macrophage to increase its production of pathogen-busting enzymes and toxins, and also to secrete more cytokines that attract phagocytic cells.

The effector T cells also secrete cytokines ❺. Cytotoxic T cells that have been activated by interacting with an antigen-presenting cell recognize these cytokines as a signal to divide repeatedly, and their many descendants differentiate into effector and memory cells ❻. All of the new cytotoxic T cells recognize and bind the same antigen—the one displayed by that first ailing cell.

If B cells are like assassins, then cytotoxic T cells are specialists in cell-to-cell combat. The effector cells start working immediately. They circulate throughout blood and interstitial fluid, and bind to any other body cell displaying the original antigen together with MHC markers. A cytotoxic T cell that binds to an ailing cell (FIGURE 34.17) releases protein-digesting enzymes and small molecules called perforins. Perforins assemble into

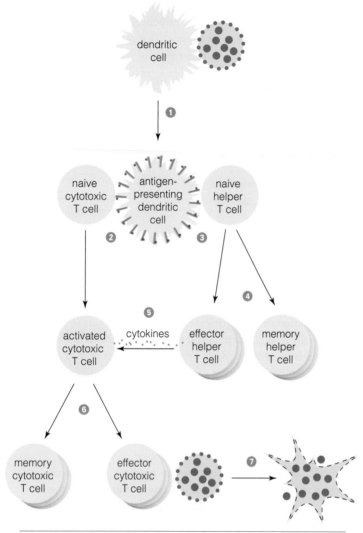

FIGURE 34.16 {Animated} A cell-mediated immune response.

❶ A dendritic cell engulfs and digests a virus-infected cell. Bits of the virus bind to MHC markers, and the complexes become displayed at the dendritic cell's surface. The dendritic cell, now an antigen-presenting cell, migrates to a lymph node.

❷ Receptors on a naive cytotoxic T cell bind to antigen–MHC complexes displayed by the dendritic cell. The interaction activates the cytotoxic T cell.

❸ Receptors on a naive helper T cell bind to antigen–MHC complexes displayed by the dendritic cell. The interaction activates the helper T cell.

❹ The activated helper T cell divides again and again. Its many descendants differentiate into effector and memory cells, each with T cell receptors that recognize the same antigen.

❺ The effector cells secrete cytokines.

❻ The cytokines induce the activated cytotoxic T cell to divide again and again. Its many descendants differentiate into effector and memory cells. Each cells bears T cell receptors that recognize the same antigen.

❼ The new effector cells circulate throughout the body. They kill any body cell that displays the viral antigen–MHC complexes on its surface.

FIGURE IT OUT: What do the large red spots represent?

Answer: Viruses

FIGURE 34.17 Cytotoxic T cells (pink) killing a cancer cell.

complexes that, like membrane attack complexes, insert themselves into the ailing cell's plasma membrane to form large channels. The channels allow the enzymes to enter the body cell, which then bursts or commits suicide ❼.

As occurs in an antibody-mediated response, memory cells form in a primary cell-mediated response. These long-lasting cells do not act immediately. If the antigen returns at a later time, the memory cells will mount a faster, stronger secondary response.

THE ROLE OF NK CELLS

In order to kill a body cell, cytotoxic T cells must recognize the MHC molecules on the surface of the cell. However, some infections or cancer can alter a body cell so that it is missing part or all of its MHC markers. NK cells are crucial for fighting such cells because, unlike cytotoxic T cells, NK cells can kill body cells that lack MHC markers. Cytokines secreted by helper T cells also stimulate NK cell division. The resulting populations of effector cells recognize and attack body cells that have antibodies bound to them. They also recognize certain proteins displayed by body cells that are under stress. Stressed body cells with normal MHC markers are not killed; only those with altered or missing MHC markers are destroyed.

Because NK cells can operate early in immune defense, they are often considered to be part of innate immunity. However, recent research has shown that they have features associated with lymphocytes of adaptive immunity: activation by cytokines, for example, and memory.

TAKE-HOME MESSAGE 34.8
Cytotoxic T cells and NK cells that form during a cell-mediated immune response kill infected body cells or those that have been altered by cancer.

National Geographic Grantee
DR. MARK MERCHANT

Crocodiles are notorious for violent territorial disputes, leaving other crocodiles with large, jagged wounds and sometimes lost limbs. Loss of a limb in swampy, bacteria-infested water would probably have a fatal outcome for a human, but severe wounds in a crocodile typically heal very rapidly and without infection.

The human immune system relies largely on adaptive immunity to combat specific infectious agents. This response can take several days to fully develop after initial infection. Crocodiles, however, rely on innate immunity. Unique antimicrobial peptides made by crocodilians are very effective at preventing infection.

National Geographic Grantee Mark Merchant is investigating these peptides for use as antibiotic drugs in humans. Most conventional antibiotics fight infection by targeting bacterial enzymes, but the fast mutation rate in bacteria can result in antibiotic-resistant strains. Crocodilian peptides act ionically with bacterial cell membranes and cause them to rupture, a strategy that makes it much more difficult for bacteria to become resistant.

Despite built-in quality controls and redundancies in immune system functions, immunity does not always work as well as it should. Its complexity is part of the problem, because there are simply more opportunities for failure to occur in systems with many components. Even a small failure in immune function can have a major effect on health.

ALLERGIES

In millions of people, exposure to a normally harmless substance stimulates an immune response. Any substance that is ordinarily harmless yet provokes such responses is called an **allergen**. Sensitivity to an allergen is an **allergy**. Drugs, foods, pollen, dust mite feces, fungal spores, and venom from bees, wasps, and other insects are among the most common allergens.

Some people are genetically predisposed to allergies. Infections, emotional stress, and changes in air temperature can trigger reactions. A first exposure to an allergen stimulates B cells to make and secrete IgE, which becomes anchored to mast cells and basophils. Upon a later exposure, antigen binds to the IgE. Binding triggers the anchoring cell to degranulate, and histamines and prostaglandins released by the cells initiate inflammation. If the allergen is detected by mast cells in the lining of the respiratory tract, the resulting inflammation constricts the airways and causes a copious amount of mucus to be secreted; sneezing, stuffed-up sinuses, and a drippy nose result (FIGURE 34.18A). Antihistamines relieve these symptoms by dampening the effects of histamines released by the degranulating cells. Other drugs can inhibit mast cell degranulation, thus preventing histamine release.

Skin rashes and other contact allergies do not involve antibodies; they are caused by a cell-mediated response to an allergen (FIGURE 34.18B).

OVERLY VIGOROUS RESPONSES

Immune defenses that eliminate a threat can also damage body tissues. Thus, multiple mechanisms that limit immune responses are always in play. Consider that one type of complement protein becomes activated spontaneously, even in the absence of infection or tissue damage. Without the fail-safe mechanism of inhibitory molecules that deactivate this protein, complement cascades would occur constantly, with disastrous results to body tissues.

Acute illnesses arise when mechanisms that limit immune responses fail. Exposure to an allergen sometimes causes a severe, whole-body allergic reaction called anaphylactic shock. Huge amounts of inflammatory molecules such as histamines and prostaglandins are released all at once in all parts of the body. Too much fluid leaks from blood

A Hay fever is caused by allergy to grass pollen. Cold-like symptoms (such as sneezing and a runny nose) are a result of inflammation of the mucous membranes in respiratory airways.

B Direct contact with an allergen can cause a rash—an itchy, irritated patch of skin. In this case, the offending allergen was nickel (a metal) in a ring.

FIGURE 34.18 Examples of allergies.

into tissues, causing a sudden and dramatic drop in blood pressure (a reaction called shock). Rapidly swelling tissues constrict the airways and may block them. Anaphylactic shock is rare but life-threatening and requires immediate treatment. It may occur at any time, upon exposure to even a tiny amount of allergen. The risks include any prior allergic reaction.

Other types of hyperactive immune responses are not as well understood. Severe episodes of asthma or septic shock occur when too many neutrophils degranulate at once. In a "cytokine storm," too many white blood cells release cytokines at the same time. The cytokine overdose triggers immediate, widespread inflammation that can cause organ failure, with potentially fatal results. Cytokine storm triggered by infection with H5N1 influenza virus

(Section 19.2) is a reason that this strain of bird flu has an unusually high mortality rate.

AUTOIMMUNE DISORDERS

People usually do not make antibodies to molecules that occur on their own healthy body cells, in part because the thymus has a built-in quality control mechanism that weeds out T cells with defective receptors. Thymus cells snip small polypeptides from a variety of body proteins and attach them to MHC markers. Maturing T cells that bind too strongly to one of these peptide–MHC complexes have TCRs that recognize a self-protein; those that do not bind at least weakly to the complexes do not recognize MHC markers. Both types of cells die. If this mechanism fails, mature lymphocytes that do not discriminate between self and nonself may be produced. Such lymphocytes can mount an **autoimmune response**, which is an immune response that targets one's own tissues. Autoimmunity is beneficial when a cell-mediated response targets cancer cells, but in most cases it is not (**TABLE 34.4**).

Antibodies to self-proteins (autoantibodies) may bind to hormone receptors, as in the case of Graves' disease. In this disease, autoantibodies that bind stimulatory receptors on the thyroid gland cause it to produce excess thyroid hormone, which quickens the body's overall metabolic rate. Antibodies are not part of the feedback loops that normally regulate thyroid hormone production. So, antibody binding continues unchecked, the thyroid continues to release too much hormone, and the metabolic rate spins out of control. Symptoms of Graves' disease include uncontrollable weight loss; rapid, irregular heartbeat; sleeplessness; pronounced mood swings; and bulging eyes.

The neurological disorder called multiple sclerosis occurs when self-reactive T cells attack myelin in the brain and spinal cord (Section 29.4). Symptoms range from weakness and loss of balance to paralysis and blindness. Specific alleles for MHC markers increase susceptibility, but a bacterial or viral infection may trigger the disorder.

IMMUNODEFICIENCY

Insufficient immune function—immune deficiency— renders an individual vulnerable to infections by opportunistic agents that are typically harmless to those in good health. Primary immune deficiencies, which are present at birth, are the outcome of mutations. Severe

allergen A normally harmless substance that provokes an immune response in some people.
allergy Sensitivity to an allergen.
autoimmune response Immune response that inappropriately targets one's own tissues.

TABLE 34.4

Examples of Autoantibodies Associated With Autoimmune Disorders

Disorder	Autoantibody Target	Affected Area
Crohn's disease	Proteins in neutrophil granules	Gastrointestinal tract
Dermatomyositis	tRNA synthesis enzyme	Muscles, skin
Diabetes mellitus type 1	Islet proteins or insulin	Pancreas
Goodpasture's syndrome	Type IV collagen	Kidney, lung
Graves' disease	TSH receptor	Thyroid
Guillain-Barré syndrome	Lipids of ganglia	Peripheral nervous system
Hashimoto's disease	TH synthesis proteins	Thyroid
Idiopathic thrombo-cytopenic purpura	Platelet glycoproteins	Blood (platelets)
Lupus erythematosus	DNA, nuclear proteins	Connective tissue
Multiple sclerosis	Myelin proteins	Central nervous system
Myasthenia gravis	Acetylcholine receptors	Neuromuscular junctions
Pemphigus vulgaris	Cadherin	Skin
Pernicious anemia	Parietal cell glycoprotein	Stomach epithelium
Polymyositis	tRNA synthesis enzyme	Muscles
Primary biliary cirrhosis	Nuclear pore proteins, mitochondria	Liver
Rheumatoid arthritis	Constant region of IgG	Joints
Scleroderma	Topoisomerase	Arteriole endothelium
Ulcerative colitis	Enzyme in neutrophil granules	Large intestine
Wegener's granulomatosis	Enzyme in neutrophil granules	Blood vessels

combined immunodeficiencies (SCIDs) are examples. Secondary immune deficiency is the loss of immune function after exposure to an outside agent, such as a virus. AIDS (acquired immunodeficiency syndrome, described in the next section) is the most common secondary immune deficiency.

TAKE-HOME MESSAGE 34.9

Normally harmless substances may induce an immune response in some people. Sensitivity to such allergens is called an allergy.

Autoimmune diseases are caused by inappropriate immune responses to normal body tissues.

Compromised immunity, which sometimes occurs as a result of mutation or environmental factors, causes an individual to be especially vulnerable to infections.

A Kaposi's sarcoma, a cancer common in older AIDS patients.

B This baby contracted AIDS from his mother's breast milk.

FIGURE 34.19 AIDS.

The most common secondary immune deficiency is **AIDS**, or acquired immunodeficiency syndrome. AIDS is a syndrome of disorders that occur as a result of infection with HIV, the human immunodeficiency virus (Section 19.1). This virus cripples the immune system, so it makes the body susceptible to infections by other pathogens and to rare forms of cancer. Worldwide, approximately 33.3 million people are currently infected (**TABLE 34.5**).

A person recently infected with HIV appears to be in good health, perhaps fighting a cold. But symptoms eventually emerge that foreshadow AIDS: fever, many enlarged lymph nodes, chronic fatigue and weight loss, and drenching night sweats. Then, infections by normally harmless microorganisms strike. Yeast infections of the mouth, esophagus, and vagina often occur, as well as a form of pneumonia caused by the fungus *Pneumocystis jiroveci*. Gastrointestinal inflammation due to infection causes diarrhea. Some cancers are also common (**FIGURE 34.19A**), as are infections by cancer-causing viruses such as Epstein–Barr virus.

HIV mainly infects macrophages, dendritic cells, and helper T cells. When HIV particles enter the body, dendritic cells engulf them. The dendritic cells then migrate to lymph nodes, where they present processed HIV antigen to naive T cells. An army of HIV-neutralizing IgG antibodies and HIV-specific cytotoxic T cells forms. For years or even decades, these responses can keep the level of HIV low. During this stage, infected people often have no symptoms of AIDS, but they can pass the virus to other people. Eventually, the level of antibodies in the blood plummets, and the production of T cells slows. Why this happens is still a major topic of research, but its effect is certain: The immune system becomes progressively less effective at fighting the virus. The number of virus particles rises, and more and more helper T cells become infected. Lymph nodes begin to swell with infected T cells. Eventually, secondary infections and tumors kill the patient.

AIDS Acquired immunodeficiency syndrome. A secondary immune deficiency that develops as the result of infection by the HIV virus.

TABLE 34.5

Global HIV and AIDS Cases

Region	AIDS Cases	% of Adults Infected
Sub-Saharan Africa	22,500,000	5.0
Caribbean Islands	240,000	1.0
Central Asia/Eastern Europe	1,400,000	0.8
Latin America	1,400,000	0.5
North America	1,500,000	0.5
Southern/Southeast Asia	4,100,000	0.3
Australia/New Zealand	57,000	0.3
Western/Central Europe	820,000	0.2
Middle East/North Africa	460,000	0.2
Eastern Asia	770,000	0.1
Approx. worldwide total	33,247,000	0.8

Source: Joint United Nations Programme HIV/AIDS, 2010

TRANSMISSION AND TREATMENT

HIV is not transmitted by casual contact; most infections are the result of having unprotected sex with an infected partner. Infected mothers can transmit HIV to a child during pregnancy, labor, delivery, or breast-feeding (**FIGURE 34.19B**). HIV also travels in tiny amounts of infected blood in the syringes shared by intravenous drug abusers, or by hospital patients in less developed countries. Many people have become infected via blood transfusions, but this transmission route is becoming rarer as most blood is now tested prior to use for transfusions. AIDS tests check for antibodies that bind to HIV antigens. These antibodies are detectable within three months of exposure to the virus.

Drugs cannot cure AIDS, but they can slow its progress. Most target processes unique to retroviral replication. RNA nucleotide analogs such as AZT interrupt HIV replication when they substitute for normal nucleotides in the viral RNA-to-DNA synthesis process. Protease inhibitors affect other parts of the viral replication cycle. A three-drug mixture of one protease inhibitor plus two reverse transcriptase inhibitors is currently the most successful AIDS therapy. This "cocktail" has changed the typical course of the disease from a short-term death sentence to a long-term, often manageable illness, and also shows promise as a treatment if given immediately after exposure to HIV.

TAKE-HOME MESSAGE 34.10

AIDS is a secondary immune deficiency caused by HIV infection. HIV infects white blood cells and so cripples the human immune system.

Immunization refers to procedures designed to induce immunity. In active immunization, a preparation that contains antigen—a **vaccine**—is administered orally or injected. The first immunization elicits a primary immune response, just as an infection would. A second immunization, or booster, elicits a secondary immune response for enhanced protection. In passive immunization, a person receives antibodies purified from the blood of another individual. Passive immunization offers immediate benefit for someone who has been exposed to a lethal agent such as tetanus, rabies, Ebola virus, or a venom or toxin. Because the antibodies were not made by the recipient's lymphocytes, effector and memory cells do not form, so benefits last only as long as the injected antibodies do.

The first vaccine was developed in the late 1700s, a result of desperate attempts to survive devastating smallpox epidemics (**FIGURE 34.20**). Edward Jenner, an English physician, injected liquid from a cowpox sore into the arm of a healthy boy. Six weeks later, Jenner injected the boy with liquid from a smallpox sore. Luckily, the boy did not get smallpox. He was immune—protected from infection. Jenner named his procedure "vaccination," after the Latin word for cowpox (*vaccinia*). Though it was still controversial, the use of Jenner's vaccine spread quickly through Europe, then to the rest of the world. The last known case of naturally occurring smallpox was in 1977.

We now know that the cowpox virus is an effective vaccine for smallpox because the antibodies it elicits also recognize smallpox virus antigens. Our increasing knowledge of the immune system has allowed us to develop vaccines for many other infectious diseases (**TABLE 34.6**). These vaccines have overwhelmingly reduced suffering and deaths, but public confidence is a necessary part of their success. When enough individuals refuse vaccination, outbreaks of preventable and sometimes fatal diseases occur.

We still have no vaccine effective against HIV infection. Antibodies produced during a normal adaptive response exert selective pressure on HIV virus, which has a very high mutation rate, so a large number of variants of the HIV virus exist. A successful HIV vaccine must efficiently recognize and neutralize all variants, including those that have not yet arisen. Immunization with live, weakened HIV virus is an effective vaccine in chimpanzees, but the risk of infection from the vaccination itself far outweighs its potential benefits in humans. Other types of vaccines have been notoriously ineffective against HIV.

immunization Any procedure designed to induce immunity to a specific disease.
vaccine A preparation introduced into the body in order to elicit immunity to a specific antigen.

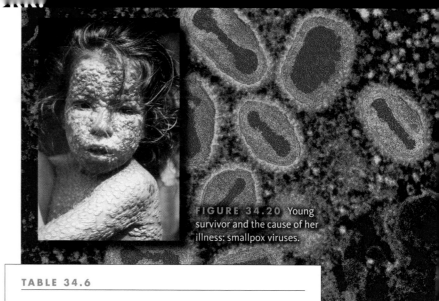

FIGURE 34.20 Young survivor and the cause of her illness: smallpox viruses.

TABLE 34.6

Recommended Immunization Schedule for Children

Vaccine	Age of Vaccination
Hepatitis B	Birth
Hepatitis B boosters	1–2 months and 6–18 months
Rotavirus	2, 4, and 6 months
DTP: diphtheria, tetanus, and pertussis (whooping cough)	2, 4, and 6 months
DTP boosters	15–18 months, 4–6 years, and 11–12 years
HiB (*Haemophilus influenzae*)	2, 4, and 6 months
HiB booster	12–15 months
Pneumococcal	2, 4, and 6 months
Pneumococcal booster	12–15 months
Inactivated poliovirus	2 and 4 months
Inactivated poliovirus boosters	6–18 months and 4–6 years
Influenza	Yearly, 6 months and older
MMR (measles, mumps, rubella)	12–15 months
MMR booster	4–6 years
Varicella (chicken pox)	12–15 months
Varicella booster	4–6 years
Hepatitis A series (2 doses)	12–23 months
HPV series (3 doses)	11–12 years
Meningococcal	11–12 years

Source: Centers for Disease Control and Prevention (CDC), 2011

TAKE-HOME MESSAGE 34.11

Administering a vaccine elicits an immune response in the recipient that protects against future encounters with a disease-causing agent.

Worldwide vaccination programs have greatly reduced suffering and deaths from many diseases. An effective vaccination program requires widespread participation.

CREDITS: (20) background, Eye of Science/Science Source; inset, James Hicks, Centers for Disease Control and Prevention.

Frankie McCullough (waving) died of cervical cancer at age 32.

Get Involved

34.12 Application: FRANKIE'S LAST WISH

FIGURE 34.21 HPV and cervical cancer. This Pap test reveals HPV-infected cervical cells among normal ones. Infected cells have enlarged, often multiple nuclei surrounded by a clear area. These changes sometimes lead to cervical cancer, which is treatable if detected early enough.

FRANKIE MCCULLOUGH HAD KNOWN FOR A FEW MONTHS THAT SOMETHING WAS NOT QUITE RIGHT. She had not had an annual checkup in many years; after all, she was only 31 and had always been healthy. She had never doubted her own invincibility until the moment she saw the doctor's face change as he examined her cervix.

The cervix is the lowest part of the uterus, or womb. Cervical cells can become cancerous, but the process is usually slow. Several precancerous stages are detectable by routine Pap tests. Precancerous and even early-stage cancerous cells can be removed from the cervix before they spread to other parts of the body. However, plenty of women like Frankie do not take advantage of regular exams. They do not see a gynecologist unless they have pain or bleeding, which can be symptoms of advanced cervical cancer. Even with treatment, 85 percent of the women who end up with this type of cancer will die within 5 years. Thousands of women die of cervical cancer each year in the United States, and many more die in places where routine gynecological testing is not a common practice.

Healthy cervical cells are transformed into cancerous ones by human papillomavirus (HPV), a virus that infects skin and mucous membranes. A few of the 100 or so different strains of HPV cause warts on the hands or feet, or in the mouth. About 30 others that infect the genital area sometimes cause genital warts, but usually there are no symptoms of infection. Genital HPV is spread very easily by sexual contact: A woman has a 50% chance of being infected with genital HPV within three years of becoming sexually active.

A genital HPV infection usually goes away on its own, but not always. A persistent infection with one of about 10 strains is the main risk factor for cervical cancer (FIGURE 34.21). Types 16 and 18 are particularly dangerous: One of the two is found in more than 70 percent of all cervical cancers.

In 2006, the U.S. Food and Drug Administration (FDA) approved Gardasil, a vaccine that protects the recipient against infection by four types of genital HPV, including types 16 and 18. Gardasil consists of viral proteins that self-assemble into virus-like particles (VLPs). These proteins are produced by a

CREDITS: (21) background, Biomedical Imaging Unit, Southampton General Hospital/Science Source; inset, In memory of Frankie McCullough.

recombinant yeast, *Saccharomyces cerevisiae*. The yeast expresses genes for one surface protein from each of four strains of HPV, so the VLPs carry no viral DNA. Thus, the VLPs are not infectious, but the antigenic proteins they consist of elicit an immune response at least as strong as infection with HPV virus.

The vaccine also prevents cervical cancer caused by these four HPV strains. It is most effective in girls who have not yet become sexually active, because they are least likely to have already become infected with HPV.

The HPV vaccine came too late for Frankie McCullough. Despite radiation treatments and chemotherapy, her cervical cancer spread quickly. She died about 18 months after being diagnosed, leaving a wish for other people: awareness. "If there is one thing I could tell a young woman to convince them to have a yearly exam, it would be not to assume that your youth will protect you. Cancer does not discriminate; it will attack at random, and early detection is the answer." Almost all women newly diagnosed with invasive cervical cancer have not had a Pap test in five years.

Summary

SECTION 34.1 The body's ability to resist and fight infections is called **immunity**. A microorganism or other antigen-bearing particle that breaches surface barriers triggers **innate immunity**, a set of general defenses that can prevent pathogens from becoming established inside the body. **Adaptive immunity**, which can specifically target billions of different **antigens**, follows. **Complement** and signaling molecules such as **cytokines** help coordinate the activities of white blood cells such as **dendritic cells**, **macrophages**, **neutrophils**, **basophils**, **mast cells**, and **eosinophils**. Lymphocytes (**B cells**, **T cells**, and **NK cells**) are white blood cells with special roles in immune responses.

SECTION 34.2 Most **normal flora** that colonize body surfaces—including the linings of tubes and cavities—do not cause disease unless they penetrate inner tissues. Vertebrates fend off pathogens (such as those that cause **dental plaque**) at body surfaces with physical, mechanical, and chemical barriers (such as **lysozyme**).

SECTION 34.3 An innate immune response can be triggered by activated complement or by phagocytic white blood cells that engulf an antigen-bearing particle. Complement activated by the presence of antigen or tissue damage attracts phagocytic cells. It also coats antigenic particles and forms complexes that kill invading cells by puncturing their plasma membranes.

Inflammation begins when white blood cells in infected or damaged tissue release signaling molecules. The molecules attract phagocytic cells and increase blood flow to the affected area, warming and reddening it. Plasma proteins that leak from capillaries cause swelling and pain. Prolonged exposure to an inflammation-provoking stimulus can cause chronic inflammation. **Fever** increases the metabolic rate and can slow pathogen replication.

SECTION 34.4 **T cell receptors** recognize antigen displayed in conjunction with **MHC markers** by an antigen-presenting cell. **B cell receptors** are **antibodies** that have not been released from a B cell. Both kinds of antigen receptors collectively have the ability to recognize billions of specific antigens, a diversity that arises from random splicing of antigen receptor genes.

SECTION 34.5 B cells and T cells carry out adaptive immune responses. **Antibody-mediated** and **cell-mediated immune responses** work together to rid the body of a specific pathogen. Phagocytic lymphocytes present antigen in adaptive responses. **Effector cells** form and target the antigen-bearing particles in a primary response. **Memory cells** that also form are reserved for a later encounter with the same antigen, in which case they trigger a faster, stronger secondary response. Phagocytic white blood cells that engulf, process, and present antigen to T cells in the spleen or lymph nodes are central to all adaptive immune responses.

SECTIONS 34.6, 34.7 B cells, assisted by T cells, antigen-presenting cells, and signaling molecules, carry out antibody-mediated immune responses. Antibodies that recognize a specific antigen are produced by B cells during these responses. Antibody binding causes **agglutination** of foreign cells, and tags antigen-bearing particles for phagocytosis. Blood typing tests for the presence of antigen on blood cells by agglutination.

SECTION 34.8 T cells interact with antigen-presenting cells to carry out cell-mediated immune responses. Cytotoxic T cells and NK cells that form in these responses kill body cells that have been altered by infection or cancer.

SECTION 34.9 **Allergens** are normally harmless substances that induce immune responses; hypersensitivity to an allergen is called **allergy**. A malfunction in the immune system or in its checks and balances can cause dangerous acute illnesses, or chronic and sometimes deadly diseases. Immune deficiency is a reduced capacity to mount an immune response. In an **autoimmune response**, a body's own cells are inappropriately recognized as foreign and attacked.

SECTION 34.10 **AIDS** is caused by the human immunodeficiency virus (HIV). An initial adaptive immune response to infection rids the body of most—but not all—of the virus. The virus infects white blood cells, so it eventually cripples the adaptive immune system.

SECTION 34.11 **Immunization** with **vaccines** designed to elicit immunity to specific disease is a critical part of worldwide health programs. Effective vaccination programs require widespread participation.

SECTION 34.12 Screenings, treatments, and vaccines for diseases such as cervical cancer are a direct outcome of our increasing understanding of the way the human body interacts with pathogens.

Self-Quiz Answers in Appendix VII

1. _____ trigger immune responses.
   a. Cytokines   d. Antigens
   b. Lysozymes   e. Histamines
   c. Antibodies   f. all of the above

2. Which of the following is *not* among the first line of defenses against infection?
   a. skin   d. resident bacterial populations
   b. acidic gastric fluid   e. complement activation
   c. lysozyme in saliva   f. flushing action of diarrhea

3. Which of the following is *not* considered to be part of an innate immune response?
   a. phagocytic cells   e. inflammation
   b. fever   f. complement activation
   c. histamines   g. presenting antigen
   d. cytokines   h. all take part

4. Which of the following is *not* part of an adaptive immune response?
   a. phagocytic cells   e. antigen receptors
   b. antigen-presenting cells f. complement activation
   c. histamines   g. antibodies
   d. cytokines   h. all take part

5. Activated complement proteins _____ .
   a. form pore complexes   c. attract phagocytic cells
   b. promote inflammation   d. all of the above

6. Name a defining characteristic of innate immunity.

7. Name a defining characteristic of adaptive immunity.

8. Antibodies are _____ .
   a. antigen receptors   c. proteins
   b. made only by B cells d. all of the above

9. A dendritic cell engulfs a bacterium, then presents bacterial bits on its surface along with a(n) _____ .
   a. MHC marker   c. T cell receptor
   b. antibody   d. antigen

10. Antibody-mediated responses are most effective against _____ .
    a. intracellular pathogens   d. both a and b
    b. extracellular pathogens   e. both b and c
    c. cancerous cells   f. a, b, and c

11. Cell-mediated responses are most effective against _____ .
    a. intracellular pathogens   d. both a and b
    b. extracellular pathogens   e. both a and c
    c. cancerous cells   f. a, b, and c

12. _____ are targets of cytotoxic T cells.
    a. Extracellular virus particles in blood
    b. Virus-infected body cells or tumor cells
    c. Parasitic worms in the liver
    d. Bacterial cells in pus
    e. Pollen grains in nasal mucus

13. Allergies occur when the body responds to _____ .
    a. pathogens   c. normally harmless substances
    b. toxins   d. all of the above

14. Which combination of the following types of antibodies and immune cells is central to hay fever?
    a. IgE and mast cells
    b. IgG and basophils
    c. IgA and lymphocytes
    d. IgM and macrophages

15. Match the immune cell with the function.
    ___ dendritic cell   a. kills virus-infected cells
    ___ B cell   b. antigen-presenter
    ___ helper T cell   c. activates other lymphocytes
    ___ NK cell   d. kills cells lacking MHC markers
    ___ cytotoxic T cell   e. makes antibodies

16. Match the immunity concept with the best description.
    ___ anaphylactic shock   a. recognizes antigen
    ___ immune memory   b. inadequate immune response
    ___ autoimmunity   c. general defense mechanism
    ___ inflammation   d. immune response
    ___ immune deficiency   against one's own body
    ___ antigen receptor   e. secondary response
    ___ antigen processing   f. systemic allergic reaction
                                  g. presenting antigen together
                                      with MHC molecules

Critical Thinking

1. In what is called transplant rejection, a tissue or organ transplanted from one human into another is immediately destroyed by the recipient's immune system. Which type of lymphocyte does the attacking?

2. Before each flu season, you get a flu shot, which consists of a vaccine against several strains of influenza virus. This year, you get "the flu" anyway. What happened? (There are at least three explanations.)

3. Elena developed chicken pox when she was in first grade. Later in life, when her children developed chicken pox, she remained healthy even though she was exposed to countless virus particles daily. Explain why.

4. Monoclonal antibodies are produced by immunizing a mouse with a particular antigen, then removing its spleen. Individual B cells producing mouse antibodies specific for the antigen are isolated from the spleen and fused with cancerous B cells from a myeloma cancer cell line. The resulting hybrid myeloma ("hybridoma") cells are cloned: Individual cells are grown in tissue culture as separate cell lines. Each line produces and secretes antibodies that recognize the antigen to which the mouse was immunized. These antibodies, which are called monoclonal antibodies, can be purified and used for research or other purposes.

Monoclonal antibodies are sometimes used in passive immunization. They are effective, but only in the immediate term. Antibodies produced by one's own immune system can last up to about six months in the bloodstream, but monoclonals delivered in passive immunization often last for less than a week. Why the difference?

CENGAGE brain.com   To access course materials, please visit www.cengagebrain.com.

Data Analysis Activities

Cervical Cancer Incidence in HPV-Positive Women   In 2003, Michelle Khan and her coworkers published their findings on a 10-year study in which they followed cervical cancer incidence and HPV status in 20,514 women. All women who participated in the study were free of cervical cancer when the test began. Pap tests were taken at regular intervals, and the researchers used a DNA probe hybridization test (Section 15.2) to detect specific types of HPV in the women's cervical cells.

The results are shown in **FIGURE 34.22** as a graph of the incidence rate of cervical cancer by HPV type. HPV-positive women are often infected by more than one type, so the data were sorted into groups based on the women's HPV status ranked by type: either positive for HPV16; or negative for HPV16 and positive for HPV18; or negative for HPV16 and HPV18 and positive for any other cancer-causing HPV; or negative for all cancer-causing HPV.

1. At 110 months into the study, what percentage of women who were not infected with any type of cancer-causing HPV had cervical cancer? What percentage of women who were infected with HPV16 also had cervical cancer?

2. In which group would women infected with both HPV16 and HPV18 fall?

3. Is it possible to estimate from this graph the overall risk of cervical cancer that is associated with infection of cancer-causing HPV of any type?

4. Do these data support the conclusion that being infected with HPV16 or HPV18 raises the risk of cervical cancer?

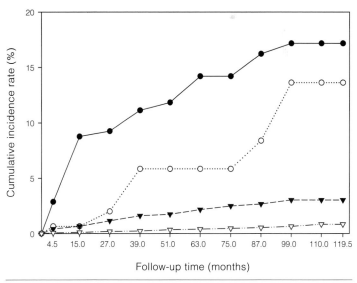

FIGURE 34.22 Cumulative incidence rate of cervical cancer correlated with HPV status in 20,514 women aged 16 years and older.

The data were grouped as follows:
● HPV16 positive
○ HPV16 negative and HPV18 positive
▼ All other cancer-causing HPV types combined
▽ No cancer-causing HPV type was detected.

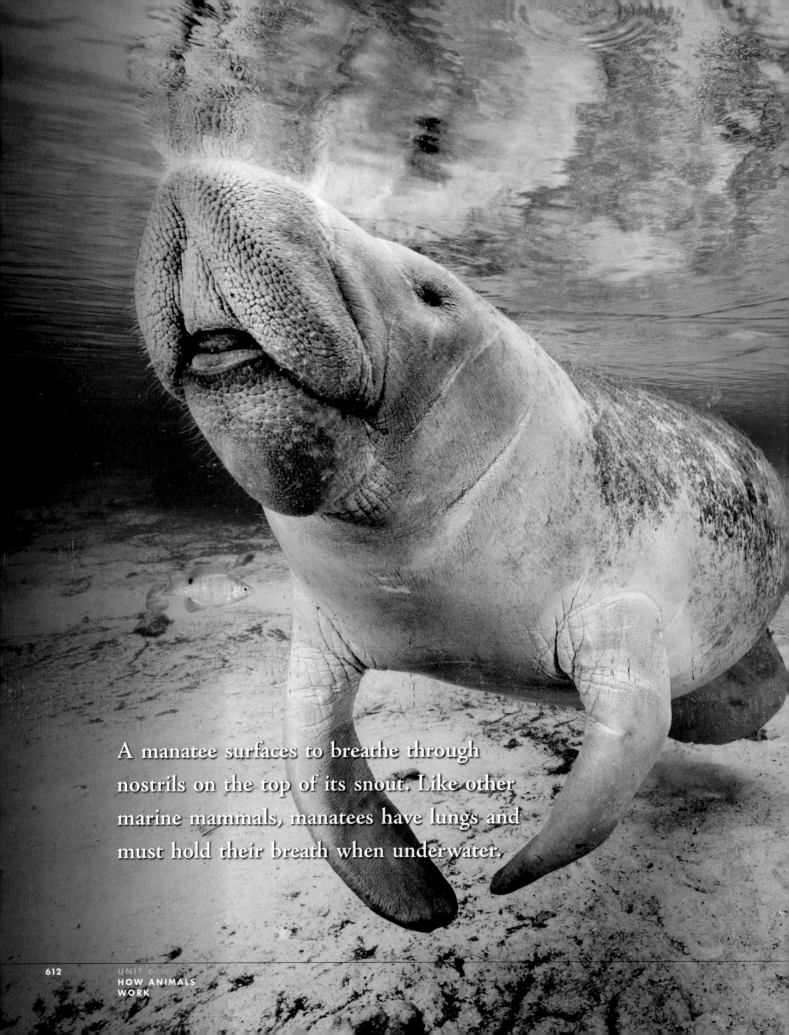

A manatee surfaces to breathe through nostrils on the top of its snout. Like other marine mammals, manatees have lungs and must hold their breath when underwater.

35

RESPIRATION

Links to Earlier Concepts

This chapter draws on your knowledge of diffusion and membrane transport (Sections 5.6, 5.7), and aerobic respiration (7.1). You will learn about respiration in invertebrates (Chapter 23) and vertebrate gills and lungs (24.2, 24.3). You will see how hemoglobin and red blood cells (9.5, 33.4) function in gas exchange, and how chemoreceptors (30.1) and the brain stem (29.9) interact to regulate breathing.

KEY CONCEPTS

RESPIRATORY SYSTEMS
Respiration is a physiological process that moves oxygen and carbon dioxide between tissues and the environment. Gills, lungs, and other respiratory organs facilitate gas exchange.

HUMAN RESPIRATORY SYSTEM
The human respiratory system consists of a system of airways that connect to paired lungs. Muscles whose contraction expands the thoracic cavity also function in respiration.

RESPIRATORY CYCLE
Inhalation is always an active process. It occurs when a part of the brain stem signals muscles to contract. The contraction increases the size of the thoracic cavity. Exhalation is usually passive.

GAS EXCHANGES
Hemoglobin binds oxygen in pulmonary capillaries and releases it near active tissues. Waste carbon dioxide is converted to bicarbonate, and carried to the lungs in plasma.

RESPIRATORY PROBLEMS
Interrupted breathing (apnea), infectious diseases (such as tuberculosis), and inflammatory conditions (such as asthma and bronchitis) interfere with normal respiratory function.

SITES OF GAS EXCHANGE

In Chapter 7 you learned about aerobic respiration, an energy-releasing pathway that requires oxygen (O_2) and produces carbon dioxide (CO_2) as summarized below:

$$C_6H_{12}O_6 + O_2 \longrightarrow CO_2 + H_2O$$

glucose · · · · · oxygen · · · · · carbon dioxide · · · · · water

This chapter focuses on **respiration**, the physiological processes that collectively supply an animal's body cells with oxygen from the environment, and deliver waste carbon dioxide to the environment.

Gases enter and leave an animal body by diffusing across a thin, moist **respiratory surface** (**FIGURE 35.1A**). A typical respiratory surface is no more than one or two cell layers thick. The respiratory surface must be thin because gases diffuse quickly only over very short distances. It must be moist because a gas can only diffuse across a living cell's lipid bilayer when it is in solution.

A second exchange of gases occurs internally, at the plasma membrane of body cells (**FIGURE 35.1B**). Here, oxygen diffuses from the interstitial fluid into a cell, and carbon dioxide diffuses in the opposite direction. In invertebrates that do not have a circulatory system, oxygen that crosses the respiratory surface reaches body cells by diffusion. In most invertebrates and all vertebrates, a circulatory system facilitates the movement of gases between the two sites of gas exchange.

FACTORS AFFECTING GAS EXCHANGE

The larger the area of a respiratory surface, the more molecules can cross it in any given time. This is why the area of a respiratory surface is often surprisingly large relative to the animal's body size. Branches and folds allow a large respiratory surface to fit in a small volume.

The concentrations of gases on either side of the respiratory surface also affect the rate of gas exchange. The steeper the concentration gradient across this surface, the faster diffusion proceeds. As a result, many animals have mechanisms that keep oxygen-rich air or water flowing over their respiratory surface. Your inhalations and exhalations move air rich in carbon dioxide away from the respiratory surface in your lungs and replace it with oxygen-rich air.

---

respiration Physiological process by which an animal body supplies cells with oxygen and disposes of their waste carbon dioxide.
respiratory protein A protein that reversibly binds oxygen when the oxygen concentration is high and releases it when oxygen concentration is low. Hemoglobin is an example.
respiratory surface Moist surface across which gases are exchanged between animal cells and the external environment.

A Cells of the respiratory surface exchange gases with both the external and internal environment.

B Other body cells exchange gases with the internal environment.

FIGURE 35.1 Two sites of gas exchange.

Respiratory proteins steepen the oxygen concentration gradient at a respiratory surface of many animals. A **respiratory protein** contains one or more metal ions that bind oxygen when oxygen concentration is high, and release it when oxygen concentration is low. Hemoglobin serves as the respiratory protein in vertebrates and some invertebrates. When an oxygen atom binds to hemoglobin, that atom no longer contributes to the oxygen concentration of blood or hemolymph. Thus, the presence of hemoglobin lowers the effective oxygen concentration in the blood and encourages faster diffusion of oxygen from the air into the blood. Hemocyanin, a copper-containing protein, is the respiratory protein in some invertebrates, including octopuses and horseshoe crabs. It is colorless when deoxygenated, and blue when carrying oxygen (**FIGURE 35.2**).

FIGURE 35.2 Hemocyanin with bound oxygen gives horseshoe crab hemolymph a blue color.

TAKE-HOME MESSAGE 35.1

Respiration comprises the physiological processes that supply cells with oxygen they need for aerobic respiration, and remove the waste carbon dioxide that this pathway produces.

A respiratory surface is a thin, moist membrane across which gases diffuse into and out of the internal environment. The larger its area, the more gas can cross in a given time.

The steepness of the concentration gradient across the respiratory membrane also affects gas exchange, with a steeper gradient increasing the rate of exchange.

Steep gradients are maintained by mechanisms that move water or air to and from the respiratory surface and by respiratory proteins that reversibly bind oxygen.

Some invertebrates that live in aquatic or continually damp land environments have neither respiratory nor circulatory organs. For example, in flatworms (Section 23.5), all gas exchange occurs across the body surface and the lining of the gastrovascular cavity. Animals that lack both respiratory and circulatory organs are either small and flat or, when larger, have cells arranged in thin layers.

Evolution of a circulatory system increased the efficiency of oxygen distribution through the body. In earthworms, a closed circulatory system carries hemoglobin-containing blood to and from a moist body wall that serves as the respiratory surface. Annelids do not have red blood cells, but some have hemoglobin in the fluid portion of their blood.

Aquatic invertebrates with a circulatory system usually have **gills**, which are folded or filamentous respiratory organs that function in gas exchange. As blood or hemolymph moves through gills, it picks up oxygen from the water and gives up carbon dioxide. Crabs and other aquatic crustaceans have gills beneath the exoskeleton of their thorax. Among mollusks, most have gills in their mantle cavity (**FIGURE 35.3A**), but some sea slugs have external gills (**FIGURE 35.3B**), and some land snails and slugs have a lung (**FIGURE 35.3C**). A **lung** is a saclike internal respiratory organ that exchanges gases with the air.

The most successful air-breathing land invertebrates are insects. A hard exoskeleton helps these animals conserve water, but it also prevents gas exchange across the body surface. Insects overcome this limitation with a **tracheal system**, a system of branching, chitin-reinforced tubes that convey air directly to tissues deep in the body.

The tracheal tubes start at spiracles, which are small openings across the exoskeleton (**FIGURE 35.3D**). There is usually a pair of spiracles per segment: one on each side of the body. Spiracles can be opened or closed to regulate the amount of oxygen that enters the body. Substances that clog spiracles are used as insecticides. For example, horticultural oils sprayed on fruit trees suffocate scale bugs, aphids, and mites by clogging spiracles.

Inside the insect body, tracheal tubes divide into finer and finer branches. At the tips of the finest branches, oxygen from air in the tube dissolves in interstitial fluid, from which it diffuses into cells. Carbon dioxide diffuses in the opposite direction, from the cells into the tracheal tubes. Because tracheal tubes deliver oxygen to fluid right next to

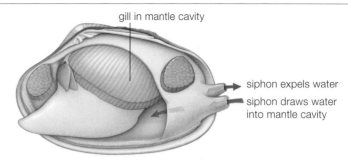

A Clam with internal gills.

B Sea slug with external gills.   C Land snail with a lung inside shell.

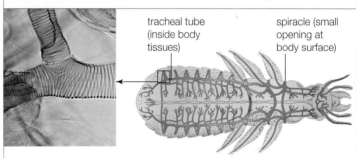

D Insect with chitin-reinforced tracheal tubes that deliver air from an opening at the body surface (a spiracle) to interstitial fluid deep inside the body.

FIGURE 35.3 Examples of invertebrate respiratory mechanisms.

cells, insects have no need for a respiratory protein such as hemoglobin or hemocyanin to transport gases in fluid.

TAKE-HOME MESSAGE 35.2

Some animals such as flatworms exchange gases only across the body wall and the lining of the gastrovascular cavity. Gases move within their body by diffusion.

Most aquatic invertebrates that have a circulatory system use internal or external gills to exchanges gases with water.

Lungs of land-dwelling mollusks and the tracheal system of insects allow exchange of gases with the air.

Insects have a system of air-filled tracheal tubes that open at the body surface and end near body cells.

gill Of an aquatic animal, a folded or filamentous respiratory organ in which blood or hemolymph exchanges gases with water.
lung Internal respiratory organ that exchanges gases with the air.
tracheal system Of insects, tubes that convey gases between the body surface and internal tissues.

CREDITS: (3A) From Starr/Taggart/Evers/Starr, Biology, 13E. © 2013 Cengage Learning; (3B) © Hal Beral VWPics/ SuperStock; (3C) Aydin Örstan; (3D) left, Micrograph Ed Reschke; right, From Russell/Wolfe/Hertz/Starr. Biology, 1e. © 2008 Cengage Learning Inc.

FISH GILLS

All fishes have gill slits that open across the pharynx (the throat region). In jawless fishes and cartilaginous fishes, gill slits are visible from the outside, whereas most bony fishes have a gill cover that hides them. In all fishes, water flows into the mouth, enters the pharynx, then exits the body through the gill slits. If you could remove the gill covers of a bony fish, you would see that the gills

FIGURE 35.4 **{Animated}** Structure and function of the gills of a bony fish.

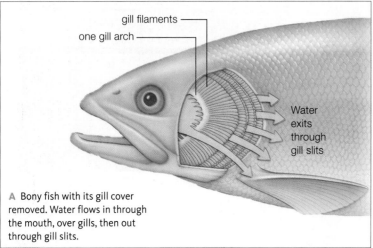

gill filaments
one gill arch
Water exits through gill slits

A Bony fish with its gill cover removed. Water flows in through the mouth, over gills, then out through gill slits.

gill arch
gill filament
respiratory surface
fold with a capillary bed inside
water flow
direction of blood flow
oxygenated blood back toward body
oxygen-poor blood from deep in body

B Two gill arches with filaments.   **C** Countercurrent flow of water and blood.

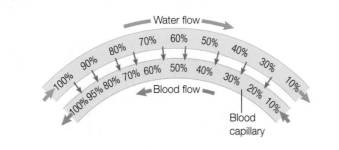

Water flow
100% 90% 80% 70% 60% 50% 40% 30%
100% 95% 80% 70% 60% 50% 40% 30% 20% 10%
Blood flow
30% 10%
Blood capillary

D Oxygen flow from water into a capillary. Percentages indicate the degree of oxygenation of water (blue) and blood (red). All along the capillary, oxygen follows its concentration gradient from water into blood.

themselves consist of bony gill arches, each with many gill filaments attached (**FIGURE 35.4A,B**). Each gill filament contains many capillary beds where blood exchanges gases with water. A mechanism called **countercurrent exchange** enhances movement of gases between blood and water. "Countercurrent" refers to that fact that water flowing over gills and blood flowing through gill capillaries move in opposite directions (**FIGURE 35.4C**). As a result, the water next to a capillary always holds more oxygen than the blood flowing inside it (**FIGURE 35.4D**). This concentration gradient makes oxygen diffuse continually from the water into the blood. Thus, the blood becomes increasingly oxygenated as it passes through the capillary.

TETRAPOD LUNGS

Vertebrate lungs evolved from outpouchings of the gut wall in the bony fishes ancestral to tetrapods (land vertebrates). Lungs may have helped these fishes survive by gulping air when the water they lived in became oxygen-poor. Lungs would also have been useful for fish that made short trips over land between ponds. Lungs became increasingly important as aquatic tetrapods began spending more time on land (Section 24.3). Gills do not function on land because, without water, the thin filaments stick together and dry out. The structure of the nostrils and throat was also modified as vertebrates moved onto land (**FIGURE 35.5**).

Amphibian larvae have external gills. As the animal develops, these gills typically disappear and are replaced by paired lungs. Unlike other tetrapods, amphibians inflate their lungs by pushing air into them (**FIGURE 35.6**). Amphibians also exchange some gases across their scale-less, thin-skinned body surface. In all amphibians, most carbon dioxide formed during aerobic respiration leaves the body across the skin.

Reptiles (including birds) and mammals have keratin-rich, waterproof skin. Their sole respiratory surface is the lining of two well-developed lungs. These animals pull air into their lungs. The lungs inflate when muscles increase the size of the thoracic cavity. As this cavity expands, pressure in the lungs declines and air is sucked inward.

In mammals and nonbird reptiles, inhaled air flows through increasingly smaller airways until it reaches tiny sacs where air is exchanged. These sacs are like a dead-end street. To leave during exhalation, air must retrace its path, flowing back out the same way it came in. Lungs do not deflate completely, so a bit of stale air remains behind even after exhalation.

countercurrent exchange Exchange of substances between two fluids moving in opposite directions.

FIGURE 35.5 Nostril modifications. In frogs and most other tetrapods, a pair of external nostrils connects the sinus cavity to the air and a pair of internal nostrils connects the sinus cavity to the throat. Thus these animals can draw air into their throat through their nose. In contrast, most bony fish have two sets of external nostrils that function in smell, but not in respiration. Water enters one set of nostrils and exits through another; there is no connection between the nostrils and the throat.

A The frog lowers the floor of its mouth, pulling air into the oral cavity through its nostrils.

B Closing the nostrils and elevating the floor of the mouth pushes air into lungs.

FIGURE 35.6 {Animated} Pushing air into frog lungs.

In birds, there are no "dead-ends," and no stale air inside the lung. Birds have small, inelastic lungs that do not expand and contract when the bird breathes. Instead, large air sacs attached to the lungs inflate and deflate (FIGURE 35.7). Oxygen-rich air flows through tiny tubes in the lung during both inhalations and exhalations. The lining of these tubes is the respiratory surface. Continual movement of air over this surface increases the efficiency of gas exchange.

We turn next to the human respiratory system. Its operating principles apply to most vertebrates.

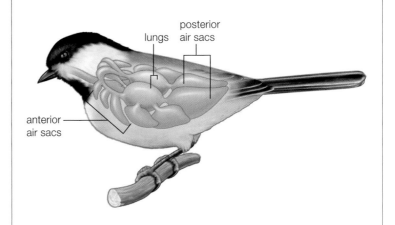

FIGURE 35.7 {Animated} Respiratory system of a bird.

Large air sacs attach to two small, inelastic lungs. Air flows in through many air tubes inside the lung, and into posterior air sacs. The lining of the tiniest of the air tubes, sometimes called air capillaries, is the respiratory surface.

It takes two respiratory cycles to move air through the lungs and air sacs of a bird's respiratory system:
Inhalation 1 — Muscles expand chest cavity, drawing air in through nostrils. Most of the air flowing in through the trachea goes to lungs and some goes to posterior air sacs.
Exhalation 1 — Anterior air sacs empty. Air from the posterior air sacs moves into lungs.
Inhalation 2 — Air in lungs moves to anterior air sacs and is replaced by newly inhaled air.
Exhalation 2 — Air in anterior air sacs moves out of the body, and air from the posterior sacs flows into the lungs.

TAKE-HOME MESSAGE 35.3

Fishes exchange gases with water flowing over their gills. Countercurrent flow of water and blood aids gas exchange.

Amphibians exchange gases across their skin and push air from their mouth into their lungs. Amniotes suck air into their lungs by expanding the size of their thoracic cavity.

Air flows in and out of mammalian lungs, but it flows continually through bird lungs.

CREDITS: (5) Steve Simzer/Shutterstock.com; (6) © Cengage Learning; (7) From Russell/Wolfe/Hertz/Starr. *Biology*, 1e. © 2008 Cengage Learning, Inc.

nasal cavity

pharynx (throat)

epiglottis

larynx (voice box)

trachea
(windpipe)

left lung

bronchus

bronchiole

diaphragm

intercostal
muscle

alveolar sac
(sectioned)

alveoli

Cast of airways (white) and blood vessels (red) in human lungs.

FIGURE 35.8 {Animated} Components of the human respiratory tract. The diaphragm and intercostal muscles also function in respiration.

 FIGURE IT OUT: Which is closer to the respiratory surface, the trachea or a bronchiole?

Answer: A bronchiole

The human respiratory system functions in gas exchange, but it also has additional tasks. We can speak, sing, or shout as air moves past our vocal cords. We have a sense of smell because airborne molecules stimulate olfactory receptors in the nose. Cells lining nasal passages and other airways help defend the body by intercepting and neutralizing airborne pathogens. The respiratory system contributes to the body's acid–base balance by expelling waste carbon dioxide that can make blood acidic and water evaporating from airways has a cooling effect on body temperature.

THE AIRWAYS

Take a deep breath. Now look at **FIGURE 35.8** to see where the air went. If you are healthy and sitting quietly, air usually enters through your nose, rather than your mouth. As air moves through your nostrils, tiny hairs filter out any large particles. Mucus secreted by cells of the nasal lining captures fine particles and airborne chemicals. Ciliated cells in the nasal lining also help remove inhaled contaminants.

Air from the nostrils enters the nasal cavity, where it is warmed and moistened. It flows next to the **pharynx**, or throat. It continues to the **larynx**, a short airway commonly known as the voice box because of the pair of vocal cords that span it (**FIGURE 35.9**). Each vocal cord consists of skeletal muscle with a cover of mucus-secreting epithelium. Contraction of the vocal cords changes the size of the **glottis**, the gap between them.

When the glottis is wide open, air flows through it silently. When muscle contraction narrows the glottis, outgoing air flowing through the tighter gap makes the vocal cords vibrate, giving rise to sounds. The tension on the cords and changes in the position of the larynx alter the sound's pitch. To get a feel for how this mechanism works, place one finger on your "Adam's apple," the laryngeal cartilage that sticks out at the front of your neck. Hum a low note, then a high one. You will feel your vocal cords vibrate and notice how laryngeal muscles shift the position of the larynx as you change the pitch of your hum.

CREDITS: (8) left, © Cengage Learning; top right, Martin Dohrn, Royal College of Surgeons/Science Source; bottom right, From Starr, Biology, 7E. © 2008 Cengage Learning.

The passage of material out of the throat is controlled by the **epiglottis**, a thin flap of membrane-covered elastic cartilage. When you swallow, the vocal cords come together to close the glottis, and the epiglottis folds down over the entrance to the larynx. As a result of these actions, food and fluids move into the esophagus, the muscular tube that connects the pharynx to the stomach. When you are breathing, the epiglottis points up, allowing air to move through the larynx into the **trachea**, or windpipe.

The cartilage-reinforced trachea branches into two similarly reinforced **bronchi** (singular, bronchus). Each bronchus delivers air to a lung. Ciliated and mucus-secreting cells in the epithelial lining of the trachea and bronchi help fend off respiratory tract infections. Bacteria and airborne particles get caught in the secreted mucus, then cilia sweep the mucus toward the throat for disposal.

THE LUNGS

The thoracic cavity holds two cone-shaped lungs, one on each side of the heart. The rib cage encloses and protects the lungs. A two-layer-thick pleural membrane lines the inner thoracic cavity wall and covers the outer surface of each lung. Fluid between the layers allows them to slide past one another as lungs change shape during breathing.

Inside each lung, air flows through finer and finer branchings of a "bronchial tree." All of these branches are **bronchioles**. Unlike the airways that lead to them, bronchioles do not have cartilage-reinforced walls. Contraction and relaxation of smooth muscle in the walls of bronchioles can alter their diameter. When you cough, your bronchioles constrict, raising the speed of air flow through them. The increased air speed helps dislodge and expel mucus. Bronchioles also constrict reflexively to protect lungs from airborne irritants such as those in smoke.

The finest bronchioles lead to the **alveoli** (singular, alveolus), the little air sacs where gases are exchanged. Collectively, alveoli provide an extensive surface for gas exchange. If the respiratory surface of all 6 million alveoli in your lungs were laid out in a single layer, they would cover more than half a tennis court!

alveoli Air sacs in the lung; gas exchange occurs across their lining.
bronchiole A small airway that leads from a bronchus to alveoli.
bronchus Airway connecting the trachea to a lung.
diaphragm Sheet of smooth muscle between the thoracic and abdominal cavities; contracts during inhalation.
epiglottis Tissue flap that folds down to prevent food from entering the airways during swallowing.
glottis Opening formed when the vocal cords relax.
larynx Short airway containing the vocal cords (voice box).
pharynx Throat; opens to airways and digestive tract.
trachea Airway to the lungs; windpipe.

vocal cords
glottis (closed)
epiglottis
base of tongue

vocal cords
glottis closed   glottis open

A Human vocal cords are located at the entrance to the larynx.

B Contraction of skeletal muscle in the cords alters the width of the glottis, the gap between them.

FIGURE 35.9 Vocal cords.

Alveoli are surrounded by pulmonary capillaries. As blood flows through these capillaries, it exchanges gases with air inside the alveoli. Remember from Section 33.2 that the pulmonary circuit of the human circulatory system pumps oxygen-poor blood to the lungs and returns oxygen-rich blood to the heart. The systemic circulation then transports oxygen-rich blood to body tissues and returns oxygen-poor, carbon dioxide–rich blood to the heart.

MUSCLES OF RESPIRATION

The **diaphragm**, a broad sheet of smooth muscle beneath the lungs, separates the thoracic cavity from the abdominal cavity. It is the only smooth muscle that can be controlled voluntarily. You can make your diaphragm contract by deliberately inhaling. The diaphragm and the intercostal muscles—the skeletal muscles between the ribs—act together to change the volume of the thoracic cavity during breathing. There are two sets of intercostal muscles. One set is external to the rib cage and functions in inhalation. The other set is inside the rib cage and acts during forced exhalation.

TAKE-HOME MESSAGE 35.4

The human respiratory system functions in gas exchange. It also has roles in smell, voice production, body defenses, acid–base balance, and temperature regulation.

Air enters through the nose or mouth. It flows through the pharynx (throat) and larynx (voice box) to a trachea that branches into two bronchi, one leading to each lung.

Inside each lung, additional branching airways deliver air to the alveoli, where gases are exchanged with blood in pulmonary capillaries. The diaphragm and muscles between the ribs alter the size of the chest cavity during breathing.

CREDITS: (9) photo, Courtesy of Kay Elemetrics Corporation; art, © Cengage Learning.

Inward
flow of air

A Inhalation. The thoracic cavity and lungs expand as the diaphragm contracts and moves downward, while the external intercostal muscles contract, lifting the rib cage.

Outward
flow of air

B Exhalation. The thoracic cavity and lungs shrink as the diaphragm relaxes and moves upward and the external intercostal muscles relax.

FIGURE 35.10 {Animated} Changes in the size of the thoracic cavity during a single respiratory cycle. The x-ray images reveal how inhalation and expiration change the lung volume.

FIGURE IT OUT: What effect does contraction of the diaphragm have on the volume of the thoracic cavity?

Answer: It increases the volume.

THE RESPIRATORY CYCLE

A **respiratory cycle** is one breath in (inhalation) and one breath out (exhalation). Inhalation is always active, and muscle contractions drive it. Changes in the volume of the lungs and thoracic cavity during a respiratory cycle alter pressure gradients between air inside and outside the respiratory tract.

When you start to inhale, the diaphragm contracts, flattening and moving downward (**FIGURE 35.10A**). Intercostal muscles on the outside of the rib cage contract, lifting the rib cage up and expanding it outward. As the thoracic cavity expands, so do the lungs. When pressure in the alveoli falls below atmospheric pressure, air follows the pressure gradient and flows into the airways.

Exhalation is usually passive. When intercostal muscles and the diaphragm relax, the lungs passively recoil and lung volume decreases. This compresses the alveoli, causing the air pressure inside them to increase above atmospheric pressure. As a result of this increase, air moves out of the lungs (**FIGURE 35.10B**).

Exhalation becomes active when you exercise vigorously or consciously attempt to expel extra air. During active exhalation, muscles of the abdominal wall contract. Pressure in the abdominal cavity increases, exerting an upward-directed force on the diaphragm. At the same time, contraction of intercostal muscles inside the rib cage pulls the thoracic wall inward and downward. As a result, the volume of the thoracic cavity decreases more than usual and additional air is forced out of the lungs.

Vital capacity, the maximum volume of air that can be moved in and out with forced inhalation and exhalation, is one measure of lung health. In an adult, the maximum capacity of the lungs is about 4 to 6 liters of air, depending on body size. However, a person typically fills his or her lungs only halfway during a normal resting inhalation. Lungs never deflate completely. As you exhale, the smallest airways collapse, temporarily trapping some air. As a result, air in alveoli is always a mix of freshly inhaled air and air left behind during the previous exhalation.

CONTROL OF BREATHING

You do not have to think about breathing. Neurons in the medulla oblongata of your brain stem (Section 29.9) function as the pacemaker for inhalation, initiating an action potential 10–20 times per minute. Nerves relay these action potentials to the diaphragm and intercostal muscles, where the stimulation results in contractions that cause inhalation. Between action potentials, the muscles relax and you exhale.

Your rate of breathing increases with activity level (**FIGURE 35.11**). When you exercise, muscle cells increase their rate of aerobic respiration and produce more CO_2. When CO_2 enters blood, it excites chemoreceptors in the carotid arteries and aorta. These receptors respond by signaling the brain. The brain itself also has chemoreceptors for CO_2. In response to signals that CO_2 is rising, the brain alters the breathing pattern, so breaths become faster and deeper. Sympathetic nervous stimulation also increases the respiratory rate during fright or excitement (Section 29.7). In many birds and mammals, a rise in body temperature triggers shallow, rapid breaths (panting). Panting helps cool a body by increasing the rate of evaporative cooling across the respiratory tract. Humans cool themselves primarily by sweating, and do not pant in response to heat.

Reflexes such as swallowing or coughing can temporarily halt breathing, but humans rarely hold their breath for more than a minute. The rise in CO_2 that results when breathing halts usually triggers a gasp for air within a minute or so.

CHOKING—A BLOCKED AIRWAY

Choking occurs when food or an object enters and blocks the larynx. A person who is choking cannot move air through the larynx, and so cannot breathe, cough, or speak. If you suspect someone is choking, encourage them to cough. If they can do so, their airway is not fully obstructed and coughing will probably clear it.

If person is choking, a rescuer can help clear the person's airway and keep them from dying of lack of air. First aid for choking involves two types of maneuvers. Blows to the back can help dislodge the foreign material with little risk of injury to internal organs (FIGURE 35.12A). If back blows are ineffective, thrusts to the choker's abdomen can raise intra-abdominal pressure, forcing the diaphragm upward. Raising air pressure inside the lungs by this maneuver can dislodge the object, allowing the victim to resume breathing normally (FIGURE 35.12B).

respiratory cycle One inhalation and one exhalation.
vital capacity Maximum amount of air moved in and out of lungs with forced inhalation and exhalation.

TAKE-HOME MESSAGE 35.5

Inhalation is always an active process. Contraction of the diaphragm and intercostal muscles expands the thoracic cavity. As a result, air pressure in alveoli declines below atmospheric pressure and air moves inward.

Exhalation is usually passive. As muscles of respiration relax, volume of the thoracic cavity declines, air pressure in alveoli rises, and air moves out of the lungs.

The lungs are never fully emptied of air.

The medulla oblongata in the brain stem controls the rate and depth of breathing.

STIMULUS

CO_2 concentration and acidity rise in the blood and cerebrospinal fluid.

RESPONSE

Chemoreceptors in wall of carotid arteries and aorta

Respiratory center in brain stem

CO_2 concentration and acidity decline in the blood and cerebrospinal fluid.

Diaphragm, Intercostal muscles

Tidal volume and rate of breathing change.

FIGURE 35.11 Respiratory response to CO_2 production during exercise. When chemoreceptors in arteries and the brain are excited by increased CO_2, they signal brain regions that govern breathing. As a result, breathing becomes deeper and faster, so more CO_2 is expelled.

A Back blows. Have the person lean forward. Use the heel of your hand to strike between the shoulder blades.

B Abdominal thrusts. Stand behind the person and place one fist below the rib cage, just above the navel, with your thumb facing inward. Cover the fist with your other hand and thrust inward and upward with both fists.

FIGURE 35.12 {Animated} Maneuvers to assist a conscious adult who is choking. The Red Cross recommends that rescuers ask if a victim is choking and wants help. If the person nods, the rescuer should alternate between a series of five back blows and five abdominal thrusts.

CREDITS: (11) photo, © C. Yokochi and J. Rohen, *Photographic Anatomy of the Human Body*, 2nd Ed., Igaku-Shoin, Ltd., 1979; art, © Cengage Learning; (12A) © Cengage Learning 2015; (12B) From Starr/Taggart/Evers/Starr, Biology, 12E. © 2009 Cengage Learning.

A Each alveolus is surrounded by a mesh of pulmonary capillaries.

B Cutaway view of an alveolus and associated pulmonary capillaries. Pores connect adjacent alveoli.

C Components of the respiratory membrane.

FIGURE 35.13 Zooming in on the respiratory membrane in human lungs.

THE RESPIRATORY MEMBRANE

Air drawn into your lungs by inhalation diffuses from an alveolus into an associated pulmonary capillary at the lung's **respiratory membrane**. This membrane consists of alveolar epithelium, capillary endothelium, and their fused basement membranes (**FIGURE 35.13**). Alveolar epithelium contains squamous cells and secretory cells. The secretory cells keep alveolar walls lubricated, so the walls do not stick together when the alveolus has to inflate.

Oxygen and carbon dioxide diffuse passively across a respiratory membrane. The net direction of movement for each gas depends on its concentration gradient across the repiratory membrane, or as we say for gases, partial pressure gradient. The partial pressure of a gas is its contribution to the pressure exerted by a mix of gases. **FIGURE 35.14** shows how the partial pressures of O_2 and CO_2 vary among air, blood, and body tissues.

OXYGEN TRANSPORT

Inhaled air has a higher partial pressure of O_2 than does blood in pulmonary capillaries. As a result, O_2 tends to diffuse from alveoli into these capillaries. Once in the blood, most O_2 diffuses into red blood cells, where it binds to hemoglobin. Hemoglobin consists of four polypeptide (globin) subunits, each with an associated iron-containing heme group (**FIGURE 35.15**). When O_2 is bound to one or more of hemoglobin's heme groups, we refer to the molecule as oxyhemoglobin.

Binding of O_2 to heme is reversible. Heme picks up O_2 in pulmonary capillaries, where the temperature is relatively cool, O_2 partial pressure is high, and CO_2 partial pressure is low. The oxygen-rich blood then flows to a systemic capillary bed, in a tissue where the temperature and partial pressure of CO_2 are higher, and the partial pressure of O_2 is lower. These conditions cause the hemes to release O_2.

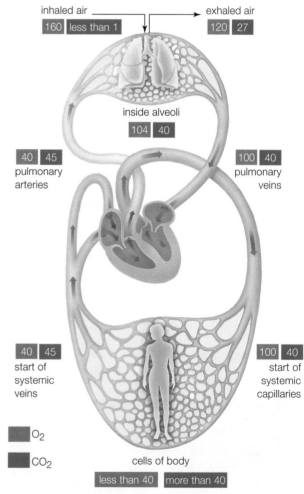

FIGURE 35.14 Partial pressures (mm Hg) for O_2 (red boxes) and CO_2 (blue boxes) in air, blood, and tissues.

 FIGURE IT OUT: Where is the biggest drop in partial pressure of O_2?

Answer: Between the start of the systemic capillaries and systemic veins

CREDITS: (13, 14) From Starr/Taggart/Evers/Starr, Biology, 13E. © 2013 Cengage Learning.

FIGURE 35.15 Hemoglobin, the oxygen-carrying protein in red blood cells. Heme groups are shown in red, globin chains in blue and green.

CARBON DIOXIDE TRANSPORT

CO_2 diffuses into capillaries from metabolically active tissues, which have higher CO_2 partial pressure than blood. Once in the blood, CO_2 is transported to the lungs in three forms. About 10 percent remains dissolved in plasma. Another 30 percent reversibly binds with hemoglobin and forms carbaminohemoglobin. However, about 60 percent of the CO_2 is transported in plasma as bicarbonate (HCO_3^-).

Bicarbonate forms inside red blood cells. An enzyme in these cells (carbonic anhydrase) catalyzes formation of carbonic acid from CO_2 and water. Carbonic acid then dissociates into bicarbonate and H^+:

$$CO_2 + H_2O \rightleftharpoons \underset{\text{carbonic acid}}{H_2CO_3} \rightleftharpoons \underset{\text{bicarbonate}}{HCO_3^- + H^+}$$

Being charged, the H^+ and bicarbonate produced by this reaction cannot diffuse across a red blood cell's plasma membrane. The H^+ binds to hemoglobin. The bicarbonate is transported into the plasma by proteins in the red blood cell's plasma membrane. When the blood reaches pulmonary capillaries, where the CO_2 partial pressure is relatively low, bicarbonate reenters the red blood cell and the above reaction is reversed. Water and CO_2 form, diffuse from the blood into alveoli, and leave the body in exhalations.

respiratory membrane Membrane consisting of alveolar epithelium, capillary endothelium, and their fused basement membranes.

TAKE-HOME MESSAGE 35.6

Oxygen diffuses across the respiratory membrane and into pulmonary capillaries, where it binds to hemoglobin in red blood cells. Hemoglobin releases oxygen near active tissues.

Carbon dioxide diffuses into capillaries in active tissues. Most combines with water to form carbonic acid, which splits into bicarbonate and H^+. Bicarbonate dissolves in plasma. In alveoli, carbon dioxide and water re-form and are exhaled.

PEOPLE MATTER

National Geographic Grantee
DR. CYNTHIA BEALL

Air pressure decreases with altitude, so air becomes "thinner." At 5,500 meters (about 18,000 feet), a given volume of air contains only half as many O_2 molecules as air at sea level. This is why people who normally live at sea level often feel dizzy, disoriented, and breathless when they visit a high elevation. Typically, members of long-established, high-altitude populations do not experience these ill effects, because natural selection has adapted these populations to their low-oxygen environment.

Dr. Cynthia Beall (at the center in the photo above) studies the adaptations of high-altitude human populations. She began her work in the 1970s, when people of the Andean plateau were the only high-altitude group whose physiology had been studied. The Andeans have an unusually high concentration of hemoglobin in their blood, a trait that allows them to maximize the amount of oxygen they acquire from each breath. Beall's comparative studies revealed that high-altitude populations in other places adapted in other ways. For example, Tibetan plateau dwellers maintain a low hemoglobin level, but take more breaths per minute. Tibetans also make more nitric oxide. This gas encourages blood vessels to widen, increasing blood flow through lung capillaries. Although the Andean and Tibetan populations both face the same selective pressure (low oxygen), a different mechanism of countering that pressure evolved in each. In Andeans, the blood composition was altered; in Tibetans, respiratory rate and blood flow were affected.

CREDITS: (15) From Starr/Evers/Starr, Biology Today and Tomorrow with Physiology, 3E. © 2010 Cengage Learning; (in text) © Courtesy of Cynthia Beall.

35.7 WHAT CAUSES RESPIRATORY DISEASES AND DISORDERS?

FIGURE 35.16 A mask that delivers pressurized air can prevent episodes of sleep apnea.

Interrupted Breathing With apnea, breathing repeatedly stops and restarts spontaneously, especially during sleep. Sleep apnea most often occurs when the tongue or other soft tissue obstructs the upper airways. Breathing may stop for up to several seconds many times each night, causing daytime fatigue. Risk for heart attacks and strokes rises with sleep apnea, because blood pressure soars when breathing stops. Obstructive sleep apnea can be reduced by changes in sleeping position or by wearing a mask that delivers pressurized air (**FIGURE 35.16**).

Sudden infant death syndrome (SIDS) occurs when an infant does not awaken from an episode of apnea. Autopsies of affected infants have demonstrated that a defect in the medulla oblongata is associated with SIDS. The defect may impair the medulla's response to potentially deadly respiratory stress. There are also environmental risk factors. Maternal smoking during pregnancy heightens the risk, and infants who sleep on their stomach are at higher risk than those who sleep on their back.

Infectious Diseases Worldwide, about one in three people is infected by *Mycobacterium tuberculosis*, the bacterial species that can cause tuberculosis (TB). Most infected people are symptom-free, but about 10 percent of those infected develop "active TB." They cough up bloody mucus, have chest pain, and find breathing difficult. If untreated, active TB can be fatal. Antibiotics can cure most infections, but they must be taken diligently for at least six months.

Pneumonia is a general term for lung inflammation caused by an infection. Bacteria, viruses, and fungi can cause pneumonia. Typical symptoms include a cough, an aching chest, shortness of breath, and fever. An x-ray reveals infected tissues filled with fluid and white blood cells instead of air.

Bronchitis, Asthma, and Emphysema Inflammation of bronchial epithelium is called bronchitis. Inflamed epithelial cells secrete extra mucus that triggers coughing. Bacteria colonize the mucus, leading to more inflammation, more mucus, and more coughing. Bronchitis often arises after an upper respiratory infection. Inhaling irritants such as cigarette smoke can cause chronic bronchitis.

With asthma, an inhaled allergen or irritant triggers inflammation, which constricts airways and thus makes breathing difficult. A tendency to have asthma is inherited, but exposure to irritants such as smoke raises the frequency of asthma attacks. An acute asthma attack is treated with inhaled drugs that dilate the airways.

With emphysema, tissue-destroying bacterial enzymes digest the thin, elastic alveolar wall. As these walls disappear, the area of the respiratory surface declines. Lungs become distended and inelastic, leaving the person constantly feeling short of breath. Some people inherit a genetic predisposition to emphysema. They do not have a functioning gene for an enzyme that inhibits bacterial attacks on alveoli. However, tobacco smoking is by far the main risk factor for emphysema.

TAKE-HOME MESSAGE 35.7

Apnea, or interrupted breathing, is caused by tissue obstructing airways or a defective respiratory pacemaker.

Tuberculosis is a widespread bacterial disease that can be fatal, although most infected people have no symptoms. Pneumonia is caused by many different pathogens.

In asthma and bronchitis, airways become inflamed and constricted. In emphysema, alveolar sacs become distended and inelastic.

Application: EFFECTS OF SMOKING

Education

FIGURE 35.17 Cigarette smoke at the junction between the trachea and the bronchi. Smoke immobilizes cilia of cells lining the airways.

EVERYONE KNOWS THAT SMOKING TOBACCO RAISES THE RISK OF LUNG CANCER. Tobacco smoke contains more than forty carcinogens (cancer-causing chemicals), and more than 80 percent of lung cancers occur in smokers. Once diagnosed with lung cancer, the majority of smokers die within a year. Female smokers are at an especially high risk of developing cancer. On average, their cancers appear earlier than men's, and with lower exposure to tobacco.

Lung cancer takes years to become large enough to be diagnosed, but tobacco smoke impairs respiratory function immediately. When the smoke enters upper airways (**FIGURE 35.17**), it immobilizes cilia that help keep pathogens and pollutants from reaching the lungs. Smoke from a single cigarette can paralyze these cilia for hours. Smoke also kills white blood cells that patrol and defend respiratory tissues, allowing pathogens to multiply in the undefended airways. The result is a heightened susceptibility to colds, asthma attacks, bronchitis, and emphysema.

Tobacco smoke also delivers a hefty dose of carbon monoxide (CO), a colorless, odorless, poisonous gas. Inhaled CO interferes with gas exchange. It binds to hemoglobin to form carboxyhemoglobin (COHb), thus blocking sites that would otherwise bind O_2. Hemoglobin binds to CO more than 200 times more tightly than oxygen. In addition, binding of CO also makes hemoglobin hold more tightly to any oxygen that it does bind. Thus, when CO is present, blood holds less oxygen and delivers less of what it does have to tissues.

Smoking cigarettes increases blood COHb by about 5 percent for each pack smoked per day. Over the short term, a blood COHb level as low as 4–6 percent can decrease a healthy young person's capacity to exercise. Over the longer term, an increased COHb level harms the heart, which must work overtime to make up for CO's suffocating effects on respiratory function.

Respiratory effects of marijuana smoke are less well studied than those of tobacco smoke, mainly because its use is illegal in most countries. We do know that marijuana smoke contains carbon monoxide and an assortment of carcinogens, including arsenic and ammonia. Marijuana smokers get an unfiltered dose of these toxins. Nevertheless, the few studies that have been done show no significant impairment of respiratory function or increased risk for lung cancer with marijuana smoking only. On the other hand, people who smoke both marijuana and tobacco have more respiratory problems than tobacco-only smokers.

Summary

SECTION 35.1 Aerobic respiration requires O_2 and releases CO_2 as a product. **Respiration** is a physiological process by which O_2 enters the internal environment and CO_2 leaves it. Both gases diffuse across a **respiratory surface**. Hemoglobin and other **respiratory proteins** facilitate gas exchange by maintaining steep concentration gradients between blood and cells.

SECTION 35.2 Some invertebrates in aquatic or damp habitats exchange gases mainly across the body surface. Many aquatic invertebrates have **gills** with blood running through them. Land snails and slugs have a simple **lung**. A **tracheal system** delivers air to cells deep inside the body of insects.

SECTION 35.3 Water and blood flow in opposing directions at fish gills, allowing a highly efficient **countercurrent exchange** of gases. Most land vertebrates have paired lungs, although amphibians also exchange gases across the skin. Frogs pull air into their mouth through their nostrils, then push it into their lungs. Other tetrapods pull air into their lungs by expanding their thoracic cavity and lungs. In mammals, gas exchange occurs at the ends of airways in tiny sacs. Birds have a more efficient system; gas exchange occurs as air flows through tubes in their lungs.

SECTION 35.4 In humans, air flows through the nose and the mouth into the **pharynx**, then the **larynx**, then the **trachea** (windpipe). The larynx contains the vocal cords, whose movements alter the size of the opening (the **glottis**) between them. When you swallow, the position of the **epiglottis** at the entrance to the larynx shifts, keeping food out of the trachea. The trachea branches into two **bronchi** that enter the lungs. These two large airways and finely branching **bronchioles** form the bronchial tree. At the ends of the finest branches of this tree are the thin-walled **alveoli**, where gas exchange occurs. The **diaphragm** at the base of the thoracic cavity and the muscles attached to ribs alter the size of the thoracic cavity during breathing.

SECTION 35.5 A **respiratory cycle** is one inhalation and one exhalation. Inhalation is active. As muscle contraction expands the chest cavity, pressure inside the lungs decreases below atmospheric pressure, so air flows into the lungs. These events are reversed during exhalation, which is normally passive. The most air that can move in and out in one cycle is the **vital capacity**. Cells in the brain stem adjust the rate and magnitude of breathing. If a foreign object lodges in the trachea and prevents breathing, it can sometimes be dislodged by blows to the back or abdominal thrusts that compress the lungs and force air outward.

SECTION 35.6 In human lungs, the alveolar wall, the wall of a pulmonary capillary, and their fused basement membranes form a thin **respiratory membrane** between air inside an alveolus and the internal environment. O_2 following its partial pressure gradient diffuses across the respiratory membrane, into the plasma of the blood, and finally into red blood cells.

Where O_2 partial pressure is high, heme in hemoglobin of red blood cells binds O_2 and forms oxyhemoglobin. Heme groups release O_2 where its partial pressure is low.

CO_2 follows its partial pressure gradient and diffuses from cells to interstitial fluid, to blood. Most CO_2 reacts with water in red blood cells, forming bicarbonate. The enzyme carbonic anhydrase speeds this reaction. The reaction is reversed in the lungs. There, CO_2 diffuses out of blood into air inside alveoli. It is expelled, along with water vapor, in exhalations.

SECTION 35.7 With apnea, breathing is interrupted by an obstructing tissue or as the result of a problem in the brain's respiratory center. Tuberculosis, pneumonia, bronchitis, and emphysema are respiratory diseases.

SECTION 35.8 Smoking tobacco raises the risk of lung cancer and damages cells that protect airways from pathogens. It also delivers carbon monoxide, a gas that interferes with oxygen delivery by binding to hemoglobin more strongly than oxygen does. Marijuana smoke also contains carbon monoxide and carcinogens.

Self-Quiz   Answers in Appendix VII

1. Respiratory proteins such as hemoglobin _____ .
   a. contain metal ions
   b. occur only in vertebrates
   c. increase the efficiency of oxygen transport
   d. both a and c

2. In _____ , gas exchange occurs at the body surface and gas is distributed by diffusion alone.
   a. earthworms   c. frogs
   b. flatworms   d. insects

3. Countercurrent flow of water and blood increases the efficiency of gas exchange in _____ .
   a. fishes   c. birds
   b. amphibians   d. all of the above

4. In human lungs, gas exchange occurs at the _____ .
   a. two bronchi   c. alveoli
   b. pleural sacs   d. both b and c

5. When you breathe quietly, inhalation is _____ and exhalation is _____ .
   a. passive; passive   c. passive; active
   b. active; active   d. active; passive

6. During inhalation, _____ .
   a. the thoracic cavity expands
   b. the diaphragm relaxes
   c. atmospheric pressure declines

7. What type of metal associates with hemoglobin?

Data Analysis Activities

Risks of Radon Radon is a colorless, odorless gas emitted by many rocks and soils. It is formed by the radioactive decay of uranium and is itself radioactive. There is some radon in the air almost everywhere, but routinely inhaling a lot of it raises the risk of lung cancer. Radon also seems to increase cancer risk far more in smokers than in nonsmokers. **FIGURE 35.18** is an estimate of how radon in homes affects risk of lung cancer mortality. Note that these data show only the risk of death for radon-induced cancers. Smokers are also at risk from lung cancers that are caused by tobacco alone.

1. If 1,000 smokers were exposed to a radon level of 1.3 pCi/L over a lifetime (the average indoor radon level), how many would die of a radon-induced lung cancer?
2. How high would the radon level have to be to cause approximately the same number of cancers among 1,000 nonsmokers?
3. The risk of dying in a car crash is about 7 out of 1,000. Is a smoker in a home with an average radon level (1.3 pCi/L) more likely to die in a car crash or of radon-induced cancer?

Radon Level (pCi/L)	Risk of Cancer Death From Lifetime Radon Exposure	
	Never Smoked	**Current Smokers**
20	36 out of 1,000	260 out of 1,000
0	18 out of 1,000	150 out of 1,000
8	15 out of 1,000	120 out of 1,000
4	7 out of 1,000	62 out of 1,000
2	4 out of 1,000	32 out of 1,000
1.3	2 out of 1,000	20 out of 1,000
0.4	<1 out of 1,000	6 out of 1,000

FIGURE 35.18 Estimated risk of lung cancer death as a result of lifetime radon exposure. Radon levels are in picocuries per liter (pCi/L). The Environmental Protection Agency considers a radon level above 4 pCi/L unsafe. To learn about testing for radon and what to do if the radon level is high, visit the EPA's Radon Information Site at www.epa.gov/radon.

8. _____ binds to hemoglobin more strongly than O_2 does.
   a. Carbon dioxide   c. Oxyhemoglobin
   b. Carbon monoxide   d. Carbonic anhydrase

9. Carbonic anhydrase in red blood cells catalyzes formation of bicarbonate from water and _____ .
   a. oxygen   c. oxyhemoglobin
   b. hemoglobin   d. carbon dioxide

10. The medulla oblongata _____ .
    a. produces hemoglobin   c. regulates breathing rate
    b. is in the forebrain   d. detects carbon monoxide

11. _____ in arteries detect changes in the CO_2 concentration of the blood.
    a. Mechanoreceptors   c. Photoreceptors
    b. Neurotransmitters d. Chemoreceptors

12. True or false? Human lungs hold some air even after forced exhalation.

13. The diaphragm is a _____ muscle.
    a. smooth   b. skeletal   c. cardiac

14. What type of organism causes tuberculosis?

15. Match the words with their descriptions.
    ___ trachea   a. muscle of respiration
    ___ pharynx   b. gap between vocal cords
    ___ alveolus   c. between bronchi and alveoli
    ___ bronchus   d. windpipe
    ___ bronchiole   e. site of gas exchange
    ___ glottis   f. airway leading to lung
    ___ diaphragm   g. throat

Critical Thinking

1. The red blood cell enzyme carbonic anhydrase contains the metal zinc. Humans obtain zinc from their diet, especially from red meat and some seafoods. A zinc deficiency does not reduce the number of red blood cells, but it does impair respiratory function by reducing carbon dioxide output. Explain why a zinc deficiency has this effect.

2. Look again at **FIGURE 35.14**. Notice that the oxygen and carbon dioxide content of blood in pulmonary veins is the same as at the start of the systemic capillaries. Notice also that systemic veins and pulmonary arteries have equal partial pressures. Explain the reason for the similarities.

3. Respiration supplies cells with the oxygen they need for aerobic respiration. Explain the role of oxygen in this energy-releasing metabolic pathway. Where is it used and what is its function?

4. A developing fetus gets oxygen from its mother's blood. Fetal capillaries run through pools of maternal blood in an organ called the placenta. As fetal blood runs through these capillaries, it exchanges substances with the maternal blood around the capillary. The hemoglobin made by a fetus is different than that made after birth. Fetal hemoglobin binds oxygen more strongly at low oxygen levels than normal hemoglobin. How would fetal hemoglobin's somewhat higher affinity for oxygen benefit the fetus?

CENGAGE To access course materials, please visit
brain www.cengagebrain.com.

An aye-aye feeding on a coconut. Constantly growing incisors allow these unusual primates to gnaw through grub-containing wood and woody nuts without wearing down their teeth.

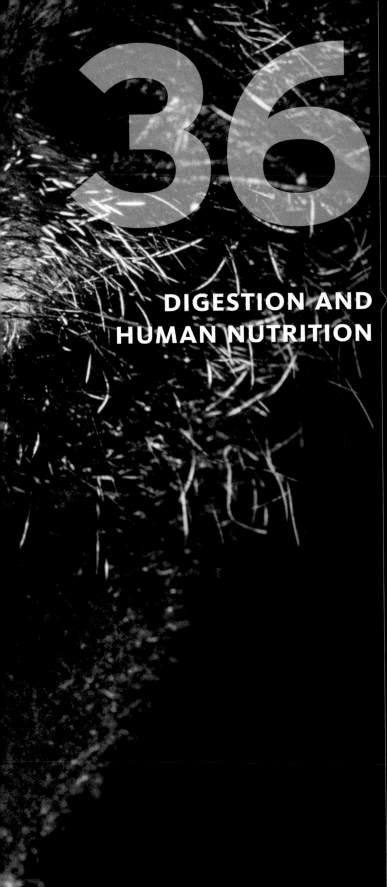

36

DIGESTION AND HUMAN NUTRITION

Links to Earlier Concepts

This chapter expands the discussion of digestive systems in Chapters 23 and 24. You will consider dietary aspects of organic compounds (Sections 3.2–3.4) and the use and storage of glucose (7.7). This chapter revisits diffusion, transport mechanisms, and osmosis (5.6–5.8); pH and cofactors (2.5, 5.5); and epithelium (28.3) and adipose tissue (28.4).

KEY CONCEPTS

ANIMAL DIGESTIVE SYSTEMS
Some invertebrates have a saclike gut, but most animals have a tubular gut with two openings. Structural differences in digestive systems can arise as adaptations to different diets.

HUMAN DIGESTIVE SYSTEM
Human digestion starts in the mouth and continues in the stomach and small intestine. Nutrient absorption begins in the small intestine. The large intestine concentrates wastes.

DIGESTION AND ABSORPTION
Digestion is the mechanical and chemical breakdown of food into its component organic subunits. Absorption is transfer of these subunits from the interior of the gut into body tissues.

HUMAN NUTRITION
A healthy diet provides all nutrients, vitamins, and minerals necessary to build body parts and maintain normal metabolism. It is low in salt, simple sugars, and saturated fats.

MAINTAINING A HEALTHY WEIGHT
Maintaining body weight requires balancing calories taken in with calories burned. A body weight far above or below normal increases the risk of health problems.

DIGESTIVE TASKS

Animals are heterotrophs that obtain the energy and raw materials they need from organic compounds made by other organisms. In sponges, individual cells engulf food particles, break them down (digest them), then expel wastes. In most other animals, digestion is extracellular. It occurs inside a hollow organ or organs whose interior opens to the outside.

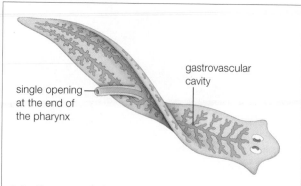

A Saclike gastrovascular cavity of a planarian flatworm.

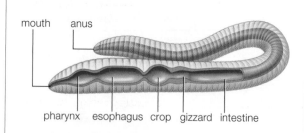

B Complete digestive tract of an earthworm, with two openings (mouth and anus) and specialized regions in between.

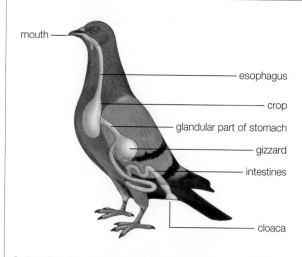

C Complete digestive tract of a bird with two openings (mouth and cloaca), and specialized regions in between.

FIGURE 36.1 {Animated} Animal digestive systems.

Animal digestion typically involves four tasks:

1. *Ingestion.* Taking food into the digestive chamber.
2. *Mechanical and Chemical Digestion.* Breaking food down into components that can be absorbed into the body. Mechanical digestion smashes food into smaller and smaller fragments. Chemical digestion breaks large polymers into their component subunits.
3. *Absorption.* Movement of nutrient molecules across the lining of the digestive chamber and into the body's internal environment.
4. *Elimination.* Expelling any leftover material that was not digested and absorbed from the body.

SAC OR TUBE?

Flatworms and cnidarians have a saclike **gastrovascular cavity** that functions in both digestion and gas exchange. This cavity has a single opening through which food enters and wastes leave. In flatworms, the opening is at the tip of a muscular pharynx (**FIGURE 36.1A**). In animals that have a gut with a single opening, each load of food must be broken down, its nutrients absorbed, and any wastes eliminated before a new load of food can enter.

Most invertebrates and all vertebrates have a **complete digestive tract**: a tubular gut with two openings (**FIGURE 36.1B,C**). Food enters a mouth at one end of the tube, and wastes leave through the other end. The body plan of a coelomate animal (Section 23.1) with a complete digestive tract is sometimes described as a "tube within a tube." The body wall is the outer tube and the tubular digestive tract lies within it, inside a coelom (**FIGURE 36.2**).

FIGURE 36.2 Tube within a tube. Schematic cross-section of a coelomate animal with a complete digestive tract.

As food travels the length of a complete digestive tract, it passes through regions specialized for food storage, food breakdown, nutrient absorption, and waste elimination. Unlike a gastrovascular cavity, a tubular gut can carry out all of these tasks simultaneously. Like you, an earthworm can take in new food even when food it ate earlier has not yet exited the digestive tract.

In some animals, digestive wastes exit through an **anus**, an opening that serves this purpose alone. In others, digestive wastes exit through a **cloaca**, a multipurpose opening that also releases urinary waste and functions in

CREDITS: (1A) © Cengage Learning; (1B) From Russel/Wolfe/Hertz/Starr, Biology, 2E. © 2011 Cengage Learning, Inc. Reproduced with permission. www.cengage.com/permissions; (1C) © Cengage Learning 2015; (2) From Starr/Evers/Starr, Biology Today and Tomorrow with Physiology, 4E. © 2013 Cengage Learning.

FIGURE 36.3 {Animated} Multiple-chambered stomach of a cow. Microbes in the first two stomach chambers break down cellulose in plant cell walls. Solids accumulate in the second chamber, forming "cud" that is regurgitated—moved back into the mouth for a second round of chewing. Nutrient-rich fluid moves from the second chamber to the third and fourth chambers, and finally to the intestine.

reproduction. Amphibians, reptiles, and birds have a cloaca (**FIGURE 36.1C**), whereas humans and other placental mammals have an anus.

PROCESSING SPECIFIC FOODS

Features of animal digestive systems are shaped by natural selection and adapt the animal to a particular diet. Consider the shape of a bird's beak. Birds do not have teeth; their jawbones are covered with a layer of the structural protein keratin that forms a beak. The size and shape of a bird's beak determines what kinds of food it can process. Hawks and other predatory birds have a sharp, curved beak that they use to tear flesh, whereas some other birds have a short, thick beak that can open seeds, or a long, narrow beak for reaching into flowers to sip nectar.

Similarly, there are four types of mammalian teeth (Section 24.7), but which types are present and their relative sizes vary among species. Carnivores (meat eaters) tend to have long, sharp canine teeth for killing prey, whereas herbivores (plant eaters) typically have small canine teeth or none at all. Rodents and some other mammals routinely chew on rough material that wears down their teeth, so they have teeth that grow continually.

anus Body opening that serves solely as the exit for wastes from a complete digestive tract.
cloaca Body opening that serves as the exit for digestive and urinary waste; also functions in reproduction.
complete digestive tract Tubelike digestive system; food enters through one opening and wastes leave through another.
gastrovascular cavity Saclike gut that also functions in gas exchange.
ruminant Hoofed mammal with a multiple-chamber stomach that adapts it to a cellulose-rich diet.

Regional specializations of the digestive tract also adapt animals to particular diets. Like other seed-eating birds, a pigeon has a large saclike food-storing region called a crop (**FIGURE 36.2C**). The bird quickly fills its crop with seeds, then digests them later, in safer places. Birds also have a gizzard, which is a chamber lined with hard protein particles. The gizzard breaks up tough foods such as seeds or bones. Compared to hawks and other meat-eating birds, seed eaters have larger gizzards relative to their body size.

Cattle, goats, sheep, and antelopes are **ruminants**, hoofed grazers with multiple stomach chambers (**FIGURE 36.3**). Microbes living inside these chambers break down cellulose, thus helping ruminants maximize the nutrients they extract from plant foods. Animals do not make enzymes that would allow them to break down cellulose on their own.

Meat does not contain cellulose, so it can be digested more quickly than plant material. As a result, meat-eating mammals typically have a shorter gut than grazers. The longer an animal's gut, the more time it takes for material to pass through, and the more processing can occur.

TAKE-HOME MESSAGE 36.1

Digestive systems mechanically and chemically degrade food into small molecules that can be absorbed into the internal environment. These systems also expel the undigested residues from the body.

Some invertebrates digest food in a gastrovascular cavity that has one opening. Most animals have a tubular digestive tract with two openings and regional specializations in between.

Some variations in gut structure reflect adaptations to particular diets.

CREDITS: (3 art) Based on A. Romer and T. Parsons, *The Vertebrate Body*, Sixth Edition, Saunders Publishing Company, 1986; (3 photo) © lightpoet/Shutterstock.com.

Like other vertebrates, humans have a complete digestive system: a tubular gut with two openings (**FIGURE 36.4A**). If the gut were stretched out in a straight line, it would extend 6.5 to 9 meters (21 to 30 feet). Its various regions specialize in digesting food, absorbing nutrients, and concentrating and storing unabsorbed waste. Salivary glands, the pancreas, and the liver are accessory organs that secrete substances into the tube (**FIGURE 36.4B**).

Food enters the body through the mouth, or oral cavity. Mechanical digestion begins when teeth rip and crush food. As a species, humans are omnivores, meaning that we are capable of digesting both plant and animal material. The structure of our teeth adapts us to a varied diet. We have all four types of mammalian teeth, and all are equally well developed (**FIGURE 36.5**). Incisors shear off bits of food. Canines tear meats. Premolars

FIGURE 36.4 {Animated} Major organs and accessory organs of the human digestive system.

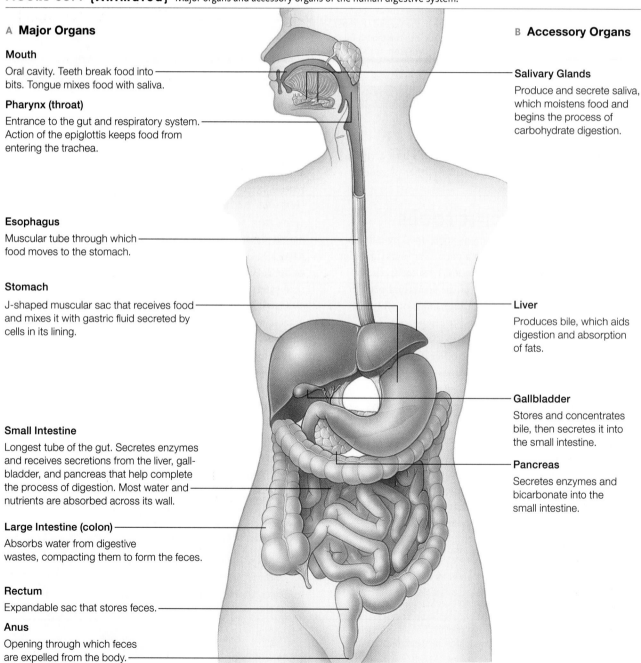

A Major Organs

Mouth
Oral cavity. Teeth break food into bits. Tongue mixes food with saliva.

Pharynx (throat)
Entrance to the gut and respiratory system. Action of the epiglottis keeps food from entering the trachea.

Esophagus
Muscular tube through which food moves to the stomach.

Stomach
J-shaped muscular sac that receives food and mixes it with gastric fluid secreted by cells in its lining.

Small Intestine
Longest tube of the gut. Secretes enzymes and receives secretions from the liver, gall-bladder, and pancreas that help complete the process of digestion. Most water and nutrients are absorbed across its wall.

Large Intestine (colon)
Absorbs water from digestive wastes, compacting them to form the feces.

Rectum
Expandable sac that stores feces.

Anus
Opening through which feces are expelled from the body.

B Accessory Organs

Salivary Glands
Produce and secrete saliva, which moistens food and begins the process of carbohydrate digestion.

Liver
Produces bile, which aids digestion and absorption of fats.

Gallbladder
Stores and concentrates bile, then secretes it into the small intestine.

Pancreas
Secretes enzymes and bicarbonate into the small intestine.

incisors
canine
premolars
molars

FIGURE 36.5
Teeth of a human adult.

and molars have broad, bumpy crowns that function as platforms for grinding and crushing food. Each tooth consists mostly of dentin, a bonelike material. The part of each tooth that extends above the gum—the crown—is covered by enamel, the hardest material in the body.

The tongue, a bundle of membrane-covered skeletal muscle, attaches to the floor of the mouth. Movements of the tongue help mix food with saliva secreted by salivary glands. **Salivary glands** are exocrine glands that open into the mouth beneath the tongue and on the inner surface of the cheeks next to the upper molars. Salivary amylase, an enzyme in saliva, begins the process of chemical digestion by breaking starch into disaccharides (two-sugar units). This reaction, like other digestive reactions, is an example of hydrolysis (Section 3.1). In addition to enzymes, saliva contains glycoproteins that combine with water to form mucus. The presence of mucus helps small food bits stick together in easy-to-swallow clumps.

Food is forced into the pharynx (throat) by swallowing. The presence of food at the back of the throat triggers a swallowing reflex. When you swallow, the epiglottis flops down and the vocal cords constrict, so the route between the pharynx and larynx is blocked. The reflex keeps food from entering the trachea and choking you.

Swallowed food enters the **esophagus**, which is a muscular tube between the pharynx and stomach. Wavelike smooth muscle contractions, called **peristalsis**, move food through the esophagus to the stomach, and through the rest of the digestive tract. The **stomach** is a stretchable sac that stores food, secretes acid and digestive enzymes, and mixes them all together.

The stomach empties into the **small intestine**, the region of the gut where most carbohydrates, lipids, and proteins are digested and from which most nutrients and water are absorbed. Secretions from the liver and pancreas assist the small intestine in these tasks.

The **large intestine** (mainly the colon) absorbs water and ions, thus compacting digestive wastes. Wastes are briefly stored in a stretchable tube, the **rectum**, before being expelled from the anus at the gut's terminal opening.

---

esophagus Muscular tube between the throat and stomach.
large intestine Organ that receives digestive waste from the small intestine and concentrates it as feces.
peristalsis Wavelike smooth muscle contractions that propel food through the digestive tract.
rectum Region where feces are stored prior to excretion.
salivary gland Exocrine gland that secretes saliva into the mouth.
small intestine Longest portion of the digestive tract, and the site of most digestion and absorption.
stomach Digestive organ that mixes food with enzymes and acid.

TAKE-HOME MESSAGE 36.2

Humans have a complete digestive system. Food processing starts in the mouth. Swallowing forces food and water from the mouth into the pharynx. Food continues through the esophagus to the stomach.

Most digestion and absorption occurs in the small intestine. The large intestine absorbs most of the remaining water and ions, which causes the wastes to compact. The rectum briefly stores the wastes before they are expelled through the anus.

The liver and pancreas produce substances that are secreted into the small intestine.

STRUCTURE AND FUNCTION

The human stomach is a muscular, stretchable sac with a sphincter at either end (**FIGURE 36.6**). A sphincter is a ring of muscle. A sphincter at the junction between two organs regulates flow between them.

The stomach has three functions. First, it stores food and controls the rate of passage to the small intestine. Second, it mechanically breaks down food. Third, it secretes substances that aid in chemical digestion.

When the stomach is empty, its inner surface is highly folded. As the stomach fills with food, these folds smooth out, increasing the stomach's capacity. In an average adult, the stomach can expand enough to hold about 1 liter of fluid (a little bit more than a quart).

Glandular epithelium, also called mucosa, lines the stomach's inner wall. Cells of this lining secrete about 2 liters of **gastric fluid** each day. Gastric fluid includes mucus, hydrochloric acid, and pepsinogen, an inactive form of the protein-digesting enzyme pepsin.

Like the heart, the stomach undergoes rhythmic contractions. Spontaneous action potentials generated in the upper portion of the stomach cause the smooth muscle in the stomach wall to contract about three times a minute. Stomach contractions mix gastric fluid with food to form a semiliquid mass called **chyme**. They also propel chyme out through the pyloric sphincter that connects the stomach to the first segment of the small intestine.

Chemical digestion of proteins begins in the stomach. The acidity of chyme denatures proteins (makes them unfold) and exposes their peptide bonds. High acidity also converts pepsinogen into pepsin. Pepsin breaks peptide bonds, snipping proteins up into smaller polypeptides.

The stomach increases or decreases its acid secretion depending on when and what you eat. Arrival of food in the stomach, especially protein, triggers endocrine cells in the stomach lining to secrete the hormone gastrin into the blood. Gastrin acts on acid-secreting cells of the stomach lining, causing them to increase their output. When the stomach is empty, gastrin secretion declines. The resulting decrease in acid secretion minimizes the likelihood that excess acidity will damage the stomach wall.

STOMACH DISORDERS

In some people, the sphincter at the entrance to the stomach (the gastroesophageal sphincter) does not close properly or opens when it should be closed. The result is gastroesophageal reflux. Acidic chyme splashes into the esophagus, causing a burning pain commonly called heartburn or acid indigestion. Occasional acid reflux can be treated with over-the-counter antacids, but a chronic problem should be discussed with a doctor. Repeated exposure to acid can damage the tissue of the esophagus and raise the risk of esophageal cancer.

Normally, a protective layer of secreted mucus prevents acid and enzymes from damaging the stomach lining and causing an ulcer (a craterlike sore). Most stomach ulcers arise after an acid-loving species of bacteria (*Helicobacter pylori*) makes its way through gastric mucus to infect cells of the stomach lining. *H. pylori* releases chemicals that increase gastrin secretion, causing the stomach to make extra acid. The heightened acidity stresses cells of the stomach lining, which in turn allows the bacteria to spread more easily. Antibiotics can halt the infection and allow the ulcer to heal. If untreated, infection with *H. pylori* raises the risk of stomach cancer.

Continual use of nonsteroidal anti-inflammatory drugs such as ibuprofen or aspirin can also cause a stomach ulcer. These drugs inhibit secretion of the mucus that protects the stomach lining.

chyme Mix of food and gastric fluid.
gastric fluid Fluid secreted by the stomach lining; contains digestive enzymes, acid, and mucus.

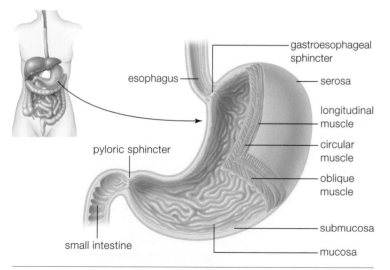

FIGURE 36.6 {Animated} Location and structure of the stomach. The folds shown on the inner surface smooth out when the stomach fills with food.

Labels: gastroesophageal sphincter; esophagus; serosa; longitudinal muscle; circular muscle; oblique muscle; pyloric sphincter; submucosa; small intestine; mucosa

> **TAKE-HOME MESSAGE 36.3**
>
> The stomach receives food from the esophagus and stretches to store it.
>
> Stomach contractions break up food and mix it with gastric fluid. They also move the resulting mixture (the chyme) into the small intestine.
>
> Chemical digestion of proteins begins in the stomach.

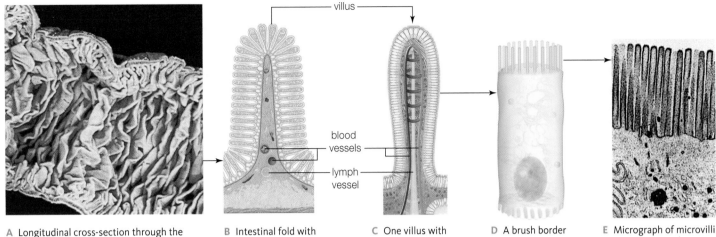

A Longitudinal cross-section through the small intestine showing its folded lining.

B Intestinal fold with villi at its surface.

C One villus with brush border cells at its surface.

D A brush border cell with microvilli at its free surface.

E Micrograph of microvilli on a brush border cell.

FIGURE 36.7 Structure of the small intestine, the longest portion of the digestive tract.

 FIGURE IT OUT: Are microvilli multicelled or smaller than a cell?   Answer: Microvilli are smaller than a cell. Villi are multicellular.

Chyme forced out of the stomach through the pyloric sphincter enters the duodenum, the initial portion of the small intestine. The small intestine is "small" only in terms of its diameter—about 2.5 cm (1 inch). It is the longest segment of the gut. Uncoiled, the adult small intestine would extend for about 5 to 7 meters (16 to 23 feet).

Most digestion and absorption takes place at the lining of the small intestine. This lining is highly folded (**FIGURE 36.7A**). Unlike the folds of an empty stomach, those of the small intestine are permanent. The surface of each fold has many **villi** (singular, villus). A villus is a hairlike multicelled projection about 1 millimeter long (**FIGURE 36.7B,C**). Millions of villi on the intestinal lining give it a furry or velvety appearance. Blood vessels and lymph vessels run through the interior of each villus.

Most of the cells at the surface of a villus have even tinier cylindrical protrusions called **microvilli** (singular, microvillus). These cells are sometimes called **brush border cells** because the many microvilli at each cell's free surface make its outer edge resemble a brush (**FIGURE 36.7D,E**). Collectively, the many folds and projections of the small intestinal lining increase its surface area by hundreds of times. As a result, the surface area of the small intestine is comparable to that of a tennis court.

Like the stomach, the small intestine has three layers of smooth muscle. The combined action of these muscles mixes the chyme, propels it forward, and forces it up against the wall of the small intestine, thus enhancing the rate of digestion and absorption (**FIGURE 36.8**).

time

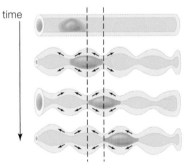

FIGURE 36.8 Muscle action in the small intestine. Contractions of rings of muscle in the wall of the small intestine cause chyme to slosh back and forth as it progresses through this organ.

brush border cell In the lining of the small intestine, an epithelial cell with microvilli at its surface.
microvilli Thin projections that increase the surface area of some epithelial cells.
villi Multicelled projections from the lining of the small intestine.

TAKE-HOME MESSAGE 36.4

The surface of the small intestine is highly folded. Each fold has many fingerlike projections (villi). Brush border cells at the surface of a villus have tiny cylindrical projections (microvilli) at their surface.

The many folds and projections of the intestinal lining greatly increase the surface area for the two functions of the small intestine—digestion and absorption.

The process of chemical digestion that began in the mouth and continued in the stomach is completed in the small intestine (**TABLE 36.1**). The lumen of the small intestine (the region inside the tube) receives chyme from the stomach, enzymes and bicarbonate from the pancreas, and bile from the gallbladder (**FIGURE 36.9**). Pancreatic enzymes work in concert with enzymes at the surface of brush border cells to complete the breakdown of large organic compounds into absorbable subunits. The bicarbonate secreted by the pancreas raises the pH of the chyme enough for digestive enzymes to function properly (Section 5.3).

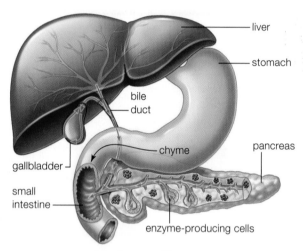

FIGURE 36.9 {Animated} Organs that contribute to the contents of the small intestine. Chyme from the stomach is joined by bile and pancreatic enzymes. Bile is produced by the liver, stored in the gallbladder, and enters the small intestine through the bile duct.

TABLE 36.1

Locations and Products of Chemical Digestion

| Organ | Type of Organic Molecule | | |
	Carbohydrate	Protein	Fat
Mouth	Salivary amylase begins digestion.		
Stomach		Acid, pepsin begin digestion.	
Small intestine	Pancreatic and small intestinal enzymes complete digestion.	Pancreatic and small intestinal enzymes complete digestion.	Bile emulsifies fats; pancreatic, small intestinal enzymes digest it.
Absorbable products	Monosaccharides (simple sugars)	Amino acids	Fatty acids, glycerol

CARBOHYDRATE DIGESTION

In the small intestine, carbohydrates are broken down into monosaccharides, or simple sugars (**FIGURE 36.10 ❶**). This process began in the mouth, where salivary amylase broke some polysaccharides into disaccharides (two-unit sugars). A pancreatic amylase continues these reactions in the small intestine. Enzymes embedded in the plasma membrane of brush border cells split disaccharides into monosaccharides. For example, sucrase breaks sucrose into glucose and fructose subunits, and lactase splits lactose into glucose and galactose. Active transport proteins move the monosaccharides from the lumen into a brush border cell. At the other side of the cell, the monosaccharides are actively transported into the interstitial fluid inside the villus ❷. From here, they enter the blood.

PROTEIN DIGESTION

Protein digestion began in the stomach, where pepsin broke proteins into polypeptides. It is completed in the small intestine, where pancreatic proteases such as trypsin and chymotrypsin break the polypeptides into smaller fragments ❸. Enzymes at the surface of the brush border cell then break these fragments first into smaller peptides, then into amino acids. Like monosaccharides, amino acids are transported into brush border cells, then out into the interstitial fluid by membrane proteins. From here, the amino acids enter the blood ❹.

FAT DIGESTION

Fat digestion occurs entirely in the small intestine. Here, bile increases the effectiveness of lipases (fat-digesting enzymes) secreted into the small intestine by the pancreas. **Bile** contains salts, pigments, cholesterol, and lipids. It is made in the liver, then stored and concentrated in the **gallbladder**. A fatty meal causes the gallbladder to contract, forcing bile out through a short duct into the small intestine.

Bile enhances fat digestion by facilitating **emulsification**, the dispersion of droplets of fat in a fluid. Water-insoluble triglycerides from food tend to clump together as fat globules. Contractions of the small intestine break big globs of fat into smaller droplets, then bile salts coat the droplets so they remain separated ❺. Compared to big globules, the many small droplets present a much greater surface area to the lipases that break triglycerides into fatty acids and monoglycerides ❻.

Being lipid soluble, fatty acids and monoglycerides produced by fat digestion can enter a villus by diffusing across the lipid bilayer of brush border cells ❼. Inside these cells, triglycerides form ❽ and become coated with proteins. The resulting lipoproteins are moved by exocytosis into

Lumen (interior) of small intestine

① carbohydrates ③ proteins

bile salts
+ fat globules ⑤ → emulsified fat droplets
(triglycerides)
⑥

② monosaccharides ④ amino acids

free fatty acids + monoglycerides + bile salts

Brush border cell

⑦

free fatty acids
+ monoglycerides

triglycerides
+ proteins

⑧
triglycerides

⑨
lipoproteins

Interstitial fluid inside a villus

① Polysaccharides are broken down to monosaccharides (simple sugars).

② Monosaccharides are actively transported into brush border cells, then out into interstitial fluid.

③ Proteins are broken down to polypeptides, then amino acids.

④ Amino acids are actively transported into brush border cells, then out into interstitial fluid.

⑤ Movements of the intestinal wall break up fat globules into small droplets. Bile salts coat the droplets so they remain separated.

⑥ Pancreatic enzymes digest the fat droplets to fatty acids and monoglycerides.

⑦ Monoglycerides and fatty acids diffuse across the plasma membrane's lipid bilayer, into brush border cells.

⑧ Inside a brush border cell, the products of fat digestion form triglycerides.

⑨ Triglycerides associate with proteins to form lipoproteins, which are expelled by exocytosis into interstitial fluid.

FIGURE 36.10 {**Animated**} Summary of digestion and absorption in the small intestine.

interstitial fluid inside a villus ⑨. From the interstitial fluid, triglycerides enter lymph vessels that eventually drain into the general circulation (Section 33.10).

In some people, components of bile accumulate to form pebble-like gallstones in the gallbladder. Most gallstones are harmless, but some block or become lodged in the bile duct. In this case, the gallbladder or gallstones are usually removed surgically. After removal of a gallbladder, all bile from the liver drains directly into the small intestine.

WATER UPTAKE

Each day, eating and drinking puts 1 to 2 liters of fluid into the lumen of your small intestine. Secretions from your stomach, accessory glands, and the intestinal lining add

another 6 to 7 liters. About 80 percent of the water that enters the small intestine moves across the intestinal lining and into the internal environment by osmosis. Transport of salts, sugars, and amino acids across brush border cells creates an osmotic gradient, and water follows that gradient from chyme into the interstitial fluid.

bile Mix of salts, pigments, and cholesterol produced in the liver, then stored and concentrated in the gallbladder; emulsifies fats when secreted into the small intestine.
emulsification Dispersion of fat droplets in a fluid.
gallbladder Organ that stores and concentrates bile.

TAKE-HOME MESSAGE 36.5

Chemical digestion is completed in the small intestine. Enzymes from the pancreas and enzymes embedded in the membrane of brush border cells break large molecules into smaller, absorbable subunits.

Bile made by the liver and stored in the gallbladder emulsifies fats, making it easier for enzymes to break them down.

Small subunits (monosaccharides, amino acids, fatty acids, and monoglycerides) enter the internal environment when they are transported into brush border cells, then out into the interstitial fluid in a villus. Most fluid that enters the gut is also absorbed across the wall of the small intestine.

STRUCTURE AND FUNCTION

Not everything that enters the small intestine can or should be absorbed. Contractions propel indigestible material, dead bacteria and mucosal cells, inorganic substances, and some water from the small intestine into the large intestine. The large intestine is wider than the small intestine, but shorter—only about 1.5 meters (5 feet) long.

As wastes travel through the large intestine, they become compacted as **feces**. The large intestine concentrates wastes by actively pumping sodium ions across its wall, into the internal environment. Water follows by osmosis.

Compared with other gut regions, material moves more slowly through the large intestine, which also has a moderate pH. These conditions favor growth of *Escherichia coli* and other bacteria that are part of our normal gut flora. *E. coli* makes vitamin B_{12} that we absorb across the lining of the large intestine.

The first part of the large intestine is a cup-shaped pouch called the cecum (**FIGURE 36.11A**). Herbivores have a large cecum containing many bacteria that help break down cellulose. The human cecum is comparatively small. In humans and many other mammals, a short, tubular **appendix** projects from the cecum. The appendix serves as a reservoir for beneficial bacteria.

Appendicitis—an inflammation of the appendix— often occurs after a bit of feces lodges in the appendix and infection sets in. It requires prompt surgical treatment. Removing an inflamed appendix prevents it from bursting and releasing bacteria into the abdominal cavity, where they could cause a life-threatening infection.

The cecum connects to the colon, the longest portion of the large intestine. The colon ascends the wall of the abdominal cavity, extends across the cavity, descends, and connects to the rectum. In many people small growths called polyps develop on the colon wall (**FIGURE 36.11B**). Most colon polyps are benign, but some become cancerous. Colonoscopy, a procedure in which clinicians use a camera to examine the colon, can detect such cancers early, thus increasing the likelihood of curing them before they spread.

Contraction of the smooth muscle in the colon wall propels the contents of the colon along. After a meal, flow of action potentials along autonomic nerves causes the colon to contract forcefully, propelling feces into the rectum. The resulting stretching of the rectum activates a defecation reflex that opens a sphincter of smooth muscle at the base of the rectum. Voluntary contraction of a sphincter of skeletal muscle at the anus provides control over the timing of defecation (expulsion of feces).

Healthy adults typically defecate once a day, on average. Emotional stress, a diet low in fiber, minimal exercise, dehydration, and some medications can lead to constipation. This means defecation occurs fewer than three times a week, is difficult, and yields small, hardened, dry feces. Occasional constipation usually goes away on its own. A chronic problem should be discussed with a doctor. Infection by a viral, bacterial, or protozoan pathogen can cause an episode of diarrhea, the frequent passing of watery feces. Autoimmune disorders that affect the gut, such as Crohn's disease, can cause chronic diarrhea.

FIGURE 36.11 A Cecum and appendix of the large intestine (colon). **B** Sketch and photo of polyps in the transverse colon.

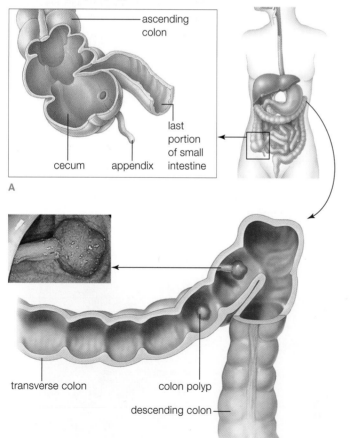

appendix Wormlike projection from the first part of the large intestine.
feces Unabsorbed food material and cellular waste that is expelled from the digestive tract.

TAKE-HOME MESSAGE 36.6

By absorbing water and mineral ions, the colon compacts undigested residues and other wastes as feces, which are stored briefly in the rectum before expulsion.

CREDITS: (11A) From Starr, Biology, 7E. © 2008 Cengage Learning; (11B) National Cancer Institute.

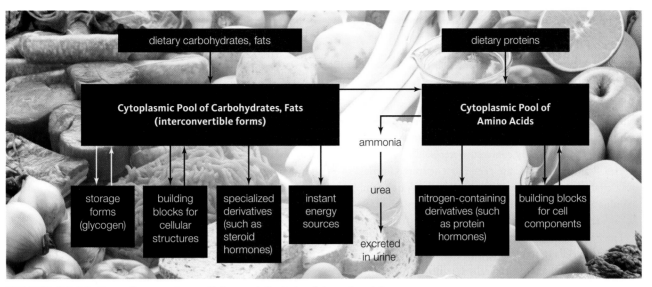

FIGURE 36.12 How cells use and reuse dietary carbohydrates, fats, and proteins.

Dietary carbohydrates, fats, and proteins are macronutrients, which are substances that we require in large amounts. Macronutrients are sources of energy and raw materials. As Section 7.7 explained, the breakdown products of these molecules can serve as reactants in the energy-releasing reactions of aerobic respiration. **FIGURE 36.12** rounds out this picture by illustrating the major routes by which the body uses organic compounds obtained from food.

The body hydrolyzes starch and sugars to release glucose, your primary source of energy. When glucose absorption exceeds the body's immediate needs, the excess is stored for later use. Blood that flows through capillaries in the small intestine carries glucose-rich blood to the liver, which stores glucose as glycogen. The liver and adipose cells also use glucose to build fats.

In addition to being an energy source, fats are used to build cell membranes and to make steroid hormones. They also help you take up fat-soluble vitamins. Your body can remodel carbohydrates to make most of the fats that it requires, but those it cannot make must come from foods. **Essential fatty acids** are those that cannot be synthesized by the body, so these fat components must be obtained from a dietary source such as nuts, seeds, and vegetable oils.

Your body uses amino acids from dietary proteins to build peptides and proteins and to make nucleotides. Although most organs do not routinely break down amino acids for a source of energy, the liver does. The amino acid's amino group is separated from its carbon skeleton, which is used to fuel the Krebs cycle. The toxic ammonia (NH_3) produced by this reaction is converted to urea, a somewhat less toxic compound that is excreted in urine.

Essential amino acids are those your body cannot make and must obtain from food. Animal proteins are usually complete, meaning they contain all of the essential amino acids in the ratio that a human needs. Soybeans and quinoa seeds are two of the few plant foods that supply all essential amino acids. Most plant proteins are incomplete, meaning they lack or have a low amount of one or more essential amino acids. You can meet your amino acid requirements with plant-based foods, but doing so requires combining these foods. Amino acids missing from one food must be provided by others. As an example, rice and beans together provide all necessary amino acids, but rice alone or beans alone do not. Complementary sources of amino acids do not need to be eaten simultaneously, but can instead be "combined" over the course of a day.

essential amino acid Amino acid that the body cannot make and must obtain from food.
essential fatty acid Fatty acid that the body cannot make and must obtain from food.

TAKE-HOME MESSAGE 36.7

Dietary carbohydrates are the body's main sources of energy.

Dietary fats are broken down for energy, and used to make membrane components and steroid hormones.

Dietary proteins provide amino acids for building peptides, proteins, and nucleotides.

Animal protein provides every amino acid a human body needs. Most plant proteins lack one or more essential amino acids, but combining plant foods can provide all you need.

CREDITS: (12) photo, @Carlos Gawronski/iStockphoto.com; art, © Cengage Learning 2015.

In addition to macronutrients, normal metabolism requires intake of vitamins and minerals.

Vitamins are organic substances that are required in the diet in very small amounts. **TABLE 36.2** lists the major vitamins humans need. Vitamins A, D, E, and K are fat soluble. Heat has little effect on these vitamins, which are abundant in both cooked and fresh foods. Because these vitamins can be stored in the body's own fat, they do not need to be eaten daily. By contrast, water-soluble vitamins such as vitamins B and C are generally not stored in the body, so they must be eaten more frequently. Water-soluble vitamins are also more sensitive to heat, so they are more easily destroyed by cooking.

The body remodels vitamin A into the visual pigment made by rod cells (Section 30.5). In the United States, milk and soy milk products are typically fortified with vitamin A, so a deficiency in this vitamin is rare. In less-developed countries, vitamin A deficiency is the most common cause of childhood blindness.

Vitamin D increases calcium uptake from the gut and encourages the retention of calcium in bone. It can be obtained from dietary sources, or made in the skin. Vitamin D production by skin requires exposure to sunlight. People with dark skin make less vitamin D than lighter-skinned people, and so are more likely to be deficient in this vitamin.

Vitamin E is an antioxidant: a molecule that prevents oxidation of other molecules by free radicals (Section 5.5). Being fat soluble, vitamin E plays an important role in protecting the lipids of cell membranes.

Vitamin K is a coenzyme that assists enzymes involved in blood clotting. (K denotes the German word *koagulation*.) Absorption of vitamin K produced by bacteria in the large intestine supplements vitamin K extraction from food.

B vitamins are used to build coenzymes that function in a variety of essential pathways. For example, vitamin B_3 (niacin) is used to make NAD, and vitamin B_2 (riboflavin) is used to make FAD. Both of these coenzymes play vital roles in aerobic respiration, as summarized in Section 7.5.

Vitamin C is needed to make collagen, the body's most abundant protein. Vitamin C also functions as an antioxidant. A deficiency causes scurvy, a disorder in which skin and bones deteriorate and wounds are slow to heal.

TABLE 36.2

Major Vitamins: Sources and Functions

Vitamin	Main Dietary Sources	Main Functions	Symptoms of Deficiency
Fat-Soluble Vitamins			
A	Orange fruits and vegetables, leafy greens, egg yolk	Component of visual pigments; maintains epithelia	Night blindness, skin problems
D	Fatty fish, egg yolk	Aids uptake and use of calcium	Weak/soft bones, rickets in children
E	Nuts, seeds, vegetable oils helps maintain cell membranes	Antioxidant, aids fat absorption	Muscle weakness, nerve damage
K	Green vegetables	Needed for blood clotting	Impaired blood clotting
Water-Soluble Vitamins			
B_1 (thiamin)	Meats, nuts, legumes	Coenzyme in carbohydrate metabolism	Beri beri (neurological and heart problems)
B_2 (riboflavin)	Meats, eggs, nuts, milk, green vegetables	Component of the coenzyme FAD	Anemia, sores in mouth, sore throat
B_3 (niacin)	Meats, fish, dairy products, nuts, legumes	Component of the coenzyme NAD	Skin and mucous membrane sores, gut pain, diarrhea, psychosis, dementia
B_6	Meats, fish, starchy vegetables, noncitrus fruits	Coenzyme in protein metabolism	Anemia, sores on lips, depression, impaired immune function
B_7 (biotin)	Meats, fish, nuts, legumes, whole grains	Coenzyme in many reactions	Hair loss, dry skin, dry eyes, fatigue, insomnia, depression
B_9 (folic acid)	Meats, fruits, green vegetables, whole grains	Coenzyme in nucleic acid synthesis and amino acid metabolism	Anemia, sores in mouth; deficiency during pregnancy causes neurological birth defects
B_{12}	Meats, seafood, dairy products	Coenzyme in amino acid synthesis	Anemia; fatigue, neurological problems
C (ascorbic acid)	Fruits (especially citrus) and vegetables	Required for collagen synthesis, antioxidant	Scurvy (anemia, bleeding gums, impaired wound healing, swollen joints)

National Geographic Explorer
DR. CHRISTOPHER GOLDEN

To conservationists, the aye-aye shown in this chapter's opening photo is an endangered lemur in need of improved protection. However, to some of the aye-aye's human neighbors, it and other endangered animals are a valuable source of food. Christopher Golden, who studies public health and ecology in rural Madagascar, has found that bushmeat is an important source of dietary iron for the local people. He says, "Everyone can get adequate protein from vegetables. However, in areas without fortification and supplementation programs, it is extraordinarily difficult to obtain adequate iron without eating meat." Golden estimates that cutting off access to bushmeat would triple the incidence of iron-deficiency anemia among the poorest Malagasy children. Among other ill effects, childhood anemia stunts growth and decreases mental capacity.

Golden is convinced that the people in his study area will eventually lose access to bushmeat, regardless of whether conservation laws are better enforced. Improved law enforcement would cut off this food supply quickly. Allowing unsustainable hunting to continue would do the same more slowly, by decimating wildlife populations. Golden argues that it is possible to protect both human health and biodiversity. He advocates ramping up efforts to prevent illegal hunting, while also providing alternative sources of meat, such as chickens. In rural Madagascar, unlike some other regions, the vast majority of bushmeat is consumed, rather than sold.

In addition to protecting wildlife, reducing bushmeat consumption would benefit public health by minimizing people's exposure to potentially dangerous viruses that infect wild animals. Golden is collaborating with Nathan Wolfe, also a National Geographic Explorer (Section 19.2), to determine what types of viruses lemurs, bats, and the other animals hunted for bushmeat carry.

Minerals are elements that are essential in the diet in small amounts. The seven minerals required in largest quantities are calcium, phosphorus, potassium, sulfur, sodium, chlorine, and magnesium. Calcium and phosphorus, the body's most abundant minerals, are components of teeth and bones. Calcium also plays a role in intercellular signaling, and phosphorus is also used to make nucleic acids. Sodium and potassium are important in nerve function, sulfur is a component of some proteins, chlorine is a component of hydrochloric acid (HCl) in gastric fluid, and magnesium is a cofactor. Deficiencies in these major elements are rare, although calcium levels may be lower in people who eat a solely plant-based diet.

Iodine, another essential mineral, is necessary to produce thyroid hormone, which has roles in development and metabolism (Section 31.5). Iodine is abundant in fish, shellfish, and seaweeds. A deficiency in this mineral causes goiter, an enlarged thyroid gland, and disrupts metabolism. In the United States, iodized salt makes deficiency rare.

Iron is an essential component of heme, the chemical group that binds to oxygen in hemoglobin (Section 35.6) and myoglobin. Heme is also a cofactor for many enzymes, including critical components of electron transfer chains (Section 5.4) and the antioxidant catalase (Section 5.5). Worldwide, iron is the mineral most commonly deficient in the diet. Symptoms of iron-deficiency anemia include fatigue, shortness of breath, dizziness, and chest pain.

> **TAKE-HOME MESSAGE 36.8**
>
> Normal metabolism requires dietary intake of essential vitamins and inorganic substances called minerals.
>
> Fat-soluble vitamins are stored in the body. Water-soluble ones are not, and must be replenished more often.
>
> Many vitamins function as antioxidants or are made into coenzymes.
>
> Essential minerals are components of important biological molecules.

mineral In the diet, an inorganic substance that is required in small amounts for normal metabolism.
vitamin Organic substance required in the diet in small amounts for normal metabolism.

Every five years, the United States government issues updated dietary guidelines designed to help people maintain a healthy weight, promote health, and prevent disease. **FIGURE 36.13** shows an example of their recommendations. You can generate your own healthy eating plan by visiting the USDA website: www.choosemyplate.gov.

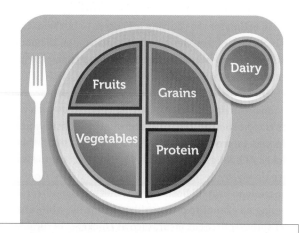

USDA Nutritional Guidelines

Food Group	Amount Recommended
Grains	6 ounces/day
Vegetables	2.5 cups/day
Fruits	2 cups/day
Dairy products	3 cups/day
Meat and beans	5.5 ounces/day

FIGURE 36.13 Example of nutritional guidelines from the United States Department of Agriculture (USDA). These recommendations are for females ages ten to thirty who get less than 30 minutes of vigorous exercise daily. Portions add up to a 2,000-kilocalorie daily intake.

TABLE 36.3

Main Types of Dietary Fats

Polyunsaturated Fatty Acids: Liquid at room temperature; essential for health.
  Omega-3 fatty acids
    Alpha-linolenic acid and its derivatives
    Sources: Nut oils, vegetable oils, oily fish
  Omega-6 fatty acids
    Linoleic acid and its derivatives
    Sources: Nut oils, vegetable oils, meat

Monounsaturated Fatty Acids: Liquid at room temperature. Main dietary source is olive oil. Beneficial in moderation.

Saturated Fatty Acids: Solid at room temperature. Main sources are meat and dairy products, palm and coconut oils. Excessive intake may raise risk of heart disease.

Trans Fatty Acids (Hydrogenated Fats): Solid at room temperature. Made from vegetable oils and used in many processed foods. Excessive intake raises risk of heart disease.

FRUITS, VEGETABLES, AND WHOLE GRAINS

Fruits, vegetables, and grains should make up the largest proportion of your diet. These foods provide sugars and starches, your primary sources of energy. The energy stored in food is measured in kilocalories, or as written on food labels, "Calories" (with a capital C). Fruits, vegetables, and grains also provide vitamins, minerals, and dietary fiber.

There are two types of fiber. Soluble fiber consists of polysaccharides that form a gel when mixed with water. Eating foods high in soluble fiber helps lower one's cholesterol level and reduces the risk of heart disease. Insoluble fiber such as cellulose does not dissolve, so it passes through the human digestive tract more or less intact. Eating insoluble fiber helps prevent constipation.

Whole grains provide more vitamins and fiber than their processed counterparts. A whole grain includes all components of a grain seed. For example, whole wheat includes bran (the fiber-rich seed coat) and wheat germ (the protein- and vitamin-rich plant embryo), as well as starchy endosperm. By contrast, white wheat flour is made solely from endosperm.

You may have noticed breads and other grain-based foods labeled as "gluten-free." Gluten is a protein found in wheat and many other grains. An estimated 1 percent of the population has a genetic disorder called celiac disease, in which gluten causes an autoimmune reaction that harms the small intestine's villi. Celiac disease is treated by eliminating gluten from the diet.

HEART-HEALTHY OILS

A healthy diet includes fats that provide energy and meet your need for essential fatty acids (**TABLE 36.3**). Essential fatty acids are polyunsaturated (Section 3.3), meaning their tails have two or more double bonds. There are two types of essential fatty acids: omega-3 fatty acids and omega-6 fatty acids. Omega-3 fatty acids, the main fat in oily fish, seem to have special health benefits. Studies suggest that a diet high in omega-3 fatty acids can reduce the risk of cardiovascular disease, lessen the inflammation associated with rheumatoid arthritis, and help diabetics control their blood glucose.

Oleic acid, the main fat in olive oil, is monounsaturated, which means its carbon tails have only one double bond. While monounsaturated fats have not been shown to have the same benefits as polyunsaturated fats, they can be beneficial if substituted for less healthy fats.

Most animal fats are saturated fats, which are solid at room temperature. Excessive intake of these fats may increase one's risk for heart disease, stroke, and some cancers. Coconut oil is also rich in saturated fats, but it has not been shown to have the negative health effects of saturated fats from animal sources.

Trans fats are synthetic fats manufactured from vegetable oils. Their molecular structure makes them even worse for you than saturated fats (Section 3.7). All food labels are now required to show the amounts of *trans* fats, saturated fats, and cholesterol per serving (**FIGURE 36.14**).

LEAN MEAT AND LOW-FAT DAIRY

Meat (including poultry and fish) is the richest source of protein and is also rich in essential iron. Choosing lean meats or fish helps minimize intake of saturated fats and cholesterol. Eating soybean products such as tofu provides complete protein without harmful fats or cholesterol, as does eating the proper combinations of plant foods such as rice and beans.

Milk and dairy products such as yogurt are good sources of protein, vitamins, and minerals, but whole milk is rich in saturated fats. Low-fat or skim alternatives are better nutritional options. People who are lactose intolerant or who wish to avoid animal products can substitute "milks" made from soybeans, rice, almonds, or other plants. Such products have the advantage of being free of saturated fats and cholesterol. Many are fortified to provide the same amount of calcium and vitamins as dairy milk.

MINIMAL ADDED SALT AND SUGAR

Salt contains two essential minerals, sodium and chloride, but both are easily obtained in sufficient quantity from unsalted foods. Eating foods with added salt elevates the body's sodium level, which raises the risk of high blood pressure in some people. Most canned and otherwise processed foods are high in salt, so replacing these items with fresh foods lowers sodium intake. Food labels show sodium content as a percentage of the recommended daily maximum for a person who has normal blood pressure.

Commercially prepared foods and drinks are often high in added sugar. The USDA estimates that added sugars contribute an astounding 16 percent of the total calories in American diets. Sodas, energy drinks, and sport drinks contribute the greatest proportion of calories. The American Heart Association recommends that women consume no more than 24 grams of sugar per day and men no more than 36 grams, from all sources. A typical can of soda has more than 30 grams of sugar.

Nutrition Facts

Serving Size 1 cup (228g)
Servings Per Container 2

Amount Per Serving

Calories 250	Calories from Fat 110

	% Daily Value*
Total Fat 12g	**18%**
Saturated Fat 3g	**15%**
Trans Fat 1.5g	
Cholesterol 30mg	**10%**
Sodium 470mg	**20%**
Total Carbohydrate 31g	**10%**
Dietary Fiber 0g	**0%**
Sugars 5g	
Protein 5g	

Vitamin A	4%
Vitamin C	2%
Calcium	20%
Iron	4%

*Percent Daily Values are based on a 2,000 calorie diet. Your Daily Values may be higher or lower depending on your calorie needs:

	Calories:	2,000	2,500
Total Fat	Less than	65g	80g
Sat Fat	Less than	20g	25g
Cholesterol	Less than	300mg	300mg
Sodium	Less than	2,400mg	2,400mg
Total Carbohydrate		300g	375g
Dietary Fiber		25g	30g

Check serving size. A package often holds more than one serving, but nutritional information is given per serving.

Avoid foods in which a large proportion of calories comes from fat.

Choose foods that provide a low percent of the recommended maximum of saturated fat, *trans* fat, cholesterol, and sodium. 20% or more is high.

Choose foods that are high in dietary fiber and low in sugar.

If you eat meat, you probably get more than enough protein.

Choose foods that provide a high percentage of your daily vitamin and mineral requirements.

This part of the label shows recommended intake of nutrients for two levels of calorie intake. Keeping fat and salt intake below recommended levels and dietary fiber above recommended levels decreases risk of some chronic health problems.

FIGURE 36.14 How to read a food label. Information on a food label can be used to ensure that you get the nutrients you need without exceeding recommended limits on less healthy substances such as salt and *trans* fats. This hypothetical label is for a ready-to-eat macaroni and cheese product.

FIGURE IT OUT: What proportion of the fat in a serving of this product comes from the least healthy forms of fat (saturated fat and *trans* fat)?

Answer: Of the total fat content in a serving (12 grams), 3 are saturated fat and 1.5 g are *trans* fat. Thus 4.5 g, or more than a third of the fat, is from unhealthy sources.

TAKE-HOME MESSAGE 36.9

Fresh fruits, vegetables, and whole grains in the diet provide carbohydrates and also vitamins, minerals, and dietary fiber essential to health.

Meat and dairy products are rich sources of protein, and meat provides iron. These animal products can also be high in saturated fats, which elevate risk of heart disease.

Processed foods are high in sodium and sugars. Excessive sodium intake increases the risk of high blood pressure. Sugar adds calories without adding nutritional value.

When the food you eat contains more energy than you need at the time, you store the excess as bond energy in organic compounds. The body's largest energy store is fat in adipose tissue. For most of our species' history, an ability to store energy as fat in adipose tissue was selectively advantageous. Putting on fat when food was abundant increased the chances of survival in the event of a later famine. However, most people in the United States now have more than enough food all of the time. As a result, about two-thirds of adults are overweight or obese.

Body mass index (BMI) is a measurement designed to help assess increased health risk associated with weight. You can calculate your body mass index with this formula:

$$BMI = \frac{weight\ (pounds) \times 703}{height\ (inches) \times height\ (inches)}$$

Generally, individuals with a BMI of 25 to 29.9 are said to be overweight. A score of 30 or more indicates obesity: an overabundance of fat in adipose tissue that may lead to severe health problems. Conversely, a BMI of 18.5 or lower is considered dangerously underweight. A low BMI can result from anorexia nervosa, an eating disorder in which a person restricts their food intake well below a healthy level as a result of an irrational fear of weight gain.

To maintain a given weight, you must balance the amount of energy in the food you eat with the energy you expend in your activities. Here is a way to estimate how many kilocalories you should take in daily to maintain a given weight. First, multiply the weight (in pounds) by 10 if you are not active physically, by 15 if you are moderately active, and by 20 if you are highly active. Next, subtract one of the following amounts from the multiplication result:

Age:	25–34	Subtract:	0
	35–44		100
	45–54		200
	55–64		300
	Over 65		400

For example, if you are 25 years old, are highly active, and weigh 120 pounds, you will require $120 \times 20 = 2,400$ kilocalories daily to maintain weight. If you want to gain weight you will require more; to lose, you will require less.

You can also lose weight by increasing the rate at which your body uses energy. Even when you are at rest, you use energy in essential processes such as breathing, generating body heat, fighting off pathogens, moving material though your digestive tract, and circulating your blood. The

TABLE 36.4

Energy Expended in Activities

Activity	Energy expended (Calories per kilogram of body weight per hour)
Sitting quietly	1
Standing	2
Walking slowly	3
Bicycling to class	4–7
Swimming	6–10
Basketball game	8
Running (5 mph)	8

amount of energy you use in these activities is your **basal metabolic rate**. Basal metabolic rate varies with lean body weight. Larger, more muscular bodies use more energy than smaller, less muscular ones. Men tend to be more muscular than women of the same weight, so their metabolic rate is higher. In both sexes, metabolic rate slows with age. Thyroid hormone level influences basal metabolic rate too. People with a high level of thyroid hormone use more energy at rest than those with a lower level.

Dieting can influence one's basal metabolic rate. Often, when people eat less, their resting metabolic rate declines. This mechanism evolved to promote survival when food became scarce. However, it is a source of great frustration to dieters who have chosen to limit their food intake in the hope of losing weight.

Exercise can help you lose weight by expending energy. **TABLE 36.4** shows energy expenditure during various activities. Exercise that increases the body's muscle mass also has the benefit of increasing the resting metabolic rate.

basal metabolic rate   Rate at which the body uses energy when you are at rest.

TAKE-HOME MESSAGE 36.10

A person who balances caloric intake with energy expenditures will maintain his or her current weight.

The rate at which your body uses energy is influenced by age, body size and muscularity, and thyroid hormone level.

Physical activity expends energy and can help reduce body weight by increasing basal metabolic rate.

36.11 Application: THE OBESITY EPIDEMIC

FIGURE 36.15 MRIs of an obese woman (left) and a woman of normal body weight (far left). With obesity, the abdomen fills with fat that squashes internal organs.

Education

THE INCREASING PREVALENCE OF OBESITY HAS DIRE IMPLICATIONS FOR PUBLIC HEALTH. Obesity increases the risk for a long list of diseases including high blood pressure, type 2 diabetes, heart disease, stroke, gallbladder disease, osteoarthritis, sleep apnea, and cancers of the uterus, breast, prostate gland, kidney, and colon.

An obese person's internal organs are hemmed in by fat (FIGURE 36.15), which can impair the organs' function. For example, breathing can become difficult because fat in the abdomen impairs the ability of the diaphragm to descend downward during inhalation.

Fat also impairs function at the cellular level. Adipose cells of people who are at a healthy weight hold a moderate amount of triglycerides. In obese people, adipose cells are overstuffed with triglycerides. Like cells that are stressed in other ways, the overstuffed adipose cells respond by sending out chemical signals that summon up an inflammatory response (Section 34.4). The resulting chronic inflammation harms organs throughout the body and increases the risk of cancer. Overstuffed adipose cells also increase their secretion of

chemical messages that interfere with the effect of insulin. Remember that this hormone encourages cells to take up sugar from the blood (Section 31.8). When insulin becomes ineffective, the result is type 2 diabetes.

In 1960, the obesity rate in the United States was 15 percent. Today it is more than double that. Multiple factors contributed to this increase. The proportion of meals consumed outside the home increased, as did the average portion sizes of restaurant meals. Soda consumption rose, and physical activity decreased. We spend more time in front of televisions and computers, and fewer of us have jobs that require physical exertion.

Preventing obesity is important. Once a person becomes obese, dieting alone is seldom effective in restoring a normal body weight. A variety of existing drugs can reduce weight somewhat, but they have negative side effects and must be taken continually to prevent rebound weight gain. Surgical procedures that reduce stomach volume can produce a dramatic sustainable weight loss, but these drastic interventions are expensive and can result in serious complications.

Summary

SECTION 36.1 A digestive system breaks down food into molecules small enough to be absorbed into the internal environment. It also stores and eliminates unabsorbed materials. Sponges digest food inside their cells, but most other animals have a digestive system.

Some invertebrates have a **gastrovascular cavity**: a saclike gut with a single opening. Most animals and all vertebrates have a **complete digestive system**: a tube with two openings (a mouth and either an **anus** or a **cloaca**). Variations in the structure of vertebrate digestive systems are adaptations to particular diets. For example, the multiple stomach chambers of **ruminants** allow them to digest grasses.

SECTION 36.2 Digestion starts in the mouth, where food is broken into bits and mixed with saliva from **salivary glands**. Swallowed food moves into the pharynx, which opens onto the **esophagus**. Wavelike contractions (**peristalsis**) of the esophagus conveys food to the **stomach**. From the stomach, food enters the **small intestine**, then the **large intestine**. Wastes are stored in the **rectum** until they are eliminated through the anus.

SECTION 36.3 A sphincter at the end of the esophagus opens to allow food into the stomach. Protein digestion begins in the stomach, a muscular sac with a glandular lining that secretes **gastric fluid**. This fluid contains acid and enzymes that help break down proteins, and mucus that protects the stomach lining. Gastric fluid mixes with food and forms **chyme** that continues to the small intestine.

SECTIONS 36.4, 36.5 The small intestine is the longest portion of the gut and has the largest surface area. Its highly folded lining has many **villi** at its surface. Each multicelled villus has a covering of **brush border cells**. These cells have **microvilli** that increase their surface area for digestion and absorption.

Chemical digestion is completed in the small intestine, as enzymes from the pancreas, bile from the gallbladder, and enzymes in the plasma membrane of brush border cells break down food molecules into absorbable components.

Carbohydrates are broken down to monosaccharides; proteins, to amino acids. Both types of breakdown products are transported across brush border cells into interstitial fluid. From there, they enter blood.

Bile made in the liver and stored and concentrated in the **gallbladder** aids in the **emulsification** of fats. Monoglycerides and fatty acids diffuse into brush border cells, where they recombine as triglycerides (fats). Proteins assemble with the fats to form lipoproteins that are expelled by exocytosis into interstitial fluid. This fluid carries the lipoproteins to lymph vessels for delivery to the blood. The small intestine is also the site of most water absorption.

SECTION 36.6 More water and ions are absorbed in the large intestine, which compacts undigested solid wastes as **feces**. Feces are stored in the rectum, a stretchable region just before the anus. The **appendix**, a short extension from the cecum (the first part of the large intestine), stores helpful bacteria.

SECTIONS 36.7, 36.8 Food is the source of molecules that serve as energy and raw materials. A healthy diet must include **essential amino acids** and **essential fatty acids**, as well as **vitamins**, which are small organic molecules, and **minerals**, which are inorganic. Plant-based diets can meet all these needs if foods are properly combined. The liver plays a central role in metabolism of food. All blood that flows through the small intestine travels next to the liver, which stores glucose as glycogen.

SECTION 36.9 Current dietary guidelines emphasize maximizing intake of fruits, vegetables, and whole grains, which provide fiber as well as nutrients. Intake of foods high in saturated fats, *trans* fats, added salt, and added sugar should be minimized.

SECTION 36.10 The ability to store fat is adaptive when food is sometimes scarce, but can be problematic when food is always plentiful. To maintain body weight, energy intake must balance with energy output. You expend some energy in **basal metabolism** even when resting, but physical activity increases energy expenditures.

SECTION 36.11 Humans store excess food energy mainly in the bonds of triglycerides in adipose cells. Obesity raises the risk of health problems. Excessive stored fat presses on internal organs and signals from stressed adipose cells trigger inflammation.

Self-Quiz   Answers in Appendix VII

1. A digestive system functions in _____ .
   a. secreting enzymes   c. eliminating wastes
   b. absorbing compounds d. all of the above

2. Protein digestion begins in the _____ .
   a. mouth   c. small intestine
   b. stomach   d. large intestine

3. Most nutrients are absorbed in the _____ .
   a. mouth   c. small intestine
   b. stomach   d. large intestine

4. Bile has a role in _____ digestion and absorption.
   a. carbohydrate   c. protein
   b. fat   d. amino acid

5. Monosaccharides and amino acids absorbed from the gut enter _____ .
   a. blood vessels   c. fat droplets
   b. lymph vessels   d. both b and c

6. Bacteria in the _____ make essential vitamins.
   a. stomach   c. large intestine
   b. small intestine   d. esophagus

Data Analysis Activities

Human Dietary Adaptation   The human *AMY-1* gene encodes salivary amylase, an enzyme that breaks down starch. The number of copies of this gene varies, and people who have more copies generally make more of the enzyme. In addition, the average number of *AMY-1* copies differs among cultural groups.

George Perry and his colleagues hypothesized that duplications of the *AMY-1* gene would confer a selective advantage in cultures in which starch is a large part of the diet. To test this hypothesis, the scientists compared the number of copies of the *AMY-1* gene among members of seven cultural groups that differed in their traditional diets. **FIGURE 36.16** shows their results.

1. Starchy tubers are a mainstay of Hadza hunter–gatherers in Africa, whereas fishing sustains Siberia's Yakut. Almost 60 percent of Yakut had fewer than 5 copies of the *AMY-1* gene. What percent of the Hadza had fewer than 5 copies?
2. None of the Mbuti (rain-forest hunter–gatherers) had more than 10 copies of *AMY-1*. Did any European Americans?
3. Do these data support the hypothesis that a starchy diet favors duplications of the *AMY-1* gene?

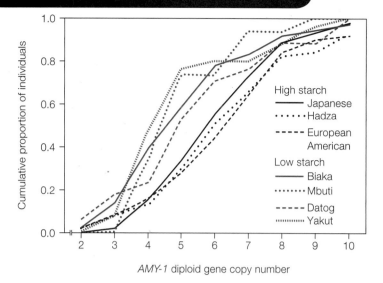

FIGURE 36.16 Number of copies of the *AMY-1* gene among members of cultures with traditional high-starch or low-starch diets. The Hadza, Biaka, Mbuti, and Datog are tribes in Africa. The Yakut live in Siberia.

---

7. The pH is lowest in the _____ .
   a. stomach   c. large intestine
   b. small intestine d. esophagus

8. Most water that enters the gut is absorbed across the lining of the _____ .
   a. stomach   c. large intestine
   b. small intestine d. esophagus

9. _____ is the mineral most often deficient in the diet.
   a. Potassium   c. Sodium
   b. Chlorine   d. Iron

10. Blood that flows through capillaries in the small intestine flows next through vessels in the _____ .
    a. stomach   c. pancreas
    b. heart   d. liver

11. Tiny filaments called _____ increase the surface area of a brush border cell in the lining of the small intestine.
    a. villi   c. microvilli
    b. cilia   d. flagella

12. _____ are a good source of soluble fiber.
    a. Dairy products c. Whole grains
    b. Lean meats   d. Sodas

13. Basal metabolic rate increases with _____ .
    a. age   c. a decrease in thyroid hormone
    b. lean body mass d. all of the above

14. Which of the following vitamins is water soluble?
    a. vitamin A   c. vitamin C
    b. vitamin D   d. vitamin K

15. Match each organ with its function.
    ___ gallbladder   a. makes bile
    ___ colon   b. compacts undigested residues
    ___ liver   c. secretes digestive enzymes into
    ___ small   the small instestine
        intestine   d. absorbs most nutrients
    ___ stomach   e. stores feces
    ___ pancreas   f. connects pharynx to stomach
    ___ esophagus   g. stores, secretes bile
    ___ rectum   h. secretes gastric fluid

Critical Thinking

1. A python can survive by eating a large meal once or twice a year. When it does eat, microvilli in its small intestine lengthen fourfold and its stomach pH drops from 7 to 1. Explain the benefits of these changes.

2. Starch and sugar have the same number of calories per gram. Yet a serving of boiled sweet potato provides about 1.2 calories per gram, while a serving of kale yields only 0.3 calories per gram. What do you think accounts for the difference in the calories your body obtains from these two plant foods?

3. List the foods you ate today. Which item was highest in fat? In protein? In insoluble fiber? In iron?

CENGAGE **brain**.com   To access course materials, please visit **www.cengagebrain.com.**

CREDIT: (16) George Perry, et. al., Diet and evolution of human amylase gene copy number variation, *Nature Genetics* 39, 1256–1260 (2007).

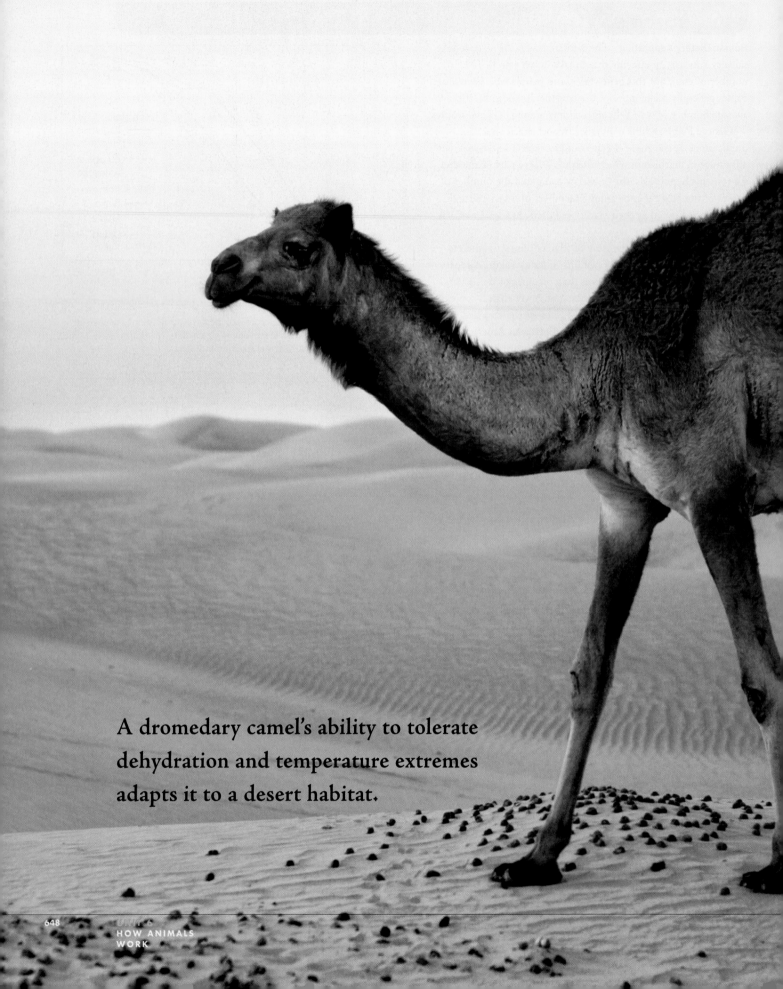

A dromedary camel's ability to tolerate dehydration and temperature extremes adapts it to a desert habitat.

37

MAINTAINING THE INTERNAL ENVIRONMENT

Links to Earlier Concepts

This chapter's discussion of fluid regulation touches on osmosis (Section 5.6) and transport proteins (5.7). We consider waste produced by aerobic respiration (7.2) and protein breakdown (36.7). The discussion of urine formation refers to epithelium (28.3), blood pressure (33.6), and the adrenal glands (31.6). We also reconsider how sweat glands (28.3) help animals regulate their body temperature (28.9).

KEY CONCEPTS

MAINTAINING EXTRACELLULAR FLUID
An animal's survival depends on maintaining the composition and volume of its extracellular fluid within a tolerable range. Most animals have organs that regulate solutes and eliminate wastes.

HUMAN URINARY SYSTEM
A human kidney cleanses the blood of wastes and forms urine. Urine travels through a ureter to the bladder, where it is stored until it is expelled through the urethra.

HOW URINE FORMS
Urine formation begins when protein-free plasma filters into kidney tubules. Reabsorption returns most water and solutes to blood. Secretion adds solutes to the urine.

ADJUSTING CORE TEMPERATURE
Metabolism produces heat. Heat is also lost to and gained from the environment. Ectotherms adjust their temperature behaviorally. Endotherms adjust it by altering their production of metabolic heat.

HUMAN BODY TEMPERATURE
Humans are ectotherms. We cool off by sweating, and warm up by shivering and by increasing metabolic heat production. A dramatic change in our core temperature can be fatal.

COMPOSITION AND COMPONENTS OF BODY FLUIDS

By weight, an animal consists mostly of water with many dissolved salts and other solutes. The fluid outside of an animal's cells—extracellular fluid—serves as the body's internal environment. In vertebrates, extracellular fluid consists mainly of interstitial fluid and plasma. Interstitial fluid fills spaces between cells, and plasma is the fluid portion of the blood.

Keeping the solute composition and volume of the extracellular fluid within ranges that cells can tolerate is a major aspect of homeostasis. Water and solute gains need to be balanced by water and solute losses. An animal loses water and solutes in feces and urine, in exhalations, and in secretions. It gains water by eating and drinking. In aquatic animals, water also moves into or out of the body by osmosis (Section 5.6) across the body surface.

FIGURE 37.1 Nitrogenous waste products.

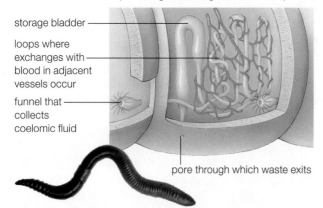

A amino group **B** ammonia

A Amino groups cleaved from proteins become **B** ammonia, which is toxic.

C uric acid

Some animals excrete ammonia directly; others first convert it to **C** uric acid or **D** urea.

D urea

Metabolic reactions alter the composition of extracellular fluid. For example, aerobic respiration adds carbon dioxide, which many animals eliminate with the assistance of respiratory organs. Breakdown of proteins produces **ammonia** (FIGURE 37.1A,B). Most animals have organs that rid their body of waste ammonia and other unwanted solutes that have entered the extracellular fluid.

ORGANS THAT ADJUST BODY FLUIDS

The simplest organs that help maintain the volume and composition of body fluid are the nephridia of some invertebrates. A **nephridium** is a tubular organ that takes up body fluid at one end and expels excess water and unwanted solutes at the other end. The waste material exits through a pore in the body wall. In planarian flatworms, a pair of nephridia function mainly to rid the body of excess water. Planarian flatworms, like other freshwater animals, have a higher solute concentration than the water around them, so water continually enters their body by osmosis.

In earthworms, each segment has a pair of nephridia that take up coelomic fluid (FIGURE 37.2A). As this fluid flows through the nephridium, essential solutes and some water leave the tube and enter adjacent blood vessels. Wastes that remain in the tube are expelled.

In most insects and spiders, tubular organs called **Malpighian tubules** take up waste solutes from hemolymph and deliver them to the gut for excretion (FIGURE 37.2B). These animals convert ammonia to **uric acid** (FIGURE 37.1C) before excreting it. Carrying out this conversion requires additional energy, but it helps the animal conserve water. Ammonia can only be excreted when

---

FIGURE 37.2 Examples of organs that regulate solute composition in invertebrates.

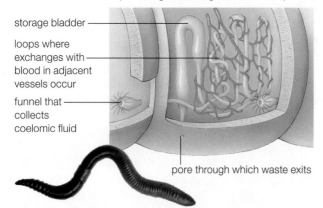

storage bladder

loops where exchanges with blood in adjacent vessels occur

funnel that collects coelomic fluid

pore through which waste exits

A Nephridium of an earthworm. Coelomic fluid enters a nephridium (green). As fluid travels through the nephridium, essential solutes leave this tube and enter adjacent blood vessels (red). Ammonia-rich waste exits the body through a pore.

Malpighian tubule

part of gut

B Malpighian tubules of a honeybee. The tubules (gold) are bathed by hemolymph of the open circulatory system. Uric acid and other waste solutes move from hemolymph into the tubules, which deliver the wastes to the gut (pink) for elimination through the anus.

	Human	Kangaroo Rat →
Daily Water Gain (milliliters):	2600 ml	60 ml
From food	33%	10%
From drink	54%	0%
By metabolism	13%	90%
Daily Water Loss (milliliters):	2600 ml	60 ml
In urine	58%	23%
In feces	8%	4%
By evaporation	34%	73%

FIGURE 37.3 Water gains and losses in humans and in desert kangaroo rats. The rats are native to deserts of the American Southwest.

dissolved in water, whereas uric acid is excreted as crystals mixed with just a tiny bit of water to produce a thick paste.

All vertebrates have a pair of **kidneys**, which are organs that filter the blood, adjust its composition, and produce urine. **Urine** consists of water and soluble wastes. The volume of urine produced varies with the amount of water an animal needs to excrete or retain. Marine bony fishes tend to lose water by osmosis, so they produce only a small amount of urine. They meet their need for water by drinking seawater, then excreting the excess salt across their gills. By contrast, freshwater bony fishes tend to gain water by osmosis, so they produce a large volume of urine. Solutes lost in urine are offset by solutes absorbed from the gut or pumped in across the gills.

Waterproof skin and highly efficient kidneys adapt amniotes (mammals, reptiles, and birds) to life on land. In birds and other reptiles, the liver converts ammonia to uric acid. Crystals of uric acid give bird droppings their whitish color. All reptiles, including birds, eliminate urinary waste through the same opening they use for feces: the cloaca.

The mammalian liver combines two ammonia molecules with carbon dioxide to form **urea** (**FIGURE 37.1D**). Converting ammonia to urea takes less energy than converting it to uric acid. However, excreting urea requires twenty to thirty times more water than excreting uric acid. Thus, a typical mammal requires more water than a bird or reptile of similar size.

Mammals cannot excrete uric acid, but those that live where access to fresh water is limited have other evolutionary adaptations that help them conserve water. The dromedary camel shown in the chapter opening photo can go weeks without water. Desert kangaroo rats (**FIGURE 37.3**) can survive without ever drinking water; they obtain all the fluid they need from their diet of seeds. Both camels and kangaroo rats have highly efficient kidneys that produce a very concentrated urine with a syruplike consistency. Both also produce extremely dry feces. The kangaroo rat is active mainly at night, and it has complex sinuses that help it take up water from air before that air is exhaled.

ammonia Nitrogen-containing compound that is a waste product of amino acid breakdown.
kidney Organ of the vertebrate urinary system that filters blood, adjusts its composition, and forms urine.
Malpighian tubules Of insects and spiders, tubular organs that take up waste solutes and deliver them to the gut for excretion.
nephridium Of some invertebrates, an organ that takes up body fluid and expels excess water and solutes through a pore at the body surface.
urea Main nitrogen-containing compound in urine of mammals.
uric acid Main nitrogen-containing compound in the urine of insects, as well as birds and other reptiles.
urine Fluid that consists of water and soluble wastes; formed and excreted by the vertebrate kidneys.

TAKE-HOME MESSAGE 37.1

All animals must balance daily gains in water and solutes with daily losses. All must rid the body of waste carbon dioxide and ammonia. Many animals convert ammonia to urea or uric acid before excreting it.

Earthworms have ammonia-excreting nephridia and insects have uric acid–excreting Malpighian tubules.

All vertebrates have two kidneys that filter blood and produce urine. The volume of urine and type of nitrogen-containing wastes excreted varies among vertebrate groups.

CREDITS: (3) left, © Cengage Learning 2015; right, Tom McHugh/Science Source.

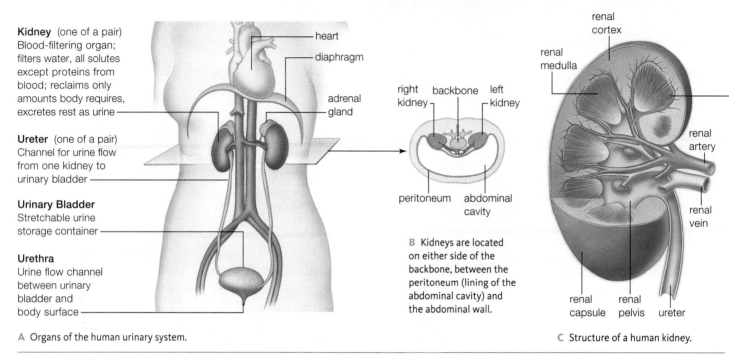

Kidney (one of a pair)
Blood-filtering organ; filters water, all solutes except proteins from blood; reclaims only amounts body requires, excretes rest as urine

Ureter (one of a pair)
Channel for urine flow from one kidney to urinary bladder

Urinary Bladder
Stretchable urine storage container

Urethra
Urine flow channel between urinary bladder and body surface

heart
diaphragm
adrenal gland

right kidney   backbone   left kidney

peritoneum   abdominal cavity

B Kidneys are located on either side of the backbone, between the peritoneum (lining of the abdominal cavity) and the abdominal wall.

renal cortex
renal medulla
renal artery
renal vein
renal capsule   renal pelvis   ureter

A Organs of the human urinary system.

C Structure of a human kidney.

FIGURE 37.4 {Animated} Components of the human urinary system and their functions.

COMPONENTS OF THE SYSTEM

FIGURE 37.4A shows organs of the human urinary system. Human kidneys are bean-shaped organs about the size of an adult fist. They lie just inside the peritoneum that lines the abdominal cavity, to the left and right of the backbone (**FIGURE 37.4B**). The outermost kidney layer, the renal capsule, consists of fibrous connective tissue (**FIGURE 37.4C**). Renal is from a Latin word, *renum*, that means "relating to the kidneys." The bulk of tissue inside the renal capsule is divided into two zones. The outer zone is renal cortex; the inner zone, renal medulla. A renal artery transports blood to each kidney and a renal vein carries blood away from it.

Inside each kidney, urine collects inside a central cavity called the renal pelvis. From there, the urine flows through a tubular **ureter** to the **urinary bladder**, a hollow, muscular organ that stores urine. When the bladder is full, stretch receptors signal motor neurons in the spinal cord. In a reflex action, these neurons cause smooth muscle in the bladder wall to contract. At the same time, sphincters encircling the **urethra**, the tube that delivers urine to the body surface, relax. As a result of these two actions, urine flows out of the body. After age two or three, the brain can override the spinal reflex and prevent urine from flowing through the urethra at inconvenient moments.

A male's urethra runs the length of the penis, and it conveys urine and semen at different times. A sphincter cuts off urine flow during erections. In females, the urethra opens onto the body surface near the vagina. The female urethra is a short tube, so infectious organisms can easily reach the urinary bladder. That is one reason why women get bladder infections more often than men do.

INTRODUCING NEPHRONS

In the next section, we discuss the three processes that rid the body of excess water and solutes in the form of urine. Understanding these processes will be simpler if you first acquaint yourself with the structures involved.

Overview of Nephron Structure A kidney has more than 1 million **nephrons**, each a microscopically small tube (tubule) of cuboidal epithelium and its associated capillaries. The tubule walls are just one cell thick, so substances diffuse or are transported easily across them.

Each nephron begins in the cortex, where its wall balloons out and folds back to form a cup-shaped **Bowman's capsule** (**FIGURE 37.5A,B**). Beyond the capsule, the nephron twists a bit and straightens out as a **proximal tubule** (the part nearest the beginning of the nephron). After extending down into the renal medulla, the nephron makes

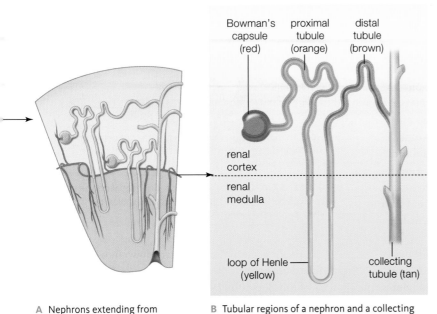

Bowman's capsule (red)　proximal tubule (orange)　distal tubule (brown)

renal cortex

renal medulla

loop of Henle (yellow)　collecting tubule (tan)

A Nephrons extending from the cortex into the medulla.

B Tubular regions of a nephron and a collecting tubule, cutaway view.

efferent arteriole

glomerulus

afferent arteriole

renal artery　renal vein

peritubular capillaries

C Blood vessels associated with nephron tubules. The glomerulus and peritubular capillaries are considered part of the nephron.

FIGURE 37.5 {Animated} Orientation and structure of a nephron, the functional unit of the kidney.

a hairpin turn called the **loop of Henle**. The tubule reenters the cortex and twists again, as the **distal tubule** (the farthest from the start of the nephron). The distal tubules of several nephrons drain into a **collecting tubule**. Many collecting tubules extend through the kidney medulla and open into the renal pelvis.

Blood Vessels Associated With Nephrons Inside each kidney, a renal artery branches into smaller arterioles called afferent arterioles. Each afferent arteriole leads to

a **glomerulus** (plural, glomeruli), a cluster of capillaries in Bowman's capsule (**FIGURE 37.5C**). Capillaries of a glomerulus have gaps between the cells that make up their walls. These gaps make the capillaries about a hundred times more permeable than a typical capillary. As blood flows through the glomerulus, blood pressure forces some fluid out through the gaps in the capillary wall and into Bowman's capsule. *Glomerulus* is the Greek word for filter.

The portion of the blood that does not leave the glomerulus and enter Bowman's capsule enters an efferent arteriole. This arteriole quickly branches into **peritubular capillaries**, which thread lacily around the nephron (*peri–*, around). Peritubular capillaries are the site for exchanges between fluid flowing through kidney tubules and the blood. From the peritubular capillaries, blood continues into venules that carry it to the renal vein.

Bowman's capsule Region of a nephron that forms a cup around the glomerulus; connects to the proximal tubule.
collecting tubule Kidney tubule that receives fluid from several nephrons and delivers it to the renal pelvis.
distal tubule Region of a kidney tubule that connects to a collecting tubule.
glomerulus Ball of leaky capillaries enclosed by Bowman's capsule.
loop of Henle U-shaped portion of a kidney tubule; connects the proximal and distal regions of the tubule.
nephron A kidney tubule and associated capillaries; filters blood and forms urine.
peritubular capillaries Capillaries that branch from an efferent arteriole; surround and exchange substances with a kidney tubule.
proximal tubule Region of kidney tubule nearest Bowman's capsule.
ureter Tube that carries urine from a kidney to the bladder.
urethra Tube through which urine from the bladder exits the body.
urinary bladder Hollow, muscular organ that stores urine.

CREDIT: (5) © Cengage Learning.

FILTRATION, REABSORPTION, AND SECRETION

Blood pressure generated by a beating heart drives **glomerular filtration**, the first step in urine formation (**FIGURE 37.6** and **FIGURE 37.7 ❶**). About 20 percent of the plasma that flows into a glomerulus is forced out through gaps in the capillary walls into Bowman's capsule. Collectively, the inner wall of Bowman's capsule and the walls of capillaries in a glomerulus function like a filter for the blood. Plasma proteins, blood cells, and platelets cannot pass through the filter. They remain in the blood and leave the glomerulus via the efferent arteriole. The protein-free plasma that enters Bowman's capsule is called filtrate. From Bowman's capsule, filtrate flows into the proximal tubule.

Only a small fraction of the filtrate actually ends up in urine. **Tubular reabsorption** returns most water and solutes to the blood. Reabsorption begins in the proximal tubule ❷, where transport proteins move sodium ions (Na^+), chloride ions (Cl^-), potassium ions (K^+), and glucose and other nutrients across the tubule wall and into peritubular capillaries. Water follows these solutes by osmosis, so it moves in the same direction.

Most water and nutrients are reabsorbed from the proximal tubule, but reabsorption occurs along the entire length of the kidney tubule. Tubular reabsorption returns about 99 percent of the water filtered into Bowman's capsule to the blood. It returns just about all of the glucose and amino acids, as well as most sodium ions, chloride ions, and bicarbonate ions.

Tubular secretion is the movement of substances from the blood in peritubular capillaries into the filtrate ❸. Membrane proteins in the walls of peritubular capillaries actively transport substances into the interstitial fluid, from which they are transported across the epithelium of the kidney tubule and enter the filtrate. Secreted substances include hydrogen ions (H^+), potassium ions (K^+), and breakdown products of foreign organic molecules such as drugs and pesticides.

CONCENTRATING THE URINE

Sip soda all day and your urine will be dilute; sleep eight hours and it will be concentrated. However, even the most dilute urine has far more solutes than plasma or typical interstitial fluid.

For water to move out of a nephron by osmosis, the interstitial fluid surrounding the nephron must have a higher solute concentration than the filtrate inside the nephron. The concentration of solutes in the interstitial fluid is constant throughout the cortex, but increases with the distance into the medulla.

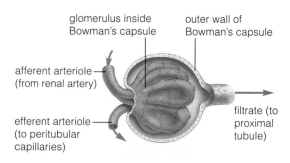

FIGURE 37.6 Glomerular filtration. Urine formation begins when blood pressure forces protein-free plasma out of the glomerular capillaries and into Bowman's capsule.

The loop of Henle carries filtrate down into the medulla, then back into the cortex. The ascending and descending arms of the loop differ in their permeabilities to water and sodium. The descending arm of the loop is permeable to water but not to sodium. The loop's ascending arm is impermeable to water and actively pumps sodium into the interstitial fluid.

A high solute concentration in interstitial fluid draws water out of filtrate as it flows through the descending loop of Henle. Then, ions are actively transported out of the filtrate as it flows through the ascending loop. Ions that leave the ascending loop contribute to the high solute concentration in the interstitial fluid.

Filtrate entering the distal tubule is less concentrated than normal body fluid. The distal tubule delivers this filtrate to the collecting tubule. Like the descending loop of Henle, this tubule extends down into the medulla. In the deepest part of the medulla, urea is pumped out of the collecting tubule, and this contributes to the high solute concentration of the interstitial fluid. As urine descends through the collecting tubule, the increasing solute concentration of the interstitial fluid around the tubule draws water outward by osmosis.

The body can adjust how much water is reabsorbed at distal tubules and collecting tubules. When the body has too little water, the Na^+ concentration in blood rises and blood pressure declines. These changes trigger secretion of hormones that cause the kidneys to concentrate the urine.

Detection by the hypothalamus of a rise in Na^+ concentration causes the hypothalamus to signal the posterior pituitary gland. In response, the posterior pituitary releases **antidiuretic hormone** (ADH). ADH makes the distal tubules and collecting tubules more permeable to water. As a result, more water is reabsorbed, and the urine becomes more concentrated.

A decline in blood pressure causes arterioles that carry blood to nephrons to release the enzyme renin. Renin sets

CREDIT: (6) From Starr/Taggart/Evers/Starr, Biology, 13E. © 2013 Cengage Learning.

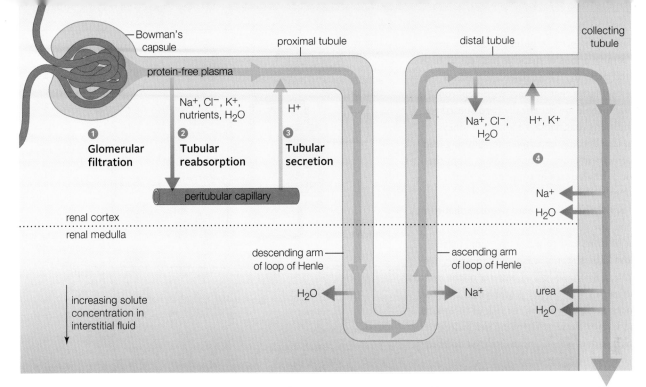

Bowman's capsule

protein-free plasma

proximal tubule

distal tubule

collecting tubule

Na⁺, Cl⁻, K⁺, nutrients, H_2O

H^+

Na⁺, Cl⁻, H_2O

H^+, K⁺

1 Glomerular filtration

2 Tubular reabsorption

3 Tubular secretion

4

peritubular capillary

Na⁺

H_2O

renal cortex
renal medulla

descending arm of loop of Henle

ascending arm of loop of Henle

increasing solute concentration in interstitial fluid

H_2O

Na⁺

urea

H_2O

urine to renal pelvis

1 Glomerular filtration. Protein-free plasma forced out of glomerular capillaries by blood pressure enters Bowman's capsule.

2 Tubular reabsorption. Essential ions, nutrients, water, in the filtrate return to the blood. Green arrows indicate reabsorption.

3 Tubular secretion. Wastes and excess ions are moved from the blood into the filtrate for elimination in urine. Blue arrows indicate secretion.

4 Hormone effects. Aldosterone increases Na⁺ reabsorption and water follows by osmosis. Antidiuretic hormone increases water reabsorption.

FIGURE 37.7 {Animated} How urine forms. Only a small segment of peritubular capillary is shown.

 FIGURE IT OUT: What process moves H^+ from peritubular capillaries into the distal tubule?

Answer: Tubular secretion

off a chain of reactions that eventually results in secretion of **aldosterone** by the adrenal glands. This hormone makes distal tubules and collecting tubules reabsorb more Na⁺ **4**. Water follows by osmosis, so less water is excreted from the body in urine; the urine becomes more concentrated.

Atrial natriuretic peptide (ANP) is a hormone that makes urine more dilute by inhibiting aldosterone secretion. Muscle cells in the heart's atria release ANP when a high blood volume causes the atrial walls to stretch.

Parathyroid hormone (PTH) regulates blood calcium level in part by adjusting the amount of calcium excreted in urine. When calcium level declines, PTH acts on the kidney to increase reabsorption of this essential ion.

aldosterone Adrenal hormone that makes kidney tubules more permeable to sodium; encourages sodium reabsorption, which leads to more water reabsorption and more concentrated urine.
antidiuretic hormone Pituitary hormone that encourages water reabsorption in the kidney, thus concentrating the urine.
glomerular filtration Protein-free plasma forced out of glomerular capillaries by blood pressure enters Bowman's capsule.
tubular reabsorption Water and solutes move from the filtrate inside a kidney tubule into the peritubular capillaries.
tubular secretion Ions and breakdown products of organic molecules move out of peritubular capillaries and into filtrate.

TAKE-HOME MESSAGE 37.3

During glomerular filtration, pressure generated by the beating heart drives water and solutes out of glomerular capillaries and into kidney tubules.

Water, some ions, glucose, and other solutes move out of the filtrate and return to the blood in peritubular capillaries, a process called tubular reabsorption.

In tubular secretion, transport proteins move urea, H^+, and K⁺ from peritubular capillaries into the nephron for excretion.

Urine concentration depends on how much water flows out of the distal tubule and the collecting tubule. Hormones affect urine concentration by their effects on the permeability of these tubules.

CREDIT: (7) From Starr/Taggart/Evers/Starr, Biology, 13E. © 2013 Cengage Learning.

The vast majority of kidney problems arise as complications of diabetes mellitus or high blood pressure. These disorders damage the capillaries that interact with nephrons. Some people are genetically predisposed to conditions that damage kidneys. Kidneys can also become impaired after filtering lead, arsenic, pesticides, or other toxins from the blood. High doses of some drugs damage kidneys too.

Kidney stones are hard deposits that form when uric acid, calcium, and other wastes settle out of urine and collect in the renal pelvis. Most kidney stones wash away in urine, but sometimes one lodges in a ureter or the urethra and causes severe pain. A stone that slows or blocks urine flow raises the risk of infections and kidney damage. Drinking too little water makes kidney stones more likely, as do obesity and a high-calcium diet.

Kidney function is measured in terms of the rate of filtration through capillaries of the glomerulus. Kidney failure occurs when this rate falls by half. Failure of both kidneys can be fatal because wastes build up in the blood and interstitial fluid. The pH rises, and changes in the concentrations of other ions, most notably Na^+ and K^+, interfere with metabolism.

Kidney dialysis removes wastes and restores proper solute concentrations in a person who has kidney failure. "Dialysis" refers to exchanges of solutes across a semipermeable membrane between two solutions. With hemodialysis, a dialysis machine is connected to a patient's blood vessel (FIGURE 37.8A). The machine pumps a patient's blood through semipermeable tubes submerged in a warm solution of salts, glucose, and other substances. As the blood flows through the tubes, wastes dissolved in the blood diffuse out and solute concentrations return to normal levels. Cleansed, solute-balanced blood is returned to the patient's body. Typically a person has hemodialysis three times a week at an outpatient dialysis center. An alternative procedure, peritoneal dialysis, can be done at home. In this procedure, the patient's peritoneal lining serves as the dialysis membrane. Each night, the patient pumps dialysis solution into his or her abdominal cavity (FIGURE 37.8B). Wastes diffuse across the peritoneal lining into the fluid, which is drained out the next morning.

Kidney dialysis can keep a person alive through an episode of temporary kidney failure. When kidney damage is permanent, dialysis must be continued for the rest of a

person's life, or until a donor kidney becomes available for transplant surgery.

Each year in the United States, about 12,000 people are recipients of kidney transplants. More than 40,000 others remain on a waiting list because there is a shortage of donated kidneys. The National Kidney Foundation estimates that every day, 17 people die of kidney failure while waiting for a transplant. Most kidneys for transplant come from deceased donors, but the number of living donors is increasing. One kidney is adequate to maintain good health, so the risks to a living donor are mainly related to the surgery—unless a donor's remaining kidney fails.

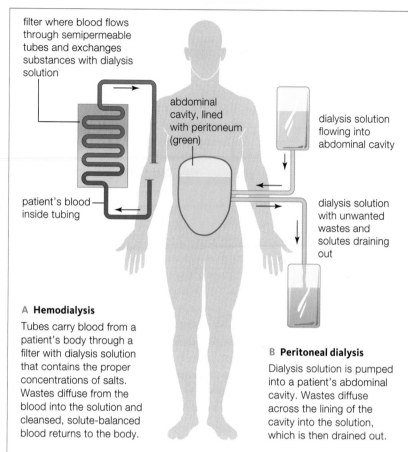

filter where blood flows through semipermeable tubes and exchanges substances with dialysis solution

abdominal cavity, lined with peritoneum (green)

dialysis solution flowing into abdominal cavity

patient's blood inside tubing

dialysis solution with unwanted wastes and solutes draining out

A Hemodialysis
Tubes carry blood from a patient's body through a filter with dialysis solution that contains the proper concentrations of salts. Wastes diffuse from the blood into the solution and cleansed, solute-balanced blood returns to the body.

B Peritoneal dialysis
Dialysis solution is pumped into a patient's abdominal cavity. Wastes diffuse across the lining of the cavity into the solution, which is then drained out.

FIGURE 37.8 {Animated} Two types of dialysis for kidney failure.

TAKE-HOME MESSAGE 37.4

Most kidney failure occurs as a complication of diabetes or high blood pressure. Kidney stones, infections, and drug reactions are less common causes.

Untreated kidney failure is fatal. Dialysis can keep a person with kidney failure alive, but it must be continued until a person dies or receives a kidney transplant.

CREDIT: (8) © Cengage Learning.

37.5 WHAT CAN URINE TESTS DETECT?

Physicians routinely check the pH and solute concentrations of urine to monitor their patients' health. Acidic urine suggests metabolic problems. Alkaline urine can indicate an infection. Sugar in the urine is evidence of diabetes. Damaged kidneys produce urine high in proteins. An abundance of some salts can be a sign of dehydration or of deficiencies in hormones that control kidney function. Urine tests can also detect chemicals produced by cancers of the kidney, bladder, and prostate gland.

Do-it-yourself urine tests have become popular. If a woman is hoping to become pregnant, she can use one test to keep track of the amount of luteinizing hormone (LH) in her urine. As the next chapter explains, a surge in LH triggers ovulation (release of an egg from an ovary). Another urine test can reveal whether a woman has become pregnant. Still another test allows older women to check for declining hormone levels in urine, a sign that they may be entering menopause.

Breakdown products of water-soluble drugs are excreted in the urine. For example, after a person smokes marijuana, his or her kidneys filter a breakdown product of the drug's active ingredient (THC) out of the blood and into the urine. It can take as long as 30 days for all molecules of the breakdown product to be removed from the body.

Water-soluble pollutants that enter the body are also excreted in urine. Thus, urine tests can reveal the extent of a person's exposure to harmful substances such as lead or pesticides. For example, urine tests were used in a recent study that revealed a positive correlation between a child's exposure to some organophosphate pesticides commonly used in agriculture and an increased risk of attention deficit hyperactivity disorders (ADHD).

The length of time it takes the kidneys to eliminate a substance from the blood depends on the efficiency of the kidneys, which varies with health and age. A toxin is eliminated from the body of a healthy 35-year-old about twice as fast it is eliminated from the body of a healthy 85-year-old.

TAKE-HOME MESSAGE 37.5

Analyzing the composition of urine can provide insights into general health, hormone levels, drug use, and exposure to toxins such as pesticides.

PEOPLE MATTER

National Geographic Explorer
DR. CHERYL KNOTT

Collecting orangutan urine in the forests of Borneo earned Cheryl Knott a place in *Popular Science* magazine's 2005 list of the worst jobs in science. Orangutans spend most of their time in trees, so Knott collects their urine from leaves (as shown above) and from plastic sheets she spreads beneath their sleeping nests. Thus far, she and her team have collected over 3,000 samples of orangutan urine.

Analysis of the urine samples, in combination with extensive observation of the animals, allows Knott to investigate how environmental changes affect orangutan nutrition and reproduction. To find out how well nourished orangutans are, Knott looks for ketones in their urine. Ketones are products of the breakdown of fat deposits. She also looks for C-peptide, a hormone that declines with weight loss. These tests tell her whether orangutans are getting enough to eat or if they have to rely on their fat reserves for energy. To determine orangutans' reproductive status, Knott checks the concentration of sex hormones in their urine.

Knott's investigations revealed why female orangutans have so few young—on average, only one every six to eight years. In most years, their rain-forest habitat provides them with enough food to survive, but not enough to reproduce. Although some rain-forest trees produce fruit each year, about every four years there is a mast fruiting when a majority of trees in these forests produce fruit. Orangutans are more likely to become pregnant during these and other periods of high fruit abundance.

The orangutans' low reproductive rate puts them a high risk of extinction from habitat loss and poaching. Knott says, "Researching orangutan reproduction helps us to better understand what we need to do to preserve the species." To learn more about Knott's efforts to save orangutans, visit the website http://savegporangutans.org.

The enzymes that carry out the metabolic reactions vital to life function best within a limited range of temperatures (Section 5.3). Thus, **thermoregulation**, the maintenance of the body's core temperature within a limited range, is an essential aspect of homeostasis.

HEAT GAINS AND LOSSES

Metabolic reactions release heat, so the heat generated by metabolism influences the temperature of an animal's body. Animals also gain heat from, and lose heat to, their surroundings. An animal's internal temperature remains stable only when the metabolic heat it produces and the heat it gains from the environment balance the heat it loses to the environment:

$$\begin{array}{ccccc} \text{change in} \\ \text{body heat} \end{array} = \begin{array}{c} \text{heat} \\ \text{produced} \end{array} + \begin{array}{c} \text{heat} \\ \text{gained} \end{array} - \begin{array}{c} \text{heat} \\ \text{lost} \end{array}$$

Body surfaces lose and gain heat by thermal radiation, conduction, convection, and evaporation. Thermal radiation is the emission of heat from a warm object into the space around it. Just as the sun radiates heat energy into space, an animal radiates metabolically produced heat. At rest, a human adult gives off as much heat as a 100-watt incandescent lightbulb.

Conduction is the transfer of heat within an object or among objects that contact one another. An animal loses heat when it contacts a cooler object, and gains heat when it contacts a warmer one. When you sit on a cold plastic chair, heat from your body is conducted to the plastic, warming it.

In convection, heat is transferred by the movement of heated air or water away from the source of heat. As air or water heats up, it rises and moves away from the object (such as a body) that warmed it.

In evaporation, a liquid becomes a vapor. Energy that powers this process typically comes from the liquid itself in the form of heat, so the remaining liquid cools (Section 2.4). When that liquid is water at a body surface, this cooling helps decrease body temperature. When it is hot, a fan can cool you by increasing the rate at which your body loses heat through evaporation.

MODES OF THERMOREGULATION

There are two main modes of thermoregulation. Invertebrates, fishes, amphibians, and nonbird reptiles are **ectotherms**, which means "heated from the outside." The body temperature of ectotherms fluctuates with the temperature of the external environment. That is why the chameleon in **FIGURE 37.9** is about the same temperature as its surroundings. Ectotherms typically have a low metabolic rate, and they lack insulating fur, hair, or

This lizard blends into the background because its body stays about the same temperature as its surroundings.

A human hand stays warm because a person produces and releases a large amount of metabolic heat.

cooler---------------->warmer

FIGURE 37.9 Endotherm and ectotherm. Photo of a chameleon (an ectothermic lizard) being held by a human (an endotherm). The image was taken using heat-sensitive film.

feathers. They regulate internal temperature by altering their position, rather than their metabolism. A lizard, for example, warms itself by basking on a rock in a sunny spot or cools itself by retreating into a shady burrow.

Most birds and mammals are **endotherms**, which means "heated from within." Compared to ectotherms, endotherms maintain their body temperature within a narrower range. They also have a higher metabolic rate. For example, a mouse uses thirty times more energy than a lizard of the same body weight. The ability to produce a large amount of metabolic heat allows endotherms to remain active in a wider range of temperatures than ectotherms. Fur, hair, or feathers insulate endotherms by minimizing heat transfers.

Some birds and mammals are **heterotherms**, animals that keep their core temperature constant some of the time, but allow it to fluctuate at other times. For example, hummingbirds have a very high metabolic rate when foraging for nectar during the day. At night, the birds' metabolic activity decreases so much that their body may become almost as cool as the surroundings.

VERTEBRATE RESPONSES TO COLD

Most vertebrates that remain active when it is very cold are endotherms. When external temperature declines, thermoreceptors in their skin send action potentials to the hypothalamus, the brain region responsible for

CREDIT: (9) NASA/JPL-Caltech/L. Hermans.

thermoregulation. Action potentials from the hypothalamus cause smooth muscle in arterioles that deliver blood to the skin to contract, so less metabolic heat reaches the body surface (**TABLE 37.1**). At the same time, muscle contractions make hair, fur, or feathers "stand up." This response creates a layer of still air next to skin, reducing the amount of heat lost by convection.

Skeletal muscles are a vertebrate's main source of metabolic heat. With prolonged exposure to cold, the hypothalamus commands these muscles to contract ten to twenty times each second. This shivering response increases metabolic heat production, but it has a high energy cost.

Brown adipose tissue helps many mammals stay warm in cold places. This tissue contains mitochondria that can release energy as heat, rather than storing it in ATP. The resulting increase in metabolic heat output is called nonshivering heat production.

Animals that hibernate during a cold season are seasonal heterotherms. While hibernating, an animal is largely inactive, and its respiratory rate, heart rate, and body temperature decline dramatically. Depending on the species, the animal may reawaken to feed periodically on stored food, or subsist entirely on fat and glycogen accumulated during the prior season. Mammalian hibernators include some bats, bears, and rodents (**FIGURE 37.10**). Many reptiles and amphibians also hibernate during winter.

VERTEBRATE RESPONSES TO HEAT

In a hot environment, a vertebrate becomes less active, thus decreasing the amount of heat produced by the activity of its skeletal muscles. Blood delivery to the skin increases, allowing more metabolic heat to escape into the surroundings. Many vertebrates also reduce their temperature by breathing rapidly (panting), which increases the rate of evaporative cooling from their respiratory tract.

Sweating is the main mechanism of cooling in primates (including humans) and large hooved mammals. Sweat glands are exocrine glands that release water and solutes through pores at the skin's surface. Evaporation of sweat cools the skin. Rodents and marsupials cannot sweat, but some of them cool off by spreading saliva on their skin. Like

TABLE 37.1

Vertebrate Responses to Cold and Heat

Stimulus	Main Responses	Outcome
Cold stress	Widespread vasoconstriction in skin; fluffing of fur or feathers to improve insulation	Conservation of body heat
	Increased muscle action; shivering; nonshivering heat production	Heat production increases
Heat stress	Widespread vasodilation in skin; in some species, panting, sweating or spreading of saliva on skin	Dissipation of heat from body
	Decreased muscle action	Heat production decreases

FIGURE 37.10 Hibernating arctic ground squirrels. In hibernation, the core body temperature of these rodents can fall below freezing. The brain is kept a bit warmer.

sweating, this cooling mechanism results in the loss of water, which must be replenished by drinking.

Desert reptiles and amphibians may become dormant during the hot, dry summer, a state called estivation. These animals remain inactive for the season inside a burrow deep beneath the soil surface.

ectotherm Animal that controls its internal temperature by altering its behavior; for example, a fish or a lizard.
endotherm Animal that tightly controls its internal temperature by adjusting its metabolism; for example, a bird or a mammal.
heterotherm Animal that sometimes maintains its temperature by producing metabolic heat, and at other times allows its temperature to fluctuate with the environment.
thermoregulation Maintaining body temperature within a limited range.

TAKE-HOME MESSAGE 37.6

Thermoregulation is an important aspect of homeostasis.

Endotherms maintain their body temperature within a narrower range than ectotherms. They also expend more energy generating metabolic heat.

Vertebrates respond to cold stress by decreasing blood flow to skin, fluffing up fur or feathers, shivering, and nonshivering heat production.

Vertebrates respond to heat stress by increasing blood flow to skin and by mechanisms that increase evaporative water loss.

37.7 HOW DO HUMANS RESPOND TO HEAT AND COLD?

As Section 28.9 explained, a negative feedback mechanism maintains the human core body temperature at about 98.6° Fahrenheit (37°C). When our core temperature rises above this point, blood flow to our skin increases and we, like other primates, begin to sweat. Humans have a denser array of sweat glands than other primates. For example, we have about ten times the number of sweat glands of a chimpanzee. Our impressive sweating capacity is thought to have arisen when our early ancestors spent much of their time walking upright across the hot, sunny savannas of equatorial Africa. Under these conditions, an increased capacity to cool the body by sweating would have been selectively advantageous.

FIGURE 37.11 Nonshivering heat production. The PET/CT scans showing metabolic activity of one person at two temperatures. Dark regions indicate areas of highest metabolic activity. In this person, brown adipose tissue in the neck and clavicle region increased its metabolic activity in response to cold.

Metabolic activity at 22°C (72°F)	Metabolic activity after two hours at 16°C (61°F)

TABLE 37.2

Impact of Increases in Cold Stress

Core Temperature	Physiological Responses
36–34°C (about 95°F)	Shivering response; faster breathing. Peripheral vasoconstriction moves blood away from body surface. Dizziness, nausea.
33–32°C (about 91°F)	Shivering response ends. Metabolic heat output declines.
31–30°C (about 86°F)	Capacity for voluntary motion is lost. Eye and tendon reflexes inhibited. Consciousness lost. Cardiac muscle action becomes irregular.
26–24°C (about 77°F)	Ventricular fibrillation sets in (Section 33.9). Death follows.

Sweating depletes the body of water and salts, a loss that can cause problems if not remedied. Most heat-related problems in otherwise healthy people occur as a result of overexertion coupled with dehydration. A rise in core body temperature above 106°F (41°C) results in heat stroke, a potentially fatal condition.

To stay safe outside on a hot day, drink plenty of water and avoid excessive exercise. If you must exert yourself, take breaks to monitor how you feel. Avoid direct sunlight, wear a hat and light-colored clothing, and use sunscreen. Sunburn impairs the skin's ability to transfer heat to the air. Also keep in mind that sweat glands of a person who is not normally exposed to heat produce less sweat than those of a person who has routine heat exposure.

In a cold environment, humans warm themselves by shivering and, in some cases, by nonshivering heat production (**FIGURE 37.11**). Exposure to cold increases the secretion of thyroid hormone (Section 31.5), which binds to cells of brown adipose tissue and encourages nonshivering heat production. People who make too little thyroid hormone cannot increase their nonshivering heat production, so they often feel cold. They also tend to be overweight, because nonshivering heat production burns a lot of calories.

Hypothermia occurs when normal mechanisms fail to keep core temperature from falling so far that function is disrupted (**TABLE 37.2**). Brain activity becomes impaired when the core body temperature falls to 95°F (35°C). Thus, "stumbles, mumbles, and fumbles" are symptoms of early hypothermia. Severe hypothermia causes loss of consciousness, disrupts heart rhythm, and can be fatal.

A person who has even moderate hypothermia may also suffer from frostbite, which results from the cold-related shift in circulation away from peripheral tissues. As these tissues cool, the interstitial fluid inside them begins to freeze. Fingers and toes are most often affected. Severe frostbite kills tissue. Dead tissue must be surgically removed to prevent infection of other body parts.

TAKE-HOME MESSAGE 37.7

Sweating is the main mechanism by which humans cool their body. Compared to other primates, humans have an enhanced capacity to sweat.

Heat-related illness usually occurs when an overexerted person does not replenish fluid lost in sweat.

In cold climates, shivering and (in most people) nonshivering heat production can help warm the body.

A decrease in core temperature can cause fatal hypothermia. Exposure of extremities to cold can cause frostbite.

CREDITS: (11) From Cold-Activated Brown Adipose Tissue in Healthy Men. van Marken Lichtenbelt, Wouter D. et al. Article DOI: 10.1056/NEJMoa0808718. © 2009 *The New England Journal of Medicine*. Reprinted with permission; (Table 37.2) © Cengage Learning.

Education

FIGURE 37.12 Facing different climatic challenges. Ituri pygmies in the Congo and Inuit people in the Canadian Arctic (inset).

AS HUMANS DISPERSED OUT OF AFRICA, THE CLIMATIC CHALLENGES THEY FACED CHANGED.
In equatorial Africa, people sweat a lot, so they lose a good deal of sodium (FIGURE 37.12). Sodium is an essential nutrient, and was a limited resource for many early populations. Thus, individuals with kidneys that reabsorbed a lot of sodium were at a selective advantage. Later, some humans migrated to colder regions, where they sweated less frequently. In cooler environments, a tendency to reabsorb a large amount of sodium from filtrate would have been less advantageous. It could even be maladaptive, because high blood sodium increases risk of hypertension and cardiovascular disorders.

Allele frequencies of some genes involved in sodium reabsorption provide evidence of a climate-related shift in selective pressure. Consider the *ACE* gene, which encodes an enzyme needed to make aldosterone. Aldosterone, you will recall, is the hormone that promotes sodium reabsorption from urine. The ancestral allele for the *ACE* gene

(*D*) is most common in modern African and Middle Eastern populations. It is less common in Europe, and least common in Asia. An alternative allele (*I*) has an insertion and encodes a less active form of *ACE*.

Distribution of *ACE* alleles in modern populations may be of medical importance. People homozygous for the *D* allele (*DD*) make more aldosterone than those with other genotypes, and so reabsorb more sodium. In modern societies, where sodium is abundant, an enhanced capacity for sodium reabsorption is likely to increase the risk for cardiovascular disorders. Some studies have found an increased risk of hypertension or heart attack with the *DD* genotype.

For humans who settled in cold climates, an ability to produce increased amounts of metabolic heat provided a selective advantage. We see the results of this selection in the distribution of alleles for genes that encode proteins involved in heat production. Alleles that result in increased nonshivering heat production tend to be highest in arctic populations.

CREDITS: (12) background, Randy Olson/National Geographic Creative; inset, Norbert Rosing/National Geographic Creative.

Summary

SECTION 37.1   Plasma and interstitial fluid are the main components of extracellular fluid. Maintaining the volume and composition of this fluid is an essential aspect of homeostasis. Organisms must balance solute and fluid gains with solute and fluid losses. They also must eliminate metabolic wastes such as the **ammonia** produced by breaking down proteins. Earthworm **nephridia** excrete ammonia. Insects convert ammonia to **uric acid**, which enters **Malpighian tubules**. Birds and other reptiles also excrete uric acid. Mammals excrete **urea** dissolved in a lot of water. All vertebrates have a pair of **kidneys** that filter the blood and produce **urine**.

SECTION 37.2   A kidney has more than a million **nephrons**, each consisting of a tubule and some associated capillaries. A **Bowman's capsule** in the renal cortex is the entrance to a nephron tubule. It receives fluid filtered out of leaky capillaries of the **glomerulus**. This fluid continues through a **proximal tubule**, a **loop of Henle** that descends into and ascends from the renal medulla, and a **distal tubule** that drains into a **collecting tubule**. **Peritubular capillaries** lie in close proximity to the tubular portion of a nephron and exchange substances with it.

Fluid from collecting tubules drains into the renal pelvis, where it is called urine. **Ureters** carry urine formed in the kidneys to the **urinary bladder**. The bladder stores urine until it is expelled through the **urethra**. Urination is a reflex, but can be overridden by voluntary control.

SECTION 37.3   Urine formation begins when **glomerular filtration** produces protein-free plasma that enters the tubular part of a nephron. Most water and solutes are returned to the blood by **tubular reabsorption**. Substances that are not reabsorbed, and substances added to the filtrate by **tubular secretion**, end up in the urine. Hormones regulate the urine's concentration and composition. **Antidiuretic hormone** makes tubules more permeable to water, so more is reabsorbed and urine is more concentrated. **Aldosterone** increases sodium reabsorption. Water follows sodium into the blood, so aldosterone indirectly concentrates the urine.

SECTIONS 37.4, 37.5   Kidneys can be harmed by chronic disease, genetic factors, infections, or drugs. When kidneys fail, frequent dialysis or a kidney transplant is required to sustain life. Analysis of urine provides information about health and hormone concentrations. Drugs and toxins such as pesticides are excreted in urine and can be detected by urine tests.

SECTION 37.6   All animals produce metabolic heat. **Thermoregulation** requires that heat produced by metabolism and gained from the environment must balance heat lost to the environment.

For **ectotherms** such as reptiles, core temperature depends more on heat exchanges with the environment than on metabolic heat production. Such animals control core temperature mainly by modifying behavior. For **endotherms** (most birds and mammals), a high metabolic rate is the primary source of heat. Endotherms regulate their core temperature mainly by controlling the production and loss of metabolic heat. **Heterotherms** tightly control core temperature part of the time, and allow it to fluctuate with the external temperature at other times. Some animals allow temperature to fluctuate daily. Those that hibernate allow it to fall during hibernation.

Animals cool their bodies by dilating blood vessels in the skin, and by sweating and panting. They retain heat in their core by constricting blood vessels in the skin and gain warmth by shivering, and by nonshivering heat production.

SECTION 37.7   Humans cool their body mainly by sweating. We have many more sweat glands than other primates. Sweating without restoring lost water and solutes raises the risk of hyperthermia. Humans warm themselves by shivering and nonshivering heat production. A decline in core body temperature can be fatal. Frostbite is damage to extremities that occurs when tissue freezes.

SECTION 37.8   Humans evolved in tropical Africa, where individuals who maintained their sodium level despite sweating were at a selective advantage. Reabsorbing extra sodium can cause health problems where salt is plentiful. Mechanisms that enhanced metabolic heat production evolved in humans who migrated to cold regions.

Self-Quiz   Answers in Appendix VII

1. A freshwater fish gains most of its water by _____ .
   a. drinking   c. osmosis
   b. eating food   d. transport across the gills

2. Breakdown of _____ produces ammonia.
   a. sugars   c. starches
   b. fats   d. proteins

3. Insects and birds excrete _____ .
   a. ammonia   c. uric acid
   b. urea   d. nucleic acid

4. Bowman's capsule, the start of the tubular part of a nephron, is located in the _____ .
   a. renal cortex   c. renal pelvis
   b. renal medulla   d. renal artery

5. Plasma fluid filtered into Bowman's capsule flows directly into the _____ .
   a. renal artery   c. distal tubule
   b. proximal tubule   d. loop of Henle

6. Blood pressure forces water and small solutes out of blood and into nephrons during _____ .
   a. glomerular filtration   c. tubular secretion
   b. tubular reabsorption   d. both a and c

Data Analysis Activities

Pesticides in Urine To carry the USDA's organic label (left), food must be produced without commonly used pesticides such as malathion and chlorpyrifos. Chensheng Lu of Emory University used urine testing to find out if eating organic food significantly affects the level of pesticide residues in a child's body (**FIGURE 37.13**). He collected urine of twenty-three children and tested it for metabolites (breakdown products) of pesticides. During the first five days, children ate their standard, nonorganic diet. For the next five days, they ate organic versions of the same foods and drinks. For the final five days, they returned to their standard diet.

1. During which phase of the experiment did the children's urine contain the lowest level of the malathion metabolite?

2. In which phase of the experiment was the most chlorpyrifos metabolite detected?

Study Phase	No. of Samples	Malathion Metabolite		Chlorpyrifos Metabolite	
		Mean (µg/liter)	Maximum (µg/liter)	Mean (µg/liter)	Maximum (µg/liter)
1. Conventional	87	2.9	96.5	7.2	31.1
2. Organic	116	0.3	7.4	1.7	17.1
3. Conventional	156	4.4	263.1	5.8	25.3

FIGURE 37.13 Levels of metabolites (breakdown products) of malathion and chlorpyrifos in the urine of children taking part in a study of effects of an organic diet. The difference in the mean level of metabolites in the organic and inorganic phases of the study was statistically significant.

3. Did switching to an organic diet lower the amount of pesticide residues excreted by the children?

4. Even in the nonorganic phases of this experiment, the highest pesticide metabolite levels detected were far below those known to be harmful. Given these data, would you spend more to buy organic foods?

7. Kidneys return most of the water and small solutes back to blood by way of _____ .
   a. glomerular filtration c. tubular secretion
   b. tubular reabsorption   d. both a and b

8. Tubular secretion moves _____ into kidney tubules.
   a. H^+ b. glucose   c. water   d. protein

9. Antidiuretic hormone makes distal tubules and collecting tubules more permeable to _____ .

10. _____ can keep people with kidney failure alive, but it cannot cure them.

11. Match each structure with a function.
   ___ ureter
   ___ Bowman's capsule
   ___ urethra
   ___ collecting tubule
   ___ pituitary gland

   a. start of nephron
   b. delivers urine to body surface
   c. carries urine from kidney to bladder
   d. secretes ADH
   e. target of aldosterone

12. Which of the following is an endotherm?
   a. a shark   b. a frog   c. a monkey   d. a snake

13. Match each term with the most suitable description.
   ___ endotherm
   ___ ectotherm
   ___ convection
   ___ conduction
   ___ thermal radiation

   a. environment dictates core temperature
   b. metabolism dictates core temperature
   c. heat transfer between objects that are in direct contact
   d. water, air current transfers heat
   e. emission of radiant energy

Critical Thinking

1. The desert kangaroo rat shown in **FIGURE 37.3** excretes a very small volume of urine relative to its size. Compared with a human nephron, kangaroo rat nephrons have a loop of Henle that is proportionally much longer. Explain how this helps the kangaroo rat conserve water.

2. Drinking too much water can be dangerous. When marathoners or other endurance athletes sweat heavily and drink lots of water, their sodium level drops. The resulting "water intoxication" can be fatal. Why is maintaining the sodium level so important?

3. In cold habitats, ectotherms are few and endotherms often show morphological adaptations to cold. Compared to closely related species that live in warmer areas, cold dwellers tend to have smaller appendages. Also, animals adapted to cool climates tend to be larger than closely related species that dwell in warmer climates. For example, the largest bear species is the polar bear and the largest penguin is Antarctica's emperor penguin. Think about heat transfers between animals and their habitat, then explain why smaller appendages and larger overall body size are advantageous in very cold places.

4. Drinking alcohol inhibits ADH secretion. What effect will drinking a beer have on the permeability of kidney tubules to sodium? To water?

CENGAGE brain.com To access course materials, please visit www.cengagebrain.com.

A newly hatched thrush, a type of songbird.
Thrushes hatch less than two weeks after an egg
is laid, when they are still blind and featherless.

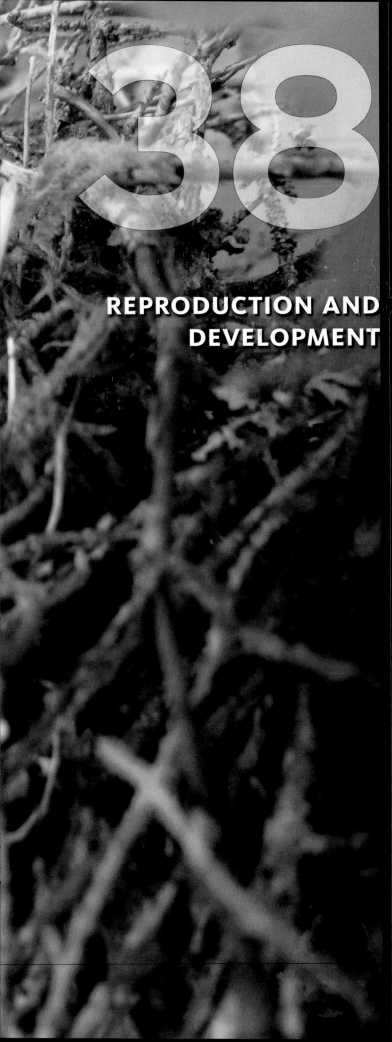

38

REPRODUCTION AND DEVELOPMENT

Links to Earlier Concepts

This chapter continues the discussion of sexual reproduction begun in Sections 12.1 and 12.2. We revisit cell differentiation (8.6) and the role of master genes in development (10.2). You will learn more about primary tissue layers (23.1), the mammalian placenta (24.7), and the function of sex hormones (31.7). We also reconsider the harmful effects of mercury (2.6), alcohol (5.9), HIV (19.1, 34.10) and endocrine disrupters (31.10).

KEY CONCEPTS

MODES OF REPRODUCTION
Most animals reproduce sexually. Fertilization may be external or internal. Developing young are nourished by egg yolk or supported by nutrients delivered across a placenta.

PRINCIPLES OF DEVELOPMENT
The same processes regulate development of all animals. Cleavage of the zygote distributes different materials to different cells. These cells then express different master genes that trigger the formation of body parts.

HUMAN REPRODUCTIVE ORGANS
Sperm form in testes, then travel through ducts to the body surface. Ovaries release eggs on a monthly basis. Egg are fertilized in oviducts, then development occurs in the uterus.

HUMAN INTERCOURSE
Sexual intercourse delivers sperm into the vagina. A variety of methods can prevent fertilization. Intercourse can transmit pathogenic bacteria, viruses, and protozoans.

HUMAN DEVELOPMENT
In humans, cleavage forms a blastocyst that implants in the uterus. A placenta connects the developing individual with its mother. Organs form in the embryo and become functional in the fetus.

Photograph by Christy Pitto, National Geographic Creative.

665

A Asexual reproduction in hydra (a cnidarian). A new individual (*left*) is budding from its parent.

B Sexual reproduction in the barred hamlet, a simultaneous hermaphrodite. Each fish lays eggs and also fertilizes its partner's eggs.

C Sexual reproduction in elephants. The male is inserting his penis into the female. Eggs will be fertilized and the offspring will develop inside the female's body.

FIGURE 38.1 Examples of animal reproduction.

ASEXUAL OR SEXUAL?

With **asexual reproduction**, a single individual produces offspring. All offspring are genetic replicas (clones) of the parent and identical to one another. This genetic uniformity can be advantageous in a stable environment where the combination of alleles that makes a parent successful is likely to do the same for its offspring (Section 11.1).

Invertebrates reproduce by a variety of asexual mechanisms. A new individual may grow on the body of its parent, a process called budding (**FIGURE 38.1A**). With fragmentation, a piece of the parent breaks off and develops into a new animal. Many corals reproduce by fragmentation. Some flatworms reproduce by transverse fission: The worm divides in two, leaving one piece headless and one tailless. Each piece then grows the missing body parts. In other animals, offspring develop from unfertilized eggs, a process called parthenogenesis. For example, a female aphid (a plant-sucking insect) can give birth to several smaller clones of herself every day. Some fishes, amphibians, lizards, and birds also produce offspring from unfertilized eggs. No mammal is known to reproduce asexually by natural means.

With **sexual reproduction**, two parents produce haploid gametes. An **egg** is a female gamete and a **sperm** is a male gamete. Gametes combine at fertilization, so offspring inherit different combinations of paternal and maternal alleles (Section 12.1).

Sexually reproducing animals incur higher genetic and energetic costs than asexual reproducers. On average, only half of a sexually reproducing parent's genetic material ends up in each of its offspring. Producing gametes has costs, and many animals spend time and energy finding and courting a mate. What benefits offset these costs? Most animals live where resources and threats change over time. In such environments, producing offspring that differ from both parents and from one another can be advantageous. Sexual reproduction increases the likelihood that some of an individual's offspring will inherit a combination of alleles that suits them to a newly changed environment.

Because sexual reproduction is most beneficial in a changing environment, some animals reproduce asexually when conditions are stable and favorable, but switch to sexual reproduction when conditions begin to change. For example, aphids produce sexual offspring when they are likely to disperse to new environments. Such dispersal occurs with crowding and in autumn.

GAMETES AND FERTILIZATION

Animal gametes form in primary reproductive organs, or **gonads**. Animals with both male and female gonads are **hermaphrodites**. Tapeworms and some roundworms are simultaneous hermaphrodites, which means they produce eggs and sperm at the same time, and can fertilize themselves. Earthworms, land snails, and slugs are simultaneous hermaphrodites too, but they require a partner. So do hamlets, a type of marine fish (**FIGURE 38.1B**). During a bout of mating, hamlet partners take turns donating and receiving sperm. Other fishes are sequential hermaphrodites, meaning they switch from one sex to another during the course of a lifetime. More typically, vertebrates have separate sexes that remain fixed for life; each individual is either male or female.

Most aquatic invertebrates, fishes, and amphibians release gametes into the water, where they combine during **external fertilization**. With **internal fertilization**, sperm fertilize an egg inside the female's body (**FIGURE 38.1C**). Internal fertilization evolved in most land animals, including insects and the amniotes.

After internal fertilization, a female may lay eggs in the environment or retain them inside her body for some portion of their development. Birds eggs develop outside the mother's body, as do eggs of most insects (**FIGURE 38.2A**). Embryos of many sharks, snakes, and lizards develop while enclosed by an egg sac in the mother's body. The eggs hatch inside the mother shortly before she gives birth to well-developed young (**FIGURE 38.2B**).

NOURISHING DEVELOPING YOUNG

A developing animal requires nutrients. Most animals are nourished by **yolk**, a thick fluid rich in proteins and lipids deposited in the egg during its formation. In birds, the proportion of yolk in an egg varies with the incubation time characteristic of the species. The average bird egg, which is about one-third yolk, takes 21 days to hatch. Kiwi birds have the longest incubation period of any bird—11 weeks. Their eggs are about two-thirds yolk by volume.

Placental mammals (Section 24.7), including humans, have almost yolkless eggs. Instead, the **placenta**, an organ that forms during pregnancy, allows exchange of substances between a mother's blood and that of her developing offspring (**FIGURE 38.2C**). Nutrients in the maternal blood diffuse into an offspring's blood and support its development.

A Yolk in eggs laid in the environment. Yolk will provide offspring of this bug with all the nutrients they need to develop.

B Yolk in an egg sac inside the mother. This recently hatched lemon shark emerging from its mother's cloaca was nourished by yolk.

C A placenta. This elk is examining her newborn calf. The placenta that allowed nutrients to diffuse from her blood into the calf's blood, dangles at the *left*. The placenta is expelled after birth.

FIGURE 38.2 How developing offspring are nourished.

TAKE-HOME MESSAGE 38.1

Some animals produce genetic copies of themselves through asexual reproduction. Most reproduce sexually, producing offspring with different combinations of parental alleles. Some can switch between asexual and sexual reproduction.

A sexually reproducing animal may produce eggs and sperm at the same time, produce both types of gametes at different times, or always produce only one type of gamete.

Fertilization is usually external in aquatic animals and internal in land-dwelling ones.

Yolk deposited during egg formation sustains development of most animals. In placental mammals, nutrients diffuse from maternal blood into the blood of the developing young.

---

asexual reproduction Reproductive mode by which offspring arise from one parent only.
egg Female gamete.
external fertilization Sperm fertilize eggs after they are released into the environment.
gonad Gamete-forming organ of an animal.
hermaphrodite Animal that has both male and female gonads, either simultaneously or at different times in its life.
internal fertilization Sperm fertilize eggs inside a female's body.
placenta Of placental mammals, organ that forms during pregnancy and allows diffusion of substances between the maternal and embryonic bloodstreams.
sexual reproduction Reproductive mode by which offspring arise from two parents and inherit genes from both.
sperm Male gamete.
yolk Nutritious material in many animal eggs.

In all sexually reproducing animals, sexual reproduction produces a zygote that develops through a series of stages to adulthood. FIGURE 38.3 illustrates the stages of development in one vertebrate, the leopard frog. In this frog, as in most amphibians, fertilization is external.

GAMETES FORM AND UNITE

Animal gametes are haploid cells that form by meiosis of diploid germ cells in gonads (Section 12.2). Male gonads are **testes** (singular, testis), which produce sperm. Female gonads are **ovaries**, which produce eggs. Meiosis of a male germ cell is accompanied by equal cytoplasmic divisions, so four sperm form from each male germ cell. By contrast, meiosis of female germ cells involves unequal cytoplasmic divisions. After each meiotic division, one cell gets the bulk of the cytoplasm. As a result, meiosis of a female germ cell yields a single egg, with a large amount of cytoplasm. Sections 38.6 and 38.7 describe how human sperm and eggs form. During fertilization, an egg and a sperm unite to form a diploid zygote. Section 38.9 explains this process in detail.

CLEAVAGE

New cells arise when **cleavage** carves up a zygote by repeated mitotic cell divisions ❶. During cleavage, the number of cells increases, but the zygote's original volume remains unchanged. As a result, cells become more numerous but smaller in size.

The cells produced by cleavage are called blastomeres. Blastomeres are not identical because maternal mRNAs are not distributed evenly throughout the egg cytoplasm. As cleavage proceeds, different blastomeres receive different amounts and types of these mRNAs. As Section 10.2 explained, the localization of different maternal mRNAs in different parts of the embryo will determine which master genes are turned on where.

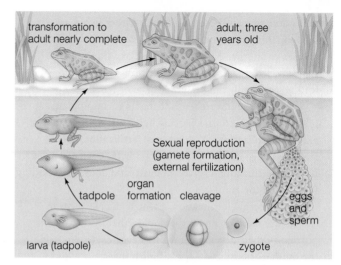

FIGURE 38.3 {Animated} Vertebrate development. *Above*, overview of reproduction and development in the leopard frog. *Opposite*, a closer look at some stages.

GASTRULATION

The end result of cleavage is a **blastula**: a ball of cells surrounding a cavity (blastocoel) full of their secretions ❷. During **gastrulation**, these cells move about and organize themselves as the layers of the **gastrula** ❸. In most animals and all vertebrates, a gastrula consists of three embryonic tissue layers, or **germ layers**. The three germ layers give rise to the same types of tissues and organs in all vertebrates (**TABLE 38.1**). This developmental similarity is evidence of a shared ancestry.

Ectoderm, the outer germ layer, forms first. It gives rise to nervous tissue and to the outer layer of skin or other body covering. **Endoderm**, the inner germ layer, is the start of the respiratory tract and gut linings. A third layer called **mesoderm** forms between the ectoderm and the endoderm. Mesoderm is the source of all muscles, connective tissues, and the circulatory system.

THE BODY TAKES SHAPE

An embryo's tissues and organs begin to form after gastrulation ❹. Many organs incorporate tissues derived from more than one germ layer. For example, the stomach's epithelial lining is derived from endoderm, and the smooth muscle that makes up the stomach wall develops from mesoderm. The next section describes tissue and organ formation in more detail.

In most animals, the individual that hatches from an egg or is born continues to grow and develop. In frogs, a larva (a tadpole) grows, then undergoes metamorphosis, a drastic remodeling of tissues into the adult form ❺.

TABLE 38.1

Fates of Vertebrate Germ Layers

Germ Layer	Organs and tissues in adult
Ectoderm (outer layer)	Outer layer (epidermis) of skin; nervous tissue
Mesoderm (middle layer)	Connective tissue of skin; skeletal, cardiac, smooth muscle; bone; cartilage; blood vessels; urinary system; gut organs; peritoneum (coelom lining); reproductive tract
Endoderm (inner layer)	Lining of gut and respiratory tract, and organs derived from these linings

CREDIT: (Table 38.1, 3) © Cengage Learning.

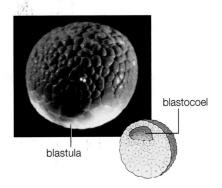

blastocoel

blastula

1 Here we show the first three divisions of cleavage, a process that carves up a zygote's cytoplasm. In this species, cleavage results in a blastula, a ball of cells with a fluid-filled cavity.

2 Cleavage is over when the blastula forms.

  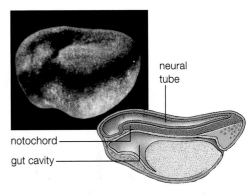

ectoderm

future gut cavity

neural plate

ectoderm

mesoderm

endoderm

neural tube

notochord

gut cavity

3 Migration of cells produces a gastrula with three primary tissue layers: an outer layer of ectoderm, a middle layer of mesoderm, and an inner layer of endoderm.

4 Organs begin to form as a primitive gut cavity opens up. A neural tube, then a notochord, and other organs form from the primary tissue layers.

Tadpole, a swimming larva with segmented muscles and a notochord extending into a tail.

Limbs grow and the tail is absorbed during metamorphosis to the adult form.

Sexually mature, four-legged adult leopard frog.

5 The frog's body form changes as it grows and its tissues specialize.

blastula Hollow ball of cells that forms as a result of cleavage.
cleavage Mitotic division of an animal cell.
ectoderm Outermost tissue layer of an animal embryo.
endoderm Innermost tissue layer of an animal embryo.
gastrula Three-layered developmental stage formed by gastrulation in an animal.
gastrulation Animal developmental process by which cell movements produce a three-layered gastrula.
germ layer One of three primary layers in an early embryo.
mesoderm Middle tissue layer of a three-layered animal embryo.
ovary Egg-producing animal gonad.
testis Sperm-producing animal gonad.

TAKE-HOME MESSAGE 38.2

Gametes form by meiosis of cells in gonads. Fertilization unites gametes to form a zygote.

A zygote undergoes cleavage, which increases the number of cells. Cleavage ends with formation of a blastula.

Rearrangement of blastula cells forms a gastrula, which in most animals has three layers.

After gastrulation, organs such as the neural tube and notochord begin to form.

Continued growth and tissue specialization produce the adult.

CELL DIFFERENTIATION

All cells in a developing animal are descended from the same zygote, so all have the same genes. How, then, do specialized tissue and organs form? From gastrulation onward, selective gene expression occurs: Different cell lineages express different subsets of genes. Selective gene expression is the key to differentiation, the process by which cells become specialized in form and function (Section 10.1).

An adult human body has about 200 differentiated cell types. As your eye developed, cells of one lineage began expressing genes for crystallin, a transparent protein. These differentiating cells formed the lens of your eye. No other cells in your body make crystallin. Keep in mind that a differentiated cell still retains the entire genome.

That is why it is possible to clone an adult animal from one of its differentiated cells (Section 8.6).

EMBRYONIC INDUCTION

Intercellular signals encourage selective gene expression. By a process called **embryonic induction**, signals from one subset of cells affect the developmental pathway of other cells. Induction often involves **morphogens**, which are substances (usually proteins) that affect gene expression in a concentration-dependent manner. Cells nearest the source of a morphogen are exposed to a high concentration of morphogen and express one set of genes. Cells farther from the source of the morphogen are exposed to a lower morphogen concentration, and express different genes.

The bicoid protein of fruit flies is an example of a morphogen. *Bicoid* is a maternal effect gene, meaning it is expressed during egg production and its product influences development. During egg production, bicoid mRNA accumulates at one end of an egg. After fertilization, this mRNA is translated into bicoid protein. The secreted bicoid protein becomes distributed in a gradient along the length of the egg. As development continues, orientation of this gradient determines which part of the embryo will become the front of the animal, and which will be the back. Where bicoid protein concentration is highest, a zygote expresses genes that cause development of anterior body structures. Where the concentration of bicoid protein is low and other morphogens are high, the zygote expresses genes that cause development of posterior body parts.

Bicoid is one of the master genes whose effects on fly development were described in Section 10.2. It is a transcription factor that affects expression of homeotic genes. As you may recall, homeotic genes are master genes whose expression results in the formation of specific body parts in local regions of the developing individual.

Embryonic induction also plays a role in formation of the vertebrate neural tube, the embryonic forerunner of the spinal cord and brain (Section 29.9). The neural tube develops from ectoderm and its formation is regulated by morphogens secreted by the notochord, which lies beneath it (**FIGURE 38.4**).

Development of the neural tube begins when the region of ectoderm overlying the notochord thickens, forming a neural plate ❶. Next, cells at the edges of the neural plate become wedge-shaped as actin microfilaments at one end of each cell shorten. These changes in cell shape cause the edges of the neural plate to fold inward, forming a depression called the neural groove ❷. With continued folding, edges of the neural plate meet at the midline and fuse to form the neural tube ❸.

FIGURE 38.4 {Animated} Neural tube formation.

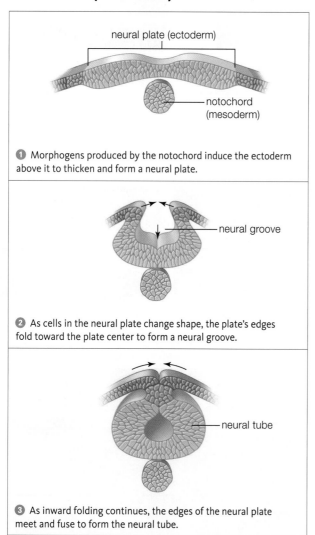

❶ Morphogens produced by the notochord induce the ectoderm above it to thicken and form a neural plate.

❷ As cells in the neural plate change shape, the plate's edges fold toward the plate center to form a neural groove.

❸ As inward folding continues, the edges of the neural plate meet and fuse to form the neural tube.

FIGURE 38.5 {Animated} Paw development in a mouse embryo. The yellow stain indicates regions where cells are undergoing apoptosis.

Cell shape changes are one mechanism of morphogenesis, the developmental process that shapes tissues and organs and determines their position within the animal body. We turn next to two additional mechanisms.

APOPTOSIS

Programmed cell death, or **apoptosis**, helps sculpt body parts. Apoptosis occurs when chemical signals cause a cell to carry out a predictable sequence of self-destruction of its parts. During apoptosis, an internal or external signal sets in motion a chain of reactions that result in the activation of self-destructive enzymes. Some of these enzymes chop up structural proteins such as cytoskeletal proteins and the histones that organize DNA. Others snip apart nucleic acids. As a result of damage to its components, the cell dies.

Apoptosis shapes a mouse paw (or human hand), which starts out as a platelike structure (**FIGURE 38.5**). As development progresses, digits become connected solely by webs of tissue. Eventually, apoptosis eliminates the webbing, freeing the individual digits. Apoptosis also makes the tail of a tadpole disappear during metamorphosis. As you will learn later in this chapter, it also eliminates the tail that forms early in human development.

CELL MIGRATIONS

Cell migrations also play a role in morphogenesis. For example, ectodermal cells that form at the tip of the neural tube (a region called the neural crest) migrate outward to positions throughout the body. The descendants of neural crest cells include the neurons and glial cells of the peripheral nervous system, and the melanocytes in skin.

Cells travel by inching along in an amoeba-like fashion (**FIGURE 38.6**). Assembly of actin microfilaments at one edge of the cell causes that portion of the cell to protrude forward. Adhesion proteins in the plasma membrane then anchor the advancing portion of the cell to a protein in the membrane of another cell or in the extracellular matrix.

A cell adheres to one point and protrudes forward.

The protruding portion of the cell attaches to a new point.

The trailing portion of the cell releases its grip.

FIGURE 38.6 Cell migration.

Once the front of a cell is thus anchored, adhesion proteins in the trailing part of the cell release their grip, and the rear of the cell is drawn forward. How does the cell know where to go? It may move in response to a concentration gradient of some chemical signal, or it may follow a "trail" of molecules that its adhesion proteins recognize. The cell stops migrating when it reaches a region where its adhesion proteins hold it tightly in place.

apoptosis Mechanism of cell suicide.
embryonic induction Embryonic cells produce signals that alter the behavior of neighboring cells.
morphogen Substance that regulates development by affecting cells in a concentration-dependent manner.

TAKE-HOME MESSAGE 38.3

All cells in an embryo have the same genes, but they express different subsets of this genome. Selective gene expression is the basis of cell differentiation.

Localization of maternal mRNAs within an egg results in localization of proteins within an embryo. Diffusion of these proteins creates a concentration gradient that influences gene expression.

Changes in cell shape, death of specific cells, and movement of cells cause tissues and organs to develop in specific shapes and in particular positions.

CREDITS: (5) Courtesy of © Paul Martin; (14 top right, (6) From Russell/Wolfe/Hertz/Starr, Biology, 1E. © 2008 Cengage Learning.

A GENERAL MODEL FOR ANIMAL DEVELOPMENT

By studying development of a diverse array of animals, researchers have come up with a general model. The key point of the model is this: Where and when particular genes are expressed determines how an animal body develops.

First, molecules confined to different areas of an unfertilized egg induce localized expression of master genes in the zygote. Products of these master genes (Section 10.2) diffuse outward, so concentration gradients for these products form along the head-to-tail and top-to-bottom axes of the developing embryo.

Second, depending on where they fall within these concentration gradients, cells in the embryo activate or suppress other master genes. The products of these genes become distributed in gradients, which affect expression of other genes, and so on.

Third, this positional information affects expression of homeotic genes that regulate which body parts appear where. One homeotic gene expressed by cells in the notochord encodes a morphogen that stimulates neural tube development in vertebrates. Like many homeotic genes, this gene occurs in other animals, including fruit flies.

CONSTRAINTS ON BODY PLANS

The developmental model described above helps explain how animal body plans can evolve, because changes in genes that regulate development will alter body form. However, some factors limit the changes that can occur.

First, physical constraints limit body form. Large body size cannot evolve in an animal that does not have circulatory and respiratory mechanisms sufficient to service cells far from the body surface. Second, an existing body framework imposes architectural constraints. For example, the ancestors of all modern land vertebrates had a body plan with four limbs. The evolution of wings in birds and bats occurred through modification of existing forelimbs, not by sprouting new limbs. Although it might be advantageous to have both wings and arms, no living or fossil vertebrate with both has been discovered.

Finally, there are phylogenetic constraints on body plans. These constraints are imposed by interactions among genes that regulate development in a lineage. As master genes evolved together, their interactions became more enmeshed in pathways that unravel if one component is not working; their interactions determine the basic body form. Mutations that dramatically alter these interactions are usually lethal.

Consider how paired bones and skeletal muscles become arrayed along a vertebrate's head-to-tail axis. This pattern arises early in development, when the mesoderm on either

A Normal zebrafish embryo with somites, bumps of mesoderm that give rise to bone and muscle.

B Embryo with a mutation that prevents somite formation. It will die in early development.

FIGURE 38.7 Lethal effect of a mutation in a zebrafish gene (*fused somites*) that functions in early development.

side of the embryo's neural tube becomes divided into blocks of cells called somites (**FIGURE 38.7A**). The somites will later develop into bones and skeletal muscles. A complex pathway involving many genes governs somite formation. Any mutation that disrupts this pathway so that somites do not form is lethal during development (**FIGURE 38.7B**). Thus, no vertebrates have an unsegmented body plan.

The number of somites that develop, and thus the length of the body, does vary among species. A zebrafish embryo has 31 somites; a cornsnake embryo has more than 300. Such differences in the number of somites arise in part from differences in how fast somites form. In snakes, somites form much more quickly than they do in zebrafish. Modifications in the rate of a developmental process often lead to differences in body form.

In short, mutations that affected development led to the variety of forms among animal lineages that we see today. These mutations brought about morphological changes through the modification of existing developmental pathways, rather than by blazing entirely new genetic trails.

TAKE-HOME MESSAGE 38.4

In all animals, cytoplasmic localization affects expression of sets of master genes shared by most animal groups. The products of these genes cause embryonic cells to form tissues and organs at certain locations.

Once a developmental pathway evolves, mutations that interrupt it can have drastic or lethal consequences.

Evolutionary changes in body form involve modifications in the details of developmental pathways.

Now that you have a general understanding of animal reproduction and development, we will turn our attention to the details of these processes in humans. In this section, we provide an overview of human development and define its stages. Prenatal (before birth) and postnatal (after birth) stages are listed in **TABLE 38.2**. The remainder of this chapter describes human reproductive anatomy and discusses human reproductive function—from gamete formation to birth—in more detail.

Human prenatal development normally lasts 38 to 40 weeks from the time of fertilization. It is sometimes discussed in terms of trimesters. The first trimester includes months one through three, the second trimester, months four through six, and the third trimester, months seven through nine.

In discussing animals, the term **embryo** generally refers to an individual from the time of first cleavage to the time when it hatches or is born. With regard to humans, the term embryo is often reserved for the period from 2 weeks to 8 weeks after fertilization. From week nine until birth, the individual is referred to as a **fetus**. During embryonic development, the human body plan is set in place and organs form. During fetal development, the organs mature and begin to function.

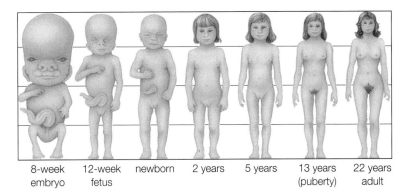

| 8-week embryo | 12-week fetus | newborn | 2 years | 5 years | 13 years (puberty) | 22 years adult |

FIGURE 38.8 Proportional changes during human development.

In humans, a birth before 37 weeks is considered premature. Premature birth increases the risk of birth defects and early death, although technological advances have allowed us to keep premature infants alive at increasingly early stages. To date, the earliest a child has been born and survived to adulthood is 21 weeks. Survival of children born before 28 weeks (7 months) is uncertain, mainly because the lungs have not fully developed. By 36 weeks, the survival rate is 95 percent.

After birth, the human body continues to grow and its body parts continue to change in proportion (**FIGURE 38.8**). During postnatal development, the head grows much more slowly than other body parts, whereas the legs grow much faster. Compared to other primates, humans have long legs for their body size. Our long-legged body is an adaptation to bipedal locomotion (upright walking). By about age 7, the legs are about 50 percent of the total body length, the proportion required for efficient walking.

Sexual maturation occurs at **puberty**. At this time gonads increase their production of sex hormones and begin to produce gametes. Secondary sexual characteristics appear. Generally bones stop growing shortly after completion of puberty. The brain is the last organ to be fully mature: Parts of the brain continue to develop until a person is about 20 years old.

embryo In animals, a developing individual from first cleavage until hatching or birth; in humans, usually refers to an individual during weeks 2 to 8 of development.
fetus Developing human from about 9 weeks until birth.
puberty Period when reproductive organs begin to function.

TAKE-HOME MESSAGE 38.5

Human prenatal development takes about 40 weeks and encompasses embryonic development and fetal development.

Humans sex organs begin to function at puberty.

TABLE 38.2

Stages of Human Development

Prenatal period

Zygote	Single cell resulting from fusion of sperm nucleus and egg nucleus at fertilization.
Blastocyst (blastula)	Ball of cells with surface layer, fluid-filled cavity, and inner cell mass.
Embryo	Individual from completion of implantation (2 weeks) until the end of week 8.
Fetus	Individual from week 9 until birth.

Postnatal period

Newborn	Individual during the first two weeks after birth.
Infant	Individual from two weeks to fifteen months.
Child	Individual from infancy to about twelve years.
Pubescent	Individual at puberty, when secondary sexual traits develop.
Adolescent	Individual from puberty until adulthood.
Adult	Begins between 18 and 25 years; bone formation and growth cease. Changes proceed slowly after this.
Old age	Aging processes result in tissue deterioration.

CREDIT: (Table 38.2, 8) © Cengage Learning.

38.6 WHAT ARE FUNCTIONS OF A MAN'S REPRODUCTIVE ORGANS?

During embryonic development, a man's testes (the male gonads) form in his abdomen, then descend into the scrotum, a pouch suspended below the pelvic girdle (**FIGURE 38.9**). Smooth muscle in the scrotum wall adjusts the position of the testes to keep them at the optimal temperature for making sperm, which is just a bit cooler than core body temperature. A testis and the scrotum that enclose it are collectively called a testicle.

At puberty, a man's testes enlarge and begin producing a large amount of **testosterone**, the main sex hormone in males. The increase in testosterone stimulates development of secondary sex characteristics such as facial hair. It also triggers formation of sperm inside the **seminiferous tubules** that make up the bulk of the testes.

Diploid male germ cells line the inner wall of each seminiferous tube (**FIGURE 38.10 ❶**). Mitosis of the germ cells produces diploid primary spermatocytes ❷. Meiosis of spermatocytes yields spermatids that differentiate to become sperm, the mature male gametes ❸. Nurse cells inside seminiferous tubules support sperm as they develop. Cells between seminiferous tubules make testosterone. Two anterior pituitary hormones, follicle-stimulating hormone (FSH) and luteinizing hormone (LH), govern testosterone secretion and sperm production. As you will learn, these hormones also act on ovaries. A releasing hormone from the hypothalamus governs secretion of LH and FSH (Section 31.3).

After sperm form, cilia push them into a coiled duct called the **epididymis** (plural, epididymides). Secretions from the epididymis wall help sperm mature. The final portion of each epididymis is continuous with a **vas deferens** (plural, vasa deferentia). The vasa deferentia, the longest ducts of the male reproductive tract, convey sperm to a short ejaculatory duct. This duct connects to the urethra, which extends through the penis to the body surface.

The **penis**, the male organ of intercourse, has a rounded head (the glans) at the end of a narrower shaft. Nerve endings in the glans make it highly sensitive to touch. The foreskin, a retractable tube of skin, covers the glans when a man is not sexually excited. In some cultures, males undergo circumcision, which is surgical removal of the foreskin. Inside the penis, connective tissue encloses three elongated cylinders of spongy tissue. When a male is sexually excited, blood flows into the spongy tissue faster than it flows out, so fluid pressure rises inside the penis and it stiffens.

Sperm stored in the epididymides and first part of the vasa deferentia continue their journey toward the body surface only when a male reaches the peak of sexual excitement and ejaculates. During ejaculation, rhythmic smooth muscle contractions propel sperm and exocrine gland secretions out of the body as a thick, white fluid called **semen**. Sperm makes up less than 5 percent of the semen's volume. The main component of semen is fluid

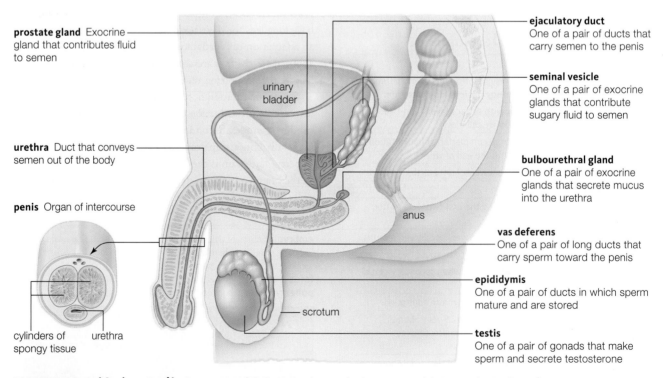

prostate gland Exocrine gland that contributes fluid to semen

urinary bladder

urethra Duct that conveys semen out of the body

penis Organ of intercourse

cylinders of spongy tissue   urethra

ejaculatory duct One of a pair of ducts that carry semen to the penis

seminal vesicle One of a pair of exocrine glands that contribute sugary fluid to semen

bulbourethral gland One of a pair of exocrine glands that secrete mucus into the urethra

anus

vas deferens One of a pair of long ducts that carry sperm toward the penis

epididymis One of a pair of ducts in which sperm mature and are stored

scrotum

testis One of a pair of gonads that make sperm and secrete testosterone

FIGURE 38.9 {Animated} Components of the human male reproductive system and their reproductive functions.

CREDIT: (9) © Cengage Learning.

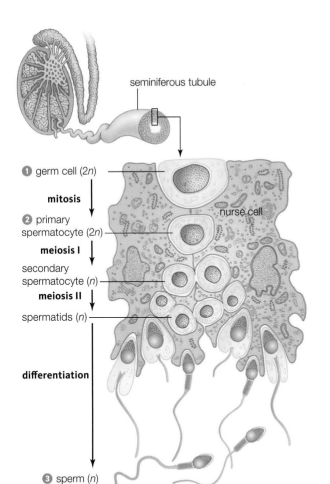

seminiferous tubule

① germ cell (2*n*)

mitosis

② primary spermatocyte (2*n*)

nurse cell

meiosis I

secondary spermatocyte (*n*)

meiosis II

spermatids (*n*)

differentiation

③ sperm (*n*)

FIGURE 38.10 {Animated} Sperm formation in the testes.

secreted by exocrine glands called **seminal vesicles**. Fructose (a sugar) in seminal fluid serves as the energy source for sperm. Secretions from the **prostate gland**, a walnut-sized exocrine gland that encircles the urethra, are the other major component of semen volume. Prostate secretions help raise the pH of the female reproductive tract, making it more hospitable to sperm. Other exocrine glands, called bulbourethral glands, secrete an alkaline mucus that neutralizes any residue of acidic urine in the urethra.

epididymis Duct where sperm mature; empties into a vas deferens.
penis Male organ of intercourse.
prostate gland Exocrine gland that contributes to semen.
semen Sperm mixed with secretions from exocrine glands.
seminal vesicles Exocrine glands that add sugary fluid to semen.
seminiferous tubules In testes, tiny tubes where sperm form.
testosterone Hormone secreted by testes; functions in sperm formation and development of male secondary sex characteristics.
vas deferens One of a pair of long ducts that carry mature sperm to the ejaculatory duct.

CREDITS: (10) top, From Starr/Evers/Starr, Biology Today and Tomorrow with Physiology, 4E. © 2013 Cengage Learning; bottom, © Cengage Learning; (in text) top, © Stewart Nicol; bottom, © Lucy Cooke/National Geographic Creative.

PEOPLE MATTER

National Geographic Grantee
DR. STEWART C. NICOL

Stewart Nicol studies spiny, ant-eating monotremes called echidnas. Monotreme means "one opening," and refers to the cloaca of these egg-laying mammals. A male monotreme's penis functions solely in reproduction, so he extends it out through his cloaca only when ready to mate.

In a short-beaked echidna (left), the male's penis is large for his size and forked, with two rosette-shaped openings at the tip of each fork. Reptiles and other monotremes have a forked penis with two openings, but the short-beaked echidna's four-barreled penis is unique.

Nicol's research has revealed that both sexes of short-beaked echidnas have multiple mates. This may be why short-beaked echidna males have large testes for their body size. Bigger testes allows production of more sperm. The more sperm a male can put into a female, the greater the chance that one of his sperm will fertilize her egg. Nicol has found evidence of sexual competition among males. In Tasmania, some impatient males mate with females who are still hibernating. Echidnas are one of the few mammals that can sustain a pregnancy during hibernation. As hibernating females appear unable to choose whom they mate with, Nicol is now investigating whether females have a mechanism for rejecting sperm.

TAKE-HOME MESSAGE 38.6

Testes, the primary reproductive organs in human males, produce sperm and make the sex hormone testosterone.

Sperm form by meiosis in seminiferous tubules.

Ducts convey sperm from a testis to the body surface. Exocrine glands that empty into these ducts provide most of the volume of semen.

The penis contains cylinders of spongy tissue that engorge with blood during sexual excitement.

FEMALE REPRODUCTIVE ANATOMY

A female's gonads—her ovaries—lie deep inside her pelvic cavity (**FIGURE 38.11A, B**). Ovaries are about the size and shape of almonds. They produce and release **oocytes**, which are immature eggs. They also secrete estrogens and progesterone, the main sex hormones in females. **Estrogens** maintain the female reproductive tract and trigger the development of female sexual traits. **Progesterone** prepares the reproductive tract for pregnancy.

Adjacent to each ovary is an **oviduct**, a hollow tube that connects the ovary to the uterus. (Oviducts are also known as Fallopian tubes.) An oocyte released from an ovary is drawn into an oviduct by movement of fingerlike projections at the oviduct's entrance. Cilia in the oviduct lining then propel the oocyte along the length of the tube. Fertilization usually occurs in an oviduct.

Each oviduct opens into the **uterus**, a hollow, pear-shaped organ above the urinary bladder. A thick layer of smooth muscle called the myometrium makes up most of the uterine wall. The uterine lining, or endometrium, consists of glandular epithelium, connective tissues, and blood vessels. A woman becomes pregnant when a blastula attaches to the endometrium and continues its development in the uterus.

The lowest portion of the uterus is a narrowed region called the **cervix**, which opens into the vagina. The **vagina**, which extends from the cervix to the body's surface, functions as the organ of intercourse and the birth canal.

Two pairs of liplike skin folds called labia enclose the surface openings of the vagina and urethra (**FIGURE 38.11C**). *Labia* is Latin for lips. Adipose tissue fills the labia majora, which are the thick outer folds. The thin inner

FIGURE 38.11 {**Animated**} Reproductive system of the human female.

A Location of reproductive organs in pelvic cavity.

C External view of reproductive organs.

Ovary One of two female gonads. Makes eggs and secretes female sex hormones (estrogens and progesterone).

Oviduct One of a pair of ducts through which oocytes are propelled from an ovary to the uterus; usual site of fertilization.

Uterus Womb, chamber in which an embryo develops. Includes myometrium (smooth muscle layer) and endometrium (epithelial lining). Narrowed lower portion (the cervix) secretes mucus into the vagina.

Vagina Organ of sexual intercourse: birth canal.

Clitoris Highly sensitive erectile organ. Only the tip is externally visible; bulk of the organ extends internally on either side of the vagina.

Labium minus One of a pair of inner skin folds (the labia minora).

Labium majus One of a pair of fatty outer skin folds (the labia majora).

B Components of the system and their functions.

CREDITS: (11A) From Starr/Taggart, Biology: The Unity and Diversity of Life, 7E. © 1995 Cengage Learning; (11B) From Starr/Taggart/Evers/Starr, Biology, 13E. © 2013 Cengage Learning; (11C) From Starr/Evers/Starr, Biology Today and Tomorrow with Physiology, 4E. © 2013 Cengage Learning.

ovary

follicle cells   primary oocyte

polar body   secondary oocyte

secondary oocyte

corpus luteum

❶ One of many immature follicles in an ovary. Each consists of a primary oocyte and the surrounding follicle cells.

❷ A fluid-filled cavity begins to form in the follicle's cell layer.

❸ The primary oocyte completes meiosis I and divides unequally, forming a secondary oocyte and a polar body.

❹ Ovulation. Rupture of the mature follicle releases a secondary oocyte coated with secreted protein and follicle cells.

❺ A corpus luteum develops from follicle cells left behind after ovulation.

❻ If pregnancy does not occur, the corpus luteum degenerates.

FIGURE 38.12 {Animated} Events during one ovarian cycle.

folds are the labia minora. An erectile organ called the clitoris lies near the anterior junction of the labia minora. The clitoris and penis develop from the same embryonic tissue and both are highly sensitive to tactile stimulation.

EGG PRODUCTION AND RELEASE

Unlike a male's germ cells, a female's germ cells do not usually divide after she is born. Mitosis of germ cells before her birth produces primary oocytes. A primary oocyte is an immature egg that has entered meiosis but stopped in prophase I (Section 12.3). When a female reaches puberty, hormonal changes prompt her primary oocytes to mature, one at a time, in an approximately 28-day ovarian cycle.

FIGURE 38.12 shows one round of this cycle. A developing oocyte and the cells around it constitute an **ovarian follicle** ❶. In the first part of the ovarian cycle, the primary oocyte enlarges and secretes a layer of proteins. Follicle cells surrounding the primary oocyte divide repeatedly to form a fluid-filled cavity ❷.

Often, more than one follicle starts to develop, but usually only one becomes fully mature. In that follicle, the primary oocyte completes meiosis I and undergoes unequal cytoplasmic division. This division produces a large secondary oocyte and a tiny **polar body** ❸, which will eventually disintegrate. The secondary oocyte begins meiosis II, then halts in metaphase II. It will not complete meiosis and become a mature egg until fertilization. At that time, a second polar body will form. It too will disintegrate.

About two weeks after the follicle began to mature, its wall ruptures and **ovulation** occurs: The secondary oocyte, polar body, and some surrounding follicle cells are ejected into the adjacent oviduct ❹. The oocyte must meet up with sperm within 24 hours for fertilization to occur.

Meanwhile, in the ovary, the cells of the ruptured follicle develop into a hormone-secreting **corpus luteum** ❺. (The name means "yellow body" in Latin and refers to its yellow color.) If pregnancy does not occur, the corpus luteum will break down ❻, and a new follicle will begin to mature.

cervix Narrow part of uterus that connects to the vagina.
corpus luteum Hormone-secreting structure that forms from follicle cells left behind after ovulation.
estrogens Hormones secreted by ovaries; causes development of female sexual traits and maintains the reproductive tract.
oocyte Immature egg.
ovarian follicle In animals, immature egg and surrounding cells.
oviduct Duct between an ovary and the uterus.
ovulation Release of a secondary oocyte from an ovary.
polar body Tiny cell produced by unequal cytoplasmic division during egg production.
progesterone Hormone secreted by ovaries; prepares the uterus for pregnancy.
uterus Muscular chamber where offspring develop; womb.
vagina Female organ of intercourse and birth canal.

TAKE-HOME MESSAGE 38.7

Ovaries, the primary reproductive organs in human females, produce eggs and secrete estrogen and progesterone.

Before birth, mitosis of female germ cells produces immature eggs. These oocytes begin meiosis, but stop in prophase I.

At puberty, primary oocytes start to mature into secondary oocytes, one at a time, on an approximately monthly basis.

A secondary oocyte released from an ovarian follicle by ovulation enters an oviduct. The oviduct conveys the oocyte to the uterus. If fertilization occurs, the resulting embryo will complete development in the uterus.

The vagina serves as the female organ of intercourse and as the birth canal.

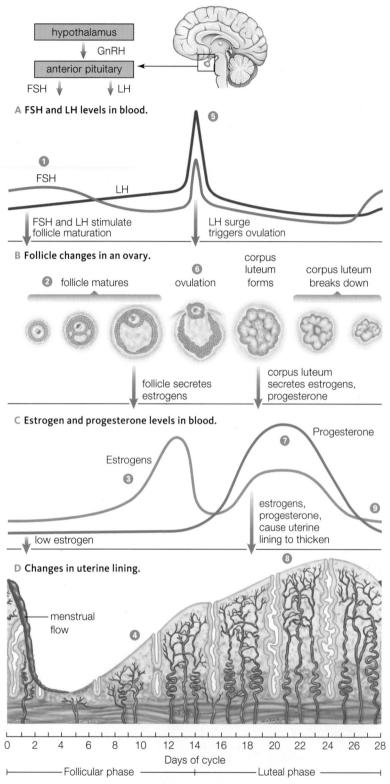

A **FSH and LH levels in blood.**

FSH

LH

FSH and LH stimulate follicle maturation

LH surge triggers ovulation

B **Follicle changes in an ovary.**

② follicle matures

ovulation

corpus luteum forms

corpus luteum breaks down

follicle secretes estrogens

corpus luteum secretes estrogens, progesterone

C **Estrogen and progesterone levels in blood.**

Progesterone

Estrogens

estrogens, progesterone, cause uterine lining to thicken

low estrogen

D **Changes in uterine lining.**

menstrual flow

| 0 | 2 | 4 | 6 | 8 | 10 | 12 | 14 | 16 | 18 | 20 | 22 | 24 | 26 | 28 |

Days of cycle

Follicular phase — Luteal phase

FIGURE 38.13 {**Animated**} Reproductive cycle of a human female. Day 1 of the cycle is the onset of menstruation.

 FIGURE IT OUT: What is the source of the progesterone secreted after ovulation?

Answer: The corpus luteum

OVARIAN AND MENSTRUAL CYCLES

The ovarian cycle described in the previous section is coordinated with cyclic changes in the uterus. We refer to the approximately monthly changes in the uterus as the **menstrual cycle**. The first day of the menstrual cycle is marked by onset of **menstruation**: the flow of bits of uterine lining and a small amount of blood from the uterus, through the cervix, and out of the vagina.

Hormones control the ovarian and menstrual cycles (**TABLE 38.3** and **FIGURE 38.13**). When the cycles begin, secretion of gonadotropin-releasing hormone (GnRH) by the hypothalamus is stimulating the pituitary to release FSH and LH ❶. As its name would suggest, **follicle-stimulating hormone** stimulates an ovarian follicle to begin maturing ❷. The interval of follicle maturation that precedes ovulation is called the follicular phase of the menstrual cycle. During follicle maturation, cells around the oocyte secrete estrogens ❸. Estrogens bind to cells of the endometrium and signal them to begin mitosis. The resulting cell divisions thicken the endometrium ❹.

As the level of estrogens increases, a positive feedback loop develops. Increased estrogen causes the hypothalamus to release more GnRH, so the pituitary releases more FSH, and the follicle grows and produces more estrogens. The rise in estrogens encourages the anterior pituitary to release **luteinizing hormone** (LH), which in females has roles in ovulation and formation of the corpus luteum.

At about the midpoint in the cycle, the increased level of estrogens in the blood causes a surge in LH secretion by the pituitary ❺. The surge of LH causes the primary oocyte to complete meiosis I and undergo cytoplasmic division. It also causes the follicle to swell and burst. Thus, the midcycle surge of LH is the trigger for ovulation ❻.

The luteal phase begins immediately after ovulation. At first the concentration of estrogens declines a bit, then LH stimulates corpus luteum formation. As the luteal phase continues, the corpus luteum secretes estrogens and a lot of progesterone ❼. Estrogens and progesterone cause the uterine lining to thicken and encourage blood vessels to grow through it. The uterus is now ready for pregnancy ❽.

Secretion of progesterone by the corpus luteum has a negative feedback effect on the hypothalamus and pituitary. The high level of progesterone causes a reduction in the secretion of FSH and LH, thus preventing maturation of other follicles and inhibiting additional ovulations.

If fertilization does not occur, the declining level of LH causes the corpus luteum to break down. As it does, estrogen and progesterone levels plummet ❾. In the uterus, the decline in estrogens and progesterone causes the thickened lining to break down, and menstruation begins.

TABLE 38.3

Events of a Menstrual Cycle Lasting Twenty-Eight Days

Phase	Events	Day of Cycle
Pre-ovulation (follicular phase)	Menstruation; endometrium breaks down	1–5
	FSH stimulates follicle growth, estrogen level rises, endometrium is rebuilt	6–13
Ovulation	High level of estrogens causes LH surge that triggers completion of meiosis in oocyte and rupture of the follicle	14
Post-ovulation (luteal phase)	Corpus luteum forms, secretes estrogens and progesterone; endometrium thickens; FSH and LH secretion are inhibited.	15–25
	Corpus luteum degenerates; estrogens and progesterone decline, allowing FSH and LH to begin to rise	26–28

Blood and endometrial tissue flow out of the vagina for 3 to 6 days. At the same time, the pituitary begins to increase its secretion of FSH and LH once again.

FROM PUBERTY TO MENOPAUSE

When a woman enters puberty, increased estrogen secretion by her ovaries results in the development of female secondary sexual traits such as breasts and pubic hair. She also begins to menstruate.

During their reproductive years, many women regularly experience discomfort a week or two before they menstruate. Estrogens and progesterone released during the cycle cause milk ducts to widen, making breasts feel tender. Other tissues may swell also, because premenstrual changes influence aldosterone secretion. This hormone stimulates reabsorption of sodium and, indirectly, water (Section 37.3).

estrous cycle Reproductive cycle in which the uterine lining thickens, and, if pregnancy does not occur, is reabsorbed.
follicle-stimulating hormone (FSH) Anterior pituitary hormone with roles in ovarian follicle maturation and sperm production.
luteinizing hormone (LH) Anterior pituitary hormone with roles in ovulation, corpus luteum formation, and sperm production.
menopause Permanent cessation of menstrual cycles.
menstrual cycle Reproductive cycle in which the uterus lining thickens and then, if pregnancy does not occur, is shed.
menstruation Flow of shed uterine tissue out of the vagina.

CREDIT: (Table 38.3) © Cengage Learning.

Cycle-associated hormonal changes can also cause depression, irritability, anxiety, and headaches, and can disrupt sleep. Regular recurrence of these symptoms is known as premenstrual syndrome (PMS). Use of oral contraceptives minimizes hormone swings and therefore PMS.

During menstruation, secretion of local signaling molecules called prostaglandins stimulates contractions of smooth muscle in the uterine wall. Many women do not feel the muscle contractions, but others experience a dull ache or sharp pains commonly known as menstrual cramps. Severe pain and heavy bleeding during menstruation are not normal and may be caused by benign tumors in the uterus called fibroids.

A woman enters **menopause** when all the follicles in her ovaries have either been released during menstrual cycles or have disintegrated as a result of normal aging. With no follicles left to mature, production of estrogen and progesterone is dramatically diminished and menstrual cycles cease. Menopause is rare among animals. It is known to occur only in humans and two species of whales.

ESTROUS CYCLES

All female placental mammals replace their uterine lining on a cyclic basis. However, most have an estrous cycle, rather than a menstrual cycle. In an **estrous cycle**, the endometrial lining is reabsorbed rather than shed, so the female never menstruates. Females with an estrous cycle are usually sexually receptive only when they can conceive, a period known as estrus or heat. The length of estrous cycles varies among species. In dogs it is about six months, whereas in mice it is six days.

In many species, a female in estrus produces signals that alert males of the species to her condition. Often a female's labia swell and she produces a discharge containing pheromones that help attract potential mates. For example, a female dog releases a thin, bloody discharge from her vagina when she is in heat.

TAKE-HOME MESSAGE 38.8

Cyclic changes in hormone levels govern the female ovarian and menstrual cycles. A releasing hormone from the hypothalamus causes secretion of FSH and LH by the anterior pituitary. FSH hormones cause follicle maturation and a surge in LH causes ovulation.

Prior to ovulation, estrogens and progesterone secreted by a maturing follicle cause the lining of the uterus to thicken. After ovulation, progesterone secreted by the corpus luteum encourages additional thickening.

If pregnancy does not occur, the corpus luteum breaks down, hormone levels drop, the endometrial lining is shed, and the cycle begins again.

SEXUAL INTERCOURSE

For males, intercourse requires an erection. The penis consists mostly of long cylinders of spongy tissue. When a male is not sexually aroused, his penis is limp, because the arteries that transport blood to its spongy tissue remain constricted. When he becomes aroused, increased activity of sympathetic nerves (Section 29.7) causes smooth muscle in the walls of these arteries to relax so that the arteries dilate. The resulting inflow of blood expands the spongy tissue and compresses veins that carry blood out of the penis. Inward blood flow now exceeds outward flow, causing an increase in internal fluid pressure. This pressure enlarges and stiffens the penis so it can be inserted into a female's vagina.

The ability to obtain and sustain an erection peaks during the late teens. As a male ages, he may have episodes of erectile dysfunction. With this disorder, the penis does not stiffen enough for intercourse. Men who have circulatory problems are most often affected. Smoking increases the risk of circulatory problems, so smokers are especially likely to have erectile dysfunction.

Drugs prescribed for erectile dysfunction act by relaxing smooth muscle in the walls of arterioles supplying the penis. However, they also dilate blood vessels elsewhere in the body and so should not be taken without a prescription.

When a woman becomes sexually excited, blood flow to the vaginal wall, labia, and clitoris increases. Glands in the cervix secrete mucus and glands on the labia (the equivalent of a male's bulbourethral glands) produce a lubricating fluid. The vagina itself does not have any glandular tissue. It is moistened by mucus from the cervix and by plasma fluid that seeps out between epithelial cells of the vaginal lining.

During intercourse, increased signals from sympathetic nerves raise the heart rate and breathing rate in both partners. The posterior pituitary steps up its oxytocin secretion. The oxytocin acts in the brain, inhibiting signals from the amygdala, the part of the brain that controls fear and anxiety (Section 29.11).

Continued mechanical stimulation of the penis or clitoris can lead to orgasm. During orgasm, endorphins flood the brain and evoke feelings of pleasure. At the same time, release of oxytocin causes rhythmic contractions of smooth muscle in both the male and female reproductive tract. In males, orgasm is usually accompanied by ejaculation, in which contracting muscles force the semen out of the penis.

THE SPERM'S JOURNEY

An ejaculation can put 300 million sperm into the vagina. FIGURE 38.14 shows the structure of a mature sperm. It is a haploid cell with a "head" packed full of DNA and tipped by an enzyme-containing cap. The enzymes help

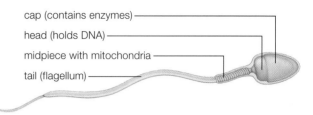

cap (contains enzymes)
head (holds DNA)
midpiece with mitochondria
tail (flagellum)

FIGURE 38.14 Structure of a human sperm.

a sperm penetrate an oocyte by partly digesting away its outer layer. At its other end, the sperm has a flagellum that allows it to swim toward an egg. The sperm does not have ribosomes, endoplasmic reticulum, or Golgi bodies. However, its midsection contains many mitochondria that supply the ATP required for flagellar movement. While in a male's body, sperm produce ATP by breaking down the fructose in seminal vesicle secretions. Once sperm enter the female reproductive tract, they take up carbohydrates from their environment to fuel movement.

To travel from the vagina into the uterus, sperm must swim through a canal in the center of the cervix. During parts of the reproductive cycle when a woman's estrogen level is low, a thick plug of acidic mucus bars the passage of sperm through this canal. As the estrogen level rises before ovulation, the cervix becomes more sperm-friendly. It begins secreting a thinner, more alkaline mucus containing glucose that the sperm can use as fuel. Even so, passing through cervical mucus is challenging, so only the strongest sperm pass through the cervix into the chamber of the uterus.

Once sperm are in the uterus, contractions of smooth muscle help move them upwards, toward the oviducts. Ovulation occurs in one ovary at a time, so only one oviduct leads to an oocyte. However, sperm randomly enter one oviduct or the other. As a result, half of them have no chance of encountering an oocyte.

FERTILIZATION

Fertilization usually happens in the upper part of an oviduct (FIGURE 38.15 ❶.). Of the millions of sperm ejaculated into the vagina, only a few hundred make it this far. Sperm live for three days after ejaculation, so fertilization can occur even if intercourse takes place a few days before ovulation.

A secondary oocyte released at ovulation retains a wrapping of follicle cells. Beneath those cells is a jelly coat composed of secreted glycoproteins ❷. The sperm makes its way between the follicle cells to the jelly coat. The plasma membrane of the sperm's head has receptors that bind species-specific proteins in the jelly. Binding these proteins triggers the release of protein-digesting enzymes from the

CREDIT: (14) From Starr/Taggart/Evers/Starr, Biology, 13E. © 2013 Cengage Learning.

1 Fertilization usually occurs in the oviduct. Sperm swim from the vagina, through the uterus, then up an oviduct (blue arrows).

Inside an oviduct, the sperm surround a secondary oocyte that was released by ovulation.

2 Enzymes released from the cap of each sperm clear a path through the jelly coat. Penetration of the secondary oocyte by a sperm causes the oocyte to release substances that harden the jelly coat and prevent additional sperm from binding.

3 The oocyte nucleus completes meiosis II, to form a nucleus with a haploid maternal genome. The sperm's tail and other organelles degenerate. Its DNA is enclosed by a membrane, forming a haploid nucleus with paternal genes.

Later, the two nuclear membranes will break down and paternal and maternal chromosomes will become arranged on a bipolar spindle in preparation for the first mitotic division.

FIGURE 38.15 {Animated} Human fertilization. The photo at the upper right is a light micrograph taken one day after fertilization.

cap on the sperm's head. The collective effect of enzyme release from many sperm clears a passage through the jelly coat to the oocyte's plasma membrane. Receptors in this membrane bind a sperm's plasma membrane and the two membranes fuse. The sperm is then drawn into the oocyte. Usually only one sperm enters the secondary oocyte. Its entry causes the egg to release substances that change the consistency of the jelly coat, making it difficult for other sperm to bind.

It only takes one sperm to fertilize an egg, but it takes the binding of many to release enough enzyme to clear a way to the egg plasma membrane. This is why a man who has healthy sperm but a low sperm count can be functionally infertile.

Remember that the secondary oocyte released at ovulation was halted in the middle of meiosis II. Binding of the sperm membrane to the oocyte membrane causes completion of meiosis. The unequal cytoplasmic division that follows produces a single mature egg—an **ovum** (plural, ova)—and the second polar body.

After a sperm penetrates an oocyte, its tail breaks down, leaving the nucleus **3**. Chromosomes in the haploid egg and sperm nuclei become the genetic material of the new zygote. The sperm also supplies a single centriole. Recall from Section 4.9 that centrioles help microtubes organize themselves. The sperm's centriole replicates to form the pair of centrioles that organize the spindle for the zygote's first mitotic division. Sperm mitochondria enter an oocyte too, but they are typically broken down. Thus, mitochondria are inherited only from the mother.

TAKE-HOME MESSAGE 38.9

An erection stiffens the penis enough for it to be inserted into the vagina. Ejaculation places sperm in the vagina. Sperm swim toward the oviducts, where fertilization occurs.

After a sperm binds to proteins in the jelly coat around a secondary oocyte, it releases enzymes that digest a path through the coat. Then the sperm enters the oocyte.

Entry of sperm into an oocyte causes the oocyte to complete meiosis II. It also alters the jelly coat so other sperm cannot bind. The haploid sperm nucleus and egg nucleus provide the genetic material of the new zygote.

ovum Mature animal egg.

CREDITS: (15-1) © Cengage Learning; (15-2, 3) From Starr/Taggart/Evers/Starr, Biology, 13E. © 2013 Cengage Learning; top right, Courtesy of Elizabeth Sanders, Women's Specialty Center, Jackson, MS.

A fertile couple who takes no precautions to prevent pregnancy has about an 85 percent chance of conceiving within a year. A variety of methods can lower the likelihood of pregnancy. The most effective option is abstinence—no intercourse. It is 100 percent effective, but difficult to sustain. **TABLE 38.4** lists common types of contraception available to people who are sexually active.

With rhythm methods, a woman tries to avoid intercourse during her fertile period. She calculates when she is ovulating by recording the timing of her menstrual

cycles, monitoring the thickness of her cervical mucus, and checking her body temperature, which usually rises around ovulation (**FIGURE 38.16**). However, ovulation can be difficult to pinpoint even with meticulous monitoring, so miscalculations are common.

Removing the penis from the vagina before ejaculation is called withdrawal. This method is often ineffective because sperm can leave the urethra prior to ejaculation. Similarly, rinsing the vagina (douching) immediately after intercourse is unreliable because sperm can swim through the cervical canal within seconds of ejaculation.

Surgical methods are highly effective, but they are meant to make a person permanently sterile. A vasectomy blocks or cuts the vas deferens. A tubal ligation blocks or cuts a woman's oviducts.

Chemical and physical barriers can stop sperm from reaching an egg. Spermicidal foams and jellies poison sperm. They are best used with a physical barrier method such as a diaphragm, which is a flexible, dome-shaped device that covers the cervix. A cervical cap is similar, but smaller than a diaphragm. Condoms are thin, tight-fitting sheaths worn over the penis. Latex types have the advantage of also protecting against sexually transmitted diseases (STDs).

An intrauterine device, or IUD, must be inserted into the uterus by a physician. Some IUDs thicken cervical mucus so much that sperm cannot swim through it. Others release copper ions that prevent an early embryo from implanting.

The birth control pill is the most common fertility control method in developed countries. "The Pill" is a mix of synthetic estrogens and progesterone-like hormones that prevents both maturation of oocytes and ovulation. The birth control patch delivers the same mixture of hormones and it blocks ovulation the same way, as do hormone injections or implants.

Emergency contraception is available if a woman has unprotected sex or a condom breaks. "Morning-after pills" prevent ovulation and work best if taken immediately after intercourse, but they can be effective up to three days later. Such pills are not meant for regular use. They can cause nausea, vomiting, abdominal pain, headache, and dizziness.

FIGURE 38.16 Rise in body temperature at the time of ovulation.

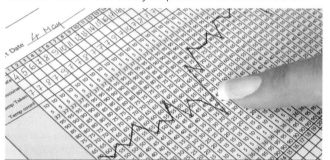

TABLE 38.4

Common Methods of Contraception

Method	Mechanism of Action	Pregnancy Rate*
Abstinence	Avoid intercourse entirely	0% per year
Rhythm method	Avoid intercourse when female is fertile	25% per year
Withdrawal	End intercourse before male ejaculates	27% per year
Vasectomy	Cut or close off male's vasa deferentia	<1% per year
Tubal ligation	Cut or close off female's oviducts	<1% per year
Condom	Enclose penis, block sperm entry to vagina	15% per year
Diaphragm, cervical cap	Cover cervix, block sperm entry to uterus	16% per year
Spermicides	Kill sperm	29% per year
Intrauterine device	Prevent sperm entry to uterus or prevent implantation	<1% per year
Oral contraceptives	Prevent ovulation	<1% per year
Hormone patches, implants, or injections	Prevent ovulation	<1% per year
Emergency contraception pill	Prevent ovulation	15–25% per use**

* Percent of pregnancies with consistent, correct use
** Not meant for regular use

TAKE-HOME MESSAGE 38.10

Couples can prevent pregnancy by avoiding sex entirely or abstaining when the woman is fertile.

Hormones delivered by pills, patches, or injections can prevent a woman from ovulating.

Temporary barriers such as condoms or a diaphragm keep sperm and egg apart, as do permanent surgical methods such as a vasectomy or tubal ligation.

38.11 WHAT ARE SEXUALLY TRANSMITTED DISEASES?

Sexually transmitted diseases (STDs) are contagious diseases that are spread by sexual contact (**TABLE 38.5**). For all STDs, women are generally more easily infected than men, and have more complications. Women can also infect their offspring during childbirth, so sexually active women who intend to become pregnant should be tested for STDs.

Trichomoniasis is an STD caused by the flagellated protozoan *Trichomonas vaginalis*. Infected women have a yellowish discharge and a sore, itchy vagina. Men usually have no symptoms. In both, untreated infection can cause infertility. An antiprotozoal drug can cure the infection.

Bacterial STDs cause a discharge from the penis and painful urination in most infected men. Women often have no initial symptoms, but they can develop pelvic inflammatory disease (PID). This secondary outcome of bacterial STDs scars the female reproductive tract and can cause infertility and chronic pain. PID also raises the risk of tubal pregnancies, in which an embryo begins to develop in the oviduct. A tubal pregnancy cannot be carried to term and must be terminated to protect the mother.

The most common bacterial STD is chlamydia, caused by *Chlamydia trachomatis*. Bacteria are also responsible for gonorrhea and syphilis. An untreated infection by the spiral-shaped bacteria (*Treponema pallidum*) that cause syphilis is especially dangerous. It can cause skin ulcers (**FIGURE 38.17**) and damage the liver, bones, and the brain. Fortunately, most bacterial STDs can be cured with antibiotics, although antibiotic-resistant strains of syphilis and gonorrhea are becoming increasingly common.

By contrast, viral STDs cannot be cured by drugs, although some medicines can relieve or prevent certain symptoms. Infection by human papillomavirus (HPV) is the most common viral STD worldwide. Most HPV strains cause benign growths called warts, but a few cause cancer. Depending on where the virus is introduced, it can cause cancer of the throat, cervix, or anus. Sexually active females should have an annual Pap smear, in which cells from the cervix are examined for signs of cancer using a microscope. A recently approved vaccine can prevent HPV infection in both males and females if given before exposure to the virus occurs (Section 34.12).

About 45 million Americans have genital herpes, which is caused by type 2 herpes simplex virus. An initial infection commonly causes small sores at the site of infection. The sores heal, but the virus remains dormant and may later be reactivated. When it is, the result is tingling, itching, and sores. Antiviral drugs help sores heal and lessen the likelihood of viral reactivation.

Infection by HIV (or human immunodeficiency virus) can cause AIDS (acquired immune deficiency syndrome).

FIGURE 38.17 Skin ulcers caused by untreated syphilis.

TABLE 38.5

Frequency and Causes of STDs

STD	U.S. Cases	Pathogen
Trichomoniasis	7,400,000	Protozoan
HPV infection	6,000,000	Virus
Chlamydia	1,200,000	Bacteria
Genital herpes	1,000,000	Virus
Gonorrhea	650,000	Bacteria
Syphilis	70,000	Bacteria
AIDS	40,000	Virus

Sections 19.1 and 19.2 described the HIV virus and Section 34.10 explained how its effects on the immune system lead to AIDS. With regard to sexual transmission, oral sex is least likely to transmit an infection. Unprotected anal sex is 5 times more dangerous than unprotected vaginal sex and 50 times more dangerous than oral sex. To reduce the risk of HIV transmission during vaginal or anal sex, doctors recommend using a latex condom and a lubricant. The lubricant helps prevent small abrasions that could allow the virus to enter the body. If you think you have been exposed to HIV, get tested as soon as possible. Early treatment may prevent development of AIDS.

TAKE-HOME MESSAGE 38.11

Viruses, bacteria, and protozoans cause common STDs.

Symptoms range from mild to life-threatening. STDs can cause infertility and infected women can pass them to offspring.

Bacterial and protozoan pathogens can be killed by drugs. Viral infections cannot be cured, but antiviral drugs reduce the effects of herpes and HIV infection. An HPV vaccine can prevent infection.

Human development starts with cleavage. Cell divisions begin within a day of fertilization, as cilia propel the zygote away from the upper portion of the oviduct where fertilization occurred (**FIGURE 38.18**). The zygote divides by mitosis to form two cells, which become four, which become eight, and so on ❶. Sometimes a cluster of four or eight cells splits in two and each cluster develops independently, resulting in identical twins. More typically, all cells adhere tightly to one another as divisions continue.

By about 5 days after fertilization, the dividing cluster of cells has reached the uterus and formed a **blastocyst**, the mammalian version of the blastula ❷. The blastocyst consists of an outer layer of cells, a cavity (the blastocoel)

filled with their fluid secretions, and an inner cell mass. Of all cells in the human blastocyst, only those in the inner cell mass give rise to the developing individual. The other cells give rise to the extraembryonic membranes that protect and support that individual.

Up to this point, the developing individual has been nourished by nutrients it absorbed from maternal secretions in the oviduct and uterus. For development to continue, the blastocyst must implant itself in the wall of the uterus, where it can obtain nutrients from the maternal bloodstream. Implantation requires direct contact between the surface of the blastocyst and cells in the lining of the uterus. Thus, before a blastocyst can implant, it must shed the protein coat that surrounds it.

Once its protein coat has ruptured, the blastocyst attaches to the lining of the uterus and begins burrowing into it ❸. During implantation, the inner cell mass develops into two flattened layers of cells that are collectively called an embryonic disk ❹. At the same time, the extraembryonic membranes typical of amniotes begin to form. A membrane called the **amnion** encloses a fluid-filled amniotic cavity between the embryonic disk and the blastocyst surface. Fluid in this cavity (amniotic fluid) acts as a buoyant cradle in which an embryo grows and moves freely, protected from temperature changes and mechanical impacts. As the amnion forms, other cells move around the inner wall of the blastocyst, forming the lining of a yolk sac. In reptiles and birds, this sac holds yolk that nourishes the developing embryo. In humans, it has no nutritional role. Some cells that form in a human yolk sac give rise to the embryo's first blood cells.

FIGURE 38.18 {Animated} Early embryonic development. Graphics 3–5 show a cross-section through the uterus.

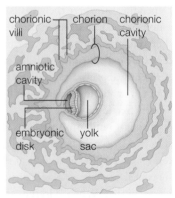

❶ **Days 1–4** Cleavage divides the zygote into an increasing number of smaller cells.

❷ **Days 5–7** The blastocyst forms, expands, then sheds its protein coat.

❸ **Days 8–9** Implantation begins. The blastocyst attaches to the wall of the uterus and begins to burrow into it.

❹ **Days 10–11** The inner cell mass develops into a two-layered embryonic disk. Extraembryonic membranes form.

❺ **Day 14** Chorionic villi (fingerlike extensions of the chorion) begin to grow into blood-filled spaces in the lining of the uterus.

As implantation continues, spaces in the uterine tissue around the blastocyst become filled with blood seeping in from ruptured maternal capillaries. The extraembryonic membrane called the **chorion** develops many tiny fingerlike projections (chorionic villi) that extend into blood-filled maternal tissues ❺. The chorion will become part of the placenta. An outpouching of the yolk sac will become the fourth extraembryonic membrane, the **allantois**. In humans, the allantois forms blood vessels of the umbilical cord that connects the fetus to the placenta.

Implantation of a blastocyst in the uterus prevents menstruation because the chorion secretes human chorionic gonadotropin (HCG). This is the first hormone that a new human produces, and it prevents degeneration of the corpus luteum. By the beginning of the third week, HCG can be detected in a mother's blood or urine. At-home pregnancy tests have a "dipstick" with a region that changes color when exposed to urine containing HCG (**FIGURE 38.19**).

Gastrulation occurs on about day 15. Cells migrate inward along a depression, the primitive streak, that forms on the disk's surface ❻. Shortly thereafter, the embryonic disk develops two folds that will merge to form a neural tube, the precursor of the spinal cord and brain ❼. Beneath the neural tube, mesoderm folds into another tube that develops into a notochord. The human notochord acts as a structural model for the backbone.

allantois Extraembryonic membrane that, in mammals, becomes part of the umbilical cord.
amnion Extraembryonic membrane that encloses an amniote embryo and the amniotic fluid.
blastocyst Mammalian blastula.
chorion Outermost extraembryonic membrane of amniotes; major component of the placenta in placental mammals.

FIGURE 38.19 Urine test for pregnancy. A dipstick containing an absorbent material is dipped in a woman's urine. If the hormone HCG is present in the urine, it reacts with antibodies and dye in the stick, and a colored line appears in the test area. If HCG is not present, a colored line appears only in the control area.

control area; line here indicates that the test is working

test area; line here indicates that HCG is present in urine

Somites form by the end of the third week ❽. They will develop into bones, skeletal muscles of the head and trunk, and the dermis of the skin that overlies them. Pharyngeal arches that will form structures in the head and neck develop ❾. In fishes, pharyngeal arches develop into gills, but a human embryo never has gills. Instead, it receives oxygen and other essential material by way of the placenta.

> **TAKE-HOME MESSAGE 38.12**
>
> Cleavage of the human zygote produces a blastocyst that implants in the mother's uterus.
>
> Projections from the blastocyst's surface invade maternal tissues. An embryonic disk that will give rise to all body tissues forms. Other parts of a blastocyst give rise to external membranes: an amnion, yolk sac, chorion, and allantois.
>
> The embryonic disk undergoes gastrulation, then the neural tube and notochord form, and pharyngeal arches develop.

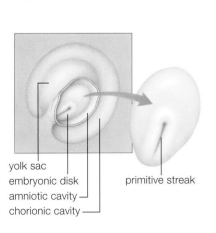

yolk sac
embryonic disk
amniotic cavity
chorionic cavity
primitive streak

❻ **Day 15** Gastrulation begins at depression called the primitive streak.

paired neural folds

neural groove (below, notochord is forming)

❼ **Day 16** Neural tube begins to form.

future brain

somites

❽ **Days 18–23** Somites develop.

pharyngeal arches

❾ **Days 24–25** Pharyngeal arches appear.

38.13 WHEN DO HUMAN ORGANS FORM AND BEGIN TO FUNCTION?

When the fourth week ends, the embryo is 500 times the size of a zygote, but still less than 1 centimeter long. It has a conspicuous tail (FIGURE 38.20). Growth slows as details of organs begin to fill in. Limbs form; paddles are sculpted into fingers and toes. Growth of the head surpasses that of all other regions. At the end of the eighth week, all organ systems have formed, apoptosis has largely eliminated the tail, and we define the individual as a human fetus.

In the second trimester (months 3–6), the sex of the fetus becomes obvious. By four months, most neurons have formed. Reflexive movements begin as developing nerves and muscles connect. Legs kick, arms wave about, and fingers grasp. The fetus frowns, squints, puckers its lips, sucks, and hiccups. Soft fetal hair (lanugo) and a thick, cheesy coating (vernix) cover the skin. Most of the hair will be shed before birth. Starting when a fetus is five months

FIGURE 38.20 Human organ development and growth.

WEEK 4

yolk sac
connecting stalk
embryo

WEEKS 5–6

forebrain

future lens

pharyngeal arches

developing heart

upper limb bud

somites

neural tube forming

lower limb bud

tail

A

actual length

head growth exceeds growth of other regions

retinal pigment

future external ear

upper limb differentiation (hand plates develop, then digital rays of future fingers; wrist, elbow start forming)

umbilical cord formation between weeks 4 and 8 (amnion expands, forms tube that encloses the connecting stalk and a duct for blood vessels)

foot plate

B

actual length

CREDITS: (20) top photos, © Lennart Nilsson/Bonnierforlagen AB; top art, From Starr/Taggart, Biology: The Unity and Diversity of Life, 7E. © 1995 Cengage Learning; bottom art, © Cengage Learning.

old, the fetal heartbeat can be heard through a stethoscope positioned on the mother's abdomen, and the mother can feel the fetus moving inside her.

By the seventh month, the fetus can detect sounds and light. In this final trimester, the fetus puts on fat. In preparation for birth, it practices muscle movements involved in breathing, inhaling amniotic fluid in place of air. Its lungs will later inflate with its first breath after birth.

placenta

WEEK 8

final week of embryonic period; embryo looks distinctly human compared to other vertebrate embryos

upper and lower limbs well formed; fingers and then toes have separated

primordial tissues of all internal, external structures now developed

tail has become stubby

C   actual length

WEEK 16
Length: 16 centimeters
        (6.4 inches)
Weight: 200 grams
        (7 ounces)

WEEK 29
Length: 27.5 centimeters
        (11 inches)
Weight: 1,300 grams
        (46 ounces)

WEEK 38 (full term)
Length: 50 centimeters
        (20 inches)
Weight: 3,400 grams
        (7.5 pounds)

During fetal period, length measurement extends from crown to heel (for embryos, it is the longest measurable dimension, as from crown to rump).

D

AN ESSENTIAL LIFE LINE

A human embryo or fetus must obtain all the materials it needs from its mother. The developing individual and its mother exchange materials by way of the placenta, a pancake-shaped, blood-engorged organ that consists of uterine lining and extraembryonic membranes (**FIGURE 38.21**). At full term, a placenta covers about a quarter of the inner surface of the uterus.

A coiled umbilical cord connects the embryo to the placenta. Embryonic blood vessels extend through this cord to the placenta, and into the chorionic villi (fingerlike projections of the chorion). These villi are surrounded by pools of maternal blood.

Maternal and embryonic bloodstreams never mix. Instead, substances move between maternal and embryonic blood by diffusing across the walls of the embryonic vessels in the chorionic villi. Oxygen diffuses from maternal blood into embryonic blood, and carbon dioxide diffuses in the opposite direction. Transport proteins assist in the movement of essential nutrients from the maternal blood into embryonic blood vessels inside the villi. One type of maternal antibody (IgG) is also transported from maternal blood into the fetal bloodstream.

In addition to providing essential substances to the embryo, the placenta produces hormones that sustain the pregnancy. From the third month of pregnancy on, it secretes the HCG, progesterone, and estrogens that encourage the ongoing maintenance of the uterine lining.

EFFECTS OF MATERNAL HEALTH AND BEHAVIOR

A pregnant woman's health and behavior can affect the development of the child she is carrying. Malnutrition raises the risk of miscarriage or stillbirth. Miscarriage is the death of an embryo or fetus before 20 weeks. Stillbirth is the death of a fetus after 20 weeks. Some maternal dietary deficiencies can result in birth defects. For example, if a mother does not eat an adequate amount of iodine, her newborn may be affected by cretinism, a disorder that affects brain function and motor skills (Section 31.5). A maternal deficiency in folate (folic acid) puts her child at risk for neural tube defects.

Some pathogens can cross the placenta and interfere with development. For example, infection by the rubella virus during the first eight weeks of pregnancy nearly always causes severe birth defects or miscarriage. Being vaccinated before pregnancy is the best way to avoid a rubella infection while pregnant. HIV and herpesviruses sometimes cross the placenta too, but these viruses are more often transmitted during delivery. A maternal case of toxoplasmosis is also

---

FIGURE 38.21 {**Animated**} Life support system of a developing human.

Artist's depiction of the view inside the uterus, showing a fetus connected by an umbilical cord to the pancake-shaped placenta.

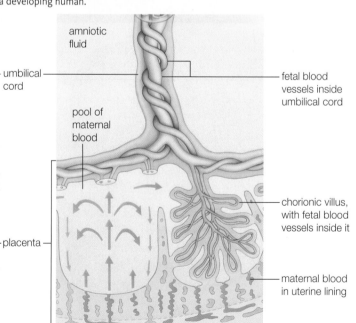

The placenta consists of maternal and fetal tissue. Fetal blood flowing in vessels of chorionic villi exchanges substances by diffusion with maternal blood around the villi. The bloodstreams do not mix.

CREDIT: (21) left, From Starr/Evers/Starr, Biology Today and Tomorrow with Physiology, 3E. © 2010 Cengage Learning; right, From Starr/Taggart, Biology: The Unity and Diversity of Life, 7E. © 1995 Cengage Learning.

a matter of concern. Toxoplasmosis is caused by a protist found in garden soil, cat feces, and undercooked meat. Because it often does not cause symptoms, a pregnant woman may become infected without realizing it. If the parasite crosses the placenta, the resulting prenatal infection can lead to developmental problems, a miscarriage, or stillbirth. To minimize the risk of these outcomes, pregnant women should eat well-cooked meat and avoid the feces of cats that have been outdoors.

Alcohol and other harmful chemicals that enter a woman's body have detrimental effects on a developing fetus because they cross the placenta. Alcohol use during pregnancy is the leading preventable cause of inborn mental impairment. When a pregnant woman drinks, her embryo or fetus feels the effects. The liver of the developing child has not fully developed, so it cannot detoxify alcohol (or other toxins) as effectively as an adult can (Section 5.9). The most dramatic effects of prenatal alcohol exposure are seen in children with fetal alcohol syndrome (FAS). Affected individuals have a small head and facial abnormalities (FIGURE 38.22). They also have slowed growth, heart malfunctions, skeletal abnormalities, mental impairment, behavioral problems, and poor coordination. Likelihood of FAS increases with the frequency of drinking and with the amount of alcohol consumed at one time. However, even moderate drinking during pregnancy may have adverse developmental effects. Most doctors now advise women who are pregnant or attempting to become pregnant to avoid alcohol entirely.

Smoking or exposure to secondhand smoke increases risk of miscarriage and adversely affects fetal growth and development. Carbon monoxide in the smoke can outcompete oxygen for the binding sites on hemoglobin, so the embryo or fetus of a smoker gets less oxygen than that of a nonsmoker. Levels of nicotine in amniotic fluid can be even higher than those in the mother's blood. Prenatal nicotine exposure increases the risk of sudden infant death syndrome (Section 35.7).

Some commonly used medications cause birth defects. Isotretinoin (Accutane), a highly effective treatment for severe acne, is often prescribed for young women. If taken early in a pregnancy, it can cause heart problems or facial and cranial deformities in the embryo. Some antidepressants also increase the risk of birth defects. Paroxetine (Paxil) and related drugs inhibit the reuptake of serotonin. Use of these drugs during early pregnancy increases the likelihood of heart malformations. Taking them later in pregnancy increases risk of fatal heart and lung disorders.

Environmental pollutants can also enter a woman's body and harm her child. Section 2.6 explained how methyl

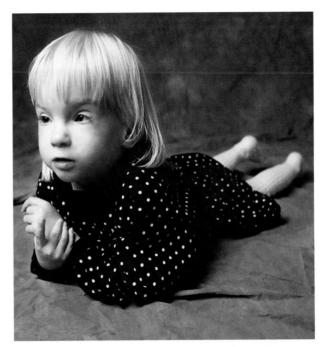

FIGURE 38.22 A child with fetal alcohol syndrome. Wide-spaced eyes, a thin upper lip, and an abnormally smooth area between the nose and lip are visible signs of FAS. Affected children are also small and often have impaired mental function and organ abnormalities.

mercury released by burning coal can get into the human food supply. Prenatal exposure to methyl mercury impairs brain development, which is why pregnant women are advised to avoid eating large predatory fish such as albacore tuna. These fish often contain high levels of methyl mercury.

Endocrine disrupters also affect prenatal development. As Section 31.10 noted, maternal exposure to phthalates during pregnancy increases the risk of reproductive abnormalities in male offspring. As another example, bisphenol-A (BPA), a chemical widely used to make plastic containers and to coat cans, reportedly has prenatal effects, including suppression of thyroid hormone production in developing males.

TAKE-HOME MESSAGE 38.14

Vessels of the embryo's circulatory system extend through the umbilical cord to the placenta, where they run through pools of maternal blood.

Maternal and embryonic blood do not mix. Rather, substances move between the maternal and embryonic bloodstreams by crossing blood vessel walls.

Some pathogens and toxins can cross the placenta and interfere with normal development.

CHILDBIRTH

A mother's body changes as her fetus nears full term, at about 38 weeks after fertilization. Until the last few weeks, her firm cervix helped prevent the fetus from slipping out of her uterus prematurely. Now, connective tissue in the cervix becomes thinner, softer, and more flexible so it can stretch during childbirth.

The birth process is known as **labor**. Typically, the amnion ruptures right before birth, so amniotic fluid drains out from the vagina. The cervical canal dilates. Strong contractions propel the fetus through the cervix, then out through the vagina (**FIGURE 38.23**).

A positive feedback mechanism operates during labor. As the fetus nears full term, it typically shifts position so that its head touches the mother's cervix. Receptors in the cervix respond to pressure by sending signals along nerves to the hypothalamus, which in turn tells the posterior lobe of the pituitary to secrete the hormone oxytocin. In a positive feedback loop, oxytocin binds to receptor on smooth muscle cells of the uterus, causing stronger uterine contractions that put additional pressure on the cervix. The added pressure

triggers more oxytocin secretion, causing more cervical stretching, and so on, until the fetus is expelled. Synthetic oxytocin is often given to induce or speed labor.

Strong muscle contractions also detach and expel the placenta from the uterus as the "afterbirth." The umbilical cord that connects the newborn to this mass of expelled tissue is clamped, cut short, and tied. The body's navel marks the former attachment site.

In the United States, more than 30 percent of births involve a cesarean section. During this surgical procedure, a doctor makes an incision in the mother's abdominal wall, then cuts open her uterus to remove the fetus.

A variety of conditions can necessitate a surgical delivery. A placenta that grows in the lower portion of the uterus and covers the cervix can make it impossible for the fetus to exit safely through the vagina. A fetus that is positioned with its feet, rather than its head, at the cervix may also have to be extracted surgically. If the placenta dislodges too early in labor or the umbilical cord becomes kinked, blood flow to the fetus is compromised and surgery may be required to ensure its safety. A cesarean section can also be used to prevent transmission of herpes or another sexually transmitted disease to an infant.

LACTATION

Before a pregnancy, a woman's breast tissue is largely adipose tissue. During pregnancy, milk ducts and mammary glands enlarge in preparation for **lactation**, or milk production. Prolactin, a hormone secreted by the mother's anterior pituitary, encourages milk synthesis. When a newborn suckles, neural signals cause the release of oxytocin. The hormone stimulates muscles around the milk glands to contract and force milk into the ducts.

Human milk includes sugar (lactose), easily digested fats and proteins, essential vitamins and minerals, and enzymes that aid in digestion. It has proteins that encourage growth of beneficial gut bacteria, and lysozyme (Section 34.2) to kill harmful bacteria. In addition, milk contains maternal antibodies that coat the lining of the newborn's throat and gut lining, lessening the risk of dangerous infections.

labor Expulsion of a placental mammal from its mother's uterus by muscle contractions.
lactation Milk production by a female mammal.

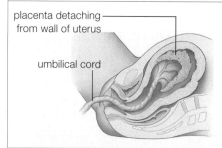

A Fetus positioned for childbirth; its head is against the mother's cervix, which is dilating (widening).

B Muscle contractions stimulated by oxytocin force the fetus out through the vagina.

C The placenta detaches from the wall of the uterus and is expelled.

FIGURE 38.23 Expulsion of fetus and afterbirth during labor. The afterbirth consists of the placenta, tissue fluid, and blood.

TAKE-HOME MESSAGE 38.15
During birth, hormonally stimulated muscle contractions force a fetus out of its mother's body. Hormones also stimulate milk production and secretion.

FIGURE 38.24 *In vitro* fertilization. A fertility specialist uses a micromanipulator to insert a human sperm into an egg.

A COUPLE THAT CANNOT CONCEIVE NATURALLY MAY TURN TO *IN VITRO* FERTILIZATION (IVF). This reproductive technology combines an egg and sperm outside the body. After fertilization, the zygote undergoes mitotic divisions, eventually forming a ball of cells (a blastocyst) that can be placed in a woman's womb to develop.

The first child conceived by IVF was born in 1976. At the time, much of the public and many scientists were appalled by the idea of what newspapers referred to as "test tube babies." Scientists worried that this new, unnatural procedure would produce children with psychological and genetic defects. Ethicists warned about the societal implications of manipulating human embryos.

Despite the initial reservations, IVF has become widely accepted and practiced. Worldwide, the technique has produced more than 3 million children. The earliest test tube babies have reached adulthood and begun having children of their own.

Research into IVF opened the way to a variety of assisted reproductive technologies. If a man makes sperm, but does not ejaculate them properly or does not ejaculate a large enough number to allow fertilization by normal means, intracytoplasmic sperm injection can put his sperm inside his partner's egg (**FIGURE 38.24**). If a woman cannot conceive, she can now obtain donated eggs and use IVF to produce a blastocyst that she can carry to term. A woman who has fertile eggs but cannot, or does not want to, carry them herself can have a blastocyst conceived by IVF implanted in a surrogate mother. Blastocysts created by IVF can be frozen away for later use. Prospective parents can also screen blastocysts before they are implanted to avoid genetic defects, or to choose a particular sex.

Summary

SECTION 38.1 **Asexual reproduction** produces genetic copies of a parent. **Sexual reproduction** yields varied offspring, and can be advantageous in environments where conditions vary. Most animals reproduce sexually and have separate sexes, but **hermaphrodites** have both male and female **gonads**; they make **sperm** and **eggs**. With **external fertilization**, gametes are released into water. Gametes meet in the female's body with **internal fertilization**, which occurs in most animals on land. Offspring may develop inside or outside the maternal body. **Yolk** helps nourish developing young of most animals. In placental mammals, young are sustained by nutrients delivered via the **placenta**.

SECTIONS 38.2–38.4 All animals go through similar developmental stages. They produce gametes in gonads: a male's **testes** or a female's **ovaries**. After fertilization takes place, **cleavage** increases the number of cells and different cells receive different components of the maternal cytoplasm. Cleavage ends with production of a **blastula**. In vertebrates, **gastrulation** forms a **gastrula** that has three **germ layers** (**ectoderm**, **mesoderm**, and **endoderm**). Organs begin forming after gastrulation.

Cells become specialized by selective gene expression. With **embryonic induction** some cells affect gene expression in other cells, as by secreting **morphogens**. Organs take shape as cells migrate, tissue layers fold, and cells commit suicide (**apoptosis**). Genes that regulate development are highly conserved. Mutations that dramatically alter development are usually fatal.

SECTION 38.5 Human prenatal development lasts about 40 weeks. From weeks 2 to 8, the individual is called an **embryo**. From week 9 to birth it is a **fetus**. An individual's sex organs mature at **puberty**.

SECTION 38.6 A human male's testes produce sperm and the sex hormone **testosterone**. Hormones from the pituitary regulate testosterone secretion and sperm production. Sperm form in **seminiferous tubules** and mature in an **epididymis** that opens into a **vas deferens**. Secretions from the **seminal vesicles** and **prostate gland** join with sperm to form **semen**. Semen leaves the body through the **penis**.

SECTIONS 38.7, 38.8 A human female's ovaries contain **ovarian follicles** that produce **oocytes** and secrete **estrogens** and **progesterone**. An **oviduct** conveys the oocyte released at **ovulation** to the **uterus**. The **cervix** of the uterus opens into the **vagina**. From puberty until **menopause**, a woman has an approximately monthly **menstrual cycle**. During a cycle, **follicle-stimulating hormone** (FSH) causes a primary oocyte to complete meiosis I, forming a secondary oocyte and a **polar body**. FSH also causes the follicle to secrete estrogen. The rise in estrogen triggers a surge of **luteinizing hormone** that, in turn, triggers ovulation. After ovulation, the **corpus luteum** secretes progesterone that primes the uterus for pregnancy. When

the corpus luteum breaks down, **menstruation** occurs. Most mammals have an **estrous cycle** instead of a menstrual cycle.

SECTIONS 38.9–38.11 Intercourse delivers sperm into the vagina. It can also transfer sexually transmitted diseases. Fertilization occurs when a sperm penetrates a secondary oocyte, causing it to complete meiosis II. The nucleus of the resulting **ovum** and that of the sperm supply the genetic material of the zygote. Pregnancy can be prevented by abstinence; with surgical, physical, or chemical barriers; and by manipulating hormones.

SECTIONS 38.12–38.14 Human fertilization usually occurs in an oviduct. Cleavage produces a **blastocyst** that implants in the uterine wall. After implantation, an **amnion** forms and encloses the embryo in fluid. The **chorion** becomes part of the placenta and the **allantois** becomes part of the umbilical cord. Gastrulation occurs at about 2 weeks; then a neural tube, pharyngeal arches, and a tail form in the early embryo. The tail disappears and organ formation ends before an individual becomes a fetus after 8 weeks.

The placenta allows exchanges between embryonic and maternal blood. Harmful substances also cross the placenta, so a mother's health, nutrition, and lifestyle can affect the growth and development of her future child.

SECTION 38.15 Hormones induce **labor** at about 38 weeks. Positive feedback governs contractions that expel a fetus and then the afterbirth. Hormones control maturation of the mammary glands and **lactation**.

SECTION 38.16 Reproductive technology such as *in vitro* fertilization can help couples with fertility problems have children.

Self-Quiz   Answers in Appendix VII

1. Most land animals have _____ fertilization.
   a. internal   b. external

2. An individual that makes eggs and sperm is a _____ .
   a. zygote   c. gastrula
   b. hermaphrodite   d. gamete

3. Testosterone is secreted by the _____ .
   a. testes   c. prostate gland
   b. hypothalamus   d. pituitary gland

4. During a menstrual cycle, a midcycle surge of _____ triggers ovulation.
   a. estrogens   b. progesterone   c. LH   d. FSH

5. The corpus luteum develops from _____ .
   a. a polar body   c. a secondary oocyte
   b. follicle cells   d. spermatogonia

6. Sexually transmitted bacteria cause _____ .
   a. trichomoniasis   c. syphilis
   b. genital herpes   d. all of the above

Data Analysis Activities

Multiple Births and Birth Defects Fertility treatments raise the risk of multiple pregnancies, which are associated with an increased risk of some birth defects. **FIGURE 38.25** shows the results of Yiwei Tang's study of birth defects reported in Florida from 1996 to 2000. Tang compared the incidence of various defects among single and multiple births. She calculated the relative risk for each type of defect based on type of birth, and corrected for other differences that might increase risk such as maternal age, income, race, and medical care during pregnancy. A relative risk of less than 1 means a defect occurs less often with multiple births than single births. A relative risk greater than 1 means that multiples are more likely to have a defect.

1. What was the most common type of birth defect in the single-birth group?
2. Was that defect more or less common in the multiple-birth group?
3. Tang found that multiples have more than twice the risk of single newborns for one type of defect. Which type?
4. Does a multiple pregnancy increase the relative risk of chromosomal defects in offspring?

	Prevalence of Defect		Relative Risk
	Multiples	Singles	
Total birth defects	358.50	250.54	1.46
Central nervous system defects	40.75	18.89	2.23
Chromosomal defects	15.51	14.20	0.93
Gastrointestinal defects	28.13	23.44	1.27
Genital/urinary defects	72.85	58.16	1.31
Heart defects	189.71	113.89	1.65
Musculoskeletal defects	20.92	25.87	0.92
Fetal alcohol syndrome	4.33	3.63	1.03
Oral defects	19.84	15.48	1.29

FIGURE 38.25 Prevalence, per 10,000 live births, of various types of birth defects among multiple and single births.

The relative risk for each defect is given after researchers adjusted for maternal age, race, previous adverse pregnancy experience, education, Medicaid participation during pregnancy, and the infant's sex and number of siblings.

7. Match each term with the most suitable description.
   ___ epididymis   a. conveys oocyte to uterus
   ___ vas deferens   b. can be inflated by blood
   ___ vagina   c. where sperm mature
   ___ seminal vesicle   d. target of vasectomy
   ___ penis   e. main contributor to semen
   ___ oviduct   f. sheds lining monthly
   ___ uterus   g. birth canal

8. A homeotic gene regulates _____ .
   a. body part formation   c. secondary sexual traits
   b. milk production   d. sperm formation

9. True or false? All blastomeres have the same cytoplasmic components and express the same genes.

10. What are the three tissues of a vertebrate gastrula?

11. A human blastocyst normally implants in _____ .
    a. an oviduct   c. the uterus
    b. a seminiferous tubule   d. the vagina

12. Match each hormone with its effect.
    ___ oxytocin   a. growth of facial hair
    ___ testosterone   b. uterus contracts
    ___ LH   c. LH, FSH are released
    ___ GnRH   d. surge causes ovulation
    ___ FSH   e. follicle develops
    ___ HCG   f. milk is produced
    ___ prolactin   g. endometrium is maintained

13. Put these human developmental events in order, from earliest to latest.
    a. blastocyst forms   d. implantation
    b. heart begins beating   e. breathing practice begins
    c. gastrulation   f. neural tube forms

Critical Thinking

1. At no point in human development does an embryo have functional gills. Explain how the embryo obtains the oxygen it requires for aerobic respiration.

2. Fraternal twins are nonidentical siblings that form when two eggs mature and are released and fertilized at the same time. Explain why an increased level of FSH raises the likelihood of fraternal twins.

3. The most common ovarian tumors in young women are teratomas. The name comes from the Greek word *teraton*, which means monster. The "monstrous" feature of these tumors is the presence of a variety of tissues, most commonly bones, teeth, fat, and hair. Explain why a tumor that arises from a germ cell can contain a wider assortment of tissues than one derived from a differentiated body cell.

CREDIT: (25) From Starr/Taggart/Evers/Starr, Biology 13E. © 2013 Cengage Learning.

A male tungara frog inflates his vocal sac to make his species-specific mating call. Female frogs are attracted by the sound of this call.

39

ANIMAL BEHAVIOR

Links to Earlier Concepts

This chapter builds on your knowledge of sensory and endocrine systems (Chapters 30, 31). You will revisit pheromones (30.3) and learn about additional effects of the hormone oxytocin (31.3). Be sure that you understand the concepts of sexual selection (17.6) and adaptation (16.2). The chapter provides many examples of scientific experiments (1.6).

KEY CONCEPTS

GENETIC FOUNDATIONS

Genes affecting the ability to detect stimuli or to respond to nervous or hormonal signals influence behavior. Genetic differences within and among species cause behavioral differences.

INSTINCT AND LEARNING

Instinctive behavior can be performed without practice, but most behavior has a learned component. Some types of learning can only occur during a certain portion of the lifetime.

ANIMAL COMMUNICATION

Animal communication signals arise only if communication benefits both signal senders and receivers. Predators sometimes take advantage of the communication behavior of their prey.

MATING AND PARENTING

In most cases, females are choosier about mates than males. Monogamy is rare in most animals. Whether there is parental care, and who delivers it, varies among animal groups.

FORMING GROUPS

Grouping together provides benefits such as protection, but also has costs such as increased competition. Self-sacrificing behavior evolved in some animals that live in large family groups.

Photograph by George Grall, National Geographic Creative.

SENSING AND RESPONDING

Like other traits, behavioral traits have a genetic basis. The structure of the nervous system determines the types of stimuli that an animal can detect and the types of responses it can make. Gene differences that affect the structure and activity of the nervous system cause many differences in behavior. Hormones interact closely with the nervous system, so genes that influence hormone action also affect behavior. Genes with influence on metabolism

FIGURE 39.1 Coastal garter snake dining on a banana slug. The snake is genetically predisposed to recognize slugs as prey. By contrast, garter snakes from inland regions where there are no banana slugs do not recognize them as food.

FIGURE 39.2 Genetic polymorphism for foraging behavior in fruit fly larvae. When a larva is placed in the center of a yeast-filled plate, its genotype at the *foraging* locus influences whether it moves a little or a lot while it feeds. Black lines show a representative larva's path.

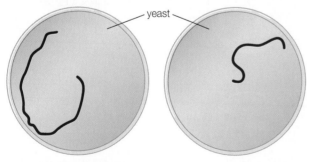

A Rovers (genotype *FF* or *Ff*) move often as they feed. When a rover's movements on a petri dish filled with yeast are traced for 5 minutes, the trail is relatively long.

B Sitters (genotype *ff*) move little as they feed. When a sitter's movements on a petri dish filled with yeast are traced for 5 minutes, the trail is relatively short.

and structural traits can also have behavioral effects. For example, singing requires both sound-making structures and sufficient energy to do so.

Like other genetically determined traits, behaviors evolve. In considering why animals behave as they do, biologists often discuss "proximate" and "ultimate" causes of a behavior. The proximate causes of a behavior are the genetic and physiological mechanisms that bring about the behavior. The ultimate cause of a behavior is the specific selective pressure that caused it to evolve. Keep in mind that not all behavior is adaptive all the time. A behavior that evolved in one context can be maladaptive in another.

VARIATION WITHIN A SPECIES

One way to investigate the genetic basis of behavior is to examine behavioral and genetic differences among members of a single species. For example, Stevan Arnold studied feeding behavior in two populations of garter snakes of the Pacific Northwest. One population lives in coastal forests, where it hunts the banana slugs common on the forest floor (**FIGURE 39.1**). The other population lives inland, where there are no banana slugs. Inland snakes eat fishes and tadpoles. The two populations differ in their inborn food preferences. When Arnold offered a slug to newborn garter snakes, offspring of coastal snakes ate it, but offspring of inland snakes ignored it.

Arnold hypothesized that inland snakes lack the genetically determined ability to associate the scent of slugs with food. He predicted that if coastal garter snakes were crossed with inland snakes, the resulting offspring would make an intermediate response to slugs. Results from his experimental crosses confirmed this prediction. We do not know which allele or alleles underlie this difference.

We know more about the genetic basis of differences in foraging behavior among fruit fly larvae. The wingless, wormlike larvae crawl about eating yeast that grows on decaying fruit. In wild fruit fly populations, about 70 percent of the fly larvae are "rovers," which means they tend to move around a lot as they feed. Rovers often leave one patch of food to seek another (**FIGURE 39.2A**). The remaining 30 percent of larvae are "sitters"; they tend to move little once they find a patch of yeast (**FIGURE 39.2B**). When food is absent, rovers and sitters move the same amount, so both are equally energetic.

The proximate cause of the difference in larval behaviors is a difference in alleles of a gene called *foraging*. Flies with a dominant allele of this gene have the rover phenotype. Sitters are homozygous for the recessive allele. The *foraging* gene encodes an enzyme involved in learning about olfactory cues. Rovers make more of the enzyme than sitters.

A Vole (*Microtus*), a type of small rodent.

B PET scan of a monogamous prairie vole's brain with many oxytocin receptors (red).

C PET scan of a promiscuous mountain vole's brain with fewer oxytocin receptors.

FIGURE 39.3 Genetic roots of mating and bonding behavior in voles. Closely related vole species vary in their behavior, and in the number and distribution of receptors for the hormone oxytocin.

make these animals ideal subjects for study of this behavior. Most voles, like most mammals, are promiscuous; they have multiple mates. However, some voles form lifelong, largely monogamous relationships. For example, in prairie voles, a permanent social bond forms after a night of repeated matings. The hormone oxytocin plays a central role in a female prairie vole's bonding behavior. When females who are part of an established pair are injected with a chemical that interferes with oxytocin action, they dump their long-term partners in favor of other males.

Females of promiscuous vole species are less influenced by oxytocin than prairie voles. When researchers compared the brains of promiscuous and monogamous species, they found a striking difference in the number and distribution of oxytocin receptors (**FIGURE 39.3B,C**). Monogamous prairie voles have many oxytocin receptors in the part of the brain associated with social learning. Promiscuous mountain voles have far fewer of these receptors.

In male voles, variations in the distribution of receptors for another hormone (arginine vasopressin, or AVP) correlate with bonding tendency. Compared to males of promiscuous vole species, males of monogamous species have more AVP receptors. Scientists isolated the prairie vole gene for the AVP receptor and used genetic engineering to insert it into the brain of male mice, which are naturally promiscuous. After this treatment, the genetically modified mice preferred a female with whom they had already mated over an unfamiliar female. These results confirm the role of AVP in fostering monogamy among male rodents.

EPIGENETIC EFFECTS

Epigenetic mechanisms (Section 10.5) sometimes cause heritable changes in behavior. For example, a female rat who did not receive much licking and grooming from her mother early in life will fail to lick and groom her own pups. The lack of tactile stimulation affects methylation patterns in a rat pup's DNA, and the resulting changes in gene expression disrupt oxytocin's influence in the adult. The methylation patterns are inherited, so this negative effect on female parental behavior can persist for generations.

The ultimate cause of the behavioral variation in larval foraging behavior is competition for food. In experimental populations with limited food, both rovers and sitters are most likely to survive to adulthood when their foraging type is rare. A rover does best when surrounded by sitters, and vice versa. Presumably, when there are lots of larvae of one type they all compete for food in the same way. Under these circumstances, a fly that behaves differently than the majority is at an advantage. As a result, natural selection maintains both alleles of the *foraging* gene.

VARIATION AMONG SPECIES

A behavior's genetic basis can sometimes be clarified by comparing related species. For example, studies of voles (**FIGURE 39.3A**) reveal that inherited differences in the number and distribution of certain hormone receptors influence mating and bonding behavior. Differences in mating behavior between closely related species of vole

TAKE-HOME MESSAGE 39.1

Many genes shape the nervous system. Such genes affect traits such as an animal's ability to sense and respond to specific stimuli.

Genetic differences affect species-specific behavior, and also differences in behavior among individuals of a species.

Epigenetic mechanisms can result in inherited behavioral tendencies.

CREDITS: (3A) © Robert M. Timm & Barbara L. Clauson, University of Kansas; (3B–C) Reprinted from *Trends in Neuroscience*, Vol. 21, Issue 2, 1998, L.J.Young, W. Zuoxin, T.R. Insel, "Neuroendocrine bases of monogamy", Pages 71–75, ©1998, with permission from Elsevier Science.

INSTINCTIVE BEHAVIOR

All animals are born with the capacity for **instinctive behavior**—an innate response to a specific and usually simple stimulus. For example, a newborn coastal garter snake behaves instinctively when it eats a banana slug in response to its smell.

The life cycle of the cuckoo bird provides several examples of instinct at work. This European bird is a "brood parasite," meaning it lays its eggs in the nest of other birds. A newly hatched cuckoo is blind, but contact with an object beside it stimulates an instinctive response. That hatchling maneuvers the object, which is usually one of its foster parents' eggs, onto its back, then shoves it out of the nest (**FIGURE 39.4A**). The cuckoo will also shove its foster parents' chicks over the side, if they happen to hatch before it does. Instinctively shoving objects out of the nest ensures the cuckoo has its foster parents' undivided attention.

Instinctive responses are advantageous only if the triggering stimulus almost always signals the same situation. Doing away with an egg benefits a cuckoo chick because the egg always houses a future competitor for food. However, instinctive responses can open the way to exploitation. Cuckoos often look nothing like the chicks they displace, yet their foster parents feed them all the same (**FIGURE 39.4B**). The cuckoo chick exploits its foster parents' instinctive urge to fill any gaping mouth in their nest with food.

TIME-SENSITIVE LEARNING

A **learned behavior** is one that is altered by experience. Instinctive behavior is sometimes modified with learning. A garter snake's initial strikes at prey are instinctive, but the snake learns to avoid dangerous or unpalatable prey. Learning may occur throughout an animal's life, or be restricted to a critical period.

Imprinting is a form of learning that occurs during a genetically determined time period early in life. For example, baby geese learn to follow the large object that looms over them after they hatch (**FIGURE 39.5A**). With rare exceptions, this object is their mother. When mature, the geese will seek out a sexual partner that appears similar to the imprinted object.

A genetic capacity to learn, combined with actual experiences in the environment, shapes most forms of behavior. For example, a male songbird has an inborn capacity to recognize his species' song when he hears older males singing it. The young male uses these overheard songs as a model for his own song. Males reared with no model or exposed only to songs of other species often sing a simplified version of their species' song.

A Young cuckoo shoving its foster parents' egg from the nest. It pushes out any object beside it.

B A foster parent (*left*) feeds a cuckoo chick (*right*) in response to a simple cue: a gaping mouth.

FIGURE 39.4 Instinctive responses to simple cues.

Many birds can only learn the details of their species-specific song during a limited period early in life. For example, a male white-crowned sparrow will not sing normally if he does not hear a male "tutor" of his own species during his first month. Hearing a same-species tutor later in life will not normalize his singing.

Most birds must also practice their song to perfect it. In one experiment, researchers temporarily paralyzed throat muscles of zebra finches who were beginning to sing. After being temporarily unable to practice, these birds never mastered their song. In contrast, temporary paralysis of throat muscles in very young birds or adults did not impair later song production. Thus, in this species, there is a critical period for song practice, as well as for song learning.

CONDITIONED RESPONSES

Nearly all animals are lifelong learners. Most learn to associate certain stimuli with rewards and others with negative consequences. With classical conditioning, an animal's involuntary response to a stimulus becomes associated with a stimulus that accompanies it. In the most famous example, Ivan Pavlov rang a bell whenever he fed a dog. Eventually, the dog's reflexive response—increased salivation—was elicited by the sound of the bell alone. Conditioned taste aversion is a type of classical conditioning in which an animal learns to avoid a food that made it sick at an earlier time. This learned response protects the animal from repeated ingestion of toxic substances. Some plants and fungi take advantage of animals' capacity for this type of learning by producing nausea-inducing substances.

With operant conditioning, an animal modifies a voluntary behavior in response to consequences of that behavior. This type of learning was first described in the context of learning experiments in the lab. A rat that presses a lever and is rewarded with a food pellet becomes more likely to press the lever again. A rat that receives a shock when it enters a particular area will quickly learn to avoid that area. In nature as well, animals learn to repeat behaviors that provide food or mating opportunities and to avoid those that cause pain.

OTHER TYPES OF LEARNING

With **habituation**, an animal learns by experience not to respond to a stimulus that has neither positive nor negative effects. Pigeons in cities often become habituated to people: The birds learned not to flee from the throngs who walk past them.

Many animals learn the landmarks in their environment. A mental map of the landmarks can be put to use when an animal needs to return home. For example, a fiddler crab foraging up to 10 meters (30 feet) away from its burrow is able to scurry straight home when it perceives a threat.

Animals also learn the details of their social landscape. They learn to recognize mates, offspring, or competitors by their appearance, calls, odor, or some combination of cues. For example, two male lobsters that meet up for the first time will fight (**FIGURE 39.5B**). Later, they will recognize one another by scent and behave accordingly, with the loser actively avoiding the winner.

With imitation learning, an animal copies behavior it observes in another individual. For example, Ludwig Huber and Bernhard Voelkl allowed marmoset monkeys to watch another marmoset open a container to get the treat inside. Some marmosets used their hands to open the container; others used their teeth. When the observing monkeys were later given a similar container, they used either their hands or their teeth depending on which technique they had observed (**FIGURE 39.5C**).

---

habituation Learning not to respond to a repeated neutral stimulus.
imprinting Learning that can occur only during a specific interval in an animal's life.
instinctive behavior An innate response to a simple stimulus.
learned behavior Behavior that is modified by experience.

TAKE-HOME MESSAGE 39.2

Instinctive behavior can initially be performed without any prior experience, as when a simple cue triggers a response. Even instinctive behavior may be modified by experience.

Certain types of learning can only occur at particular times in the life cycle.

Learning can affect both voluntary and involuntary behaviors.

A **Imprinting.** Nobel laureate Konrad Lorenz with geese that imprinted on him. Under normal circumstances, newborn geese imprint on and follow their mother.

B **Social learning.** Captive male lobsters fight at their first meeting. The loser remembers the winner's scent and avoids him. Without another meeting, memory of the defeat lasts up to two weeks.

C **Imitative learning.** Marmosets given an opportunity to observe another marmoset opening a container filled with food later opened the container the same way. The marmoset above had observed another opening a container with its teeth.

FIGURE 39.5 Experimental demonstrations of animal learning.

Communication signals are evolved cues that transmit information from one member of a species to another. A communication signal arises and persists only if it benefits both the signal sender and the signal receiver. If signaling is disadvantageous for either party, then natural selection will tend to favor individuals that do not send or respond to it.

Pheromones are chemical signals that convey information among members of a species. Signal pheromones cause a rapid shift in the receiver's behavior. Sex attractants that help males and females of many species find each other are one example. The alarm pheromone a honeybee emits when she perceives a threat to her hive is another. Alarm pheromone causes other honeybees to rush out of the hive and attack the potential intruder. Priming pheromones cause longer-term responses, as when a chemical in the urine of male mice triggers ovulation in females. Producing a pheromone requires less energy than calling or gesturing. However, the amount of information a pheromone can convey is limited; it is either released or not. Properties of acoustical, visual, and tactile signals vary continuously, and so can convey more information.

A Courtship display in albatrosses. The display involves a series of coordinated movements, some accompanied by calls.

B Threat display of a male collared lizard. This display allows rival males to assess one another's strengths without engaging in a potentially damaging fight.

FIGURE 39.6 Examples of visual communication.

When bee moves straight up comb, recruits fly straight toward the sun.

FIGURE 39.7 {Animated} Honeybee waggle dance. Orientation of dancer's straight run (middle of the figure 8) conveys where food is, relative to the direction of the sun.

Acoustical signals often advertise the presence of an animal or group of animals. Many male vertebrates, including songbirds, whales, frogs, some fish, and many insects, make sounds to attract prospective mates. In many cases, sounds made by males also function in territoriality. Some birds and mammals give alarm calls that inform others of potential threats. A prairie dog makes one kind of call when it sees an eagle and another when it sees a coyote. Upon hearing the call, other prairie dogs respond appropriately: They either dive into burrows (to escape an eagle's attack) or stand erect (to spot the coyote).

Properties of acoustical signals vary depending on whether or not the sender benefits by revealing its position. Sounds that lure mates or offspring are typically easily localized, whereas alarm calls are not.

Visual communication is most widespread in animals that have good eyesight and are active during the day. Most bird courtship involves coordinated visual signaling (**FIGURE 39.6A**). Selection favors clear signals, so movements that serve as signals often become exaggerated. Body form may evolve in concert with movements, as when bright-colored feathers enhance a courtship display. A courtship display assures a prospective mate that the displayer is of the correct species and is in good health.

Threat displays advertise good health too, but they serve a different purpose. When two potential rivals meet, a threat display demonstrates each individual's strength and how well armed it is (**FIGURE 39.6B**). If the rivals are not evenly matched, the weaker individual retreats, and both benefit by avoiding a fight that could lead to injury.

With tactile displays, touch transmits information. For example, after discovering food, a foraging honeybee worker returns to the hive and dances in the dark, surrounded by a crowd of fellow workers. The speed and orientation of

pheromone Chemical that serves as a communication signal between members of an animal species.

**UNIT 7
PRINCIPLES OF
ECOLOGY**

CREDITS: (6A) G. Ziesler/ZEFA; (6B) © Eitan Grunwald, www.herptrips.com; (7) © Cengage Learning.

When bee moves straight down comb, recruits fly to source directly away from the sun.

When bee moves to right of vertical, recruits fly at 90° angle to right of the sun.

her dance convey information about the distance of and direction to the food (**FIGURE 39.7**).

Predators sometimes tap into signaling systems of prey. For example, calls made by a male tungara frog (shown in the chapter opening photo) attract females. Unfortunately, such calls also attract frog-eating bats (**FIGURE 39.8**). As another example, fireflies attract mates by producing flashes of light in a characteristic pattern. Some female fireflies prey on males of other species. When a predatory female sees the flash from a male of the prey species, she flashes back as if she were a female of his own species. When he approaches ready to mate, she captures and eats him.

FIGURE 39.8 Intercepted signals. A frog-eating bat with a male tungara frog. Both female frogs and frog-eating bats locate male frogs by listening for the males' courtship call.

TAKE-HOME MESSAGE 39.3

A chemical, visual, acoustical, or tactile communication signal transfers information from one individual to another of the same species. Both signaler and receiver benefit from the transfer.

Signals can draw attention of predators as well as intended receivers. Features of signals reflect a balance between the benefit of sending information and the potential cost of signaling.

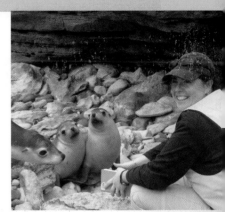

National Geographic Explorer
DR. ISABELLE CHARRIER

Some animals are able to recognize individuals by their voice. Isabelle Charrier says, "My scientific interest is in understanding how animals are able to identify each other individually by voice, especially in species showing strong environmental and ecological constraints. Colonial birds and mammals are good models for this problem: Vocal recognition between mates or between parents and offspring is effective and reliable in spite of the high background noise and the high risk of confusion between individuals."

Much of Charrier's research focuses on seals and related marine mammals. These animals spend most of their life at sea, but come ashore to give birth and nurse their young. Charrier's field studies span the globe, from walrus colonies in the Arctic to sea lion colonies in Australia. She has studied the features of vocal signals and their role in recognition in interactions between mothers and pups, between males and females, and between territorial males. She says "My favorite field experience was when I did my Ph.D.: I stayed nearly nine months on Amsterdam Island [French Subantarctic island] to study Subantarctic fur seals. This was so great, to study mother–pup vocal recognition from birth until weaning. You can really develop special interactions with the animals by being on the colony for hours every day." Her greatest challenge has been studying walruses in the Arctic. She says, "You fight every day with the weather and sea conditions, and walruses are quite difficult to find and approach. It results in a great amount of frustration, but walruses are amazing to study."

As for why she does her research, she says, "Learning more about animal communication systems is not only important for our general knowledge, but also an essential approach and a powerful tool to protect some species and their environment."

A Male hangingfly dangling a moth as a gift for a potential mate.

B Male fiddler crabs (*top*) wave their one enlarged claw to attract a female (*bottom*).

C Male sage grouse gather on a communal display ground, where they dance, puff out their neck, and make booming calls.

FIGURE 39.9 How to impress a female.

MATING SYSTEMS

Animal mating systems have traditionally been categorized as promiscuous, polygamous, or monogamous. In recent years, studies that integrate paternity analysis with behavioral observations have shown that species do not always fit cleanly into these categories. Members of a species often vary in their behavior.

Some animals such as prairie voles form a pair bond, which means two individuals mate, preferentially spend time together, and cooperate in rearing offspring. However, the participants in a pair bond may also seize opportunities for matings with other individuals. A paternity study of the prairie voles discussed in Section 39.1 found that 7 percent of pair-bonded females produced litters of mixed male parentage; and 15 percent of pair-bonded males sired offspring with females other than their partner. Thus, prairie voles are now described as socially monogamous, but genetically promiscuous. As a species, they form an exclusive social relationship with a single partner. However, the genetic composition of their offspring reflects a tendency to mate with multiple partners.

Even social monogamy is rare in most animals, with the exception of birds. An estimated 90 percent of birds are socially monogamous. Among this group, the vast majority of species that have been examined for paternity patterns are genetically promiscuous. This is not surprising as promiscuity benefits both males and females by increasing the genetic diversity among the offspring they produce.

Multiple matings can also provide another benefit: more offspring. This benefit usually applies most strongly to males. Sperm are energetically inexpensive to produce, so a male's reproductive success is usually limited by access to mates. By contrast, the main limit on a female's reproductive success is her capacity to produce large, yolk-rich eggs or, in mammals, to carry developing young.

When one sex exerts selection pressure on the other, we expect sexual selection to occur (Section 17.6). In many species, females choose among males on the basis of their ability to provide necessary resources. For example, a female hangingfly will only mate with a male while feeding on prey that he has provided as a "nuptial gift" (**FIGURE 39.9A**).

In other species, males establish a mating territory, an area that includes resources that females require for reproduction. A **territory** is an area from which an animal or group of animals actively exclude others. A male fiddler crab's territory is a stretch of shoreline in which he excavates a burrow. Fiddler crabs have **sexual dimorphism**, in which body forms of males and females differ. A male has one oversized claw (**FIGURE 39.9B**) and during mating season, he stands outside his burrow waving it. The claw is used both in the courtship display and in territorial disputes with other males. Females attracted by a male's display check out the location and dimensions of his burrow before mating with him. Burrow location and size are important because they affect development of the larvae.

In mammals such as elephant seals and elk, the strongest males hold large territories, and mate with all of the females inside the area. Other males may never get to mate at all unless they sneak into an area under another male's control.

In some birds such as sage grouse, males converge at a communal display ground called a **lek**. Males stamp their feet and emit booming calls by puffing and deflating their large neck pouches for female onlookers (**FIGURE 39.9C**). The most popular males mate with many females.

PARENTAL CARE

Parental care requires time and energy that an individual could otherwise invest in reproducing again. It arises only if the genetic benefit of providing care (increased offspring survival now) offsets the cost (reduced opportunity to produce offspring later). If the parental care provided by a single parent is sufficient to successfully rear an offspring, individuals who spare themselves this cost by leaving parental duties to their mate are at a selective advantage.

Which sex cares for the young varies by species. In about 90 percent of mammals, the female rears young (**FIGURE 39.10A**). In the remaining 10 percent, both sexes participate. No mammal relies solely on male parental care. Female mammals sustain developing young in their body, so they have a greater investment in newborns than males. Also, most male mammals do not lactate, although in two fruit bat species, both males and females nurse the young.

Most fishes provide no parental care, but in those that do, this duty usually falls to the male. Males guard eggs until they hatch (**FIGURE 39.10B**) or, in the case of sea horses, protect them inside their body. The prevalence of male parental care in fishes may be related to sex differences in how fertility changes with age. A female fish's fertility increases dramatically with age, whereas a male's does not. Thus, a female fish who invests energy in care forgoes more future reproduction than a male fish does.

In birds, two-parent care is most common (**FIGURE 39.10C**). Chicks of birds that cooperate in care of their young tend to hatch while in a relatively helpless state. Chicks of sage grouse and other birds in which females alone provide care tend to hatch when more fully developed.

A Female grizzly bears care for their cub for as long as two years.

B Male clownfish guard eggs (*right*) until they hatch.

C Male and female terns cooperate in the care of their chick.

FIGURE 39.10 Who cares for the young?

lek Of some birds, a communal mating display area for males.
sexual dimorphism Distinct male and female body forms.
territory Area an animal or group occupies and defends.

FIGURE 39.11 A selfish herd. Sardines attempt to hide behind one another as a predatory sailfish attacks.

Most animals live solitary lives, coming together only to mate. However, some spend time in groups. A group may be a temporary, like a herd of zebras or a school of fish, or it may be more permanent, like a prairie dog colony or a wolf pack. A tendency to group together, whether briefly or for the longer term, will evolve only if the benefits of being near others outweigh the costs.

BENEFITS OF GROUPS

In many species, grouping together reduces the risk of predation. There is safety in numbers. Whenever animals cluster, individuals at the margins of the group inadvertently shield others from predators. A **selfish herd** is a temporary aggregation that arises when animals hide behind one another to escape a threat. Small fish form a selfish herd when under attack by a predator (**FIGURE 39.11**).

In a group, multiple individuals can be on the alert for predators. In some cases, an animal that spots a threat will warn others of its approach. Birds, monkeys, meerkats, and prairie dogs are among the animals that make alarm calls in response to a predator. Even in species that do not make alarm calls, individuals can benefit from the vigilance

of others. Often, when an animal notices another group member beginning to flee, it will do likewise. In what is called the "confusion effect," a predator has a more difficult time picking out a specific individual to pursue when a group of prey is scattering.

Not all prey groups flee from predators. Some present a united defense. For example, when threatened by wolves, musk oxen stand back to back, presenting an imposing display of sharp horns. Sawfly caterpillars also gather in a group. When a hungry bird approaches, the caterpillars rear up and vomit partly digested eucalyptus leaves. In experiments, birds presented with such a slimy cluster eat fewer caterpillars than birds that were offered caterpillars one at a time.

Social animals form more permanent multigenerational groups, in which members benefit by cooperating in some tasks. Members of a social group are usually relatives. Wolves and lions are social animals who cooperate in catching prey. Cooperative hunting allows a group of predators to capture larger or faster prey. Even so, cooperative hunting is often no more efficient than hunting alone. In one study, researchers observed that a solitary lion catches prey about 15 percent of the time. Two lions hunting together catch prey twice as often as a solitary lion, but having to share the spoils of the hunt means the amount of food per lion is the same. When more lions join a hunt, the success rate per lion falls. Wolves have a similar pattern. Among carnivores that hunt cooperatively, hunting success is usually not the major advantage of group living. Individuals hunt together, but also cooperate in fending off scavengers (**FIGURE 39.12**), caring for one another's young, and defending their territory.

Group living can also facilitate learning by imitation. Imitative tool production is an example. Chimpanzees strip leaves from branches to make "fishing sticks," simple tools that they use to capture insects as food. Different groups of chimpanzees use slightly different methods of tool-shaping and insect-fishing. In each group, individuals learn by imitating the behavior of others.

COSTS OF GROUP LIVING

Grouping together has costs. Individuals that group together are easier for predators to locate and for parasites and contagious diseases to infect. Members of a group also compete more for resources. Consider how many seabirds form dense breeding colonies in which competition for space and food is intense (**FIGURE 39.13**). Given the opportunity, a pair of breeding herring gulls will cannibalize the eggs and even the chicks of their neighbors.

DOMINANCE HIERARCHIES

Cost and benefits are often not equally distributed among members of a group. Many animals that live in permanent groups form a **dominance hierarchy**. In this type of social system, dominant animals get a greater share of resources and breeding opportunities than subordinate ones. Typically, dominance is established by physical confrontation. In most wolf packs, one dominant male breeds with one dominant female. The other members of the pack are nonbreeding brothers and sisters, aunts and uncles. All hunt and carry food back to individuals that guard the young in their den.

Why would a subordinate give up resources and often breeding privileges? Challenging a strong individual can be dangerous, as is living on one's own. Subordinates get their chance to reproduce by outliving a dominant peer.

---

dominance hierarchy Social system in which resources and mating opportunities are unequally distributed within a group.
selfish herd Temporary group that forms when individuals cluster to minimize their individual risk of predation.
social animal Animal that lives in a multigenerational group in which members, who are usually relatives, cooperate in some tasks.

FIGURE 39.12 Lionesses enjoy the results of a communal hunt, while spotted hyenas try to steal a share.

FIGURE 39.13 A colony of nesting penguins. Parasites spread easily through such colonies and the colony's large size makes it easy for predators to find.

TAKE-HOME MESSAGE 39.5

Individual animals sometimes form a temporary group that reduces their risk of predation.

Animals that live in permanent social groups cooperate in tasks such as hunting and rearing young.

Costs of grouping include increased risk of disease and parasitism, and increased competition for resources.

A Honeybee queen surrounded by sterile worker females.

B Naked mole-rat worker in its burrow.

FIGURE 39.14 Examples of eusocial animals.

From a genetic standpoint, the greatest cost an individual can pay for living in a group is the failure to breed. Yet, in some animals, a social system has evolved in which permanently sterile workers care cooperatively for the offspring of just a few breeding individuals. Such animals are said to be eusocial. **Eusocial animals** live in a multigenerational family group in which sterile workers carry out all tasks essential to the group's welfare, while other members of the group produce offspring.

Most eusocial animals are members of the order Hymenoptera, which includes bees, wasps, and ants. Some bees and wasps are eusocial, as are all ants. In all eusocial hymenoptera, the workers that maintain and defend a colony are sterile females. For example, the only egg-laying female in a honeybee colony is the queen (**FIGURE 39.14A**). Termites are also eusocial, but a termite colony has both male and female workers.

Only two species of eusocial vertebrates are known. Both are African mole-rats, mouse-sized rodents that live in underground burrows (**FIGURE 39.14B**). A clan of eusocial mole-rats includes a reproductive female, one or two reproductive males, and their worker offspring. Workers of both sexes dig the burrows, care for the young, provide the clan with food, and defend it.

Workers in a eusocial species engage in **altruistic behavior**, which in biology means behavior that enhances another individual's reproductive success at the altruist's

expense. According to William Hamilton's **theory of inclusive fitness**, genes that promote altruism can evolve if those helped are relatives. If an individual with an allele that promotes altruism helps enough others with same allele, the frequency of that allele will increase, despite the reduced reproductive success of the altruist.

It is easy to see the genetic advantage of caring for one's own offspring. They have copies of some of your genes. However, remember that in a sexually reproducing diploid species, each offspring typically inherits half its genes from its mother and half from its father. Thus each individual shares only 50 percent of its genes with each of its parents. It also shares 50 percent of its genes with any of its siblings (brothers and sisters). By sacrificing its own reproductive success to help rear its siblings, a sterile worker promotes copies of its own "self-sacrifice" genes in these close relatives.

In all eusocial species, sterile workers assist fertile relatives with whom they share genes. Honeybees and ants may have an added incentive to make sacrifices. Hymenoptera have a haplodiploid sex determination system, in which diploid females develop from fertilized eggs and haploid males from unfertilized ones. As a result, female hymenopterans share 75 percent of their genes with their sisters. This may help explain why eusociality has arisen many times in this order.

In mole-rats, eusocial behavior is thought to have evolved mainly as a result of ecological factors. Mole-rats live in a very dry habitat where burrowing is difficult and food supplies are patchy. Dispersing from an existing clan and starting a new one is unlikely to be successful. Thus, most individuals do better by staying and assisting their relatives.

altruistic behavior Behavior that benefits others at the expense of the individual.
eusocial animal Animal that lives in a multigenerational group in which many sterile workers cooperate in all tasks essential to the group's welfare, while a few members of the group produce offspring.
theory of inclusive fitness Alleles associated with altruism can be advantageous if the expense of this behavior to the altruist is outweighed by increases in the reproductive success of relatives.

TAKE-HOME MESSAGE 39.6

Eusocial animals live in family groups in which many sterile workers care for the young of a few breeding individuals.

In eusocial bees and ants, all workers are female. In termites and mole-rats, there are both male and female workers.

The theory of inclusive fitness explains how genes that favor altruism can evolve if individuals help close relatives.

Ecological factors can also favor evolution of eusociality. In mole-rats, a harsh habitat makes it difficult for individuals to leave an established clan and breed elsewhere.

Education

FIGURE 39.15 Africanized honeybee workers stand guard at their hive entrance. If a threat appears, they will release an alarm pheromone.

HONEYBEES STING ONLY IN DEFENSE. Stinging is an evolved response to the threat of animals that raid hives for honey. The European bees used as pollinators of domestic crops and in commercial honey production have been selectively bred to have a high threat threshold. Africanized bees, known in the popular press as "killer bees," are more easily put on the defensive (**FIGURE 39.15**).

Africanized honeybees arose in Brazil in the 1950s. Bee breeders there had imported African bees in the hope of breeding an improved pollinator for this region's tropical orchards. Some of the African imports escaped and mated with European honeybees that had already become established there. Descendants of the resulting hybrids expanded northward and have now become established in much of the United States.

All honeybees can sting only once, and all make the same kind of venom, but Africanized bees sting with less provocation, respond to threats in greater numbers, and are more persistent in pursuit of perceived threats. Vibrations, as from a lawn mower or construction equipment, have triggered several attacks.

What makes Africanized honeybees so testy? One factor is a greater response to the alarm pheromone that workers release in response to a threat. Workers inside the hive detect this chemical signal and rush out to drive off the intruder. Researchers tested the response of Africanized honeybees and European honeybees to alarm pheromone by positioning a cloth near the entrance of hives and releasing an artificial pheromone. Africanized bees flew out of a hive and attacked the cloth faster than European bees, and they plunged six to eight times as many stingers into the cloth.

Human deaths from Africanized bee stings remain rare: There have been about 20 since the bees arrived in the United States in 1990. However, even a single sting can be fatal to someone allergic to honeybee venom. In addition, bee stings are highly painful and people who receive a large number of stings often require hospitalization. Livestock and pet animals have also been stung, in some cases fatally. Thus, the spread of Africanized bees through the United States is a matter of concern.

Summary

SECTION 39.1 Behavior is a response to stimuli. Genes that influence the nervous or endocrine systems often affect behavior. Studies of behavioral differences within a species or among closely related species can shed light on the proximate (genetic and physiological) and ultimate (evolutionary) causes of a behavior. Epigenetic effects can also influence behavior.

SECTION 39.2 **Instinctive behavior** is inborn; it occurs without any prior experience. Instinctive responses are often triggered by a simple stimulus.

Learned behavior arises in response to experience. Most behavior has a learned component. **Imprinting** is time-sensitive learning. With **habituation**, an animal learns to disregard certain frequently encountered stimuli. Animals also form mental maps, learn the identity of other individuals, develop conditioned responses, and imitate observed behaviors.

SECTION 39.3 Animals communicate by means of chemical, visual, acoustical, or tactile signals. Chemical signals called **pheromones** may elicit an immediate change in behavior, or cause a physiological change that affects behavior over the longer term.

Signaling systems are adaptive only when they benefit both the sender and the receiver. Evolution influences properties of signals, as when courtship calls are easily localized, but alarm calls are not. Predators sometimes take advantage of the communication system of their prey.

SECTION 39.4 Animal mating systems vary among species, and often within species. Monogamy is rare. Even among species that form pair bonds, either or both partners may mate with others. Both males and females benefit by mating with multiple partners, but males tend to be less choosy about mates than females. Sexual selection favors traits that give an individual a competitive edge in attracting mates. Some male birds display for females at a **lek**. In other animals, males establish and defend a **territory** that contains resources that females need. With territorial systems, some males have many mates, whereas other do not mate at all. Territorial animals may have **sexual dimorphism.**

Parental care evolves when the cost in terms of lost opportunities to produce additional offspring later is offset by the benefit of increased survival among current offspring. Which parent or parents care for offspring varies among animal groups. In mammals, maternal care is the rule and no cases of sole paternal care are known. In fishes that provide care, the care-giver is usually male. In birds, both parents usually cooperate in rearing young.

SECTION 39.5 Most animals are solitary, but some form temporary or long-term groups. Animals may temporarily come together as a **selfish herd** in response to the threat of predation. **Social animals** form multigenerational groups and benefit by cooperating in tasks such as defense or rearing the young. With a **dominance hierarchy**, resource and mating opportunities are distributed unequally among group members. Species that live in large groups incur costs, including increased disease and parasitism, and more intense competition for resources.

SECTION 39.6 Honeybees, ants, termites, and some rodents called mole-rats are **eusocial animals**: They live in colonies with overlapping generations and have a reproductive division of labor. Most colony members do not reproduce; they assist their relatives instead.

The **theory of inclusive fitness** states that **altruistic behavior** can be perpetuated when altruistic individuals help their reproducing relatives. Altruistic individuals help perpetuate alleles that lead to their altruism by promoting reproductive success of close relatives who are likely to share these alleles.

SECTION 39.7 "Killer bees" are a hybrid of African and European honeybee strains. Their defensive stinging behavior is triggered more easily than that of other honeybees and they sting in greater numbers.

Self-Quiz   Answers in Appendix VII

1. Genes affect the behavior of individuals by _____ .
   a. influencing the development of nervous systems
   b. affecting how individuals respond to hormones
   c. determining which stimuli can be detected
   d. all of the above

2. Stevan Arnold offered slug meat to newborn garter snakes from different populations to test his hypothesis that the snakes' response to slugs _____ .
   a. was shaped by indirect selection
   b. is an instinctive behavior
   c. is based on pheromones
   d. is adaptive

3. The proximate cause of feeding differences between sitter and rover fruit flies is _____ .
   a. a difference in alleles at one locus that affects learning
   b. natural selection related to competition for food
   c. a difference in alleles for oxytocin receptors
   d. a difference in their ability to find food

4. The honeybee dance transmits information about _____ by way of tactile signals.
   a. predators   c. location of food
   b. mating opportunities   d. amount of honey

5. A _____ is a chemical that conveys information between individuals of the same species.
   a. pheromone   c. hormone
   b. neurotransmitter   d. all of the above

6. In what group of vertebrates is monogamy and cooperative care of the young by two parents most common?

Data Analysis Activities

Nestling Responses to Alarm Calls As adults, the Australian songbirds known as scrubwrens give different alarm calls depending on whether a predatory bird is on the ground or in flight. The length of the call indicates the urgency of the threat. Scrubwrens make well-concealed nests on the ground, so predators on the ground pose more of a threat to nestlings than those flying above. By contrast, flying predators pose more of a threat to adults. To gauge the response of scrubwren nestlings to parental alarm calls, Dirk Platzen recorded the calls and played them to 5- and 11-day-old nestlings. **FIGURE 39.16** shows how playback of the recordings affected the rate at which chicks made peeping sounds.

1. Which type of alarm call reduced peeping most in 11-day-old nestlings? Which had the least effect?
2. Given that a predator on the ground poses the greatest threat to young birds, which response would you expect to be greatest in 5-day-old nestlings? Is it?
3. Which types of calls did chicks become increasingly responsive to as they aged?

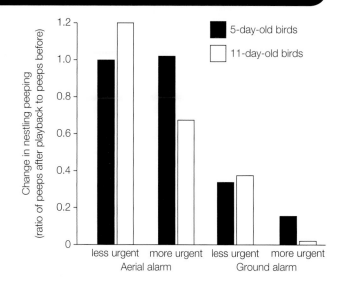

FIGURE 39.16 Change in peeping behavior of 5-day-old nestlings (black bars) and 11-day-old nestlings (white bars) in response to playback of alarm calls by their parent. A value of 0 indicates complete suppression of nestling peeps, 1 indicates no change, and a value above 1 indicates an increase in peeping.

7. List two possible benefits of living in a group.

8. All honeybee workers are _____ .
   a. male   c. female
   b. sterile   d. b and c

9. Eusocial insects _____ .
   a. live in extended family groups
   b. include termites, honeybees, and ants
   c. show a reproductive division of labor
   d. all of the above

10. In fishes that provide parental care, that care is most often delivered by _____ .
   a. the male parent   c. siblings
   b. the female parent   d. both parents

11. Match the terms with their most suitable description.
   ___ altruistic behavior   a. time-dependent form of learning
   ___ selfish herd   b. communal display area
   ___ habituation   c. learning to ignore a stimulus
   ___ lek   d. defended area with resources
   ___ territory   e. assisting another individual at one's own expense
   ___ imprinting   f. unequal distribution of benefits
   ___ dominance hierarchy   g. involuntary response becomes tied to a stimulus
   ___ classical conditioning   h. individuals hide behind others

Critical Thinking

1. For billions of years, the only bright objects in the night sky were stars or the moon. Night-flying moths use them to navigate a straight line. Today, the instinct to fly toward bright objects causes moths to exhaust themselves fluttering around streetlights and banging against brightly lit windowpanes. This behavior clearly is not adaptive, so why does it persist?

2. A female chimpanzee engages in sex only during her fertile period, which is advertised by a swelling of her external genitals. Bonobos, the closest relatives of the chimpanzees, are more sexually active than chimpanzees. Female bonobos mate even when they are not fertile. In both species, mating is promiscuous; each female mates with many males. By one hypothesis, female promiscuity may help prevent male infanticide. Chimpanzee males have been observed to kill infants in the wild, but this behavior has never been observed among bonobos.

Explain why it would be disadvantageous for a male to kill the infant of a female with whom he had sex. How might the bonobo female's increased sexual activity lower likelihood of male infanticide?

CENGAGE brain.com To access course materials, please visit www.cengagebrain.com.

CREDIT: (16) Platzen, D. & Magrath, R., "Adaptive differences in response to two types of parental alarm call in altricial nestlings," Proceedings of the Royal Society of London 2005, Series B; Biological Sciences, vol. 272. pp. 1101–1106, by permission of The Royal Society.

CHAPTER 39
ANIMAL
BEHAVIOR

709

A red knot sandpiper, marked with
leg bands for an ongoing study of
its rapidly declining population.

40

POPULATION ECOLOGY

Links to Earlier Concepts

Earlier chapters explored the evolutionary history and genetic nature of populations, including those of humans (Sections 1.1, 17.1, 24.12). Now you will consider ecological factors that limit population growth. Again, science does not address social issues—in this case, how exponential growth affects human lives (1.7). It can only help explain how ecological conditions and events sustain a population's growth, or put a stop to it.

KEY CONCEPTS

THE VITAL STATISTICS
Ecologists describe a population in terms of its size, density, and the distribution of its members. They often use sampling methods to determine these statistics.

EXPONENTIAL GROWTH
With unlimited resources, a population will grow exponentially. Although the growth rate remains constant, the number of individuals added increases with each generation.

LIMITS ON INCREASES IN SIZE
Density-dependent factors such as increased competition for resources slow population growth. Density-independent factors such as extreme weather can also affect population size.

LIFE HISTORY PATTERNS
Natural selection affects how quickly organisms mature, how often they reproduce, and the number of young per breeding event. Different environments favor different patterns of investment in offspring.

THE HUMAN POPULATION
Technological innovations have allowed human populations to sidestep some limits on growth and expand into new habitats. We are now using resources at an unsustainable rate.

A Clumped distribution of hippopotamuses. B Near-uniform distribution of nesting seabirds. C Random distribution of dandelions.

FIGURE 40.1 Population distribution patterns.

SIZE, DENSITY, AND DISTRIBUTION

A population, remember, is a group of interbreeding individuals of the same species in a specified area (Section 17.1). Members of a population breed with one another more than they breed with members of other populations. Many factors affect the size and structure of a population, and the study of those factors is called population ecology. **Ecology** is a branch of biology that deals with how organisms interact with one another and the environment. Ecology is not the same as environmentalism, which is advocacy for protection of the environment. However, environmentalists often cite results of ecological studies when drawing attention to environmental concerns.

SIZE, DENSITY, AND DISTRIBUTION

Demographics are statistics that describe a population. These include population size, density, and distribution, which we discuss here, as well as age structure and fertility rates, which we consider in Section 40.6.

Population size is the total number of individuals in a population. **Population density** is the number of individuals per unit area or volume. Examples of population density include the number of dandelions per square meter of lawn or the number of amoebas per milliliter of pond water. **Population distribution** describes the location of individuals relative to one another. Members of a population may be clumped together, be an equal distance apart, or be distributed randomly. The most common population distribution pattern is a clumped one, in which members of the population are closer to one another than would be predicted by chance alone. A patchy distribution of resources encourages clumping. Hippopotamuses clump in muddy river shallows (**FIGURE 40.1**). A cool, damp, north-facing slope may be covered with ferns, whereas an adjacent drier south-facing slope has none. Limited dispersal ability increases the likelihood of a clumped distribution:

As the saying goes, the nut does not fall far from the tree. Asexual reproduction is another source of clusters. It produces colonies of coral and vast stands of some trees. Finally, as Section 39.5 explained, some animals benefit by grouping together.

Intense competition for limited resources can produce a near uniform distribution, with individuals more evenly spaced than would be expected by chance. Creosote bushes in deserts of the American Southwest grow in this pattern. Competition for limited water among the root systems keeps the plants from growing in close proximity. Similarly, seabirds in breeding colonies often show a near uniform distribution. Each nesting bird aggressively repels others that get within reach of its beak (**FIGURE 40.1B**).

A random distribution occurs when resources are distributed uniformly through the environment, and proximity to others neither benefits nor harms individuals. For example, when the wind-dispersed seeds of dandelions land on the uniform environment of a suburban lawn, dandelion plants grow in a random pattern (**FIGURE 40.1C**). Wolf spider burrows are also randomly distributed relative to one another. When seeking a burrow site, the spiders neither avoid one another nor seek one another out.

Often, the scale of the area sampled and the timing of a study influence the observed demographics. For example, seabirds are spaced almost uniformly at a nesting site, but the nesting sites are clumped along a shoreline. The birds crowd together during the breeding season, but disperse when breeding is over.

SAMPLING A POPULATION

It is often impractical to count all members of a population, so biologists frequently use sampling techniques to estimate population size. **Plot sampling** estimates the total number of individuals in an area on the basis of direct counts in a small portion of the area. For example, ecologists might estimate the number of grass plants in a grassland, or the number of clams in a mudflat, by measuring the number of individuals in several 1-meter by 1-meter square plots. To estimate total population size, scientists first determine the average number of individuals per sample plot. They then multiply that average by the number of plots that would fit in the population's range. Estimates derived from plot sampling are most accurate when species are not very mobile and conditions across their habitat are uniform.

Mark–recapture sampling is used to estimate the population size of mobile animals. With this technique, animals are captured, marked with a unique identifier of some sort, then released. After marked individuals return to the population, scientists capture another sample of the population. The proportion of marked animals in the second sample is taken to be representative of the proportion marked in the population as a whole. Suppose 100 deer are captured, marked, and released. Later, 50 of these deer are recaptured along with 50 unmarked deer. Marked deer constitute half the recaptured group, so the group previously caught and marked (100 deer) must have been half of the population. Thus the total population is estimated at 200.

Information about the traits of individuals in a sample plot or capture group can be used to infer properties of the population as a whole. For example, if half the recaptured deer are of reproductive age, half of the population is assumed to share this trait.

---

demographics Statistics that describe a population.
ecology Study of interactions among organisms, and among organisms and their environment.
mark–recapture sampling Method of estimating population size of mobile animals by marking individuals, releasing them, then checking the proportion of marks among individuals recaptured at a later time.
plot sampling Using demographics observed in sample plots to estimate demographics of a population as a whole.
population density Number of individuals per unit area.
population distribution Location of population members relative to one another; clumped, uniformly dispersed, or randomly dispersed.
population size Total number of individuals in a population.

TAKE-HOME MESSAGE 40.1

Demographics such as size, density, and distribution pattern are used to describe populations. Demographics of a population are often inferred on the basis of a study of a smaller subgroup within that population.

Environmental conditions and interactions among individuals can influence a population's demographics, which often change over time.

PEOPLE MATTER

National Geographic Grantee
DR. KAREN DeMATTEO

A Chesapeake Bay retriever named Train helps Karen DeMatteo study jaguars, puma, ocelots, oncillas, and bush dogs. Individuals of these species occur at low density in the dense South American forest, so locating them is a challenge. DeMatteo could have used standard survey technology (such as radio telemetry or camera traps) to get information, but those methods have some weaknesses. For example, an animal could avoid the part of the forest where a camera is set up. So, DeMatteo decided to look instead for what the animals leave behind in the forest—their scat (feces).

This is where Train comes in. Like other dogs, he has a terrific sense of smell, and he has been trained to use it to find specific types of scat. He behaves like a drug-sniffing dog, except instead of alerting his handler when he finds a drug, he alerts DeMatteo when he finds predator scat. DeMatteo collects the scat that Train finds, and later analyzes its DNA in the laboratory. Results of this analysis, along with GPS and spatial mapping locations of where scat was found, allow DeMatteo to determine the predators' distribution and understand differences in habitat use. DeMatteo says, "The goal is to expand our knowledge of how these species move through the landscape so we can determine locations for biological corridors/wildlife crossings that maximize animal movement and minimize human–wildlife conflict."

40.2 WHY DOES THE SIZE OF A POPULATION CHANGE?

Starting Size of Population		Net Monthly Increase	New Size of Population
2,000	× r =	800	2,800
2,800	× r =	1,120	3,920
3,920	× r =	1,568	5,488
5,488	× r =	2,195	7,683
7,683	× r =	3,073	10,756
10,756	× r =	4,302	15,058
15,058	× r =	6,023	21,081
21,081	× r =	8,432	29,513
29,513	× r =	11,805	41,318
41,318	× r =	16,527	57,845
57,845	× r =	23,138	80,983
80,983	× r =	32,393	113,376
113,376	× r =	45,350	158,726
158,726	× r =	63,490	222,216
222,216	× r =	88,887	311,103
311,103	× r =	124,441	435,544
435,544	× r =	174,218	609,762
609,762	× r =	243,905	853,667
853,667	× r =	341,467	1,195,134

A Increases in size over time. Note that the net increase becomes larger with each generation.

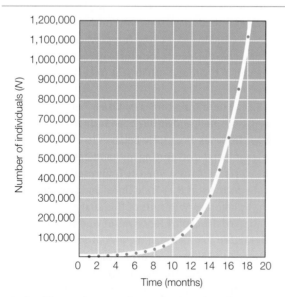

B Graphing numbers over time produces a J-shaped curve.

FIGURE 40.2 {Animated} Exponential growth in a hypothetical population of mice with a per capita rate of growth (r) of 0.4 per mouse per month and a population size of 2,000.

IMMIGRATION AND EMIGRATION

In nature, populations continually change in size. Individuals are added to a population by births and **immigration**, the arrival of new residents that previously belonged to another population. Individuals are removed from it by deaths and **emigration**, the departure of individuals who take up permanent residence elsewhere.

In many animal species, young of one or both sexes leave the area where they were born to breed elsewhere. For example, young freshwater turtles typically emigrate from their parental population and become immigrants at another pond some distance away. By contrast, seabirds typically breed where they were born. However, some individuals may emigrate and end up at breeding sites more than a thousand kilometers away. The tendency of individuals to emigrate to a new breeding site is usually related to resource availability and crowding. As resources decline and crowding increases, the likelihood of emigration rises.

ZERO TO EXPONENTIAL GROWTH

If we set aside the effects of immigration and emigration, we can define **zero population growth** as an interval during which the number of births is balanced by an equal number of deaths. As a result, population size remains unchanged, with no net increase or decrease in the number of individuals.

We can measure births and deaths in terms of rates per individual, or per capita. *Capita* means head, as in a head count. Subtract a population's per capita death rate (d) from its per capita birth rate (b) and you have the **per capita growth rate**, or r:

$$ b \quad - \quad d \quad = \quad r $$

b (per capita birth rate)	−	d (per capita death rate)	=	r (per capita growth rate)

Imagine 2,000 mice living in the same field. If 1,000 mice are born each month, then the birth rate is 0.5 births per mouse per month (1,000 births/2,000 mice). If 200 mice die one way or another each month, then the death rate is 200/2,000 or 0.1 deaths per mouse per month. Thus, r is 0.5 – 0.1, or 0.4 per mouse per month.

As long as r remains constant and greater than zero, **exponential growth** will occur, which means that the population's size will increase by the same proportion of its total in every successive time interval. We can calculate population growth (G) for each interval based on the number of individuals (N) and the per capita growth rate:

$$ N \quad \times \quad r \quad = \quad G $$

N (number of individuals)	×	r (per capita growth rate)	=	G (population growth per unit time)

Our hypothetical population of field mice consists of 2,800 after one month (**FIGURE 40.2A**). A net increase of 800 fertile mice has increased the number of breeders. If all of the fertile mice reproduce, the population size will expand by 1,120 individuals (2,800 $\times$ 0.4). The total population size is now 3,920. At this growth rate, the number of mice would rise from 2,000 to more than 1 million in under two years! Graphing the increases against time results in a J-shaped curve, which is characteristic of exponential population growth (**FIGURE 40.2B**).

With exponential growth, the number of new individuals added increases each generation, although the per capita growth rate stays the same. Exponential population growth is analogous to compound interest in a bank account. The annual interest *rate* stays fixed, yet every year the *amount* of interest paid increases. The annual interest paid into the account adds to the size of the balance, so the next interest payment will be based on the increased balance. Similarly, with exponential growth, the number of individuals added increases in each generation.

Imagine a single bacterium in a culture flask. After thirty minutes, the cell divides in two. Those two cells divide, and so on every thirty minutes. If no cells die between divisions, then the population size will double in every interval—from 1 to 2, then 4, 8, 16, 32, and so on. After 9–1/2 hours, there have been nineteen doublings, so the population now consists of more than 500,000 cells. Ten hours (twenty doublings) later, there are more than a million. Curve 1 in **FIGURE 40.3** is a plot of this increase.

Now suppose that 25 percent of the descendant cells die every thirty minutes in our hypothetical population of bacteria. In this scenario, it takes seventeen hours, not ten, for that population to reach 1 million. Thus, deaths slow the rate of increase but do not stop exponential growth (curve 2 in **FIGURE 40.3**). Exponential growth will occur in

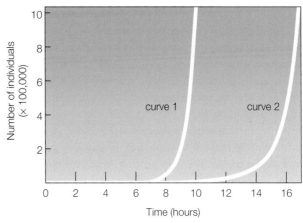

FIGURE 40.3 Effect of deaths on the rate of increase for two hypothetical populations of bacteria, both starting with one cell. Plot the population growth for bacterial cells that reproduce every half hour and you get growth curve 1. Next, plot the population growth of bacterial cells that divide every half hour, with 25 percent dying between divisions, and you get growth curve 2. Deaths slow the rate of increase, but as long as the birth rate exceeds the death rate, exponential growth will continue.

any population in which the birth rate exceeds the death rate—in other words, as long as *r* is greater than zero.

BIOTIC POTENTIAL

The growth rate for a population under ideal conditions is its **biotic potential**. This is a theoretical rate at which the population would grow if shelter, food, and other essential resources were unlimited and there were no predators or pathogens. Factors that affect biotic potential include the age at which reproduction typically begins, how long individuals remain reproductive, and the number of offspring that are produced each time an individual reproduces. Microbes such as bacteria have some of the highest biotic potentials, whereas large-bodied mammals have some of the lowest.

Regardless of the species, populations seldom reach their biotic potential because of the effects of limiting factors, a topic we discuss in detail in the next section.

biotic potential Maximum possible population growth rate under optimal conditions.
emigration Movement of individuals out of a population.
exponential growth A population grows by a fixed percentage in successive time intervals; the size of each increase is determined by the current population size.
immigration Movement of individuals into a population.
per capita growth rate (r) Of a population, the change in individuals added over some time interval, divided by the number of individuals in the population.
zero population growth Interval in which births equal deaths.

TAKE-HOME MESSAGE 40.2

The size of a population depends on its birth rate, death rate, immigration, and emigration.

Exponential growth occurs when the per capita growth rate (*r*) of a population is stable and greater than one. With exponential growth, more and more individuals are added with each successive generation.

Most populations never achieve the maximal possible growth rate for their species, because of limiting factors.

40.3 WHAT CONSTRAINS POPULATION GROWTH?

DENSITY-DEPENDENT FACTORS

No population can grow exponentially forever. As the degree of crowding increases, **density-dependent limiting factors** cause birth rates to slow and death rates to rise, so the rate of population growth decreases. These factors include predation, parasitism and disease, and competition for a limited resource.

Any natural area has limited resources. Thus, as the number of individuals in an area increases, so does **intraspecific competition**: competition among members of the same species. As a result of increased competition, some individuals fail to secure what they need to survive and reproduce. Competition has a detrimental effect even on winners, because energy they use in competition for resources is not available for reproduction. Essential resources for which animals might compete include food, water, hiding places, and nesting sites (**FIGURE 40.4**). Plants compete for nutrients, water, and access to sunlight.

Parasitism and contagious disease increase with crowding because the closer individuals are to one another, the more easily parasites and pathogens can spread. Predation increases with density too, because predators often concentrate their efforts on the most abundant prey.

LOGISTIC GROWTH

Logistic growth occurs when density-dependent factors affect population size over time (**FIGURE 40.5**). When the population is small, density-dependent limiting factors have little effect and the population grows exponentially ❶. Then, as population size and the degree of crowding rise, these factors begin to limit growth ❷. Eventually, the population size levels off at the environment's carrying capacity ❸. **Carrying capacity (K)** is the maximum number of individuals that a population's environment can support indefinitely. The result is an S-shaped curve.

The equation that describes logistic growth is:

$$(r \times N)\frac{(K - N)}{K} = G$$

As with the exponential growth equation, G is growth per unit time, r is the per capita growth rate, and N is current population size. K is carrying capacity. The $(K−N)/K$ part of the equation represents the proportion of carrying capacity not yet used. As a population grows, this proportion decreases, so G becomes smaller and smaller. At carrying capacity, the equation become $G=rN(0)$, which means no individuals are added.

Carrying capacity is species-specific, environment-specific, and can change over time ❹. For example, the carrying capacity for a plant species decreases when nutrients in the soil become depleted. Human activities also affect carrying capacity. For example, human harvest of horseshoe crabs has decreased the carrying capacity for red knot sandpipers (shown in the chapter opening photo). Horseshoe crab eggs are these birds' main food during their long-distance migration.

DENSITY-INDEPENDENT FACTORS

Sometimes, natural disasters or weather-related events affect population size. A volcanic eruption, hurricane, or flood can decrease population size. So can human-caused events such

FIGURE 40.4 Example of a limiting factor. Wood ducks build nests only inside tree hollows of specific dimensions (*left*). In some places, lack of access to appropriate hollows now limits the size of the wood duck population. Adding artificial nesting boxes (*right*) to these environments can help increase the size of the duck populations.

FIGURE 40.5 Logistic growth. Note the initial S-shaped curve.
❶ At low density, the population grows exponentially.
❷ As crowding increases, density-dependent limiting factors slow the rate of growth.
❸ Population size levels off at the carrying capacity for that species.
❹ Any change in the carrying capacity will result in a corresponding shift in population size.

FIGURE IT OUT: How does adding nest boxes affect the carrying capacity for wood duck populations? Answer: It increases carrying capacity.

FIGURE 40.6 Overshoot and crash. A reindeer herd introduced to an island in 1944 increased in size exponentially, then crashed after an especially cold and snowy winter in 1963–64.

as an oil spill. These events are called **density-independent limiting factors**, because crowding does not influence the likelihood of their occurrence or the magnitude of their effect.

In nature, density-dependent and density-independent factors often interact to determine a population's size. Consider what happened after the 1944 introduction of 29 reindeer to St. Matthew Island, an uninhabited island off the coast of Alaska. When biologist David Klein visited the island in 1957, he found 1,350 well-fed reindeer (**FIGURE 40.6**). Klein returned in 1963 and counted 6,000 reindeer. The population had soared far above the island's carrying capacity. A population can temporarily overshoot an environment's carrying capacity, but the high density cannot be sustained. Klein observed that some effects of density-dependent limiting factors were already apparent. For example, the

average body size of the reindeer had decreased. When Klein returned in 1966, only 42 reindeer survived. The single male had abnormal antlers, and was thus unlikely to breed. There were no fawns. Klein figured out that thousands of reindeer had starved to death during the winter of 1963–1964. That winter was unusually harsh, with low temperatures, high winds, and 140 inches of snow. Most reindeer, already in poor condition as a result of increased competition, starved when deep snow covered their food. A population decline had been expected—a population that exceeds its carrying capacity usually shrinks and falls below that capacity—but bad weather magnified the extent of the crash. By the 1980s, there were no reindeer left on the island.

carrying capacity (K) Maximum number of individuals of a species that a particular environment can sustain; can change over time.
density-dependent limiting factor Factor that limits population growth and has a greater effect in dense populations; for example, competition for a limited resource.
density-independent limiting factor Factor that limits population growth and arises regardless of population size; for example, a flood.
intraspecific competition Competition for resources among members of the same species.
logistic growth A population grows exponentially at first, then growth slows as population size approaches the environment's carrying capacity for that species.

TAKE-HOME MESSAGE 40.3

Carrying capacity is the maximum number of individuals of a population that can be sustained indefinitely by the resources in a given environment.

With logistic growth, the growth of a population is fastest when its individuals are at low density, then it slows as the population size approaches the carrying capacity of its environment.

The effects of density-dependent factors such as disease cause a logistic growth pattern. Density-independent factors such as natural disasters also affect population growth.

A population's growth rate is affected by its members' **life history**, which is the schedule of how individuals allocate resources to reproduction over the course of their lifetime. Life history traits include the age at which reproduction begins, the frequency of reproduction, and the number of offspring produced during each reproductive event.

TABLE 40.1

Life Table for an Annual Plant Cohort*

Age Interval (days)	Survivorship (number surviving at start of interval)	Number Dying During Interval	Death Rate (number dying/ number surviving)	"Birth" Rate During Interval (number of seeds from each plant)
0–63	996	328	0.329	0
63–124	668	373	0.558	0
124–184	295	105	0.356	0
184–215	190	14	0.074	0
215–264	176	4	0.023	0
264–278	172	5	0.029	0
278–292	167	8	0.048	0
292–306	159	5	0.031	0.33
306–320	154	7	0.045	3.13
320–334	147	42	0.286	5.42
334–348	105	83	0.790	9.26
348–362	22	22	1.000	4.31
362–	0	0	0	0
		996		

* *Phlox drummondii; data from W. J. Leverich and D. A. Levin, 1979.*

TIMING OF BIRTHS AND DEATHS

One way to investigate life history traits is to focus on a **cohort**—a group of individuals born during the same interval—from their time of birth until the last one dies. Ecologists often divide a natural population into age classes and record the age-specific birth rates and mortality. The resulting data is summarized in a life table (**TABLE 40.1**).

Information about age-specific death rates can also be illustrated by a **survivorship curve**, a plot that shows how many members of a cohort remain alive over time. Ecologists have described three types of curves. A type I curve is convex, indicating that the death rate remains low until relatively late in life (**FIGURE 40.7A**). Humans and other large mammals that produce and care for one or two offspring at a time show this pattern. A diagonal type II curve indicates that the death rate of the population does not vary much with age (**FIGURE 40.7B**). In lizards, small mammals, and large birds, old individuals are about as likely to die of disease or predation as young ones. A type III curve is concave, indicating that the death rate for a population peaks early in life (**FIGURE 40.7C**). Marine animals that release eggs into water have this type of curve, as do plants that release enormous numbers of tiny seeds.

r-SELECTION AND *K*-SELECTION

To produce offspring, an individual must invest resources that it could otherwise use to grow and maintain itself. Species differ in the manner in which they distribute parental investment among offspring and over the course

FIGURE 40.7 {Animated} Survivorship curves. Gray lines are theoretical curves. Red dots are data from field studies.

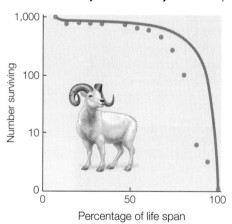

A Type I curve. Mortality is highest late in life. Data for Dall sheep (*Ovis dalli*).

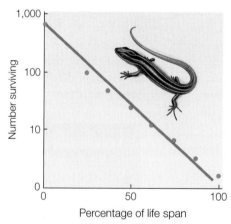

B Type II curve. Mortality varies little with age. Data for five-lined skink (*Eumeces fasciatus*).

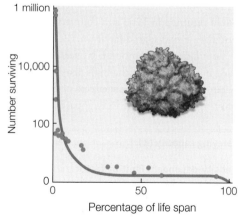

C Type III curve. Mortality is highest early in life. Data for a desert shrub (*Cleome droserifolia*).

FIGURE IT OUT: Based on the death rates listed for the annual plant in Table 40.1, what type of survivorship curve does that plant have?

Answer: A type III curve, with mortality highest early in life.

CREDIT: (7) © Cengage Learning 2015.

Opportunistic life history	Equilibrial life history
shorter development	longer development
early reproduction	later reproduction
fewer breeding episodes, many young per episode	more breeding episodes, few young per episode
less parental investment per young	more parental investment per young
higher early mortality, shorter life span	low early mortality, longer life span
result of *r*-selection	result of *K*-selection

A Fly laying many eggs.

B Whale with its single calf.

FIGURE 40.8 Two types of life history. Most species have a mix of opportunistic and equilibrial life history traits.

of their lifetime. Life history patterns vary continuously among species, but ecologists have described two theoretical extremes at either end of this continuum. Both maximize the number of offspring that will be produced and survive to adulthood, but they do so under very different environmental conditions.

When a species lives where conditions vary in an unpredictable manner, its populations seldom reach the carrying capacity of their environment. As a result, there is little competition for resources and deaths occur mainly as a result of density-independent factors. Such conditions favor an opportunistic life history, in which individuals produce as many offspring as possible, as quickly as possible. Opportunistic species are said to be subject to **r-selection**, because they maximize *r*, the per capita growth rate. They tend to have a short generation time and small body size. Opportunistic species usually have a type III survivorship curve, with mortality heaviest early in life. For example, weedy plants such as dandelions have an opportunistic life history. They mature within weeks, produce many tiny seeds, then die. Flies are opportunistic animals. A female fly can lay hundreds of small eggs in a temporary food source such as a rotting tomato (**FIGURE 40.8A**).

When a species lives in a more stable environment, its populations often approach carrying capacity. Under these circumstances, the ability to successfully compete for resources has a major influence on reproductive success. Thus, an equilibrial life history, in which parents produce a few, high-quality offspring, is adaptive. Equilibrial species are shaped by **K-selection**, in which adaptive traits provide a competitive advantage when population size is near carrying capacity (*K*). Such species tend to have a large body and a long generation time. This type of life history is typical of large mammals that take years to reach adulthood and begin reproducing. For example, a female blue whale reaches maturity at the age of 6 to 10 years. She then produces only

one large calf at a time, and continues to invest in the calf by nursing it after its birth (**FIGURE 40.8B**). Similarly, a coconut palm grows for years before beginning to produce a few coconuts at a time. In both whales and coconut palms, a mature individual produces young for many years.

Some species have mixes of traits that cannot be explained by *r*-selection or *K*-selection alone. For example, century plants (a type of agave) and bamboo are large and long-lived, but they reproduce only once. Atlantic eels and Pacific salmon are unusual among vertebrates in also having a one-shot reproductive strategy. Such a strategy can evolve when opportunities for reproduction are unlikely to be repeated. In the century plant and bamboo, climate conditions that favor reproduction occur only rarely. In the eels and salmon, physiological changes related to migration between fresh water and salt water make a repeat journey impossible.

cohort Group of individuals born during the same interval.
K-selection Selection that favors traits that allow their bearers to outcompete others for limited resources; occurs when a population is near its environment's carrying capacity.
life history A set of traits related to growth, survival, and reproduction such as life span, age-specific mortality, age at first reproduction, and number of breeding events.
r-selection Selection that favors traits that allow their bearers to produce the most offspring the most quickly; occurs when population density is low and resources are abundant.
survivorship curve Graph showing how many members of a cohort remain alive over time.

TAKE-HOME MESSAGE 40.4

Tracking a group of same-aged individuals from birth to death reveals patterns of reproduction and survival. These data can be summarized in life tables or survivorship curves.

Different life history patterns are adaptive under different environmental conditions and population densities.

FIGURE 40.9 {Animated} How predation affects life history traits in guppies. David Reznik (shown above) and John Endler carried out an experiment using wild guppies that had evolved in the presence of a predator (pike cichlid) that preferentially preys on large guppies. Control group guppies remained in their home pool with pike cichlids. Other guppies were moved to a guppy-free pool with a predator (killifish) that preferentially eats small guppies. Data at left show the average age and weight at maturity for descendants of both groups 11 years after the study began.

Many species are subject to different types of predation at different stages in their life cycle. In some cases, this predation pressure can influence life history traits.

AN EXPERIMENTAL STUDY

A long-term study by the evolutionary biologists John Endler and David Reznick illustrates the effect of predation on life history traits. Endler and Reznick studied populations of guppies, small fishes that are native to shallow freshwater streams in the mountains of Trinidad (**FIGURE 40.9**). The scientists focused their attention on a region where many small waterfalls prevent guppies in one part of a stream from moving easily to another. As

a result of these natural barriers, each stream holds several populations of guppies that have very little gene flow between them (Section 17.7).

The waterfalls also keep guppy predators from moving from one part of the stream to another. The main guppy predators, killifishes and cichlids, differ in size and prey preferences. The relatively small killifish preys mostly on immature guppies, and ignores the larger adults. The cichlids are bigger fish. They tend to pursue mature guppies and ignore small ones.

Some parts of the streams hold one type of predator but not the other. Thus, different guppy populations face different predation pressures. Reznick and Endler

CREDITS: (9) photo, © Helen Rodd; art, © Cengage Learning 2015 based on data from Reznick D.A., Bryga H., and Endler J.A. (1990) *Nature* 346: 357–359.

discovered that guppies in regions with cichlids grow faster and are smaller at maturity than guppies in regions with killifish. Guppies in populations hunted by cichlids also reproduce earlier, have more offspring at a time, and breed more frequently.

Were these differences in life history traits genetic, or did some environmental variation cause them? To find out, the biologists collected guppies from both cichlid- and killifish-dominated streams. They reared the groups in separate aquariums under identical predator-free conditions. Two generations later, the groups continued to show the differences observed in natural populations. The researchers concluded that differences between guppies preyed on by different predators have a genetic basis.

Reznick and Endler hypothesized that the predators act as selective agents on guppy life history patterns. They made a prediction: If life history traits evolve in response to predation, then these traits will change when a population is exposed to a new predator that favors different prey traits. To test their prediction, they found a stream region above a waterfall that had killifish but no guppies or cichlids. To this region, they introduced guppies from a site below the waterfall, where there were cichlids but no killifish. Thus, at the experimental site, guppies that had previously lived only with cichlids (which eat large guppies) were now exposed to killifish (which eat smaller ones). The control site was the downstream region below the waterfall, where relatives of the transplanted guppies still coexisted with cichlids.

Reznick and Endler revisited the stream over the course of eleven years and thirty-six generations of guppies. They monitored traits of guppies above and below the waterfall. The recorded data showed that guppies at the upstream experimental site were evolving. Exposure to a previously unfamiliar predator caused changes in the guppies' rate of growth, age at first reproduction, and other life history traits. By contrast, guppies at the control site showed no such changes. Reznick and Endler concluded that life history traits in guppies can evolve rapidly in response to the selective pressure exerted by predation.

COLLAPSE OF A FISHERY

The evolution of life history traits in response to predation is not merely of theoretical interest. It has economic importance. Just as guppies evolved in response to predators, a population of Atlantic codfish (*Gadus morhua*) evolved in response to human fishing pressure. From the mid-1980s to early 1990s, the number of fishing boats targeting the North Atlantic population of codfish increased. As the yearly catch rose, the age of sexual maturity shifted, and fishes that reproduce while young and small became a larger

FIGURE 40.10 Fishermen with a prized catch, a large Atlantic codfish. Both sport fishermen and commercial fisherman preferentially harvested the largest codfish.

component of the population. These early-reproducing individuals were at an advantage because both commercial fisherman and sports fishermen preferentially caught and kept larger fish (**FIGURE 40.10**). Fishing pressure continued to rise until 1992, when declining cod numbers caused the Canadian government to ban cod fishing in some areas. That ban, and later restrictions, came too late to stop the Atlantic cod population from crashing. In some areas, the population declined by 97 percent and still shows no signs of recovery.

Looking back, it is clear that life history changes were an early sign that the North Atlantic cod population was in trouble. Had biologists recognized what was happening, they might have been able to save the fishery and protect the livelihood of more than 35,000 fishers and associated workers. Ongoing monitoring of the life history data for other economically important fishes may help prevent similar disastrous crashes in the future.

TAKE-HOME MESSAGE 40.5

The action of a predator that preferentially focuses on prey individuals of a particular size can exert directional selection on life history traits of a prey species.

When humans are the predator, monitoring life history changes in the prey population can help prevent the overharvesting of that species.

40.6 HOW HAS THE SIZE OF THE HUMAN POPULATION CHANGED OVER TIME?

EXPANSIONS AND INNOVATIONS

For most of its history, the human population grew very slowly (**FIGURE 40.11**). The growth rate began to pick up about 10,000 years ago, and it soared during the past two centuries. Three trends promoted the large increases. First, humans expanded into new habitats. Second, they developed technologies that increased the carrying capacity of their habitats. Third, they sidestepped limiting factors that typically restrain population growth.

Modern humans evolved in Africa by about 200,000 years ago, and by 43,000 years ago, their descendants were established in much of the world (Section 24.12). The invention of agriculture about 11,000 years ago provided a more dependable food supply than traditional hunting and gathering. In the middle of the eighteenth century, people learned to harness energy in fossil fuels to operate machinery. This innovation opened the way to high-yielding mechanized agriculture and improved food distribution systems. Food production was further enhanced in the early 1900s, when the invention of synthetic nitrogen fertilizers increased crop yields. The invention of synthetic pesticides in the mid-1900s also contributed to increased food production.

Disease has historically dampened human population growth. During the mid-1300s, one-third of Europe's population was lost in a pandemic known as the Black Death. Beginning in the mid-1800s, an increased understanding of the link between microorganisms and illness led to improvements in food safety, sanitation, and medicine. People began to pasteurize foods and drinks, heating them to kill harmful bacteria. They also began to protect their drinking water.

Advances in sanitation also lowered the death rate associated with medical treatment. In the mid-1800s, Ignaz Semmelweis, a physician in Vienna, began urging doctors to wash their hands between patients. His advice was largely ignored until after his death, when Louis Pasteur popularized the idea that unseen organisms cause disease. Acceptance of this idea also revolutionized surgery, which had been carried out without regard for cleanliness.

A worldwide decline in death rates without an equivalent drop in birth rates is responsible for the ongoing explosion in human population size. The population is now more than 7 billion and is expected to reach 9 billion by 2050.

FERTILITY AND FUTURE GROWTH

Birth rates have begun to slow as a result of contraception use. The **total fertility rate** of a population is the number of offspring a woman would be expected to have during her reproductive years given the current age-specific birth

FIGURE 40.11 Growth curve (red) for the world human population.

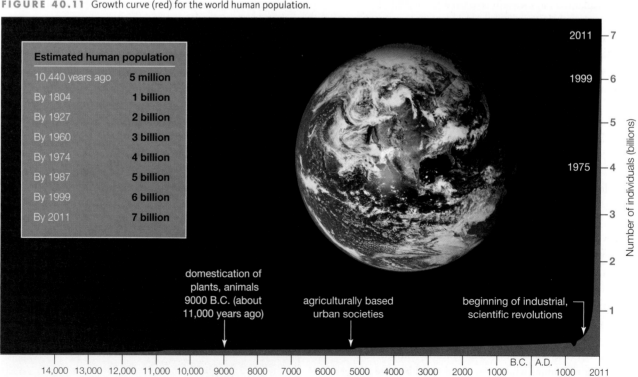

Estimated human population	
10,440 years ago	5 million
By 1804	1 billion
By 1927	2 billion
By 1960	3 billion
By 1974	4 billion
By 1987	5 billion
By 1999	6 billion
By 2011	7 billion

CREDITS: (11) photo, NASA; art, © Cengage Learning 2014.

rate. In 1950, the total fertility rate for humans averaged 6.5 worldwide. By 2012, it had declined to 2.6, but it still remains above the **replacement fertility rate**—the number of children a woman must bear to replace herself with one daughter of reproductive age. At present, the replacement fertility rate is 2.1 for developed countries, and as high as 2.5 in some developing countries. (It is higher in developing countries because more daughters die before reaching the age of reproduction.) As long as the total fertility rate exceeds the replacement rate, the human population will continue to grow.

Age structure, which is the distribution of individuals among age groups, affects the rate of population growth. Individuals are often categorized as pre-reproductive, reproductive, or post-reproductive. Members of the pre-reproductive category have a capacity to produce offspring when mature. Along with reproductive individuals, they constitute a population's **reproductive base**.

FIGURE 40.12 shows age structure diagrams for the world's three most populous countries. China and India already have more than one billion people apiece; together, they hold 38 percent of the world population. Next in line is the United States, with more than 315 million. Notice the size of the reproductive base in each diagram. The broader the base of an age structure diagram, the greater the proportion of young people, and the greater the expected growth. Government policies that favor couples who have only one child have helped China to narrow its pre-reproductive base.

Even if every couple now living decides to have no more than two children, two factors will keep the world population increasing for many years. First, longevity continues to increase. Second, the population has a broad pre-reproductive base; about a quarter of the world population has not yet begun to reproduce.

---

age structure Distribution of population members among various age categories.
replacement fertility rate Number of children a woman must bear to replace herself with one daughter of reproductive age.
reproductive base Of a population, members of the reproductive and pre-reproductive age categories.
total fertility rate Expected number of children a women will bear over the course of a lifetime.

CREDIT: (12) © Cengage Learning.

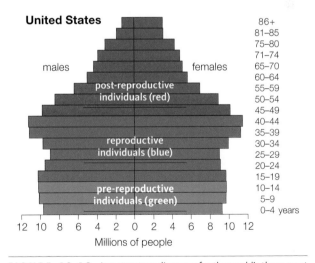

FIGURE 40.12 Age structure diagrams for the world's three most populous countries. The width of each bar represents the number of individuals in a 5-year age group. The *left* side of each chart indicates males; the *right* side, females.

FIGURE IT OUT: Which country has the largest number of men in the 45 to 49 age group?

Answer: China

40.7   HOW DOES INDUSTRIALIZATION AFFECT HUMAN POPULATION GROWTH?

A DEMOGRAPHIC TRANSITION

Demographic factors vary among countries, with the most highly developed countries having the lowest birth rates and infant mortality, and the highest life expectancy. The **demographic transition model** describes how changes in population growth often unfold in four stages of economic development (**FIGURE 40.13**).

Living conditions are harshest during the preindustrial stage, before technological and medical advances become widespread. Birth and death rates are both high, so the growth rate is low **1**.

In the transitional stage, food production and health care improve as industrialization begins. The death rate drops fast, but the birth rate declines more slowly **2**. As a result, the rate of population growth increases. Many of the world's least developed countries are in this stage. Examples include Afghanistan, Haiti, Cambodia, and Ethiopia.

During the industrial stage, when industrialization is in full swing, the birth rate declines. People move from rural areas to towns and cities, where birth control is often more easily available and couples tend to want smaller families. The birth rate moves closer to the death rate, and the population grows less rapidly **3**. The United States is in this stage.

In the postindustrial stage, a population's growth rate becomes negative. The birth rate falls below the death rate, and population size slowly decreases **4**. Japan and some European countries are in this stage.

The demographic transition model was developed based on analysis of what happened when western Europe and

TABLE 40.2	
Ecological Footprints*	
Country	Hectares per Capita
United States	8.0
Canada	7.0
France	5.0
United Kingdom	4.9
Japan	4.7
Mexico	3.0
Brazil	2.9
China	2.2
India	0.9

* Global Footprint Network, 2010 data

North America industrialized in the late 1800s. Whether it can accurately predict changes in modern developing countries remains to be seen. Less developed countries now receive aid from highly developed countries, but must also compete against these countries in a global market.

DEVELOPMENT AND CONSUMPTION

What is Earth's carrying capacity for humans? There is no simple answer to this question. For one thing, we cannot predict what new technologies may arise or the effects they will have. For another, different types of societies require different amounts of resources to sustain them. On a per capita basis, people in highly developed countries use far

FIGURE 40.13 {Animated} Demographic transition model. The model correlates changes in population growth with industrialization.

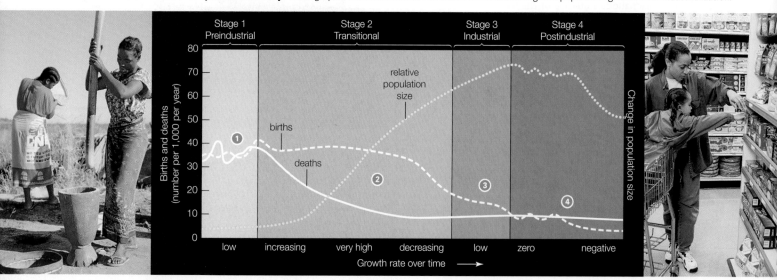

more resources than those in less developed countries, and they also generate more waste and pollution.

Ecological footprint analysis is one widely used method of measuring and comparing resource use. An **ecological footprint** is the amount of Earth's surface required to support a particular level of development and consumption in a sustainable fashion. It includes the amount of area required to grow crops, graze animals, produce forest products, catch fish, hold buildings, and take up any carbon emitted by burning fossil fuels.

In 2010, the per capita global footprint for the human population was 2.7 hectares, or about 6.5 acres (**TABLE 40.2**). The world's two most populous countries, China and India, were below that average, whereas the per capita footprint of the United States was more than three times the average. In other words, the lifestyle of an average person in the United States requires three times as much of Earth's sustainable resources as the lifestyle of an average world citizen. It requires more than eight times the resources of a person in India.

The United States is unlikely to lower its resource consumption to match that of India. In fact, billions of people in India, China, and other less developed nations dream that one day they or their offspring will enjoy the same type of lifestyle as the average American.

Ecological footprint analysis tells us that, with current technology, Earth may not have enough resources to make those dreams come true. The Global Footprint Network estimates that for everyone now alive to live like an average person in the United States would require the resources of five Earths. Such analysis suggests that the human population is currently living well beyond its ecological means and is in the process of racking up a deficit that will take its toll on future generations.

---

demographic transition model Model describing the changes in human birth and death rates that occur as a region becomes industrialized.
ecological footprint Area of Earth's surface required to sustainably support a particular level of development and consumption.

TAKE-HOME MESSAGE 40.7

Historically, population growth has slowed after countries have industrialized. The same trend may eventually occur in currently developing countries.

The most highly developed countries have relatively low growth rates, but they consume a disproportionately large share of Earth's resources.

The current global level of resource use is unsustainable, and the requirement for resources is expected to rise.

40.8 A HONKIN' MESS

Application: Sustainability

FIGURE 40.14 California park overrun by Canada geese.

CANADA GEESE WERE HUNTED TO NEAR EXTINCTION IN THE LATE 1800S. In the early 1900s, federal laws and international treaties were put in place to protect them and other migratory birds. In recent decades, the number of geese in the United States has soared. For example, in 1970, Michigan had about 9,000 geese; today, it has 300,000. These plant-eating birds often congregate at golf courses and parks (**FIGURE 40.14**). They are considered pests because they produce large amounts of slimy, green feces that soil shoes, feet, and clothing.

Controlling the number of Canada geese poses a challenge because several different populations spend time in the United States. In the past, nearly all Canada geese seen in the United States were migratory. The geese nested in northern Canada, flew to the United States to spend the winter, then returned to Canada. Most Canada geese still migrate, but some populations have lost this trait. During the winter, migratory birds often mingle with nonmigratory ones.

Life is more difficult for migratory geese than for nonmigratory ones. Flying hundreds of miles to and from a northern breeding area takes lots of energy and is dangerous. Compared to a migratory bird, one that stays put can devote more energy to producing young. If the nonmigrant lives in a suburban or urban area, it also benefits from an unnatural abundance of food (grass) and an equally unnatural lack of predators. Not surprisingly, the biggest increases in Canada geese have been among nonmigratory birds that live where humans are plentiful. We have increased the carrying capacity for these birds.

In 2006, increasing complaints about Canada geese led the U.S. Fish and Wildlife Service to encourage wildlife managers to look for ways to reduce nonmigratory Canada goose populations, without harming migratory ones.

Summary

SECTION 40.1 **Ecology** is the study of interactions among organisms and their living and nonliving environment. Ecologists describe a population in terms of its **demographics**. They estimate **population size** by using a sampling method such as **plot sampling** or **mark–recapture sampling**. Other demographics include **population density** and **population distribution**. Most populations have a clumped distribution.

SECTION 40.2 A population's per capita birth rate minus its per capita death rate gives us *r*, the **per capita growth rate**. When birth rate and death rate are equal, there is **zero population growth**.

A population in which *r* is a value greater than zero undergoes **exponential growth**. The increase in size in any interval is determined by the equation $G = r \times N$, where *G* is population growth and *N* is the number of individuals. With exponential growth, a graph of population size against time produces a J-shaped growth curve. The maximum possible exponential growth rate under optimal conditions is the population's **biotic potential**.

Emigration and **immigration** of individuals can also affect population size.

SECTION 40.3 The effects of **density-dependent limiting factors** such as disease and **intraspecific competition** lead to **logistic growth**: a population begins growing exponentially, then growth slows as the population size approaches its environment's **carrying capacity**. With logistic growth, population size over time plots out as an S-shaped curve. Carrying capacity varies by species, among environments, and over time. A population may temporarily overshoot carrying capacity, then crash.

Density-independent limiting factors such as extreme weather events can also influence the growth rate of a population, but their effect does not vary with crowding.

SECTIONS 40.4, 40.5 The time to maturity, number of reproductive events, number of offspring per event, and life span are aspects of a **life history** pattern. Such patterns can be studied by following a **cohort**, a group of individuals born at the same time. Three types of **survivorship curves** are common: a high death rate late in life, a constant death rate at all ages, or a high death rate early in life. Life histories have a genetic basis and are subject to natural selection. At low population density, **r-selection** favors quickly producing as many offspring as possible. At a higher population density, **K-selection** favors investing more time and energy in fewer, higher-quality offspring. Most populations have a mixture of both *r*-selected and *K*-selected traits. Predation can also affect life history traits.

SECTION 40.6 The human population has surpassed 7 billion. Expansion into new habitats and the invention of agriculture allowed early increases. Medicine and technology have allowed greater increases. Today, the global **total fertility rate** is declining, but it remains above the **replacement fertility rate**. The **age structure** varies among countries, with some having a broad **reproductive base** that will cause numbers to increase for at least sixty years.

SECTION 40.7 The **demographic transition model** predicts that population growth slows with advancing economic development. Some of the world's least developed countries remain in the earliest stages of their demographic transition. World resource consumption will probably continue to rise because nations continue to develop and a highly developed nation has a much larger **ecological footprint** than a developing one. However, with current technology, Earth does not have enough resources to support the existing population in the style of developed nations.

SECTION 40.8 Human activities have caused shifts in the size of some Canada goose populations in the United States. Most recently, there has been a dramatic rise in nonmigratory populations of these birds because we have increased their carrying capacity.

Self-Quiz   Answers in Appendix VII

1. Most commonly, individuals of a population show a _____ distribution through their habitat.

2. The rate at which population size grows or declines depends on the rate of _____ .
   a. births   c. immigration   e. a and b
   b. deaths   d. emigration   f. all of the above

3. Suppose 200 fish are marked and released in a pond. The following week, 200 fish are caught and 100 of them have marks. How many fish are in this pond?

4. A population of worms is growing exponentially in a compost heap. Thirty days ago there were 400 worms and now there are 800. How many worms will there be thirty days from now, assuming conditions remain constant?

5. For a given species, the maximum rate of increase per individual under ideal conditions is its _____ .
   a. biotic potential   c. environmental resistance
   b. carrying capacity   d. density control

6. _____ is a density-independent factor that influences population growth.
   a. Resource competition   c. Predation
   b. Infectious disease   d. Harsh weather

7. A life history pattern for a population is a set of adaptive traits such as _____ .
   a. longevity   c. age at reproductive maturity
   b. fertility   d. all of the above

8. The human population is now over 7 billion. It reached 6 billion in _____ .
   a. 2007   b. 1999   c. 1802   d. 1350

Data Analysis Activities

Monitoring Iguana Populations In 1989, Martin Wikelski began a long-term study of marine iguana populations in the Galápagos Islands. He marked the iguanas on two islands—Genovesa and Santa Fe—and collected data on how their body size, survival, and reproductive rates varied over time. The iguanas eat algae and have no predators, so deaths typically result from food shortages, disease, or old age. His studies showed that the iguana populations decline during El Niño events, when water surrounding the islands heats up.

In January 2001, an oil tanker ran aground and leaked a small amount of oil into the water near Santa Fe. **FIGURE 40.15** shows the number of marked iguanas that Wikelski and his team counted just before the spill and about a year later.

1. Which island had more marked iguanas at the time of the first census?

2. How much did the population size on each island change between the first and second census?

3. Wikelski concluded that changes on Santa Fe were the result of the oil spill, rather than a factor common to both islands. How would the census numbers be different from those he observed if an adverse event had affected both islands?

FIGURE 40.15 Shifting numbers of marked marine iguanas on two Galápagos islands. An oil spill occurred near Santa Fe just after the January 2001 census (orange bars). A second census was carried out in December 2001 (green bars).

---

9. Compared to the less developed countries, the highly developed ones have a higher _____ .
   - a. death rate
   - b. birth rate
   - c. total fertility rate
   - d. resource consumption rate

10. An increase in infant mortality will _____ a population's replacement fertility rate.
   - a. raise
   - b. lower
   - c. not affect

11. Species that usually colonize empty habitats are more likely to have traits that are favored by _____ .
   - a. *r*-selection
   - b. *K*-selection

12. All members of a cohort are the same _____ .
   - a. sex
   - b. size
   - c. age
   - d. weight

13. Match each term with its most suitable description.

   ___ carrying capacity
   ___ exponential growth
   ___ biotic potential
   ___ limiting factor
   ___ logistic growth

   - a. maximum rate of increase per individual under ideal conditions
   - b. population growth plots out as an S-shaped curve
   - c. maximum number of individuals sustainable by the resources in a given environment
   - d. population growth plots out as a J-shaped curve
   - e. essential resource that restricts population growth when scarce

Critical Thinking

1. When researchers moved guppies from pools with cichlids that eat large guppies to pools with killifish that eat small ones, life history traits were not the only traits that changed. Over generations, male guppies became more colorful. Why do you think this change occurred?

2. Each summer, a giant saguaro cactus produces tens of thousands of tiny black seeds. Most die, but the few that land in a sheltered spot sprout the following spring. The saguaro is a slow-growing CAM plant (Section 6.5). After fifteen years, it may be only knee high, and it will not flower for another fifteen years. It may live for 200 years. Saguaros share their habitat with annuals such as poppies, which sprout, form seeds, and die in just a few weeks. Speculate on how these different life histories can both be adaptive in the same desert environment.

3. Age structure diagrams for two hypothetical populations are shown below. Describe the growth rate of each population and discuss the current and future social and economic problems that each is likely to face.

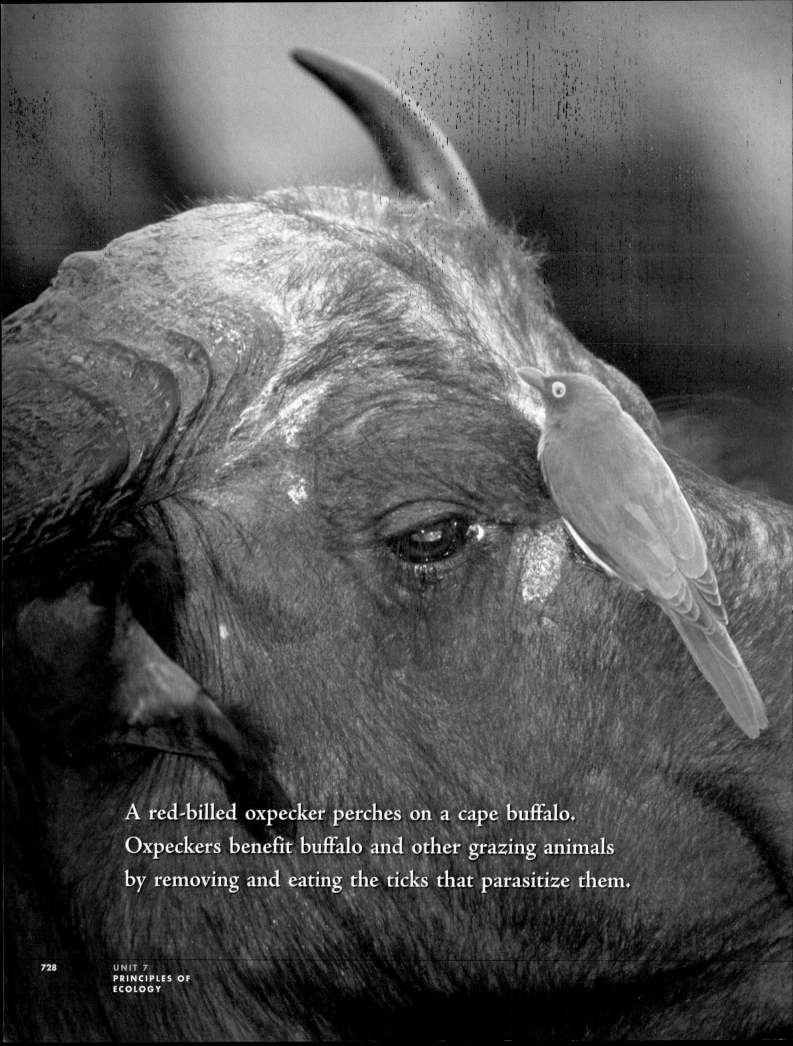

A red-billed oxpecker perches on a cape buffalo.
Oxpeckers benefit buffalo and other grazing animals
by removing and eating the ticks that parasitize them.

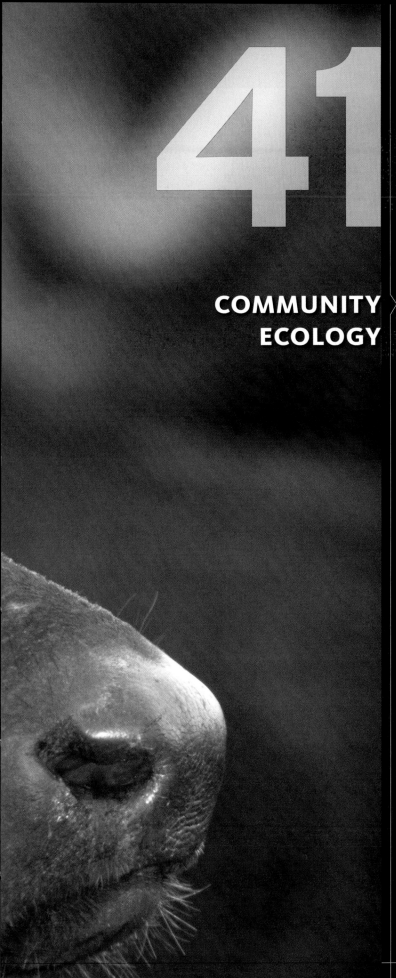

41

COMMUNITY ECOLOGY

Links to Earlier Concepts

In this chapter you will revisit biogeography and take a closer look at global patterns in species distribution (Section 16.1). You will be reminded of effects of pathogens (19.2) and how species interactions lead to natural selection (17.11). You will see examples of field experiments (1.6) and apply what you know about populations and factors affecting their growth (40.1–40.3).

KEY CONCEPTS

COMMUNITY CHARACTERISTICS

Physical characteristics of the environment and interactions among species affect the number of species in a community and their relative abundance.

FORMS OF SPECIES INTERACTIONS

Interspecific interactions such as commensalism, mutualism, competition, predation, and parasitism can influence the population size of participating species.

CHANGES IN COMMUNITIES

The composition of a community changes over time, but the exact outcome of future changes is difficult to predict. Random factors and disturbances can influence community structure.

EFFECTS OF A SINGLE SPECIES

The addition or loss of a single species can have a dramatic effect on the population size of other species within a community. Some species foster diversity by their presence.

LESSONS FROM ISLANDS

The number of species on an island depends on immigration and extinction rates. A model based on studies of islands helps scientists predict how many species will live in a particular community.

The type of place where a species normally lives is its **habitat**. In any specific habitat, all the species that live there constitute a **community**. Communities often nest one inside another. For example, we find a community of microbial organisms inside the gut of a termite. That termite is part of a larger community of organisms living on a fallen log. The log-dwellers are part of a larger forest community.

Even communities that are similar in scale differ in their species diversity. There are two components to species diversity. The first, species richness, refers to the number of species. The second is species evenness, or the relative abundance of each species. For example, a pond that has five fish species in nearly equal numbers has a higher species diversity than a pond with one abundant fish species and four rare ones.

Community structure is dynamic, which means that in any community, the array of species and their relative abundances tends to change over time. Communities change over a long time span as they form and then age. They also change over the short term as a result of disturbances.

Geography and climate affect community structure. Factors such as soil quality, sunlight intensity, rainfall, and temperature vary with latitude and elevation. Tropical regions receive the most sunlight energy and have the most even temperature. For most plants and animal groups, the number of species is greatest in the tropical regions near the equator, and declines as you move toward the poles. Tropical forest communities have more types of trees than temperate ones. Similarly, tropical reef communities are more diverse than comparable communities farther from the equator.

Species interactions also influence community structure. In some cases, the effect is indirect. For example, when

TABLE 41.1

Direct Two-Species Interactions

Type of Interaction	Effect on Species 1	Effect on Species 2
Commensalism	Helpful	None
Mutualism	Helpful	Helpful
Interspecific competition	Harmful	Harmful
Predation, herbivory, parasitism, parasitoidism	Helpful	Harmful

songbirds eat caterpillars, the birds indirectly benefit trees that the caterpillars feed on, while directly reducing the abundance of caterpillars.

Biologists categorize direct species interactions by their effects on both participating species (**TABLE 41.1**). For example, **commensalism** helps one species and has no effect on the other. Commensal orchids live attached to the trunk or branches of a tree (**FIGURE 41.1**). Having a perch in the light benefits the orchid, and the tree is unaffected. Relationships are considered commensal only when one species benefits, and the other neither benefits nor is harmed by the relationship. Should evidence of either effect come to light, the relationship is reclassified.

Species interactions may be fleeting or long term. **Symbiosis**, which means "living together," refers to a relationship in which two species have a prolonged close association. Two species that interact closely for generations often coevolve, regardless of whether one species helps or harms another. As Section 17.11 explained, coevolution is an evolutionary process in which each species acts as a selective agent that shifts the range of variation in the other.

commensalism Species interaction that benefits one species and neither helps nor harms the other.
community All species that live in a particular area.
habitat Type of environment in which a species typically lives.
symbiosis One species lives in or on another in a commensal, mutualistic, or parasitic relationship.

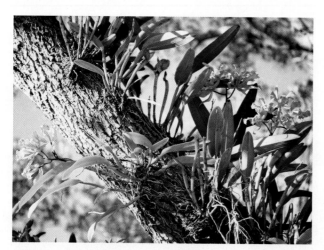

FIGURE 41.1 Commensal orchids on a tree trunk. The orchids benefit by growing on the tree, which is unaffected by their presence.

TAKE-HOME MESSAGE 41.1

The types and abundances of species in a community are affected by physical factors such as climate and by biological factors such as interactions among species.

With commensalism, one species benefits from an interaction that has no effect on its partner species. A commensalism in which one species lives on or in another is a type of symbiosis.

FIGURE 41.2 Obligate mutualists: a yucca moth on a yucca flower. Yucca moths mate on such flowers. Afterward, the female gathers pollen from one flower and carries it with her to another flower that has not yet begun to produce pollen. She lays her eggs in the second flower's ovary, then uses the pollen she brought along to fertilize it. By pollinating the flower, she ensures that seeds will form to feed her larvae. Moth larvae eat some seeds, but plenty survive to give rise to new yucca plants.

Mutualism is an interspecific interaction that benefits both participants. Flowering plants and their pollinators are a familiar example. In some cases, two species coevolve a mutual dependence. For example, each species of yucca plant is pollinated by one species of yucca moth, whose larvae develop only on that plant (**FIGURE 41.2**). More often, mutualistic relationships are less exclusive. Most flowering plants have more than one pollinator, and most pollinators service more than one species of plant.

Photosynthetic organisms often supply sugars to their nonphotosynthetic partners, as when plants lure pollinators with nectar. In addition, many plants make sugary fruits that attract seed-dispersing animals. Plants also provide sugars to mycorrhizal fungi and nitrogen-fixing bacteria. The plants' fungal or bacterial symbionts return the favor by supplying their host with other essential nutrients. Similarly, photosynthetic dinoflagellates provide sugars to reef-building corals, and photosynthetic bacteria or algae in a lichen feed their fungal partner.

Animals often share ingested nutrients with mutualistic microorganisms that live in their gut. For example, *Escherichia coli* bacteria in your colon provide you with vitamin K in return for a steady food supply and a nice, warm place to live.

mutualism Species interaction that benefits both species.

Other mutualisms involve protection. For example, an anemonefish and a sea anemone fend off one another's predators (**FIGURE 41.3**). Ants protect bull acacia trees from leaf-eating insects, and in return the tree houses the ant in special hollow thorns and provides them with sugar-rich foods. The oxpecker bird shown in the chapter's opening photo protects its partner from ticks, which it eats.

From an evolutionary standpoint, mutualism is best described as reciprocal exploitation. Each individual increases its fitness by extracting a resource, such as protection or food, from its partner. If taking part in the mutualism has a cost, such as the cost of producing nectar, selection favors individuals who minimize that cost. For example, a flower that produces the minimum amount of nectar necessary to attract pollinators will do better than one that expends more energy to produce additional nectar.

FIGURE 41.3 Mutualism between a sea anemone and a pink anemone fish. The tiny but aggressive fish chases away predatory butterfly fishes that would like to bite off tips of the anemone's stinging tentacles. The fish cannot survive and reproduce without the protection of an anemone. The anemone does not need a fish to protect it, but it does better with one.

TAKE-HOME MESSAGE 41.2

A mutualism is a species interaction in which each species benefits by associating with the other.

In each species, individuals who maximize the benefit they receive while minimizing their costs will be favored.

CREDITS: (2) © Darlyne A. Murawski/National Geographic Creative; (3) © Thomas W. Doeppner.

TYPES OF COMPETITION

Interspecific competition, which is competition among members of different species, is not usually as intense as intraspecific competition. The requirements of two species might be similar, but they are never as close as they are for members of one species.

Each species has a unique set of ecological requirements and roles that we refer to as its **ecological niche**. Both physical and biological factors define the niche. Aspects of an animal's niche include the temperature range it can tolerate, the species it eats, and the places it can breed. A description of a flowering plant's niche would include its soil, water, light, and pollinator requirements. The more similar the niches of two species are, the more intensely those species will compete.

Competition takes two forms. With interference competition, one species actively prevents another from accessing some resource. As an example, one species of scavenger will often chase another away from a carcass (**FIGURE 41.4**). As another example, some plants use chemicals to fend off potential competition. Aromatic compounds that ooze from tissues of sagebrush plants, black walnut trees, and eucalyptus trees seep into the soil around these plants. The chemicals prevent other kinds of plants from germinating or growing.

In exploitative competition, species do not interact directly; by using the same resource, each reduces the amount of the resource available to the other. For example, deer and blue jays both eat acorns in oak forests. The more acorns the deer eat, the fewer are available for the jays.

COMPETITIVE EXCLUSION

Deer and blue jays share a fondness for acorns, but each also has other sources of food. Any two species usually differ at least a bit in their resource requirements. Species compete most intensely when the supply of a shared resource is an important limiting factor for both.

In the 1930s, G. Gause conducted experiments with two species of ciliated protozoans (*Paramecium*) that compete for the same prey: bacteria. He cultured the *Paramecium* species separately and together (**FIGURE 41.5**). Within weeks, population growth of one species outpaced the other, which went extinct. This and other experiments are the basis for the concept of **competitive exclusion**: Whenever two species require the same limited resource to survive or reproduce, the better competitor will drive the less competitive species to extinction in that habitat.

When resource needs of competitors are not exactly the same, competing species continue to coexist, but the presence of each reduces the carrying capacity (Section 40.3) of the habitat for the other. For example, the reproductive success of a flowering plant is decreased by competition from other species that flower at the same time and rely on the same pollinators.

FIGURE 41.4 Interference competition among scavengers. A golden eagle attacks a fox with its talons to drive it away from a resource—the moose carcass in the foreground.

Paramecium

FIGURE 41.5 {**Animated**} Results of competitive exclusion between two *Paramecium* species that compete for the same food. When the two species were grown together, *P. aurelia* drove *P. caudatum* to extinction.

CREDITS: (4) © Pekka Komi; (5) left, Michael Abbey/Science Source; right, © Cengage Learning.

Even strikingly different organisms can influence one another through competition. Wolf spiders and carnivorous plants called sundews compete for insect prey in Florida swamps. Sundews grown in the presence of wolf spiders make fewer flowers than sundews in spider-free enclosures. Presumably, competition for insect prey reduces the energy the plants could devote to flowering.

RESOURCE PARTITIONING

Resource partitioning is an evolutionary process by which species become adapted to use a shared limiting resource in a way that minimizes competition. Consider three species of annual plants that commonly coexist in abandoned fields. All require water and nutrients, but the roots of each species take resources up from a different depth. This variation allows the plants to coexist. Similarly, eight species of woodpecker coexist in Oregon forests. All feed on insects and nest in hollow trees, but the details of their foraging behavior and nesting preferences vary. Differences in nesting time also reduce competitive interactions.

Resource partitioning arises as a result of the directional selection that occurs when species with similar requirements share a habitat and compete for a limiting resource. In each species, those individuals who differ most from the competing species have the least competition and thus leave the most offspring. Over generations, directional selection leads to **character displacement**: The range of variation for one or more traits is shifted in a direction that lessens the intensity of competition for a limiting resource. For example, competing seed-eating birds might evolve greater differences in bill size so they can eat different seeds.

---

character displacement As a result of competition between two species, the species become less similar in their resource requirements.
competitive exclusion Process whereby two species compete for a limiting resource, and one drives the other to local extinction.
ecological niche All of a species' requirements and roles in an ecosystem.
interspecific competition Competition between members of two species.
resource partitioning Evolutionary process whereby species become adapted in different ways to access different portions of a limited resource; allows species with similar needs to coexist.

TAKE-HOME MESSAGE 41.3

In some competitive interactions, one species controls or blocks access to a resource, regardless of whether it is scarce or abundant. In other interactions, one species is better than another at exploiting a shared resource.

When two species compete, individuals whose needs are least like those of the competing species are favored.

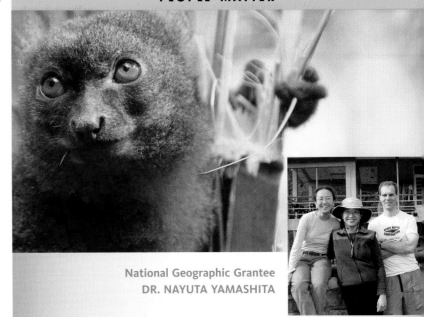

PEOPLE MATTER

National Geographic Grantee
DR. NAYUTA YAMASHITA

In animals, resource partitioning often involves evolved differences in feeding behavior. Nayuta Yamashita (above left) and her colleagues Chia Tan (center) and Chris Vinyard (right) investigate how differences in body form influence food usage among primates. They find three species of bamboo lemurs (Section 24.8) that coexist in Madagascar of particular interest. Yamashita says, "The lemurs are all bamboo specialists that feed on the same species of giant bamboo, though they eat different parts."

To find out the mechanisms by which the lemurs divvy up their food supply, Yamashita measured physical properties of the bamboo they eat and compared the shapes of the lemurs' teeth and jaws. She also measured how much force their jaws could exert. Results of these studies revealed that differences in bite force reflect resource partitioning. The greater bamboo lemur (shown in the photo above) has the most powerful bite, and is the only bamboo lemur that can access the toughest part of the bamboo plant—the pith inside mature shoots.

Yamashita is also investigating another interesting aspect of bamboo lemur feeding: their ability to ingest cyanide. The bamboo that the lemurs eat contains a lot of this poison, yet the lemurs eat it with no apparent ill effect.

PREDATOR AND PREY ABUNDANCE

With **predation**, one species (the predator) captures, kills, and digests another species (the prey). The abundance of prey species in a community affects how many predators it can support. The number of predators reduces the number of prey, but the extent of this effect depends partly on how the predator species responds to changes in prey density. With some predators, such as web-spinning spiders, the proportion of prey killed is constant, so the number killed in any given interval depends solely on prey density. As the number of flies in an area increases, more and more become caught in a web. More often, the number of prey killed depends in part on the time it takes predators to capture, eat, and digest prey. As prey density increases, the rate of kills rises steeply at first because there are more prey to catch. Eventually, the rate of increase slows, because a predator is exposed to more prey than it can handle at one time. A wolf that just killed a caribou will not hunt another until it has eaten and digested the first one.

A Wasp that can inflict a painful sting. Like many stinging bees and wasps, it has a yellow and black pattern.

B Fly, which lacks a stinger, mimics the color pattern of stinging insects.

FIGURE 41.7 Mimicry.

FIGURE 41.6 Graph of the number of Canadian lynx (*dashed* line) and snowshoe hares (*solid* line), based on counts of pelts sold by trappers to Hudson's Bay Company during a ninety-year period.

Predator and prey populations sometimes rise and fall in a cyclical fashion. **FIGURE 41.6** shows historical data for the numbers of lynx and their main prey, the snowshoe hare. Both populations rise and fall over an approximately ten-year cycle, with predator abundance lagging behind prey abundance. Field studies indicate that lynx numbers fluctuate mainly in response to hare numbers. However, the size of the hare population is affected by the abundance of the hare's food as well as the number of lynx. Hare populations continued to rise and fall even when predators were experimentally excluded from areas.

PREDATOR–PREY ARMS RACES

Predator and prey exert selection pressure on one another. Suppose a mutation arises that gives a prey species a more effective defense. Over generations, directional selection will cause this mutation to spread through the prey population. If some members of a predator population have a trait that makes them better at thwarting the improved defense, they and their descendants will be at an advantage. Thus, predators exert selection pressure that favors improved prey defense, which in turn exerts selection pressure on predators, and so it goes over many generations.

You have already learned about some defensive adaptations. Many prey species have hard or sharp parts that make them difficult to eat. Think of a snail's shell or a sea urchin's spines. Others contain chemicals that taste bad or sicken predators. Most defensive compounds in animals come from the plants they eat. For example, a monarch butterfly caterpillar takes up chemicals from the milkweed that it feeds on. A bird that later eats the butterfly will be sickened by these chemicals and avoid similar butterflies.

Prey animals use a variety of mechanisms to fend off a predator. Section 1.6 described how eyespots and a hissing sound protect some butterflies. A lizard's tail may detach from the body and wiggle a bit as a distraction. Many animals, including skunks, exude or squirt a foul-smelling, irritating repellent when frightened. Bees and wasps sting.

Well-defended prey often have warning coloration, a conspicuous color pattern that predators learn to avoid. For example, many species of stinging wasps and bees have a pattern of black and yellow stripes (**FIGURE 41.7A**). The similar appearance of bees and wasps is an example of one type of **mimicry**, an evolutionary pattern in which one species comes to resemble another. Bees and wasps benefit from their similar appearance. The more often a predator is stung by a black-and-yellow-striped insect, the less likely it is to attack a similar-looking insect.

In another type of mimicry, prey masquerade as a species that has a defense they lack. For example, some flies that cannot sting resemble bees or wasps that can (**FIGURE 41.7B**). The fly benefits when predators avoid it after an encounter with the better-defended look-alike species.

Camouflage is a body form and coloration pattern that allows an animal to blend into its surroundings, and thus avoid detection. For example, snowshoe hares such as the one in **FIGURE 41.6** turn white in winter, making it harder for predators to spot them in a snowy landscape.

Predators can benefit from camouflage too (**FIGURE 41.8**). Other predator adaptations include sharp teeth and claws that can pierce protective hard parts. Speedy prey select for faster predators. For example, the cheetah, the fastest land animal, can run 114 kilometers per hour (70 mph). Its preferred prey, Thomson's gazelles, run 80 kilometers per hour (50 mph).

PLANT–HERBIVORE ARMS RACE

With **herbivory**, an animal eats a plant or plant parts. The number and type of plants in a community can influence the number and type of herbivores present. Two types of defenses have evolved in response to herbivory. Some plants have adapted to withstand and recover quickly from herbivory. For example, prairie grasses are seldom killed by native grazers such as bison. The grasses store enough resources in roots to grow back lost shoots. Other plants have traits that deter herbivory. Such traits include spines or

camouflage Coloration or body form that helps an organism blend in with its surroundings and escape detection.
herbivory An animal feeds on plants or plant parts.
mimicry An evolutionary pattern in which one species becomes more similar in appearance to another.
predation One species captures, kills, and eats another.

A Frilly pink body parts of a flower mantis help hide it from insect prey attracted to the real flowers.

B Fleshy protrusions give a scorpionfish the appearance of an algae-covered rock. Fish that come close for a nibble end up as prey.

FIGURE 41.8 **Camouflage**.

thorns, leaves that are hard to chew or digest, and chemicals that taste bad or sicken herbivores. Ricin, the toxin made by castor bean plants (Section 9.6), sickens many herbivores. Caffeine in coffee beans and nicotine in tobacco leaves are evolved defenses against insects.

Existence of plant defenses favors herbivores capable of overcoming those defenses. For example, a capacity to withstand cyanide evolved in the bamboo-eating lemurs discussed in the prior section. Similarly, eucalyptus leaves contain toxins that make them poisonous to most mammals, but not to koalas. Specialized liver enzymes allow koalas to break down toxins made by a few eucalyptus species.

TAKE-HOME MESSAGE 41.4

Predation benefits predators and harms prey. Predator numbers may fluctuate in response to prey availability.

Predators can coevolve with their prey. Herbivores coevolve with the plants that they eat.

With mimicry, one species benefits by its resemblance to another species.

41.5 HOW DO PARASITES AND THEIR HOSTS INTERACT?

PARASITISM

With **parasitism**, one species (the parasite) benefits by feeding on another (the host), without immediately killing it. Endoparasites such as parasitic roundworms live and feed

A Endoparasitic roundworms in the intestine of a host pig.

B Ectoparasitic ticks attached to and sucking blood from a finch.

C Ectoparasitic dodder (*Cuscuta*), also known as strangleweed or devil's hair. This parasitic flowering plant has almost no chlorophyll. Leafless stems wrap around a host plant, and modified roots absorb water and nutrients from the host plant's vascular tissue.

FIGURE 41.9 Parasites inside and out.

inside their host (**FIGURE 41.9A**). An ectoparasite such as a tick feeds while attached to a host's external surface (**FIGURE 41.9B**).

A parasitic way of life has evolved in members of a diverse variety of groups. Bacterial, fungal, protistan, and invertebrate parasites feed on vertebrates. Lampreys (Section 24.2) attach to and feed on other fish. There are even a few parasitic plants that withdraw nutrients from other plants (**FIGURE 41.9C**).

Parasites usually do not kill their host immediately. In terms of evolutionary fitness, killing a host too fast is bad for the parasite. Ideally, a host will live long enough to give a parasite time to produce some offspring. The longer the host survives, the more parasite offspring can be produced. Thus, parasites with less-than-fatal effects on hosts are at a selective advantage.

Although parasites typically do not kill their hosts, many still have an important impact on a host population. Most pathogens are parasites that cause disease in their hosts. Even when a parasite does not cause obvious symptoms, its presence can weaken a host, making it more vulnerable to predation or less attractive to potential mates. Some parasites cause their host to become sterile. Others shift the sex ratio among their host's offspring.

Adaptations to a parasitic lifestyle include traits that allow the parasite to locate hosts and to feed undetected. For example, ticks that feed on mammals or birds move toward a source of heat and carbon dioxide, which may be a potential host. A chemical in tick saliva acts as a local anesthetic, preventing the host from noticing the feeding tick. Endoparasites often have traits that help them evade a host's immune defenses.

Among hosts, traits that fend off parasites or reduce the toll that a parasite takes on fitness are favored. Many animals groom or preen themselves to remove ectoparasites. One type of seabird (the crested auklet) secretes a citrus-scented compound that it spreads on its feathers as a tick repellent. Chimpanzees and other primates sometimes fold up tough, indigestible leaves and swallow them whole, a practice that helps rid their gut of parasitic worms.

PARASITOIDS

As many as 15 percent of all insects may be **parasitoids**, which lay their eggs in other insects. Larvae that hatch from the eggs develop in the host's body, eat its tissue, and eventually kill it. Parasitoids reduce the size of a host population in two ways. First, as the parasitoid larvae grow inside their host, they withdraw nutrients and prevent it from reproducing. Second, the presence of these larvae eventually leads to the death of the host.

CREDITS: (9A) © C. James Webb/Phototake USA; (9B) Bill Hilton, Jr., Hilton Pond Center; (9C) © The Samuel Roberts Noble Foundation, Inc.

FIGURE 41.10 **Biological pest control.** A commercially raised parasitoid wasp about to deposit a fertilized egg in an aphid. This wasp is used to reduce aphid populations. After the egg hatches, a wasp larva devours the aphid from the inside.

FIGURE 41.11 **Brood parasitism.** Ants tend a caterpillar of the Alcon blue butterfly, which smells like an ant and imitates sounds made by the queen ant. Ant workers feed the caterpillar more eagerly than their own larvae and will even feed it ant larvae if food runs short.

BIOLOGICAL PEST CONTROL

Parasites and parasitoids are commercially-raised and released in target areas as a form of **biological pest control** in which a pest's natural enemies are used to reduce its numbers (**FIGURE 41.10**). Biological pest control has some advantages over pesticides. Most chemical insecticides kill a wide variety of insects, including some that help control pests. Insecticides also have negative effects on human health. By contrast, the parasites and parasitoids used as biological control agents usually target only a limited number of species.

For a species to be an effective biological control agent, it must be adapted to take advantage of a specific host species and to survive in that species' habitat. The ideal biological control agent excels at finding the target host species, has a population growth rate comparable to the host's, and has offspring that disperse widely.

Introducing a species into a community as a biological control agent always entails some risks. The introduced parasites sometimes attack nontargeted species in addition to, or instead of, those that they were expected to control. For example, parasitoid wasps were introduced to Hawaii to control stinkbugs that feed on some Hawaiian crops. Instead, the parasitoids decimated the population of koa bugs, Hawaii's largest native bug. Introduced parasitoids have also been implicated in ongoing declines of many native Hawaiian butterfly and moth populations.

biological pest control Use of a pest's natural enemies to control its population size.
brood parasitism One egg-laying species benefits by having another raise its offspring.
parasitism Relationship in which one species withdraws nutrients from another species, without immediately killing it.
parasitoid An insect that lays eggs in another insect, and whose young devour their host from the inside.

BROOD PARASITISM

With **brood parasitism**, one egg-laying species benefits by having another raise its offspring. The host species suffers by squandering care on unrelated individuals. The European cuckoos described in Section 39.2 are brood parasites, as are North American cowbirds. Not having to invest in parental care allows a female cowbird to produce a large number of eggs, as many as thirty in a single reproductive season.

The presence of brood parasites decreases the reproductive rate of the host species and favors host individuals that detect and eject foreign young. Some avian brood parasites counter this host defense by producing eggs that closely resemble those of their host species. In cuckoos, different subpopulations have different host preferences and egg coloration. Females of each subpopulation lay eggs that closely resemble those of their preferred host.

As another example, some butterflies such as the Alcon blue butterfly outsource care of their young to ants (**FIGURE 41.11**). Caterpillars of these butterflies smell like an ant and make sounds similar to those made by ants. Worker ants, fooled by these false cues, carry the caterpillars into their nest, where they care for them as if they were members of the colony, feeding them and protecting them from predators.

> ### TAKE-HOME MESSAGE 41.5
> Parasites feed on living host individuals, harming them by withdrawing nutrients from them.
>
> Parasitoids reduce the number of host organisms by preventing reproduction and eventually killing the host.
>
> Brood parasites reduce the reproductive rate of hosts by tricking them into caring for young that are not their own.

CREDITS: (10) © Peter J. Bryant/Biological Photo Service; (11) © Darlyne A. Murawski/National Geographic Creative.

A The 1980 Mount Saint Helens eruption wiped out the biological community at the base of this Cascade volcano.

B In less than a decade, pioneer species had arrived and the process of primary succession had begun.

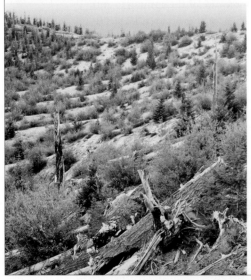

C Twelve years later, seedlings of Douglas firs had taken hold.

FIGURE 41.12 {Animated} An example of succession.

SUCCESSIONAL CHANGE

Species composition of a community changes over time. Often, some species alter the habitat in ways that allow others to come in and replace them. This type of change, which takes place over a long interval, is referred to as ecological succession.

Primary succession begins when **pioneer species** colonize a barren habitat that lacks soil, such as land exposed by the retreat of a glacier, a newly formed volcanic island, or a region where volcanic material has buried existing soil (**FIGURE 41.12**). The earliest pioneers to colonize such environments are often mosses and lichens (Sections 21.2 and 22.3), which are small, have a brief life cycle, and can tolerate intense sunlight, extreme temperature changes, and little or no soil. Some hardy annual flowering plants with wind-dispersed seeds are also frequent pioneers. Pioneer species help build and improve the soil. In doing so, they often set the stage for their own replacement. Many pioneer species partner with nitrogen-fixing bacteria, so they can grow in nitrogen-poor habitats. Seeds of later species find shelter inside mats of the pioneers. Organic wastes and remains accumulate and, by adding volume and nutrients to soil, this material helps other species take hold. Later successional species often shade and eventually displace earlier ones.

In **secondary succession**, a disturbed area within a community recovers. If improved soil is still present, secondary succession can occur fast. It commonly occurs in abandoned agricultural fields and burned forests.

When the concept of ecological succession was first developed in the late 1800s, it was thought to be a predictable and directional process that culminates in a "climax community," an array of species that persists over time and is reconstituted in the event of a disturbance. Ecologists now realize that the species composition of a community changes frequently, and in unpredictable ways. Communities do not journey along a well-worn path to some predetermined climax state. Random events can determine the order in which species arrive in a habitat and thus affect the course of succession in unpredictable ways.

Ecologists had an opportunity to investigate these factors after the 1980 eruption of Mount Saint Helens leveled about 600 square kilometers (235 square miles) of forest in Washington State (**FIGURE 41.12**). They recorded the natural pattern of colonization and carried out experiments in plots inside the blast zone. The results of these and other studies showed that the presence of some pioneers helped certain other, later-arriving plants become established, whereas the presence of other pioneers kept the same late successional species out.

CREDITS: (14A) R. Barrick/USGS; (14B) USGS; (14C) P. Frenzen, USDA Forest Service.

EFFECTS OF DISTURBANCE

The type and rate of disturbances also influence species composition in communities. According to the **intermediate disturbance hypothesis**, species richness is greatest in habits where disturbances are moderate in their intensity or frequency. In such habitats, there is enough time for new colonists to arrive and become established but not enough for competitive exclusion to cause extinctions:

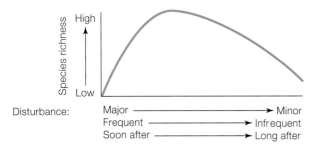

In communities repeatedly subjected to a particular type of physical disturbance, individuals that withstand or benefit from that disturbance have a selective advantage. For example, some plants in areas subject to periodic fires produce seeds that germinate only after a fire. Seedlings of these plants benefit from the lack of competition for resources in newly burned areas. Other plants have an ability to resprout quickly after a fire (**FIGURE 41.13**). Because different species respond differently to fire, the frequency of this disturbance affects competitive interactions. Human suppression of naturally occurring fires can change the composition of a biological community by allowing species that are not fire-adapted to outcompete fire-adapted ones that previously predominated.

Some species are especially intolerant of physical disturbance of their environment. These **indicator species** are the first to decline or disappear when conditions change, so they can provide an early warning of environmental degradation. For example, a decline in a trout population can be an early sign of problems in a stream, because trout are highly sensitive to pollutants and cannot tolerate low oxygen levels. Some lichens are intolerant of air pollution and serve as indicators of air quality (**FIGURE 41.14**).

indicator species Species whose presence and abundance in a community provides information about conditions in the community.
intermediate disturbance hypothesis Species richness is greatest in communities with moderate levels of disturbance.
pioneer species Species that can colonize a new habitat.
primary succession A new community becomes established in an area where there was previously no soil.
secondary succession A new community develops in a site where a community previously existed.

FIGURE 41.13 Adapted to disturbance. Some woody shrubs, such as this toyon, resprout from their roots after a fire. In the absence of occasional fire, toyons are outcompeted and displaced by species that grow faster but are less fire resistant.

FIGURE 41.14 Indicator species. Lichens take up nutrients—and pollutants—from airborne dust, so many cannot survive where the level of air pollution is high. The U.S. Forest Service monitors the types and numbers of lichens on tree trunks as part of its program to assess the health of forest communities.

TAKE-HOME MESSAGE 41.6

Succession is a process in which one array of species replaces another over time. It can occur in a barren, soilless habitat (primary succession), or in a habitat where a community previously existed (secondary succession).

Physical factors affect succession, but so do species interactions and disturbances. As a result, the course that succession will take in a community is difficult to predict.

Some species are especially intolerant of certain physical changes to the environment, and the size of their populations can serve as an indicator of the state of an environment.

The loss or addition of one species sometimes alters the abundance of many other species in a community.

KEYSTONE SPECIES

A **keystone species** is a species that has a disproportionately large effect on a community relative to its abundance. It is named for the central, wedge-shaped stone in a stone arch; a keystone keeps other stones in place. Robert Paine coined the term "keystone species" as a result of his experiments on the rocky shores of California's coast. Species in the rocky intertidal zone withstand pounding surf by clinging to rocks. A rock to cling to is a limiting factor. Paine set up control plots with the sea star *Pisaster ochraceus* and its main prey—chitons, limpets, barnacles, and mussels. Then he removed all sea stars from his experimental plots.

Sea stars prey mainly on mussels. With sea stars gone from experimental plots, mussels took over, crowding out seven other species of invertebrates (**FIGURE 41.15**).

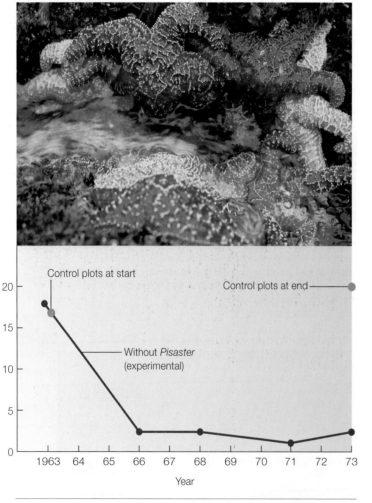

FIGURE 41.15 Effect of removal of the sea star *Pisaster* on the number of species in tide pools. Sea stars were not removed from control plots.

Paine concluded that sea stars are a keystone species. They normally keep the number of prey species in the intertidal zone high by preventing competitive exclusion by mussels.

Keystone species need not be predators. For example, beavers are keystone species in some communities. These large, herbivorous rodents cut down trees by gnawing through their trunks. The beaver then uses the felled trees to build a dam, thus creating a deep pool where a shallow stream would otherwise exist. By altering the physical conditions in a section of the stream, the beaver affects the types of fish and aquatic invertebrates that can live there.

EXOTIC SPECIES

The arrival of a new species in a community can also cause dramatic changes. When you hear someone speaking enthusiastically about exotic species, you can safely bet the speaker is not an ecologist. An **exotic species** is a nonnative species, one that evolved in one community, then dispersed from its home and became established elsewhere.

As the pace of global travel and trade have picked up, so has the rate of species introductions. More than 4,500 exotic species have become established in the United States. An estimated 25 percent of Florida's plant and animal species are exotics. In Hawaii, 45 percent are exotic. Some species were brought in for use as food crops, to brighten gardens, or to provide textiles. Other species arrived as stowaways along with cargo from distant regions. Increased dispersal rates among pest species are an unanticipated side effect of increased global trade and improvements in shipping. Speedier ships make quicker trips, increasing the likelihood that pests hidden in cargo holds will survive a journey.

Many exotic species have little impact on their adopted community, but others are invasive. An invasive species harms an existing community. The water mold that is currently killing off oaks in the Pacific Northwest (Section 20.6) is an invasive species, as are the fungi that currently threaten North America's bats (Section 22.3) and frogs (Section 22.5). Sea lampreys are considered an invasive species in the Great Lakes (Section 24.2).

As another example, consider the vine called kudzu (*Pueraria lobata*). Native to Asia, it was introduced to the American Southeast as a food for grazers and to control erosion, but it quickly became an invasive weed. Kudzu overgrows trees, telephone poles, houses, and almost everything else in its path (**FIGURE 41.16A**).

Gypsy moths (*Lymantria dispar*) are an invasive species too. They entered the northeastern United States in the mid-1700s and now range into the Southeast, Midwest, and Canada. Gypsy moth caterpillars (**FIGURE 41.16B**) preferentially feed on oaks. Loss of leaves to gypsy moths

A Kudzu native to Asia is overgrowing trees across the southeastern United States.

B Gypsy moth caterpillars native to Europe and Asia now feed on oaks in much of the United States.

C Nutrias native to South America now abound in freshwater marshes of the Gulf States.

FIGURE 41.16 Three exotic species that are altering natural communities in the United States. To learn more about invasive species in the United States, visit the National Invasive Species Information Center online at www.invasivespeciesinfo.gov.

weakens the trees, making them less efficient competitors and more susceptible to parasites.

Large semiaquatic rodents called nutrias (*Myocastor coypus*) were imported from South America for their fur. Today, descendants of animals that either escaped or were intentionally released thrive in freshwater marshes and along rivers in twenty states (**FIGURE 41.16C**). Their appetite for plants threatens native vegetation and crop plants, and their burrowing contributes to marsh erosion and damages levees, increasing the risk of flooding.

Most invasive species have a far greater impact in their new home than they did in the community in which they evolved. When a species leaves its community of origin

behind, it also leaves behind the competitors, predators, and parasites with which it coevolved and which helped to keep its numbers in check. If the invasive species is a parasite, predator, or herbivore, it also leaves behind hosts or prey that had coevolved with it and had defenses against it. As a result, an invasive species often reaches a higher population density in its new home than it achieved in its old one.

TAKE-HOME MESSAGE 41.7

Keystone species greatly influence the diversity and abundance of other species within their community.

An exotic species evolved in one community and now lives in another. It is considered invasive if it threatens other members of its new community.

When an invasive species enters a new community, it encounters species that have not evolved defenses against it. Thus invasive species often have a greater impact in their new community than they did in their community of origin.

exotic species A species that evolved in one community and later became established in a different one.
keystone species A species that has a disproportionately large effect on community structure relative to its abundance.

CREDITS: (16A) Danny E Hooks/Shutterstock.com; (16B) Photo by Scott Bauer, USDA/ARS; (16C) © Greg Lasley Nature Photography, www.greglasley.net.

Islands are natural laboratories for population studies. They have also been laboratories for community studies. Consider Surtsey, an island that appeared in the mid-1960s when an undersea volcano erupted 33 kilometers (21 miles) from the coast of Iceland (**FIGURE 41.17**). Bacteria and fungi were early colonists. The first vascular plant became established on the island in 1965. Mosses appeared two years later and thrived. The first lichens were found five years after that. The rate at which vascular plants were introduced to the island picked up dramatically after a seagull colony became established in 1986.

The number of species on Surtsey will not continue increasing forever. How many species will there be when the number levels off? According to the **equilibrium model of island biogeography**, the number of species living on any island reflects a balance between immigration rates for new species and extinction rates for established ones.

Two factors determine the equilibrium number of species (**FIGURE 41.18**). First, there is a **distance effect**; islands far from a source of colonists receive fewer immigrants than those closer to a source. Most species cannot disperse very far, so they will not turn up far from a mainland. Second, there is an **area effect**; an island's size affects both immigration rates and extinction rates. More colonists will happen upon a larger island simply by virtue of its size. Also, big islands are more likely to offer a variety of habitats, such as high and low elevations. These options make it more likely that a new arrival will find a suitable habitat. Finally, big islands can support larger populations of species than small islands. The larger a population, the less likely it is to become locally extinct as the result of some random event. For example, a fire large enough to wipe out the population of a small island might leave survivors on a larger island.

Robert H. MacArthur and Edward O. Wilson developed the equilibrium model of island biogeography in the late 1960s. Since then, the model has been modified and its use has been expanded to help scientists think about habitat islands, which are natural settings surrounded by a "sea" of habitat that has been disturbed by humans. Many parks and wildlife preserves fit this description. Island-based models can help ecologists estimate the size of an area needed to ensure survival of a species that inhabits it.

FIGURE 41.17 Vascular plant colonization of Surtsey, a volcanic island shown forming in the inset photo. Seagulls first began nesting on the island in 1986.

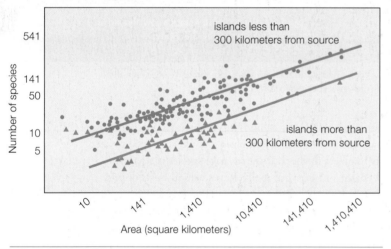

FIGURE 41.18 {Animated} Island biodiversity patterns.

Distance effect: Species richness on islands of a given size declines as distance from a source of colonists rises. Green circles are values for islands less than 300 kilometers from the colonizing source. Orange triangles are values for islands more than 300 kilometers (190 miles) from a source of colonists.

Area effect: Among islands the same distance from a source of colonists, larger islands tend to support more species than smaller ones.

FIGURE IT OUT: Which is likely to have more species, a 100-km² island more than 300 km from a colonizing source or a 500-km² island less than 300 km from a colonist source?

Answer: The 500-km² island

area effect Larger islands have more species than small ones.
distance effect Islands close to a mainland have more species than those farther away.
equilibrium model of island biogeography Model that predicts the number of species on an island based on the island's area and distance from the mainland.

CREDITS: (17) photo, © Pierre Vauthey/Sygma/Corbis; art, From Starr/Taggart/Evers/Starr, Biology, 13E. © 2013 Cengage Learning; (18) © Cengage Learning.

TAKE-HOME MESSAGE 41.8

Studies of islands helped biologists understand how the area of a community and its distance from a source of colonist species influences the species richness of the community.

Sustainability

FIGURE 41.19 Nest mounds of red imported fire ants in a Texas field. The inset photo shows the ants attacking a quail egg.

RED IMPORTED FIRE ANTS (*SOLENOPSIS INVICTA*) ARRIVED IN THE SOUTHEASTERN UNITED STATES IN THE 1930s. These natives of South America probably arrived as stowaways on a cargo ship. They are invasive and have established colonies as far west as California and as far north as Kansas and Delaware.

The spread of red imported fire ants poses a threat to wildlife. Competition from these invasive ants typically causes a region's native ant populations to decline, and the resulting change in species composition can harm ant-eating animals. For example, the Texas horned lizard feeds mainly on native harvester ants, and cannot eat the red imported fire ants that have largely replaced its natural prey. Red imported fire ants also harm native species by feeding on their eggs and feeding on or stinging their young. Ground-nesting animals such as quail are especially vulnerable to fire ant predation (FIGURE 41.19).

The presence of red imported fire ants can even affect native plants. The ants interfere with pollination by displacing or preying on native pollinators such as ground-nesting bees. They also impede dispersal of native plants whose seeds would normally be spread by native ants that the fire ants have replaced.

Given the problems the imported ants are causing in the United States, you might wonder what things are like in their native South America.

The ants are not considered much of a concern there, in part because they are far less common. In South America, parasites, predators, and diseases keep the ants' numbers in check.

Invicta means "invincible" in Latin, and *S. invicta* lives up to its name. Pesticides do not slow the spread of this species. To fight the ants, scientists have now turned to biological controls, enlisting the help of the ants' natural enemies.

Phorid flies are parasitoids that target red imported fire ants. The flies kill their host in a rather gruesome way. A female fly pierces the cuticle of an adult ant, then lays an egg in the ant's soft tissues. The egg hatches into a larva, which grows and eats its way through the tissues to the ant's head. When the larva is ready to undergo metamorphosis, it secretes an enzyme that makes the ant's head fall off. The fly larva then develops into an adult within the shelter of the detached ant head.

Several phorid fly species have been introduced in various southern states. The flies seem to be surviving, reproducing, and increasing their range. They are not expected to kill off all *S. invicta* in affected areas. Rather, the hope is that the flies will reduce the density of invading colonies.

Ecologists are also exploring other options. They are testing effects of imported pathogenic fungi or protists that infect *S. invicta* but not native ants. Another idea is to introduce a parasitic South American ant that invades *S. invicta* colonies and kills the egg-laying queens.

CREDITS: (19) background, Photography by B. M. Drees, Texas A&M University, http://fireant.tamu; inset, © James Mueller.

Summary

SECTION 41.1   Each species in a **community** occupies a certain **habitat** characterized by physical and chemical features and by the array of other species living in it. The number of species in a community tends to be greatest in the tropics. Species interactions affect community structure. With **commensalism**, one species benefits and the other is unaffected. A **symbiosis** is an interaction in which one species lives in or on another.

SECTION 41.2   In a **mutualism**, both species benefit from an interaction. Some mutualists cannot complete their life cycle without the interaction. Mutualists who maximize their own benefits while limiting the cost of cooperating are at a selective advantage.

SECTION 41.3   A species' roles and requirements define its unique **ecological niche**. With **interspecific competition**, two species with similar resource requirements are harmed by one another's presence. When one competitor drives the other to local extinction, we call the process **competitive exclusion**. Competing species with similar requirements become less similar when directional selection causes **character displacement**. This change in traits allows **resource partitioning**.

SECTION 41.4   **Predation** benefits a predator at the expense of the prey it captures, kills, and eats. Predators and their prey exert selective pressures on one another. Evolved prey defenses include **camouflage** and **mimicry**. Predators have traits that allow them to overcome prey defenses. With **herbivory**, an animal eats a plant or plant parts. Plants have traits that discourage herbivory or that allow a quick recovery from the loss of shoots.

SECTION 41.5   **Parasitism** involves feeding on a host without killing it. **Parasitoids** are insects that lay eggs on a host insect, then larvae devour the host. Parasites and parasitoids are often used in **biological pest control**. A **brood parasite** steals parental care from another species.

SECTION 41.6   Ecological succession is the sequential replacement of one array of species by another over time. **Primary succession** happens in new habitats. **Secondary succession** occurs in disturbed ones. The first species of a community are **pioneer species**. Their presence may help, hinder, or not affect later colonists.

Modern models of succession emphasize the unpredictability of the outcome as a result of chance events, ongoing changes, and disturbance. The **intermediate disturbance hypothesis** predicts that a moderate level of disturbance keeps a community diverse. An **indicator species** is highly sensitive to disturbance and can provide information about the health of the environment.

SECTION 41.7   **Keystone species** play a major role in determining the composition of a community. Removal of a keystone species or introduction of an **exotic species** can dramatically alter community structure.

SECTION 41.8   A community supports a finite number of species. The **equilibrium model of island biogeography** predicts the number of species that an island will sustain based on the **area effect** and the **distance effect**. Scientists can use this model to predict the number of species that habitat islands such as parks can sustain.

SECTION 41.9   Arrival of an invasive exotic species such as the red imported fire ant can decrease populations of native species that compete for the same resources. Natural enemies of the ants are now being used to reduce their numbers.

Self-Quiz   Answers in Appendix VII

1. The type of place where a species typically lives is called its _____ .
   - a. niche
   - b. habitat
   - c. community
   - d. population

2. Which cannot be a symbiosis?
   - a. mutualism
   - b. parasitism
   - c. commensalism
   - d. interspecific competition

3. Lizards that eat flies they catch on the ground and birds that eat flies they catch in the air are engaged in _____ competition.
   - a. exploitative
   - b. interference
   - c. intraspecific
   - d. interspecific
   - e. both a and d
   - f. both b and c

4. _____ can lead to resource partitioning.
   - a. Mutualism
   - b. Parasitism
   - c. Commensalism
   - d. Interspecific competition

5. Match the terms with the most suitable descriptions.
   - ___ mutualism
   - ___ parasitism
   - ___ commensalism
   - ___ predation
   - ___ interspecific competition

   - a. one free-living species feeds on another and usually kills it
   - b. two species interact and both benefit by the interaction
   - c. two species interact and one benefits while the other is neither helped nor harmed
   - d. one species feeds on another but usually does not kill it
   - e. two species access a resource

6. A tick is a(n) _____ .
   - a. brood parasite
   - b. ectoparasite
   - c. endoparasite

7. By a currently favored hypothesis, species richness of a community is greatest between physical disturbances of _____ intensity or frequency.
   - a. low
   - b. intermediate
   - c. high
   - d. variable

8. _____ species are the first to colonize a new habitat.

Data Analysis Activities

Biological Control of Fire Ants Ant-decapitating phorid flies are just one of the biological control agents used to battle imported fire ants. Researchers have also enlisted the help of a fungal parasite that infects the ants and slows their production of offspring. An infected colony dwindles in numbers and eventually dies out. Are these biological controls useful against imported fire ants? To find out, USDA scientists treated infested areas with either traditional pesticides or pesticides plus biological controls (both flies and the parasite). The scientists left some plots untreated as controls. **FIGURE 41.20** shows the results.

1. How did population size in the control plots change during the first four months of the study?

2. How did population size in the two types of treated plots change during this same interval?

3. If this study had ended after the first year, would you conclude that biological controls had a major effect?

4. How did the two types of treatment (pesticide alone versus pesticide plus biological controls) differ in their longer-term effects? Which is most effective?

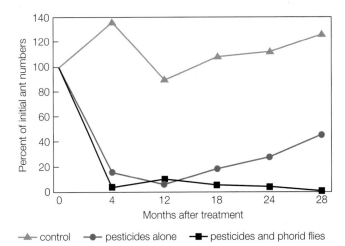

FIGURE 41.20 Effects of two methods of controlling red imported fire ants. The graph shows the numbers of red imported fire ants over a 28-month period. Orange triangles represent untreated control plots. Green circles are plots treated with pesticides alone. Black squares are plots treated with pesticide and biological control agents (phorid flies and a fungal parasite).

---

9. Growth of a forest in an abandoned corn field is an example of _____ .
   a. primary succession   c. secondary succession
   b. resource partitioning   d. competitive exclusion

10. Species richness is greatest in communities _____ .
   a. near the equator   c. near the poles
   b. in temperate regions   d. that recently formed

11. If you remove a species from a community, the population size of its main _____ is likely to increase.
   a. parasite   b. competitor   c. predator

12. A _____ has another species rear its young.
   a. mutualist   c. brood parasite
   b. pioneer species   d. exotic species

13. Herbivory benefits _____ .
   a. the herbivore   c. both a and b
   b. the plant   d. neither a nor b

14. Match the terms with the most suitable descriptions.
   ___ area effect
   ___ pioneer species
   ___ indicator species
   ___ keystone species
   ___ exotic species
   ___ resource partitioning

   a. greatly affects other species
   b. first species established in a new habitat
   c. more species on large islands than small ones at same distance from the source of colonists
   d. species that is especially sensitive to changes in the environment
   e. allows competitors to coexist
   f. often outcompete, displace native species of established community

Critical Thinking

1. With antibiotic resistance rising, researchers are looking for ways to reduce the use of antibiotics. Some cattle once fed antibiotic-laced food now get probiotic feed instead, with cultured bacteria that can establish or bolster populations of helpful bacteria in the animal's gut. The idea is that if a large population of beneficial bacteria is in place, then harmful bacteria cannot become established or thrive. Which ecological principle is guiding this research?

2. Phasmids are plant-eating insects that mimic leaves or sticks, as shown at the *left*. Most rest during the day, and feed at night. If they do move in daytime, they do so very slowly. If disturbed, a phasmid will fall to the ground and lie motionless. Speculate on selective pressures that could have shaped phasmid morphology and behavior. Suggest an experiment to test a hypothesis about how its appearance or behavior may be adaptive.

CENGAGE brain.com To access course materials, please visit www.cengagebrain.com.

An energy and nutrient transfer. The caterpillar is tapping into the sunlight energy that this leaf captured and stored in the chemical bonds of sugars. The caterpillar also obtains nutrients such as nitrogen that the plant took up from the soil and used to build its leaves.

42

ECOSYSTEMS

Links to Earlier Concepts

This chapter returns to the concept of a one-way flow of energy in nature (Sections 1.2, 5.1) and looks at nitrogen-fixing bacteria (19.5), soil erosion, and leaching (26.1) in the context of nitrogen cycling. You will be reminded of properties of chemical bonds (2.3) and the pathways of photosynthesis (6.3) and aerobic respiration (7.1). You will see how slow movements of Earth's crust (16.5) influence the cycling of some nutrients.

KEY CONCEPTS

ORGANIZATION OF ECOSYSTEMS
A one-way flow of energy and cycling of nutrients among species maintain an ecosystem. Nutrients and energy are transferred through food chains that interconnect as food webs.

BIOGEOCHEMICAL CYCLES
In a biogeochemical cycle, a nutrient moves slowly among its environmental reservoirs (air, water, and rocks). Nutrients move more quickly into, through, and out of food webs.

THE WATER CYCLE
Most of Earth's water is in its oceans. Evaporation, condensation, precipitation, and flow of rivers and streams move water. Water also transports soluble forms of some nutrients.

THE CARBON CYCLE
Most of Earth's carbon is in rocks, but organisms take carbon up from water or the air. Carbon dioxide is one of the atmospheric greenhouse gases that help keep Earth's surface warm.

NITROGEN AND PHOSPHORUS CYCLES
Plants take up soluble forms of nitrogen and phosphorus from soil. Nitrogen is abundant in air, but only certain bacteria can use this form. Phosphorus has no major gaseous form; most of it is in rocks.

An **ecosystem** is a community of organisms together with the nonliving components of their environment. It is an open system, because it requires ongoing inputs of energy to persist. Most ecosystems also gain nutrients from and lose nutrients to other ecosystems.

Features of ecosystems vary widely. In climate, soil type, array of species, and other features, prairies differ from forests, which differ from tundra and deserts. Reefs differ from the open ocean, which differs from streams and lakes. Yet, despite these differences, ecologists have found that all systems are alike in many aspects.

PRODUCERS AND CONSUMERS

All ecosystems run on energy that **producers** capture from the environment (**FIGURE 42.1**). Producers are autotrophs (Section 6.1), meaning they obtain energy directly from the environment and use an inorganic form of carbon to build sugars. In most ecosystems, photoautotrophs such as plants, algae, and photosynthetic protists and bacteria are the main producers. In some dark environments such as deep-sea hydrothermal vent ecosystems, chemoautotrophs fill this role. As Section 19.4 explained, chemoautotrophs are bacteria or archaea that fuel the assembly of their food by oxidizing (removing electrons from) inorganic substances such as hydrogen sulfide.

Primary production is the rate at which an ecosystem's producers capture and store energy. Day length, temperature, and the availability of nutrients, including nitrogen and phosphorus, affect the rate of photosynthesis and so influence primary production. As a result, primary production can vary seasonally within an ecosystem and also differs among ecosystems. Per unit area, primary production on land tends to be higher than that in the oceans. However, because oceans cover about 70 percent of Earth's surface, marine producers—photosynthetic bacteria and protists—contribute nearly half of the global net primary production.

As Section 1.2 explained, **consumers** obtain energy and carbon by feeding on tissues and remains of producers and one another. We describe consumers by their diets. Herbivores eat plants. Carnivores eat the flesh of animals. Parasites live inside or on a living host and feed on its tissues. Omnivores eat both animals and plants. **Detritivores** such as earthworms eat small bits of decaying organic matter, or detritus. **Decomposers** feed on wastes and remains, breaking them down into inorganic building blocks. Bacteria, archaea, and fungi serve as decomposers.

ENERGY FLOW, NUTRIENT CYCLING

Energy captured by producers is converted to bond energy in organic molecules. This energy is released by metabolic

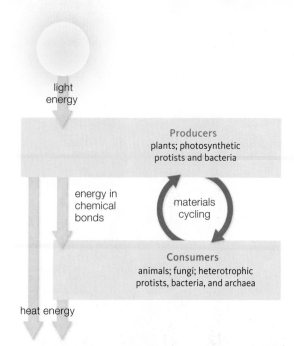

FIGURE 42.1 {Animated} One-way flow of energy (yellow arrows) and nutrient cycling (blue arrows) in the most common type of ecosystem. All light energy that enters the system eventually returns to the environment as heat energy that is not reused. By contrast, nutrients are continually recycled.

reactions that give off heat. Energy flow through living organisms is a one-way process because producers cannot capture the energy of heat in chemical bonds, so it escapes from the ecosystem (Section 5.1). In contrast, nutrients cycle within an ecosystem. Producers take up hydrogen, oxygen, and carbon from inorganic sources such as the air and water. They also take up dissolved nitrogen, phosphorus, and other necessary minerals. Nutrients that producers used to build their bodies are used in turn to build the bodies of the consumers who eat them. When producers or consumers die, decomposition returns nutrients to the environment, from which producers take them up again.

TROPHIC STRUCTURE

Ecologists often look at energy transfers in terms of who eats whom. The hierarchy of feeding relationships in an ecosystem is the ecosystem's trophic structure. *Troph* refers to feeding, as in autotroph, which means self-feeding. In any ecosystem, all organisms at the same **trophic level** are the same number of transfers away from that system's source of energy. Producers are at the first trophic level. The primary consumers that eat them are at the second trophic level. The second-level consumers eat primary consumers, and so on.

A **food chain** is a sequence of steps by which some energy captured by primary producers is transferred to higher trophic levels. For example, in one tallgrass prairie food chain, energy flows from grasses to grasshoppers, to sparrows, and finally to bird-eating hawks (**FIGURE 42.2**). At the first trophic level in this food chain, grasses and other plants are the producers. At the second trophic level, grasshoppers are primary consumers. At the third trophic level, sparrows that eat grasshoppers are second-level consumers. At the fourth trophic level, hawks that eat sparrows are third-level consumers.

Energy captured by producers usually passes through no more than four or five trophic levels. Even in ecosystems with many species, the number of participants in each food chain is limited. The inefficiency of energy transfers constrains the length of food chains. Only 5 to 30 percent of the energy in tissues of an organism at one trophic level ends up in tissues of an organism at the next trophic level.

Several factors limit the efficiency of transfers. All organisms lose energy as metabolic heat, and this energy is not available to organisms at the next trophic level. Also, some energy gets stored in molecules that most consumers cannot break down. For example, most carnivores cannot access energy tied up in bones, scales, hair, feathers, or fur. Many herbivores cannot digest cellulose and lignin that reinforce the tissues of plants.

---

consumer Organism that obtains energy and carbon by feeding on tissues, wastes, or remains of other organisms.
decomposer Organism that feeds on biological remains and breaks organic material down into its inorganic subunits.
detritivore Consumer that feeds on small bits of organic material.
ecosystem A biological community and its environment.
food chain Description of who eats whom in one path of energy flow through an ecosystem.
primary production The rate at which an ecosystem's producers capture and store energy.
producer An organism that obtains energy directly from the environment and carbon from inorganic sources; an autotroph.
trophic level Position of an organism in a food chain.

TAKE-HOME MESSAGE 42.1

An ecosystem is a community of autotrophic producers and heterotrophic consumers that interact with one another and with their nonliving environment.

Nutrients cycle within an ecosystem, but energy flows through in one direction only.

Ecosystems vary in their primary production. Marine ecosystems generally have a lower primary production per unit area than land ecosystems.

Energy and nutrients are passed up food chains. Inefficiency of energy transfers limits the number of steps in food chains.

hawk

Fourth Trophic Level
Third-level consumer

sparrow

Third Trophic Level
Second-level consumer

grasshopper

Second Trophic Level
Primary consumer

big bluestem grass

First Trophic Level
Producer

FIGURE 42.2 {Animated} Food chain. An example of who eats whom in a tallgrass prairie ecosystem in Kansas. Yellow arrows indicate energy flow. Plants are the main producers. Sunlight energy they capture and store in their tissues supplies the energy that the ecosystem's consumers require.

 FIGURE IT OUT: Which of these organisms are heterotrophs?

Answer: All of the consumers are heterotrophs. They cannot make their own food.

CREDITS: (3) From left, top row, © Bryan & Cherry Alexander/Science Source; © Dave Mech; © Tom & Pat Leeson, Ardea London Ltd.; 2nd row, © Paul J. Fusco/Science Source; © Tom Wakefield/Bruce Coleman, Inc.; © E. R. Degginger/Science Source; 3rd row, © Tom McHugh/Science Source; © Tom J. Ulrich/Visuals Unlimited; © Dave Mech; mosquito, Photo by James Gathany, Centers for Disease Control; flea, © Edward S. Ross; 4th row, © Jim Steinborn; © Jim Riley; © Matt Skalitzky; earthworm, © Peter Firus, flagstaffotos.com.au; art, © Cengage Learning.

An organism that participates in one food chain usually has a role in many others as well. The food chains of an ecosystem cross-connect as a **food web**. FIGURE 42.3 shows some participants in an arctic food web.

Most food webs include both **grazing food chains**, in which herbivores eat producers, and **detrital food chains**, in which producers die and are then consumed by detritivores. Herbivores tend to be relatively large animals such as mammals, whereas detritivores tend to be smaller animals such as worms or insects.

In most land ecosystems, the bulk of the energy that gets stored in producer tissues moves through detrital food chains. For example, in an arctic ecosystem, voles, lemmings, and hares eat some living plant parts. However, far more

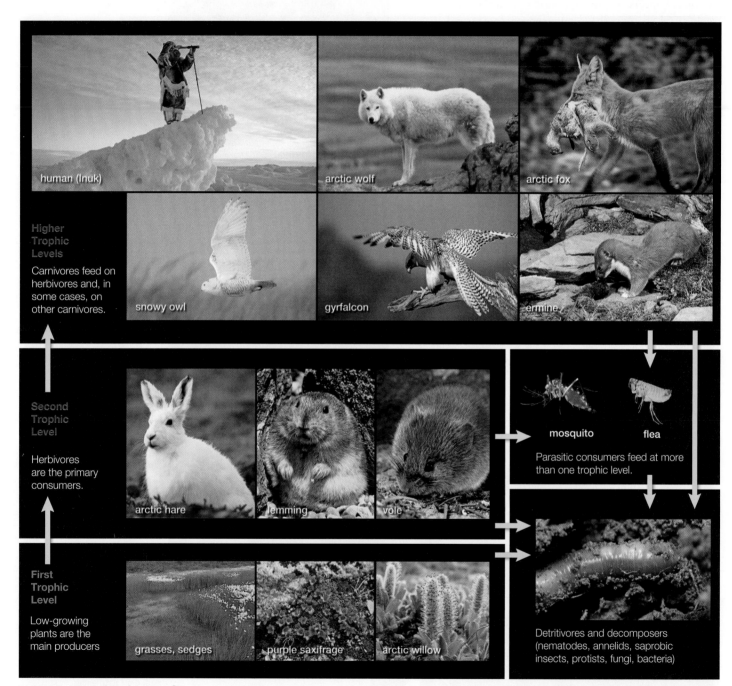

human (Inuk)

arctic wolf

arctic fox

Higher Trophic Levels

Carnivores feed on herbivores and, in some cases, on other carnivores.

snowy owl

gyrfalcon

ermine

mosquito   flea

Parasitic consumers feed at more than one trophic level.

Second Trophic Level

Herbivores are the primary consumers.

arctic hare

lemming

vole

First Trophic Level

Low-growing plants are the main producers

grasses, sedges

purple saxifrage

arctic willow

Detritivores and decomposers (nematodes, annelids, saprobic insects, protists, fungi, bacteria)

FIGURE 42.3 {Animated} Some organisms in an arctic food web. Yellow arrows indicate path of energy flow (point from eaten to eater).

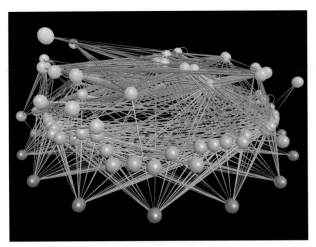

FIGURE 42.4 Computer model for a land food web in East River Valley, Colorado. Balls signify species. Their colors identify trophic levels, with producers (coded red) at the bottom and top predators (yellow) at top. The connecting lines thicken, as they go from an eaten species to the eater.

plant material ends up as detritus. Bits of dead plant material sustain detritivores such as nematodes and soil-dwelling insects.

Understanding food webs helps ecologists predict how ecosystems will respond to change. Neo Martinez and his colleagues constructed the food web diagram shown in **FIGURE 42.4**. By comparing different food webs, Martinez realized that trophic interactions connect species more closely than people thought. On average, each species in a food web was typically two links away from all other species. Ninety-five percent of species were within three links of one another, even in large communities with many species. As Martinez concluded in his paper about these findings, "Everything is linked to everything else." He cautioned that the extinction of any species in a food web has a potential impact on many other species.

---

detrital food chain Food chain in which energy is transferred directly from producers to detritivores.
food web Set of cross-connecting food chains.
grazing food chain Food chain in which energy is transferred from producers to grazers (herbivores).

TAKE-HOME MESSAGE 42.2

Two types of food chains connect in most food webs. Tissues of living producers are the base for grazing food chains. Producer remains are the base for detrital food chains.

Even in complex ecosystems, trophic interactions link each species in a food web with many others.

A food web diagram is one way of depicting the trophic relationships of species in a particular ecosystem. Ecological pyramid diagrams are another. A biomass pyramid shows the amount of organic material in the bodies of organisms at each trophic level at a specific time. An energy pyramid shows the amount of energy that flows through each trophic level in a given interval. **FIGURE 42.5** shows ecological pyramids for one freshwater spring ecosystem in Florida.

Most commonly, producers account for most of the biomass in a pyramid, and top carnivores contribute relatively little. The Florida ecosystem has lots of aquatic plants but very few gars (a top predator in this ecosystem). Similarly, if you walk through a prairie, you will see more grams of grass than of coyote.

An energy pyramid is always broadest at the bottom. This is why people promote a vegetarian diet by touting the ecological benefits of "eating lower on the food chain." They are referring to the energy losses in transfers between plants, livestock, and humans. When a person eats a plant, he or she gets most of the calories in that food. When a plant is used to feed livestock, only a small percentage of that food's calories ends up in meat a person can eat. Thus, feeding a population of meat-eaters requires far greater crop production than sustaining a population of vegetarians.

FIGURE 42.5 {Animated} Ecological pyramids for Silver Springs, an aquatic ecosystem in Florida.

A Biomass pyramid (grams per square meter).

B Energy flow pyramid (kilocalories per square meter per year).

TAKE-HOME MESSAGE 42.3

Ecological pyramids depict the distribution of materials and energy among the trophic levels of an ecosystem.

42.4 WHAT IS A BIOGEOCHEMICAL CYCLE?

FIGURE 42.6 Generalized biogeochemical cycle. For any nutrient, the cumulative amount in all environmental reservoirs far exceeds the amount in living organisms.

In a **biogeochemical cycle**, an essential element moves from one or more environmental reservoirs, through the biological component of an ecosystem, and then back to the reservoirs (**FIGURE 42.6**). Depending on the element, environmental reservoirs may include Earth's rocks and sediments, waters, and atmosphere.

Chemical and geologic processes move elements to, from, and among environmental reservoirs. For example, elements locked in rocks can become part of the atmosphere as a result of volcanic activity. As one of Earth's crustal plates moves under another, rocks on the seafloor can be uplifted so they become part of a landmass. On land, the rocks are exposed to the erosive forces of wind and rain. As the rocks are slowly broken down, elements in them enter rivers, and eventually seas. Compared to the movement of elements among organisms of an ecosystem, the movement of elements among nonbiological reservoirs is far slower. Processes such as erosion and uplifting operate over thousands or millions of years.

biogeochemical cycle A nutrient moves among environmental reservoirs and into and out of food webs.

TAKE-HOME MESSAGE 42.4

A biogeochemical cycle is the slow movement of a nutrient among environmental reservoirs and into, through, and out of food webs.

42.5 WHAT IS THE WATER CYCLE?

The **water cycle** moves water from the ocean to the atmosphere, onto land, and back to the oceans (**FIGURE 42.7**). Sunlight energy causes evaporation, the conversion of liquid water to water vapor. Water vapor that enters the cool upper layers of the atmosphere condenses into droplets, forming clouds. When droplets get large and heavy enough, they fall as precipitation—as rain, snow, or hail.

Oceans cover about 70 percent of Earth's surface, so most rainfall returns water directly to the oceans. Most precipitation that falls on land seeps into the ground. Some of this water remains between soil particles as **soil water**. Plant roots can tap into this water source. Water that drains through soil layers often collects in **aquifers**, which are natural underground reservoirs consisting of porous rock layers. **Groundwater** is water in soil and aquifers. Water that falls on impermeable rock or on saturated soil becomes **runoff**: It flows over the ground into streams. The flow of groundwater and surface water returns water to oceans.

Movement of water results in movement of other nutrients. Carbon, nitrogen, and phosphorus all have soluble forms that flowing water can carry from place to place. As water trickles through soil, it brings nutrients from topsoil into deeper soil layers. As a stream flows over limestone, water slowly dissolves the rock and carries carbonates back to the seas where the limestone formed.

The vast majority of Earth's water (97 percent) is in oceans, and most fresh water is frozen as ice (**TABLE**

FIGURE 42.7 {Animated} The water cycle. Water moves from the ocean to the atmosphere, land, and back. The arrows identify processes that move water.

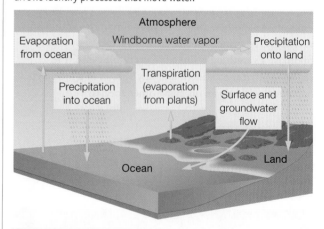

aquifer Porous rock layer that holds some groundwater.
groundwater Soil water and water in aquifers.
runoff Water that flows over soil into streams.
soil water Water between soil particles.
water cycle Movement of water among Earth's oceans, atmosphere, and the freshwater reservoirs on land.

CREDITS: (6) photo, Jack Scherting, USC&GS, NOAA; inset, © Cengage Learning; (7) © Cengage Learning.

42.1). Thus, the fresh water available to meet human needs and sustain land ecosystems is limited. Water overdrafts are now common—humans remove water from aquifers, lakes, or rivers faster than natural processes replenish it.

Aquifers supply about half of the drinking water in the United States. Overdrawing water from an aquifer can lower the water table, which is the topmost level at which the rock is saturated with water. When the water table falls, wells that tap an aquifer can run dry.

Consider what has happened to the largest aquifer in the United States, the Ogallala aquifer. This aquifer stretches from South Dakota to Texas and supplies irrigation water for 27 percent of the nation's crops. For the past thirty years, withdrawals have exceeded replenishment by a factor of ten. As a result, the water table has dropped as much as 50 meters (150 feet) in some regions.

Water in many rivers is currently over-allocated, meaning the amount of water promised to various stakeholders such as cities and farmers exceeds the amount that currently flows through the river. In such rivers, diversion of water for human use results in lowered or nonexistent flow in some portion of the river. The lack of water can have a devastating effect on biological communities that depend on the river. Rivers convey sediment and nutrients as well as water, so decreased flow alters ecosystems by slowing delivery of these materials to the river's delta, the region where the river approaches the sea.

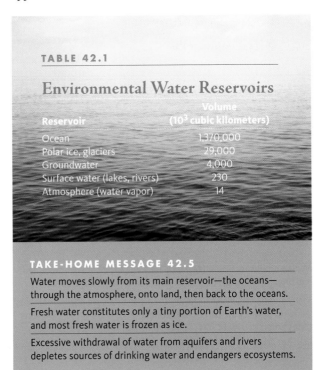

TABLE 42.1

Environmental Water Reservoirs

Reservoir	Volume (10³ cubic kilometers)
Ocean	1,370,000
Polar ice, glaciers	29,000
Groundwater	4,000
Surface water (lakes, rivers)	230
Atmosphere (water vapor)	14

TAKE-HOME MESSAGE 42.5

Water moves slowly from its main reservoir—the oceans—through the atmosphere, onto land, then back to the oceans.

Fresh water constitutes only a tiny portion of Earth's water, and most fresh water is frozen as ice.

Excessive withdrawal of water from aquifers and rivers depletes sources of drinking water and endangers ecosystems.

PEOPLE MATTER

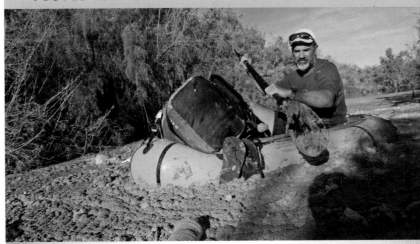

National Geographic Grantee
JONATHAN WATERMAN

For million of years, the Colorado River has flowed from its source high in the Rocky Mountains to the Gulf of Mexico. Today, the river often does not reach the sea; its waters instead irrigate cropland and flow into pipes that supply cities such as Los Angeles, Las Vegas, Phoenix, and Denver.

In 2008, author Jonathan Waterman set out to raft the length of the Colorado River, intending to document the extent and causes of its decline. He says, "I saw a river being both depleted and salted thick by farms." In Mexico, the river essentially disappeared. "Fifty miles from the sea, 1.5 miles south of the Mexican border, I saw the river evaporate into a scum of phosphates and discarded water bottles." (See the photo above.) Waterman ended up walking for ten days through what should have been the river's delta region. Eventually he reached a tributary, the Rio Hardy, which he rafted until it too ran dry about 12 miles from the sea.

Waterman detailed the story of his journey and of the Colorado River's plight in his book *Running Dry: A Journey from Source to Sea Down the Colorado River*. He says of his books, "All were underlain by the premise that we can affect change in human behavior, to protect and preserve wild places, or human life." With regard to the Colorado River, Waterman's optimism about the possibility of change may be well-founded. In 2012, the governments of the United States and Mexico agreed to increase water flow through the Colorado's delta region through at least 2017.

42.6 HOW DOES CARBON MOVE THROUGH ECOSYSTEMS?

THE CARBON CYCLE

In the **carbon cycle**, natural processes move carbon among Earth's atmosphere, oceans, soils, and into and out of food webs (**FIGURE 42.8**). It is an **atmospheric cycle**, a biogeochemical cycle in which a gaseous form of the element plays a significant role.

On land, plants take up carbon dioxide from the atmosphere and incorporate it into their tissues when they carry out photosynthesis ❶. Plants and most other land organisms release carbon dioxide into the atmosphere by the process of aerobic respiration ❷.

The greatest flow of carbon between nonbiological reservoirs takes place between the atmosphere and the oceans. The air holds about 750 gigatons of carbon, mainly in the form of carbon dioxide (CO_2). Seawater holds 38,000–40,000 gigatons of dissolved carbon, primarily in bicarbonate (HCO_3^-) and carbonate (CO_3^{2-}) ions. Bicarbonate ions form when atmospheric carbon dioxide dissolves in water ❸. Aquatic producers take up bicarbonate

and convert it to CO_2 that they use in photosynthesis. As on land, aquatic organisms carry out aerobic respiration and release carbon dioxide ❹.

Earth's rocks and sediments form its single greatest reservoir of carbon, with more than 65 million gigatons. Limestone is a sedimentary rock that forms over millions of years when sediments containing calcium carbonate shells of marine organisms such as foraminifera (Section 20.3) become compacted ❺. Limestone and other rocks derived from marine sediments can be uplifted onto land by movements of tectonic plates (Section 16.5). Producers do not take up carbon from rocks and sediment, so carbon in these reservoirs has little effect on these ecosystems.

Soil contains about 1,600 gigatons of carbon, more than twice as much as the atmosphere. The carbon in soil resides in humus and in living soil organisms. Over time, bacteria and fungi in the soil decompose humus and release carbon dioxide into the air. The speed of decomposition increases with temperature. In a tropical forest, decomposition and

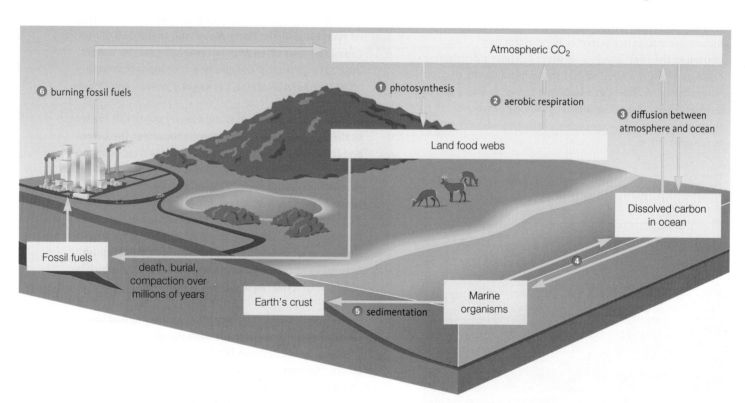

FIGURE 42.8 {Animated} The carbon cycle.

❶ Carbon enters land food webs when plants take up carbon dioxide from the air for use in photosynthesis.

❷ Carbon returns to the atmosphere as carbon dioxide when plants and other land organisms carry out aerobic respiration.

❸ Carbon diffuses between the atmosphere and the ocean. Bicarbonate forms when carbon dioxide dissolves in seawater.

❹ Marine producers take up bicarbonate for use in photosynthesis, and marine organisms release carbon dioxide from aerobic respiration.

❺ Many marine organisms incorporate carbon into their shells. After they die, these shells become part of the sediments. Over time, the sediments become carbon-rich rocks such as limestone and chalk in Earth's crust.

❻ Burning of fossil fuels derived from the ancient remains of plants puts additional carbon dioxide into the atmosphere.

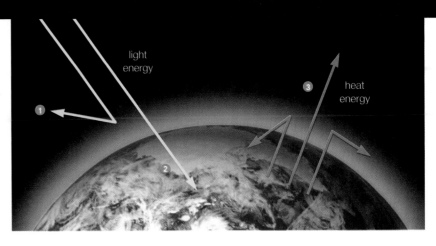

FIGURE 42.9 {**Animated**} Greenhouse effect.

1 Earth's atmosphere reflects some sunlight energy back into space.

2 More light energy reaches and warms Earth's surface.

3 Earth's warmed surface emits heat energy. Some of this energy escapes through the atmosphere into space. But some is absorbed and then emitted in all directions by greenhouse gases. The emitted heat warms Earth's surface and lower atmosphere.

FIGURE IT OUT: Do greenhouse gases reflect heat energy toward the Earth?

Answer: No. The gases absorb heat energy, then reemit it in all directions.

nutrient uptake proceed rapidly, so most of the forest's carbon is stored in living plants, rather than in soil. By contrast, in temperate zone forests and grasslands, soil holds more carbon than the plants do. The most carbon-rich soils are in the arctic, where low temperature hampers decomposition, and in peatbogs (Section 21.2), where acidic, anaerobic conditions do the same.

Fossil fuels such as coal, oil, and natural gas are another carbon reservoir. Such fuels are carbon-rich remains of ancient photosynthesizers. Fossil fuels hold an estimated 5,000 gigatons of carbon. Until the Industrial Revolution, this carbon, like that in rocks, had little impact on ecosystems. However, we now withdraw 4 to 5 gigatons of carbon from fossil fuel reservoirs each year **6**. Our use of this fuel puts more carbon dioxide into the air than can dissolve in the oceans. Each year, about 2 percent of the extra carbon we release by burning fossil fuels dissolves in seawater. The other 98 percent increases the carbon dioxide level of the atmosphere.

THE GREENHOUSE EFFECT

The ongoing rise in atmospheric carbon dioxide is a matter of concern. Atmospheric carbon dioxide helps keep Earth warm enough for life. In what is known as the **greenhouse effect**, sunlight heats Earth's surface, then carbon dioxide and other "greenhouse gases" absorb some heat radiating from the surface and reradiate it toward Earth (**FIGURE 42.9**). Without the greenhouse effect, heat from Earth's surface would escape into space, leaving the planet cold and lifeless.

atmospheric cycle Biogeochemical cycle in which a gaseous form of an element plays a significant role.
carbon cycle Movement of carbon, mainly between the oceans, atmosphere, and living organisms.
global climate change A rise in average temperature that is altering climate patterns around the world.
greenhouse effect Warming of Earth's lower atmosphere and surface as a result of heat trapped by greenhouse gases.

Given the greenhouse effect, we would predict that increases in the atmospheric concentration of carbon dioxide and other greenhouse gases would raise the temperature of Earth's surface. Evidence supports this prediction. In 2013, the carbon dioxide content of Earth's atmosphere rose above 400 parts per million for the first time in several million years. The result is **global climate change**, a trend toward rising temperature and shifts in other climate patterns.

Earth's climate has always varied over time. During ice ages, much of the planet was covered by glaciers. Other periods were warmer than the present, and tropical plants and coral reefs thrived at now-cool latitudes. Scientists can correlate past large-scale temperature changes with shifts in Earth's orbit, which varies in a regular fashion over 100,000 years, and Earth's tilt, which varies over 40,000 years. Changes in solar output and volcanic eruptions also affect Earth's temperature. However, there is a consensus among scientists that these factors do not play a major role in the current temperature rise, whereas the rise in greenhouse gases does. We discuss the consequences of global climate change in more detail in Section 44.6, when we consider human effects on the biosphere.

TAKE-HOME MESSAGE 42.6

Most of Earth's carbon is in rocks. Not much carbon moves out of this reservoir into the world of life.

Oceans and soils hold more carbon than the air. Carbon flows continually between these reservoirs and into and out of food webs. Producers take up carbon dioxide for photosynthesis, and all organisms release carbon dioxide as a result of aerobic respiration.

At present, burning of fossil fuels is releasing carbon into the air faster than the ocean can absorb it. As a result, the atmospheric concentration of carbon dioxide is increasing.

Carbon dioxide is a greenhouse gas. The presence of such gases in the atmosphere is essential to keeping Earth's surface warm enough to support life. However, the increasingly high level of these gases is causing global climate change.

CREDITS: (9) photo, NASA; art, © Cengage Learning.

42.7 HOW DOES NITROGEN MOVE THROUGH ECOSYSTEMS?

THE NITROGEN CYCLE

Nitrogen moves in an atmospheric cycle known as the **nitrogen cycle** (FIGURE 42.10). The main nitrogen reservoir is the atmosphere, which is about 80 percent nitrogen gas. Nitrogen gas consists of two atoms of nitrogen held together by a triple covalent bond as N_2, or $N\equiv N$. Recall from Section 2.3 that a triple bond holds atoms together more strongly than a single or double bond would.

All organisms use nitrogen to build ATP, nucleic acids, and proteins. Photosynthetic organisms also use it to build chlorophyll. Despite the universal need for nitrogen and the abundance of atmospheric nitrogen, no eukaryote can make use of nitrogen gas. Eukaryotes do not have an enzyme that can break the strong bond between the two nitrogen atoms.

Certain types of bacteria and archaea can break the triple bond. They carry out **nitrogen fixation**, combining nitrogen atoms in nitrogen gas with hydrogen to produce ammonia (NH_3). Ammonia dissolves to form ammonium (NH_4^+) ❶. Biological nitrogen fixation has a high activation energy (Section 5.2); it requires an input of 16 molecules of ATP to convert one molecule of nitrogen to ammonia.

You have already learned about two major groups of nitrogen-fixers. Nitrogen-fixing cyanobacteria live in aquatic habitats, soil, and as components of lichens (Sections 19.5 and 22.3). Other nitrogen-fixing bacteria live on their own in soil, or inside plant parts such as nodules on roots of peas and other legumes (Section 26.3). Some deep-sea archaea also fix nitrogen.

An additional small amount of ammonium forms as a result of lightning-fueled reactions in the atmosphere. Energy from the lightning causes nitrogen gas to react with atmospheric water vapor.

Plants can take up ammonium from soil water ❷ and use it in metabolic reactions. Animals meet their nitrogen needs by eating plants or one another. Bacterial and fungal decomposers return ammonium to the soil when they break down organic wastes and remains, a process called ammonification ❸.

Nitrification is a two-step, oxygen-requiring process that converts ammonium to nitrates (NO_3^-) ❹. First, ammonia-oxidizing bacteria or archaea convert ammonium to nitrite (NO_2^-), then nitrite-oxidizing bacteria convert nitrites to nitrates. Like ammonium, nitrates can be taken up and used by plants ❺. Nitrification is essential to ecosystem health because it prevents ammonium from accumulating to toxic concentrations. We make use of the bacteria that carry out this process in sewage treatment plants. Sewage contains large amounts of ammonium formed from urea excreted in urine (Section 37.1).

FIGURE 42.10 {Animated} Nitrogen cycle in a land ecosystem.

CREDIT: (10) © Cengage Learning.

Tractor applying industrially produced, nitrogen-rich fertilizer to a cornfield. Nitrogen is the nutrient that most commonly limits corn growth. The inset photo shows corn grown with adequate nitrogen (*left*) and in nitrogen-deficient soil (*right*).

Conversion of nitrates to nitrogen gas is called **denitrification** ❻. This anaerobic reaction is carried out mainly by bacteria. In sewage treatment plants, denitrifying bacteria are used to remove nitrates from wastewater before the water is released into the environment. In ecosystems, denitrification results in a decline in the amount of soluble nitrogen available to producers.

ALTERATIONS TO THE CYCLE

In the early 1900s, scientists invented a method of fixing atmospheric nitrogen and producing ammonium on an industrial scale. This process allowed production of synthetic nitrogen fertilizers that have boosted crop yields (**FIGURE 42.11**). These fertilizers have helped feed a rapidly increasing human population. However, their use has also disrupted the biological portion of the nitrogen cycle. A lot of nitrate from synthetic fertilizers is carried away from croplands in runoff and nitrate contamination of aquatic ecosystems encourages algal blooms (Section 20.10). When nitrate contaminates drinking water, it can pose a threat to human health. Among other effects, ingested

nitrate inhibits iodine uptake by the thyroid gland and may increase the risk of thyroid cancer. The U.S. Environmental Protection Agency (EPA) has set a maximum standard for nitrate in public drinking water and requires periodic testing to ensure this standard is met.

Humans also interfere with the nitrogen cycle by burning wood and fossil fuels. Combustion of these materials releases nitrous oxide gas (N_2O) into the atmosphere. An increase in atmospheric nitrous oxide is a matter of concern for two reasons. First, nitrous oxide is a greenhouse gas, and a highly persistent and effective one. It can remain in the atmosphere for more than 100 years, and it traps 300 times as much heat as an equivalent amount of CO_2. Second, nitrous oxide contributes to destruction of the ozone layer. As Section 18.4 explains, ozone high in the atmosphere protects life at Earth's surface from damaging effects of ultraviolet radiation. We discuss ozone destruction in more detail in Section 44.5.

> **TAKE-HOME MESSAGE 42.7**
>
> Nitrogen-fixing prokaryotes convert gaseous nitrogen to ammonium that plants take up and use. Other prokaryotes convert ammonium to nitrites and nitrates. Still others change nitrates into nitrogen gas, which can escape from an ecosystem.
>
> Use of synthetic nitrogen fertilizer and burning of fossil fuels add nitrogen-containing pollutants to ecosystems.

denitrification Conversion of nitrates or nitrites to nitrogen gas.
nitrification Conversion of ammonium to nitrate.
nitrogen cycle Movement of nitrogen among the atmosphere, soil, and water, and into and out of food webs.
nitrogen fixation Conversion of nitrogen gas to ammonia.

Atoms of phosphorus are highly reactive, so phosphorus does not occur naturally in its elemental form. Most of Earth's phosphorus is bonded to oxygen as phosphate (PO_4^{3-}), an ion that occurs in rocks and sediments. In the **phosphorus cycle**, phosphorus passes quickly through food webs as it moves from land to ocean sediments, then slowly back to land (**FIGURE 42.12**). Because little phosphorus exists in a gaseous form and its major reservoir is sedimentary rock, the phosphorus cycle is called a **sedimentary cycle**.

In the geochemical portion of the phosphorus cycle, weathering and erosion move phosphates from rocks into soil, lakes, and rivers ❶. Leaching and runoff carry dissolved phosphates to the ocean ❷. Here, most phosphorus comes out of solution and settles as rocky deposits along continental margins ❸. Slow movements of Earth's crust can uplift these deposits onto land ❹, where weathering releases phosphates from rocks once again.

All organisms require phosphorus as a component of nucleic acids and phospholipids. The biological portion of the phosphorus cycle begins when producers take up phosphate. Land plants take up dissolved phosphate from the soil water ❺. Land animals get phosphates by eating the plants or one another. Phosphorus returns to the soil in the wastes and remains of organisms ❻.

Like nitrogen, phosphorus is often a limiting factor for plant growth, so fertilizers usually contain both phosphorus and nitrogen. Phosphate-rich rock is mined for this purpose. Guano, which is phosphate-rich droppings from seabird or bat colonies, is also mined and used as fertilizer. Also like nitrogen, phosphates often run off from the site where they are applied and enter aquatic habitats. The influx of phosphorus can encourage the growth of aquatic producers, resulting in an algal bloom.

phosphorus cycle Movement of phosphorus among Earth's rocks and waters, and into and out of food webs.
sedimentary cycle Biochemical cycle in which the atmosphere plays little role and rocks are the major reservoir.

TAKE-HOME MESSAGE 42.8

Rocks are the main phosphorus reservoir. Weathering and erosion of rock move phosphates into soil and water. Plants take up dissolved phosphates from the soil.

Phosphate can be a limiting nutrient for plants, so phosphate-rich rock and guano are mined for use as fertilizer. However, excess phosphate from these or other sources can result in an algal bloom when it enters aquatic habitats.

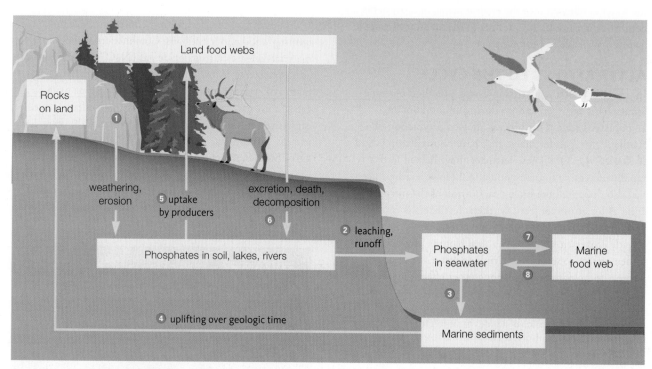

FIGURE 42.12 {Animated} The phosphorus cycle.

Sustainability

FIGURE 42.13 Loon with its fish prey. Along with nutrients, the loon takes in any toxic pollutants that accumulated in the fish's body.

NUTRIENTS ARE NOT THE ONLY THINGS THAT MOVE UP FOOD CHAINS. Pollutants enter food chains and pass from one trophic level to the next.

By the process of **bioaccumulation**, an organism's tissues store a pollutant taken up from the environment, causing the amount in the body to increase over time. The ability of some plants to bioaccumulate toxic substances makes them useful in phytoremediation of polluted soils (Section 26.7).

In animals, hydrophobic chemical pollutants ingested or absorbed across skin tend to accumulate in fatty tissues. The amount of pollutants in an animal's body increases over time, so longer-lived species tend to be more affected by fat-soluble pollutants than shorter-lived ones. Within a species, old individuals tend to have a higher pollutant load than younger ones.

The concentration of a chemical in organisms increases as the pollutant moves up a food chain,

a process known as **biological magnification**. As a result of bioaccumulation and biological magnification, even seemingly low concentrations of pollutants in an environment can cause harm, with long-lived animals at the top of food chains being most affected.

For example, tissues of a fish-eating bird such as a loon contain contaminants that the bird took in from the bodies of the fish it ate (**FIGURE 42.13**). Loons in many regions contain high levels of methylmercury, a neurotoxin produced by coal-burning power plants (Section 2.6). The higher the mercury level in a lake, the lower the bird's reproductive success. Among other ill effects, loons with a high mercury level show impaired parental behavior.

bioaccumulation The concentration of a chemical pollutant in the tissues of an organism rises over the course of the organism's lifetime.
biological magnification A chemical pollutant becomes increasingly concentrated as it moves up through food chains.

Summary

SECTION 42.1 There is a one-way flow of energy into and out of an **ecosystem**, and a cycling of materials among the organisms within it. All ecosystems have inputs and outputs of energy.

Producers convert energy from an inorganic source (usually light) into chemical bond energy. **Primary production**, the rate at which producers capture and store energy, can vary over time and between locations.

Consumers feed on producers or one another. For example, **detritivores** eat small bits of organic remains; **decomposers** break wastes and remains down into their inorganic components.

A **food chain** shows one path of energy and nutrient flow among organisms. Each organism in a food chain is at a different **trophic level**, with the primary producer being the first level and consumers at higher levels. The inefficiency of energy transfers from one trophic level limits most food chains to four or five links.

SECTION 42.2 The many food chains within an ecosystem interconnect to form a **food web**. Most food webs include both **grazing food chains**, in which herbivores eat producers, and **detrital food chains**, in which producers die and are then consumed by detritivores. As a result of the multiple connections through food webs, a change that affects one species in an ecosystem will have effects on many others.

SECTION 42.3 Energy pyramids and biomass pyramids show how energy and organic compounds are distributed among organisms within an ecosystem. All energy pyramids are largest at their base.

SECTION 42.4 In the nonbiological portion of a **biogeochemical cycle**, an element moves among environmental reservoirs such as Earth's atmosphere, rocks, and waters. In the biological portion of the cycle, elements move through an ecosystem's food web, then return to the environment.

SECTION 42.5 In the **water cycle**, evaporation, condensation, and precipitation move water from its main reservoir—the oceans—into the atmosphere, onto land, then back to oceans. Water that falls onto land may become part of the **groundwater**, which means it may be become **soil water** or be stored in an **aquifer**. Alternatively, it may become **runoff**. The water cycle helps move soluble forms of other nutrients.

Earth has a limited amount of freshwater, most of which is frozen as ice. Overwithdrawing water from rivers or aquifers to meet human needs can harm other species.

SECTION 42.6 The main reservoir for carbon is rocks, but the **carbon cycle** moves carbon mainly among seawater, the air, soils, and living organisms in an **atmospheric cycle**. Carbon dioxide contributes to the **greenhouse effect**. Greenhouse gases keep Earth's surface warm enough to support life. However, as a result of fossil fuel consumption and other human activities, the levels of these gases are increasing. The increase correlates with and is considered the most likely cause of the ongoing **global climate change**.

SECTION 42.7 The **nitrogen cycle** is an atmospheric cycle. Air is the main reservoir for N_2, a gaseous form of nitrogen that plants cannot use. Plants can take up and use ammonium that bacteria produce by **nitrogen fixation**. Fungi and bacteria that act as decomposers add ammonium derived from remains to the soil. Plants also use nitrates that some bacteria produce from ammonium through **nitrification**. Nitrogen is returned to the air by bacteria that carry out **denitrification** of nitrates. Humans add extra nitrogen to ecosystems by using synthetic fertilizer and by burning fossil fuels, which releases nitrous oxide.

SECTION 42.8 The **phosphorus cycle** is a **sedimentary cycle** with no significant atmospheric component. Phosphorus from rocks dissolves in water and is taken up by producers. Phosphate-rich rocks and deposits of bird droppings are mined for use as fertilizer.

SECTION 42.9 Toxic substances move up through food chains in the same way that nutrients do. Such toxins accumulate in the bodies of organisms, a process called **bioaccumulation**. Predators end up with high levels of these toxins because of **biological magnification**; when they eat prey, they ingest all the toxins that accumulated in the prey's body over its lifetime, and each predator typically eats many prey.

Self-Quiz Answers in Appendix VII

1. In most ecosystems, producers use energy from _____ to build organic compounds.
   a. inorganic chemicals   c. heat
   b. sunlight   d. lower trophic levels

2. Decomposers are commonly _____ .
   a. fungi   c. plants
   b. bacteria   d. a and b

3. Organisms at the first trophic level _____ .
   a. capture energy from a nonliving source
   b. are eaten by organisms at higher trophic levels
   c. are shown at the bottom of an energy pyramid
   d. all of the above

4. Primary productivity on land is affected by _____ .
   a. nutrient availability   c. temperature
   b. amount of sunlight   d. all of the above

5. A(n) _____ is an autotroph.
   a. producer   c. detritivore
   b. herbivore   d. top carnivore

Data Analysis Activities

Rising Atmospheric Carbon To assess the impact of human activity on the carbon dioxide level in Earth's atmosphere, it helps to take a long view. One useful data set comes from deep core samples of Antarctic ice. The oldest ice core that has been fully analyzed dates back a bit more than 400,000 years. Air bubbles trapped in the ice provide information about the gas content in Earth's atmosphere at the time the ice formed. Combining ice core data with more recent direct measurements of atmospheric carbon dioxide—as in **FIGURE 42.14**—can help scientists put current changes in the atmospheric carbon dioxide into historical perspective.

1. What was the highest carbon dioxide level between 400,000 B.C. and 0 A.D.?
2. During this period, how many times did carbon dioxide reach a level comparable to that measured in 1980?
3. The industrial revolution occurred around 1800. How much did carbon dioxide levels change in the 800 years prior to the event? In 175 years after it?
4. Did carbon dioxide levels rise more between 1800 and 1975 or between 1980 and 2013?

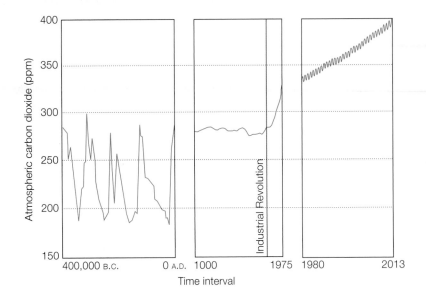

FIGURE 42.14 Changes in atmospheric carbon dioxide levels. Direct measurements began in 1980. Earlier data are based on air bubbles in ice cores. The oscillations in the directly measured data result from seasonal differences in photosynthesis.

6. Most of Earth's fresh water is _____ .
   a. in lakes and streams   c. frozen as ice
   b. in aquifers and soil   d. in bodies of organisms

7. Earth's largest carbon reservoir is _____ .
   a. the atmosphere   c. seawater
   b. sediments and rocks   d. living organisms

8. Carbon is released into the atmosphere by _____ .
   a. photosynthesis   c. burning fossil fuels
   b. aerobic respiration   d. b and c

9. Greenhouse gases _____ .
   a. help keep Earth's surface warm enough for life
   b. are released by natural and human activities
   c. include nitrous oxide and carbon dioxide
   d. all of the above

10. The _____ cycle is a sedimentary cycle.
    a. phosphorus   c. nitrogen
    b. carbon   d. water

11. Earth's largest phosphorus reservoir is _____ .
    a. the atmosphere   c. sediments and rocks
    b. bird droppings   d. living organisms

12. Most plants obtain _____ by taking it up from the air.
    a. nitrogen   c. phosphorus
    b. carbon   d. a and b

13. Nitrogen fixation converts _____ to _____ .
    a. nitrogen gas; ammonia   c. ammonia; nitrates
    b. nitrates; nitrites   d. nitrites; nitrogen oxides

14. Soil in _____ is richest in carbon.
    a. the arctic   b. the tropics   c. temperates zones

15. Match each term with its most suitable description.
    ___ carbon dioxide   a. contains triple bond
    ___ bicarbonate   b. product of nitrogen fixation
    ___ ammonium   c. marine carbon source
    ___ nitrogen gas   d. greenhouse gas

Critical Thinking

1. Marguerite has a vegetable garden in Maine. Eduardo has one in Florida. List the variables that could cause differences in the primary production of these gardens.

2. A watershed is an area in which all rainfall drains into a particular river. Find out which watershed you live in at the *Science in Your Watershed* site at http://water.usgs.gov/wsc.

3. The sulfur cycle is another important biogeochemical cycle. Rocks are the main reservoir for sulfur, but some sulfur compounds are dissolved in water, and sulfur oxide occurs in the atmosphere. Which of these sources do you think plants tap to meet their need for sulfur? Which essential biological compounds contain sulfur?

4. Rather than using fertilizer, a farmer may rotate crops, planting legumes one year, then another crop, then legumes again. Explain how crop rotation keeps soil fertile.

CENGAGE brain.com To access course materials, please visit www.cengagebrain.com.

The Congo rain forest in central Africa, Earth's second largest tropical rain forest. Year-round warmth and rainfall support a diverse variety of evergreen, broadleaf trees. Their continual photosynthesis removes an enormous amount of carbon dioxide from the atmosphere.

43

THE BIOSPHERE

Links to Earlier Concepts

In this chapter, you will consider the biosphere (Section 1.1) as a whole, revisit properties of water (2.4), and see how carbon-fixing pathways (6.5), soils (26.1), herbivory (41.4), and fire (41.6) affect plant distribution. We compare regional primary production (42.1) and learn more about the effects of global climate change (42.6), succession (41.6), and morphological convergence (16.7).

KEY CONCEPTS

AIR CIRCULATION PATTERNS

Latitudinal differences in the amount of solar energy reaching the ground cause air to move away from the equator, giving rise to major surface winds and latitudinal patterns in rainfall.

CURRENTS AND CLIMATES

Heating of the tropical seas sets ocean waters in motion. The circulating water affects climate on land. Interactions between oceans, air, and land influence coastal climates.

LAND BIOMES

A biome consists of geographically separated regions that have a similar climate and soils, and so support similar types of vegetation. Biomes vary in their productivity and species-richness.

FRESHWATER ECOSYSTEMS

Lakes undergo succession. In temperate zones, seasonal temperature changes determine when water within a lake mixes. Properties of a river, and the life it supports, vary along its length.

COASTAL AND MARINE ECOSYSTEMS

Life thrives in coastal wetlands, on coral reefs, and in the ocean's upper, sunlit water. Organisms also live in the ocean's deeper, darker waters and on the seafloor.

Photograph by Frans Lanting, National Geographic Creative.

The biosphere includes all places where life exists on Earth (Section 1.1). The geographical distribution of species within the biosphere depends largely on climate. **Climate** refers to average weather conditions, such as cloud cover, temperature, humidity, and wind speed, over time. Regional climates differ because many factors that influence winds and ocean currents vary from place to place.

SEASONAL EFFECTS

Each year, Earth rotates around the sun in an elliptical path (**FIGURE 43.1**). Seasonal changes in day length and

A Summer solstice (June). Northern Hemisphere is most tilted toward sun; has its longest day.

D Spring equinox (March). Sun's direct rays fall on equator; length of day equals length of night.

B Autumn equinox (September). Sun's direct rays fall on equator; length of day equals length of night.

C Winter solstice (December). Northern Hemisphere is most tilted away from sun; has its shortest day.

FIGURE 43.1 **Effects of Earth's tilt and yearly rotation around the sun.** The 23° tilt of Earth's axis causes the Northern Hemisphere to receive more intense sunlight and have longer days in summer than in winter.

FIGURE 43.2 **Latitudinal variation in the intensity of sunlight at ground level.** For simplicity, we depict two equal parcels of incoming radiation on an equinox, a day when incoming rays are perpendicular to Earth's axis. Rays that fall on high latitudes **A** have passed through more atmosphere (blue) than those that fall near the equator **B**. Compare the length of the green lines. (Atmosphere is not to scale.)

In addition, energy in the rays that fall at the high latitude is spread over a greater area than energy that falls on the equator. Compare the length of the red lines.

As a result of these two factors, the amount of sunlight energy that reaches the Earth's surface decreases with increasing latitude.

temperature arise because Earth's axis is not perpendicular to the plane of this ellipse, but rather tilts at a 23-degree angle. In June, when the Northern Hemisphere is angled toward the sun, it receives more intense sunlight and has longer days than the Southern Hemisphere (**FIGURE 43.1A**). In December, the opposite occurs (**FIGURE 43.1C**). Twice a year—on spring and autumn equinoxes—Earth's axis is perpendicular to incoming sunlight. On these days, every place on Earth has 12 hours of daylight and 12 hours of darkness (**FIGURE 43.1B,D**).

In each hemisphere, the extent of seasonal change in day length increases with latitude. At 25° north or south of the equator, the longest day length is a bit less than 14 hours. By contrast, 60° north or south of the equator, the longest day length is nearly 19 hours.

AIR CIRCULATION AND RAINFALL

On any given day, equatorial regions receive more sunlight energy than higher latitudes for two reasons. First, fine particles of dust, water vapor, and greenhouse gases absorb some solar radiation or reflect it back into space. Sunlight traveling to high latitudes passes through more atmosphere to reach Earth's surface than light traveling to the equator, so less energy reaches the ground at high latitudes (**FIGURE 43.2A**). Second, energy in an incoming parcel of sunlight is spread out over a smaller surface area at the equator than at the higher latitudes (**FIGURE 43.2B**). As a result, Earth's surface warms more at the equator than at the poles.

Knowing about two properties of air can help you understand how regional differences in surface warming give rise to global air circulation and rainfall patterns. First, as air warms, it becomes less dense and rises. Hot-air balloonists take advantage of this effect when they take off from the ground by heating the air inside their balloon. Second, warm air can hold more water than cooler air. This is why you can "see your breath" in cold weather; water vapor in warm exhaled air condenses into droplets when exposed to the cold outside your body.

The global air circulation pattern begins at the equator, where intense sunlight heats air and causes evaporation from the ocean. The result is an upward movement of warm, moist air (**FIGURE 43.3A**). As this air rises to higher altitudes, it cools and flows north and south, releasing moisture as rain. This rain supports tropical rain forests such as the one shown in the photo that opens this chapter.

By the time the air reaches 30° north or south of the equator, it has given up most moisture, so little rain falls here. Many of the world's great deserts are about 30° from the equator. The air has also cooled, so it sinks toward Earth's surface (**FIGURE 43.3B**).

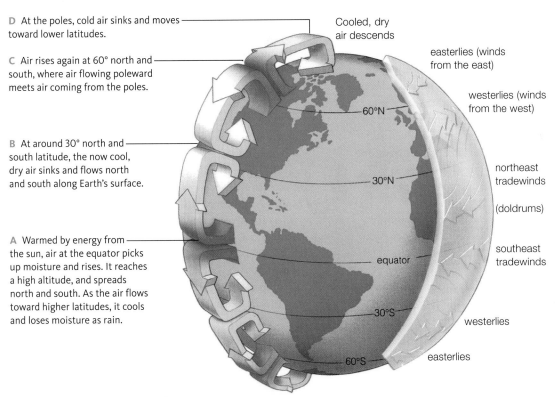

D At the poles, cold air sinks and moves toward lower latitudes.

C Air rises again at 60° north and south, where air flowing poleward meets air coming from the poles.

B At around 30° north and south latitude, the now cool, dry air sinks and flows north and south along Earth's surface.

A Warmed by energy from the sun, air at the equator picks up moisture and rises. It reaches a high altitude, and spreads north and south. As the air flows toward higher latitudes, it cools and loses moisture as rain.

Cooled, dry air descends

easterlies (winds from the east)

westerlies (winds from the west)

60°N

30°N

northeast tradewinds

(doldrums)

southeast tradewinds

equator

30°S

westerlies

60°S

easterlies

E Major winds near Earth's surface do not blow directly north and south because of the effects of Earth's rotation. Winds are deflected to the right in the Northern Hemisphere and to the left in the Southern Hemisphere.

FIGURE 43.3 {**Animated**} Global air circulation patterns.

As air continues flowing along Earth's surface toward the poles, it again picks up heat and moisture. At a latitude of about 60°, warm, moist air rises again, losing moisture as it does so (**FIGURE 43.3C**). The resulting rains support temperate zone forests.

Cold, dry air descends near the poles (**FIGURE 43.3D**). Precipitation is sparse, and polar deserts form.

SURFACE WIND PATTERNS

Major wind patterns arise as air in the lower atmosphere moves continually from latitudes where air is sinking toward those where air is rising. Earth's rotation affects the direction of these winds. Air masses are not attached to Earth's surface, so the Earth spins beneath them, moving fastest at the equator and most slowly at the poles. Thus, as an air mass moves away from the equator, the speed at which the Earth rotates beneath it continually slows. As a result, major winds trace a curved path relative to the Earth's surface (**FIGURE 43.3E**). In the Northern Hemisphere, winds curve toward the right of their initial direction; in the Southern Hemisphere, they curve toward the left. For example, between 30° north and 60° north, surface air

traveling toward the North Pole is deflected right, or toward the east. Winds are named for the direction from which they blow, so prevailing winds in the United States are westerlies—they blow from west to east.

Winds blow most consistently from one region where air is rising to another such location. Where air actually rises, winds are intermittent, as in the doldrums near the equator.

climate Average weather conditions in a region.

TAKE-HOME MESSAGE 43.1

Equatorial regions receive more sunlight energy than higher latitudes.

Sunlight-induced heating drives the rise of moisture-laden air at the equator. This air cools as it moves north and south, releasing rains that support tropical forests. Deserts form where cool, dry air sinks. Sunlight energy also drives moisture-laden air aloft at 60° north and south latitude. This air gives up moisture as it flows toward the equator or the pole.

Major surface winds arise as air in the lower atmosphere moves toward latitudes where air rises and away from latitudes where it sinks. These winds trace a curved path relative to Earth's surface because of Earth's rotation.

OCEAN CURRENTS

Latitudinal variations in sunlight affect ocean temperature and set major currents in motion. At the equator, vast volumes of water warm and expand, making the sea level about 8 centimeters (3 inches) higher than it is at either pole. The existence of this "slope" starts sea surface water moving toward the poles. As the water moves toward cooler latitudes, it gives up heat to the air above it.

Enormous volumes of water flow as ocean currents. Directional movement of surface currents is influenced by the major winds, Earth's rotation, and the distribution of land masses. Surface currents circulate clockwise in the Northern Hemisphere and counterclockwise in the Southern Hemisphere (**FIGURE 43.4**).

Swift, deep, and narrow currents of water flow away from the equator along the east coast of continents. Along the east coast of North America, warm water flows north, as the Gulf Stream. Slower, shallower, broader currents of cold water parallel the west coast of continents and flow toward the equator.

Ocean currents affect climate. For example, Pacific Northwest coasts are cool and foggy in summer because the cold California current chills the air, and water condenses out of the cooled air as droplets. As another example, Boston and Baltimore are warm and muggy in summer because air masses pick up heat and moisture from the warm Gulf Stream, then flow over these cities.

REGIONAL EFFECTS

Differences in the ability of water and land to absorb and release heat give rise to coastal breezes. In the daytime, land warms faster than water. As air over land warms and rises, cooler offshore air moves in to replace it (**FIGURE 43.5A**). After sundown, land cools more quickly than the water, so the breezes reverse direction (**FIGURE 43.5B**).

Differential heating of water and land also causes **monsoons**, which are winds that change direction seasonally. Consider how the continental interior of Asia heats up in the summer, so air rises above it. Moist air from over the warm Indian Ocean, which is to the south, moves in to

FIGURE 43.4 Major climate zones correlated with surface currents and surface drifts of the world ocean. Warm surface currents start moving from the equator toward the poles, but prevailing winds, Earth's rotation, gravity, the shape of ocean basins, and landforms influence the direction of flow. Water temperatures, which differ with latitude and depth, contribute to regional differences in air temperature and rainfall.

warm surface current **cold surface current**

CREDIT: (4) NASA.

replace the rising air, and this north-blowing wind delivers heavy rains. In the winter, the continental interior is cooler than the ocean. As a result, cool, dry wind blowing from the north toward southern coasts causes a seasonal drought.

Proximity to an ocean moderates climate. Seattle, Washington has much milder winters than Minneapolis, Minnesota, even though Seattle is slightly farther north. Air over Seattle draws heat from the adjacent Pacific Ocean, a heat source not available to Minneapolis. Mountains, valleys, and other surface features of the land affect climate too. Suppose you track a warm air mass after it picks up moisture off California's coast. It moves inland as wind from the west, and piles up against the Sierra Nevada, a high mountain range that parallels the coast. The air cools as it rises in altitude and loses moisture as rain (**FIGURE 43.6**). The result is a **rain shadow**, a semiarid or arid region of sparse rainfall on the leeward side of high mountains. *Leeward* is the side facing away from the wind. The Himalayas, Andes, Rockies, and other great mountain ranges cast similar rain shadows.

---

monsoon Wind that reverses direction seasonally.
rain shadow Dry region downwind of a coastal mountain range.

A In afternoons, land is warmer than the sea, so a breeze blows onto shore.

B In evenings, the sea is warmer than land, so the breeze blows out to sea.

FIGURE 43.5 Coastal breezes.

TAKE-HOME MESSAGE 43.2

Surface ocean currents are set in motion by latitudinal differences in solar radiation. Currents are affected by winds and by Earth's rotation.

The collective effects of winds and ocean currents around landforms determine regional climate patterns.

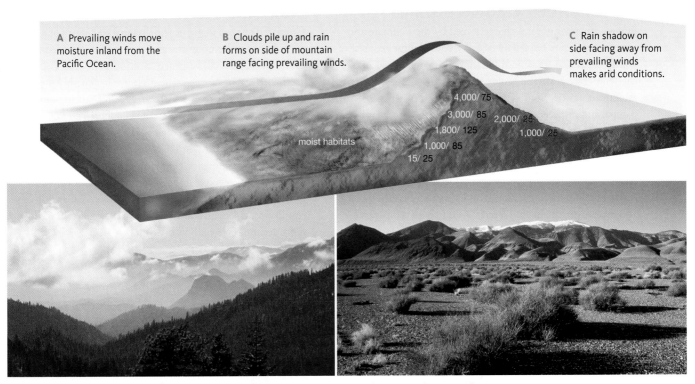

A Prevailing winds move moisture inland from the Pacific Ocean.

B Clouds pile up and rain forms on side of mountain range facing prevailing winds.

C Rain shadow on side facing away from prevailing winds makes arid conditions.

4,000/ 75
3,000/ 85   2,000/ 25
1,800/ 125   1,000/ 25
1,000/ 85
15/ 25
moist habitats

FIGURE 43.6 {Animated} Rain shadow effect. On the side of mountains facing away from prevailing winds, rainfall is light. Black numbers signify annual precipitation, in centimeters, averaged on both sides of the Sierra Nevada, a mountain range. White numbers signify elevations, in meters.

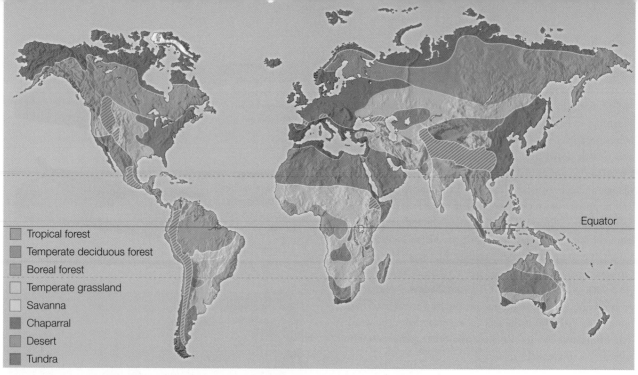

FIGURE 43.7 Major biomes. Climate is the main factor determining the distribution of biomes.

- Tropical forest
- Temperate deciduous forest
- Boreal forest
- Temperate grassland
- Savanna
- Chaparral
- Desert
- Tundra

Equator

DIFFERENCES AMONG BIOMES

Biomes are areas of land characterized by their climate and type of vegetation (**FIGURE 43.7**). Most biomes consist of widely separated areas on different continents. For example, the temperate grassland biome includes areas of North American prairie, South African veld, South American pampa, and Eurasian steppe. Grasses and other nonwoody flowering plants constitute the bulk of the vegetation in all of these regions.

Rainfall and temperature are the main determinants of the type of biome in a given region. Desert biomes get the least annual rainfall, grasslands and shrublands get more, and forests get the most. Deserts occur where temperatures soar the highest and tundra where they drop the lowest.

Soils also influence biome distribution. Soils consist of a mixture of mineral particles and varying amounts of humus (Section 26.1). Water and air fill spaces between soil particles. Soil properties vary depending on the types, proportions, and compaction of particles. Deserts have sandy or gravelly, fast-draining soil with little topsoil. Topsoil tends to be deepest in natural grasslands, where it can be more than one meter thick. For this reason, grasslands are often converted to agricultural uses.

Climate and soils affect primary production, so primary production varies among biomes.

SIMILARITIES WITHIN A BIOME

Unrelated species living in widely separated parts of a biome often have similar body structures that arose by the process of morphological convergence (Section 16.7). For example, cacti with water-storing stems that live in North American deserts are similar to euphorbs with water-storing stems that live in African deserts. Cacti and euphorbs do not share an ancestor with a water-storing stem. Rather, this feature evolved independently in the two groups as a result of living in similar environments. Similarly, an ability to carry out C4 photosynthesis evolved independently in grasses growing in warm grasslands on different continents. Under hot, dry conditions, C4 photosynthesis is more efficient than the more common C3 pathway (Section 6.5).

biome A region (often discontinuous) characterized by its climate and dominant vegetation.

TAKE-HOME MESSAGE 43.3

Biomes are vast expanses of land dominated by distinct kinds of plants that support characteristic communities. They vary in their primary productivity.

Evolution often produces similar solutions to environmental challenges in different regions of a biome.

CREDIT: (7) From RUSSELL/HERTZ/MCMILLAN. Biology, 2E. © 2012 Cengage Learning.

O horizon:
Sparse litter

A–E horizons:
Continually leached;
iron, aluminum left
behind impart red
color to acidic soil

B horizon:
Clays with silicates,
other residues of
weathering

FIGURE 43.8 Tropical rain forest. The graphic to the right shows the soil profile.

Tropical rain forests dominated by evergreen broadleaf trees form mainly between latitudes 10° north and south in equatorial Africa, the East Indies, Southeast Asia, South America, and Central America. Rain falls throughout the year and sums to an annual total of 130 to 200 centimeters (50 to 80 inches). The regular rains, combined with an average warm temperature of 25°C (77°F) and little variation in day length, allows photosynthesis to continue year-round. Of all land biomes, tropical forests have the greatest primary production. Per unit area, they remove more carbon from the atmosphere than other forests or grasslands.

Tropical rain forest is also the most structurally complex and species-rich biome. The forest has a multilayer structure (**FIGURE 43.8**). Its broadleaf trees can stand 30 meters (100 feet) tall. The trees often form a closed canopy that prevents most sunlight from reaching the forest floor. Vines and epiphytes (plants that grow on another plant, but do not withdraw nutrients from it) thrive in the shade beneath the canopy. Compared to other land biomes, tropical rain forests have the greatest variety and numbers of insects, as well as the most diverse collection of birds and primates. Age is key to this diversity: Tropical rain forest is the oldest modern biome. Some rain forests have existed for more than 50 million years, so there has been plenty of time for many evolutionary branchings to occur.

Trees in tropical rain forests shed leaves continually, but decomposition and mineral cycling happen so fast in this warm, moist environment that litter does not accumulate. The soil is highly weathered and heavily leached. Being a poor nutrient reservoir, this soil is not well suited to agriculture. Nevertheless, deforestation is an ongoing threat to tropical rain forests. Tropical forests are located in developing countries with fast-growing human populations who look to the forest as a source of lumber, fuel, and potential cropland. As human populations expand, more and more trees fall to the ax.

Deforestation in any region leaves fewer trees to remove carbon dioxide from the atmosphere. In rain forests, it also causes the extinction of species found nowhere else in the world. Among the potential losses are plants that make potentially life-saving chemicals. Two chemotherapy drugs, vincristine and vinblastine, were extracted from the rosy periwinkle, a low-growing plant native to Madagascar's rain forests. Today, these drugs help fight leukemia, lymphoma, breast cancer, and testicular cancer.

tropical rain forest Highly productive and species-rich biome in which year-round rains and warmth support continuous growth of evergreen broadleaf trees.

TAKE-HOME MESSAGE 43.4

Near the equator, year-round warmth and rains support tropical rain forests, the most productive, structurally complex, and species-rich biome.

A North American temperate deciduous forest in fall.

FIGURE 43.9 **Cool forest biomes.**

B Boreal forest (taiga) in Siberia.

TEMPERATE DECIDUOUS FORESTS

Temperate deciduous forests are dominated by broadleaf trees that lose all their leaves seasonally before a cold winter. Leaves often turn color before dropping (**FIGURE 43.9A**). Trees remain dormant while water is locked in snow and ice. In the spring, when conditions again favor growth, deciduous trees flower and put out new leaves. Also during the spring, leaves that were shed the prior autumn decay to form a rich humus. Rich soil and a somewhat open canopy that lets some sunlight through allows shorter understory plants to flourish.

Temperate deciduous forests are limited to the Northern Hemisphere, occurring in parts of eastern North America, western and central Europe, and areas of Asia, including Japan. In all these regions, 50 to 150 centimeters (about 20–60 inches) of precipitation falls throughout the year. Winters are cool and summers are warm.

North America has the most species-rich examples of this biome, with different tree species characterizing forests in different regions. For example, Appalachian forests include mainly oaks, whereas beeches and maples dominate Ohio's forests.

CONIFEROUS FORESTS

Conifers (trees with seed-bearing cones) are the main plants in coniferous forests. Although conifers do shed and replace their leaves, they do so continually, not all at once like deciduous trees. Conifer leaves are typically needle-shaped, with a thick cuticle and stomata that are sunk below the leaf surface. These adaptations help conifers conserve water during drought or times when the ground is frozen. As a group, conifers tolerate poorer soils and drier habitats than most broadleaf trees.

Conifers also withstand cold better than other trees. The most extensive land biome is the coniferous forest that sweeps across northern Asia, Europe, and North America (**FIGURE 43.9B**). It is known as **boreal forest**, or taiga, which means "swamp forest" in Russian. Pine, fir, and spruce predominate. Most rain falls in the summer. Winters are long, cold, and dry. Also in the Northern Hemisphere, montane coniferous forests extend southward through the great mountain ranges. Spruce and fir dominate at the highest elevations. At lower elevations, the mix becomes firs and pines. Conifers also dominate temperate lowlands along the Pacific coast from Alaska into northern California. These forests hold the world's tallest trees: Sitka spruce to the north, and coast redwoods to the south.

We find other conifer-dominated ecosystems in the eastern United States. About a quarter of New Jersey is pine barrens, a mixed forest of pitch pines and scrub oaks that grow in sandy, acidic soil. Pine forest covers about one-third of the Southeast. Fast-growing loblolly pines that dominate these forests are a major source of lumber.

---

boreal forest Extensive high-latitude forest of the Northern Hemisphere; conifers are the predominant vegetation.
temperate deciduous forest Northern Hemisphere biome in which the main plants are broadleaf trees that lose their leaves in fall and become dormant during cold winters.

TAKE-HOME MESSAGE 43.5

Temperate broadleaf forests grow in the Northern Hemisphere where cold winters prevent year-round growth.

Conifers dominate high-latitude boreal forests (taiga), which are Earth's most extensive biome.

Plants adapted to periodic lightning-ignited fires dominate grasslands, savanna, and chaparral.

Grasslands form in the interior of continents between deserts and temperate forests. Their soils are rich, with a deep layer of topsoil, so they are often converted to cropland. Annual rainfall is enough to keep desert from forming, but not enough to support woodlands. Low-growing grasses and other nonwoody plants tolerate strong winds, sparse and infrequent rain, and intervals of drought. Growth tends to be seasonal. Constant trimming by grazers, along with periodic fires, keeps trees and most shrubs from taking hold. When fire is suppressed by human activity, the low-growing grasses may be overgrown by woody plants.

North America's temperate grasslands, called prairies, once covered much of the continent's interior, where summers are hot and winters are cold and snowy. The prairies supported herds of elk, pronghorn antelope, and bison (**FIGURE 43.10A**) that were prey to wolves. Today, these predators and prey are largely absent from most of their former range. Nearly all prairies have been plowed under and now sustain production of wheat and other crops.

Savannas are broad belts of grasslands with a few scattered shrubs and trees. Savannas lie between the tropical forests and hot deserts of Africa, India, and Australia. In these regions, temperature remains high year-round, but rain falls seasonally. Africa's savannas are famous for their abundant wildlife. Herbivores include giraffes, zebras, a variety of antelopes, and immense herds of wildebeests (**FIGURE 43.10B**).

Chaparral is a biome dominated by drought-resistant, fire-adapted shrubs whose small, leathery leaves help them withstand drought. Chaparral occurs along the western coast of continents, between 30 and 40 degrees north or south latitude. Mild winters bring a moderate amount of rain, and the summer is hot and dry. Chaparral is California's most extensive ecosystem (**FIGURE 43.10C**). It also occurs in regions that border the Mediterranean, and in Chile, Australia, and South Africa. Many chaparral plants produce aromatic oils that help fend off insects, but also make them highly flammable. After a fire, plants resprout from roots and fire-resistant seeds germinate.

chaparral Biome of dry shrubland in regions with hot, dry summers and cool, rainy winters.
grassland Biome in the interior of continents; perennial grasses and other nonwoody plants adapted to grazing and fire predominate.
savanna Biome dominated by perennial grasses with a few scattered shrubs and trees.

A In Kansas, tallgrass prairie with grazing bison.

B African savanna with grazing wildebeest.

C California chaparral dominated by shrubby plants with leathery leaves. Deer are the main grazers here.

FIGURE 43.10 Fire-adapted biomes.

TAKE-HOME MESSAGE 43.6

Plants in grasslands, savanna, and chapparal have adaptations that allow them to withstand or recover after periodic fires.

Grasslands have a deep layer of topsoil and are often converted to farmland.

CREDITS: (10A) Joel Sartore/National Geographic Creative; (10B) Jonathan Scott/Planet Earth Pictures; (10C) Jack Wilburn/Animals Animals.

Deserts receive an average of less than 10 centimeters (4 inches) of rain per year. They cover about one-fifth of Earth's land surface and many are located at about 30° north and south latitude, where dry air sinks. Rain shadows also reduce rainfall. For example, Chile's Atacama Desert is on the leeward side of the Andes, and the Himalayas prevent rain from falling in China's Gobi desert.

Lack of rainfall keeps the humidity in deserts low. With little water vapor to block the sun's rays, intense sunlight reaches and heats the ground. At night, the lack of insulating water vapor in the air allows the temperature to fall fast. As a result, deserts tend to have larger daily temperature shifts than other biomes. Desert soils have very little topsoil. They also tend to be somewhat salty, because rain that falls usually evaporates before seeping into the ground. Rapid evaporation allows any salt in rainwater to accumulate at the soil surface.

ADAPTED TO DROUGHT

Despite their harsh conditions, most deserts support some plant life. Desert plants often have spines or fuzz at their surface. In addition to deterring herbivory, these structures reduce water loss by trapping some water and thus keeping the humidity around the stomata high. Where rains fall seasonally, some plants reduce water loss by producing leaves only after a rain, then shedding them when dry conditions return. Other desert-adapted plants store water in their tissues. For example, the stem of a barrel cactus has a spongy pulp that holds water. The stem swells after a rain, then shrinks as the plant uses stored water.

Woody desert shrubs such as mesquite and creosote have extensive, efficient root systems that take up the little water that is available. Mesquite roots can tap into water that lies as much as 60 meters (197 feet) beneath the soil surface.

Alternative carbon-fixing pathways also help desert plants minimize water loss. Cacti, agaves, and euphorbs are CAM plants, which open their stomata only at night when temperature declines (Section 6.5). This reduces the water they lose to evaporation.

Most deserts contain a mix of annuals and perennials (**FIGURE 43.11**). The annuals are adapted to desert life by a life cycle that allows them to sprout and reproduce in the short time that the soil is moist.

DESERT CRUST

A desert crust forms at the surface of many desert soils. The crust is a community that can include cyanobacteria, lichens, mosses, and fungi (**FIGURE 43.12**). These organisms secrete organic molecules that glue them and the surrounding soil particles together. The resulting crust

FIGURE 43.11 Sonoran Desert after the rains. Perennial cacti are surrounded by annual wildflowers.

FIGURE 43.12 Desert crust.

benefits members of the larger desert community in several ways. Bacteria in the crust fix nitrogen (Section 19.5), making this nutrient available to plants. The crust also holds soil particles in place. When the fragile connections within the desert crust are broken, the soil can blow away. Negative effects of such disturbance increase when windblown soil buries healthy crust in an undisturbed area, killing more crust organisms and allowing more soil to take flight.

desert Biome with little rain and low humidity; plants that have water-storing and water-conserving adaptations predominate.

TAKE-HOME MESSAGE 43.7

The desert biome has low rainfall; poor, salty soil; and large swings in daily temperature.

Desert plants have water-conserving adaptations.

A diverse community of plants, fungi, and microorganisms holds desert soil particles together, forming a crustlike structure at the soil surface.

Arctic tundra extends between the ice cap of the North Pole and the belts of boreal forests in the Northern Hemisphere. Most of this biome in northern Russia and Canada. Arctic tundra is Earth's youngest modern biome; it first appeared about 10,000 years ago when glaciers retreated at the end of the last ice age.

Conditions in this biome are harsh; snow blankets the ground for as long as nine months of the year. Annual precipitation is usually less than 25 centimeters (10 inches), and cold temperature keeps the snow that does fall from melting. During a brief summer, plants grow fast under the nearly continuous sunlight (**FIGURE 43.13**). Lichens and shallow-rooted, low-growing plants are the main producers.

Even at midsummer, only the surface layer of tundra soil thaws. Below that lies **permafrost**, a layer of frozen soil that is as much as 500 meters (1,600 feet) thick in places. Permafrost acts as a barrier that prevents drainage, so the soil above it remains perpetually waterlogged. The cool, anaerobic conditions in this soil slow decay, so organic remains can build up. Organic matter in permafrost makes the arctic tundra one of Earth's greatest stores of carbon.

FIGURE 43.13 Arctic tundra in the summer.

arctic tundra Highest-latitude Northern Hemisphere biome, where low, cold-tolerant plants survive with only a brief growing season.
permafrost Continually frozen soil layer that lies beneath arctic tundra and prevents water from draining.

TAKE-HOME MESSAGE 43.8

Arctic tundra prevails at high latitudes, where short, cool summers alternate with long, cold winters.

Arctic tundra is the youngest biome, and organic matter frozen in the permafrost makes it one of Earth's greatest stores of carbon.

PEOPLE MATTER

National Geographic Explorer
DR. KATEY WALTER ANTHONY

Thawing permafrost releases methane, the same flammable gas used to heat homes and cook meals. In arctic lakes, the released methane bubbles up from the depths in a way that is hard to quantify—until the first clear ice of fall captures a snapshot of emissions from the lake in bubbles at its surface. To test whether a frozen bubble contains methane, ecologist Katey Walter Anthony has an assistant plunge a pick into a bubble while she holds a match near it. If the bubble is methane, the gas ignites, as shown in the photo above.

Walter Anthony says the amount of methane bubbling up out of arctic lakes is troubling, because some of it seems to be coming not from bottom mud but from deeper geologic reservoirs that had previously been securely capped by permafrost—and that contain hundreds of times more methane than is in the atmosphere now. By venting methane into the atmosphere, the lakes are amplifying the global warming that created them: Methane is a greenhouse gas that traps 25 times more heat than carbon dioxide. Increased Arctic methane release could amplify global warming over the next few centuries.

"If we could only capture the gas, it would make a great energy source," Walter Anthony says. Unlike coal, methane burns without spewing sulfur dioxide or mercury, or leaving ash behind.

With this section, we turn our attention to Earth's waters. We begin here with freshwater systems, continue to coasts in the next section, then dive into the oceans.

LAKES

A lake is a body of standing fresh water. If sufficiently deep, it will have zones that differ in their physical characteristics and species composition (**FIGURE 43.14**). Nearest shore is the littoral zone. Here, sunlight penetrates all the way to the lake bottom and aquatic plants are the main producers. A lake's open waters include an upper, well-lit limnetic zone, and a profundal zone where light does not penetrate. The main producers in the limnetic zone are members of the

phytoplankton, a group of photosynthetic microorganisms that includes green algae, diatoms, and cyanobacteria. They serve as food for zooplankton, which are tiny consumers such as copepods. In the profundal zone, there is not enough light for photosynthesis, so consumers depend on food produced above. Debris that drifts down feeds detritivores and decomposers.

Nutrient Content and Succession Like a habitat on land, a lake undergoes succession; it changes over time. A newly formed lake is oligotrophic: deep, clear, and nutrient-poor, with low primary productivity (**FIGURE 43.15**). Over time, the lake becomes eutrophic. **Eutrophication** refers to processes, either natural or artificial, that enrich a body of water with nutrients. The increase in nutrients allows more producer growth, and primary productivity rises.

Seasonal Changes Temperate zone lakes undergo seasonal changes that affect primary productivity. Unlike most substances, water is not most dense in its solid state (ice). As water cools, its density increases until it reaches 4°C (39°F). Below this temperature, any additional cooling decreases water's density—which is why ice floats on water (Section 2.4). In an ice-covered lake, water just under the ice is near freezing and at its lowest density. The densest (4°C) water is at the bottom (**FIGURE 43.16A**).

In spring, winds cause currents that lead to a spring overturn, during which oxygen-rich water in the surface layers moves down and nutrient-rich water from the lake's depths moves up (**FIGURE 43.16B**). After the spring overturn, longer days and the dispersion of nutrients through the water encourage primary productivity.

In summer, a lake has three layers (**FIGURE 43.16C**). The upper layer is warm and oxygen-rich. Below this is a thermocline, a thin layer where temperature falls rapidly. Beneath the thermocline is the coolest water. The upper and lower waters on either side of this boundary do not mix. As a result, decomposers deplete oxygen dissolved near the lake bottom, and nutrients near the lake bottom cannot escape into surface waters. Nutrient shortages limit growth and production declines.

In autumn, the lake's upper waters cool, the thermocline vanishes, and a fall overturn occurs (**FIGURE 43.16D**). Oxygen-rich water moves down while nutrient-rich water moves up. This overturn brings nutrients to the surface and favors a brief burst of primary productivity. However, unlike the spring overturn, it does not lead to sustained production because decreasing light and temperature slow photosynthesis. Primary productivity will not peak again until after the next spring overturn.

FIGURE 43.14 **Lake zonation.** A lake's littoral zone extends all around the shore to a depth where rooted aquatic plants stop growing. Its limnetic zone is the open water where light penetrates and photosynthesis occurs. Below the limnetic zone is the cooler, dark water of the profundal zone.

FIGURE 43.15 **An oligotrophic lake.** Crater Lake in Oregon is a collapsed volcano that filled with snowmelt. It began filling about 7,700 years ago; from a geologic standpoint, it is a young lake.

CREDITS: (14) © Cengage Learning; (15) © Lindsay Douglas/Shutterstock.com.

STREAMS AND RIVERS

Flowing-water ecosystems start as freshwater springs or seeps. As water flows downslope, streams grow and merge. Rainfall, snowmelt, geography, altitude, and shade cast by plants affect flow volume and temperature. Minerals in rocks beneath the flowing water dissolve in it, affecting the water's solute concentrations. Because water in different parts of a river moves at different speeds, contains different solutes, and differs in temperature, the species composition of a river varies along its length (**FIGURE 43.17**).

THE ROLE OF DISSOLVED OXYGEN

The amount of oxygen dissolved in water is one of the most important factors affecting aquatic organisms. More oxygen dissolves in cooler, fast-flowing water than in warmer, still water. Thus, an increase in water temperature or decrease in its flow rate can cause aquatic species with high oxygen needs to suffocate.

In freshwater habitats, aquatic larvae of mayflies and stoneflies are the first invertebrates to disappear when the oxygen content of the water decreases. These insect larvae are active predators that demand considerable oxygen, so they serve as indicator species. Gilled snails disappear, too. Declines in populations of invertebrates can have cascading effects on the fishes that feed on them. Fishes can also be more directly affected. Trout and salmon are especially intolerant of low oxygen. Carp (including goldfish) are among the most tolerant; they survive tepid, stagnant water in ponds and tiny fish bowls.

No fishes can survive when the oxygen content of water falls below 4 parts per million. Leeches thrive as most competing invertebrates disappear. In waters with the lowest oxygen concentration, annelids called sludge worms (*Tubifex*) often are the only animals. The worms are colored red by their large amount of hemoglobin, which allows them to exploit low-oxygen habitats where predators and competition for food are scarce.

---

eutrophication Nutrient enrichment of an aquatic habitat.

TAKE-HOME MESSAGE 43.9

Within a lake, amounts of light, dissolved oxygen, and nutrients vary with depth. Primary productivity varies with a lake's age and—in temperate zones—with the season.

Rivers move nutrients into and out of ecosystems. Characteristics such as temperature and nutrient content usually vary along the length of a river.

Species differ in their dissolved oxygen needs. Cold, fast-moving water holds more oxygen than still, warm water.

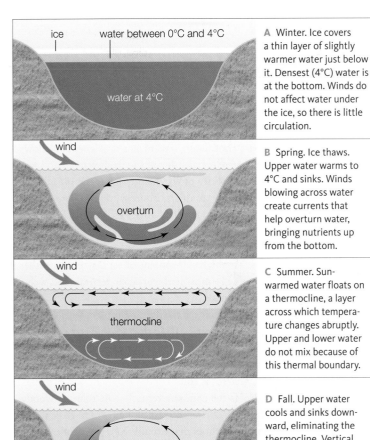

A Winter. Ice covers a thin layer of slightly warmer water just below it. Densest (4°C) water is at the bottom. Winds do not affect water under the ice, so there is little circulation.

B Spring. Ice thaws. Upper water warms to 4°C and sinks. Winds blowing across water create currents that help overturn water, bringing nutrients up from the bottom.

C Summer. Sun-warmed water floats on a thermocline, a layer across which temperature changes abruptly. Upper and lower water do not mix because of this thermal boundary.

D Fall. Upper water cools and sinks downward, eliminating the thermocline. Vertical currents mix water that was separated during the summer.

FIGURE 43.16 {Animated} Seasonal changes in a temperate zone lake.

FIGURE IT OUT: Which overturn results in the greatest rise in productivity?

Answer: The spring overturn, because increased nutrient availability is accompanied by increased light.

FIGURE 43.17 **Effect of turbulence.** As water flows over rocks, it picks up soluble minerals and becomes aerated, so it contains more oxygen.

COASTAL WETLANDS

An **estuary** is a partly enclosed body of water where fresh water from a river or rivers mixes with seawater. Seawater is denser than fresh water, so fresh water floats on top of the seawater where they meet. The size and shape of the estuary, and the rate at which freshwater flows into it, determine how quickly the saltwater and fresh water mix and the effects of tides. In all estuaries, an influx of water from upstream continually replenishes nutrients and allows a high level of productivity. Incoming fresh water also carries silt. Where the velocity of water flow slows, the silt falls to the bottom, forming mudflats. Photosynthetic bacteria and protists in biofilms on mudflats often account for a large portion of an estuary's primary production. Plants adapted to withstand changes in water level and salinity also serve as producers. The high salt content of estuary plants makes them unpalatable to most herbivores, so detrital food webs typically predominate.

Cordgrass (*Spartina*) is the dominant plant in the salt marshes of many estuaries along the Atlantic coast (**FIGURE 43.18A**). It is adapted to life in estuaries by an ability to withstand immersion during high tides and to tolerate salty, waterlogged, anaerobic soil.

"Mangrove" is the common term for salt-tolerant woody plants common in sheltered areas along tropical coasts. Prop roots, adventitious roots that extend from the trunk, help the plant stay upright (**FIGURE 43.18B**).

A Cordgrass (*Spartina*) in a South Carolina salt marsh. Salt taken up in water by roots is excreted by glands on the leaves.

B Mangroves along the shore in Florida. Specialized cells at the surface of some exposed prop roots allow gas exchange with air.

FIGURE 43.18 Two types of coastal wetlands.

Upper littoral zone Submerged only during the highest tide of the lunar cycle.

Midlittoral zone Regularly submerged during high tide and exposed at low tide.

Lower littoral zone Exposed only during the lowest tide of the lunar cycle.

FIGURE 43.19 Vertical zonation in the intertidal zone.

ROCKY AND SANDY SEASHORES

As with lakes, an ocean's shoreline is the littoral zone. This zone can be divided into three vertical regions that differ in their physical characteristics and species diversity (**FIGURE 43.19**). The upper littoral zone, which is also called the splash zone, regularly receives ocean spray but is submerged only during the highest of high tides. This zone gets the most sun, but has the fewest species. The midlittoral zone is covered by water during an average high tide and dry during a low tide. The lower littoral zone, exposed only during the lowest tide of the lunar cycle, is home to the most species.

You can easily see the zonation along a rocky shore. Multicelled algae ("seaweeds") that cling to rocks are the main producers, and grazing food chins predominate. Primary consumers include snails and sea urchins. Zonation is less obvious on sandy shores where detrital food chains start with material washed ashore. Some crustaceans eat detritus in the upper littoral zone. Nearer to the water, other invertebrates feed as they burrow through the sand.

estuary A highly productive ecosystem where nutrient-rich water from a river mixes with seawater.

TAKE-HOME MESSAGE 43.10

Estuaries are highly productive areas where fresh water and seawater mix.

Mangrove wetlands form along sheltered tropical coasts.

Grazing food chains predominate on rocky shores, and detrital food chains on sandy shores.

CREDITS: (18A) © Annie Griffiths Belt/Corbis; (18B) © Douglas Peebles/Corbis; (19) Courtesy of J. L. Sumich, *Biology of Marine Life*, 7th ed., W. C. Brown, 1999.

Coral reefs are wave-resistant formations that consist primarily of calcium carbonate secreted by many generations of coral polyps. Reef-forming corals live mainly in shallow, clear, warm waters between latitudes 25° north and 25° south. About 75 percent of all coral reefs are in the Indian and Pacific Oceans. A healthy reef is home to living corals and a huge number of other species (**FIGURE 43.20**). Biologists estimate that about a quarter of all marine fish species are associated with coral reefs.

Australia's Great Barrier Reef parallels Queensland for 2,500 kilometers (1,550 miles). This is the largest reef in the world, and it is also the largest example of biological architecture. Scientists estimate that it began forming about 600,000 years ago. Today, the Great Barrier Reef supports about 500 coral species, 3,000 fish species, 1,000 kinds of mollusks, and 40 kinds of sea snakes.

Photosynthetic dinoflagellates live inside the tissues of all reef-building corals (Section 23.4). Dinoflagellates live protected with the coral's tissues, where they receive plenty of carbon dioxide. In return, they provide the coral with oxygen and sugars.

Stress can cause a coral to expel its dinoflagellates. Because dinoflagellates give the coral its color, expelling these protists turns the coral white, an event called **coral bleaching**. When a coral is stressed for more than a short time, the dinoflagellate population in the coral's tissues cannot rebound and the coral dies, leaving its bleached hard parts behind (**FIGURE 43.21**).

The incidence of coral bleaching events has been increasing. Rising sea temperatures and sea level associated with global climate change most likely play a role. People also stress reefs by discharging sewage and other pollutants into coastal waters, by causing erosion that clouds water with sediments, and by destructive fishing practices. Fishing nets break pieces off corals. Fishermen hoping to capture reef fishes for the pet trade use explosives or sodium cyanide to stun the fishes, and destroy corals in the process. Invasive species also threaten reefs. Hawaiian reefs are threatened by exotic algae, including several species imported for cultivation during the 1970s.

Human-induced damage to reefs is taking a huge toll. For example, the Indo-Pacific region, the global center for reef diversity, lost about 3,000 square kilometers (1,160 square miles) of living coral reef each year between 1997 and 2003.

coral bleaching A coral expels its photosynthetic dinoflagellate symbionts in response to stress and becomes colorless.
coral reef Highly diverse marine ecosystem centered around reefs built by living corals that secrete calcium carbonate.

FIGURE 43.20 Healthy coral reef near Fiji. The coral gets its color from pigments of symbiotic dinoflagellates that live in its tissues and supply it with sugars.

FIGURE 43.21 "Bleached" reef near Australia. The coral skeletons shown here belong mainly to staghorn coral (*Acropora*), a genus especially likely to undergo coral bleaching.

TAKE-HOME MESSAGE 43.11

Coral reefs form by the action of living corals that lay down a calcium carbonate skeleton. Photosynthetic dinoflagellates in the coral's tissues are necessary for the coral's survival.

Rising water temperature, pollutants, fishing, and exotic species contribute to loss of reefs.

Declines in coral reefs will affect the enormous number of fishes and invertebrate species that make their home on or near the reefs.

CREDITS: (20) © John Easley, www.johneasley.com; (21) © Dr. Ray Berkelmans, Australian Institute of Marine Science.

FIGURE 43.22 Life at a hydrothermal vent on the seafloor. Giant tube worms are the most conspicuous members of this deep sea community. These annelids can grow more than 2 meters in length. The bright red plume that extends from the worm's tube gets its color from hemoglobin, the same pigment in your red blood cells. The red plume captures oxygen and dissolved sulfur from the seawater around it. As an adult, the worm never eats. Rather, sulfur absorbed by the worm serves as the energy source for chemoautotrophic bacteria that live inside it and provide it with sugars. The worms in turn serve as food for crabs that nibble on their exposed plumes.

The ocean's open waters are the **pelagic province**. This province includes the water over continental shelves and the more extensive waters farther offshore. In the ocean's upper, bright waters, phytoplankton such as single-celled algae and bacteria are the primary producers, and grazing food chains predominate. Depending on the region, some light may penetrate as far as 1,000 meters (more than a half mile) beneath the sea surface. Below that, organisms live in continual darkness, and organic material that drifts down from above serves as the basis of detrital food chains.

The **benthic province** is the ocean bottom, its rocks, and sediments. Species richness is greatest on continental shelves (the underwater edges of continents). The benthic province also includes largely unexplored species-rich regions, including seamounts and hydrothermal vents.

Seamounts are undersea mountains that stand 1,000 meters or more tall, but are still below the sea surface. They attract large numbers of fishes and are home to many marine invertebrates. Like islands, seamounts often are home to species that evolved there and live nowhere else.

At **hydrothermal vents**, hot water rich in dissolved minerals spews out from an opening on the ocean floor. The water is seawater that seeped into cracks in the ocean floor at the margins of tectonic plates and was heated by heat energy from within the Earth. Minerals in this water settle out when it mixes with the cold deep-sea water. Chemoautotrophic bacteria and archaea that obtain energy by removing electrons from minerals are the main producers

in food webs that include diverse invertebrates, including large numbers of tube worms (**FIGURE 43.22**).

Life exists even in the deepest sea. A remote-controlled submersible that sampled sediments in the deepest part of the ocean (the Mariana Trench) brought up foraminifera that live 11 kilometers (7 miles) below the surface. Sediment samples from deep in the Mediterranean Sea turned up another surprise, tiny animals that do not use oxygen. The animals, called loriciferans, live between sand grains and are distant relatives of insects and nematodes. They are the only animals known to live their lives entirely without oxygen.

---

benthic province The ocean's sediments and rocks.
hydrothermal vent Place where hot, mineral-rich water streams out from an underwater opening in Earth's crust.
pelagic province The ocean's open waters.
seamount An undersea mountain.

TAKE-HOME MESSAGE 43.12

In the pelagic province's upper waters, photosynthesis supports grazing food chains. In deeper, darker waters of this province, organisms feed mainly on detritus that drifts down from above.

The benthic province has pockets of high species diversity at undersea mountains (seamounts) and near hydrothermal vents. A hydrothermal vent ecosystem does not run on energy from the sun; the producers are chemoautotrophs rather than photoautotrophs.

Application:

EFFECTS OF EL NIÑO

Low abundance of phytoplankton in the equatorial Pacific during an El Niño.

High abundance of phytoplankton in the equatorial Pacific during a La Niña.

Education

FIGURE 43.23 Satellite photos showing the effect of El Niño on primary productivity in the Pacific Ocean.

FLUCTUATIONS IN CLIMATE INFLUENCE THE DISTRIBUTION AND ABUNDANCE OF ORGANISMS. Consider the effects of El Niño, a recurring climate event in which equatorial waters of the eastern and central Pacific Ocean warm above their average temperature. The term El Niño means "baby boy" and refers to Jesus; it was first used by Peruvian fishermen to describe local weather changes and a shortage of fishes that occurred in some years around Christmas. Scientists now know that during an El Niño, marine currents interact with the atmosphere in ways that influence weather patterns worldwide.

During an El Niño, unusually warm water flows toward eastern Pacific coasts, displacing currents that would otherwise bring up nutrients from the deep. Without these nutrients, marine primary producers decline in numbers (FIGURE 43.23). The dwindling producer populations and warming water cause a decrease in populations of small, cold-water fishes, as well as the larger consumers that rely on them, such as seals and sea lions.

An El Niño causes rainfall patterns to shift worldwide. In the El Niño winter of 1997–1998, torrential rains caused flooding and landslides along eastern Pacific coasts, while Australia and Indonesia suffered from drought-driven crop failures and raging wildfires. An El Niño typically brings cooler, wetter weather to the American Gulf states, and reduces the likelihood of hurricanes.

An El Niño usually persists for 6 to 18 months. It may be followed by an interval in which the temperature of the eastern Pacific remains near its average, or by a La Niña. During a La Niña, eastern Pacific waters become cooler than average. As a result, the west coast of the United States gets little rainfall and the likelihood of hurricanes in the Atlantic increases.

Outbreaks of human disease often occur during an El Niño. For example, the increased ocean temperature in the Pacific leads to an increased incidence of cholera. Copepods, a type of small crustacean, serve as a reservoir for cholera-causing bacteria between disease outbreaks. During an El Niño, the rise in the temperature of the ocean's surface results in a rise in the number of cholera-carrying copepods. An El Niño also brings an increase in malaria to coastal communities in South Asia and Latin America.

The United States National Oceanographic and Atmospheric Administration (NOAA) monitors sea surface temperature and studies El Niño events. NOAA's goal is to determine how El Niño affects global weather patterns and the extent of its effects. Such studies could help us develop a method of predicting when an El Niño or La Niña event is likely to occur and which regions are at a heightened risk for flooding, drought, hurricanes, or epidemics as a result. Predicting and planning for such occurrences could help prevent or minimize their harmful effects. The current data on sea surface temperature, as well as information about the monitoring program, are available on NOAA's website at www.elnino.noaa.gov.

SECTIONS 43.1, 43.2 Global air circulation patterns affect **climate** and the distribution of communities within the biosphere. Air is set in motion when sunlight heats tropical regions more than higher latitudes. Ocean currents distribute heat worldwide and influence weather patterns. Interactions between ocean currents, air currents, and landforms determine where regional phenomena such as **rain shadows** or **monsoons** occur.

SECTION 43.3 **Biomes** are characterized by a particular type of vegetation. Many biomes include multiple discontinuous areas. Climate and soil properties affect the distribution of biomes.

SECTIONS 43.4, 43.5 The broadleaf evergreen trees that predominate in **tropical rain forests** grow all year. These enormously productive forests are home to a large number of species. Tropical rain forest is the oldest existing biome. Trees in **temperate deciduous forests** shed their leaves all at once just before a cold winter that prevents growth. Conifers that dominate Northern Hemisphere high-latitude boreal forests withstand cold and drought better than broadleaf trees.

SECTION 43.6 **Grasslands** dominated by plants adapted to fire and grazing form in the somewhat moist interior of midlatitude continents. **Savannas** include fire-adapted grasses and scattered shrubs. Shrubby, fire-adapted **chaparral** is common in California and other coastal regions with hot, dry summers and cool, wet winters.

SECTION 43.7 Deserts form in regions with little precipitation and widely fluctuating temperature. Drought-adapted plants dominate. Desert crust holds soil particles in place and provides plants with nutrients.

SECTION 43.8 The Northern Hemisphere's **arctic tundra** is dominated by short plants that grow only during the brief, cool summer when daylight is abundant. Tundra is the youngest biome, and its **permafrost** is a great reservoir of carbon.

SECTION 43.9 Gradients in light, temperature, dissolved gases, and nutrients affect the distribution of species in aquatic ecosystems. Lakes undergo a natural process of **eutrophication**, becoming more productive over time. In temperate zone lakes, a spring overturn and a fall overturn cause vertical mixing of waters.

SECTIONS 43.10–43.12 Nutrient-rich fresh water mixes with seawater in an **estuary**. Mangrove wetlands form on sheltered tropical coasts. Along rocky shores, multicellular algae form the base for grazing food chains. On sandy shores, detrital food chains predominate.

Accumulated calcium carbonate skeletons of coral polyps form **coral reefs**. Photosynthetic dinoflagellates in the corals are producers for this ecosystem. Many marine species associate with reefs. When stressed, a coral may eject its photosynthetic symbionts, an event called **coral bleaching**.

Life exists throughout the ocean. In the **pelagic province**, grazing food chains predominate in sunlit waters. Detritus forms the base for food chains in deeper, darker waters. **Seamounts** are regions of high diversity in the **benthic province**. At **hydrothermal vents**, chemoautotrophic bacteria and archaea are the producers.

SECTION 43.13 Interactions among Earth's air and waters affect weather worldwide and have effects on human health, as when the Pacific warms during an El Niño and then cools during a La Niña.

Self-Quiz Answers in Appendix VII

1. The Northern Hemisphere is most tilted toward the sun in _____ .
   a. spring   b. summer   c. autumn   d. winter

2. Which latitude will have the most hours of daylight on the summer solstice?
   a. 0° (the equator)   c. 45° north
   b. 30° north   d. 60° north

3. Warm air _____ and it holds _____ water than cold air.
   a. sinks; less   c. sinks; more
   b. rises; less   d. rises; more

4. A rain shadow is a reduction in rainfall _____ .
   a. on the inland side of a coastal mountain range
   b. during an El Niño event
   c. that results from global warming

5. The Gulf Stream is a current that flows _____ along the eastern coast of the United States.
   a. north to south   b. south to north

6. _____ have a deep layer of humus-rich topsoil.
   a. Deserts   c. Rain forests
   b. Grasslands   d. Seamounts

7. Biomes differ in their _____ .
   a. climate   c. soils
   b. dominant plants   d. all of the above

8. Grasslands most often are found _____ .
   a. at 30° north and south   c. in interior of continents
   b. at high altitudes   d. all of the above

9. Permafrost underlies _____ .
   a. arctic tundra   c. boreal forest
   b. temperate forest d. all of the above

10. The warmer water is, the _____ oxygen it can hold.
    a. more   b. less

11. Chemoautotrophic bacteria and archaea are the primary producers for food webs _____ .
    a. in mangrove wetlands   c. on coral reefs
    b. at seamounts   d. at hydrothermal vents

Data Analysis Activities

Changing Sea Temperatures In an effort to predict El Niño or La Niña events in the near future, the National Oceanographic and Atmospheric Administration collects information about sea surface temperature (SST) and atmospheric conditions. Scientists compare monthly temperature averages in the eastern equatorial Pacific Ocean to historical data and calculate the difference (degree of anomaly) to see if El Niño conditions, La Niña conditions, or neutral conditions are developing. El Niño is a rise in the average SST above 0.5°C. A decline of the same amount is La Niña. **FIGURE 43.24** shows data for nearly 39 years.

1. When did the greatest positive temperature deviation occur during this time period?

2. What type of event, if any, occurred during the winter of 1982–1983? What about the winter of 2001–2002?

3. During a La Niña event, less rain than normal falls in the American West and Southwest. In the time interval shown, what was the longest interval without a La Niña event?

FIGURE 43.24 Sea surface temperature anomalies (differences from the historical mean) in the eastern equatorial Pacific Ocean. A rise above the dashed red line is an El Niño event; a decline below the blue line is La Niña.

4. What type of conditions were in effect in the fall of 2007 when California suffered severe wildfires?

---

12. Corals rely on symbiotic _____ for sugars.
    a. fungi
    c. dinoflagellates
    b. bacteria
    d. green algae

13. Which of the following biomes borders on boreal forest?
    a. savanna
    c. tundra
    b. taiga
    d. chaparral

14. Unrelated species living in geographically separated parts of a biome may resemble one another as a result of _____ .
    a. competitive interactions
    b. morphological convergence
    c. morphological divergence
    d. coevolution

15. Match the terms with the most suitable description.
    ___ tundra
    ___ chaparral
    ___ desert
    ___ savanna
    ___ estuary
    ___ boreal forest
    ___ prairie
    ___ tropical rain forest
    ___ hydrothermal vents

    a. broadleaf forest near equator
    b. partly enclosed by land; where fresh water and seawater mix
    c. African grassland with trees
    d. low-growing plants at high latitudes or elevations
    e. dry shrubland
    f. at latitudes 30° north and south
    g. mineral-rich, superheated water supports communities
    h. conifers dominate
    i. North American grassland

Critical Thinking

1. On April 26, 1986, a meltdown occurred at the Chernobyl nuclear power plant in Ukraine. Nuclear fuel burned for nearly ten days and released 400 times more radioactive material than the atomic bomb that dropped on Hiroshima. Winds carried radioactive fallout around the globe. By 1998, the rate of thyroid abnormalities in children living downwind from the site was nearly seven times as high as for those upwind; their thyroid gland concentrated the iodine radioisotopes. Chernoboyl is at 51° north latitude. In what direction did the major winds carry the fallout after the accident?

2. Owners of off-road recreational vehicles would like increased access to government-owned deserts. Some argue that it is the perfect place for off-roaders because "There's nothing there." Do you agree?

3. Rita Colwell, the scientist who discovered why cholera outbreaks often occur during an El Niño, is concerned that global climate change could increase the incidence of this disease. By what mechanism might global warming cause an increase in cholera outbreaks?

CENGAGE brain.com To access course materials, please visit www.cengagebrain.com.

Young elephants and their keepers at David Sheldrick Wildlife Trust in Kenya. Poaching and human–wildlife conflicts left the elephants motherless at an early age. They will need human care for eight to ten years before they can survive in the wild.

44

HUMAN EFFECTS ON THE BIOSPHERE

Links to Earlier Concepts

This chapter considers the causes of an ongoing mass extinction (Section 16.6) in light of human population growth (40.6). We look again at effects of species introductions and will draw on your knowledge of pH (2.5), the ozone layer (18.4), plant nutrition (26.1), and water and nutrient cycles (42.5–42.8).

KEY CONCEPTS

AN EXTINCTION CRISIS

Humans have increased the frequency of extinctions by overharvesting, and by habitat degradation and fragmentation. The extent of species losses is not fully known.

HARMFUL LAND USES

Plowing grasslands and cutting forests have long-term and long-range effects. By allowing soil erosion and affecting rainfall patterns, these practices make it difficult to restore plant cover.

EFFECTS OF POLLUTANTS

Some airborne pollutants fall to Earth in acid rain. Others harm the protective ozone layer or contribute to global climate change.

CONSERVING BIODIVERSITY

Earth's biodiversity is the product of billions of years of evolution. Conservation biologists prioritize which areas to protect by assessing which are most threatened and most biodiverse.

REDUCING NEGATIVE IMPACTS

Extraction of fuel and other nonrenewable resources harms the environment. Using such resources carefully can help reduce threats to biodiversity.

A White abalone.

B Pyne's ground plum.

C Texas blind salamander.

D Florida perforate reindeer lichen.

FIGURE 44.1 Examples of endangered species native to the United States. To learn more about these and other threatened and endangered species, visit the United States Fish and Wildlife Service's endangered species website at www.fws.gov/endangered/.

Extinction, like speciation, is a natural process. Species arise and become extinct on an ongoing basis. Scientists estimate that 99 percent of all species that have ever lived are now extinct. The rate of extinction picks up dramatically during a mass extinction, when many kinds of organisms in many different habitats become extinct in a relatively short period. We are currently in the midst of such an event. Unlike most previous mass extinctions, this one is not the inevitable result of a physical catastrophe such as a volcanic eruption or asteroid impact. Humans are the driving force behind the current rise in extinctions and our actions will determine the extent of the losses.

An **endangered species** is a species that faces extinction in all or part of its range. A **threatened species** is one that is likely to become endangered in the near future. Keep in mind that not all rare species are threatened or endangered. Some species have always been uncommon. A species is considered endangered when one or more of its populations have declined or are declining.

CAUSES OF SPECIES DECLINE

When European settlers first arrived in North America, they found between 3 and 5 billion passenger pigeons. In the 1800s, commercial hunting caused a steep decline in the bird's numbers. The last time anyone saw a wild passenger pigeon was 1900, and he shot it. The last captive member of the species died in 1914.

We continue to overharvest species. The crash of the Atlantic codfish population, described in Section 40.5, is one recent example. Another is the fate of the white abalone, a gastropod mollusk native to kelp forests off the coast of California (**FIGURE 44.1A**). Heavy harvesting of this species during the 1970s reduced the population to about 1 percent of its original size. In 2001, it became the first invertebrate to be listed as endangered by the United States Fish and Wildlife Service. Although some white abalone remain in the wild, population density remains too low for effective reproduction. The species' only hope for survival

is a program of captive breeding. If this program succeeds, individuals will be reintroduced to the wild.

Species are overharvested not only as food, but also for use in traditional medicine, for the pet trade, and for ornamentation. Some orchids prized by collectors have become nearly extinct in the wild. Most of the orphan elephants shown in the chapter opening photo lost their mother to poachers who kill to obtain ivory tusks. The majority of elephant tusks harvested this way end up in China, in the form of decorative carved objects.

Overharvest directly reduces population size, but humans also affect species indirectly by altering their habitat. Many species requires a highly specific type of habitat, and any degradation, fragmentation, or destruction of that habitat reduces population numbers.

An **endemic species** remains confined to the area in which it evolved. Such species are more likely to go extinct as a result of habitat degradation than species with a more widespread distribution. Consider Pyne's ground plum (**FIGURE 44.1B**), a flowering plant that lives only in cedar glades near a rapidly growing city in Tennessee. The plant is threatened by conversion of its habitat to homes and industrial use. Texas blind salamanders (**FIGURE 44.1C**) are among the species endemic to Edwards Aquifer, a series of water-filled, underground limestone formations. Excessive withdrawals of water, along with water pollution, threaten the salamander and other species in the aquifer. A lichen endemic to Florida is endangered by development of its scrubland habitat (**FIGURE 44.1D**).

Deliberate or accidental species introductions can also pose a threat (Section 41.7). Rats that reached islands by stowing away on ships attack and endanger many ground-nesting birds that evolved in the absence of egg-eating ground predators. Exotic species also cause problems by outcompeting native ones. For example, California's native golden trout declined after European brown trout and eastern brook trout were introduced into California's mountain streams for sport fishing.

CREDITS: (1A) John Butler, NOAA; (1B, D) Joel Sartore/National Geographic Creative; (1C) Joe Fries, U.S. Fish & Wildlife Service.

Decline or extinction of one species can endanger others. Consider running buffalo clover and the buffalo that graze on it. Both were once common in the Midwest. The plants thrived in the open woodlands where soil was enriched by buffalo droppings and periodically disturbed by the animals' hooves. Buffalo helped to disperse the clover's seeds. When buffalo were hunted to near extinction, buffalo clover populations declined as well.

THE UNKNOWN LOSSES

The International Union for Conservation of Nature and Natural Resources (IUCN) monitors threats to species worldwide. Its species listings have historically focused on vertebrates. Scientists have only recently begun to consider the threats to invertebrates and to plants. Our impact on protists and fungi is largely unknown, and the IUCN does not address threats to bacteria or archaea.

Microbiologist Tom Curtis is among those making a plea for increased research on microbial ecology and microbial diversity. He argues that we have barely begun to comprehend the vast number of microbial species and to understand their importance. Curtis writes, "I make no apologies for putting microorganisms on a pedestal above all other living things. For if the last blue whale choked to death on the last panda, it would be disastrous but not the end of the world. But if we accidentally poisoned the last two species of ammonia-oxidizers, that would be another matter. It could be happening now and we wouldn't even know . . ." Ammonia-oxidizing bacteria play an essential role in the nitrogen cycle by converting ammonia in wastes and remains to nitrites (Section 42.7). Without them, wastes would pile up and plants would not have access to the nitrogen they need to grow.

---

endangered species Species that faces extinction in all or a part of its range.
endemic species Species that remains restricted to the area where it evolved.
threatened species Species likely to become endangered in the near future.

TAKE-HOME MESSAGE 44.1

Species often decline when humans destroy or fragment natural habitat by converting it to human use, or degrade it through pollution or withdrawal of an essential resource.

Humans also directly cause declines by overharvesting species.

Global travel and trade can introduce exotic species that harm native ones.

The number of endangered species remains largely unknown.

PEOPLE MATTER

National Geographic Explorer
DR. PAULA KAHUMBU

Linking conservationists with members of the public and with one another is one of Paula Kahumbu's main goals. She says, "Conservationists do crucial work on a shoestring, cut off from the rest of the world. They're in remote, isolated places, some even risking their lives, with no chance of getting on the international radar screen. Meanwhile, millions of people who care about the catastrophic loss of wildlife and habitats aren't sure how to help." Kahumbu is executive director of WildlifeDirect (http://wildlifedirect.org), an online platform that gives conservationists a way to share day-by-day challenges and victories via blogs, diaries, videos, photos, and podcasts. Thanks to her efforts, people concerned about wildlife and wild places can view problems in real time and track the impact of their own contributions. The site attracts thousands of visitors daily, with online donations going directly to projects across Africa, Asia, and South America.

Information from conservationists involved with WildlifeDirect helped Kahumbu recognize an important conservation issue in Africa—misuse of the insecticide carbofuran. This chemical, which is banned for use on food crops in the United States and for all uses in Europe, remains widely available in Africa. Reports flowing into Wildlife Direct revealed that some farmers were using carbofuran-laced carcasses to poison lions that they believed threatened livestock. This practice caused declines in endangered lions, hyenas, and vultures. Others put carbofuran into irrigated rice fields to deliberately kill water birds for consumption as human food. Although both harmful practices have declined as a result of the efforts of Kahumbu and other conservationists, she continues to work toward a ban on the sale of carbofuran in Africa.

Kahumbu began her conservation work with research on African elephants and she remains a strong advocate for their protection. She favors a global ban on all trade in ivory, increased efforts to detect smuggled ivory, and stiffer penalties for those who take part in any aspect of the ivory trade.

With this section, we begin a survey of some of the ways that human activities threaten species by destroying or degrading habitats.

DESERTIFICATION

Deserts naturally expand and contract over geological time as climate conditions vary. However, human activities sometimes result in the rapid conversion of a grassland or woodland to desert, a process called **desertification**. As human populations increase, greater numbers of people are forced to farm in areas that are ill-suited to agriculture. Others allow livestock to overgraze in grasslands. In both cases, desertification can occur.

A well-documented instance of desertification occurred in the United States during the mid-1930s, when large portions of prairie on the southern Great Plains were plowed under to plant crops. This plowing exposed deep prairie topsoil to the force of the region's constant winds. Then came a drought, and the result was an economic and ecological disaster. Winds carried more than a billion tons of topsoil aloft as sky-darkening dust clouds turned the region into what came to be known as the Dust Bowl (**FIGURE 44.2A**). Tons of displaced soil fell to earth as far away as New York City and Washington, D.C.

Today, Africa's Sahara desert is expanding south into the Sahel region. Overgrazing in this region strips grasslands of their vegetation and allows winds to erode the soil. Winds carry the soil aloft and westward (**FIGURE 44.2B**). Soil particles land as far away as the southern United States and the Caribbean. In China's northwestern regions, overplowing and overgrazing have expanded the Gobi desert so that dust clouds periodically darken skies above Beijing. Winds carry some of the dust across the Pacific to the west coast of the United States.

Drought encourages desertification, which results in more drought in a positive feedback cycle. Plants cannot thrive in a region where the topsoil has blown away. With less transpiration (Section 26.4), less water enters the atmosphere, so local rainfall decreases.

The best way to prevent desertification is to avoid farming in areas subject to high winds and periodic drought. If these areas must be used, methods that do not repeatedly disturb the soil can minimize risk of desertification.

DEFORESTATION

The amount of forested land is currently stable or increasing in North America, Europe, and China, but tropical forests continue to disappear at an alarming rate. In Brazil, increases in the export of soybeans and free-range beef have helped make the country the world's seventh-largest economy. However, this economic expansion has come at the expense of the country's woodlands and forests (**FIGURE 44.3**).

Deforestation has detrimental effects beyond the immediate destruction of forest organisms. For example, deforestation encourages flooding because water runs off into streams, rather than being taken up by tree roots. Deforestation also raises risk of landslides in hilly areas. Tree roots tend to stabilize the soil. When they are removed, waterlogged soil becomes more likely to slide.

Soils of deforested areas become nutrient-poor because of the increased loss of nutrient ions in runoff. **FIGURE**

FIGURE 44.2 Dust storms, one outcome of desertification.

A Dust cloud in the Great Plains during the 1930s.

B Dust blows across the Atlantic from North Africa.

FIGURE 44.3 **Deforestation. Cropland that once was rainforest extends right up to the edge of Iguaçu National Park, a World Heritage Site that straddles the border between Brazil and Argentina. Threatened primates and large cats are among the species that rely on this forest habitat.**

44.4 shows results of an experiment in which scientists deforested a region in New Hampshire and monitored the nutrient content of runoff. Deforestation caused a spike in loss of essential soil nutrients such as calcium.

Like desertification, deforestation affects local climate. The loss of plants means reduced transpiration, so the amount of local rainfall declines. In shady forests, transpiration also results in evaporative cooling. When a forest is cut down, shade disappears and the evaporative cooling ceases. Thus, the temperature in a deforested area is typically higher than in an adjacent forested area.

Once a tropical forest has been logged, the resulting nutrient losses and drier, hotter conditions can make it impossible for tree seeds to germinate or for seedlings to survive. Thus, deforestation can be difficult to reverse.

Because forests take up and store huge amounts of carbon dioxide (Section 25.8), ongoing forest losses also contribute to global climate change by increasing the atmospheric concentration of this greenhouse gas.

FIGURE 44.4 **{Animated}** Effect of experimental deforestation on nutrient losses from soil. After deforestation, calcium (Ca) levels in runoff increased sixfold (gray). An undisturbed plot in the same forest showed no increase during this time (green).

desertification Conversion of dry grassland to desert.

TAKE-HOME MESSAGE 44.2

Desertification occurs when excess plowing or grazing of a grassland causes soil to blow away. With fewer plants, rainfall declines.

Deforestation increases flooding and loss of soil nutrients, raises the local temperature, and decreases rainfall. Changes in soil and temperature produced by deforestation make it difficult for new trees to become established.

A Juvenile sea lion with ring of discarded plastic around its neck. As the animal grows, the plastic will cut into its neck, causing a wound and impairing its ability to feed.

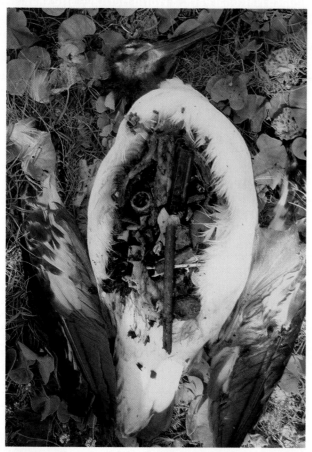

B Recently deceased Laysan albatross chick, dissected to reveal the contents of its gut. Scientists found more than 300 pieces of plastic inside the bird. One of the pieces had punctured its gut wall, resulting in its death. The chick was fed the plastic by its parents, who gathered the material from the ocean surface, mistaking it for food.

FIGURE 44.5 Perils of plastic.

Seven billion people use and discard a lot of stuff. Where does all the waste go? Historically, unwanted material was buried in the ground or dumped out at sea. Trash was out of sight, and also out of mind.

We now know that burying garbage can contaminate groundwaters, as when lead from discarded batteries seeps into the ground. We also know that solid waste dumped into oceans harms marine life (FIGURE 44.5). In the United States, solid municipal waste can no longer legally be dumped at sea. Nevertheless, plastic constantly enters our coastal waters. Foam cups and containers from fast-food outlets, plastic shopping bags, plastic water bottles, and other litter ends up in storm drains. From there it is carried to streams and rivers that can convey it to the sea. A seawater sample taken near the mouth of the San Gabriel River in southern California had 128 times as much plastic as plankton by weight.

Once in the ocean, trash can persist for a surprisingly long time. Components of a disposable diaper will last for more than 100 years, as will fishing line. A plastic bag will be around for more than 50 years, and a cigarette filter for more than 10.

Ocean currents can carry bits of plastic for thousands of miles. These plastic bits can end up accumulating in some areas of the ocean. Consider the Great Pacific Garbage Patch, a region of the north central Pacific that the media often describes as an "island of trash." In fact, the plastic is not easily visible. Rather, the garbage patch is a region where a high concentration of confetti-like plastic particles swirl slowly around an area as large as the state of Texas. The small bits of plastic absorb and concentrate toxic compounds such as pesticides and industrial chemicals from the seawater around them, making the plastic all the more harmful to marine organisms that mistakenly eat it. Scientists recently estimated that fish living in mid-depth water of the north central Pacific consume as much as 240,000 tons of this chemically tainted plastic each year.

You can help reduce the impact of plastic trash by choosing more durable objects over disposable ones, and avoiding plastic products when other, less environmentally harmful alternatives exist. If you use plastic, be sure to recycle or dispose of it properly.

TAKE-HOME MESSAGE 44.3

Plastic trash often ends up in the ocean, where it harms marine life.

You can minimize your environmental impact by avoiding disposable plastic goods and by recycling.

Plastic trash is one example of a pollutant. **Pollutants** are natural or man-made substances released into soil, air, or water in greater than natural amounts. The presence of a pollutant disrupts the physiological processes of organisms that evolved in its absence, or that are adapted to lower levels of it. Some pollutants come from a few distinct sites, or point sources. Pollutants that come from point sources are usually the easiest to control: Identify the few sources of the pollutant, and you can take action there. It is more difficult to deal with pollution from nonpoint sources, which are more numerous and widely dispersed.

Sulfur dioxide and nitrogen oxide gases are common air pollutants. Most sulfur dioxide pollution comes from point sources—coal-burning power plants and smelters (factories that extract metals from ore). Nitrogen oxides come largely from nonpoint sources such as cars and other vehicles that burn gas and oil, and the agricultural use of synthetic, nitrogen-rich fertilizers.

Sulfur dioxide and nitrogen oxides coat dust particles when the weather is dry. Dry acid deposition occurs when this coated dust falls to the ground. Wet acid deposition, or **acid rain**, occurs when pollutants react with gases and water vapor in air and fall as acidic precipitation. The pH of unpolluted rainwater is about 5.6 (Section 2.5). The pH of acid rain can be as low as 2. In the United States, federal regulations limiting sulfur dioxide emissions have helped reduce the acidity of precipitation (**FIGURE 44.6A**). The world's main sulfur dioxide emitters are now China and India, where industrialization and coal use continue to rise.

Acid rain that falls on or drains into waterways, ponds, and lakes affects aquatic organisms. For example, heightened acidity impairs the growth of diatoms, which serve as producers in many lakes. The high acidity of some streams in the northeastern United States and Canada has contributed to a decline in populations of Atlantic salmon. These salmon breed and lay their eggs in streams, but spend most of their life in the ocean. A young salmon exposed to acidic water cannot make the physiological changes necessary for a transition to life in saltwater.

Acid rain that falls on forests burns tree leaves and increases the pH of soil water. As acidic water drains through soil, positively charged hydrogen ions displace positively charged nutrient ions such as calcium, so soil loses these nutrients. The acidity also causes soil particles to release metals such as aluminum that can harm plants. The combination of nutrient-poor soil and exposure to toxic metals weakens trees, making them more susceptible to insects and pathogens, and thus more likely to die (**FIGURE 44.6B**). Effects are most pronounced at high elevations where trees are frequently exposed to clouds of acidic fog.

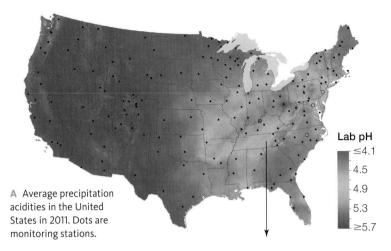

A Average precipitation acidities in the United States in 2011. Dots are monitoring stations.

Lab pH

≤4.1
4.5
4.9
5.3
≥5.7

B Dying trees in Great Smoky Mountains National Park, where acid rain harms leaves and causes loss of nutrients from soil.

FIGURE 44.6 {Animated} Acid rain in the United States.

  FIGURE IT OUT: Is rain more acidic on the East Coast or the West Coast?

Answer: The East Coast

acid rain Low-pH rain that forms when sulfur dioxide and nitrogen oxides mix with water vapor in the atmosphere.
pollutant A substance that is released into the environment by human activities and interferes with the function of organisms that evolved in the absence of the substance or with lower levels.

TAKE-HOME MESSAGE 44.4

Burning fossil fuels, metal production, and use of synthetic nitrogen fertilizer contribute to the acidification of rain and to dry acid deposition.

Increased acidity in water and soil impairs the health and development of many types of organisms.

CREDITS: (6A) Courtesy of National Atmospheric Deposition; (6B) Frederica Georgia/Science Source.

CHAPTER 44
**HUMAN EFFECTS ON
THE BIOSPHERE**

789

DEPLETION OF THE OZONE LAYER

In the upper layers of the atmosphere, between 17 and 27 kilometers (10.5 and 17 miles) above sea level, the ozone (O_3) concentration is so great that scientists refer to this region as the **ozone layer**. The ozone layer benefits living organisms by absorbing most ultraviolet (UV) radiation from incoming sunlight. UV radiation, remember, damages DNA and causes mutations (Section 8.5).

In the mid-1970s, scientists noticed that Earth's ozone layer was thinning. Its thickness had always varied a bit with the season, but now the average level was declining steadily from year to year. By the mid-1980s, the spring ozone thinning over Antarctica was so pronounced that people began referring to the lowest-ozone region as an "ozone hole" (**FIGURE 44.7A**).

Declining ozone quickly became an international concern. With a thinner ozone layer, people would be exposed to more UV radiation, the main cause of skin cancers. Higher UV levels also harm wildlife, which do not have the option of avoiding sunlight. In addition, exposure to higher-than-normal UV levels affects plants and other producers, slowing the rate of photosynthesis and the release of oxygen into the atmosphere.

Chlorofluorocarbons, or CFCs, are the main ozone destroyers. These odorless gases were once widely used as propellants in aerosol cans, as coolants, and in solvents and plastic foam. In response to the potential threat posed by the thinning ozone layer, countries worldwide agreed in 1987 to phase out the production of CFCs and other ozone-destroying chemicals. As a result of that agreement (the Montreal Protocol), the concentrations of CFCs in the atmosphere are no longer rising dramatically (**FIGURE 44.7B**). However, CFCs break down quite slowly, so scientists expect them to remain at a level that significantly thins the ozone layer for several decades.

NEAR-GROUND OZONE POLLUTION

Near the ground, where ozone levels are naturally low, ozone is considered a pollutant. Ground-level ozone forms when nitrogen oxides and volatile organic compounds released by burning or evaporating fossil fuels are exposed to sunlight. Warm temperature speeds the reaction. Thus, ground-level ozone tends to vary daily (being higher in the daytime) and seasonally (being higher during the summer).

Ozone does not persist for long, so ozone emitted into the lower atmosphere never makes it to the ozone layer where would be useful. In the lower atmosphere, this strong oxidizing agent irritates the eyes and respiratory tracts of people and wildlife and interferes with plant growth.

You can help reduce ozone pollution by avoiding actions that put fossil fuels or their combustion products into the air at times that favor ozone production. For example, on hot, sunny, still days, postpone filling your gas tank or using gasoline-powered appliances such as lawn mowers until the evening, when there is less sunlight to power the conversion of pollutants to ozone.

ozone layer High atmospheric layer with a high concentration of ozone (O_3) that prevents much ultraviolet radiation from reaching Earth's surface.

A Ozone levels in the upper atmosphere in September 2012, the Antarctic spring.

Purple indicates the least ozone, with blue, green, and yellow indicating increasingly higher levels.

Check the current status of the ozone hole at NASA's website (http://ozonewatch.gsfc.nasa.gov/).

Antarctica

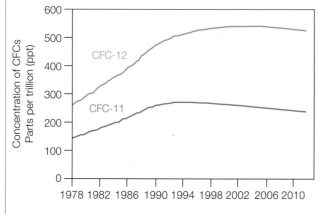

B Concentration of two CFCs in the upper atmosphere. These pollutants destroy ozone. A worldwide ban on CFCs has successfully halted the rise in atmospheric CFC concentration.

FIGURE 44.7 Destruction of the ozone layer.

TAKE-HOME MESSAGE 44.5

Certain synthetic chemicals destroy ozone in the upper atmosphere's protective ozone layer. This layer shields us and other life from UV radiation in sunlight.

Evaporation and burning of fossil fuels increase the amount of ozone in the lower atmosphere, where the gas is considered a harmful pollutant.

CREDITS: (7A) NASA Ozone Watch; (7B) From www.esrl.noaa.gov.

44.6 WHAT ARE THE EFFECTS OF GLOBAL CLIMATE CHANGE?

Muir Glacier in Alaska (1940)

Muir Glacier in Alaska (2004)

FIGURE 44.9 Melting glaciers, one sign of a warming world. Water from melting glaciers contributes to rising sea level.

Ongoing climate change affects ecosystems worldwide. How is the global climate changing? Most notably, average temperatures are increasing (**FIGURE 44.8**). Warming is more pronounced at temperate and polar latitudes than at the equator.

Rising temperature elevates sea level by two mechanisms. Water expands as it is heated, and heating also melts sea ice and glaciers (**FIGURE 44.9**). Together, thermal expansion and the addition of meltwater from glaciers cause sea level to rise. In the past century, the sea level has risen about 20 centimeters (8 inches). As a result, some coastal wetlands are disappearing underwater.

The warming climate is already having widespread effects on biological systems. Temperature changes are important cues for many temperate zone species. Abnormally warm spring temperatures are causing deciduous trees to put leaves out earlier, and spring-blooming plants to flower earlier. Animal migration times and breeding seasons are also shifting. Species arrays in biological communities are changing as warmer temperatures allow some species to expand their range to higher latitudes or elevations. Of course, not all species can move or spread quickly, and warmer temperatures are expected to drive some of these species to extinction. For example, warming of tropical waters is already stressing reef-building corals and increasing the frequency of coral bleaching events.

Global warming is just one aspect of global climate change. Temperature affects evaporation, winds, and currents, so many weather patterns are expected to change as global temperature continues to rise. For example, warmer temperatures are correlated with extremes in rainfall patterns: periods of drought interrupted by unusually heavy rains. In addition, warmer seas tend to increase the intensity of hurricanes.

As Section 42.6 explained, the most widely accepted explanation for global climate change is the rising levels of greenhouse gases such as carbon dioxide. Fossil fuel combustion is the single biggest source of greenhouse gas emissions, and the use of these fuels is still rising as large nations such as China and India become increasingly industrialized. Reducing greenhouse gas emissions will be a challenge, but efforts are under way to increase the efficiency of processes that require fossil fuels, to shift to alternative energy sources such as solar and wind power, and to develop innovative ways to store carbon dioxide.

FIGURE 44.8 Rising temperature. The temperature anomaly is the deviation from average temperature in the period 1951–1980.

TAKE-HOME MESSAGE 44.6

The rise in global temperature is causing the sea level to rise, and is affecting weather patterns.

These changes are altering the range of some species, threatening others with extinction, and disrupting the structure of biological communities.

THE VALUE OF BIODIVERSITY

Every nation has some amount of biological wealth, which we call **biodiversity**. A region's biodiversity is measured at three levels: the genetic diversity within species, species diversity, and ecosystem diversity. Biodiversity is currently declining at all three levels, in all regions.

Conservation biology addresses these declines. The goals of this relatively new field of biology are (1) to survey the range of biodiversity, and (2) to find ways to maintain and use biodiversity to benefit human populations by encouraging people to value their region's natural resources and use those resources in nondestructive ways.

Why should we protect biodiversity? From a selfish standpoint, doing so is an investment in our future. Healthy ecosystems are essential to the survival of our species. Other organisms produce the oxygen we breathe and the food we eat. They remove waste carbon dioxide from the air and decompose and detoxify wastes. Plants take up rain and hold soil in place, preventing erosion and reducing the risk of flooding. We are still discovering medically valuable compounds produced by wild species. Wild relatives of crop plants are reservoirs of genetic diversity that plant breeders draw on to protect and improve crops.

There are ethical reasons to preserve biodiversity too. All living species are the result of an ongoing evolutionary process that stretches back billions of years. Each species has a unique combination of traits, and extinction removes that collection of traits from the world forever.

SETTING PRIORITIES

Protecting biological diversity is often a tricky proposition. Even in developed countries, people often oppose environmental protections because they fear such measures will have adverse economic consequences. However, taking care of the environment can make good economic sense. With a bit of planning, people can both preserve and profit from their biological wealth.

The resources available for conserving areas are limited, so conservation biologists must often make difficult choices about which areas should be targeted for protection first. These biologists identify **hot spots**, places that are home to species found nowhere else and are under great threat of destruction. Once identified, hot spots can take priority in worldwide conservation efforts.

On a broader scale, conservation biologists define ecoregions, which are land or aquatic regions characterized by climate, geography, and the species found within them. The most widely used ecoregion system was developed by scientists of the World Wildlife Fund and defines 867 distinctive land ecoregions that they hope to maintain. **FIGURE 44.10** shows the locations and conservation status of ecoregions. Those that are critical or endangered are considered the top priority for conservation efforts.

The Klamath–Siskiyou forest in southwestern Oregon and northwestern California is one of North America's endangered ecoregions (**FIGURE 44.11**). It is home to many rare conifers. Two endangered birds, the northern

FIGURE 44.10 The location and conservation status of the land ecoregions deemed most important by the World Wildlife Fund.

Critical or endangered ecoregion
Vulnerable ecoregion
Stable or intact ecoregion
No information available

CREDIT: (10) From Starr/Taggart/Evers/Starr, Biology, 13E. © 2013 Cengage Learning; based on © World Wildlife Fund.

spotted owl and the marbled murrelet, nest in old-growth parts of the forest, and endangered coho salmon breed in streams that run through the forest. Logging threatens all of these species.

By focusing on hot spots and critical ecoregions rather than on individual endangered species, scientists hope to maintain ecosystem processes that naturally sustain biological diversity.

PRESERVATION AND RESTORATION

Worldwide, many ecologically important regions have been protected in ways that benefit local people. The Monteverde Cloud Forest in Costa Rica is one example. During the 1970s, George Powell was studying birds in this forest, which was rapidly being cleared. Powell decided to buy part of the forest as a nature sanctuary. His efforts inspired individuals and conservation groups to donate funds, and much of the forest is now protected as a private nature reserve. The reserve's plants and animals include more than 100 mammal species, 400 bird species, and 120 species of amphibians and reptiles. It is one of the few habitats left for jaguars and ocelots. A tourism industry centered on the reserve provides economic benefits to local people.

Sometimes an ecosystem is so damaged, or there is so little of it left, that conservation alone is not enough to sustain biodiversity. **Ecological restoration** is work designed to bring about the renewal of a natural ecosystem that has been degraded or destroyed.

For example, ecological restoration is occurring in Louisiana's coastal wetlands. More than 40 percent of the coastal wetlands in the United States are in Louisiana. These marshes are an ecological and economic treasure, but they are in trouble. Dams and levees built upstream of the marshes keep back sediments that would normally replenish sediments lost to the sea. Channels cut through the marshes for oil exploration and extraction have encouraged erosion, and the rising sea level threatens to flood the existing plants. Since the 1940s, Louisiana has lost an area of marshland the size of Rhode Island. Restoration efforts now under way aim to reverse some of those losses (**FIGURE 44.12**).

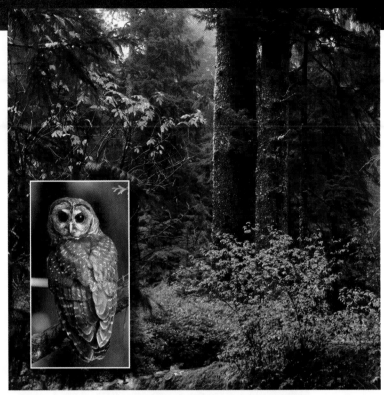

FIGURE 44.11 Klamath–Siskiyou forest, one of North America's critical ecoregions. Endangered northern spotted owls (inset) are endemic to this coniferous forest.

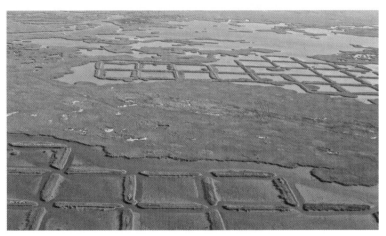

FIGURE 44.12 Ecological restoration in Louisiana's Sabine National Wildlife Refuge. Where marshland has become open water, sediments are barged in and marsh grasses are planted on them. The squares are new sediment with marsh grass.

---

biodiversity Of a region, the genetic variation within species, variety of species, and variety of ecosystems.
conservation biology Field of applied biology that surveys biodiversity and seeks ways to maintain and use it nondestructively.
ecological restoration Actively altering an area in an effort to restore an ecosystem that has been damaged or destroyed.
hot spot Threatened region that is habitat for species not found elsewhere and is considered a high priority for conservation efforts.

CREDITS: (11) main, David Patte, USFWS; inset, USFWS; (12) Diane Borden-Bilot, U.S. Fish and Wildlife Service.

A Bingham copper mine near Salt Lake City, Utah. This open pit mine is 4 kilometers (2.5 miles) wide and 1,200 meters (0.75 miles) deep, the largest man-made excavation on Earth.

FIGURE 44.13 Environmental costs of resource extraction.

B Pelican covered with oil that accidentally escaped from a deep sea-drilling platform in the Gulf of Mexico.

Ultimately, the health of life on Earth depends on our ability to recognize that the principles of energy flow and of resource limitation, which govern the survival of all systems of life, do not change. We must take note of these principles and find a way to live within our limits. The goal is living sustainably, which means meeting the needs of the present generation without reducing the ability of future generations to meet their own needs.

Promoting sustainability begins with recognizing the environmental consequences of one's own lifestyle. People in industrial nations use enormous quantities of resources, and the extraction, delivery, and use of these resources has negative effects on biodiversity. In the United States, the size of the average family has declined since the 1950s, while the size of the average home has doubled. All of the materials used to build and furnish those larger homes come from the environment. For example, an average new home contains about 500 pounds of copper in its wiring and plumbing.

Where does copper come from? Like most other nonrenewable mineral elements used in manufacturing, most copper is mined from the ground (**FIGURE 44.13A**). Surface mining strips an area of vegetation and soil, creating

an ecological dead zone. Mining puts dust into the air, creates mountains of rocky waste, and can contaminate nearby waterways.

Minerals are mined worldwide and globalization makes it difficult to know the source of the raw materials in products you buy. Keep in mind that resource extraction in developing countries is often carried out under regulations that are less strict or less stringently enforced than those in the United States. As a result, the environmental impact of mining is even greater in these countries.

Nonrenewable mineral resources are used in electronic devices such as phones, computers, televisions, and MP3 players. Constantly trading up to the newest device may be good for the ego and the economy, but it is bad for the environment. Reducing consumption by fixing existing products is a sustainable resource use, as is recycling. Obtaining nonrenewable materials by recycling reduces the

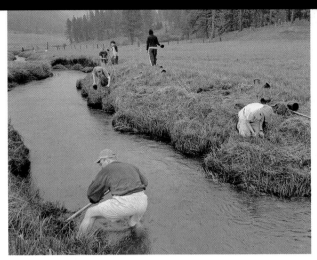

FIGURE 44.14 Volunteers restoring the Little Salmon River in Idaho so that salmon can migrate upstream to their breeding grounds.

FIGURE 44.15 Polar bears investigate an American submarine that surfaced in ice-covered Arctic waters.

need for extraction of those resources, and it also helps keep materials out of landfills.

Reducing your energy use is another way to promote sustainability. Fossil fuels such as petroleum, natural gas, and coal supply most of the energy used by developed countries. You already know that burning these nonrenewable fuels contributes to global warming and acid rain. In addition, extracting and transporting these fuels can have negative impacts, as when oil spills harm aquatic species (FIGURE 44.13B).

Renewable energy sources have their own drawbacks. For example, dams in rivers of the Pacific Northwest generate renewable hydroelectric power, but they also prevent endangered salmon from returning to streams above the dam to breed. Similarly, wind turbines can harm birds and bats. Manufacture of panels used to collect solar energy requires using nonrenewable mineral resources, and production of the panels generates pollutants.

In short, all commercially produced energy has negative environmental impacts, so the best way to minimize your impact is to use less energy.

If you want to make more of a difference, learn about the threats to ecosystems in your own area. Support efforts to preserve and restore local biodiversity. Many ecological restoration projects are supervised by trained biologists but carried out primarily through the efforts of volunteers (FIGURE 44.14).

TAKE-HOME MESSAGE 44.8

Extraction of material and energy for usage has effects that threaten biodiversity. Reducing energy consumption and recycling and reusing materials help minimize our impact.

WE BEGAN THIS BOOK WITH A STORY OF BIOLOGISTS WHO VENTURED INTO A REMOTE NEW GUINEA FOREST, AND THEIR EXCITEMENT AT THE MANY PREVIOUSLY UNKNOWN SPECIES THAT THEY DISCOVERED (SECTION 1.9). At the far end of the globe, a U.S. submarine surfaced in Arctic waters and found polar bears on the ice-covered sea. The polar bears were about 445 kilometers (270 miles) from the North Pole and 805 kilometers (500 miles) from the nearest land (FIGURE 44.15).

Even such seemingly remote regions are no longer beyond the reach of human explorers—and human influence. In the Arctic, unusually warm temperatures are affecting the seasonal cycle of sea ice melting and formation. In recent years, sea ice has begun to thin and to break up earlier in the spring and to form later in the fall. A decrease in the persistence of sea ice is bad news for polar bears. They can only reach their main prey—seals—by traveling across ice. A longer ice-free period means less time for bears to feed.

We have only recently come to realize the effects that our actions can have on other species. A century ago, Earth's biological resources seemed inexhaustible. Now we know that many practices we began while largely ignorant of how natural systems operate take a heavy toll on the biosphere. It would be presumptuous to think that we alone have had a profound impact on the world of life. As long ago as the Proterozoic, photosynthetic cells were irrevocably changing the course of evolution by enriching the atmosphere with oxygen. Over life's existence, the evolutionary success of some groups ensured the decline of others. What is new is the increasing pace of change and the capacity of our own species to recognize and perhaps to moderate its role in this increase.

CREDITS: (14) Mountain Visions/NOAA; (15) U.S. Navy photo by Chief Yeoman Alphanso Braggs.

CHAPTER 44 HUMAN EFFECTS ON THE BIOSPHERE 795

SECTION 44.1 Extinction is a natural process, but we are in the midst of a human-caused mass extinction, with numbers of **threatened species** and **endangered species** rising. **Endemic species** are especially likely to be at risk. Overharvesting, species introductions, and habitat destruction, degradation, and fragmentation can push species toward extinction. We know about only a tiny fraction of the species that are currently under threat.

SECTION 44.2 Overplowing or overgrazing of grassland can cause **desertification**. Both desertification and deforestation affect soil properties and can alter rainfall patterns. Changes caused by deforestation are especially difficult to reverse.

SECTION 44.3 Human populations discard large amounts of trash. Chemicals that seep out of buried trash can contaminate groundwater. Trash, especially plastic, that washes into or is dumped into oceans poses a threat to marine life.

SECTION 44.4 Burning coal releases sulfur dioxide, and burning oil or gas releases nitrogen oxides. These **pollutants** react with gases and water vapor in air, then fall to earth as **acid rain**. The resulting increase in the acidity of soils and waters can sicken or kill organisms.

SECTION 44.5 The **ozone layer** in the upper atmosphere protects against incoming UV radiation. Chemicals known as CFCs were banned when they were found to cause thinning of the ozone layer. Near the ground, where the ozone concentration is naturally low, ozone emitted as a result of fossil fuel use is considered a pollutant. It irritates animal respiratory tracts and interferes with photosynthesis by plants.

SECTION 44.6 Global climate change resulting from an increase in greenhouse gases is causing glaciers to melt, thus raising the sea level. It also is affecting the range of species, allowing some to move into higher elevations or latitudes. Other species such as corals are showing signs of temperature-related stress. In addition, global climate change is expected to alter rainfall patterns and the intensity of hurricanes.

SECTION 44.7 Genetic diversity, species diversity, and ecosystem diversity are components of **biodiversity**, which is declining in all regions. **Conservation biology** involves surveying biodiversity and developing strategies to protect it and allow its sustainable use. Because resources are limited, biologists often focus on **hot spots**, where many unique species are under threat. They also attempt to ensure that portions of all ecoregions are protected. When an ecosystem has been totally or partially degraded, **ecological restoration** can help restore biodiversity.

SECTION 44.8 Extraction of nonrenewable mineral resources and fuels have detrimental effects on an ecosystem. Individuals can help sustain biodiversity by limiting their energy use and by reducing resource consumption through reuse and recycling.

SECTION 44.9 Human activities affect other species, even in remote places such as the Arctic. For example, polar bears in the Arctic are threatened by thinning sea ice, which is one effect of global climate change. Although humans are not the first species to change conditions on Earth in a way that harms other species, we are the first to do so with an understanding of our effects and while having the option of altering our behavior.

Self-Quiz   Answers in Appendix VII

1. A(n) _____ species has population levels so low it is at great risk of extinction in the near future.
   a. endemic   c. threatened
   b. endangered   d. indicator

2. Species are threatened by habitat _____ .
   a. fragmentation   c. destruction
   b. degradation   d. all of the above

3. Deforestation _____ .
   a. increases mineral runoff from soil
   b. decreases local temperature
   c. increases local rainfall
   d. all of the above

4. Sulfur dioxide released by coal-burning power plants contributes to _____ .
   a. ozone destruction   c. acid rain
   b. sea level rise   d. desertification

5. The "hole" in the ozone layer is most pronounced in _____ over _____ .
   a. fall; the Arctic   c. spring; Antarctica
   b. fall; the equator   d. spring; the equator

6. An increase in the size of the ozone hole would be expected to _____ .
   a. increase skin cancers   c. both a and b
   b. reduce respiratory disorders

7. A large amount of plastic has accumulated in a region of the north central Pacific as a result of _____ .
   a. global warming   c. ozone depletion
   b. ocean currents   d. acid rain

8. Global climate change is causing _____ .
   a. a decrease in sea level   c. acid rain
   b. glacial melting   d. all of the above

9. The Montreal Protocol banned use of _____ , which contribute(s) to ozone depletion.
   a. DDT   c. fossil fuels
   b. CFCs   d. sulfur dioxides

Data Analysis Activities

Arctic PCB Pollution Winds carry chemical contaminants produced and released at temperate latitudes to the Arctic, where the chemicals enter food webs. As a result of biological magnification, top carnivores in arctic food webs, including people and polar bears, end up with high concentrations of these chemicals. Arctic people who eat a lot of local wildlife tend to have unusually high levels of industrial chemicals called polychlorinated biphenyls, or PCBs, in their body. The Arctic Monitoring and Assessment Programme studies the effects of these industrial chemicals on the health and reproduction of Arctic people. FIGURE 44.16 shows how sex ratio at birth varies with average maternal PCB levels among people native to the Russian Arctic.

1. Which sex was more common in offspring of women with less than 1 microgram per milliliter of PCB in serum?
2. At what PCB concentrations were women more likely to have daughters?
3. In some villages in Greenland, nearly all recent newborns are female. Would you expect PCB levels in those villages to be above or under 4 micrograms per milliliter?

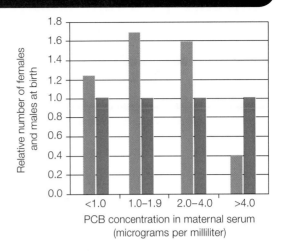

FIGURE 44.16 Effect of maternal PCB concentration on sex ratio of newborns in human populations native to the Russian Arctic. Blue bars indicate the relative number of males born per one female (pink bars).

10. A highly threatened region that is home to many unique species is a(n) _____ .
    a. ecoregion   b. biome   c. hot spot   d. community

11. Biodiversity refers to _____ .
    a. genetic diversity   c. ecosystem diversity
    b. species diversity   d. all of the above

12. Restoring a marsh that has been damaged by human activities is an example of _____ .
    a. biological magnification   c. ecological restoration
    b. bioaccumulation   d. globalization

13. Individuals help sustain biodiversity by _____ .
    a. reducing resource consumption
    b. reusing materials
    c. recycling materials
    d. all of the above

14. Match the terms with the most suitable description.
    ____ hot spot
    ____ ozone
    ____ biodiversity
    ____ acid rain
    ____ endemic species
    ____ nonpoint source of pollution
    ____ global climate change
    ____ deforestation
    ____ desertification

    a. good up high; bad nearby
    b. tree loss alters rainfall pattern and is difficult to reverse
    c. can increase dust storms
    d. evolved in one region and remains there
    e. coal-burning is major cause
    f. involves release of pollutant in many areas
    g. has unique threatened species
    h. cause of rising sea level
    i. genetic, species, and ecosystem diversity

Critical Thinking

1. In one seaside community in New Jersey, the U.S. Fish and Wildlife Service suggested trapping and removing feral cats (domestic cats that live in the wild). The goal was to protect some endangered wild birds (plovers) that nested on the town's beaches. Many residents were angered by the proposal, arguing that the cats have as much right to be there as the birds. Do you agree? Why or why not?

2. Burning fossil fuel puts excess carbon dioxide into the atmosphere, but deforestation and desertification also affect the atmospheric carbon dioxide concentration. Explain why a global decrease in the amount of vegetation is contributing to the rise in carbon dioxide.

3. The magnitude of acid rain's effects can be influenced by the properties of the rock that the rain runs over. Acid rain is least likely to significantly acidify lakes in regions where the bedrock consists of calcium carbonate–rich limestone or marble. How does the presence of these rocks mitigate the effects of acid rain?

4. Some of the bits of plastic that end up in the ocean contain phthalates, which are known endocrine disrupters (Section 31.10). How might consumption of such plastic affect the survival and reproduction of vertebrates that accidentally eat the plastic?

CENGAGE **brain**.com To access course materials, please visit www.cengagebrain.com.

Appendix I. Periodic Table of the Elements

The symbol for each element is an abbreviation of its name. Some symbols for elements are abbreviations for their Latin names. For instance, Pb (lead) is short for *plumbum*; the word "plumbing" is related—ancient Romans made their water pipes with lead.

Elements in each vertical column of the table behave in similar ways. For instance, all of the elements in the far right column of the table are inert gases; they do not interact with other atoms. In nature, such elements occur only as solitary atoms.

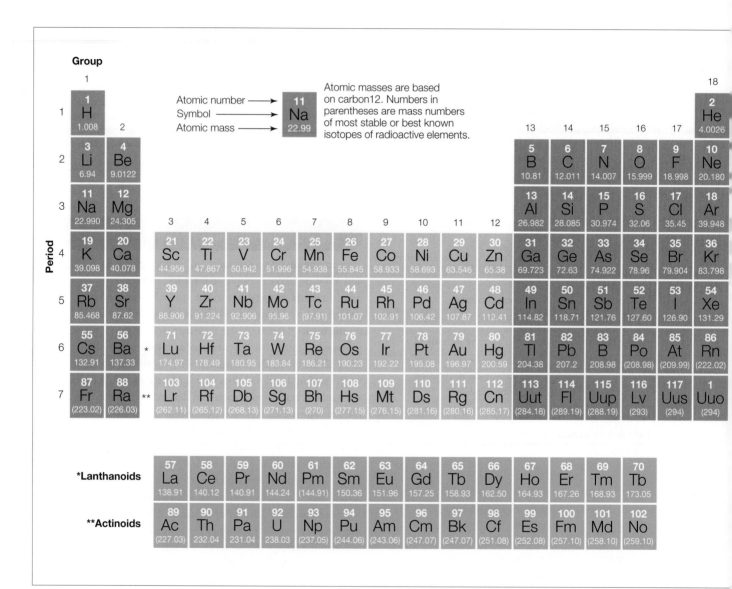

Appendix II. The Amino Acids

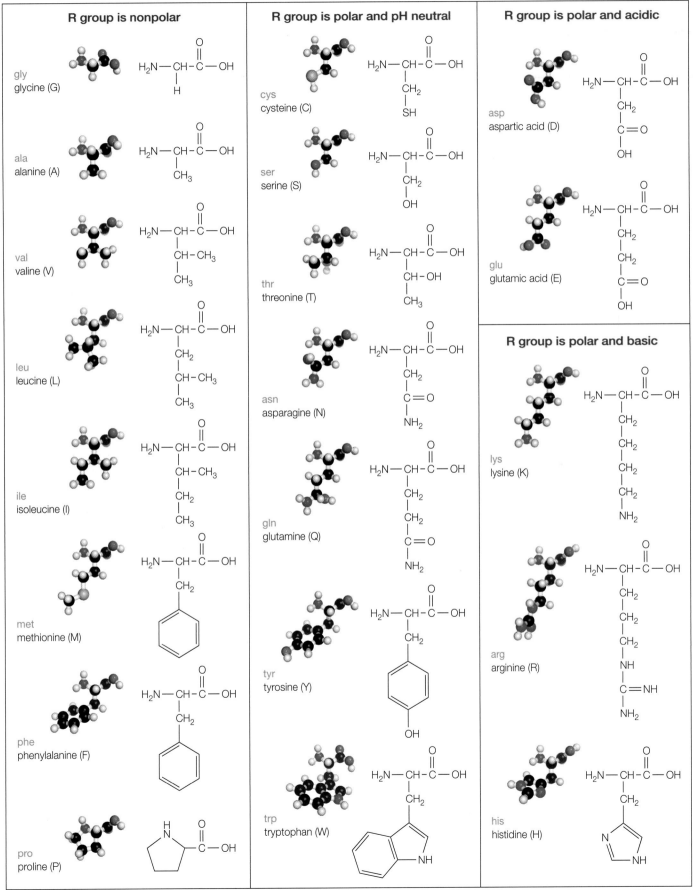

R group is nonpolar

gly
glycine (G)

$H_2N-CH-C-OH$ with $=O$ and H below

ala
alanine (A)

$H_2N-CH-C-OH$ with $=O$ and CH_3

val
valine (V)

$H_2N-CH-C-OH$ with $=O$, $CH-CH_3$, CH_3

leu
leucine (L)

$H_2N-CH-C-OH$ with $=O$, CH_2, $CH-CH_3$, CH_3

ile
isoleucine (I)

$H_2N-CH-C-OH$ with $=O$, $CH-CH_3$, CH_2, CH_3

met
methionine (M)

$H_2N-CH-C-OH$ with $=O$, CH_2, benzene ring

phe
phenylalanine (F)

$H_2N-CH-C-OH$ with $=O$, CH_2, benzene ring

pro
proline (P)

R group is polar and pH neutral

cys
cysteine (C)

$H_2N-CH-C-OH$ with $=O$, CH_2, SH

ser
serine (S)

$H_2N-CH-C-OH$ with $=O$, CH_2, OH

thr
threonine (T)

$H_2N-CH-C-OH$ with $=O$, $CH-OH$, CH_3

asn
asparagine (N)

$H_2N-CH-C-OH$ with $=O$, CH_2, $C=O$, NH_2

gln
glutamine (Q)

$H_2N-CH-C-OH$ with $=O$, CH_2, CH_2, $C=O$, NH_2

tyr
tyrosine (Y)

$H_2N-CH-C-OH$ with $=O$, CH_2, benzene ring, OH

trp
tryptophan (W)

$H_2N-CH-C-OH$ with $=O$, CH_2, indole ring, NH

R group is polar and acidic

asp
aspartic acid (D)

$H_2N-CH-C-OH$ with $=O$, CH_2, $C=O$, OH

glu
glutamic acid (E)

$H_2N-CH-C-OH$ with $=O$, CH_2, CH_2, $C=O$, OH

R group is polar and basic

lys
lysine (K)

$H_2N-CH-C-OH$ with $=O$, CH_2, CH_2, CH_2, CH_2, NH_2

arg
arginine (R)

$H_2N-CH-C-OH$ with $=O$, CH_2, CH_2, CH_2, NH, $C=NH$, NH_2

his
histidine (H)

$H_2N-CH-C-OH$ with $=O$, CH_2, imidazole ring, N, NH

Glycolysis

FIGURE A Glycolysis breaks down one glucose molecule into two 3-carbon pyruvate molecules for a net yield of two ATP. Enzyme names are indicated in green; parts of substrate molecules undergoing chemical change are highlighted blue.

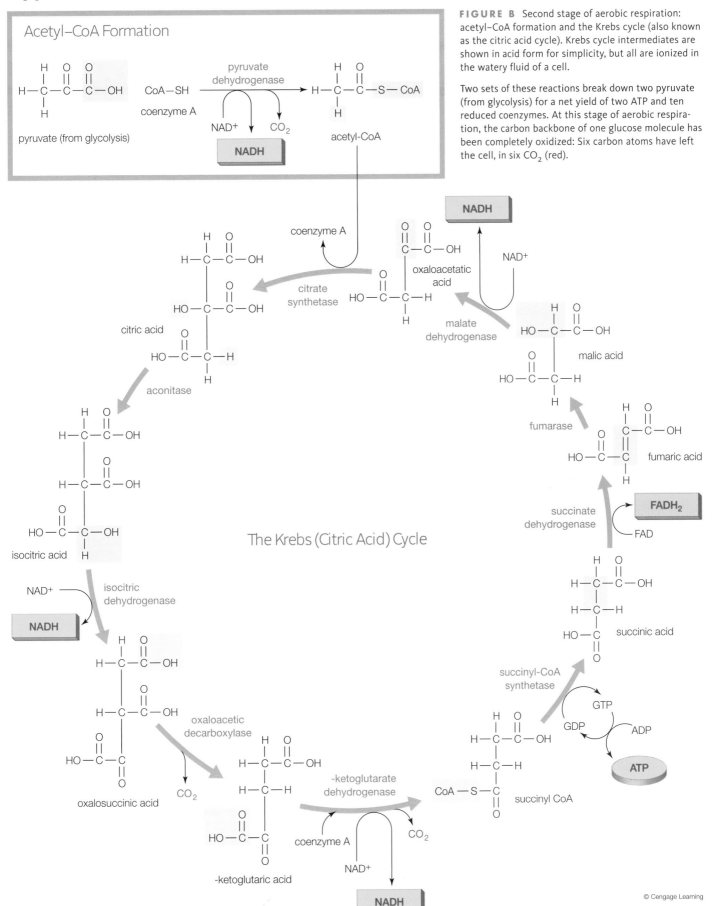

FIGURE B Second stage of aerobic respiration: acetyl–CoA formation and the Krebs cycle (also known as the citric acid cycle). Krebs cycle intermediates are shown in acid form for simplicity, but all are ionized in the watery fluid of a cell.

Two sets of these reactions break down two pyruvate (from glycolysis) for a net yield of two ATP and ten reduced coenzymes. At this stage of aerobic respiration, the carbon backbone of one glucose molecule has been completely oxidized: Six carbon atoms have left the cell, in six CO_2 (red).

Acetyl–CoA Formation

pyruvate (from glycolysis)

CoA—SH
coenzyme A

pyruvate dehydrogenase

NAD^+ CO_2 NADH

acetyl-CoA

The Krebs (Citric Acid) Cycle

coenzyme A

citrate synthetase

citric acid

aconitase

isocitric acid

NAD^+ isocitric dehydrogenase   NADH

oxalosuccinic acid

oxaloacetic decarboxylase CO_2

-ketoglutaric acid

-ketoglutarate dehydrogenase   coenzyme A CO_2 NAD^+ NADH

succinyl CoA

succinyl-CoA synthetase   GDP   GTP   ADP   ATP

succinic acid

succinate dehydrogenase   FAD   FADH₂

fumaric acid

fumarase

malic acid

malate dehydrogenase NAD^+ NADH

oxaloacetatic acid

FIGURE C Details of the Calvin–Benson cycle. These light-independent reactions of photosynthesis use ATP and NADPH to fix carbon from carbon dioxide. The enzyme rubisco catalyzes the attachment of CO_2 to RuBP. The resulting PGA molecules are converted to PGAL, and the complex series of reactions that follow shuffle carbon atoms among sugar molecules to regenerate RuBP. One molecule of glucose is produced for six CO_2 molecules that enter the reactions. Water and some of the molecular participants are not shown, for clarity.

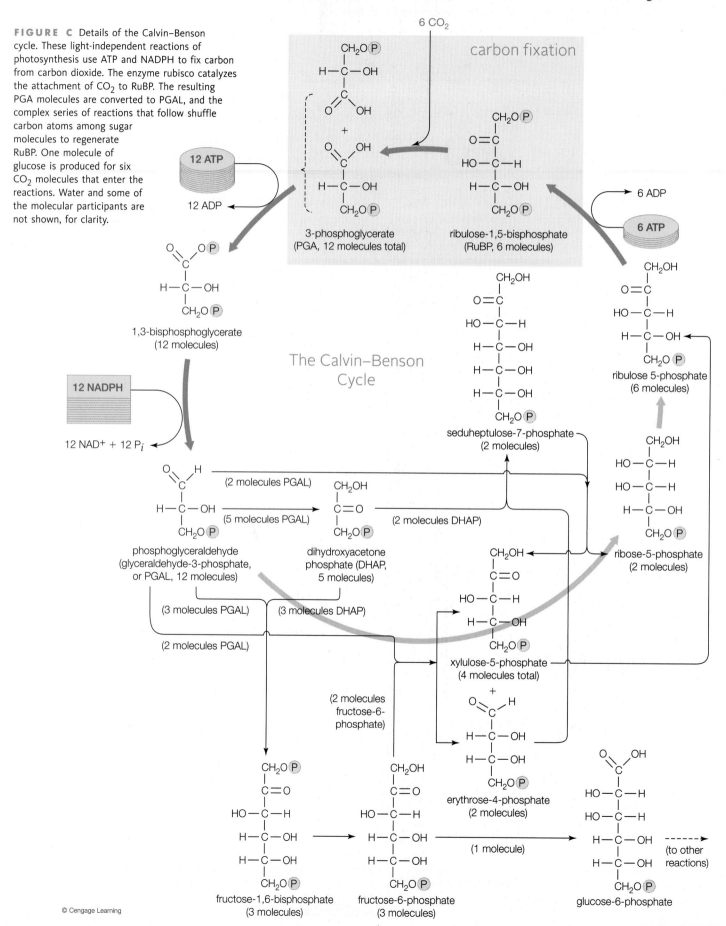

Appendix IV. A Plain English Map of the Human Chromosomes

Haploid set of human chromosomes. The banding patterns characteristic of each type of chromosome appear after staining with a reagent called Giemsa. The locations of some of the 20,065 known genes (as of November, 2005) are indicated. Also shown are locations that, when mutated, cause some of the genetic diseases discussed in the text.

Chromosome 1
- sweet taste receptors
- Rh blood type
- marijuana receptor
- (anorexia nervosa susceptibility)
- leptin receptor
- TSH β chain
- lamin A (progeria)
- Duffy blood group antigen

Chromosome 2
- LH/choriogonadotropin receptor (micropenis)
- CD8; cytotoxic T cell antigen
- antibody light chain
- lactase
- (cleft palate)
- glucagon

Chromosome 3
- oxytocin receptor
- HIV receptor
- rhodopsin
- (alkaptonuria)
- (sucrose intolerance)
- somatostatin

Chromosome 4
- (achondroplasia)
- (Huntington disease)
- (Ellis-van Creveld syndrome)
- alcohol dehydrogenase (susceptibility to alcoholism)
- red hair color

Chromosome 5
- Cri-du-chat syndrome
- bitter taste receptor
- growth hormone receptor (pituitary dwarfism)
- interleukin-4

Chromosome 6
- (gluten intolerance)
- HLA/MHC
- tumor necrosis factor
- α chains of HCG, FSH, LH, and TSH
- estrogen receptor

Chromosome 7
- cytochrome c
- elastin
- DLX 5/6 homeotic genes
- CFTR (cystic fibrosis)
- leptin (obesity)
- (blue-deficient colorblind)
- TCR β subunit

Chromosome 8
- gonadotropin releasing hormone
- helicase (Werner's syndrome)
- corticotropin releasing hormone

Chromosome 9
- (galactosemia)
- (cerebral palsy)
- (Friedreich ataxia)
- (fructose intolerance)
- ABO blood group

Chromosome 10
- vitamin B-12 receptor
- mannose binding protein
- perforin
- (gluten intolerance)

Chromosome 11
- hemoglobin β chain (sickle cell anemia)
- insulin
- parathyroid hormone
- catalase
- PAX6 (aniridia)
- FSH, β chain
- tyrosinase (albinism)

Chromosome 12
- CD4
- helper T cell antigen
- oncogene KRAS2 (lung cancer, bladder cancer, breast cancer)
- keratins
- lysozyme
- (phenylketonuria)
- aldehyde dehydrogenase (alcohol intolerance)

Chromosome 13
- ribosomal RNA
- BRCA 2 (breast cancer)
- (gastroesophageal reflux)

Chromosome 14
- ribosomal RNA
- presinilin (Alzheimer's)
- TSH receptor
- immunoglobulin heavy chains

Chromosome 15
- ribosomal RNA
- fibrillin 1 (Marfan syndrome)
- (Tay-Sachs disease)

Chromosome 16
- hemoglobin α chain
- DNAse I (lupus)

Chromosome 17
- (Canavan disease)
- p53 tumor antigen
- NF1 (neurofibromatosis)
- serotonin transporter
- BRCA 1 (breast, ovarian cancer)
- Growth hormone

Chromosome 18
- B cell apoptosis regulator (B cell lymphoma)
- myelin basic protein

Chromosome 19
- LDL receptor (coronary artery disease)
- insulin receptor
- brown hair color
- green/blue eye color
- (Warfarin resistance)
- HCG, β chain
- LH, β chain

Chromosome 20
- prion protein (Creutzfeld-Jacob disease)
- oxytocin
- GHRH (acromegaly)

Chromosome 21
- ribosomal RNA
- interferon receptors
- (bipolar disorder, early onset)

Chromosome 22
- ribosomal RNA
- immunoglobulin light chains
- myoglobin

Chromosome X
- dystrophin (muscular dystrophy)
- (anhidrotic ectodermal dysplasia)
- IL2RG (SCID-X1)
- XIST X chromosome inactivation control
- (hemophilia B)
- (hemophilia A)
- (red-deficient colorblind)
- (green-deficient colorblind)

Chromosome Y
- sex determining region Y (SRY)
- (no sperm)
- male stature

Actively-spreading ridges and transform faults

Total spreading rate, cm/year

Major active fault or fault zone; dashed where nature, location, or activity uncertain

Normal fault or rift; hachures on downthrown side

Reverse fault (overthrust, subduction zones); generalized; barbs on upthrown side

Volcanic centers active within the last one million years; generalized. Minor basaltic centers and seamounts omitted.

This NASA map summarizes the tectonic and volcanic activity of Earth during the past 1 million years. The reconstructions at far right indicate positions of Earth's major land masses through time.

Eurasian Plate

Baikal

Rift

Tan-Lu F.

Altyn Tagh F.

Arabian
Plate

Indian
Plate

3.0

2.7

Somalia
Plate

1.4

1.5   S.W. Indian
Ocean Ridge

1.4

Pacific
Plate

Marina Trench

Philippines
Plate

Caroline
Plate

Ontong-Java
Plateau

Java Trench

Australian
Plate

Darling F.

S.E. Indian Ocean Ridge

7.2

7.5

Alpine F.

Antarctic   Plate

P.D.L

90°   180°   45°   0°   45°   90°

Appendix VI. Units of Measure

LENGTH

1 kilometer (km) = 0.62 miles (mi)
1 meter (m) = 39.37 inches (in)
1 centimeter (cm) = 0.39 inches

To convert	multiply by	to obtain
inches	2.25	centimeters
feet	30.48	centimeters
centimeters	0.39	inches
millimeters	0.039	inches

AREA

1 square kilometer = 0.386 square miles
1 square meter = 1.196 square yards
1 square centimeter = 0.155 square inches

VOLUME

1 cubic meter = 35.31 cubic feet
1 liter = 1.06 quarts
1 milliliter = 0.034 fluid ounces = 1/5 teaspoon

To convert	multiply by	to obtain
quarts	0.95	liters
fluid ounces	28.41	milliliters
liters	1.06	quarts
milliliters	0.03	fluid ounces

WEIGHT

1 metric ton (mt) = 2,205 pounds (lb) = 1.1 tons (t)
1 kilogram (kg) = 2.205 pounds (lb)
1 gram (g) = 0.035 ounces (oz)

To convert	multiply by	to obtain
pounds	0.454	kilograms
pounds	454	grams
ounces	28.35	grams
kilograms	2.205	pounds
grams	0.035	ounces

TEMPERATURE

Celcius (°C) to Fahrenheit (°F): $°F = 1.8 \, (°C) + 32$

Fahrenheit (°F) to Celsius: $°C = \dfrac{(°F - 32)}{1.8}$

	°C	°F
Water boils	100	212
Human body temperature	37	98.6
Water freezes	0	32

Appendix VII. Answers to Self-Quizzes and Genetics Problems

CHAPTER 1

1.	a	1.1
2.	c	1.1
3.	energy, nutrients	1.2
4.	homeostasis	1.2
5.	d	1.2
6.	reproduction	1.2
7.	d	1.2
8.	a, d, e	1.1–1.4
9.	Animals	1.3
10.	a, b	1.1, 1.3
11.	domains	1.4
12.	b	1.5
13.	b	1.7
14.	b	1.7
15.	c	1.1
	e	1.7
	b	1.4
	d	1.5
	a	1.5
	f	1.2

CHAPTER 2

1.	a	2.1
2.	b	2.1
3.	d	2.2
4.	d	2.1
5.	b	2.2
6.	a	2.3
7.	a	2.3
8.	c	2.3
9.	c	2.4
10.	c	2.4
11.	d	2.2, 2.5
12.	a	2.5
13.	c	2.5
14.	b	2.4
15.	c	2.4
	b	2.1
	d	2.4
	a	2.1, 2.2
	f	2.4
	e	2.1, 2.2

CHAPTER 3

1.	c	3.1
2.	four	3.1
3.	b	3.1, 3.3, 3.4
4.	e	3.2, 3.6
5.	c	3.3
6.	False	3.3, 3.7
7.	b	3.3
8.	starch, cellulose, glycogen	3.2
9.	e	3.3
10.	d	3.4, 3.6
11.	d	3.5
12.	d	3.6
13.	a amino acid	3.4
	b carbohydrate	3.2
	c polypeptide	3.4
	d fatty acid	3.3
14.	c	3.3
	a	3.2
	b	3.3
15.	g	3.4
	a	3.3
	b	3.4
	c	3.3
	d	3.6
	j	3.3
	f	3.6
	i	3.4

	h	3.2
	e	3.2

CHAPTER 4

1.	c	4.1
2.	c	4.1
3.	c	4.1, 4.4
4.	b	4.1
5.	b	4.3
6.	c	4.3
7.	a	4.3
8.	b	4.5
9.	a	4.6
10.	c	4.7
11.	a	4.6
12.	c, b, d, a	4.6
13.	d	4.10
14.	a	4.10
15.	c	4.7
	g	4.8
	e	4.4, 4.6
	d	4.5
	a	4.10
	b	4.4, 4.9
	f	4.1, 4.5

CHAPTER 5

1.	c	5.1
2.	b	5.1
3.	d	5.1
4.	a	5.2
5.	c	5.2
6.	c	5.2
7.	temperature, pH, salt, pressure	5.3
8.	d	5.4
9.	a	5.5
10.	more/less	5.6
11.	c	5.6, 5.7
12.	b	5.7
13.	a	5.6
14.	d	5.8
15.	c	5.2
	e	5.8
	f	5.1
	b	5.2
	a	5.5
	g	5.6
	h	5.7
	d	5.7

CHAPTER 6

1.	autotroph: weed; heterotrophs: cat, bird, caterpillar	6.1
2.	c	6.1
3.	a	6.3
4.	d	6.4
5.	b	6.3, 6.4
6.	b	6.4
7.	c	6.4
8.	c	6.3, 6.5
9.	b	6.5
10.	b	6.5
11.	a	6.1
12.	b	6.5, 6.6
13.	f	6.5
	h	6.5
	g	6.4
	d	6.4
	e	6.5
	b	6.1, 6.3

	a	6.1
	c	6.1

CHAPTER 7

1.	False	7.1
2.	d	7.1, 7.3
3.	a	7.1, 7.6
4.	c	7.3
5.	b	7.1, 7.4, 7.5
6.	d	7.1, 7.6
7.	e	7.4
8.	b	7.4
9.	c	7.5
10.	c	7.5
11.	c	7.6
12.	d	7.7
13.	f	7.6
14.	c	7.5
15.	b	7.4
	d	7.3
	a	7.3, 7.6
	c	7.4, 7.7
	e	7.3
	f	7.2

CHAPTER 8

1.	c	8.2
2.	c	8.2
3.	b	8.2
4.	b	8.2
5.	a	8.3
6.	b	8.3
7.	b	8.3
8.	a	8.4
9.	d	8.4
10.	c	8.2, 8.4
11.	b	8.4
12.	d	8.3, 8.4
13.	d	8.5
14.	d	8.6
15.	d	8.1
	b	8.6
	a	8.2
	g	8.3
	e	8.4
	h	8.4
	c	8.3
	f	8.5

CHAPTER 9

1.	c	9.1
2.	b	9.2
3.	a	9.1
4.	c	9.1
5.	a	9.1
6.	b	9.1, 9.3
7.	b	9.2
8.	c	9.3
9.	a	9.3
10.	a	9.3
11.	a	9.2
12.	a	9.2, 9.4
13.	b	9.2, 9.4
14.	c	9.4
15.	c	9.3
	b	9.2
	e	9.4
	a	9.2
	f	9.3
	d	9.2

CHAPTER 10

1.	d	10.1
2.	d	10.1, 10.2
3.	b	10.1
4.	b	10.1
5.	h	10.1
6.	b	10.1
7.	c	10.2
8.	c	10.2
9.	d	10.2
10.	b	10.2
11.	b	10.3
12.	b	10.3
13.	c	10.3
14.	b	10.4
15.	f	10.2
	a	10.3
	b	10.1, 10.4
	e	10.3
	c	10.1
	d	10.5

CHAPTER 11

1.	e	11.1
2.	b	11.1
3.	d	11.1
4.	e	11.1
5.	c	11.2
6.	c	11.1
7.	a	11.1
8.	c	11.1
9.	a	11.1
10.	d	11.3
11.	interphase, prophase, metaphase, anaphase, telophase	11.2
12.	d	11.5
13.	a	11.5
14.	c	11.3
	f	11.2
	a	11.5
	g	11.3
	b	11.3
	e	11.5
	d	11.2
	h	11.4
15.	d	11.2
	b	11.2
	c	11.2
	e	11.1
	a	11.2
	f	11.3

CHAPTER 12

1.	b	12.1
2.	b	12.2
3.	c	12.1, 12.4, 12.6
4.	d	12.2
5.	b	12.2
6.	a	12.2
7.	Sister chromatids are still attached	12.3
8.	c	12.3
9.	b	12.4
10.	a	12.4
11.	e	12.1, 12.4
12.	b	12.4, 12.5
13.	c	12.3
	d	12.3
	a	12.1
	f	12.2
	e	12.2

	b	12.1, 12.6
	g	12.4

CHAPTER 13

1.	b	13.1
2.	a	13.1
3.	b	13.2
4.	b	13.2
5.	c	13.2
6.	a	13.2, 13.3
7.	b	13.2
8.	d	13.3
9.	c	13.3
10.	c	13.4
11.	b	13.4
12.	Continuous variation	13.6
13.	b	13.3
	d	13.2
	a	13.1
	c	13.1

CHAPTER 14

1.	b	14.1
2.	b	14.1
3.	a	14.1
4.	b	14.2
5.	False	14.3
6.	d	14.2, 14.3
	(could be due to both parents carrying an autosomal recessive allele, or the mom carrying an x-linked recessive allele)	
7.	d	14.3
8.	X from mom, Y from dad	14.3
9.	d	14.2
10.	Y-linked inheritance (this is a critical thinking question)	14.3
11.	d	14.5
12.	b	14.5
13.	True	14.5
14.	c	14.5
15.	c	14.5
	e	14.4
	f	14.5
	b	14.4
	a	14.1
	d	14.4

CHAPTER 15

1.	c	15.1
2.	a	15.1
3.	b	15.1
4.	b	15.2
5.	c	15.2
6.	b	15.3
7.	b	15.3
8.	d	15.2, 15.4
9.	d	15.4
10.	True	15.6
11.	b	15.6
	d	15.6
	e	15.5
	f	15.1
12.	d	15.5
13.	b	15.6
14.	a	15.2
	d	15.1

c	15.1
e	15.3
b	15.1
15. c	15.4
f	15.5
d	15.6
b	15.4
a	15.5
e	15.5

CHAPTER 16

1. b	16.1
2. c	16.1, 16.7
3. d	16.2
4. b	16.2
5. b	16.3
6. d	16.4
7. Gondwana	16.6
8. a	16.1–16.3
c	16.6
d	16.5
e	16.3, 16.5
f	16.9
9. morphological divergence	16.7
10. d	16.7
11. b	16.8
12. 66	16.9
13. e	16.7, 16.8
14. b	16.2
d	16.1, 16.3
g	16.2
e	16.4
c	16.7
f	16.7
a	16.3

CHAPTER 17

1. a	17.1
2. c	17.1, 17.7
3. a, c, b	17.3–17.5
4. d	17.6
5. d	17.6
6. b	17.7
7. f	17.1, 17.2, 17.7
8. allopatric speciation	17.9
9. d	17.6, 17.8
10. d	17.12
11. c	17.12
(this is a critical thinking question)	
12. c	17.12
13. b	17.12
14. c	17.7
e	17.6
g	17.11
b	17.7
d	17.12
f	17.11
a	17.11
h	17.12

CHAPTER 18

1. c	18.1
2. a	18.1
3. c	18.2
4. a	18.2
5. a	18.2
6. c	18.4
7. b	18.5
8. b	18.4

9. c	18.2
10. a	18.4
11. d	18.5, 18.6
12. c	18.5
13. d	18.6
14. a	18.1
c	18.5
b	18.3
e	18.5
f	18.6
d	18.6

CHAPTER 19

1. c	19.1
2. b	19.3
3. c	19.1
4. b	19.1
5. d	19.2
6. c	19.3
7. one	19.4
8. c	19.5
9. d	19.5
10. d	19.5
11. c	19.6
12. d	19.2, 19.7
13. a	19.4
14. b	19.6
a	19.1
a	19.2
b	19.6
b	19.6
15. d	19.5
e	19.7
a	19.3
f	19.1
b	19.8
c	19.8

CHAPTER 20

1. c	20.2
2. d	20.3
3. b	20.2
4. c	20.4
5. b	20.5
6. a	20.7
7. d	20.7
8. c	20.4
9. c	20.6
10. d	20.6
11. c	20.7
12. a	20.8
13. a	20.2
14. a	20.7
15. d	20.9
g	20.5
a	20.3
b	20.6
f	20.6
c	20.7
e	20.6

CHAPTER 21

1. c	21.1, 21.2
2. a	21.1, 21.3
(ferns produce spores, not seeds)	
3. b	21.2
4. c	21.3
5. a	21.4
6. e	21.2, 21.3, 21.5
7. b	21.5, 21.6
8. True	21.3

9. c	21.6
10. a	21.2
11. a	21.1
12. c	21.7
13. b	21.5
14. c	21.2
d	21.3
a	21.5
b	21.6
15. c	21.4
i	21.1
a	21.1
b	21.1
e	21.1
f	21.6
d	21.3
g	21.3
h	21.4

CHAPTER 22

1. c	22.1
2. a	22.1
3. b	22.1
4. a	22.3
5. d	22.2
6. c	22.2
7. c	22.2
8. d	22.2
9. b	22.4
10. d	22.3
11. a	22.3
12. c	22.4
13. b	22.5
14. a	22.3
15. d	22.1
b	22.1
a	22.1
f	22.2
g	22.2
c	22.3
e	22.3

CHAPTER 23

1. False	23.1
2. d	23.1
3. a	23.4
4. a	23.5
5. b	23.11
6. a	23.7
7. b	23.2
8. a	23.1, 23.9
9. c	23.9, 23.11
10. b	23.12
11. b	23.6, 23.7
12. d	23.11
13. b	23.12
f	23.7
d	23.3
h	23.4
c	23.5
a	23.8
g	23.6
e	23.9

CHAPTER 24

1. c	24.1
2. c	24.1
3. a	24.2
4. b	24.2
5. d	24.3
6. c	24.4
7. f	24.4, 24.5

8. a	24.5
9. b	24.9
10. c	24.6
11. c	24.11
12. b	24.1
i	24.2
g	24.3
f	24.8
c	24.6
d	24.7
a	24.7
h	24.7
e	24.10

CHAPTER 25

1. b	25.2
2. c	25.2
3. a, b	25.2
4. b	25.3
5. False	25.5
6. c	25.2, 25.6
7. c	25.4
8. a	25.3, 25.5
9. b, c	25.3
10. d	25.5
11. b	25.5
12. a	25.6
13. b	25.6
14. b	25.7
15. c	25.6
d	25.2, 25.4
e	25.6
a	25.3
b	25.3
f	25.1, 25.4
g	25.2, 25.4

CHAPTER 26

1. f	26.1
2. b	26.1
3. e	26.2
4. b	26.2
5. b	26.3
6. c	26.4
7. d	26.4
8. d	26.4
9. c	26.6
10. c	26.5
11. c	26.5
12. a	26.5
13. b	26.6
14. a	26.6
15. c	26.5
g	26.1
e	26.6
b	26.2
d	26.4
h	26.4
f	26.6
a	26.4

CHAPTER 27

1. pollination	27.1
2. a, b, c	27.1, 27.13
3. b	27.1
4. b	27.1
5. c	27.3
6. c	27.3
7. d	27.4
8. d	27.3, 27.4
9. c	27.5
10. a	27.5

11. e	27.6–27.9
12. c	27.11
13. b	27.10
d	27.10
a	27.10
f	27.11
c	27.11
e	27.10
14. c	27.9
15. c	27.9
e	27.7
b	27.10
a	27.8
d	27.9

CHAPTER 28

1. a	28.3
2. a	28.3
3. a	28.3
4. b	28.4
5. b	28.4
6. c	28.4
7. c	28.5
8. a	28.5
9. d	28.6
10. a	28.8
11. a	28.7
12. b	28.9
13. a	28.8
14. c	28.3
15. b	28.3
j	28.3
a	28.4
c	28.8
d	28.5
h	28.3
f	28.8
i	28.3
e	28.4
g	28.3

CHAPTER 29

1. a	29.2
2. c	29.3
3. b	29.4
4. a	29.5
5. a	29.4
6. c	29.7
7. a	29.7
8. b	29.11
9. c	29.12
10. c	29.1
11. b	29.9
12. a	29.8
13. j	29.9
d	29.5
g	29.11
b	29.9
h	29.10
a	29.9
e	29.1
i	29.7
c	29.8
f	29.8

CHAPTER 30

1. b	30.2
2. c	30.1
3. c	30.2
4. e	30.3
5. d	30.2
6. b	30.8

7. b	30.7
8. a	30.2
9. b	30.7
10. c	30.5
11. d	30.4
12. b	30.4
13. a	30.8
14. c	30.3
15. d	30.5
g	30.7
f	30.5
a	304.
h	30.5
e	30.3
b	30.8
i	30.7
c	30.3

CHAPTER 31

1. a	31.1
2. b	31.3
3. a	31.3
4. d	31.1
5. c	31.8
6. a	31.5
7. b	31.8
8. d	31.5
9. c	31.5
10. c	31.5
11. c	31.7
12. d	31.6
f	31.5
c	31.5
e	31.8
a	31.4
b	31.3
13. b	31.9
14. d	31.4
c	31.5
b	31.6
g	31.7
f	31.7
e	31.8
a	31.8

CHAPTER 32

1. a	32.2
2. c	32.7
3. b	32.4
4. a	32.3
5. a	32.3
6. biceps	32.4
7. a	32.4
8. b	32.5
9. d	32.5
10. d	32.6
11. c	32.6
12. d	32.6
13. a	32.8
14. c	32.1
15. h	32.4
f	32.5
g	32.8
e	32.3
i	32.5
c	32.3
b	32.2
d	32.3
a	32.7

CHAPTER 33

1. a	33.1
2. d	33.1
3. pulmonary	33.1
4. c	33.4
5. b	33.4
6. a	33.4
7. b	33.3
8. d	33.3
9. a	33.6
10. b	33.8
11. d	33.3
12. a	33.2
13. b	33.10
14. b	33.9
15. f	33.1
a	33.10
e	33.3
g	33.3
b	33.3
c	33.8
d	33.2

CHAPTER 34

1. d	34.1
2. e	34.2, 34.3
3. g	34.3
4. h	34.3–34.8
5. d	34.3
6. Immediate, fixed, general, and no antigen memory are all correct.	34.1, 34.3
7. Self/nonself discrimination, diversity, specificity, and memory are all correct.	34.5
8. d	34.4, 34.6
9. a	34.5
10. b	34.5, 34.6
11. e	34.5, 34.8
12. b	34.5, 34.7
13. c	34.9
14. a	34.9
15. b	34.6, 34.8
e	34.4
c	34.6
d	34.8
a	34.8
16. f	34.9
e	34.5
d	34.9
c	34.3
b	34.9
a	34.4
g	34.5

CHAPTER 35

1. d	35.1
2. b	35.2
3. a	35.3
4. c	35.4
5. d	35.5
6. a	35.5
7. iron	35.6
8. b	35.8
9. d	35.6
10. c	35.5
11. d	35.5
12. True	35.5
13. a	35.4
14. bacteria	35.7
15. d	35.4
g	35.4
e	35.4
f	35.4
c	35.4
b	35.4
a	35.4

CHAPTER 36

1. d	36.1
2. b	36.3
3. c	36.5
4. b	36.5
5. a	36.5
6. c	36.6
7. a	36.3, 36.5, 36.6
8. b	36.5
9. d	36.8
10. d	36.7
11. c	36.4
12. c	36.9
13. b	36.10
14. c	36.8
15. g	36.5
b	36.6
a	36.5
d	36.4
h	36.3
c	36.5
f.	36.2
e.	36.6

CHAPTER 37

1. c	37.2
2. d	37.2
3. c	37.2
4. a	37.3
5. b	37.4
6. a	37.4
7. b	37.4
8. a	37.4
9. water	37.4
10. dialysis	37.5
11. c	37.3
a	37.3
b	37.3
e	37.4
d	37.4
12. c	37.6
13. b	37.6
a	37.6
d	37.6
c	37.6
e	37.6

CHAPTER 38

1. a	38.1
2. b	38.1
3. a	38.6
4. c	38.8
5. b	38.7
6. c	38.11
7. c	38.6
d	38.10
g	38.7
e	38.6
b	38.6
a	38.7
f	38.8
8. a	38.3
9. False	38.2
10. endoderm, mesoderm, ectoderm	38.2
11. c	38.12
12. b	38.15
a	38.6
d	38.8
c	38.8
e	38.8
g	38.12
f	38.15
13. a, d, c, f	38.12
b, e	38.13

CHAPTER 39

1. d	39.1
2. b	39.1
3. a	39.1
4. c	39.3
5. a	39.3
6. birds	39.4
7. cooperation in predator detection, defense, rearing young, learning by imitation, defending territory	39.5
8. d	39.6
9. d	39.6
10. a	39.4
11. e	39.6
h	39.5
c	39.2
b	39.4
d	39.4
a	39.2
f	39.5
g	39.2

CHAPTER 40

1. clumped	40.1
2. f	40.2
3. 400	40.1
4. 1,600	40.2
5. a	40.2
6. d	40.3
7. d	40.4
8. b	40.6
9. d	40.7
10. a	40.6
11. a	40.4
12. c	40.4
13. c	40.3
d	40.2
a	40.2
e	40.3
b	40.3

CHAPTER 41

1. b	41.1
2. d	41.1, 41.3
3. e	41.3
4. d	41.3
5. b	41.2
d	41.5
c	41.1
a	41.4
e	41.3
6. b	41.5
7. b	41.6
8. Pioneer	41.6
9. c	41.6
10. a	41.1
11. b	41.3
12. c	41.5
13. a	41.4
14. c	41.8
b	41.6
d	41.6
a	41.7
f	41.7
e	41.3

CHAPTER 42

1. b	42.1
2. d	42.1
3. d	42.1
4. d	42.1
5. a	42.1
6. c	42.5
7. b	42.5
8. d	42.6
9. d	42.6, 42.7
10. a	42.8
11. c	42.8
12. b	42.6
13. a	42.7
14. d	42.6
15. d	42.6
c	42.6
b	42.7
a	42.7

CHAPTER 43

1. b	43.1
2. d	43.1
3. d	43.1
4. a	43.2
5. b	43.2
6. b	43.2
7. d	43.3
8. c	43.6
9. a	43.8
10. b	43.9
11. d	43.12
12. c	43.11
13. c	43.3
14. b	43.3
15. d	43.8
e	43.6
f	43.7
c	43.6
b	43.10
h	43.5
i	43.6
a	43.4
g	43.12

CHAPTER 44

1. b	44.1
2. d	44.1
3. a	44.2
4. c	44.4
5. c	44.5
6. a	44.5
7. b	44.3
8. b	44.6
9. b	44.5
10. c	44.7
11. d	44.7
12. c	44.7
13. d	44.8
14. g	44.7
a	44.5
i	44.7
e	44.4
d	44.1
f	44.4
h	44.6
b	44.2
c	44.2

Appendix VII. Answers to Self-Quizzes and Genetics Problems (continued)

CHAPTER 13: GENETICS PROBLEMS

1. Yellow is recessive. Because F_1 plants have a green phenotype and must be heterozygous, green must be dominant over the recessive yellow.

2. a. *AB*
   b. *AB, aB*
   c. *Ab, ab*
   d. *AB, Ab, aB, ab*

3. a. All offspring will be *AaBB*.

4. A mating of two M^L cats yields 1/4 *MM*, 1/2 M^LM, and 1/4 M^LM^L. Because M^LM^L is lethal, the probability that any one kitten among the survivors will be heterozygous is 2/3.

5. Because both parents are heterozygous (Hb^AHb^S), each child has a 1 in 4 possibility of inheriting two Hb^S alleles and having sickle cell anemia.

6. The data reveal that these genes do not assort independently because the observed ratio is very far from the 9:3:3:1 ratio expected with independent assortment. Instead, the results can be explained if the genes are located close to each other on the same chromosome.

CHAPTER 14: GENETICS PROBLEMS

1. Autosomal recessive. If the allele was inherited in a dominant pattern, individuals in the last generation would all have the phenotype. If it was X-linked, offspring of the first generation would all have the phenotype.

2. a. Human males (XY) inherit their X chromosome from their mother.
   b. A male with an X-linked allele produces two kinds of gametes: one with an X chromosome (and the X-linked allele), and the other with a Y chromosome.
   c. A female homozygous for an X-linked allele produces one type of gamete, which carries the X-linked allele.
   d. A female heterozygous for an X-linked allele produces two types of gametes: one that carries the X-linked allele, and another that carries the partnered allele on the homologous chromosome.

3. As a result of translocation, chromosome 21 may get attached to the end of chromosome 14. The new individual's chromosome number would still be 46, but its somatic cells would have the translocated chromosome 21 in addition to two normal chromosomes 21.

4. 50 percent

Glossary

abscisic acid (ABA) Plant hormone involved in stomata function and stress responses; inhibits germination. **466**

abscission Process by which plant parts are shed. **466**

acid Substance that releases hydrogen ions when it dissolves in water. **32**

acid rain Low-pH rain that forms when sulfur dioxide and nitrogen oxides mix with water vapor in the atmosphere. **789**

actin Globular protein that plays a role in cell movements; main component of thin filaments in myofibrils. **561**

action potential Abrupt reversal of the charge difference across a plasma membrane. **501**

activation energy Minimum amount of energy required to start a reaction. **80**

activator Transcription factor that increases the rate of transcription. **164**

active site Of an enzyme, pocket in which substrates bind and a reaction occurs. **82**

active transport Energy-requiring mechanism in which a transport protein pumps a solute across a cell membrane against its concentration gradient. **90**

adaptation (adaptive trait) A heritable trait that enhances an individual's fitness in a particular environment. **257**

adaptive immunity Of vertebrate animals, a set of immune defenses that can be tailored to specific pathogens encountered by an organism during its lifetime. Characterized by self/nonself recognition, specificity, diversity, and memory. **590**

adaptive radiation Macroevolutionary pattern in which a burst of genetic divergences from a lineage gives rise to many new species. **292**

adaptive trait *See* adaptation.

adhering junction Cell junction composed of adhesion proteins that connect to cytoskeletal elements. Fastens animal cells to each other and basement membrane. **69**

adhesion protein Plasma membrane protein that helps cells stick to one another and (in animals) to extracellular matrix. **57**

adipose tissue Connective tissue that specializes in fat storage. **485**

adrenal cortex Outer portion of an adrenal gland; secretes aldosterone and cortisol. **544**

adrenal gland Endocrine gland located atop the kidney. **544**

adrenal medulla Inner portion of an adrenal gland; secretes epinephrine and norepinephrine. **544**

aerobic Involving or occurring in the presence of oxygen. **115**

aerobic respiration Oxygen-requiring metabolic pathway that breaks down sugars to produce ATP. Includes glycolysis, acetyl–CoA formation, the Krebs cycle, and electron transfer phosphorylation. **114**

age structure Of a population, the distribution of its members among various age categories. **723**

agglutination The clumping together of foreign cells bound by antibodies; the clumps attract phagocytic cells. Basis of blood typing tests. **601**

AIDS Acquired immunodeficiency syndrome. A secondary immune deficiency that develops as the result of infection by the HIV virus. **606**

alcoholic fermentation Anaerobic sugar breakdown pathway that produces ATP, CO_2, and ethanol. **122**

aldosterone Adrenal hormone that makes kidney tubules more permeable to sodium; encourages sodium reabsorption, which in turn increases water reabsorption and concentrates the urine. **655**

allantois Extraembryonic membrane that, in mammals, becomes part of the umbilical cord. **685**

allele frequency Abundance of a particular allele in a population's gene pool. **275**

alleles Forms of a gene with slightly different DNA sequences; may encode slightly different versions of the gene's product. **192**

allergen A normally harmless substance that provokes an immune response in some people. **604**

allergy Sensitivity to an allergen. **604**

allopatric speciation Speciation pattern in which a physical barrier ends gene flow between populations. **288**

allosteric regulation Control of enzyme activity by a regulatory molecule or ion that binds to a region outside the enzyme's active site. **84**

alternation of generations Of land plants and some algae, a life cycle that includes haploid and diploid multicelled bodies. **338**

alternative splicing Post-translational RNA modification in which some exons are removed or joined in various combinations. **151**

altruistic behavior Behavior that benefits others at the expense of the individual. **706**

alveoli Air sacs in the lung; gas exchange occurs across their lining. **619**

amino acid Small organic compound that is a subunit of proteins. Consists of a carboxyl group, an amine group, and a characteristic side group (R), all typically bonded to the same carbon atom. **44**

amino acid–derived hormone An amine (modified amino acid), peptide, or protein that functions as a hormone. **536**

ammonia Nitrogen-containing compound (NH_3) formed by breakdown of amino acids. **650**

amnion Extraembryonic membrane that encloses an amniote embryo and the amniotic fluid. **684**

amniote Vertebrate whose egg has waterproof membranes that allow it to develop away from water; a reptile, bird, or mammal. **401**

amoeba Single-celled protist that extends pseudopods to move and to capture prey. **340**

amoebozoan Shape-shifting heterotrophic protist with no pellicle or cell wall; an amoeba or slime mold. **340**

amphibian Tetrapod with scaleless skin; develops in water, then lives on land as a carnivore with lungs. For example, a frog or salamander. **404**

anaerobic Occurring in the absence of oxygen. **115**

analogous structures Similar body structures that evolved separately in different lineages (by morphological convergence). **267**

anaphase Stage of mitosis during which sister chromatids separate and move toward opposite spindle poles. **181**

aneuploid Having too many or too few copies of a particular chromosome. **230**

angiosperms Highly diverse seed plant lineage; only plants that make flowers and fruits. **356**

animal A eukaryotic heterotroph that is made up of unwalled cells and develops through a series of stages. Most ingest food, reproduce sexually, and move. **9, 376**

animal hormone Intercellular signaling molecule that is secreted by an endocrine gland or cell and travels in the blood. **536**

annelid Segmented worm with a coelom, complete digestive system, and closed circulatory system. **384**

antenna Of some arthropods, sensory structure on the head that detects touch and odors. **389**

anther Of a flower, the part of the stamen that produces pollen. **454**

anthropoid primate Humanlike primate; monkey, ape, or human. **411**

Glossary (continued)

antibody Y-shaped antigen receptor protein, made only by B cells; antibody bound to antigenic particles activates complement and triggers effector cell function such as phagocytosis. **596**

antibody-mediated immune response Immune response in which antibodies are produced in response to an antigen. **598**

anticodon In a tRNA, set of three nucleotides that base-pairs with an mRNA codon. **153**

antidiuretic hormone Pituitary hormone that encourages water reabsorption in the kidney, thus concentrating the urine. **654**

antigen A molecule or particle that the immune system recognizes as nonself. Its presence in the body triggers an immune response. **590**

antioxidant Substance that prevents oxidation of other molecules. **86**

anus Body opening that serves solely as the exit for wastes from a tubular digestive tract. **630**

aorta Large artery that receives oxygenated blood pumped out of the heart's left ventricle. **572**

ape Common name for a tailless nonhuman primate; a gibbon, orangutan, gorilla, chimpanzee, or bonobo. **411**

apical dominance In plants, effect in which a lengthening shoot tip inhibits the growth of lateral buds. **464**

apical meristem Meristem in the tip of a shoot or root; gives rise to primary growth (lengthening) in a plant. **432**

apicomplexan Parasitic protist that reproduces inside cells of its host; for example, the protist that causes malaria. **336**

apoptosis Mechanism of cell suicide. **671**

appendicular skeleton Of vertebrates, bones of the limbs or fins and bones that connect these structures to the axial skeleton. **557**

appendix Wormlike projection from the first part of the large intestine; serves as a reservoir for bacteria. **638**

aquifer Porous rock layer that holds some groundwater. **752**

arachnids Land-dwelling arthropods with no antennae and four pairs of walking legs; spiders, scorpions, mites, and ticks. **390**

archaea Singular **archaean**. Group of single-celled organisms that lack a nucleus but are more closely related to eukaryotes than to bacteria. **8**

arctic tundra Highest-latitude Northern Hemisphere biome, where low, cold-tolerant plants survive with only a brief growing season. **773**

area effect Larger islands have more species than small ones. **742**

arteriole Blood vessel that conveys blood from an artery to capillaries. **578**

artery Large-diameter vessel that carries blood away from the heart. **570**

arthropod Invertebrate with jointed legs and a hard exoskeleton that is periodically molted. **389**

asexual reproduction Reproductive mode of eukaryotes by which offspring arise from a single parent only. **178**, **666**

atmospheric cycle Biogeochemical cycle in which a gaseous form of an element plays a significant role. For example, the carbon cycle. **754**

atom Fundamental building block of all matter. Consists of varying numbers of protons, neutrons, and electrons. **4**

atomic number Number of protons in the atomic nucleus; determines the element. **24**

ATP Adenosine triphosphate. Nucleotide that consists of an adenine base, a ribose sugar, and three phosphate groups. Functions as a subunit of RNA and as a coenzyme in many reactions. Important energy carrier in cells. **46**

ATP/ADP cycle Process by which cells regenerate ATP. ADP forms when a phosphate group is removed from ATP, then ATP forms again as ADP gains a phosphate group. **87**

atrioventricular (AV) node Clump of cells that conveys excitatory signals between the atria and ventricles. **575**

atrium Heart chamber that receives blood from veins. **574**

australopith Extinct African hominins in the genus *Australopithecus*; some are considered likely human ancestors. **413**

autoimmune response Immune response that inappropriately targets one's own tissues. **605**

autonomic nervous system Division of the peripheral nervous system that relays signals to and from internal organs and glands. **506**

autosome A chromosome that is the same in males and females. **137**

autotroph Producer. An organism that makes its own food using energy from the environment and carbon from inorganic molecules such as CO_2. **100**

auxin Plant hormone that causes lengthening; also has a central role in growth by coordinating the effects of other hormones. **464**

AV node *See* atrioventricular node.

axial skeleton Bones of the main body axis; skull, backbone, and rib cage. **557**

axon Of a neuron, a cytoplasmic extension that transmits electrical signals along its length and secretes chemical signals at its endings. **500**

bacteria Singular bacterium. The most diverse and well-known group of prokaryotes. **8**

bacteriophage Virus that infects bacteria. **133**, **316**

balanced polymorphism Maintenance of two or more alleles for a trait at high frequency in a population. **283**

bark In woody plants, all living and dead tissue that lies outside of the vascular cambium. **433**

Barr body Inactivated X chromosome in a cell of a female mammal. The other X chromosome is active. **168**

basal body Organelle that develops from a centriole; occurs at base of cilium or flagellum. **67**

basal metabolic rate Rate at which a body uses energy when at rest. **644**

base Substance that accepts hydrogen ions when it dissolves in water. **32**

basement membrane Secreted layer that attaches an epithelium to an underlying tissue. **482**

base-pair substitution Type of mutation in which a single base pair changes. **156**

basophil Circulating white blood cell that releases the contents of its granules in response to antigen or injury. **591**

B cell B lymphocyte. White blood cell that can make antibodies. Central to antibody-mediated immune responses. **591**

B cell receptor Antigen receptor on the surface of a B cell; an antibody that has not been released from the B cell's plasma membrane. **597**

bell curve Bell-shaped curve; typically results from graphing frequency versus distribution for a trait that varies continuously. **216**

benthic province The ocean's sediments and rocks. **778**

bilateral symmetry Having paired structures so the right and left halves are mirror images. **376**

bile Mix of salts, pigments, and cholesterol produced in the liver, then stored and concentrated in the gallbladder; emulsifies fats when secreted into the small intestine. **636**

Glossary (continued)

binary fission Method of asexual reproduction that divides one bacterial or archaeal cell into two identical descendant cells. **320**

bioaccumulation The concentration of a chemical pollutant in the tissues of an organism rises over the course of the organism's lifetime. **759**

biodiversity Scope of variation among living organisms; the genetic variation within species, variety of species, and variety of ecosystems. **8, 792**

biofilm Community of microorganisms living within a shared mass of secreted slime. **59**

biogeochemical cycle A nutrient moves among environmental reservoirs and into and out of food webs. **752**

biogeography Study of patterns in the geographic distribution of species and communities. **254**

biological magnification A chemical pollutant becomes increasingly concentrated as it moves up through food chains. **759**

biological pest control Use of a pest's natural enemies to control its population size. **737**

biology The scientific study of life. **4**

bioluminescence Light emitted by a living organism. **335**

biomarker Substance found only or mainly in cells of one type. **307**

biome A region (often discontinuous) characterized by its climate and dominant vegetation. **768**

biosphere All regions of Earth where organisms live. **5**

biotic potential Maximum possible population growth rate under optimal conditions. **715**

bipedalism Habitual upright walking. **412**

bird Feathered reptile of a lineage in which the body became adapted for flight. **408**

bivalve Mollusk with a hinged two-part shell. For example, a clam. **386**

blastocyst Mammalian blastula. **684**

blastula Hollow ball of cells that forms as a result of cleavage. **668**

blood Circulatory fluid of a closed circulatory system. In vertebrates, a fluid connective tissue consisting of plasma and cellular components (red cells, white cells, platelets) that form in bones. **485, 570**

blood–brain barrier Protective mechanism that prevents unwanted substances from entering cerebrospinal fluid. **508**

blood pressure Pressure exerted by blood against a vessel wall. **579**

bone tissue Connective tissue made up of cells surrounded by a mineral-hardened matrix of their own secretions. **485**

boreal forest Extensive high-latitude forest of the Northern Hemisphere; conifers are the predominant vegetation. **770**

bottleneck Reduction in population size so severe that it reduces genetic diversity. **284**

Bowman's capsule Region of a nephron tubule that forms a cup around the glomerulus; coveys filtrate to the proximal tubule. **652**

brain Central control organ of a nervous system; receives and integrates sensory information, regulates internal conditions, and sends out signals that result in movements. **498**

bronchiole A small airway that leads from a bronchus to alveoli. **619**

bronchus Airway connecting the trachea to a lung. **619**

brood parasitism One egg-laying species benefits by having another raise its offspring. **737**

brown alga Multicelled marine protist with a brown accessory pigment in its chloroplasts. **337**

brush border cell In the lining of the small intestine, an epithelial cell with microvilli at its surface. **635**

bryophyte Nonvascular plant; a moss, liverwort, or hornwort. **348**

buffer Set of chemicals that can keep the pH of a solution stable by alternately donating and accepting ions that contribute to pH. **32**

C3 plant Type of plant that uses only the Calvin–Benson cycle to fix carbon. **106**

C4 plant Type of plant that minimizes photorespiration by fixing carbon twice, in two cell types. **107**

calcitonin Thyroid hormone that encourages bone to take up and incorporate calcium. **543**

Calvin–Benson cycle Cyclic carbon-fixing pathway that builds sugars from CO_2; the light-independent reactions of photosynthesis. **106**

camera eye Eye with an adjustable opening and a single lens that focuses light on a retina. **524**

camouflage Coloration or body form that helps an organism blend in with its surroundings and escape detection. **735**

CAM plant Type of plant that conserves water by fixing carbon twice, at different times of day. **107**

cancer Disease that occurs when a malignant neoplasm physically and metabolically disrupts body tissues. **185**

capillary Small-diameter blood vessel; exchanges with interstitial fluid occur across its wall. **570**

carbohydrate Molecule that consists primarily of carbon, hydrogen, and oxygen atoms in a 1:2:1 ratio. Complex kinds (e.g., cellulose, starch, glycogen) are polymers of simple kinds (sugars). **40**

carbon cycle Movement of carbon, mainly between the oceans, atmosphere, and living organisms. **754**

carbon fixation Process by which carbon from an inorganic source such as carbon dioxide becomes incorporated (fixed) into an organic molecule. **106**

cardiac cycle Sequence of contraction and relaxation of heart chambers that occurs with each heartbeat. **574**

cardiac muscle tissue Muscle of the heart wall. **486**

carpel Floral reproductive organ that produces female gametophytes; consists of an ovary, stigma, and often a style. **356, 454**

carrying capacity (K) Of a species, the maximum number of individuals that a particular environment can sustain; can change over time. **716**

cartilage Connective tissue that consists of cells surrounded by a rubbery matrix of their own secretions. **484**

cartilaginous fish Jawed fish with a skeleton of cartilage; a shark, ray, or skate. **402**

Casparian strip Waxy band between the plasma membranes of abutting root endodermal cells; forms a seal that prevents soil water from seeping through cell walls into the vascular cylinder. **442**

catalysis The acceleration of a reaction rate by a molecule that is unchanged by participating in the reaction. **82**

cDNA Complementary strand of DNA synthesized from an RNA template by the enzyme reverse transcriptase. **239**

cell Smallest unit of life; at minimum, consists of plasma membrane, cytoplasm, and DNA. **4**

cell cortex Reinforcing mesh of microfilaments under a plasma membrane. **66**

cell cycle A series of events from the time a cell forms until its cytoplasm divides. **178**

cell junction Structure that connects a cell to another cell or to extracellular matrix; e.g., tight junction, adhering junction, or gap junction (of animals); plasmodesmata (of plants). **69**

Glossary *(continued)*

cell-mediated immune response Immune response involving cytotoxic T cells and NK cells that destroy infected or cancerous body cells. **598**

cell plate A disk-shaped structure that forms during cytokinesis in a plant cell; matures as a cross-wall between the two new nuclei. **182**

cell theory Theory that all organisms consist of one or more cells, which are the basic unit of life; all cells come from division of preexisting cells; and all cells pass hereditary material to offspring. **52**

cellular slime mold Amoeba-like protist that feeds as a single predatory cell; under unfavorable conditions, it joins with others to form a multicellular spore-bearing structure. **340**

cell wall Rigid but permeable structure that surrounds the plasma membrane of some cells. **59**

cellulose Tough, insoluble carbohydrate that is the major structural material in plants. **40**

central nervous system Of vertebrates, the brain and spinal cord. **499**

central vacuole Large, fluid-filled vesicle in many plant cells. **62**

centriole Barrel-shaped organelle from which microtubules grow. **67**

centromere Of a duplicated eukaryotic chromosome, constricted region where sister chromatids attach to each other. **136**

cephalization Evolutionary trend whereby nerve cells and sensory structures become concentrated in the head of a bilateral animal. **376, 498**

cephalopod Predatory mollusk that has a closed circulatory system and moves by jet propulsion. For example an octopus or squid. **387**

cerebellum Hindbrain region that coordinates voluntary movements. **510**

cerebral cortex Outer gray matter layer of the cerebrum; region responsible for most complex behavior. **512**

cerebrospinal fluid Fluid that surrounds the brain and spinal cord and fills spaces (ventricles) within the brain. **508**

cerebrum Forebrain region that controls higher functions. **510**

cervix Narrow part of uterus that connects to the vagina. **676**

chaparral Biome of dry shrubland in regions with hot, dry summers and cool, rainy winters. **771**

character Quantifiable, heritable characteristic or trait. **294**

character displacement Evolutionary process in which two competing species become less similar in their resource requirements over time. **733**

charge Electrical property; opposite charges attract, and like charges repel. **24**

chelicerates Arthropod group with specialized feeding structures (chelicerae) and no antennae; arachnids and horseshoe crabs. **390**

chemical bond An attractive force that arises between two atoms when their electrons interact; joins atoms as molecules. *See* covalent bond, ionic bond. **28**

chemoautotroph Organism that uses carbon dioxide as its carbon source and obtains energy by oxidizing inorganic molecules. **321**

chemoheterotroph Organism that obtains energy and carbon by breaking down organic compounds. **321**

chemoreceptor Sensory receptor that responds to a chemical. **520**

chlorophyll *a* Main photosynthetic pigment in plants. **100**

chloroplast Organelle of photosynthesis in the cells of plants and photosynthetic protists. Has two outer membranes enclosing semifluid stroma. Light-dependent reactions occur at its inner thylakoid membrane; light-independent reactions, in the stroma. Stores excess sugars as starch. **65**

choanoflagellate Heterotrophic freshwater protist with a flagellum and a food-capturing "collar." May be solitary or colonial. **341**

chordate Animal with an embryo that has a notochord, dorsal nerve cord, pharyngeal gill slits, and a tail that extends beyond the anus. A lancelet, tunicate, or vertebrate. **400**

chorion Outermost extraembryonic membrane of amniotes; major component of the placenta in placental mammals. **685**

chromosome A structure that consists of DNA and associated proteins; carries part or all of a cell's genetic information. **136**

chromosome number The total number of chromosomes in a cell of a given species. **136**

chyme Mix of food and gastric fluid. **634**

chytrid Fungus that makes flagellated spores. **365**

ciliate Single-celled, heterotrophic protist with many cilia. **335**

cilium Plural, **cilia** Short, movable structure that projects from the plasma membrane of some eukaryotic cells. **66**

circadian rhythm A biological activity that is repeated about every 24 hours. **470**

circulatory system Organ system consisting of a heart or hearts and vessels that distribute circulatory fluid through a body. May be closed or open. **570**

clade A group whose members share one or more defining derived traits. **294**

cladistics Making hypotheses about evolutionary relationships among clades. **295**

cladogram Evolutionary tree diagram that shows evolutionary connections among a group of clades. **295**

cleavage Mitotic division of an animal cell. **668**

cleavage furrow In a dividing animal cell, the indentation where cytoplasmic division will occur. **182**

climate Average weather conditions in a region. **764**

cloaca Body opening that serves as the exit for digestive waste and urine; also functions in reproduction. **402, 630**

cloning vector A DNA molecule that can accept foreign DNA and be replicated inside a host cell. **239**

closed circulatory system Circulatory system in which blood flows through a continuous network of vessels; all materials are exchanged across the walls of those vessels. **384, 570**

club fungus Fungus that produces spores in club-shaped structures during sexual reproduction. **365**

cnidarian Radially symmetrical invertebrate with two tissue layers; uses tentacles with stinging cells to capture food. For example, a jelly or a sea anemone. **380**

cnidocyte Stinging cell unique to cnidarians. **380**

coal Fossil fuel formed over millions of years by compaction and heating of plant remains. **352**

cochlea Coiled, fluid-filled structure in the inner ear; holds the mechanoreceptors (hair cells) involved in hearing. **528**

codominance Effect in which the full and separate phenotypic effects of two alleles are apparent in heterozygous individuals. **212**

codon In an mRNA, a nucleotide base triplet that codes for an amino acid or stop signal during translation. **152**

coelom A fluid-filled body cavity between the gut and body wall; it is lined with tissue derived from mesoderm. **377**

coenzyme An organic molecule that functions as a cofactor; e.g., NAD. **86**

coevolution The joint evolution of two closely interacting species; macroevolutionary pattern in which each species is a selective agent for traits of the other. **293**

cofactor A metal ion or organic molecule that associates with an enzyme and is necessary for its function. **86**

cohesion Property of a substance that arises from the tendency of its molecules to resist separating from one another. **31**

cohesion–tension theory Explanation of how transpiration creates a tension that pulls a cohesive column of water upward through xylem, from roots to shoots. **445**

cohort Group of individuals born during the same interval. **718**

coleoptile Rigid sheath that protects a growing embryonic shoot of monocots. **461**

collecting tubule Kidney tubule that receives fluid from several nephrons and delivers it to the renal pelvis. **653**

collenchyma Simple plant tissue composed of living cells with unevenly thickened walls; provides flexible support. **424**

colonial organism Organism composed of many similar cells, each capable of living and reproducing on its own. **332**

colonial theory of animal origins Hypothesis that the first animals evolved from a colonial protist. **378**

commensalism Species interaction that benefits one species and neither helps nor harms the other. **730**

community All populations of all species in a given area. **5, 730**

compact bone Dense bone that makes up the shaft of long bones. **558**

companion cell In phloem, specialized parenchyma cell that provides a partnered sieve element with metabolic support. **446**

comparative morphology The scientific study of similarities and differences in body plans. **255**

competitive exclusion Process whereby two species compete for a limiting resource, and one drives the other to local extinction. **732**

complement A set of proteins that circulate in inactive form in blood; activated complement proteins attract phagocytic white blood cells, coat antigenic particles, and puncture lipid bilayers. **590**

complete digestive tract Tubelike digestive system; food enters through one opening and wastes leave through another. **630**

compound Molecule that has atoms of more than one element. **28**

compound eye Of some arthropods, a motion-sensitive eye made up of many image-forming units, each with its own lens. **389, 524**

concentration Amount of solute per unit volume of a solution. **32**

condensation Chemical reaction in which an enzyme builds a large molecule from smaller subunits; water also forms. **39**

cone cell Photoreceptor that provides sharp vision and allows detection of color. **526**

conjugation Mechanism of horizontal gene transfer in which one prokaryote passes a plasmid to another. **320**

connective tissue Animal tissue with an extensive extracellular matrix; provides structural and functional support. **484**

conservation biology Field of applied biology that surveys biodiversity and seeks ways to maintain and use it nondestructively. **792**

consumer Organism that obtains energy and carbon by feeding on tissues, wastes, or remains of other organisms; a heterotroph. **6, 748**

continuous variation Range of small differences in a shared trait. **216**

contractile vacuole In freshwater protists, an organelle that collects and expels excess water. **333**

control group In an experiment, group of individuals identical to an experimental group except for the independent variable under investigation. **13**

coral bleaching A coral expels its photosynthetic dinoflagellate symbionts in response to stress and becomes colorless. **777**

coral reef Highly diverse marine ecosystem centered around reefs built by living corals that secrete calcium carbonate. **777**

cork Plant tissue that waterproofs, insulates, and protects the surfaces of woody stems and roots. **433**

cork cambium Lateral meristem that gives rise to periderm in plants. **433**

cornea Clear, protective covering at the front of a vertebrate eye; helps focus light on the retina. **525**

corpus luteum Hormone-secreting structure that forms from follicle cells left behind after ovulation. **677**

cortisol Adrenal cortex hormone that influences metabolism and immunity; secretions rise with stress. **544**

cotyledon Seed leaf of a flowering plant embryo. **357**

countercurrent exchange Exchange of substances between two fluids moving in opposite directions. **616**

covalent bond Chemical bond in which two atoms share a pair of electrons. **28**

critical thinking The act of judging information before accepting it. **12**

crossing over Process by which homologous chromosomes exchange corresponding segments of DNA during prophase I of meiosis. **198**

crustaceans Mostly marine arthropods with a calcium-hardened cuticle and two pairs of antennae; for example lobsters, crabs, krill, and barnacles. **390**

cuticle Secreted covering at a body surface. **69, 346**

cyanobacteria Photosynthetic, oxygen-producing bacteria. **322**

cytokines Signaling molecules secreted by white blood cells to coordinate their activities during immune responses. **591**

cytokinesis Cytoplasmic division; process in which a eukaryotic cell divides in two after mitosis or meiosis. **182**

cytokinin Plant hormone that promotes cell division in shoot apical meristem and cell differentiation in root apical meristem. Often interacts antagonistically with auxin. **464**

cytoplasm Semifluid substance enclosed by a cell's plasma membrane. **52**

cytoskeleton Network of interconnected protein filaments that support, organize, and move eukaryotic cells and their parts. *See* microtubules, microfilaments, intermediate filaments. **66**

data Experimental results. **13**

decomposer Organism that feeds on wastes and remains; breaks organic material down into its inorganic subunits. **323, 748**

deductive reasoning Using a general idea to make a conclusion about a specific case. **12**

deletion Mutation in which one or more nucleotides are lost from DNA. **156**

demographics Statistics that describe a population. **712**

demographic transition model Model describing the changes in human birth and death rates that occur as a region becomes industrialized. **724**

denature To unravel the shape of a protein or other large biological molecule. **46**

dendrite Of a motor neuron or interneuron, a cytoplasmic extension that receives chemical signals sent by other neurons and converts them to electrical signals. **500**

dendritic cell Phagocytic white blood cell that patrols solid tissues; important antigen-presenting cell in adaptive immune responses. **591**

denitrification Conversion of nitrates or nitrites to nitrogen gas. **757**

dense, irregular connective tissue Connective tissue that consists of randomly arranged fibers and scattered fibroblasts. **484**

dense, regular connective tissue Connective tissue that consists of fibroblasts arrayed between parallel arrangements of fibers. **484**

density-dependent limiting factor Factor that limits population growth and has a greater effect in dense populations; for example, competition for a limited resource. **716**

density-independent limiting factor Factor that limits population growth and acts regardless of population size; for example a flood. **717**

dental plaque On teeth, a thick biofilm composed of bacteria, their extracellular products, and saliva proteins. **592**

dependent variable In an experiment, a variable that is presumably affected by an independent variable being tested. **13**

derived trait A novel trait present in a clade but not in the clade's ancestors. **294**

dermal tissues Tissues that cover and protect the plant body. *See* epidermis, periderm. **422**

dermis Deep layer of skin that consists of connective tissue with nerves and blood vessels running through it. **491**

desert Biome with little rain and low humidity; plants that have water-storing and water-conserving adaptations predominate. **772**

desertification Conversion of dry grassland to desert. **786**

detrital food chain Food chain in which energy is transferred directly from producers to detritivores. **750**

detritivore Consumer that feeds on small bits of organic material. **748**

deuterostomes Lineage of bilateral animals in which the second opening on the embryo surface develops into a mouth; includes echinoderms and chordates. **377**

development Multistep process by which the first cell of a new multicelled organism gives rise to an adult. **7**

diaphragm Muscle between the thoracic and abdominal cavities; contracts during inhalation. **619**

diastole Relaxation phase of the cardiac cycle. **574**

diastolic pressure Blood pressure when ventricles are relaxed. **579**

diatom Single-celled photosynthetic protist with a brown accessory pigment in its chloroplasts and a two-part silica shell. **337**

differentiation Process by which cells become specialized during development; occurs as different cells in an embryo begin to use different subsets of their DNA. **142**

diffusion Spontaneous spreading of molecules or ions. **88**

dihybrid cross Cross between two individuals identically heterozygous for two genes; for example $AaBb \times AaBb$. **210**

dikaryotic Having two genetically distinct nuclei in a cell ($n + n$). **365**

dinoflagellate Single-celled, aquatic protist that moves with a whirling motion; may be heterotrophic or photosynthetic. **335**

dinosaur Group of reptiles that includes the ancestors of birds; became extinct at the end of the Cretaceous. **406**

diploid Having two of each type of chromosome characteristic of the species ($2n$). **137**

directional selection Mode of natural selection that shifts an allele's frequency in a consistent direction, so phenotypes at one end of a range of variation are favored. **278**

disruptive selection Mode of natural selection in which traits at the extremes of a range of variation are adaptive, and intermediate forms are not. **281**

distal tubule Region of a kidney tubule that delivers filtrate to a collecting tubule. **653**

distance effect Islands close to a mainland have more species than those farther away. **742**

DNA Deoxyribonucleic acid. Carries hereditary information that guides development and other activities; consists of two chains of nucleotides (adenine, guanine, thymine, and cytosine) twisted into a double helix. **7, 46**

DNA cloning Set of methods that uses living cells to make many identical copies of a DNA fragment. **238**

DNA library Collection of cells that host different fragments of foreign DNA, often representing an organism's entire genome. **240**

DNA ligase Enzyme that seals gaps in double-stranded DNA. **138**

DNA polymerase DNA replication enzyme. Uses one strand of DNA as a template to assemble a complementary strand of DNA from nucleotides. **138**

DNA profiling Identifying an individual by analyzing the unique parts of his or her DNA. **244**

DNA replication Process by which a cell duplicates its DNA before it divides. **138**

DNA sequence Order of nucleotides in a strand of DNA. **135**

DNA sequencing *See* sequencing.

dominance hierarchy Social system in which resources and mating opportunities are unequally distributed within a group. **705**

dominant Refers to an allele that masks the effect of a recessive allele paired with it in heterozygous individuals. **207**

dormancy Period of temporarily suspended metabolism. **456**

dosage compensation Mechanism in which X chromosome inactivation equalizes gene expression between males and females. **168**

double fertilization Mode of fertilization in flowering plants in which one sperm cell fuses with the egg, and a second sperm cell fuses with the endosperm mother cell. **456**

duplication Repeated section of a chromosome. **228**

echinoderms Invertebrates with a water–vascular system and hardened plates and spines embedded in the skin or body. Radials as adults, but bilateral as larvae. For example, a sea star. **394**

ECM *See* extracellular matrix.

ecological footprint Area of Earth's surface required to sustainably support a particular level of development and consumption. **725**

ecological niche All of a species' requirements and roles in an ecosystem. **732**

ecological restoration Actively altering an area in an effort to restore an ecosystem that has been damaged or destroyed. **793**

ecology Study of interactions among organisms, and among organisms and their environment. **712**

ecosystem A community interacting with its environment through a one-way flow of energy and cycling of materials. **5, 748**

ectoderm Outermost tissue layer of an animal embryo. **376, 668**

ectotherm Animal whose body temperature varies with that of its environment; controls its internal temperature by altering its behavior; for example, a fish or a lizard. **406, 658**

Glossary (continued)

effector cell Antigen-sensitized B cell or T cell that forms in an immune response and acts immediately. **598**

egg Female gamete. **666**

electron Negatively charged subatomic particle. **24**

electronegativity Measure of the ability of an atom to pull electrons away from other atoms. **28**

electron transfer chain Array of enzymes and other molecules in a cell membrane that accept and give up electrons in sequence, thus releasing the energy of the electrons in small, usable steps. **85**

electron transfer phosphorylation Process in which electron flow through electron transfer chains sets up a hydrogen ion gradient that drives ATP formation. **104**

electrophoresis Laboratory technique that separates DNA fragments by size. **242**

element A pure substance that consists only of atoms with the same number of protons. **24**

embryo In animals, a developing individual from first cleavage until hatching or birth; in humans, usually refers to an individual in weeks 2 to 8 of development. **673**

embryonic induction Embryonic cells produce signals that alter the behavior of neighboring cells. **670**

emergent property A characteristic of a system that does not appear in any of the system's component parts. **4**

emerging disease A disease that was previously unknown or has recently begun spreading to a new region. **318**

emigration Movement of individuals out of a population. **714**

emulsification Dispersion of fat droplets in a fluid. **636**

endangered species A species that faces extinction in all or a part of its range. **784**

endemic species Species that remains restricted to the area where it evolved. **784**

endergonic Describes a reaction that requires a net input of free energy to proceed. **80**

endocrine gland Ductless gland; aggregation of epithelial cells that secrete a hormone or hormones into the blood. **483, 538**

endocytosis Process by which a cell takes in a small amount of extracellular fluid (and its contents) by the ballooning inward of the plasma membrane. **92**

endoderm Innermost tissue layer of an animal embryo. **376, 668**

endodermis Outer layer of the vascular cylinder in a plant root; sheet of cells just outside the pericycle. **430**

endomembrane system Series of interacting organelles (endoplasmic reticulum, Golgi bodies, vesicles) between nucleus and plasma membrane; produces lipids, proteins. **62**

endoplasmic reticulum (ER) Organelle that is a continuous system of sacs and tubes extending from the nuclear envelope. Smooth ER makes lipids and breaks down carbohydrates and fatty acids; rough ER modifies polypeptides made by ribosomes on its surface. **63**

endorphin One type of natural painkiller molecule. **521**

endoskeleton Internal skeleton made up of hardened components such as bones. **401, 556**

endosperm Nutritive tissue in the seeds of flowering plants. **357, 456**

endospore Resistant resting stage of some soil bacteria. **323**

endosymbiont hypothesis Theory that mitochondria and chloroplasts evolved from bacteria that entered and lived in a host cell. **308**

endotherm Animal that maintains its temperature by adjusting its production of metabolic heat; for example, a bird or mammal. **406, 658**

energy The capacity to do work. **78**

enhancer In eukaryotic cells, a binding site in DNA for an activator. **164**

entropy Measure of how much the energy of a system is dispersed. **78**

enzyme Protein or RNA that speeds up a chemical reaction without being changed by it. **39**

eosinophil Circulating white blood cell with granules; specialized to combat multicelled parasites that are too large for phagocytosis. **591**

epidermis Outermost tissue layer. In young plants, dermal tissue. In animals, the epithelial layer of skin. **424, 490**

epididymis Duct where sperm mature; empties into a vas deferens. **674**

epigenetic Refers to heritable changes in gene expression that are not the result of changes in DNA sequence. **172**

epiglottis Tissue flap that folds down to prevent food from entering the trachea during swallowing. **619**

epistasis Polygenic inheritance, in which a trait is influenced by multiple genes. **213**

epithelial tissue Sheetlike animal tissue that covers outer body surfaces and lines internal tubes and cavities. **482**

equilibrium model of island biogeography Model that predicts the number of species on an island based on the island's area and distance from the mainland. **742**

ER *See* endoplasmic reticulum.

erosion *See* soil erosion.

esophagus Muscular tube that connects the pharynx (throat) to the stomach. **633**

essential amino acid Amino acid that the body cannot make and must obtain from food. **639**

essential fatty acid Fatty acid that the body cannot make and must obtain from food. **639**

estrogens Sex hormones that function in reproduction and cause development of female secondary sexual characteristics; secreted by the ovaries. **545, 676**

estrous cycle Reproductive cycle in which the uterine lining thickens, and, if pregnancy does not occur, is reabsorbed. **679**

estuary A highly productive ecosystem where nutrient-rich water from a river mixes with seawater. **776**

ethylene Gaseous plant hormone that participates in germination, abscission, ripening, and stress responses. **467**

eudicot Flowering plant in which the embryo has two seed leaves (cotyledons). For example, a tomato, cherry, or cactus. **357**

eugenics Idea of deliberately improving the genetic qualities of the human race. **248**

euglenoid Flagellated protozoan with multiple mitochondria; may be heterotrophic or have chloroplasts descended from green algae. **333**

eukaryote Organism whose cells characteristically have a nucleus; a protist, fungus, plant, or animal. **8**

eusocial animal Animal that lives in a multigenerational group in which many sterile workers cooperate in all tasks essential to the group's welfare, while a few members of the group produce offspring. **706**

eutrophication Nutrient enrichment of an aquatic habitat. **774**

evaporation Transition of a liquid to a vapor. **31**

evolution Change in a line of descent. **256**

evolutionary tree Diagram showing evolutionary connections. **295**

exaptation Evolutionary adaptation of an existing structure for a completely new purpose. **292**

exergonic Describes a reaction that ends with a net release of free energy. **80**

exocrine gland Gland that secretes milk, sweat, saliva, or some other substance through a duct. **483**

exocytosis Process by which a cell expels a vesicle's contents to extracellular fluid. **92**

exon Nucleotide sequence that remains in an RNA after post-transcriptional modification. **151**

exoskeleton Of some invertebrates, hard external parts that muscles attach to and move. **389**, **556**

exotic species A species that evolved in one community and later became established in a different one. **740**

experiment A test designed to support or falsify a prediction. **12**

experimental group In an experiment, a group of individuals who have a certain characteristic or receive a certain treatment as compared with a control group. **13**

exponential growth A population grows by a fixed percentage in successive time intervals; the size of each increase is determined by the current population size. **714**

external fertilization Sperm and eggs unite in the external environment. **667**

extinct Refers to a species that no longer has living members. **292**

extracellular fluid Of a multicelled organism, body fluid outside of cells; serves as the body's internal environment. **480**

extracellular matrix (ECM) Complex mixture of cell secretions; its composition and function vary by cell type. E.g., basement membrane of epithelial tissue. **68**

extreme halophile Organism adapted to life in a highly salty environment. **326**

extreme thermophile Organism adapted to life in a very high-temperature environment. **326**

facilitated diffusion Passive transport mechanism in which a solute follows its concentration gradient across a membrane by moving through a transport protein. **90**

fat Lipid that consists of a glycerol molecule with one, two, or three fatty acid tails. *See* saturated fat, unsaturated fat. **42**

fatty acid Organic compound that consists of a chain of carbon atoms with an acidic carboxyl group at one end. Carbon chain of saturated types has single bonds only; that of unsaturated types has one or more double bonds. **42**

feces Unabsorbed food material and cellular waste that is expelled from the digestive tract. **638**

feedback inhibition Regulatory mechanism in which a change that results from some activity decreases or stops the activity. **84**

fermentation A metabolic pathway that breaks down sugars to produce ATP and does not require oxygen. E.g., lactate fermentation. **114**

fertilization Fusion of two gametes to form a zygote; part of sexual reproduction. **195**

fetus Developing human from about 9 weeks until birth. **673**

fever A temporary, internally induced rise in core body temperature above the normal set point. **595**

fibrin Threadlike protein formed during blood clotting from the soluble plasma protein fibrinogen. **577**

fibrous root system Root system composed of an extensive mass of similar-sized adventitious roots; typical of monocots. **430**

first law of thermodynamics Energy cannot be created or destroyed. **78**

fitness Degree of adaptation to an environment, as measured by an individual's relative genetic contribution to future generations. **257**

fixed Refers to an allele for which all members of a population are homozygous. **284**

flagellated protozoan Protist belonging to an entirely or mostly heterotrophic lineage with no cell wall and one or more flagella. **333**

flagellum Long, slender cellular structure used for locomotion through fluid surroundings. **59**

flatworm Bilaterally symmetrical invertebrate with organs but no body cavity; for example, a planarian or tapeworm. **382**

flower Specialized reproductive structure of a flowering plant. **356**, **454**

fluid mosaic Model of a cell membrane as a two-dimensional fluid of mixed composition. **56**

follicle-stimulating hormone (FSH) Anterior pituitary hormone with roles in ovarian follicle maturation and sperm production. **678**

food chain Description of who eats whom in one path of energy flow through an ecosystem. **749**

food web Set of cross-connecting food chains. **750**

foraminifera Heterotrophic single-celled protists with a porous calcium carbonate shell and long cytoplasmic extensions. **334**

fossil Physical evidence of an organism that lived in the ancient past. **255**

founder effect After a small group of individuals found a new population, allele frequencies in the new population differ from those in the original population. **284**

fovea Retinal region where cone cells are most concentrated. **526**

free radical Atom with an unpaired electron; most are highly reactive and can damage biological molecules. **27**

frequency-dependent selection Mode of natural selection in which a trait's adaptive value depends on its frequency in a population. **283**

fruit Mature ovary of a flowering plant; often with accessory parts; encloses a seed or seeds. **357**, **458**

FSH *See* follicle-stimulating hormone.

functional group An atom (other than hydrogen) or a small molecular group bonded to a carbon of an organic compound; imparts a specific chemical property. **39**

fungus Single-celled or multicellular eukaryotic consumer that digests food outside its body, then absorbs the resulting breakdown products. Has chitin-containing cell walls. **9**, **364**

gallbladder Organ that stores and concentrates bile produced by the liver. **636**

gamete Mature, haploid reproductive cell; e.g., an egg or a sperm. **194**

gametophyte Multicelled, haploid, gamete-producing body that forms in the life cycle of land plants and some multicelled algae. **338**, **346**

ganglion Cluster of nerve cell bodies. **498**

gap junction Cell junction that forms a closable channel across the plasma membranes of adjoining animal cells. **69**

gastric fluid Fluid secreted by the stomach lining; contains digestive enzymes, acid, and mucus. **634**

gastropod Mollusk in which the lower body consists of a broad "foot"; for example, a snail or slug. **386**

gastrovacular cavity Saclike gut that also functions in gas exchange. **380**, **630**

gastrula Three-layered structure formed by gastrulation during animal development. **668**

gastrulation Animal developmental process by which cell movements produce a three-layered gastrula. **668**

gene A part of a chromosome that encodes an RNA or protein product in its DNA sequence. Unit of hereditary information. **148**

gene expression Process by which the information in a gene guides assembly of an RNA or protein product. **149**

gene flow The movement of alleles into and out of a population. **285**

gene pool All the alleles of all the genes in a population; a pool of genetic resources. **275**

gene therapy Treating a genetic defect or disorder by transferring a normal or modified gene into the affected individual. **248**

genetically modified organism (GMO) Organism whose genome has been modified by genetic engineering. **246**

genetic code Complete set of sixty-four mRNA codons. **152**

genetic drift Change in allele frequency due to chance alone. **284**

genetic engineering Process by which deliberate changes are introduced into an individual's genome. **246**

genetic equilibrium Theoretical state in which an allele's frequency never changes in a population's gene pool. **276**

genome An organism's complete set of genetic material. **240**

genomics The study of genomes. **244**

genotype The particular set of alleles that is carried by an individual's chromosomes. **207**

genus plural **genera** A group of species that share a unique set of traits; first part of a species name. **10**

geologic time scale Chronology of Earth's history; correlates geologic and evolutionary events. **264**

germ cell Immature reproductive cell that gives rise to haploid gametes when it divides. **194**

germinate To resume metabolic activity after dormancy. **456**

germ layer One of three primary layers in an early embryo. **668**

GH See growth hormone.

gibberellin Plant hormone that induces stem elongation; also helps seeds break dormancy. **465**

gill Of an aquatic animal, a folded or filamentous respiratory organ in which blood or hemolymph exchanges gases with water. **615**

global climate change A currently ongoing rise in average temperature that is altering climate patterns around the world. **755**

glomeromycete Fungus that partners with plant roots; fungal hyphae grow inside the cell walls of root cells. **365**

glomerular filtration Protein-free plasma forced out of glomerular capillaries by blood pressure enters Bowman's capsule. **654**

glomerulus In a kidney, a ball of leaky capillaries enclosed by Bowman's capsule. **653**

glottis Opening formed when the vocal cords relax. **618**

glucagon Pancreatic hormone that raises blood glucose level. **546**

glycolysis Set of reactions in which a six-carbon sugar (such as glucose) is broken down to two pyruvate for a net yield of two ATP. First part of carbohydrate-breakdown pathways. **116**

GMO See genetically modified organism.

Golgi body Membrane-enclosed organelle that modifies proteins and lipids, then packages the finished products into vesicles. **63**

gonad Gamete-forming organ of an animal; testes or ovaries. **666**

Gondwana Supercontinent that existed before Pangea, more than 500 million years ago. **263**

Gram-positive bacteria Bacteria with thick cell walls that are colored purple when prepared for microscopy by Gram staining. **323**

grassland Biome in the interior of continents; perennial grasses and other nonwoody plants adapted to grazing and fire predominate. **771**

gravitropism Plant growth in a direction influenced by gravity. **468**

gray matter Central nervous system tissue that consists of neuron axon terminals, cell bodies, and dendrites, along with some neuroglial cells. **508**

grazing food chain Food chain in which energy is transferred from producers to grazers (herbivores). **750**

green alga Single-celled, colonial, or multicelled photosynthetic protist that has chloroplasts containing chlorophylls *a* and *b*. **338**

greenhouse effect Warming of Earth's lower atmosphere and surface as a result of heat trapped by greenhouse gases. **755**

ground tissues Tissues that make up the bulk of the plant body; all plant tissues other than vascular and dermal tissues. **422**

groundwater Soil water and water in aquifers. **752**

growth In multicelled species, an increase in the number, size, and volume of cells. **7**

growth factor Molecule that stimulates mitosis and differentiation. **184**

growth hormone (GH) Anterior pituitary hormone that regulates growth and metabolism. **541**

guard cell One of a pair of cells that define a stoma across the epidermis of a plant leaf or stem. **446**

gymnosperm Seed plant whose seeds are not enclosed within a fruit; a conifer, cycad, ginkgo, or gnetophyte. **354**

habitat Type of environment in which a species typically lives. **730**

habituation Learning not to respond to a repeated neutral stimulus. **699**

half-life Characteristic time it takes for half of a quantity of a radioisotope to decay. **260**

haploid Having one of each type of chromosome characteristic of the species. **194**

heart Muscular organ that pumps blood through a body. **570**

hemolymph Fluid that circulates in an open circulatory system. **570**

hemostasis Process by which blood clots in response to injury. **577**

herbivory An animal feeds on plants or plant parts. **735**

hermaphrodite Animal that has both male and female gonads, either simultaneously or at different times in its life. **379**, **666**

heterotherm Animal that sometimes maintains its temperature by producing metabolic heat, and at other times allows its temperature to fluctuate with the environment. **658**

heterotroph Consumer. An organism that obtains carbon from organic compounds assembled by other organisms. **100**

heterozygous Having two different alleles of a gene; describes genotype of a diploid organism. **207**

hippocampus Brain region essential to formation of declarative memories. **513**

histone Type of protein that structurally organizes eukaryotic chromosomes. **136**

HIV (human immunodeficiency virus) Virus that causes AIDS. **317**

homeostasis Process in which an organism keeps its internal conditions within tolerable ranges by sensing and responding to change. **7**

homeotic gene Type of master gene; its expression controls formation of specific body parts during development. **166**

hominin Human or an extinct primate species more closely related to humans than to any other primates. **412**

Homo erectus Extinct hominin that arose about 1.8 million years ago in East Africa; migrated out of Africa. **414**

Homo habilis Extinct hominin; earliest named *Homo* species; known only from Africa, where it arose 2.3 million years ago. **414**

homologous chromosomes Chromosomes with the same length, shape, and genes. In sexual reproducers, one member of a homologous pair is paternal and the other is maternal. **179**

homologous structures Body structures that are similar in different lineages because they evolved in a common ancestor. **266**

Homo neanderthalensis Extinct hominin; closest known relative of *H. sapiens*; lived in Africa, Europe, Asia. **414**

homozygous Having identical alleles of a gene; describes genotype of a diploid organism. **207**

horizontal gene transfer Transfer of genetic material between existing individuals. **320**

hormone *See* animal hormone or plant hormone.

hot spot Threatened region that is habitat for species not found elsewhere and is considered a high priority for conservation efforts. **792**

human immunodeficiency virus *See* HIV.

humus Decaying organic matter in soil. **440**

hybrid The heterozygous offspring of a cross or mating between two individuals that breed true for different forms of a trait. **207**

hydrocarbon Compound or region of one that consists only of carbon and hydrogen atoms. **38**

hydrogen bond Attraction between a covalently bonded hydrogen atom and another atom taking part in a separate covalent bond. Collectively, they impart special properties to liquid water and stabilize the structure of biological molecules. **30**

hydrolysis Water-requiring chemical reaction in which an enzyme breaks a molecule into smaller subunits. **39**

hydrophilic Describes a substance that dissolves easily in water. **30**

hydrophobic Describes a substance that resists dissolving in water. **30**

hydrostatic skeleton Of soft-bodied invertebrates, a fluid-filled chamber that muscles exert force against, redistributing the fluid. **380, 556**

hydrothermal vent Underwater opening where hot, mineral-rich water streams out from an underwater opening in Earth's crust. **302, 778**

hypertonic Describes a fluid that has a high solute concentration relative to another fluid separated by a semipermeable membrane. **88**

hypha Component of a fungal mycelium; a filament made up of cells arranged end to end. **364**

hypothalamus Forebrain region that controls processes related to homeostasis and has endocrine functions. **511, 540**

hypothesis Testable explanation of a natural phenomenon. **12**

hypotonic Describes a fluid that has a low solute concentration relative to another fluid separated by a semipermeable membrane. **88**

immigration Movement of individuals into a population. **714**

immunity The body's ability to resist and fight infections. **590**

immunization Any procedure designed to induce immunity to a specific disease. **607**

imprinting Learning that can occur only during a specific interval in an animal's life. **698**

inbreeding Mating among close relatives. **285**

incomplete dominance Effect in which one allele is not fully dominant over another, so the heterozygous phenotype is an intermediate blend between the two homozygous phenotypes. **212**

independent variable In an experiment, variable that is controlled by an experimenter in order to explore its relationship to a dependent variable. **13**

indicator species Species whose presence and abundance in a community provides information about conditions in the community. **739**

induced-fit model Substrate binding to an active site improves the fit between the two. **82**

inductive reasoning Drawing a conclusion based on observation. **12**

inferior vena cava Vein that delivers blood from the lower body to the heart. **573**

inflammation A local response to tissue damage or infection; characterized by redness, warmth, swelling, and pain. **594**

inheritance Transmission of DNA to offspring. **7**

innate immunity In all multicelled organisms, set of immediate, general defenses against infection. **590**

inner ear Fluid-filled cochlea and vestibular apparatus. **528**

insect Most diverse arthropod group; members have six legs, two antennae, and, in some groups, wings. **392**

insertion Mutation in which one or more nucleotides become inserted into DNA. **156**

instinctive behavior An innate response to a simple stimulus. **698**

insulin Pancreatic hormone that lowers blood glucose level. **546**

intermediate disturbance hypothesis Species richness is greatest in communities with moderate levels of disturbance. **739**

intermediate filament Stable cytoskeletal element that structurally supports cell membranes and tissues. **66**

internal fertilization Sperm fertilize eggs inside a female's body. **667**

interneuron Neuron that both receives signals from and sends signals to other neurons. Located mainly in the brain and spinal cord. **500**

interphase In a eukaryotic cell cycle, the interval between mitotic divisions when a cell grows, roughly doubles the number of its cytoplasmic components, and replicates its DNA. **178**

interspecific competition Competition between members of different species. **732**

interstitial fluid Fluid in spaces between body cells. **480**

intervertebral disk Cartilage disk between two vertebrae. **556**

intraspecific competition Competition for resources among members of the same species. **716**

intron Nucleotide sequence that intervenes between exons and is removed during post-transcriptional modification. **151**

inversion Structural rearrangement of a chromosome in which part of the DNA becomes oriented in the reverse direction. **228**

invertebrate Animal that does not have a backbone. **376**

ion Charged atom. **27**

ionic bond Type of chemical bond in which a strong mutual attraction links ions of opposite charge. **28**

iris Circular muscle that adjusts the shape of the pupil to regulate how much light enters the eye. **525**

Glossary (continued)

isotonic Describes two fluids with identical solute concentrations and separated by a semipermeable membrane. **88**

isotopes Forms of an element that differ in the number of neutrons their atoms carry. **24**

jawless fish Fish with a skeleton of cartilage, no fins or jaws; a lamprey or hagfish. **402**

joint Region where bones meet. **559**

karyotype Image of an individual's set of chromosomes arranged by size, length, shape, and centromere location. **137**

key innovation An evolutionary adaptation that gives its bearer the opportunity to exploit a particular environment much more efficiently or in a new way. **292**

keystone species A species that has a disproportionately large effect on community structure relative to its abundance. **740**

kidney Organ of the vertebrate urinary system that filters blood, adjusts its composition, and forms urine. **651**

kinetic energy The energy of motion. **78**

knockout An experiment in which a gene is deliberately inactivated in a living organism; also, an organism that carries a knocked-out gene. **166**

Krebs cycle Cyclic pathway that, along with acetyl–CoA formation, breaks down pyruvate to carbon dioxide in aerobic respiration's second stage. **118**

K-selection Selection favoring traits that allow their bearers to outcompete others for limited resources; occurs when a population is near its environment's carrying capacity. **719**

labor Process of giving birth; expulsion of a placental mammal from its mother's uterus by muscle contractions. **690**

lactate fermentation Anaerobic sugar breakdown pathway that produces ATP and lactate. **122**

lactation Milk production by a female mammal. **690**

lancelet Invertebrate chordate that has a fishlike shape and retains the defining chordate traits into adulthood. **400**

large intestine Organ that receives digestive waste from the small intestine and concentrates it as feces. **633**

larva Sexually immature stage in some animal life cycles. **379**

larynx Short airway containing the vocal cords (voice box). **618**

lateral meristem Vascular cambium or cork cambium; cylindrical sheet of meristem that runs lengthwise through shoots and roots; gives rise to secondary growth (thickening) in a plant. **432**

law of independent assortment During meiosis, members of a pair of genes on homologous chromosomes tend to be distributed into gametes independently of other gene pairs. **210**

law of nature Generalization that describes a consistent natural phenomenon for which there is incomplete scientific explanation. **18**

law of segregation The two members of each pair of genes on homologous chromosomes end up in different gametes during meiosis. **209**

leaching Process by which water moving through soil removes nutrients from it. **440**

learned behavior Behavior that is modified by experience. **698**

lek Of some birds, a communal mating display area for males. **703**

lens Disk-shaped structure that bends light rays so they fall on an eye's photoreceptors. **524**

lethal mutation Mutation that alters phenotype so drastically that it causes death. **274**

LH See luteinizing hormone.

lichen Composite organism consisting of a fungus and green algae or cyanobacteria. **368**

life history A set of traits related to growth, survival, and reproduction such as life span, age-specific mortality, age at first reproduction, and number of breeding events. **718**

ligament Strap of dense connective tissue that holds bones together at a joint. **559**

light-dependent reactions First stage of photosynthesis; metabolic pathway that converts light energy to chemical energy. A noncyclic pathway produces oxygen; a cyclic pathway does not. **103**

light-independent reactions Second stage of photosynthesis; metabolic pathway that uses ATP and NADPH to assemble sugars from water and CO_2. E.g., Calvin–Benson cycle in C3 plants. **103**

lignin Material that strengthens the cell walls of vascular plants. **68, 346**

limbic system Group of structures deep in the brain that function in expression of emotion. **513**

lineage Line of descent. **256**

linkage group All genes on a chromosome. **211**

lipid A fat, steroid, or wax. **42**

lipid bilayer Double layer of lipids (mainly phospholipids) arranged tail-to-tail; structural foundation of all cell membranes. **43**

loam Soil with roughly equal amounts of sand, silt, and clay. **440**

lobe-finned fish Jawed fish with fleshy fins that contain bones; a coelacanth or lungfish. **403**

locomotion Self-propelled movement from place to place. **554**

locus Location of a gene on a chromosome. **206**

logistic growth A population grows exponentially at first, then growth slows as population size approaches the environment's carrying capacity for that species. **716**

loop of Henle U-shaped portion of a kidney tubule; connects the proximal and distal regions of the tubule. **653**

loose connective tissue Connective tissue that consists of fibroblasts and fibers scattered in a gel-like matrix. **484**

lung Internal respiratory organ that exchanges gases with the air. **615**

luteinizing hormone (LH) Anterior pituitary hormone; with roles in ovulation, corpus luteum formation, and sperm production. **678**

lymph Fluid in the lymph vascular system. **584**

lymph node Small mass of lymphatic tissue through which lymph filters; contains many lymphocytes (B and T cells). **584**

lymph vascular system System of vessels that takes up interstitial fluid and carries it (as lymph) to the blood. **584**

lysogenic pathway Bacteriophage replication path in which viral DNA becomes integrated into the host's chromosome and is passed to the host's descendants. **317**

lysosome Enzyme-filled vesicle that breaks down cellular wastes and debris. **62**

lysozyme Antibacterial enzyme in body secretions such as saliva and mucus. **593**

lytic pathway Bacteriophage replication pathway in which a virus immediately replicates in its host and kills it. **316**

macroevolution Large-scale evolutionary patterns and trends; e.g., adaptive radiation, exaptation. **292**

macrophage Phagocytic white blood cell that patrols tissues and tissue fluids. **591**

Malpighian tubules Of insects and spiders, tubular organs that take up waste solutes and deliver them to the gut for excretion. **650**

mammal Animal with hair or fur; females secrete milk from mammary glands. **409**

mark–recapture sampling Method of estimating population size of mobile animals by marking individuals, releasing them, then checking the proportion of marks among individuals recaptured at a later time. **713**

marsupial Mammal in which young are born at an early stage and complete development in a pouch on the mother's surface. **409**

mass number Of an isotope, the total number of protons and neutrons in the atomic nucleus. **24**

mast cell Stationary white blood cell that releases the contents of its granules in response to antigen as well as signaling molecules from the endocrine and nervous system. Factor in inflammation. **591**

master gene Gene encoding a product that affects the expression of many other genes. **166**

mechanoreceptor Sensory receptor that responds to pressure, position, or acceleration. **520**

medulla oblongata Hindbrain region that influences breathing and controls reflexes such as coughing and vomiting. **510**

megaspore Of seed plants, haploid spore that forms in an ovule and gives rise to an egg-producing gametophyte. **352, 456**

meiosis Nuclear division process that halves the chromosome number. Basis of sexual reproduction. **194**

melatonin Pineal gland hormone that regulates sleep–wake cycles and seasonal changes. **542**

membrane potential Voltage difference across a cell membrane; arises from differences in charge on opposite sides of the membrane. **501**

memory cell Long-lived, antigen-sensitized B cell or T cell that forms in a primary response and is held in reserve to act in a secondary response. **598**

meninges Membranes that enclose the brain and spinal cord. **508**

menopause Permanent cessation of menstrual cycles. **679**

menstrual cycle Reproductive cycle in which the uterus lining thickens and then, if pregnancy does not occur, is shed. **678**

menstruation Flow of shed uterine tissue out of the vagina. **678**

meristem In a plant, a zone of undifferentiated cells; all plant growth arises from divisions of meristem cells. **432**

mesoderm Middle tissue layer of a three-layered animal embryo. **376, 668**

mesophyll Photosynthetic parenchyma. **425**

messenger RNA (mRNA) RNA that has a protein-building message. **148**

metabolic pathway Series of enzyme-mediated reactions by which cells build, remodel, or break down an organic molecule. **84**

metabolism All of the enzyme-mediated chemical reactions by which cells acquire and use energy as they build and break down organic molecules. **39**

metamorphosis Dramatic remodeling of body form during the transition from larva to adult. **389**

metaphase Stage of mitosis at which all chromosomes are aligned midway between spindle poles. **181**

metastasis The process in which malignant cells of a neoplasm spread from one part of the body to another. **185**

methanogen Organism that produces methane gas (CH_4) as a metabolic by-product. **326**

MHC markers Self-proteins on the surface of human body cells. **596**

microevolution Change in allele frequency. **275**

microfilament Cytoskeletal element composed of actin subunits. Reinforces cell membranes; functions in movement and muscle contraction. **66**

microspore Of seed plants, a haploid spore formed in pollen sacs; gives rise to a pollen grain. **352, 456**

microtubule Hollow cytoskeletal element composed of tubulin subunits. Involved in movement of a cell or its parts. **66**

microvilli Thin projections that increase the surface area of some epithelial cells. **482, 635**

middle ear Eardrum and the tiny bones that transfer sound to the inner ear. **528**

mimicry An evolutionary pattern in which one species becomes more similar in appearance to another. **735**

mineral In the diet, an inorganic substance that is required in small amounts for normal metabolism. **641**

mitochondrion Double-membraned organelle that produces ATP by aerobic respiration in eukaryotes. **64**

mitosis Nuclear division mechanism that maintains the chromosome number. Basis of body growth and tissue repair in multicelled

eukaryotes; also asexual reproduction in some multicelled eukaryotes and many single-celled ones. **178**

model Analogous system used to test an object or event that cannot be tested directly. **12**

mold Fungus that grows as a mass of asexually reproducing hyphae. **365**

molecule Two or more atoms joined by chemical bonds. **4**

mollusk Invertebrate with a reduced coelom and a mantle. For example, a bivalve, gastropod, or cephalopod. **386**

molting Periodic shedding of an outer body layer or part. **388**

monocot Flowering plant with one seed leaf (cotyledon). For example, a grass, orchids, or palm. **357**

monohybrid cross Cross between two individuals identically heterozygous for one gene; e.g., $Aa \times Aa$. **208**

monomers Molecules that are subunits of polymers. **39**

monophyletic group An ancestor in which a derived trait evolved, together with all of its descendants. **294**

monotreme Egg-laying mammal. **409**

monsoon Wind that reverses direction seasonally. **766**

morphogen Substance that regulates development by affecting cells in a concentration-dependent manner. **670**

morphological convergence Evolutionary pattern in which similar body parts (analogous structures) evolve separately in different lineages. **266**

morphological divergence Evolutionary pattern in which a body part of an ancestor changes in its descendants. **266**

motor neuron Neuron that controls a muscle or gland. **500**

motor protein Type of energy-using protein that interacts with cytoskeletal elements to move the cell's parts or the whole cell. **66**

motor unit One motor neuron and the muscle fibers it controls. **563**

mRNA *See* messenger RNA.

multicellular organism Organism that consists of interdependent cells of multiple types. **310, 332**

multiple allele system Gene for which three or more alleles persist in a population at relatively high frequency. **212**

Glossary (continued)

muscle tension Force exerted by a contracting muscle. **563**

muscle tissue Tissue that consists mainly of contractile cells. **486**

mutation Permanent change in the nucleotide sequence of DNA. **140**

mutualism Species interaction that benefits both species. **731**

mycelium Mass of threadlike filaments (hyphae) that make up the body of a multicelled fungus. **364**

mycorrhiza Mutually beneficial partnership between a fungus and a plant root. **368**

myelin Fatty material produced by neuroglial cells; insulates axons and thus speeds conduction of action potentials. **503**

myofibril Within a muscle fiber, a threadlike contractile component made up of sarcomeres arranged end to end. **561**

myoglobin Muscle protein that reversibly binds oxygen. **564**

myosin ATP-dependent motor protein; makes up the thick filaments in a sarcomere. **561**

myriapod Long-bodied terrestrial arthropod with one pair of antennae and many similar segments; a centipede or millipede. **390**

natural killer cell *See* NK cell.

natural selection Differential survival and reproduction of individuals of a population based on differences in shared, heritable traits. Driven by environmental pressures. **257**

nectar Sweet fluid exuded by some flowers; attracts animal pollinators. **455**

negative feedback mechanism A change causes a response that reverses the change; important mechanism of homeostasis. **492**

neoplasm An accumulation of abnormally dividing cells. **184**

nephridium Of some invertebrates, an organ that takes up body fluid and expels excess water and solutes through a pore at the body surface. **650**

nephron A kidney tubule and associated capillaries; filters blood and forms urine. **652**

nerve Neuron fibers bundled inside a sheath of connective tissue. **498**

nerve cord Bundle of nerve fibers running the length of a body. **498**

nerve net Of cnidarians, a mesh of interacting neurons with no central control organ. **380**, **498**

nervous tissue Animal tissue composed of neurons and supporting cells; detects stimuli and controls responses to them. **487**

neuroglial cell Cell that supports neurons. **498**

neuromuscular junction Synapse between a neuron and a muscle. **504**

neuron One of the cells that make up communication lines of nervous systems; transmits electrical signals along its plasma membrane and sends chemical messages to other cells. **487**, **498**

neurosecretory cell Specialized neuron that secretes a hormone into the blood in response to an action potential. **540**

neurotransmitter Chemical signal released by axon terminals of a neuron. **504**

neutral mutation A mutation that has no effect on survival or reproduction. **274**

neutron Uncharged subatomic particle. **24**

neutrophil Most abundant circulating phagocytic white blood cell. **591**

niche *See* ecological niche.

nitrification Conversion of ammonium to nitrate. **756**

nitrogen cycle Movement of nitrogen among the atmosphere, soil, and water, and into and out of food webs. **756**

nitrogen fixation Incorporation of nitrogen gas (N_2) into ammonia (NH_3). **322**, **756**

NK cell Natural killer cell. Lymphocyte that can kill cancer cells undetectable by cytotoxic T cells. **591**

node A region of stem where new shoots form. **426**

nondisjunction Failure of sister chromatids or homologous chromosomes to separate during nuclear division. **230**

nonvascular plant Plant that does not have xylem and phloem; a bryophyte such as a moss. **346**

normal flora Microorganisms that typically live on human surfaces, including the interior tubes and cavities of the digestive and respiratory tracts. **324**, **592**

notochord Stiff rod of connective tissue that runs the length of the body in chordate larvae or embryos. **400**

nuclear envelope A double membrane that constitutes the outer boundary of the nucleus. Pores in the membrane control which substances can cross. **61**

nucleic acid Polymer of nucleotides; DNA or RNA. **46**

nucleic acid hybridization Convergence of complementary nucleic acid strands. Arises because of base-pairing interactions. **138**

nucleoid Of a bacterium or archaeon, region of cytoplasm where the DNA is concentrated. **59**

nucleolus In a cell nucleus, a dense, irregularly shaped region where ribosomal subunits are assembled. **61**

nucleoplasm Viscous fluid enclosed by the nuclear envelope. **61**

nucleosome A length of chromosomal DNA wound twice around a spool of histone proteins. **136**

nucleotide Small organic compound that is a subunit of nucleic acids. Consists of a five-carbon sugar, nitrogen-containing base, and one or more phosphate groups. E.g., adenine, guanine, cytosine, thymine, uracil. **46**

nucleus Of a eukaryotic cell, organelle with a double membrane that holds, protects, and controls access to the cell's DNA. **8**, **52** Of an atom, core region occupied by protons and neutrons. **24**

nutrient Substance that an organism needs for growth and survival but cannot make for itself. **6**

olfactory receptor Chemoreceptor involved in the sense of smell. **522**

oncogene Gene that helps transform a normal cell into a tumor cell. **184**

oocyte Immature egg. **676**

open circulatory system Circulatory system in which hemolymph leaves vessels and flows among tissues before returning to the heart. **386**, **570**

operator In prokaryotes, a binding site in DNA for a repressor. **164**

operon Group of genes together with a promoter–operator DNA sequence that controls their transcription. **170**

organ In multicelled organisms, a structure that consists of tissues engaged in a collective task. **5**

organelle Structure that carries out a specialized metabolic function inside a cell; e.g., a mitochondrion. **52**

organic Describes a molecule that consists mainly of carbon and hydrogen atoms. **38**

organism Individual that consists of one or more cells. **4**

organs of equilibrium Sensory organs that respond to body position and motion; function in sense of balance. **530**

organ system In multicelled organisms, set of organs that interact closely in a collective task. **5**

Glossary (continued)

osmosis Diffusion of water across a selectively permeable membrane; occurs when the fluids on either side of the membrane are not isotonic. **89**

osmotic pressure Amount of turgor that prevents osmosis into cytoplasm or other hypertonic fluid. **89**

outer ear External ear (pinna) and the air-filled auditory canal. **528**

ovarian follicle In animals, immature egg and surrounding cells. **677**

ovary In flowering plants, the enlarged base of a carpel, inside which one or more ovules form and eggs are fertilized. Matures as a fruit. **356, 454** In animals, an egg-producing gonad. **668**

oviduct Duct between an ovary and the uterus. **676**

ovulation Release of a secondary oocyte from an ovary. **677**

ovule Of seed plants, reproductive structure in which egg-bearing gametophyte develops; after fertilization, it matures into a seed. **352, 454**

ovum Mature animal egg. **681**

ozone layer Upper atmospheric region with a high concentration of ozone (O_3) that screens out incoming UV radiation. **307, 790**

pain Perception of tissue injury. **521**

pain receptor Sensory receptor that responds to tissue damage. **520**

pancreas Organ that secretes digestive enzymes into the small intestine, and the hormones insulin and glucagon into the blood. **546**

Pangea Supercontinent that formed about 270 million years ago. **262**

parapatric speciation Speciation pattern in which populations speciate while in contact along a common border. **291**

parasitism Relationship in which one species withdraws nutrients from another species, without immediately killing it. **736**

parasitoid An insect that lays eggs in another insect, and whose young devour their host from the inside. **736**

parasympathetic neurons Neurons of the autonomic system that encourage digestion and other "housekeeping" tasks. **506**

parathyroid glands Four small endocrine glands on the rear of the thyroid that secrete parathyroid hormone. **543**

parathyroid hormone Hormone that regulates the concentration of calcium ions in the blood. **543**

parenchyma Simple tissue composed of living cells with different functions depending on location; main component of ground tissue. **424**

passive transport Membrane-crossing mechanism that requires no energy input. **90**

pathogen Disease-causing agent. **318**

PCR *See* polymerase chain reaction.

pedigree Chart showing the pattern of inheritance of a trait through generations in a family. **222**

pelagic province The ocean's open waters. **778**

pellicle Layer of proteins that gives shape to many unwalled, single-celled protists. **333**

penis Male organ of intercourse. **674**

peptide Short chain of amino acids linked by peptide bonds. **44**

peptide bond A bond between the amine group of one amino acid and the carboxyl group of another. Joins amino acids in proteins. **44**

per capita growth rate (*r*) Of a population, the change in individuals added over some time interval, divided by the number of individuals in the population. **714**

perception The meaning a brain derives from a sensation. **520**

pericycle In a plant, layer of cells just inside the endodermis of a root vascular cylinder. **430**

periderm Plant dermal tissue that replaces epidermis during secondary growth of woody stems and roots. **433**

periodic table Tabular arrangement of all known elements by their atomic number. **24**

peripheral nervous system Of vertebrates, nerves that carry signals between the central nervous system and the rest of the body. **499**

peristalsis Wavelike smooth muscle contractions that propel food through the digestive tract. **633**

peritubular capillaries Capillaries that surround a kidney tubule and exchange substances with it during urine formation. **653**

permafrost Continually frozen soil layer that lies beneath arctic tundra and prevents water from draining. **773**

peroxisome Enzyme-filled vesicle that breaks down amino acids, fatty acids, and toxic substances. **62**

pH Measure of the number of hydrogen ions in a fluid. Decreases with increasing acidity. **32**

phagocytosis "Cell eating"; an endocytic pathway by which a cell engulfs particles such as microbes or cellular debris. **92**

pharynx Throat; opens to airways and digestive tract. **618**

phenotype An individual's observable traits. **207**

pheromone Chemical that serves as a communication signal among members of an animal species. **522, 700**

phloem Complex vascular tissue of plants; its living sieve elements compose sieve tubes that distribute sugars. Each sieve element has an associated companion cell that provides it with metabolic support. **346, 425**

phospholipid A lipid with a phosphate group in its hydrophilic head, and two nonpolar tails typically derived from fatty acids. Major component of cell membranes. **43**

phosphorus cycle Movement of phosphorus among Earth's rocks and waters, and into and out of food webs. **758**

phosphorylation A phosphate-group transfer. **87**

photoautotroph Organism that obtains carbon from carbon dioxide and energy from light. **321**

photoheterotroph Organism that obtains carbon from organic compounds and energy from light. **321**

photolysis Process by which light energy breaks down a molecule. **104**

photoperiodism Biological response to seasonal changes in the relative lengths of day and night. **470**

photoreceptor Sensory receptor that responds to light. **520**

photorespiration Reaction in which rubisco attaches oxygen instead of carbon dioxide to ribulose bisphosphate. **106**

photosynthesis Metabolic pathway by which most autotrophs use light energy to make sugars from carbon dioxide and water. Converts light energy into chemical bond energy. **6**

photosystem Cluster of pigments and proteins that converts light energy to chemical energy in photosynthesis. **104**

phototropism Plant growth in a direction influenced by light. **468**

phylogeny Evolutionary history of a species or group of species. **294**

phytochrome A light-sensitive pigment that helps set plant circadian rhythms based on length of night. **470**

Glossary (continued)

pigment An organic molecule that selectively absorbs light of certain wavelengths. Reflected light imparts a characteristic color. E.g., chlorophyll. **100**

pilus A protein filament that projects from the surface of some bacterial cells. **59**

pineal gland Endocrine gland in the brain; secretes melatonin under low-light or dark conditions. **542**

pioneer species Species that can colonize a new habitat. **738**

pituitary gland Endocrine gland in the forebrain; interacts closely with the adjacent hypothalamus. **540**

placenta Of placental mammals, organ that forms during pregnancy and allows diffusion of substances between the maternal and embryonic bloodstreams. **667**

placental mammal Mammal in which maternal and embryonic bloodstreams exchange materials by means of a placenta. **409**

placozoans Group of tiny marine animals having a simple asymmetrical body and a small genome; considered an ancient lineage. **378**

plankton Community of tiny drifting or swimming organisms. **334**

plant Multicelled, typically photosynthetic eukaryote; develops from an embryo that forms on the parent and is nourished by it. **9, 346**

plant hormone Extracellular signaling molecule of plants that exerts its effect at very low concentration. E.g., auxin, gibberellin. **463**

plaque *See* dental plaque.

plasma Fluid portion of blood. **576**

plasma membrane A cell's outermost membrane; controls movement of substances into and out of the cell. **52**

plasmid Of many prokaryotes, a small ring of nonchromosomal DNA. **59**

plasmodesmata Cell junctions that form an open channel between the cytoplasm of adjacent plant cells. **69**

plasmodial slime mold Protist that feeds as a multinucleated mass and forms a spore-bearing structure when environmental conditions become unfavorable. **340**

plastid One of several types of double-membraned organelles in plants and algal cells; for example, a chloroplast or amyloplast. **65**

platelet Cell fragment that helps blood clot. **577**

plate tectonics theory Theory that Earth's outer layer of rock is cracked into plates, the slow movement of which rafts continents to new locations over geologic time. **262**

pleiotropy Effect in which a single gene affects multiple traits. **213**

plot sampling Using demographics observed in sample plots to estimate demographics of a population as a whole. **712**

polar body Tiny cell produced by unequal cytoplasmic division during egg production. **677**

polarity Separation of charge into positive and negative regions. **28**

pollen grain Walled, immature male gametophyte of a seed plant. Forms in an anther. **347, 454**

pollen sac Of seed plants, reproductive structure in which pollen grains develop. **352**

pollination Arrival of pollen on a receptive stigma of a seed plant. **352, 454**

pollination vector Environmental agent that moves pollen grains from one plant to another. **454**

pollinator An animal that facilitates pollination by moving pollen from one plant to another. **358, 454**

pollutant A substance that is released into the environment by human activities and interferes with the function of organisms that evolved in the absence of the substance or with lower levels. **789**

polymer Molecule that consists of multiple monomers. **39**

polymerase chain reaction (PCR) Method that rapidly generates many copies of a specific section of DNA. **240**

polypeptide Long chain of amino acids linked by peptide bonds. **44**

polyploid Having three or more of each type of chromosome characteristic of the species. **230**

pons Hindbrain region that influences breathing and serves as a bridge to the adjacent midbrain. **510**

population A group of organisms of the same species who live in a specific location and breed with one another more often than they breed with members of other populations. **5, 274**

population density Number of individuals per unit area. **712**

population distribution Location of population members relative to one another; clumped, uniformly dispersed, or randomly dispersed. **712**

population size Total number of individuals in a population. **712**

positive feedback mechanism A response intensifies the conditions that caused its occurrence. **502**

potential energy Stored energy. **79**

Precambrian Period from 4.6 billion to 542 million years ago. **310**

predation One species captures, kills, and eats another. **734**

prediction Statement, based on a hypothesis, about a condition that should exist if the hypothesis is correct. **12**

pressure flow theory Explanation of how a difference in turgor between sieve elements in source and sink regions pushes sugar-rich fluid through a sieve tube in a plant. **447**

primary endosymbiosis Over generations, evolution of an organelle from bacteria that entered a host cell and lived inside it. **332**

primary growth Of a plant, lengthening of young shoots and roots; originates at apical meristems. **432**

primary motor cortex Region of frontal lobe that controls voluntary movement. **512**

primary production The rate at which an ecosystem's producers capture and store energy. **748**

primary succession A new community becomes established in an area where there was previously no soil. **738**

primary wall The first cell wall of young plant cells. **68**

primate Mammal having grasping hands with nails and a body adapted to climbing; for example, a lemur, monkey, ape, or human. **410**

primer Short, single strand of DNA that base-pairs with a targeted DNA sequence. **138**

prion Infectious protein. **46**

probability The chance that a particular outcome of an event will occur; depends on the total number of outcomes possible. **16**

probe Short fragment of DNA labeled with a tracer; designed to hybridize with a nucleotide sequence of interest. **240**

producer Organism that makes its own food using energy and nonbiological raw materials from the environment; an autotroph. **6, 748**

product A molecule that is produced by a reaction. **80**

progesterone Sex hormone secreted by ovaries; prepares a female body for pregnancy and helps maintain a pregnancy. **545, 676**

prokaryote Informal name for a single-celled organism without a nucleus; a bacterium or archaean. **8**

Glossary (continued)

promoter In DNA, a sequence to which RNA polymerase binds. **150**

prophase Stage of mitosis during which chromosomes condense and become attached to a newly forming spindle. **181**

prostate gland Exocrine gland that contributes to semen. **675**

protein Organic molecule that consists of one or more polypeptides. **44**

proteobacteria Most diverse bacterial lineage. **322**

protist Eukaryote that is not a plant, fungus, or animal. **8, 332**

protocell Membranous sac that contains interacting organic molecules; hypothesized to have formed prior to the earliest life forms. **304**

proton Positively charged subatomic particle. **24**

proto-oncogene Gene that, by mutation, can become an oncogene. **184**

protostomes Lineage of bilateral animals in which the first opening on the embryo surface develops into a mouth. **377**

proximal tubule Region of kidney tubule nearest Bowman's capsule. **652**

pseudocoelom Unlined body cavity around the gut. **377**

pseudopod A temporary protrusion that helps some eukaryotic cells move and engulf prey. **67**

puberty Period when reproductive organs begin to function. **673**

pulmonary artery Vessel that carries oxygen-poor blood from the heart to a lung. **572**

pulmonary circuit Circuit through which blood flows from the heart to the lungs and back. **571**

pulmonary vein Vessel carrying oxygen-rich blood from a lung to the heart. **572**

pulse Brief expansion of artery walls that occurs when ventricles contract. **578**

Punnett square Diagram used to predict the genetic and phenotypic outcome of a breeding or mating. **208**

pupil Adjustable opening through which light enters the eye. **525**

pyruvate Three-carbon end product of glycolysis. **116**

radial symmetry Having parts arranged around a central axis, like the spokes of a wheel. **376**

radioactive decay Process by which atoms of a radioisotope emit energy and/or subatomic

particles when their nucleus spontaneously breaks up. **25**

radioisotope Isotope with an unstable nucleus. **24**

radiolaria Heterotrophic single-celled protists with a porous shell of silica and long cytoplasmic extensions. **334**

radiometric dating Method of estimating the age of a rock or fossil by measuring the content and proportions of a radioisotope and its daughter elements. **260**

rain shadow Dry region downwind of a coastal mountain range. **767**

ray-finned fish Jawed fish with fins supported by thin rays derived from skin; member of most diverse lineage of fishes. **403**

reabsorption *See* tubular reabsorption.

reactant A molecule that enters a reaction and is changed by participating in it. **80**

reaction Process of molecular change, in which reactants become products. **39**

receptor protein Plasma membrane protein that triggers a change in cell activity after binding to a particular substance. **57**

recessive Refers to an allele with an effect that is masked by a dominant allele on the homologous chromosome. **207**

recognition protein Plasma membrane protein that identifies a cell as belonging to self (one's own body or species). **57**

recombinant DNA A DNA molecule that contains genetic material from more than one organism. **238**

rectum Region of the large intestine in which feces are stored prior to excretion. **633**

red alga Photosynthetic protist; typically multicelled, with chloroplasts containing red accessory pigments (phycobilins). **338**

red blood cell Hemoglobin-filled blood cell that carries oxygen. **576**

red marrow Bone marrow that makes blood cells. **558**

redox reaction Oxidation–reduction reaction, in which one molecule accepts electrons (it becomes reduced) from another molecule (which becomes oxidized). Also called electron transfer. **85**

reflex Automatic response that occurs without conscious thought or learning. **508**

replacement fertility rate Number of children a woman must bear to replace herself with one daughter of reproductive age. **723**

repressor Transcription factor that reduces the rate of transcription. **164**

reproduction Processes by which parents produce offspring. *See* sexual reproduction, asexual reproduction. **7**

reproductive base Of a population, members of the reproductive and pre-reproductive age categories. **723**

reproductive cloning Technology that produces genetically identical individuals. **142**

reproductive isolation The end of gene flow between populations. **286**

reptile Amniote subgroup that includes lizards, snakes, turtles, crocodilians, and birds. **406**

resource partitioning Evolutionary process whereby species become adapted in different ways to access different portions of a limited resource; allows species with similar needs to coexist. **733**

respiration Physiological process by which an animal body supplies cells with oxygen and disposes of their waste carbon dioxide. **614**

respiratory cycle One inhalation and one exhalation. **620**

respiratory membrane Membrane consisting of alveolar epithelium, capillary endothelium, and their fused basement membranes. **622**

respiratory protein A protein that reversibly binds oxygen when the oxygen concentration is high and releases it when oxygen concentration is low. For example, hemoglobin. **614**

respiratory surface Moist surface across which gases are exchanged between animal cells and the external environment. **614**

resting potential Membrane potential of a neuron at rest. **501**

restriction enzyme Type of enzyme that cuts DNA at a specific nucleotide sequence. **238**

retina Photoreceptor-containing layer of tissue in an eye. **524**

retrovirus RNA virus that uses the enzyme reverse transcriptase to produce viral DNA in a host cell. **317**

reverse transcriptase An enzyme that uses mRNA as a template to make a strand of cDNA. **239**

rhizoid Threadlike structure that holds a nonvascular plant in place. **348**

rhizome Stem that grows horizontally along or under the ground. **350**

ribosomal RNA (rRNA) RNA that is part of ribosomes. **148**

ribosome Organelle of protein synthesis. An intact ribosome has two subunits, each

Glossary *(continued)*

composed of rRNA and proteins. Ribosomes are not enclosed by membranes. **59**

ribozyme RNA that functions as an enzyme. **305**

RNA Ribonucleic acid. Nucleic acid with roles in gene expression; consists of a single-stranded chain of nucleotides (adenine, guanine, cytosine, and uracil). *See* messenger RNA, transfer RNA, ribosomal RNA. **46**

RNA polymerase Enzyme that carries out transcription. **150**

RNA world Hypothetical early interval when RNA served as the genetic information. **305**

rod cell Photoreceptor that is active in dim light; provides coarse perception of image and detects motion. **526**

root hairs Hairlike, absorptive extensions of an epidermal cell on the surface of a plant root. **430**

root nodules Of some plant roots, swellings that contain nitrogen-fixing bacteria. **443**

roundworm Cylindrical worm with a pseudocoelom. **388**

rRNA *See* ribosomal RNA.

r-selection Selection that favors traits that allow their bearers to produce many offspring quickly; occurs when population density is low and resources are abundant. **719**

rubisco Ribulose bisphosphate carboxylase. Carbon-fixing enzyme of the Calvin–Benson cycle. **106**

ruminant Hoofed mammal with a multiple-chamber stomach that adapts it to a cellulose-rich diet. **631**

runoff Water that flows over soil into streams. **752**

sac fungi Fungi that form spores in a sac-shaped structure during sexual reproduction. **365**

salivary gland Exocrine gland that secretes saliva into the mouth. **633**

salt Compound that releases ions other than H+ and OH– when it dissolves in water. **30**

sampling error Difference between results derived from testing an entire group of events or individuals, and results derived from testing a subset of the group. **16**

SA node *See* sinoatrial node.

sarcomere Contractile unit of skeletal and cardiac muscle. **561**

sarcoplasmic reticulum Specialized endoplasmic reticulum in muscle cells; stores and releases calcium ions. **563**

saturated fat Triglyceride that has three saturated fatty acid tails. **42**

savanna Biome dominated by perennial grasses with a few scattered shrubs and trees. **771**

science Systematic study of the observable world. **12**

scientific method Systematically making, testing, and evaluating hypotheses about the natural world. **13**

scientific theory Hypothesis that has not been disproven after many years of rigorous testing. **18**

sclerenchyma Simple plant tissue composed of cells that die when they are mature; their lignin-reinforced cell walls remain and structurally support plant parts. Includes fibers, sclereids. **424**

SCNT *See* somatic cell nuclear transfer.

seamount An undersea mountain. **778**

secondary endosymbiosis Evolution of an organelle from a protist that itself contains organelles that arose by primary endosymbiosis. **332**

secondary growth Of a plant, thickening of older stems and roots; originates at lateral meristems. **432**

secondary sexual characteristics Traits that differ between the sexes but do not play a direct role in reproduction. **545**

secondary succession A new community develops in a site where a community previously existed. **738**

secondary wall Lignin-reinforced wall that forms inside the primary wall of a plant cell. **68**

second law of thermodynamics Energy disperses spontaneously. **78**

second messenger Molecule that forms inside a cell when a hormone binds to a receptor in the plasma membrane; sets in motion reactions that alter activity inside the cell. **537**

sedimentary cycle Biochemical cycle in which the atmosphere plays little role and rocks are the major reservoir. **758**

seed Embryo sporophyte of a seed plant packaged with nutritive tissue inside a protective coat. **347, 458**

seedless vascular plant Plant that disperses by releasing spores and has xylem and phloem. For example, a club moss or fern. **350**

segmentation Having a body composed of similar units that repeat along its length. **377**

selfish herd Temporary group that forms when individuals cluster to minimize their individual risk of predation. **704**

semen Sperm mixed with secretions from exocrine glands. **674**

semicircular canals Organs of equilibrium that respond to rotation and angular movement of the head; part of the vestibular apparatus. **530**

semiconservative replication Describes the process of DNA replication, which produces two copies of a DNA molecule: one strand of each copy is new, and the other is parental. **139**

seminal vesicles Exocrine glands that add sugary fluid to semen. **675**

seminiferous tubules In testes, tiny tubes in which sperm form. **674**

sensation Detection of a stimulus. **520**

sensory adaptation Slowing or cessation of a sensory receptor's response to an ongoing stimulus. **520**

sensory neuron Neuron that is activated when its receptor endings detect a specific stimulus, such as light or pressure. **500**

sensory receptor Cell or cell component that responds to a specific stimulus, such as temperature or light. **492**

sequencing Method of determining the order of nucleotides in DNA. **242**

sex chromosome Member of a pair of chromosomes that differs between males and females. **137**

sex hormone Steroid hormone produced by gonads; functions in reproduction and may affect secondary sexual characteristics. **545**

sexual dimorphism Difference in appearance between males and females of a species. **282, 702**

sexual reproduction Reproductive mode by which offspring arise from two parents and inherit genes from both. **192, 666**

sexual selection Mode of natural selection in which some individuals outreproduce others because they are better at securing mates. **282**

shell model Model of electron distribution in an atom. **26**

short tandem repeat In chromosomal DNA, sequences of a few nucleotides repeated multiple times in a row. Used in DNA profiling. **216**

sieve elements Living plant cells that compose sugar-conducting sieve tubes of phloem. Each sieve tube consists of a stack of sieve elements that meet end to end at sieve plates. **446**

sieve tube Sugar-conducting tube of phloem; consists of stacked sieve elements. **446**

single-nucleotide polymorphism (SNP) One-nucleotide DNA sequence variation carried by a measurable percentage of a population. **244**

sink Region of plant tissue where sugars are being used or stored. **447**

sinoatrial (SA) node Cardiac pacemaker; group of cells that spontaneously emits rhythmic action potentials that result in contraction of cardiac muscle. **575**

sister chromatids The two attached DNA molecules of a duplicated eukaryotic chromosome; attachs at the centromere. **136**

sister groups The two lineages that emerge from a node on a cladogram. **295**

skeletal muscle fiber Multinucleated contractile cell that runs the length of a skeletal muscle. **561**

skeletal muscle tissue Muscle that interacts with skeletal elements to move body parts; under voluntary control. **486**

sliding-filament model Explanation of how interactions among actin and myosin filaments shorten a sarcomere and bring about muscle contraction. **562**

small intestine Longest portion of the digestive tract, and the site of most digestion and absorption. **633**

smooth muscle tissue Muscle that lines blood vessels and forms the wall of hollow organs. **486**

SNP *See* single-nucleotide polymorphism.

social animal Animal that lives in a multigenerational group in which members, who are usually relatives, cooperate in some tasks. **704**

soil erosion Loss of soil under the force of wind and water. **440**

soil water Water between soil particles. **752**

solute A substance dissolved in a solvent. **30**

solution Uniform mixure of solute completely dissolved in solvent. **30**

solvent Liquid that can dissolve other substances. **30**

somatic cell nuclear transfer (SCNT) Reproductive cloning method in which the DNA of an adult donor's body cell is transferred into an unfertilized egg. **142**

somatic nervous system Division of the peripheral nervous system that controls skeletal muscles and relays sensory signals about movements and external conditions. **506**

somatic sensations Sensations such as touch and pain that arise when sensory neurons in skin, muscle, or joints are activated. **521**

sorus Cluster of spore-producing capsules on a fern leaf. **350**

source Region of a plant tissue where sugars are being produced or released from storage. **446**

speciation Evolutionary process in which new species arise. **286**

species Unique type of organism designated by genus name and specific epithet. Of sexual reproducers, often defined as one or more groups of individuals that can potentially interbreed, produce fertile offspring, and do not interbreed with other groups. **10**

specific epithet Second part of a species name. **10**

sperm Male gamete. **666**

sphincter Ring of muscle that controls passage through a tubular organ or body opening. **560**

spinal cord Portion of the central nervous system that connects peripheral nerves with the brain. **508**

spindle Temporary structure that moves chromosomes during nuclear division; consists of microtubules. **181**

spirochetes Bacteria that resemble a stretched-out spring. **323**

spleen Large lymphoid organ that functions in immunity and filters pathogens, old red blood cells, and platelets from the blood. **584**

sponge Aquatic invertebrate that has no tissues or organs and filters food from the water. **379**

spongy bone Lightweight bone with many internal spaces; contains red marrow. **558**

sporophyte Spore-forming diploid body that forms in the life cycle of land plants and some multicelled algae. **338, 346**

stabilizing selection Mode of natural selection in which an intermediate form of a trait is adaptive, and extreme forms are not. **280**

stamen Floral reproductive organ that produces male gametophytes; typically consists of an anther on the tip of a filament. **356, 454**

stasis Evolutionary pattern in which a lineage persists with little or no change over evolutionary time. **292**

statistically significant Refers to a result that is statistically unlikely to have occurred by chance. **16**

stem cell Cell that can divide to produce more stem cells or differentiate into specialized cell types. **493**

steroid Type of lipid with four carbon rings and no fatty acid tails. **43**

steroid hormone Lipid-soluble hormone derived from cholesterol. **537**

stigma Of a flower, the upper part of the carpel. Adapted to receive pollen. **454**

stoma Plural **stomata**. Opening across a plant's cuticle and epidermis; can be opened for gas exchange or closed to prevent water loss. **346**

stomach Digestive organ that mixes food with enzymes and acid. **633**

strobilus Of some nonflowering plants, a spore-forming, cone-shaped structure composed of modified leaves. **351**

stroma The cytoplasm-like fluid between the thylakoid membrane and the two outer membranes of a chloroplast. Site of light-independent reactions of photosynthesis. **103**

stromatolite Rocky structures composed of layers of bacterial cells and sediments. **307**

substrate Of an enzyme, a reactant that is specifically acted upon by the enzyme. **82**

substrate-level phosphorylation The formation of ATP by the direct transfer of a phosphate group from a substrate to ADP. **116**

superior vena cava Vein that delivers blood from the upper body to the heart. **573**

surface-to-volume ratio A relationship in which the volume of an object increases with the cube of the diameter, and the surface area increases with the square. Limits cell size. **53**

survivorship curve Graph showing how many members of a cohort remain alive over time. **718**

suspension feeder Animal that filters food from water around it. **379**

symbiosis One species lives in or on another in a commensal, mutualistic, or parasitic relationship. **730**

sympathetic neurons Neurons of the autonomic system that are activated during stress and danger. **506**

sympatric speciation Speciation pattern in which speciation occurs within a population, in the absence of a physical barrier to gene flow. **290**

synapse Region where a neuron's axon terminals transmit signaling molecules (neurotransmitter) to another cell. **504**

synaptic integration The summation of excitatory and inhibitory signals by a postsynaptic cell. **505**

Glossary (continued)

systemic acquired resistance In plants, inducible whole-body resistance to a wide range of pathogens and abiotic stressors. **473**

systemic circuit Circulatory circuit through which blood flows from the heart to the body tissues and back. **571**

systole Contractile phase of the cardiac cycle. **574**

systolic pressure Blood pressure when ventricles are contracting. **579**

T cell T lymphocyte. White blood cell central to adaptive immunity. E.g., helper T cell, cytotoxic T cell. **591**

T cell receptor (TCR) Antigen receptor on the surface of a T cell. **596**

taiga *See* boreal forest.

taproot system An enlarged primary root together with all of the lateral roots that branch from it. Typical of eudicots. **430**

taste receptor Chemoreceptor involved in the sense of taste. **523**

taxonomy The science of naming and classifying species. **10**

taxon, plural taxa Group of organisms that share a unique set of traits. **10**

telomere Noncoding, repetitive DNA sequence at the end of eukaryotic chromosomes; protects the coding sequences from degradation. **183**

telophase Stage of mitosis during which chromosomes arrive at opposite spindle poles and decondense, and two new nuclei form. **181**

temperate deciduous forest Northern Hemisphere biome in which the main plants are broadleaf trees that lose their leaves in fall and become dormant during cold winters. **770**

temperature Measure of molecular motion. **31**

tendon Strap of dense connective tissue that connects a skeletal muscle to bone. **560**

territory Area an animal or group of animals occupies and defends. **702**

testcross Method of determining genotype by tracking a trait in the offspring of a cross between an individual of unknown genotype and an individual known to be homozygous recessive. **208**

testis Sperm-producing animal gonad. **668**

testosterone Hormone secreted by testes; functions in sperm formation and development of male secondary sex characteristics. **545, 674**

tetrapod Vertebrate with four legs, or a descendant thereof. **401**

thalamus Forebrain region that relays signals to the cerebrum; affects sleep–wake cycles. **511**

theory of inclusive fitness Alleles associated with altruism can be advantageous if the expense of this behavior to the altruist is outweighed by increases in the reproductive success of relatives. **706**

therapeutic cloning The use of SCNT to produce human embryos for research purposes. **142**

thermoreceptor Temperature-sensitive sensory receptor. **520**

thermoregulation Maintaining body temperature within a limited range. **658**

thigmotropism Plant growth in a direction influenced by contact. **469**

threatened species Species likely to become endangered in the near future. **784**

threshold potential Neuron membrane potential at which gated sodium channels open, causing an action potential to occur. **502**

thylakoid membrane A chloroplast's highly folded inner membrane system; forms a continuous compartment in the stroma. Site of light reactions of photosynthesis. **103**

thymus Hormone-producing gland in which T lymphocytes (T cells) mature. **584**

thyroid gland Endocrine gland in the base of the neck that secretes thyroid hormone and calcitonin. **542**

thyroid hormone Iodine-containing hormones that collectively increase metabolic rate and play a role in development. **542**

tight junctions In animals, arrays of adhesion proteins that join epithelial cells and collectively prevent fluids from leaking between them. **69**

tissue In multicelled organisms, specialized cells organized in a pattern that allows them to perform a collective function. **4**

tissue culture propagation Laboratory method in which individual plant cells (typically from meristem) are induced to form embryos. **462**

topsoil Uppermost soil layer; contains the most organic matter and nutrients for plant growth. **440**

total fertility rate Expected number of children a women will bear over the course of a lifetime. **722**

tracer A molecule with a detectable component; researchers can track it after delivery into a body or other system. **25**

trachea Airway to the lungs; windpipe. **619**

tracheal system Of insects, tubes that convey gases between the body surface and internal tissues. **615**

tracheids Tapered cells of xylem that die when mature; their interconnected, pitted walls remain and form water-conducting tubes in plants. **444**

tract Bundle of axons in the central nervous system. **508**

trait An observable characteristic of an organism or species. **10**

transcription Process by which enzymes assemble an RNA using the nucleotide sequence of a gene as a template. **148**

transcription factor Protein that influences transcription by binding directly to DNA; for example, an activator or repressor. **164**

transfer RNA (tRNA) RNA that delivers amino acids to a ribosome during translation. **148**

transgenic Refers to a genetically modified organism that carries a gene from a different species. **246**

translation Process by which a polypeptide chain is assembled from amino acids in the order specified by an mRNA. **149**

translocation Of a chromosome, major structural change in which a broken piece gets reattached in the wrong location. In a plant, movement of organic compounds through phloem. **228, 446**

transpiration Evaporation of water from aboveground plant parts. **445**

transport protein Protein that allows specific ions or molecules to cross a membrane. Those that function in active transport require an energy input, as from ATP; those that function in facilitated difussion require no energy input. **57**

transposable element Segment of DNA that can move spontaneously within or between chromosomes. **228**

triglyceride A fat with three fatty acid tails. **42**

tRNA *See* transfer RNA.

trophic level Position of an organism in a food chain. **748**

tropical rain forest Highly productive and species-rich biome in which year-round rains and warmth support continuous growth of evergreen broadleaf trees. **769**

tropism In plants, directional growth response to an environmental stimulus. **468**

trypanosome Parasitic flagellated protist with a single mitochondrion and a flagellum that runs along the back of the cell. **333**

Glossary (continued)

tubular reabsorption Water and solutes move from the filtrate inside a kidney tubule into the peritubular capillaries. **654**

tubular secretion Ions and breakdown products of organic molecules move out of peritubular capillaries and into filtrate. **654**

tumor A neoplasm that forms a lump. **184**

tunicate Invertebrate chordate that loses most of its defining chordate traits during the transition to adulthood. **400**

turgor Pressure that a fluid exerts against a wall, membrane, or other structure that contains it. **89**

unsaturated fat Triglyceride that has one or more unsaturated fatty acid tails. **42**

urea Main nitrogen-containing compound in urine of mammals. **651**

ureter Tube that carries urine from a kidney to the bladder. **652**

urethra Tube through which urine from the bladder exits the body. **652**

uric acid Main nitrogen-containing compound in the urine of insects, as well as birds and other reptiles. **650**

urinary bladder Hollow, muscular organ that stores urine. **652**

urine Fluid that consists of water and soluble wastes; formed and excreted by the vertebrate kidneys. **651**

uterus Muscular chamber where offspring develop; womb. **676**

vaccine A preparation introduced into the body in order to elicit immunity to a specific antigen. **607**

vacuole A membrane-enclosed, fluid-filled organelle that isolates or disposes of waste, debris, or toxic materials. **62**

vagina Female organ of intercourse and birth canal. **676**

variable In an experiment, a characteristic or event that differs among individuals or over time. **12**

vascular bundle In a stem or leaf, multistranded bundle formed by xylem, phloem, and sclerenchyma fibers. **426**

vascular cambium Lateral meristem that produces secondary xylem and phloem in plants. **433**

vascular cylinder Central column of vascular tissue in a plant root. **430**

vascular plant Plant with xylem and phloem. **346**

vascular tissues Tissues that distribute water and nutrients through a plant body. *See* xylem, phloem. **422**

vas deferens One of a pair of long ducts that carry mature sperm to the ejaculatory duct. **674**

vasoconstriction Narrowing of a blood vessel when smooth muscle that rings it contracts. **578**

vasodilation Widening of a blood vessel when smooth muscle that rings it relaxes. **578**

vector Of a disease, an animal that carries the pathogen from one host to the next. **318**

vegetative reproduction Growth of new roots and shoots from extensions or fragments of a parent plant; form of asexual reproduction in plants. **462**

vein In plants, a vascular bundle in a leaf or other structure. In animals with a circulatory system, a large-diameter vessel that returns blood to the heart. **428, 570**

ventricle Heart chamber that pumps blood into arteries. **574**

venule Blood vessel that conveys blood from capillaries to a vein. **581**

vernalization In plants, stimulation of flowering in spring by prolonged exposure to low temperature in winter. **471**

vertebrae Bones of the backbone, or vertebral column. **556**

vertebral column Backbone. **556**

vertebrate Animal with a backbone. **400**

vesicle Small, membrane-enclosed organelle; different kinds store, transport, or break down their contents; e.g., a peroxisome or lysosome. **62**

vessel elements Of xylem, cells that form in stacks and die when mature; their pitted walls remain to form water-conducting tubes in plants. Each tube consists of a stack of vessel elements that meet end to end at perforation plates. **444**

vestibular apparatus System of fluid-filled sacs and canals in the inner ear; contains organs of equilibrium. **530**

villi Singular **villus**. Multicelled projections from the lining of the small intestine. **635**

viral recombination Multiple strains of virus infect a host simultaneously and swap genes. **319**

viroid Small noncoding RNA that can infect plants. **319**

virus Noncellular, infectious particle of protein and nucleic acid; replicates only in a host cell. **316**

visceral sensations Sensations that arise when sensory neurons associated with organs inside body cavities are activated. **521**

visual accommodation Process of making adjustments to lens shape so light from an object falls on the retina. **525**

vital capacity Maximum amount of air moved in and out of lungs with forced inhalation and exhalation. **620**

vitamin Organic substance required in the diet in small amounts for normal metabolism. **640**

vomeronasal organ Pheromone-detecting organ of vertebrates. **523**

water cycle Movement of water among Earth's oceans, atmosphere, and the freshwater reservoirs on land. **752**

water mold Heterotrophic protist that grows as a mesh of nutrient-absorbing filaments. **337**

water–vascular system Of echinoderms, a system of fluid-filled tubes and tube feet that function in locomotion. **394**

wavelength Distance between the crests of two successive waves. **100**

wax Water-repellent mixture of lipids with long fatty acid tails bonded to long-chain alcohols or carbon rings. **43**

white blood cell Blood cell with a role in housekeeping and defense. **576**

white matter Central nervous system tissue consisting mainly of myelinated axons. **508**

wood Accumulated secondary xylem inside the cylinder of vascular cambium in an older plant stem or root. **433**

X chromosome inactivation Developmental shutdown of one of the two X chromosomes in the cells of female mammals. **168**

xylem Complex vascular tissue of plants; its dead tracheids and vessel elements distribute water and dissolved minerals through the plant body. **346, 425**

yeast Fungus that lives as single cell. **364**

yellow marrow Bone marrow that is mostly fat; fills cavity in most long bones. **558**

yolk Nutritious material in many animal eggs. **667**

zero population growth Interval in which births equal deaths. **714**

zygote Cell formed by fusion of two gametes at fertilization; the first cell of a new individual. **195**

zygote fungi Fungi that live in damp places and form a thick-walled zygospore during sexual reproduction. **365**

Index

Index (continued)

Index *(continued)*

Index (continued)

Index (continued)

Index (continued)

Index (continued)

Index (continued)

Index (continued)